Fatigue in composites

Fatigue in composites

Science and technology of the
fatigue response of fibre-reinforced plastics

**Edited by
Bryan Harris**

CRC Press
Boca Raton Boston New York Washington, DC

WOODHEAD PUBLISHING LIMITED
Cambridge England

Published by Woodhead Publishing Limited, Abington Hall, Abington
Cambridge CB1 6AH, England
www.woodhead-publishing.com

Published in North America by CRC Press LLC
2000 Corporate Blvd, NW
Boca Raton FL 33431, USA

First published 2003, Woodhead Publishing Ltd and CRC Press LLC
© 2003, Woodhead Publishing Ltd
The authors have asserted their moral rights.

British Library Cataloguing in Publication Data
A catalogue record for this book is available from the British Library.

Library of Congress Cataloging in Publication Data
A catalog record for this book is available from the Library of Congress.

Woodhead Publishing ISBN 1 85573 608 X
CRC Press ISBN 0-8493-1767-3
CRC Press order number: WP1767

Typeset by Ann Buchan (Typesetters), Middx, England
Printed by TJ International, Padstow, Cornwall, England

Contents

Preface xiii
Acknowledgements xvi
Contributor contact details xvii

Part I   Introduction to fatigue in composites 1

1   A historical review of the fatigue behaviour of fibre-reinforced plastics 3
B. Harris, Materials Research Centre, University of Bath, UK
    1.1   Introduction 3
    1.2   Fatigue phenomena in fibre composites 4
    1.3   Concluding comments 30
    1.4   Bibliography 31
    1.5   References 31

2   Fatigue test methods, problems and standards 36
G. D. Sims, National Physical Laboratory, London, UK
    2.1   Introduction 36
    2.2   Fatigue data requirements 36
    2.3   Fatigue testing requirements 38
    2.4   Fatigue test equipment 39
    2.5   Artefacts in fatigue testing 42
    2.6   Standardized test methods 52
    2.7   Precision data 56
    2.8   Data presentation 58
    2.9   Concluding comments 59
    2.10   Future trends 61
    2.11   Acknowledgements 61
    2.12   References 62

3   Fatigue under multiaxial stress systems 63
M. M. Shokrieh, Iran University of Science and Technology, Tehran, Iran,
and L. B. Lessard, McGill University, Montreal, Canada
    3.1   Introduction 63

3.2	Fatigue failure criteria	63
3.3	Material properties degradation	68
3.4	Progressive fatigue damage modelling	78
3.5	Material characterization	80
3.6	Experimental evaluation of the model	93
3.7	Conclusions	108
3.8	References	109

Part II   Micromechanical aspects of fatigue in composites   115

4   The effects of aggressive environments on long-term behaviour   117
F.R. Jones, University of Sheffield, UK

4.1	Introduction	117
4.2	Aqueous environments	117
4.3	Moisture sensitivity of resins	120
4.4	Thermal spiking	123
4.5	Thermomechanical response of matrix resins	123
4.6	Effect of moisture on composite performance	126
4.7	Fibre-dominated properties	129
4.8	Role of the matrix and interface	135
4.9	Environmental stress-corrosion cracking (ESCC) of GRP	137
4.10	Designing for stress-corrosion resistance	142
4.11	Non-aqueous environments	143
4.12	Conclusions	145
4.13	References	145

5   The effect of the interface on the fatigue performance of fibre composites   147
C. Galiotis and C. Koimtzoglou, Institute of Chemical Engineering and High Temperature Processes, Foundation for Research and Technology, Greece and Materials Department, University of Patras, Greece

5.1	Introduction	147
5.2	Effect of interface parameters on fatigue performance	147
5.3	Effect of other parameters that indirectly affect the interface on fatigue performance	155
5.4	Effect of fatigue loading on interface	163
5.5	Conclusions	168
5.6	References	170

6   Delamination fatigue   173
R. Martin, Materials Engineering Research Laboratory, UK

6.1	Introduction	173
6.2	The interlaminar fracture mechanics approach for fatigue	175
6.3	Characterizing delamination in fatigue	177
6.4	Modelling a delamination	183
6.5	Using fracture mechanics analysis as a design tool	184
6.6	Structural integrity prediction	187
6.7	References	187

7 The fatigue of hybrid composites 189
G. F. Fernando, Cranfield University, UK and F. A. A. Al-Khodairi, Saudi
Basic Industries Corporation, Saudi Arabia
    7.1   Introduction 189
    7.2   Comparison of fatigue data 195
    7.3   Materials and experimental procedures...................... 198
    7.4   Results and discussion................................... 202
    7.5   Fractography 233
    7.6   Conclusions 236
    7.7   Acknowledgements 237
    7.8   References 238

8 Non-destructive evaluation of damage accumulation 242
A.P. Mouritz, RMIT University, Australia
    8.1   Introduction 242
    8.2   Acoustic NDE techniques 243
    8.3   Acoustic emission 254
    8.4   Radiography 256
    8.5   Thermographic NDE methods 259
    8.6   Eddy currents.. 259
    8.7   Moiré interferometry 259
    8.8   Summary and concluding remarks 261
    8.9   Acknowledgements 262
    8.10   Information sources..................................... 262
    8.11   References 262

Part III   Fatigue in different types of composites 267

9 Short-fibre thermoset composites 269
G. Caprino, University of Naples "Federico II", Italy
    9.1   Introduction 269
    9.2   Structure and composition of short-fibre thermoset composites........ 270
    9.3   Static behaviour....................................... 270
    9.4   Fatigue behaviour 278
    9.5   Conclusions 292
    9.6   References 292

10 Woven-fibre thermoset composites 296
N. K. Naik, Indian Institute of Technology, Bombay, India
    10.1   Introduction 296
    10.2   Fatigue performance of laminated composites 298
    10.3   Woven-fabric laminated composites........................ 299
    10.4   Fatigue testing 303
    10.5   Fatigue damage in woven-fabric composites 304
    10.6   Fatigue loading: stiffness, strength and life 308
    10.7   Recent studies of the fatigue behaviour of WF composites 310
    10.8   Future trends 310
    10.9   Nomenclature 311
    10.10 References 311

11 Fatigue of thermoplastic composites 314
E.K. Gamstedt and L.A. Berglund, KTH, Sweden
   11.1   Introduction 314
   11.2   Thermoplastics 316
   11.3   Continuous-fibre composites............................ 321
   11.4   Short-fibre composites 331
   11.5   Future of thermoplastic composites 334
   11.6   References 335

12 Fatigue of wood and wood panel products 339
M.P. Ansell, University of Bath, UK
   12.1   Introduction 339
   12.2   The structure and properties of wood and timber 339
   12.3   Fatigue life of wood and panel products 343
   12.4   Dynamic property changes in fatigue of wood and panel products 349
   12.5   Fatigue damage development in wood and panel products 356
   12.6   Fatigue in timber joints 357
   12.7   Fatigue of natural fibre composites 358
   12.8   Conclusions 358
   12.9   Acknowledgements 358
   12.10 References 359

Part IV   Life-prediction methods for constant stress and variable stress 363

13 Physical modelling of damage development in structural composite materials under stress 365
P.W.R. Beaumont, Cambridge University, UK
   13.1   Introduction 365
   13.2   A framework for understanding damage development 365
   13.3   A question of design route 367
   13.4   A question of physical modelling 369
   13.5   A question of fatigue 372
   13.6   Physical modelling of fatigue damage development.................. 376
   13.7   Physical modelling of fatigue damage development at stress concentrators 396
   13.8   Computer implementation 408
   13.9   Summary and final remarks 409
   13.10 Acknowledgements 410
   13.11 References 410

14 Micromechanical models 413
K. Reifsnider and S. Case, Virginia Tech, USA
   14.1   Introduction 413
   14.2   Damage accumulation in composite materials 414
   14.3   Changes in stiffness.................................... 416
   14.4   Changes in local material strength 417
   14.5   Strength: an internal state variable and damage metric.............. 419
   14.6   Strength of a composite material: 'Critical element' concepts 419

14.7   Non-uniform stress states: characteristic material dimensions 421
14.8   Strength evolution 421
14.9   Applications 426
14.10   Conclusions 429
14.11   Acknowledgements 430
14.12   References 430

15 A computational meso-damage model for life prediction for laminates 432
P. Ladevèze and G. Lubineau, LMT Cachan, France
15.1   Introduction 432
15.2   The damage scenarios on the micro structural scale (Fig. 15.1) 432
15.3   The 3D damage model for laminates according to scenarios 3 and 4 433
15.4   The 'micro' modelling of laminate composite for scenarios 1 and 2 434
15.5   Mesomodel of the laminated composite (Fig. 15.4) 436
15.6   Comparison with experiments for $[0_n/90_m]_s$ 437
15.7   Perspectives 440
15.8   References 441

**16 A statistical study of the fatigue performance of fibre-reinforced
composite laminates** 442
*X. Diao, PreciCad Inc., Canada, L. Ye and Y-W. Mai, University of Sydney,
Australia*
16.1   Introduction 442
16.2   Fatigue and methodology 443
16.3   Statistical model 447
16.4   Stress redistribution function 449
16.5   Evaluation of fatigue performance of composite laminates 453
16.6   Concluding remarks 463
16.7   Acknowledgements 468
16.8   References 468

**17 Analysis of matrix crack-induced delamination in composite laminates
under static and fatigue loading** 470
*M. Kashtalyan, University of Aberdeen and C. Soutis, University of
Sheffield, UK*
17.1   Introduction 470
17.2   Stiffness properties of cracked laminates with delaminations 471
17.3   Delamination onset and growth prediction 486
17.4   Conclusions 496
17.5   Acknowledgements 498
17.6   References 499
17.7   Appendices 500

18 Fatigue strength of composites under variable plane stress 504
T.P. Philippidis and A.P. Vassilopoulos, University of Patras, Greece
18.1   Introduction 504
18.2   Life prediction under combined stress: theoretical considerations 505
18.3   Experimental and property evaluation 509

18.4	Verification of life prediction methodology	516
18.5	Structural application example: Inboard part of a rotor blade	520
18.6	Concluding remarks	521
18.7	References	523

19 Life prediction under service loading spectra 526
L.J. Lee and K.E. Fu, National Cheng Kung University, Taiwan

19.1	Introduction	526
19.2	Stiffness degradation under block-type loading spectrum	528
19.3	Statistical distribution of fatigue life	531
19.4	Experimental program	532
19.5	Experimental verification	533
19.6	Conclusions	544
19.7	References	545

20 A parametric constant-life model for prediction of the fatigue lives of fibre-reinforced plastics 546
B. Harris, University of Bath, UK

20.1	Introduction	546
20.2	The nature of fatigue processes in composites	546
20.3	Cracks in composites	547
20.4	Life prediction: the alternatives	548
20.5	A parametric constant-life model for life prediction	550
20.6	Conclusions	565
20.7	Acknowledgements	567
20.8	References	567

21 A neural-network approach to fatigue-life prediction 569
J.A. Lee and D.P. Almond, University of Bath, UK

21.1	Introduction	569
21.2	Background	570
21.3	Biological neural networks	570
21.4	Multi-variate non-linear mappings	570
21.5	Artificial neural network models	573
21.6	The use of artificial neural networks in practice	577
21.7	Application of artificial neural networks to the analysis of fatigue life data	579
21.8	Optimum artificial neural network architecture	580
21.9	Selection of inputs for training the artificial neural network	580
21.10	Constant stress amplitude fatigue	580
21.11	New material application	581
21.12	Block-loading data analysis	582
21.13	Suggested procedure for applying neural networks to fatigue life data	583
21.14	Comparison with other methods	585
21.15	Future trends	588
21.16	Acknowledgements	588
21.17	References	588

Part V   Fatigue in practical situations 591

22 The fatigue performance of composite structural components 593
M.D. Gilchrist, University College Dublin, Ireland
22.1   Introduction 593
22.2   General approach....................................... 593
22.3   Damage growth and life prediction 595
22.4   An approach to full-scale testing......................... 598
22.5   Reliability 599
22.6   Applications.. 599
22.7   Conclusions 616
22.8   References 616
22.9   Appendix 619
22.10 Nomenclature 620

23 Fatigue of joints in composite structures 621
J. Schön and R. Starikov, Swedish Defence Research Agency, Sweden
23.1   Introduction 621
23.2   Composite joints 621
23.3   Fatigue in adhesive joints 625
23.4   Fatigue in bolted joints 633
23.5   Outlook 639
23.6   Summary 640
23.7   References 641

24 Fatigue in filament-wound structures 644
D. Perreux and F. Thiébaud, Laboratoire de Mécanique Appliquée RC,
France
24.1   Introduction 644
24.2   Brief overview of literature on pipe behaviour 645
24.3   Breadboard fixtures 646
24.4   Fatigue behaviour of bi-directional [+55/–55] glass-fibre/epoxy-matrix
       filament-wound pipes 648
24.5   Conclusions 655
24.6   References 655

25 Fatigue of FRP composites in civil engineering applications 658
J.M.C. Cadei, FaberMaunsell Ltd, UK
25.1   Introduction 658
25.2   Composite material applications in civil engineering 658
25.3   Typical fatigue loadings in civil engineering structures 667
25.4   Fatigue behaviour of composite structures and components 671
25.5   Design and analysis of structures for fatigue 677
25.6   Case study: FRP road deck fatigue performance (TRL test programme on
       ACCS Roadway Panel) 679
25.7   Operational aspects 684
25.8   Concluding remarks 685

25.9   References 685

26 Fatigue in aerospace applications 686
A.J. Davies, QinetiQ, UK and P.T. Curtis, Dstl, UK
25.1   Introduction 686
26.2   Overview of fatigue performance of aerospace materials. 688
26.3   Fatigue life prediction 692
26.4   Damage mechanisms 695
26.5   Airframe structural elements 698
26.6   Conclusions 706
26.8   Acknowledgements 707
26.9   References 707

27 Fatigue and durability of marine composites 709
P. Davies and D. Choqueuse, IFREMER, Centre de Brest, France and A. Roy,
CRITT Matériaux, Rochefort, France
27.1   Introduction 709
27.2   Specific nature of the marine environment 711
27.3   Marine composites 715
27.4   Durability of marine laminates 717
27.5   Durability of sandwich materials 719
27.6   Assemblies 720
27.7   Slamming impact response 722
27.8   Cylinders for underwater applications 724
27.9   Future directions 727
27.10 References 727

Index 730

Preface

I first became aware of the phenomenon of fatigue in 1955 when, as a metallurgy student at the University of Birmingham, I attended a final-year course on the subject given by Dr Trevor Broome. In my mind, there are still two strongly associated memories from that time. The first is that almost the top item in Broome's reading list was, unexpectedly, Neville Shute's novel *No Highway*. This novel, written in 1948, paints an uncannily prescient picture of the in-flight fatigue failure of the tail-plane of a transatlantic airliner. The second memory from that time is that the Head of Department at Birmingham, Professor A J Murphy, was heading a government inquiry into the catastrophic mid-air failures of the De Havilland Comets as a result of low-cycle fatigue crack growth. Shute's explanation of fatigue as being due to some 'nuclear' process that led to 'crystallization' and therefore brittleness may have been wide of the mark, but his description of the large-scale fatigue testing of a tail-plane at the Royal Aircraft Establishment at Farnborough (now, sadly, known as Dstl or QinetiQ (!), depending on which part of the establishment you are dealing with) was to become a reality at the RAE following the Comet disasters, and many years later, when I became a regular visitor to Farnborough, the sight of a similar, if larger-scale test on a Concorde tail-plane never failed to remind me of *No Highway*, Trevor Broome, and the Comets. Curiously, there remains a very active interest in the Comets, with a dedicated website, and a recent British television programme raised a few hackles among survivors of the design team.

After leaving the university, I had nothing more to do with fatigue until after I began working on carbon-fibre composites at the University of Sussex. Under the tutelage of Dr Leslie Phillips from the RAE, one of the co-inventors of the process of making high-performance carbon fibres from polyacrylonitrile, I began work in 1966 with Peter Beaumont on a study of the fatigue behaviour of the newly available carbon-fibre-reinforced plastics (CFRPs) and since that time, neither Beaumont nor I have ever stopped working on the fatigue of composites. During the 1960s and 1970s it was frequently difficult to persuade aircraft engineers that the new-fangled CFRPs suffered from fatigue. They weren't metals, after all, and everyone knew that only metals suffered from fatigue. And this, despite the fact that there had been published reports on the fatigue behaviour of glass-fibre-reinforced plastics (GRPs*) since the early 1950s. How things have changed!

By a strange quirk of coincidence, as preparations for this book were getting under way, another airliner accident was reported from the USA. In November 2001 the tail fin of an American Airlines Airbus A300 fell off seconds before that plane crashed after take-off in New York. In all, 265 people were killed, and questions were immediately raised about the composite make-up of that tail fin. In an area where the tail connects to the fuselage, ultrasonic tests revealed a flaw which was described as a possible tiny ply separation within the layered carbon fibre. A report published in November 2002 indicates that the investigation into the cause of the failure is still proceeding, and that the cause will probably not be decided until next year. The investigation has now shown that the jet twice ran into the wake of a Boeing 747 five miles ahead of it, at which time the rudder began to swing back and forth violently. Seven seconds later, the composite tail fin started to break off. This was apparently the first time that anyone had been aware of the in-flight failure of a major aircraft structural component made of composite materials. Investigators have learned since the accident that sharp rudder actions can put sufficient stress on the tail fin to cause it to snap off. So far, no mention appears to have been made of the possibility of fatigue, and indeed it may be that fatigue is not implicated. But the official reaction to the incident is interesting. The planes were not taken out of service, an Airbus spokesman claiming that 'If damage is not visible, then we know it does not affect the strength of the material, and it will not grow during the service life of the airplane. A visual inspection will be adequate to find any anomaly that would be of concern.' Is such confidence well-founded?

It is now well established that fibre composites, like metals, exhibit a form of degradation in service that can be described as 'fatigue'. A simplistic description of the phenomenon is that under cyclic loading conditions, the load-bearing capacity of the material falls with time and this results in failures at stress levels which are often well below the ordinary (monotonic) engineering strength. The mechanisms by which this deterioration occurs in composites are quite different from, and much more complicated than, those which are responsible for fatigue phenomena in metals, but the problems facing the designer are similar. From the engineer's point of view, the challenge is to choose materials and use them in such a way as to avoid failures within the design life of a component or structure. In order to achieve this, it is necessary to understand the mechanisms of degradation in service and to be able to predict the life of a given composite under particular design conditions. In principle, achievement of the first of these should lead with confidence to the second, but at the present time our progress towards a state of understanding where one follows from the other is less than perfect.

Research into the fatigue response of fibre composites has been carried out since the materials themselves first began to be a subject of serious study. Some of the first papers on the fatigue behaviour of glass-reinforced plastics, for example, were published in the USA by Boller in the 1950s and 60s, and shortly after this Owen and his collaborators at Nottingham University in the UK were reporting the results of work on early carbon-fibre-reinforced plastics (CFRPs). Simultaneously, Baker and co-workers at Rolls Royce, also in the UK, were laying the foundations for an understanding of the fatigue behaviour of metal-matrix composites (MMCs). While much of this early work on fatigue involved pheno-

---

*In this book, we shall use the abbreviations CFRP and GRP. This is the most common usage, and reflects the fact that GRPs were known and named long before carbon fibres were invented. It also avoids the potential confusion often caused by American insistence on calling carbon fibre 'graphite', even though it was well established right from the early days that the structure of carbon fibres was turbostratic and not truly graphitic. In US terminology, then, GFRP often means graphite-fibre-reinforced plastic.

menological studies, it quickly became apparent that an understanding of the microstructural damage mechanisms responsible for failure under cyclic loading was a prerequisite for the development of new fatigue-resistant materials and, in the longer term, for the prediction of fatigue life, and the names of Reifsnider in the USA and Talreja in Denmark (now also in the USA) began to be associated with key developments in the emerging field of damage mechanics. And since the build-up of fatigue damage is essentially a stochastic process, vital statistical interpretations of fatigue behaviour, again with life prediction as the objective, were made, among others, by Hahn, Talreja, Whitney, and Yang.

Initially, research into the fatigue behaviour of fibre-reinforced plastics (FRPs) was driven largely by the aerospace industry, and much of the work was funded by that industry and by government. In the half-century or so since FRPs were first developed, the picture, as far as applications are concerned, has changed substantially and aerospace is now only one of several fields where designers are seeking (and using) the latest of these materials which offer them the desirable benefits of high strength and stiffness combined with low density. It is perhaps for this reason more than any other that it seems an appropriate time to produce a new survey of our current level of knowledge of the Achilles heel – the fatigue behaviour of composites – and extend it to deal with the wider range of problems met with by designers in automotive, marine, and structural engineering.

It is intended that this work will provide a practical encyclopaedic text book for designers as well as being an authoritative reference source for materials scientists.

Acknowledgements

I am indebted to Woodhead Publishing Limited for offering me the opportunity to edit a major reference work that deals with a subject on which I have spent most of my research career. The task has been enormously eased and simplified by the care and professionalism of the company's editorial staff, and I should particularly like to thank Emma Starr for taking on the major organizational burden and for executing it so smoothly in the background that I have been almost unaware of it.

A book of this kind is naturally only as good as the papers that it contains, and in this I count myself most fortunate to have contributions from a group of authors who are established and acknowledged leaders in their individual fields. Many of these authors I also count as my friends, since the composites fatigue community has been sufficiently small in the past for it to be possible to know almost all of the leading authorities. I offer my sincere thanks to all of the contributors for finding the time to write their chapters in the course of what I know from experience are very busy lives. I hope that in time the book will repay them for their efforts.

Bryan Harris
Materials Research Centre
University of Bath, Somerset, England

Contributor contact details

Chapters 1 & 20

Professor Bryan Harris
Materials Research Centre
Department of Engineering and Applied
    Science
University of Bath
Bath
Somerset
UK

Tel: +44 (0) 1225 826447
E-mail: b.harris@bath.ac.uk

Chapter 2

Dr Graham D. Sims
National Physical Laboratory
    Materials Centre
Teddington
Middlesex
TW11 0LW
UK

Tel: +44 (0) 20 8943 6564
Fax: +44 (0) 20 8614 0433
E-mail: graham.sims@npl.co.uk

Chapter 3

Professor Mahmood M. Shokrieh
Mechanical Engineering Department
Iran University of Science and Technology

Narmak
Tehran 16844
Iran

Tel.: +98 911 288 7925
Fax: +98 21 749 1206
E-mail: shokrieh@iust.ac.ir

Professor L. B. Lessard
Department of Mechanical Engineering
McGill University
817 Sherbrooke St West
Montreal
Quebec
Canada
H3A 2K6

Tel: +1 514 398-6305
Fax: +1 514 398-6305
E-mail: larry.lessard@mcgill.ca

Chapter 4

Professor F. R. Jones
Department of Engineering Materials
University of Sheffield
Sir Robert Hadfield Building
Sheffield
S1 3JD
UK

Tel: +44 (0) 114 222 5477
E-mail: f.r.jones@sheffield.ac.uk

Chapter 5

Professor C. Galiotis[1,2] & Dr C. Koimtzoglou[1]
[1] Institute of Chemical Engineering and High Temperature Processes
Foundation for Research & Technology – Hellas
Stadiou Street
Platani
PO Box 1414
GR-265 04
Patras
Greece

[2] Materials Science Department
School of Natural Science
University of Patras
GR-265 04
Patras
Greece

Tel: +30 610-965 255
Fax: +30 610-965 223
E-mail: c.galiotis@iceht.forth.gr
        ckoim@iceht.forth.gr

Chapter 6

Dr Rod Martin
Materials Engineering Research Laboratory Ltd
Tamworth Road
Hertford
SG13 7DG
UK

Tel: +44 (0) 1992 510803
Fax: +44 (0) 1992 586439
E-mail: rmartin@merl-ltd.co.uk

Chapter 7

Dr G. F. Fernando
Engineering Systems Department
Cranfield University
RMCS, Shrivenham
Swindon
SN6 8LA
UK

Tel: +44 (0) 1793 785146
E-mail: G.F.Fernando@rmcs.cranfield.ac.uk

Dr F. A. A. Al-Khodairi
Polymer Research Technology
Saudi Basic Industries Corporation
PO Box 42503
Riyadh 11551
Saudi Arabia

Chapter 8

Professor A. P. Mouritz
School of Aerospace, Mechanical and Manufacturing Engineering
RMIT University
GPO Box 2476V
Melbourne
Victoria 3001
Australia

Tel: +61 3 9925 8069
Fax: +61 3 9925 8099
E-mail: adrian.mouritz@rmit.edu.au

Chapter 9

Professor G. Caprino
Department of Materials and Production Engineering
University of Naples "Federico II"
Piazzale Tecchio 80
80125
Napoli
Italy

E-mail: caprino@unina.it

Chapter 10

Professor N. K. Naik
Aerospace Engineering Department
Indian Institute of Technology – Bombay
Powai
Mumbai - 400 076
India

Tel: +91 22 2576 7114
Fax: +91 22 2572 2602
E-mail: nknaik@aero.iitb.ac.in

Chapter 11

Dr E. K. Gamstedt
Department of Solid Mechanics
Royal Institute of Technology (KTH)
SE-10044 Stockholm
Sweden

Tel: +46 8 790 7553
Fax: +46 8 411 2418
E-mail: kristofer@hallf.kth.se

Professor L. A. Berglund
Department of Aeronautical and Vehicle
    Engineering
Royal Institute of Technology (KTH)
SE-10044 Stockholm
Sweden

Tel: +46 8 790 8118
Fax: +46 8 796 6080
E-mail: blund@kth.se

Chapter 12

Dr Martin P. Ansell
Department of Engineering and Applied
    Science
University of Bath
Bath
BA2 7AY
UK

Tel: +44 (0) 1225 386432
Fax: +44 (0) 1225 386098
E-mail: m.p.ansell@bath.ac.uk

Chapter 13

Dr P. W. R. Beaumont
Cambridge University Engineering Depart-
    ment
Trumpington Street
Cambridge
UK

Tel: +44 (0) 1223 332600
Fax: +44 (0) 1223 332662
E-mail: pwrb@eng.cam.ac.uk

Chapter 14

Professor K. Reifsnider, Alexander Giacco
    Professor of Engineering Science and
    Mechanics and Professor S. Case
120 Patton Hall
Virginia Tech
Blacksburg
VA 24061-0219
USA

E-mail: mrl@vt.edu

Chapter 15

Professor P. Ladevèze and Dr G. Lubineau
ENS Cachan
CNRS
Université Paris 6
61 avenue du Président Wilson
94235 Cachan Cedex
France

Tel: +33 (0) 1 47 40 22 41
Fax: +33 (0) 1 47 40 27 85
E-mail: ladeveze@lmt.ens-cachan.fr

Chapter 16

Professor Lin Ye and Professor Yiu-Wing
    Mai
Centre for Advanced Materials Technology
    (CAMT)
University of Sydney
Sydney
NSW 2006
Australia

Tel: +61 2 9351 2290/2341
Fax: +61 2 9351 3760
E-mail: mai@aeromech.usyd.edu.au

Dr Xiaoxue Diao
PreciCad Inc.
350 Boulevard Charest Est, 1st floor
Quebec G1K 3H4
Canada

Tel: 514 485 4292
Fax: 514 485 4234
E-mail: xiaoxue.diao@ps.ge.com

Chapter 17

Professor C. Soutis
Head of Aerospace Engineering
University of Sheffield
Faculty of Engineering
Mappin Street
Sheffield
S1 3JD
UK

Tel: +44 (0) 114 2227811
Fax: +44 (0) 114 2227890
E-mail: c.soutis@sheffield.ac.uk

Dr M. Kashtalyan
School of Engineering and Physical
    Sciences
University of Aberdeen
Fraser Noble Building
King's College
Aberdeen
AB24 3UE
UK

Tel: +44 (0) 1224 272519
Fax: +44 (0) 1224 272519
E-mail: m.kashtalyan@abdn.ac.uk

Chapter 18

Professor T. P. Philippidis & Dr A. P.
    Vassilopoulos
Section of Applied Mechanics
Department of Mechanical Engineering and
    Aeronautics
University of Patras
PO Box 1401
University Campus
265 04, Rion
Greece

Tel/Fax: +30 261 0997235
E-mail: philippidis@mech.upatras.gr
         vassilopoulos@mech.upatras.gr

Chapter 19

Dr K. E. Fu and Professor L. J. Lee
Institute of Aeronautics and Astronautics
National Cheng Kung University
Tainan
Taiwan 70101
ROC

E-mail: ljlee@mail.iaa.ncku.edu.tw

Chapter 21

Dr J. A. Lee and Professor D. P. Almond
Department of Engineering and Applied
    Science
University of Bath
Bath
BA2 7AY
UK

E-mail: d.p.almond@bath.ac.uk

Chapter 22

Professor M. D. Gilchrist
Department of Mechanical Engineering
University College Dublin
Belfield
Dublin 4
Ireland

Tel: +353 1 7161884
Fax: +353 1 2830534
E-mail: michael.gilchrist@ucd.ie

Chapter 23

Dr J. Schön
Swedish Defence Research Agency FOI
SE-172 90 Stockholm
Sweden

Tel: +46 8 55503595
Fax: +46 8 55503869
E-mail: snj@foi.se

Dr R. Starikov
Swedish Defence Research Agency FOI
FFA
SE-172 90 Stockholm
Sweden

E-mail: Romsta@foi.se

Chapter 24

Professor D. Perreux and Dr Frédéric
   Thiébaud
Laboratoire de Mécanique Appliquée RC
24 rue de l'Epitaphe
25000 Besançon
France

Tel: +33 (0) 3 81 66 60 12
Fax: +33 (0) 3 81 66 67 00
E-mail: dominique.perreux@univ-fcomte.fr

Chapter 25

Dr John M. C. Cadei
FaberMaunsell Ltd
160 Croydon Road
Beckenham
Kent
BR3 4DE
UK

Tel: +44 (0) 870 905 0906
Fax: +44 (0) 20 8663 6723
E-mail: john.cadei@fabermaunsell.com

Chapter 26

Dr A. J. Davies
QinetiQ
Farnborough
Hampshire
UK

E-mail: Ajdavies1@qinetiq.com

Professor P. T. Curtis
Dstl Farnborough
Materials and Structures Group
Hampshire
UK

E-mail: ptcurtis@taz.dstl.gov.uk

Chapter 27

Dr Peter Davies
Materials & Structures Group
   (TMSI/RED/MS)
IFREMER Centre de Brest
BP70 29280 Plouzané
France

Tel: +33 2 98 22 4777
Fax: +33 2 98 22 4535
E-mail: Peter.Davies@ifremer.fr

Mr Dominique Choqueuse
Materials & Structures Group (TMSI/RED/
   MS)
IFREMER Centre de Brest
BP70 29280 Plouzané
France

Tel: +33 2 98 22 4163
Fax: +33 2 98 22 4535
E-mail: dchoq@ifremer.fr

Dr Annette Roy
CRITT Matériaux
BP 115 - 40 bis avenue Marcel Dassault
17303 Rochefort Cedex
France

Tel : 05 46 83 92 03
Fax : 05 46 99 65 88
E-mail: critt.mpc@libertysurf.fr

Part I

Introduction to fatigue in composites

1

A historical review of the fatigue behaviour of fibre-reinforced plastics

B. Harris, Materials Research Centre, University of Bath, UK

1.1   Introduction

The engineer's perception of the phenomenon of fatigue is so closely linked with the behaviour of homogeneous, isotropic, metallic materials that there has often been a tendency to treat modern fibre composites as though they were metals. At the outset, the test methods used to study fatigue in composites were the same as those used for metals, and the interpretation of the results of such tests has often been clouded by ideas about what constitutes metallic fatigue failure. It is normal that a designer wanting to substitute a composite for a metal component should want to test the new material by applying a cyclic loading régime of the same kind as that which the component would be required to sustain in service in order to prove that the composite will perform as well as the metal. But it is wrong to assume *a priori* that there is some universal mechanism by which fluctuating loads will inevitably result in failure at stresses below the normal monotonic failure stress of the material.

Metallic fatigue, which accounts for a large percentage of engineering failures, has been intensively studied for more than a century. Design data have been accumulated for every conceivable engineering metal and alloy, and the engineer has access to a comprehensive set of rules, some empirical and some based on scientific understanding, with which to deal with any given design requirement. The fact that designers often choose to ignore these rules accounts for the many fatigue failures that should never have happened. Fatigue in metals often progresses by the initiation of a single crack and its intermittent propagation until catastrophic failure which occurs with little warning. In ordinary high-cycle (low-stress) fatigue, the properties of the metal remote from the crack may be only slightly changed during fatigue. The usual effect of fatigue at low stresses is simply to harden the metal slightly. Generally speaking, a stronger material will have a higher fatigue resistance, the fatigue ratio (fatigue limit divided by tensile strength) being roughly constant.

It was common at one time for users of composite materials to express the belief that composite materials – more specifically, carbon-fibre-reinforced plastics – did not suffer from fatigue. This is all the more astonishing in view of the fact that from the earliest days of composites development, their fatigue behaviour was a subject of serious study. What was usually implied was that, because most CFRPs were extremely stiff in the fibre direction, the working strains in practical components at conventional design stress levels were usually far too low to initiate any of the local damage mechanisms that might otherwise have caused deterioration under cyclic loads. The use of composites like CFRPs only at very low working strains raises two important issues. The first is the obvious one that, by using expensive, high-performance materials at small fractions of their available strength, we are over-designing and using them uneconomically. The second is that since anisotropy is a characteristic of composites that we accept and must design for, a stress system that develops only a small working strain in the main fibre direction may nevertheless cause strains normal to the fibres or at the fibre/resin interface which are high enough to cause the kind of deterioration that we call fatigue damage. In designing with composites, therefore, we cannot ignore fatigue. It follows that, in addition to needing to understand the mechanisms by which fatigue damage occurs in composites, we need access to procedures by which the development and accumulation of this damage, and therefore the likely life of the material (or component) in question, can be reliably predicted.

1.2   Fatigue phenomena in fibre composites

1.2.1   Damage in composites

Unlike metals, composite materials are inhomogeneous (on a gross scale) and anisotropic. They accumulate damage in a general rather than a localized fashion, and failure does not always occur by the propagation of a single macroscopic crack. The micro-structural mechanisms of damage accumulation, including fibre breakage and matrix cracking, debonding, transverse-ply cracking, and delamination, occur sometimes independently and sometimes interactively, and the predominance of one or the other may be strongly affected by both materials variables and testing conditions.

   At low levels of stress in monotonic loading, or early in life during cyclic loading, most types of composite sustain damage. This damage is distributed throughout the stressed region, and although it does not always immediately reduce the strength of the composite, it often reduces the stiffness. Such strength reductions as might occur (in the process described as 'wear-out') are sometimes off-set in the early stages of life by slight increases in strength, or 'wear-in'. These increases may be a result of the slightly improved fibre alignment which follows small, stress-induced, viscoelastic or creep deformations in the matrix. Later in life the amount of damage accumulated in some region of the composite may be so great that the residual load-bearing capacity of the composite in that region falls to the level of the maximum stress in the fatigue cycle and failure ensues, as shown schematically in Fig. 1.1. This process may occur gradually, when it is simply referred to as degradation, or catastrophically, when it is termed 'sudden-death'. Changes of this kind do not necessarily relate to the propagation of a single crack, and this must be recognized when attempting to interpret composites fatigue data obtained by methods developed for metallic materials.

   When a pre-existing crack is present in a composite it may or may not propagate under the action of a cyclic load, depending upon the nature of the composite. In highly anisotropic composites of high V_f, for example, the crack will often refuse to propagate normal to the fibres (mode 1) but will be diverted into a splitting mode, sometimes resulting in end-to-end splitting which simply eliminates the crack. By contrast, in GRP laminates containing woven-roving or chopped-strand mat reinforcement crack tip damage may remain localized

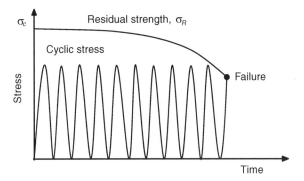

Fig. 1.1   Degradation of composite strength by wear-out until the residual strength σ_R falls from the normal composite strength σ_c to the level of the fatigue stress, at which point failure occurs.

by the complex geometry of the fibre array and the crack may proceed through this damaged zone in a fashion analogous to the propagation of a crack in a plastically deformable metal.[1]

Howe and Owen[2] (1972) studied the accumulation of damage during cyclic loading with the object of obtaining useful working relationships of the Miner-rule type[3] that might be used in design. With the aid of optical microscopy they studied the development of debonding sites and resin cracks in chopped-strand-mat/polyester composites and they suggested that, although debonding did not itself cause reductions in strength, it served to initiate resin cracks which did weaken the material. For resin cracking they proposed a non-linear damage law, independent of stress level, which gives the damage Δ as

$$\Delta = \Sigma \left[A \left(\frac{n}{N} \right) + B \left(\frac{n}{N} \right)^2 \right] \qquad [1.1]$$

where n is the number of cycles sustained by the composite at a stress which would normally cause failure after N cycles, and A and B are constants. B is negative and Δ is equal to unity at failure. They used a modification of this law to predict residual strength after cycling of CSM/polyester laminates, this strength being dependent upon the growth of resin cracks. Different damage mechanisms accumulated damage at different rates through the life cycle, as shown in Fig. 1.2. The damage development laws are likely to be different for each specific damage mechanism and will also be structure dependent, as illustrated by the results of crack-density measurements shown in Fig. 1.3.[4] These measurements were made on a T800/5245 CFRP laminate of $[(\pm45,0_2)_2]_s$ lay-up, and it can be seen that the development of cracks in the outer (unconstrained) and inner (constrained) 45° plies proceeds at quite different rates: the saturation levels for the two types of crack are also quite different.

The observed changes in the mechanical properties of fatigued composites are unlikely to be caused by a single damage mechanism. Detailed studies of the damage processes occurring during cycling of CFRP materials[5] show that sequences of damage occur through-out life, and these sequences can be mapped, as shown in Fig. 1.4, on a conventional $\sigma/\log N_f$ diagram. It seems likely that each damage-mechanism curve, including the final failure curve (i.e. the $\sigma/\log N_f$ curve), represents part of an S-shaped decay curve of the kind postulated by Talreja,[6] although in the experimental window we see only a part of each curve. It is also supposed that at sufficiently low stresses, corresponding to some notional endurance limit, all curves will flatten out and converge at large numbers of cycles. The concept of accumulation of damage leading to ultimate failure is embodied in the early cumulative-damage theory of Hashin and Rotem.[7]

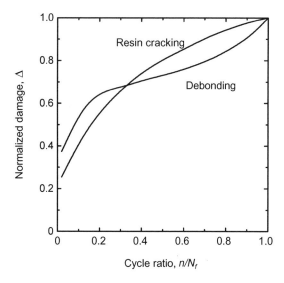

Fig. 1.2   Normalized plots of two types of damage, which occur during the fatigue cycling of a CSM/polyester laminate (redrawn from Howe and Owen[2]).

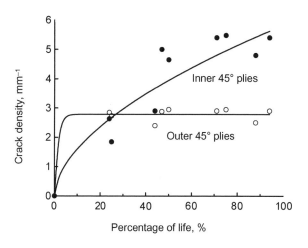

Fig. 1.3   Density of cracks in 45° plies in a $[(\pm45,0_2)_2]_s$ T800/5245 CFRP laminate during cycling at a peak stress of 1 GPa and an R ratio of 0.1.[4]

1.2.2   Experimental scatter and the definition of failure

Smith and Owen[8] demonstrated the extent to which variability affects the results of fatigue tests and emphasized the importance of replicate testing. This variability stems not only from the statistical nature of the progressive damage which leads to failure, but is more particularly due to the variable quality of many commercial composite materials. They also pointed out that in many kinds of composite the number of cycles to complete separation of the broken halves of a sample is a definition of failure that becomes quite meaningless if the

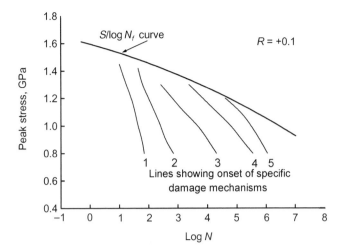

Fig. 1.4   Schematic damage mechanism maps for a T800/5245 $[(\pm45,0_2)_2]_s$ CFRP laminate tested in repeated tension fatigue $(R = 0.1)$.[5]

sample has lost its integrity and its ability to sustain an applied stress as a result of extensive resin cracking, arguing the need for careful (and relevant) definition of the failure criterion, although they accept that the use of debonding or the onset of resin cracking, say, as failure criteria would drastically impair the economic use of a material like GRP.

It is not surprising, given the nature of composites, that the variability of their fatigue response is even greater than that associated with metallic materials. Stress/life data may be obtained by testing single samples at many different stress levels, or by carrying out replicate tests at rather fewer stresses: the latter is usually considered to be the more satisfactory method because it provides statistical information at each stress, and provides probability/ stress/life curves in addition to median-life or mean-life curves. One of the problems is to know how many replicate tests should be done at each stress level since, given the cost of fatigue-testing programmes, the smaller the number of tests that can be used to establish a 'safe' $\sigma/\log N_f$ curve, the better. From a statistical point of view it is often expected that at least 20 replicate tests at each stress may be necessary before the user can have any confidence in a statistical analysis of results (see, for example, Lee et al.).[9]

A variety of distributions have been used to characterize fatigue lives, but the three-parameter Weibull function is often considered to be the most appropriate model for this purpose. The form of the cumulative distribution function used for fatigue is:

$$P(N_f;a,b,m) = 1 - \exp\left[-\left(\frac{N_f - a}{b} \right)^m \right]$$ [1.2]

where P is the probability of a life N_f, and a, the location parameter, defines a number of cycles for which there is zero probability of failure. For metallic materials, the value of the shape parameter m is often in the range $2 < m < 6$,[10] whereas several recent studies[11–13] suggest that $1 < m < 2$ for the fatigue of CFRPs.

Although we often work in terms of median or mean lives when discussing fatigue data, it is important to recognize that to the designer of critical structures, such as aircraft components, the requirements are much more restrictive, and it is likely that the desired failure probability for such a structure would be at a very low level, say 5%, instead of the

50% level implied by the median life. The use of the Weibull model to determine design allowables for the fatigue of composites has also been discussed by King.[14] An even more rigorous 'life' parameter may be the minimum extreme value obtained from an application of the theory of extreme values.[15] Extreme-value models are appropriate models for describing many engineering phenomena and systems where the relevant parameters are the characteristic largest and characteristic smallest values of a distribution.

A useful feature of the Weibull model is its reproductive property.[16] A consequence of this property is that, for a population of results that is well modelled by the Weibull distribution, certain other features of the population, such as the minimum extreme values, will also be described by a Weibull distribution. Thus, the exact distribution of the smallest observations in sets of data that are described by a Weibull model also fits a Weibull model. If we have replicate data sets of fatigue lives at a given stress and R ratio which is described by the two-parameter version of equation [1.2], with shape parameter m and scale parameter b (a being equal to 0), the smallest observations of these data sets also exhibit a Weibull distribution similar to that of the parent distribution and with the same value of the shape factor m but rescaled by $n^{1/m}$. The characteristic minimum value for a test sample of n tests will therefore be $(b/n^{1/m})$ and the modal value (i.e. the most probable value) of the distribution will be given by:

$$\frac{b}{n^{\frac{1}{m}}}\left(1 - \frac{1}{m}\right)^{\frac{1}{m}}$$

If, on the other hand, the desired level of failure probability happens to be the 5% level ($q = 0.05$), then the appropriate value of 'life' is given by:

$$b\left[\ln\left(\frac{1}{1-q}\right)\right]^{\frac{1}{m}}$$

Thus, from a series of replicate data sets of fatigue lives at various cyclic stress levels, a stress/life/probability (or $S/N/P$) diagram resembling that shown in Fig. 1.5 may be drawn, provided the distribution parameters b and m can be obtained for each data set. From a design point of view, the lower curve in this diagram, representing some given failure probability, is clearly of more interest to the engineer than any other part of the data, but it can only be obtained by statistical means which requires reliable values of the two distribution parameters b and m. This implies, as we have said, replicate data sets of 20 or more test results for each stress level and R ratio, a requirement which carries with it a serious time/cost disincentive. Whitney[11] has shown, however, that where only small numbers of life values are available at a number of different stress levels, the data may be pooled to give an overall value of the Weibull shape parameter m, this value then being used to obtain working stress/loglife curves for any given failure probability. This is done by normalizing each test-stress data set with respect to either the characteristic life b (the scale factor of the Weibull distribution for the data set) or the median life for the data set, pooling all data sets for *all* stress levels and *all* R ratios, and then re-ranking them in order to allot a new failure probability function to each point. The virtue of this procedure is that a much larger population is being used to derive the value of the Weibull shape parameter and calculations of an expected life based on that m value will be much more reliable than ones obtained from the much smaller data sets for each individual stress level. Further discussion of this topic is given in the context of life prediction later in this volume.[17]

Definitions of 'failure' and the establishment of failure criteria are closely linked subjects

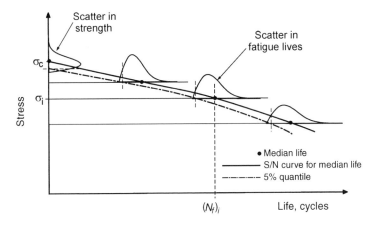

Fig. 1.5   Effects of variability in strength and fatigue life on the definition of the $\sigma/\log N_f$ curve. The scatterband of lives is jointly defined by the upper and lower probability limits of the fatigue data sets and the monotonic strength distribution.

which together lead towards solutions of the fundamental problem in fatigue design, which is life prediction. It has long been recognized that the wide variety of composite types and lay-ups makes it uneconomical to determine fatigue life curves by experiment alone.[18] The virtues of attempting to build unified life-prediction models incorporating both micro-structural and micromechanical aspects of composite response have been presented by Hashin and Rotem[18] and Petermann and Plumtree[19] and these themes are widely explored in later sections of this book devoted to life-prediction methods.

In recent years, following the increased use of high-performance reinforced plastics in aircraft, a somewhat more aggressive criterion of failure has sometimes been adopted, particularly where 'normal' service may involve the exposure of a component to low-velocity impact damage. Impact damage at high energy levels will seriously impair the load-bearing ability of the composite, and especially its resistance to compressive loads. But even at energy levels which are too low to leave any visible mark on the surfaces of the laminate there may well be internal damage which could grow under the influence of subsequent cyclic loading. This has led to the introduction of a requirement of 'zero-growth', i.e. the definition of a threshold strain level below which any impact damage in the material is stable, a concept akin to the notion of the endurance limit in the fatigue of ferrous metals and alloys. The difference is that little direct experimental evidence is available to suggest that fibre-reinforced plastics show a true fatigue (or endurance) limit. An illustration of the concept of a damage-growth threshold is shown in Fig. 1.6 taken from some recent experiments on the real-time monitoring of impact-damage CFRP by means of a new technique know as acoustography.[20]

1.2.3   Stress/life and strain/life curves
Much of the early work on the fatigue of fibre composites reflects the wider body of knowledge relating to the fatigue of metals. This is not unreasonable since the established methods of accumulating and analysing metallic fatigue data provided a reliable means of describing fatigue phenomena and designing against fatigue. Weibull's seminal text in this field[21] remains an important source for workers on composites fatigue. The danger was, and

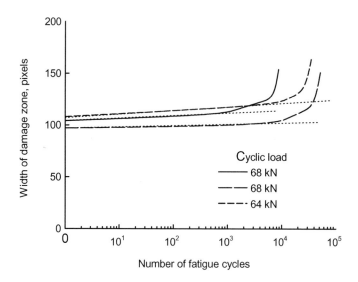

Fig. 1.6   Growth in the width of an impact-damage zone during subsequent fatigue cycling in repeated compression. The material is a 4 mm thick AS4/8552 carbon-fibre/epoxy laminate of $[45/0/-45/90]_{2S}$ lay-up.[20]

is, in making the assumption that the underlying mechanisms of material behaviour that give rise to the classical stress/life (S/N or $\sigma/\log N_f$) curve are the same in both metals and composites.

Before the development of fracture mechanics and its use in treating metallic fatigue as a crack-growth problem, the only available design information on fatigue behaviour was the $\sigma/\log N_f$ curve. This represented the perceived nature of fatigue in terms of experimental results, but gave no indication of the mechanisms of fatigue damage, of the presence or behaviour of cracks, or of changes in the characteristics of the material as a consequence of the fatigue process. The curve represents the stress to cause failure in a given number of cycles, usually either the mean or median life of a series of replicate tests at the same stress. Despite the anomaly (from a mathematical viewpoint) of plotting the dependent variable on the abscissa rather than vice versa, the $\sigma/\log N_f$ curve is nevertheless a useful starting point for the designer, provided due attention has been paid to the statistical aspects of data generation, so that the apparently simple failure envelope which it defines is associated with failure probabilities rather than with some simplistic fail/no-fail criterion. It can then be used, as many designers prefer, without any consideration of the underlying fatigue damage. Although stress/life plots are usually semi-logarithmic, there is no mechanistic reason for this.

Some of the earliest stress/life curves for fibre composites were published by Boller[22-26] in the 1950s and 60s. Two groups of Boller's data, showing the effects of different kinds of resin matrices and different laminate lay-ups, are reproduced in Fig. 1.7.[24] The effects illustrated in these and other curves published by Boller are quite complex, and not easily explained, but it is interesting to note that a unidirectional GRP laminate is more susceptible to fatigue damage than those with lay-ups containing fibres aligned in directions other than the stress direction.

By contrast, when the first fatigue experiments began to be carried out on early unidirectional carbon-fibre-reinforced plastics, these materials appeared to be very fatigue resistant, to the extent that in repeated-tension cycling, the $\sigma/\log N_f$ curve was flat and

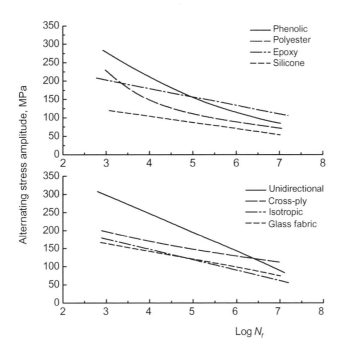

Fig. 1.7   Stress/life curves for GRP composites, showing the influence of different matrix resins and the influence of different laminate lay-ups. The data are redrawn from one of the publications of Boller.[24] Upper graphs for un-notched specimens of 181 glass-fabric reinforced resins tested at 0° to the warp at 23 °C and 50% relative humidity (RH). Lower graphs for notched specimens of epoxy-based laminates tested at 38 °C and 100% RH.

remained almost entirely within the scatterband for monotonic tensile failures, as shown in the lower graph of Fig. 1.8.[27,28] These composites, which were reinforced with the high-modulus (HM, or Type 1) species of carbon fibre, had very low failure strains. The fatigue response was therefore effectively dominated by tensile failure of the fibres alone and the slight reduction in resistance after 10^6 or 10^7 cycles appeared to be a result of small viscoelastic (creep) strains rather than to cycling effects *per se*.[29] Only in torsion or bending tests was the slope of the σ/log N_f increased as these different stress systems allowed other damage mechanisms to occur, as the upper graph in Fig. 1.8 illustrates.

A very small failure strain is often a disadvantage in engineering materials (some of the early CFRPs were extremely brittle) and developments in carbon-fibre manufacture led to materials that possessed higher failure strains (lower elastic moduli), although these improvements were often offset by concomitant reductions in strength. By the end of the 1970s, the most common polyacrylonitrile-based fibres, designated HMS, HTS and XAS, covered a range of moduli from about 400 GPa down to 200 GPa, and the tensile stress/loglife data for unidirectional laminates reinforced with these fibres fell approximately on straight lines with slopes which increased with decreasing fibre stiffness.[30] Jones *et al.*[31] showed that there was a linear relationship between the slopes of these σ/log N_f curves and the elastic moduli of the reinforcing fibres.

The dominant damage mechanisms in fibre composites vary both with the nature of the composite (the particular combination of fibres and matrices, reinforcement lay-up, etc.), and with the loading conditions (tension, bending, compression, etc.), and results for any one material under a given stress condition may appear to fit no general pattern. This is easily

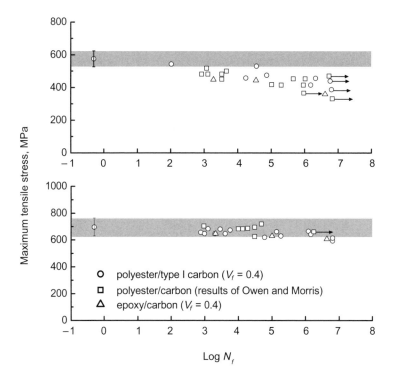

Fig. 1.8   Early results of Beaumont and Harris[27] and Owen and Morris[28] for unidirectional carbon/ epoxy and carbon/polyester composites fatigue tested in tension (lower graph) and flexure (upper graph). The shaded bands represent the scatterband of monotonic strength values.

illustrated with reference to the gradual accumulation of results and materials development over the last two decades or so.

First, the forms of stress/life curves for various kinds of GRP have long been familiar to researchers, as was the fact that the fall of the curve with reducing stress was considerable. This fall, or average slope, is an indication of the fatigue resistance of the material, a more rapid fall being indicative of a greater susceptibility to fatigue damage. Mandell[32] attempted to show that fatigue damage in GRP materials can be explained simply in terms of a gradual deterioration of the load-bearing fibres. He analysed a great deal of data to demonstrate that the behaviour of composites with long or short fibres, in any orientation, and with any matrix, can be explained in this way. He did this by effectively forcing σ/log N_f curves to fit a linear law of the form:

$$\sigma = \sigma_t - B\log N_f \qquad\qquad [1.3]$$

where σ is the peak cyclic (tensile stress), σ_t is the monotonic tensile fracture stress, N_f is the fatigue life of the material at stress σ, and B is a constant, as illustrated in Fig. 1.9. For a wide and disparate range of GRP materials, including moulded reinforced thermoplastics, Mandell obtained a constant value of about 10 for the ratio σ_t/B, with very little spread. In principle, the idea that the controlling mechanism in the fatigue of composites is the gradual deterioration of the load-bearing fibres is logical and inevitable. What controls the actual life of any given sample or composite type is simply the manner in which other mechanisms, such as transverse-ply cracking in 0/90 laminates, or local resin cracking in woven-cloth

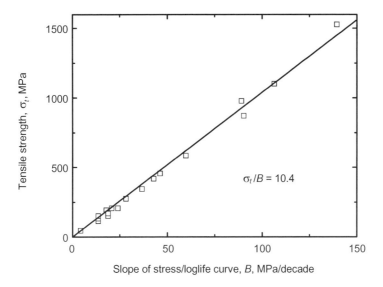

Fig. 1.9   Relationship between composite tensile strength and the slope of the fatigue σ/log N_f curve (after Mandell[32]). Data points taken by Mandell from the literature represent a wide range of GRP composites.

composites, modify the rate of accumulation of damage in the load-bearing fibres. Nevertheless, a single mechanistic model which includes randomly reinforced dough-moulding compounds and injection-moulded thermoplasts as well as woven and non-woven laminates is unexpected.

The σ/log N_f curves for many GRP materials are rarely linear, however. With GRP there are two factors which complicate the appearance of the stress/life curves. As a consequence of the high failure strain of the glass fibres and their sensitivity to moisture,

- the tensile strengths of GRP materials are sensitive to strain-rate and temperature
- during cycling at large strains there is usually a significant rise in temperature as a result of hysteretic heating which is not easily dissipated by the non-conducting constituents of the GRP.

The effects of these features have been demonstrated by Sims and Gladman.[33,34] First, when fatigue tests are carried out at constant frequency over the whole stress range of interest, the deformation rate is usually considerably greater than the rates normally used for measuring the monotonic strength. As a result, since it is common for the strength to be included as the point on the extreme left of the σ/log N_f curve, that measured strength is often actually lower than a value measured at the fatigue-test frequency. Second, if tests are run at constant frequency, the effective strain rate at each stress level will be different (higher at lower stresses), and the measured life values for each stress will not be associated with a common baseline of material behaviour, i.e. the fatigue curve will refer to a range of stresses σ, which are proportions of a variable material property, say $\sigma_t(\dot{\varepsilon})$, instead of the material property that we normally define as the strength σ_t. And third, as the peak stress level falls and the life of the sample extends, the degree of hysteretic heating rises and the effective baseline strength of the material therefore also falls, so reversing the effect of the higher effective deformation rate. Sims and Gladman showed that the only way to avoid the effects of these interacting processes is to ensure that all σ/log N_f curves for GRP materials are determined at a fixed rate of load application (RLA), that the material strength is measured at the same RLA, and that

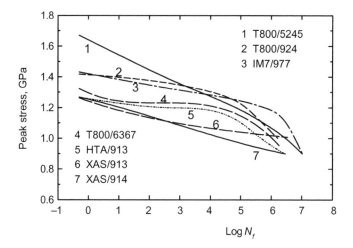

Fig. 1.10   Stress/median-life curves for repeated-tension fatigue ($R = 0.1$) for seven varieties of carbon-fibre composite, all with the lay-up $[(\pm45,0_2)_2]_s$.[35]

the hysteretic effects are either eliminated or accounted for. These corrections can make substantial differences to the shapes of stress/life curves and to the validity of the design data obtained from them: many otherwise curved σ/log N_f graphs are also rendered more linear by these corrective measures. By contrast with GRP, carbon-fibre composites are largely rate-insensitive and, because they deform less than GRP under working loads and are reasonably highly conducting, hysteretic heating effects are usually absent.

Increasing awareness on the part of designers of the qualities of fibre composites, and of carbon-fibre composites in particular, resulted in demands for fibres with combinations of strength and stiffness which were different from those which characterized the earlier materials. A particular call was for higher failure strains in association with high strength, and these demands led to developments in carbon-fibre manufacture and the availability of a much wider range of fibre characteristics. The fatigue performance of composites based on these newer fibres is clearly different from that of earlier CFRPs, as illustrated by the results shown in Fig. 1.10,[35] and the monotonic strength characteristics of the reinforcing fibres are not directly translated into the fatigue response, i.e. the strongest fibres do not always generate the most fatigue-resistant composites. And whereas the earliest of CFRP composites had approximately linear σ/log N_f curves, the newer, increasingly 'high-performance' composites sometimes show downward curvature.

This downward curvature also occurs in composites reinforced with Kevlar-49 aromatic polyamide (aramid) fibres.[31,36] Typical behaviour of a cross-plied KFRP composite is compared with those of similar GRP and CFRP materials in Fig. 1.11,[31] plotted here in terms of initial peak strain, rather than stress. The composites are comparable in every respect except for the reinforcing fibres. The performance of the KFRP over the first three decades is similar to that of the CFRP in that the slopes of the strain/life curves are similar. However, at maximum cyclic strain (or stress) levels only marginally below the tensile-failure scatter band the fatigue resistance deteriorates rapidly, and a change in controlling failure mode occurs. At the highest stress levels (first three or four decades in Fig. 1.11) failure of the KFRP occurs by the normal fibre-dominated failure process. At lower stresses, however, (much larger numbers of cycles) the internal structural weaknesses of the aramid filaments are exposed to the effects of the cyclic stress and the fibres themselves exhibit much lower

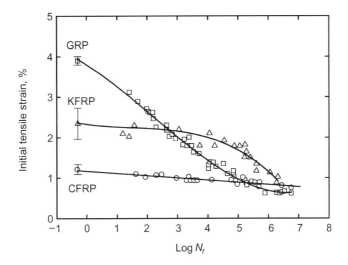

Fig. 1.11   Strain/life curves for $[(0,90)_2]_s$ laminates of composites reinforced with HTS carabon, Kevlar and E-glass fibres, all in the same Code-69 epoxy resin[31] (repeated tension fatigue, $R = 0.1$: RH = 65%).

fatigue resistance. The three curves all appear to be levelling out beyond 10^7 cycles at approximately the same strain level.

These results for carbon, glass and aramid laminates illustrate very well a strain-control model of fatigue proposed by Talreja.[6] He suggested that the strain/loglife curves for polymer–matrix composites may be thought of in terms of three régimes within which separate mechanisms control fatigue failure. At high stress levels fibre breakage occurs (with or without interfacial debonding) which leads to failures within the normal tensile failure scatter band of the 0° plies. At lower cyclic stress levels, however, although statistical fibre breakage still occurs, it does not lead so rapidly to composite destruction and other competing mechanisms then have time to occur. These other mechanisms – matrix cracking, interfacial shear failure, etc. – can then influence the overall damage state provided the composite working strain level is sufficiently high, and the slope of the strain/loglife curve therefore begins to fall. There is, however, some notional fatigue-limit strain for the matrix itself and if working strains do not rise above this level the composite should not, in principle, fail in fatigue. The strain/loglife curve ought therefore to flatten out again and something in the nature of an endurance limit should be observed. Whether or not some or all of these stages are observed will clearly depend on the characteristics of the constituents and the lay-up geometry. In Fig. 1.11, where the influence of the fibre deformation characteristics is more visible than in a stress/life plot, it can be seen that high working strains in the GRP prevent the establishment of stage 1 of the Talreja model, the curve moving almost immediately into stage 2, whereas the higher stiffness of the Kevlar fibre delays this transition in the aramid composites. Working strains in the CFRP are rarely sufficiently high as to exceed the matrix fatigue limit and so the strain/life curve (like the σ/log N_f curve) retains the low slope, characteristic of stage 1, for the entire stress range shown. Tests on composite materials are usually discontinued before the third section levels out completely, so that we are unsure whether a true fatigue limit exists.

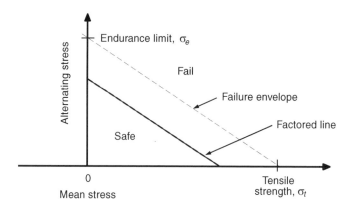

Fig. 1.12   Schematic illustration of a constant-life or Goodman diagram. The stress σ_e is the endurance fatigue limit, and σ_t is the material tensile strength.

1.2.4   Constant-life diagrams

In order to use stress/life information for design purposes, a common procedure is to cross-plot the data to show the expected life (or expected stress for some particular probability of failure) for a given combination of the alternating component of stress σ_{alt}, defined as half the stress range $\frac{1}{2}(\sigma_{max} - \sigma_{min})$, and the mean stress σ_m, which is $\frac{1}{2}(\sigma_{max} + \sigma_{min})$. A stress ratio R, is defined as $\sigma_{min}/\sigma_{max}$. In metallic fatigue it was assumed that compression stresses were of no significance because they acted only to close fatigue cracks, unlike tensile forces. Master diagrams of this kind are presented in a variety of forms, all more or less equivalent, but the most familiar is that which is usually referred as the Goodman diagram (Fig. 1.12). For design purposes, it was useful to have an equation to represent the fail/safe boundary in this diagram, and it is the linear relationship of Fig. 1.12 that is associated with the name of Goodman[37] although others have been proposed, including the earlier parabolic relationship of Gerber.[38] The linear and parabolic 'laws' have been modified to include safety factors on one or both of the stress components.

An important question, for metals as well as for composites, relates to the minimum number of fatigue-test results that are needed to define the failure envelope with a level of reliability sufficient for engineering design of critical components. And although the discussion of $\sigma/\log N_f$ curves in the last section dealt only with tension/tension cycling, the diagram in Fig. 1.12 implies the presence of increasing levels of compression stress as a radius vector sweeps anti-clockwise from the mean-stress axis beyond an angle of 45°. Since it is a well-known feature of the mechanical behaviour of composites that the compression strength is often lower than the tensile strength, the effect of compression stresses in fatigue is of no small significance.

Early examples of the derivation of constant-life diagrams were given by Boller,[24] Owen and Morris,[28] Owen,[39] Schütz and Gerharz,[40] and Kim,[41] although these authors did not develop the constant-life diagrams for life-prediction purposes. The constant-life diagram of Schütz and Gerharz for a quasi-isotropic $[(0_2, \pm45)_2, 90]_s$ CFRP laminate is shown in Fig. 1.13. Harris and co-workers[35,13] have shown that the effects of R ratio can be illustrated by presenting the fatigue data on a normalized constant-life diagram by means of the function:

$$a = f(1 - m)^u(c + m)^v \qquad [1.4]$$

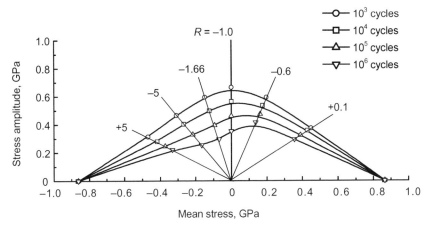

Fig. 1.13   Constant-life plots for a $[(0_2, \pm45)_2, 90]_S$ CFRP laminate. (Data from Schütz and Gerharz.[40])

where $a = \sigma_{alt}/\sigma_t$, $m = \sigma_m/\sigma_t$ and $c = \sigma_c/\sigma_t$ (definitions of σ_{alt} and σ_m were given in Section 2.1, and σ_t and σ_c are the monotonic tensile and compressive strengths, respectively). The stress function f depends on the test material, and in particular on the value of the ratio σ_c/σ_t, and the exponents u and v, usually quite close to each other in value, are functions of log N_f. The authors have developed this model as the basis of a life-prediction procedure with wide-ranging applicability and a full treatment of this work is given later in this volume.[17]

1.2.5   Damage accumulation: residual stiffness and strength

The progressive damage which occurs in a composite sample during fatigue will affect the mechanical properties of the material to an extent which depends on the composition and lay-up of the composite and on the mode of testing. In a unidirectional, high-modulus CFRP, for example, there may be no significant changes in composite stiffness prior to failure.[27] By contrast, in cross-plied (0/90) GRP and CFRP laminates transverse-ply cracking occurs early in the life of the sample, causing a significant stiffness reduction, perhaps of the order of 10%. Thereafter, for the greater part of the life following this initial deterioration there may be little further change in stiffness (although longitudinal cracks may appear as a result of the lateral constraint imposed by the transverse plies) until close to failure when the elastic modulus falls rapidly.[42,43] An illustration of the extent of this progressive damage is shown in the x-ray photograph of Fig. 1.14,[54] showing both transverse and longitudinal cracking in a 0/90 laminate of XAS-carbon/PEEK after cycling in repeated tension. We note that even the use of a high-toughness matrix like PEEK does not eliminate this cracking. Boniface and Ogin[44] have shown that this kind of transverse-crack growth can be satisfactorily modelled by the Paris crack-growth relationship with exponents p between 2 and 6. When the reinforcement is in the form of a woven fabric, the occurrence of transverse-ply cracking is hindered, and the changes in stiffness accompanying cycling are less marked. Even in laminates containing only ±45 and 0° plies there may be no fall in stiffness until near to failure. Many authors have discussed the changes in stiffness that occur during cycling, and some have developed life-prediction models which are based on the relationship between stiffness and accumulated damage.[45–48] The microstructural damage events which lead to these changes are readily monitored by means of such methods as acoustic emission analysis.[5,29]

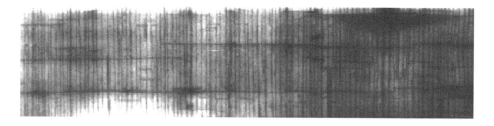

Fig. 1.14   X-ray photograph of a 0/90 carbon-fibre/PEEK composite after 8.5×10^5 fatigue cycles in repeated tension at a peak stress of 200 MPa.[54] The tensile loading axis is parallel with the long side of the photograph.

It is a matter of common experience that both the rigidities and strengths of composite materials are adversely affected by repeated loading as damage accumulates in the material. In some circumstances, both strength and stiffness may initially increase slightly as the fibres in off-axis plies or slightly misaligned fibres in 0° plies re-orient themselves in the visco-elastic matrix under the influence of tensile loads, but the dominating effect is that due to the accumulating damage in the material. The deterioration during cycling is more rapid the higher the stress, as shown in Fig. 1.15. In accordance with the wear-out model, the end-point of each residual-strength curve in this diagram lies on the normal $\sigma/\log N_f$ curve for the material.

In their work on a comparable group of CFRP, GRP and KFRP cross-plied laminates, Adam et al.[49] found that the shapes of the residual strength curves for all three materials were similar and could be represented by an interaction curve of the form:

$$t^a + s^b = 1 \qquad\qquad [1.5]$$

where t is a function of the number of cycles n, sustained at a given stress σ_{max}, for which the expected fatigue life is N_f:

$$t = \frac{\log n - \alpha}{\log N_f - \alpha} \qquad\qquad [1.6]$$

The constant α is equal to $\log(0.5)$ and simply accounts for the fact that the normal strength of the material corresponds to the lower limit of the cycles scale at ½ cycle (assuming repeated-tension cycling: the factor would be 0.25 for fully reversed cycling). The normalized residual strength ratio s is defined as:

$$s = \frac{\sigma_R - \sigma_{max}}{\sigma_t - \sigma_{max}} \qquad\qquad [1.7]$$

where σ_t is again the monotonic tensile strength of the material and σ_R is the residual strength after cycling at a peak fatigue stress σ_{max}. The exponents a and b are materials- and environment-dependent parameters which may have physical significance although they must be obtained by curve fitting. For rate-sensitive materials like GRP and KFRP, σ_t and σ_R must be determined at the same loading rate as that used for the fatigue cycling. The loss in strength, $(\sigma_t - \sigma_R)$, due to cycling may then be regarded as a damage function:

$$\Delta = 1 - s = (1 - t^a)^{\frac{1}{b}} \qquad\qquad [1.8]$$

The shape of the curve can, in principle, vary from a linear form (with $a = b = 1$), through a circular quadrant for powers of two, to an extremely angular variation for very high powers. Since both the gradual wear-out and 'sudden-death' type of behaviour can be

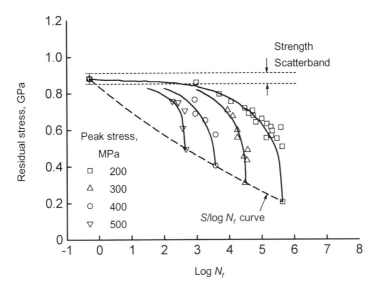

Fig. 1.15   Residual strength curves for samples of 0/90 GRP laminate subjected to fatigue cycling at an R ratio of 0.1 and various stress levels.[49]

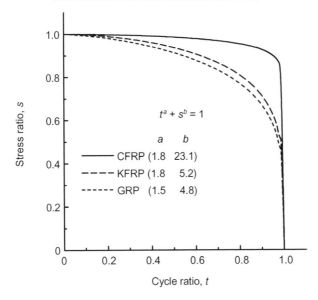

Fig. 1.16   Normalized residual strength curves for three comparable 0/90 laminates consisting of HTS carbon, Kevlar-49 and E-glass fibres in a common epoxy resin.[49] The values of the exponents for the fitted curves are shown in brackets.

accommodated within a single general model, a treatment of this kind has advantages over non-normalizing procedures. Despite apparent mechanistic dissimilarities in the fatigue behaviour of the three types of composite studied in this work, the residual strength results suggested that a common mechanism of damage accumulation led to final failure since the damage law of equation [1.5], with suitably chosen values of a and b, fits all of the data for all three materials, as shown in Fig. 1.16. Having established the values of a and b for a given material, the residual strength for any fatigue stress can then be evaluated:

$$\sigma_R = (\sigma_t - \sigma_{max})(1 - t^a)^{\frac{1}{b}} + \sigma_{max} \qquad\qquad [1.9]$$

or, alternatively, the remaining life $(N_f - n)$ can be estimated. Although it seems unlikely that a single mathematical model could cope with the whole range of composite types and lay-ups available, and this model certainly requires validation for each system of interest – materials, lay-ups, stress systems – this validation would be reasonably economical of test time and material, given that the interaction curve could be deduced from relatively few data.

The foregoing discussion suggests that the changes in mechanical properties of fatigued composites may be caused by a single damage mechanism, but this is unlikely to be the case. Detailed studies of the damage processes occurring during cycling of CFRP materials[5] show that sequences of damage occur throughout life, and these sequences can be mapped, as shown in Fig. 1.4, on a conventional $\sigma/\log N_f$ diagram. One of the problems of developing damage-growth models for life-prediction purposes is that the damage development laws are likely to be different for each specific damage mechanism and will be structure dependent.

1.2.6   Factors affecting fatigue behaviour of reinforced plastics

1.2.6.1   Fibre type

Brittle fibres such as glass, boron and carbon should not show the characteristic weakness of metals under fatigue loading conditions. In principle, then, composites containing them should also be fatigue resistant if the fibres carry the major part of the load and if the reinforcing phase is not so extensible as to permit large elastic or viscoelastic deformations of the matrix as a function of time. These conditions are fulfilled when composites unidirectionally reinforced with high-modulus fibres like carbon or boron are tested in repeated tension, and their $\sigma/\log N_f$ curves are, in general, very flat, as illustrated in Fig. 1.8. As cycling continues, however, small viscoelastic movements in the resin can allow local redistributions of stress which permit some random fibre damage to occur, and similar damage will occur in the neighbourhood of any stress concentrations. As a function of time, then, rather than as a function of the number of stress reversals, damage levels will build up to some critical level when the composite strength is no longer above the peak cyclic stress level, and failure will occur.

For manufacturing reasons (for example, to secure good 'drape' characteristics when doubly curved surfaces are required) there is considerable advantage in using woven fabrics as reinforcements, and it would be expected that the use of fabric reinforcements would affect the fatigue response. Curtis and Moore[50] showed that both the monotonic tensile strength and the fatigue strengths of CFRP laminates reinforced with woven fabric were poorer than those of similar materials made with non-woven fibres, mainly as a consequence of the distortion in the load-carrying 0° fibres and the stresses induced at weave cross-over points. However, when the fabric was oriented at 45° to the loading direction both tensile and fatigue performances were slightly better than for non-woven material. A more detailed review of the fatigue of fabric-reinforced laminates is given later in this volume by Naik.[51]

1.2.6.2   The matrix and environment

Fatigue tests on reinforced plastics show clearly that the matrix and interface are the weak links as far as fatigue resistance is concerned. Early work of Owen[52] and his collaborators suggested that lower reactivity resins gave better low-stress fatigue life in GRP, the optimum resin content being between 25 and 30 vol.%, although variations in resin content affected the fatigue strength at 10^6 cycles hardly at all by comparison with their effect on tensile strength. The results of Boller[24] in Fig. 1.7 indicate more marked effects, but although they suggest that the fatigue response of the laminate is better the more rigid the resin, the conclusion is not clear cut. By contrast with GRP, variations in resin properties were found by Owen et al.[39] to have little effect on the fatigue strength of CFRP. Kawai et al.[53] have recently explored in depth the effects of matrix ductility and progressive damage on the fatigue strengths of un-notched and notched carbon-fibre fabric laminates.

Any materials treatment or processing that can improve the resistance of the matrix to crack propagation or the interfacial adhesion is likely to improve fatigue properties. Conversely, exposure of reinforced plastics to water often results in some degree of plasticization of the matrix and weakening of the interfacial bond, and in GRP and aramid-fibre composites it may also affect the performance of the fibres themselves.[31] It follows that the fatigue of almost all FRP will be environment-sensitive, the least sensitive being those consisting of moisture-resistant plastics like the polyaryls (PEEK, etc.) reinforced with carbon fibres which are themselves insensitive to degradation in moist atmospheres.[54]

A wide-ranging review of the effects of the properties of the constituents on the fatigue performance of composites has been published by Konur and Matthews.[55]

1.2.6.3   Hybrid composites

A composite containing two (or more) types of reinforcing fibre in a common matrix is described as a 'hybrid' composite. Much attention has been lavished on the subject of hybrids, partly because of an early notion that in some curious way synergistic or 'some-thing-for-nothing' effects could be obtained by the used of mixed fibres. A brief review has been given by Harris.[56]

The simplest expectation for the fatigue stress/life curve of such a material would be that it would fall between those of the two single-fibre components, but published results do not present a clear picture on which to base predictive models. We should expect that the overall fatigue response would depend upon the extent to which the particular fibre mix controlled strain levels in the composites, and, if aramid fibres were involved, on the extent to which the intra-fibrillar weakness of that fibre was exposed to the stress. Some early experiments by Phillips et al.[57] on woven-cloth GRP/CFRP laminates suggested that adding CFRP to GRP improves its fatigue resistance more or less in proportion to the amount of CFRP added, i.e. in accordance with the rule of mixtures. Hofer et al.[58] also found that the fatigue stress of unidirectional HTS-carbon/S-glass hybrids obeyed the rule of mixtures when in the as-manufactured state, but showed a positive deviation from linear – i.e. a synergistic effect – when the composites were hygrothermally aged. Fernando et al.[36] found that the failure stresses for lives of 10^5 and 10^6 cycles for unidirectional carbon/Kevlar-49/epoxy hybrids were linear functions of composition for both repeated tension and tension/compression loading. But since the tensile strengths of the same series of hybrids were given by the failure-strain model, the fatigue ratio (fatigue stress for a given life divided by the tensile failure stress) showed a marked positive deviation from the linear weighting rule. The same workers[59] found that unidirectional CFRP/GRP fatigue strengths fell above a linear relation-ship, and the fatigue ratio therefore showed an even more marked synergistic effect. This suggests that factors controlling monotonic tensile (and compression) failure do not necessarily continue to determine failure under cyclic loading conditions, and that for fatigue applications there appear to be positive benefits in using hybrids in place of single-fibre composites.

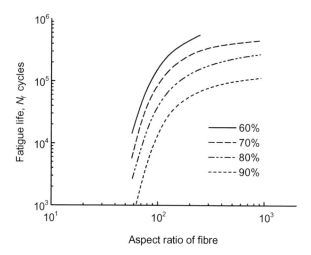

Fig. 1.17   Fatigue life versus aspect ratio for an applied stress of the indicated percentage of the composite tensile strength. The materials are short-fibre-reinforced boron/epoxy composites; repeated tension.[61]

1.2.6.4   Short-fibre composites

Although the fatigue resistance of high-V_f composites reinforced with continuous, aligned, rigid fibres is usually high, short-fibre composites of all kinds are much less resistant to fatigue damage because the weaker matrix is required to sustain a much greater proportion of the fluctuating load. Local failures are easily initiated in the matrix and these can destroy the integrity of the composite even though the fibres remain intact. The interface region is particularly susceptible to fatigue damage since the shear stresses at the interface may be reversing their direction at each cycle and there is always a high shear-stress concentration at fibre ends. It is also possible that in both random and aligned short-fibre composites the ends of fibres and weak interfaces can become sites for fatigue-crack initiation.

The beneficial effects of short fibres in materials like injection-moulding compounds have been well known for 40 years or more, and although increases in strength in such materials are modest, increases in toughness are much greater. Since fatigue resistance depends in part on strength and in part on crack resistance, it would therefore be expected that these benefits would be advantageously translated into fatigue response. Lomax and O'Rourke[60] reported that the endurance limit of polycarbonate at two million cycles is increased by a factor of seven when the polymer is filled with 40 vol.% of 6.4 mm long glass fibres. Lavengood and Gulbransen[61] determined the number of cycles to failure of short-fibre boron/epoxy composites and found that for cycling at any given fraction of the failure stress the fatigue life increased rapidly with fibre aspect ratio, levelling off at ℓ/d ratios of about 200. This therefore represents a critical aspect ratio above which the fatigue strength is a constant proportion of the flexural strength, as shown in Fig. 1.17. Lavengood and Gulbransen also studied the behaviour of aligned asbestos/epoxy composites and found them to behave in roughly the same way as boron/epoxy composites containing 25 mm-long fibres. Owen *et al.*[62] showed that the fatigue strength at a million cycles of polyester resin reinforced with random glass-fibre mat varied between 15 and 45% of the ultimate tensile strength. Huffine *et al.*[63] studied the tension and flexural fatigue behaviour of glass/epoxy composites containing 44 vol.% of aligned E-glass fibres 12.5 mm long. Their results suggested that this material was potentially useful for dynamic structural applications since it appeared to have an endurance limit of 40% of the ultimate tensile strength.

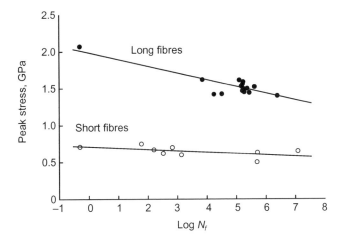

Fig. 1.18   Stress/loglife data for unidirectional composites of XAS/914 carbon/epoxy laminates reinforced with continuous and discontinuous fibres ($R = 0.1$).[67]

Harris et al.[64] studied the fatigue behaviour of commercial polyester dough-moulding compounds (DMCs) in both the dry and wet-aged conditions and for samples with drilled holes. Their results were characterized by a good deal of scatter, but indicated that in the low-stress (long-life) range the effects of moisture and stress concentrations were less marked than in the higher stress range. They showed that when their results were normalized by dividing by tensile strength, the σ/log N_f curve for the DMC fell only slightly more rapidly than the curves for other types of GRP. Atzori et al.[65] investigated the effects of a wide range of material and environmental variables on the fatigue behaviour of moulding compounds and developed a rule for estimating the fatigue strength from the monotonic tensile strength that was a modification of that of Mandell shown in Fig. 1.9.

In some cases the fatigue resistance of the matrix plastic has been found to be diminished by reinforcement with short fibres. For example, Shaver and Abrams[66] found that randomly reinforced glass/nylon composites had only half the endurance of the unfilled polymer. It should also be noted that the fatigue behaviour of most reinforced plastics will always be worse when the material is exposed to a wet environment.

Direct comparisons of the fatigue responses of otherwise identical composites reinforced with continuous and discontinuous fibres of the same type are relatively rare because the manufacturing processes are usually quite different. However, a comparison for some unidirectionally reinforced XAS/914 CFRP composites is shown in Fig. 1.18.[67] The continuous-fibre composites were hot pressed from conventional prepreg, and a well-aligned prepreg for the short-fibre materials, containing chopped fibres 3 mm long, was produced by the glycerol-alignment method: the fibre volume fraction was 0.35. Although the strength of the short-fibre composite is much lower than that of the continuous-fibre laminate, its fatigue response, as characterized by the slope of the σ/log N_f curve, is better and if the fatigue data are all normalized with respect to the monotonic tensile strengths of the two materials, the rate of fall-off for the conventional laminate is much greater than that for the short-fibre composite. Working with similar aligned short-fibre composites, Moore[68] also found that the fatigue behaviour of these materials compared favourably with those of continuous-fibre composites, although progressive cracking occurred from the fibre ends and fibre surface effects appeared to give more problems. It appears that less fibre damage

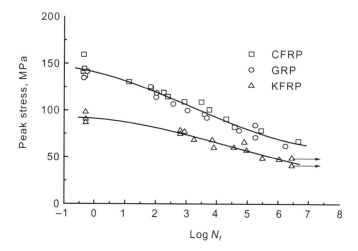

Fig. 1.19   Stress/loglife curves for the same materials as those of reference 31 but tested at 45° to the main fibre directions: $R = 0.1$; RH = 65%.[31]

resulting from fatigue can occur if the fibres are already short, and the short-fibre ends do not seem to act as sources of further damage. It is not certain what the effect of fibre length would be in aligned composites such as these, but Hitchen *et al.*[69] have shown that in random-short-fibre carbon/epoxy composites the fatigue life is independent of fibre length at any stress level. They also showed that the more flexible the matrix, the shorter the fatigue life. Friedrich *et al.*[70] found that the incorporation of short glass or carbon fibres into PEEK injection-moulding compounds produced only slight improvements in the fatigue and fracture toughness of this material. It has also been shown that the microstructural geometry related to injection moulding conditions has important effects on the fatigue-crack growth in short-carbon-fibre-reinforced PEEK composites.[71]

1.2.6.5   Interleaving
The concept of introducing soft regions, sometimes referred to as softening strips, into a fibre composite to provide barriers to crack growth and so raise the intrinsic toughness of the material has been well established since the mid-1970s and has been the subject of numerous academic papers despite being only relatively recently patented by a company that was not involved in the original idea.[72–77] A recent detailed review has been published by Kim and Mai.[78] The mechanisms by which this extra toughness is gained vary with composite type and direction of crack growth. For example, in the classic work of Favre,[73] the effect of interleaving with resin or polymer films was to increase the tendency to delamination or splitting parallel with the reinforcing fibre layers, whereas in other papers a crack propagating rapidly through a stiffer, more brittle composite is slowed when it passes through an interface into a more flexible region. Partridge and her co-workers extended the interleaving idea to investigate the possible effect on fatigue resistance, and were able to show a positive improvement despite the overall reduction in fibre content that interleaving brings. This topic is reviewed later in this book in the chapter by Fernando.[79]

1.2.6.6   Loading conditions
When the stress is not simply tensile, uniaxial, and aligned with the fibres more severe loads are placed on the matrix and the fatigue resistance of the composite is reduced. This occurs in simple flexural fatigue and tension/compression loading of undirectional composites, and

also in fatigue tests on any kind of laminated materials. Ramani and Williams,[80] for example, tested 18-ply (0±30) carbon/epoxy laminates in various combinations of axial tension/ compression cycling and showed an increasingly adverse effect on fatigue resistance as the compressive stress component was increased. Kunz and Beaumont[81] and Berg and Salama[82] showed that fatigue cracks propagated in CFRP during purely compressive cycling through the spreading of zones of fibre buckling failure. Compressive buckling is a characteristic mode of failure in many kinds of fibre-reinforced materials and it is usually initiated by local matrix shear failures, sometimes associated with debonding in imperfectly bonded compos- ites. Ramani and Williams observed extensive shear damage resulting from matrix shear and from interlaminar and interfacial weakness.

Compression and shear stress systems will also be likely to be even more damaging to composites containing aramid fibres than to CFRP or GRP, as indicated by the familiar poor compression response of KFRP. The shear weakness is also exhibited in tensile fatigue of ±45° KFRP laminates, by comparison with similar samples of CFRP and GRP, as shown in Fig. 1.19.[31] In this mode of stressing the matrix and interface would normally be expected to dominate composite behaviour, the fibre characteristics playing little part. This is demon- strated by the CFRP and GRP results in Fig. 1.19, but the intrafibrillar weakness of the aramid fibre results in a considerable reduction in composite fatigue resistance, and microscopic observations of KFRP samples that have failed in this mode clearly show the kinking and splitting of the fibres resulting from this weakness (Fig. 1.20). Similarly, when tested in torsion the weak parts of a composite (i.e. the resin and the interface) are loaded directly by the shear forces the strength and rigidity of the fibres contributing relatively little to fatigue resistance and the torsional rigidity of the material falls substantially during cycling.[83]

Because of the costly and time-consuming nature of fatigue-testing programmes the first test data that are obtained for any given material are almost determined under the simplest loading conditions, namely constant-stress testing, initially in repeated tension or flexure and subsequently with different R ratios. The carrying out of tests under variable-stress conditions and with multi-axial stresses is often left to the component or demonstrator test stage, and is sometimes not done at all. We refer briefly here to work in these areas, but leave more detailed considerations to other authors in this book.

1.2.6.6.1   Block loading and variable stresses

In most fatigue environments the mean and alternating stress amplitudes vary and may be presented as a spectrum of the frequency of occurrence of different stress levels. The concept of deterioration as a result of damage accumulation within the material with stress cycling is used in combination with the notion of residual strength, and the damage is quantified such that a parameter Δ represents the fraction of catastrophic damage sustained after n cycles (where $n < N_f$) so that at failure $\Delta = 1$ and $n = N_f$. Thus, Δ_i represents the fractional damage after cycling at a stress σ_i for a fraction of life n_i/N_i. Various forms of damage law have been used, the most common of which is the Palmgren–Miner linear damage rule. The accumulation of damage is postulated to be linear with number of cycles, and independent of the value of the stress:

$$\Delta = n/N \qquad\qquad [1.10]$$

Thus, if the load spectrum is divided into blocks with n_i cycles at stress levels σ_i, equation [1.10] applies incrementally to each block and the total damage is the sum of the individual 'block' damages, irrespective of the order of their application, so that:

Fig. 1.20   Splitting and kinking damage in Kevlar-49 fibres after fatigue cycling.[36]

$$\Delta = \Sigma \frac{n_i}{N_i} \qquad\qquad [1.11]$$

where Δ has the value of unity at failure. This well known, though rarely obeyed, rule was originally proposed for the prediction of the life of metallic components undergoing fatigue, and although a standard feature in texts on fatigue it has usually been viewed with suspicion by designers because it is often found to give non-conservative results, predicting lives greater than those observed experimentally. The definition of damage in equation [1.10] is not, of course, a mechanistic concept. It has been applied to many kinds of engineering materials, regardless of the actual nature of the damage mechanisms that contribute to the gradual deterioration and ultimate failure of an engineering component subject to cyclic loading.

The simplest step forward from the linear damage rule is the use of non-linear functions which retain the damage parameter Δ, as defined by equation [1.11]. Marco and Starkey,[84] for example, proposed a simple non-linear function of the form:

$$\Delta = (n/N)\beta \qquad\qquad [1.12]$$

where β is a function of stress amplitude. The condition for failure when $\Delta = 1$ is still satisfied and the Miner rule is a special case of this law with β = unity. The empirical damage law of equation [1.1] developed by Howe and Owen[2] is a special case of the Marco–Starkey model.

Experimental studies of fatigue under conditions of variable stress have been carried out in two ways. The simpler method is to investigate the effects of switching stresses between two or more predetermined levels at regular intervals, while the more complex is to define a spectrum of load levels more representative of real service conditions, usually established by strain-gauging a component on an operating system – an aircraft wing, for example. Analysis of results from the first of these alternatives is somewhat easier, but the second is clearly more directly relevant to the practical application. Harris et al.[85] and Schaff and Davidson[86] have described two-block tests, and Adam et al.[87] and Harris et al.[85] have described the results of four-block test sequences. Adam et al. carried out simple four-unit block-loading sequences on samples of a $[(\pm 45,0_2)_2]_s$ T800/5245 CFRP laminate. They first carried out a series of all-tension (TTTT) experiments for which the numbers of cycles at each of the stress levels were chosen so that the block should account for 20% of the lifetime of the specimen if Miner's rule were to be obeyed. Each unit in the sequence should therefore have contributed 5% of the total damage to failure. Since the contribution to the total life of the specimen by each of the units within the block programme is 5% of the median life, each block of four units therefore had a notional Miner number M of 0.2, i.e.

$$\frac{n_1}{m(N_1)} + \frac{n_2}{m(N_2)} + \frac{n_3}{m(N_3)} + \frac{n_4}{m(N_4)} = M = 0.2 \qquad [1.13]$$

where n_i is the number of cycles in the unit and $m(N_i)$ is the median life at that particular stress level. If Miner's rule is followed, the block should repeat itself 5 times before failure occurs. Following the first all-tension (TTTT) series, the next stage was to introduce a compressive element into the loading sequence so as to construct TTCT blocks.

It is logical to assume that if the life data for a given constant stress level are randomly distributed then the Miner sum M defined by equation [1.13], should be similarly distributed, regardless of whether the mean value or median value of M is equal to unity. The Miner sums from all six groups for each sequence were therefore pooled and analysed in terms of the Weibull model which showed that there was a marked difference between the mean values of the Miner number for the two groups of tests, 1.1 for the TTTT sequence, and 0.36 for the TTCT sequence. It appears, then, that the Miner rule is valid for all-tension block-loading sequences for this material, and the effect of introducing a single compression block into an otherwise all-tension group was clearly highly damaging, Miner's law no longer being obeyed and by a substantial margin, the mean life having been reduced by some 60% as a result of the substitution. Similarly, the substitution of a repeated tension unit into an all-compression sequence also resulted in a marked reduction in the mean Miner sum. It is therefore the process of stress reversal which is damaging rather than the actual sequence or the actual stress levels. This has serious consequences for designers since most practical cycling régimes are likely to include stress excursions into both tension and compression. This is certainly true of the familiar 'FALSTAFF' and other load-spectrum sequences used in the laboratory to represent actual life conditions for aircraft components.

Although studies of damage accumulation processes have been correlated moderately satisfactorily with fatigue testing régimes involving a limited number of stress levels, it is even more necessary to make good correlations when variable-amplitude or flight-loading sequences are used for practical design purposes, and a number of authors have written about this kind of analysis.[88–90] Shütz and Gerharz[40] reported results of life-prediction experiments with HT-carbon/epoxy laminates of $0.4V_f$ and $(0_2,\pm45,0_2,\pm45,90)_s$ construction. They used flight-spectrum tests typical of the conditions at an aircraft wing root, and they also obtained conventional fatigue data at a range of different R values from which they made Miner-rule life predictions at two mean stress levels for comparison with the variable-amplitude test results. The linear-damage rule predicted lives up to three times those actually measured – far too wide a margin for comfortable design work – and they concluded that this was probably due to damage contributed by low-load cycles in the compressive region which is not accounted for in the Miner estimate. The strength-degradation model of Yang and Jones[91] is claimed to be capable of predicting statistical distributions of fatigue life and residual strength as well as the effects of sequences of variable-amplitude loadings of glass/epoxy laminates.

1.2.6.6.2   Complex stresses

For most practical purposes, designers require models of behaviour that can predict failure under realistic combinations of stresses, rather than for the idealized uniaxial stress conditions under which most laboratory tests are carried out. There has been a great deal of research on complex-stress failure criteria. Twenty or more models have been proposed, although the differences between many of them are quite small, and designers throughout the world remain in dispute as to the 'best' model. Some of the key areas of disagreement have been exposed recently in two Special Issues of the journal *Composites Science and Technology* devoted to evaluating a wide range of popular failure criteria against validated experimental results.[92,93] The main difficulty in accepting one or other of the common methods is that their validity can usually only be tested over limited ranges of combined stress because of the complexity and cost of the test samples and test procedures for such experiments – tubes under combined tension, torsion and internal pressure, for example. Most of the existing failure criteria are in fact restricted to conditions of plane stress (thin plates) and some are only applicable to orthotropic materials.

Typical examples of complex-stress failure criteria are the maximum-stress criterion and the maximum-strain-energy criterion, and the differences between these in predicting the orientation-dependence of the strength of a single lamina are well known. The former takes into account that a unidirectional laminate will fail by different mechanisms at different angles, but is not able to allow for interactions between failure modes or stresses. The disadvantage of the strain-energy approach is that it does not take account of different failure modes. In its formal form it is an interactive model, although the interaction usually has to be allowed for empirically. The virtue of the strain-energy criterion in the eyes of many designers is that it is represented by a single equation instead of three (or five if compression failure is included). Although single-expression models are easy to work with mathematically, they are subject to the very serious criticism that they are truly appropriate only for homogeneous materials and do not take account of the different physical failure modes that occur in composites as the relative orientations of the stress and symmetry axes change. Homogenization methods of this kind result in single elliptical failure envelopes which can apparently be defined from only three or four data points obtained under straightforward experimental conditions. But they are incapable of distinguishing between fibre and matrix failures, or allowing for alternative matrix damage processes, such as cracking and ductile shear failure. Hart-Smith[94] has been particularly vociferous in condemning the quadratic models used by Tsai and his collaborators (and embodied in much of the currently available computer design software). He maintains that it is scientifically incorrect to use polynomial interaction failure models whenever the mechanism of failure of the laminate changes with stress and maintains that separate failure criteria are needed for the fibres, the matrix and the interface. He has argued for the adoption of a maximum-shear-stress (Tresca) model because it automatically introduces truncations related to changes in failure mode which the quadratic models do not, and satisfactorily explains in-plane laminate test data in all of the stress quadrants.

Among the earliest of attempts to explore the validity of extant complex-stress failure models under cyclic loading conditions were the work of Owen and collaborators[95–97] and of Smith and Pascoe.[98,99] These early papers illustrate the difficulties of applying models appropriate for homogeneous solids to inhomogeneous composites. However, as levels of understanding of materials behaviour and appreciation of the importance of the mechanistic approach have developed, the reliability of failure complex-stress failure models under cyclic conditions has improved, as illustrated in the papers of Philippidis and Vassilopoulos[100] and of Shokrieh and Lessard[101] later in this volume.

1.2.6.6.3   Prior impact damage

While fibre composites are finding increasing application in aerospace structures as a consequence of their high specific stiffness and strength, a major factor limiting the design of fibre-composite structures is their relative weakness under impact by foreign bodies.[102–104] Low-velocity impact damage is inevitable in service. It may be caused during manufacture, by careless handling, for example, or in service, by hailstones, bird strike, etc. It may also occur during maintenance, perhaps by accidentally dropped tools. Low-velocity impact damage is often undetectable by the naked eye,[105] even when it severely reduces the structural integrity of the component, and many research programs have been undertaken in an attempt to obtain better understanding of the impact response of composite materials. It is of particular concern that the compression strength is likely to be more markedly affected by low-velocity impact damage than the tensile strength, as illustrated by some results of Beheshty and Harris[106] shown in Fig. 1.21, although the relative effects depend upon the level of impact energy and the composite lay-up. An example of the effects of this kind of damage on the stress/life curves of a typical CFRP laminate is shown in Fig. 1.22;[106] it can be seen that the more serious effect on compression strength is carried through into the fatigue behaviour.

   In recent years there has also been work on the fatigue response of impact-damaged materials,[107–110] although their behaviour under a wide range of loading conditions from pure tension to pure compression cycling has not been extensively studied. The influences of low-velocity impact damage on the fatigue life and reliability of the affected structure are therefore not well characterized and the post-impact fatigue behaviour, even for a material for which the fatigue response in the undamaged state is well known, is still imperfectly understood. The influences of this kind of damage on the fatigue life and reliability of the affected structure are not well recognized and, in consequence, the prediction of fatigue life for impact-damaged materials is still far from satisfactory.

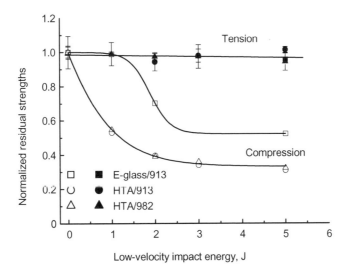

Fig. 1.21   Effect of low-velocity impact on the residual compression and tensile strengths of HTA/913 and HTA/982 CFRP laminates and E-glass/913[106] (data are normalized with respect to the strength of the undamaged material). All laminates are of lay-up $[(\pm 45,0_2)_2]_s$.

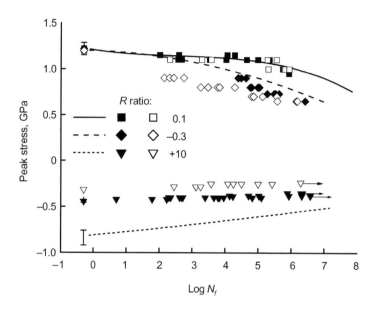

Fig. 1.22 σ/log N_f curves for HTA/982 CFRP laminate of $[(\pm45,0_2)_2]_s$ lay-up after damage by low-velocity impacts of 1 J (solid symbols) and 2 J (open symbols).[109] The lines are polynomial curves fitted to the data for the virgin laminate.

1.3   Concluding comments

The traditional view of fatigue as a materials characteristic, substantially coloured by our long-standing experience of the fatigue of metals and alloys, is equally applicable to the response of fibre composites under cyclic loading conditions, although the microstructural and mesostructural mechanisms which are responsible for the deterioration of composites are quite different. The picture of fatigue in fibre-reinforced plastics that has been presented here covers a wide range of fibre and matrix types, and of laminate structures, and it is clear that the level of appreciation of phenomenological aspects of composites fatigue is very great. This is, of course, necessary if designers with composites are to have confidence in their materials. One of the problems that is encountered in the composites field, however, is that new materials are developed and introduced at a somewhat higher rate than was common when metals and alloys were the main source of structural materials for engineering. As a consequence, a designer may often be faced with the dilemma that a new material is being considered, perhaps on the basis of its known excellent performance in terms of ordinary mechanical properties, thermal properties, density, etc., for introduction into an application where cyclic loading may also be a problem and yet there may be little or no fatigue-test data available. Life-prediction methods which are based on mechanistic models of materials degradation under load have, in the past, always been the preferred approach of materials scientists. The logic of this is inescapable, but it could be said that no generally applicable model of this kind has yet been able to supplant the only perceived acceptable alternative, *viz*. the carrying out of a full fatigue-test programme.

1.4   Bibliography

BROUTMAN L J (Editor) (1974), *Fracture and Fatigue*, Composite Materials Series vol. 5, (Academic Press, New York & London) ISBN: 0-12-136505-0.

HANCOCK J R (Editor) (1975), *Fatigue of Composite Materials: STP 569* (American Society for Testing and Materials, Philadelphia, USA).

REIFSNIDER K L and LAURAITIS K N (Editors) (1977), *Fatigue of Filamentary Composite Materials: STP 636* (American Society for Testing and Materials, Philadelphia, USA), ISBN: 0-8031-0347-6.

ASTM (1981), *Fatigue of Fibrous Composite Materials: STP 723* (American Society for Testing and Materials, Philadelphia, USA), ISBN: 0-8031-0719-6.

REIFSNIDER K L (Editor) (1982), *Damage in Composite Materials: STP 775* (American Society for Testing and Materials, Philadelphia, USA).

O'BRIEN K T (Editor) (1983), *Long-Term Behaviour of Composites: STP 813* (American Society for Testing and Materials, Philadelphia, USA).

HAHN H T (Editor) (1986), *Composite Materials: Fatigue and Fracture 1: STP 907* (American Society for Testing and Materials, Philadelphia, USA).

TALREJA R (1987), *Fatigue of Composite Materials* (Technomic Publishing Co Inc, Lancaster PA, USA), ISBN:87762-516-6.

LAGACE P A (Editor) (1989), *Composite Materials: Fatigue and Fracture 2: STP 1012* (American Society for Testing and Materials, Philadelphia, USA) ISBN: 0-8031-1190-8.

AGGARWAL B D and BROUTMAN L J (1990), *Analysis and Performance of Fibre Composites (Second Edition),* (John Wiley Interscience, New York).

O'BRIEN T K (Editor) (1991), *Composite Materials: Fatigue and Fracture 3: STP 1110* (American Society for Testing and Materials, Philadelphia, USA), ISBN: 0-8031-1419-2.

REIFSNIDER K L (Editor) (1991), *Fatigue of Composite Materials,* Composite Materials Series volume 4 (Elsevier Science BV, Amsterdam), ISBN: 0-44-70507-4.

STINCHCOMB W W and ASHBAUGH J E (Editors) (1993), *Composite Materials: Fatigue and Fracture 4: STP 1156* (American Society for Testing and Materials, Philadelphia, USA), ISBN: 0-8031-1498-2.

TALREJA R (Editor) (1994), *Damage Mechanics of Composite Materials,* Composite Materials Series vol. 9 (Elsevier Science BV, Amsterdam), ISBN: 0-444-88852-7.

MARTIN R H (Editor) (1995), *Composite Materials: Fatigue and Fracture 5*: STP 1230 (American Society for Testing and Materials, Philadelphia, USA), ISBN: 0-8031-2012-5.

CARDON A, FUKUDA H and REIFSNIDER K L (Editors) (1996), *Progress in Durability Analysis of Structural Composite Systems* (AA Balkema, Rotterdam), ISBN: 90-5410-809-6.

DEGALLAIX S, BATHIAS C and FOUGÈRES R (Editors) (1997), Proceedings of the First International Conference on *Fatigue of Composites (ICFC),* Paris (Société Française de Métallurgie et de Matériaux, Paris).

ARMANIOS E A (Editor) (1997), *Composite Materials: Fatigue and Fracture 6: STP 1285* (American Society for Testing and Materials, Philadelphia, USA), ISBN: 0-8031-2411-2.

BUCINELL R B (Editor) (1998), *Composite Materials: Fatigue and Fracture 7: STP 1330* (American Society for Testing and Materials, Philadelphia, USA), ISBN: 0-8031-2609-3.

1.5   References

1. OWEN M J and BISHOP P T (1974), Crack-growth relationships for glass-reinforced plastics and their application in design, *J Phys D: Appl Phys,* **7,** 1214–1224.
2. HOWE R J and OWEN M J (1972), Accumulation of damage in a glass-reinforced plastic under tensile and fatigue loading, in *Proceedings of the Eighth International Reinforced Plastics Congress* (British Plastics Federation, London), 137–148.
3. MINER M A (1945), *J Appl Mech,* **12,** A159–164.
4. GRIMM B (1996), Unpublished results, Department of Materials Science and Engineering, University of Bath, Bath, UK.
5. CHEN A S and HARRIS B (1993), Fatigue-induced damage mechanisms in CFRP composites, *J Mater Sci,* **28,** 2013–2027.
6. TALREJA R (1981), Fatigue of composite materials: damage mechanism and fatigue life diagrams, *Proc Roy Soc (Lond),* **A378,** 461–475.

7. HASHIN Z and ROTEM A (1978), A cumulative-damage theory of fatigue failure, *Mater Sci and Engg*, **34**, 147–160.

8. SMITH T R and OWEN M J (1968), *Proceedings of the 6th International Reinforced Plastics Congress* (British Plastics Federation London), paper 27.

9. LEE J A, HARRIS B, ALMOND D P and HAMMETT F (1997), Fibre composite fatigue-life determination, *Composites*, **28A**, 5–15.

10. FREUDENTHAL A M and GUMBEL E J (1953), On the statistical interpretation of fatigue tests, *Proc Roy Soc (Lond)*, **A216**, 309–332.

11. WHITNEY J M (1981), in *Fatigue of Fibrous Composite Materials STP 723* (American Society for Testing and Materials, Philadelphia, USA), 133–151.

12. GATHERCOLE N, REITER H, ADAM T and HARRIS B (1994), Life prediction for fatigue of T800/5245 carbon-fibre composites: I Constant-amplitude loading, *Int J Fatigue*, **16**, 523–532.

13. BEHESHTY M H, HARRIS B and ADAM T (1999), An empirical fatigue-life model for high-performance fibre composites with and without impact damage, *Compos A: Appl Sci & Manuf*, **A30**, 971–987.

14. KING R L (1987), The determination of design allowable properties for advanced composite materials, *GEC Journal*, **5**, 76–87.

15. CASTILLO E (1988), *Extreme Value Theory In Engineering* (Academic Press, Boston/London).

16. BURY K V (1975), *Statistical Models in Applied Science* (J Wiley & Sons, London).

17. HARRIS B (2003), A parametric constant-life model for prediction of the fatigue lives of fibre-reinforced plastics, this volume, pp 546–568.

18. HASHIN Z and ROTEM A (1973), A fatigue failure criterion for fibre-reinforced materials, *J Compos Mater*, **7**, 153–163.

19. PETERMANN J and PLUMTREE A (2001), A unified fatigue failure criterion for unidirectional laminates, *Compos A: Appl Sci Manuf*, **32**, 107–118.

20. CHEN A S, ALMOND D P and HARRIS B (2001), Real-time monitoring of fatigue-induced damage growth in composite materials by Acoustography, *Compos Sci & Technol*, **61**, 2437–2444.

21. WEIBULL W (1961), *Fatigue Testing and Analysis of Results* (Pergamon, Oxford, for AGARD, NATO, Paris)

22. BOLLER K H (1952), *Tests of glass-fabric-based laminates subjected to axial loading*: Forest Products Laboratory Report 1823 (US Forest Products Laboratory).

23. BOLLER K H (1957), Fatigue properties of fibrous glass-reinforced plastic laminates subjected to various conditions, *Modern Plastics*, **34**, 163–180; 185–186; 293.

24. BOLLER K H (1964), Fatigue characteristics of reinforced-plastics laminates subjected to axial loading, *Modern Plastics*, **41**, 145–150; 188.

25. BOLLER K H (1965), Effect of pre-cyclic stresses on the fatigue life of reinforced-plastics laminates, *Modern Plastics*, **42**, 162–173.

26. BOLLER K H (1966), Wright Air Force Laboratories Technical Report AFML TR 66–54 (Wright Air Development Centre Dayton Ohio).

27. BEAUMONT P W R and HARRIS B (1972), The effect of environment on fatigue and crack-propagation in carbon-fibre reinforced epoxy resin, in *Proceedings of an International Conference on Carbon Fibres: Their Composites and Applications* (Plastics Institute, London), 283–291.

28. OWEN M J and MORRIS S (1972), in *Proceedings of an International Conference on Carbon Fibres: Their Composites and Applications* (Plastics Institute, London), 292–302.

29. FUWA M, HARRIS B and BUNSELL A R (1975), Acoustic emission during cyclic loading of carbon fibre reinforced plastics, *J Phys D Applied Physics*, **8**, 1460–1471.

30. STURGEON J B (1975), Fatigue testing of carbon-fibre-reinforced plastics, in *Proceedings of the 28th Annual Technical Conference of Reinforced Plastics/Composites Inst of SPI* (Society for Plastics Industry, New York), paper 12B.

31. JONES C J, DICKSON R F, ADAM T, REITER H and HARRIS B (1984), The environmental fatigue behaviour of reinforced plastics, *Proc Roy Soc (Lond)*, **A396**, 315–338.

32. MANDELL J F (1982), Fatigue behaviour of fibre-resin composites, in *Developments in Reinforced Plastics 2* (editor G Pritchard), (Applied Science Publishers, London), 67–108.

33. SIMS G D and GLADMAN D G (1978), Effect of test conditions on the fatigue strength of a glass-fabric laminate: I Frequency, *Plastics & Rubber: Mater & Applic*, **1**, 41–48.

34. SIMS G D and GLADMAN D G (1980), Effect of test conditions on the fatigue strength of a glass-fabric laminate: II Specimen condition, *Plastics & Rubber: Mater & Applic*, **3**, 122–128.

35. HARRIS B, GATHERCOLE N, LEE J A, REITER H and ADAM T (1997), Life prediction for constant-stress

fatigue in carbon-fibre composites, *Phil Trans Roy Soc (Lond)*, **A355**, 1259–1294.

36. FERNANDO G, DICKSON R F, ADAM T, REITER H and HARRIS B (1988), Fatigue behaviour of hybrid composites: I Carbon/Kevlar hybrids, *J Mater Sci*, **23**, 3732–3743.

37. GOODMAN J (1899), *Mechanics Applied to Engineering* (Longman Green, Harlow, UK).

38. GERBER W (1874), *Z Bayer Archit Ing Ver*, **6**, 101.

39. OWEN M J (1974), Fatigue of carbon-fibre-reinforced plastics, Chapter 8 in *Fracture and Fatigue* (Editor LJ Broutman): Composite Materials Series vol. 5, Series Editors LJ Broutman and RH Krock, (Academic Press, New York & London), 341–369.

40. SCHÜTZ D and GERHARZ J J (1977), Fatigue strength of a fibre-reinforced material, *Composites*, **8**, 245–250.

41. KIM R Y (1988), Fatigue behaviour, *Composites Design* (4th Edition: editor SW Tsai), (Think Composites, Dayton, Ohio, USA), chapter 19.

42. REIFSNIDER K L and JAMISON R D (1982), *Int J Fatigue*, **4**, 187–198.

43. POURSARTIP A and BEAUMONT P W R (1982), *Proc IUTAM Symposium Mechanics of Composite Materials*, VPI, Blacksburg, Virginia, USA.

44. BONIFACE L and OGIN S L (1989), *J Compos Mater*, **23**, 735–754.

45. CAMPONESCHI E T and STINCHCOMB W W (1982), Stiffness reduction as an indicator of damage in graphite/epoxy laminates, in *Composite Materials: Testing and Design – 6* (ASTM STP 787, editor IM Daniel) (American Society for Testing and Materials, Philadelphia, USA), 225–246. HWANG W B and HAN K S (1986), Fatigue of composites–fatigue modulus concept and life prediction, *J Compos Mater*, **20**, 154–165.

46. ROTEM A (1989), Stiffness change of a graphite/epoxy laminate under reverse fatigue loading, *J Compos Technol & Research*, **11**, 59–64.

47. YANG J N, LEE L J and SHEU D Y (1992), Modulus reduction and fatigue damage of matrix-dominated composite laminates, *Compos Struct*, **21**, 91–100.

48. EL MAHI A, BERTHELOT J M and BRILLAUD J (1995), Stiffness reduction and energy release rate of cross-ply laminates during fatigue testing, *Compos Struct*, **30**, 123–130.

49. ADAM T, DICKSON R F, JONES C J, REITER H and HARRIS B (1986), A power law fatigue damage model for fibre-reinforced plastic laminates, *Proc Inst Mech Engrs: Mech Eng Sci*, **200(C3)**, 155–166.

50. CURTIS P T and MOORE B B (1985), A comparison of the fatigue performance of woven and non-woven CFRP laminates, in *Proceedings of the Fifth International Conference on Composite Materials (ICCM5)* San Diego (editors WC Harrigan, J Strife and AK Dhingra) (Metallurgical Society of AIME, Warrendale, PA, USA), 293–314.

51. NAIK N K (2003), The fatigue of woven-fibre thermoset composites, this volume pp 296–313.

52. OWEN M J (1970), Fatigue, in *Glass Reinforced Plastics* (editor B Parkyn), (Iliffe, London), 251–267

53. KAWAI M, MORISHITA M, FUZI K, SAKURAI T and KEMMOCHI K (1996), Effects of matrix ductility and progressive damage on the fatigue strengths of un-notched and notched carbon-fibre plain-weave roving fabric laminates, *Compos A: Appl Sci Manuf*, **A27**, 493–502.

54. DICKSON R F, JONES C J, HARRIS B, LEACH D C and MOORE D R (1985), Environmental fatigue behaviour of carbon fibre reinforced poly(ether ether ketone), *J Mater Sci*, **20**, 60–70.

55. KONUR O and MATTHEWS F L (1989), Effect of the properties of the constituents on the fatigue performance of composites: a review, *Composites*, **20**, 317–328.

56. HARRIS B (1989), Hybrid fibre-resin composites, in *Concise Encyclopaedia of Composite Materials* (editor A Kelly), (Pergamon Press, Oxford), 142–146.

57. PHILLIPS L N, BRADLEY J S and STURGEON J B (1976), RAE (Farnborough) Technical Memorandum MAT241, (Ministry of Defence Procurement Executive, UK).

58. HOFER K E, STANDER M and BENNETT L C (1978), *Polymer Engg Sci*, **18**, 120–127.

59. DICKSON R F, FERNANDO G, ADAM T, REITER H and HARRIS B (1989), Fatigue behaviour of hybrid composites: II Carbon/glass hybrids, *J Mater Sci*, **24**, 227–233.

60. LOMAX J W and O'ROURKE J T (1966), in *Proceedings of the 21st Annual Technical Conference of Reinforced Plastics/Composites Institute of SPI, (Society for Plastics Industry*, New York), paper X–5.

61. LAVENGOOD R E and GULBRANSEN L D (1969), Effects of aspect ratio on the fatigue life of short-boron-fibre reinforced composites, *Polymer Eng Sci*, **19**, 365.

62. OWEN M J, DUKES R and SMITH T R (1969), *Proceedings of the 24th Annual Technical Conference of Reinforced Plastics/Composites Institute of SPI* (Society for Plastics Industry New York), paper 14A.

63. HUFFINE C L, SOLUM D F and WACHTLER (1973), in *Failure Modes In Composites* (editor I Toth), (Metallurgical Society of AIME, New York), 455–471.

64. HARRIS B, ANKARA A O, CAWTHORNE D and BYE S M T (1977), Cyclic loading and the strength of dough moulding compounds, *Composites*, **8**, 185–189.
65. ATZORI B, QUARESIMIN M and TRATTENERO G (1994), in *Proceedings of the 2nd International Seminar Experimental Techniques and Design in Composite Materials* (editor M S Found), Sheffield, Sept 1994, (Sheffield Academic Press Sheffield UK), 193–211.
66. SHAVER R G and ABRAMS E F (1971), in *Proceedings of the Annual Technical Conference of SPE*, **17**, 378–381.
67. HARRIS B, REITER H, ADAM T, DICKSON R F and FERNANDO G (1990), Fatigue behaviour of carbon fibre reinforced plastics, *Composites*, **21**, 232–242.
68. MOORE B B (1982), in *Proceedings of the 3rd Risø Symposium Fatigue & Creep of Composite Materials*, Sept 1982 (editors H Lilholt & R Talreja), (Risø National Laboratory, Roskilde, Denmark), 245–257.
69. HITCHEN S A, OGIN S L and SMITH P A (1995), Effect of fibre length on fatigue of short-carbon-fibre/epoxy composites, *Composites*, **26**, 303–308.
70. FRIEDRICH K, WALTER R, VOSS H and KARGER-KOCSIS J (1986), *Composites*, **17**, 205–216.
71. EVANS W J, ISAAC D H and SAIB K D (1996), The effect of short carbon fibres reinforcement on fatigue crack growth in PEEK, *Compos A: Appl Sci Manuf*, **27**, 547–554.
72. BUNSELL A R and HARRIS B (1976), Hybrid carbon/glass fibre composites, *Proceedings of ICCM1 First Int Conference on Composite Materials* (Editors E Scala, E Anderson, I Toth and BR Noton), (Metallurgical Society of AIME, Warrendale, PA, USA), 174–190.
73. FAVRE J P (1977), Improving the fracture energy of carbon-fibre-reinforced plastics by delamination promoters, *J Mater Sci*, **12**, 43–50.
74. SUN C T and LUO J (1985), Failure loads for notched graphite/epoxy laminates with a softening strip, *Compos Sci & Technol*, **22**, 121–134.
75. PARTRIDGE I, VIRLOUVET P, CHUBB J and CURTIS P T (1989), Developments in the Science and Technology of Composites: *Proceedings of the 3rd European Conference on Composite Materials (ECCM3)* (editors AR Bunsell, P Lamicq, and A Massiah), (EACM, Bordeaux and Elsevier, London), 451–456.
76. ALTUS E and ISHAI O (1990), The effect of soft interleaved layers on the combined transverse-cracking/delamination mechanisms in composite laminates, *Compos Sci & Technol*, **39**, 13–27.
77. SINGH S and PARTRIDGE I K (1995), Mixed-mode fracture in an interleaved carbon-fibre/epoxy composite, *Compos Sci & Technol*, **55**, 319–327.
78. KIM J K and MAI Y W (1998), *Engineered Interfaces in Fibre-Reinforced Composites*, (Elsevier Science, Oxford), section 8.3.2, 345 *et seq.*
79. FERNANDO G (2003), The effect of interleaving on the fatigue behaviour of fibre composites, this volume, pp 189–241.
80. RAMANI S V and WILLIAMS D P (1976), in *Failure Modes in Composite* (Metallurgical Society of AIME, New York), 115–140.
81. KUNZ S C and BEAUMONT P W R (1975), in *Fatigue of Composite Materials* STP 569 (American Society for Testing and Materials, Philadelphia, USA), 71–91.
82. BERG C A and SALAMA N (1972), Compressive fatigue in fibre-reinforced materials, *J Materials*, **7**, 216–230.
83. PHILLIPS D C and SCOTT J M (1976), AERE Technical Report AERE G645 (Atomic Energy Authority, Harwell, UK).
84. MARCO S M and STARKEY W L (1954), Effect of complex stress-time cycles on the fatigue properties of metals, *ASME Trans*, **76**, 627.
85. HARRIS B, GATHERCOLE N, REITER H and ADAM T (1997), Fatigue of carbon-fibre-reinforced plastics under block loading conditions, *Compos A: Appl Sci Manuf*, **A28**, 327–337.
86. SCHAFF J R and DAVIDSON B D (1997), Life-prediction methodology for composite structures: 1 Constant-amplitude and two-stress-level fatigue, *J Compos Mater*, **31**, 128–157.
87. ADAM T, GATHERCOLE N, REITER H and HARRIS B (1994), Life prediction for fatigue of carbon-fibre composites: II Variable-amplitude loading, *Int J Fatigue*, **16**, 533–548.
88. GERHARZ J J (1982), Mechanisms of fatigue damage and fatigue testing, in *Practical Considerations of Design Fabrication and Tests for Composite Materials* – AGARD Lecture Series no 124 (Director B Harris), (AGARD/NATO Neuilly Paris), paper 7.
89. CLARKE G and VAN BLARICUM T J (1987), Load spectrum modification effects on fatigue of impact-damaged carbon-fibre composite coupons, *Composites*, **18**, 243–251.
90. SCHAFF J R and DAVIDSON B D (1997), Life-prediction methodology for composite structures: 2 spectrum fatigue, *J Compos Mater*, **31**, 158–181.

91. YANG J N and JONES D L (1981), Load-sequence effects on the fatigue of un-notched composite materials, *Fatigue of Fibrous Composite Materials STP 723* (American Society for Testing and Materials, Philadelphia, USA), 213–232.

92. HINTON M J, SODEN P and KADDOUR A S (Editors) (1998), Failure criteria in fibre-reinforced polymer composites: Part A Comparison of models, *Compos Sci & Technol*, **58**, 999–1254.

93. HINTON M J, SODEN P and KADDOUR A S (Editors) (2002), Failure criteria in fibre-reinforced polymer composites: Part B Comparison between theories and experiments, *Compos Sci & Technol*, **62**, 1479–1798.

94. HART-SMITH L J (1991), in *Proceedings of a meeting on Failure of Polymeric Composite Structures: Mechanisms and Criteria for the Prediction of Performance*, St Albans, UK, September 1991, (SERC/IMechE London), 19–31.

95. OWEN M J and FOUND M S (1972), Static and fatigue failure of glass-fibre-reinforced polyester resins under complex stress conditions, in *Solid/Solid Interfaces, Proceedings of Faraday Special Discussions* no. 2, (Chemical Society London), 77–89.

96. OWEN M J and GRIFFITHS J R (1978), Evaluation of biaxial stress failure surfaces for a glass-fabric-reinforced polyester resin under static and fatigue loading, *J Mater Sci*, **113**, 1521–1537.

97. FOUND M S (1985), A review of the multiaxial fatigue testing of fibre-reinforced plastics, in *Multiaxial Fatigue: STP 853* (Editors KJ Miller and MW Brown), (American Society for Testing and Materials, Philadelphia, USA), 381–395.

98. SMITH E W and PASCOE K J (1989), Biaxial fatigue of a glass-fibre-reinforced composite: I Fatigue and fracture behaviour, in *Biaxial and Multiaxial Fatigue EGF3* (Editors MW Brown and KJ Miller), (Mechanical Engineering Publications Ltd, I Mech E, London), 367–396.

99. SMITH E W and PASCOE K J (1989), Biaxial fatigue of a glass-fibre-reinforced composite: II Failure criteria for fatigue and fracture, in *Biaxial and Multiaxial Fatigue EGF3* (Editors MW Brown and KJ Miller), (Mechanical Engineering Publications Ltd, I Mech E, London), 397–421.

100. PHILIPPIDIS T P and VASSILOPOULOS (2003), *The fatigue strength of composites under variable plane stress*, this volume pp 505–525.

101. SHOKRIEH M M and LESSARD L B (2003), *Multiaxial fatigue*, this volume pp 63–113.

102. CANTWELL W J, CURTIS P T and MORTON J (1984), Impact and subsequent fatigue damage growth in carbon fibre laminates, *Int. J Fatigue*, **6**, 113–118.

103. CANTWELL W J and MORTON J (1991), The impact resistance of composite materials – a review, *Composites*, **22**, 347–362.

104. SOUTIS C and CURTIS P T (1996), Prediction of post-impact compressive strength of CFRP laminated composites, *Compos Sci and Technol*, **56**, 677–684.

105. RICHARDSON M O W and WISHEART M J (1996), Review of low-velocity impact properties of composite materials, *Composites*, **27A**, 1123–1131.

106. BEHESHTY M H and HARRIS B (1998), A constant-life model of fatigue behaviour for carbon-fibre composites: the effect of impact damage, *Compos Sci & Technol*, **58**, 9–18.

107. STELLBRINK K K U (1982), Influence of low-velocity impact on the fatigue behaviour of CFRP laminates, *Fatigue and Creep of Composite Materials*, Ch.36, 319–327.

108. CANTWELL W, CURTIS P and MORTON J (1983), Post-impact fatigue performance of carbon fibre laminates with non-woven and mixed-woven layers, *Composites*, **14**, 301–305.

109. RAMKUMAR R L (1983), Effect of low-velocity impact damage on the fatigue behaviour of graphite/epoxy laminates, *Long-Term Behaviour of Composites*, ASTM STP 813, editor TK O'Brien, (American Society for Testing and Materials, Philadelphia, USA), 116–135.

110. CLARK G and SAUNDERS D S (1991), Morphology of impact damage growth by fatigue in carbon fibre composite laminates, *Materials Forum*, **15**, 333–342.

2

Fatigue test methods, problems and standards

G.D. Sims, National Physical Laboratory, London, UK

2.1   Introduction

The repetitive loading of a composite material causes degradation due to the accumulation of discrete micro-damage (e.g. fibre fractures, fibre/matrix debonds, matrix cracks) or macro-crack propagation, aided in some cases by an aggressive environment, including moisture. The engineer requires knowledge of the effect of these loading cycles on the life of the product or component in order to ensure they are safe for the intended service life or can be replaced prior to failure. To satisfy this need, fatigue test programmes are used to establish the resistance of a material to repetitive loading. The data are often normalized with respect to the static or slow rate strength data measured typically in a monotonically loaded test of 30–90 seconds duration. Due to the long timescale and the high cost of fatigue testing, it is important to choose the fatigue test conditions correctly and ensure that all test artefacts are removed or minimized. Several of these artefacts are illustrated using results obtained for a commercially produced glass-fibre fabric epoxy laminate with a low scatter in the ultimate tensile strength (i.e. coefficient of variation equal to 2.5%) that has been used extensively at NPL for investigating the effect of test conditions on the measured fatigue data.

This chapter reviews the basics of fatigue test methods, difficulties that need to be avoided and the degree of standardization achieved.

2.2   Fatigue data requirements

Some of the related reasons why fatigue test programmes are undertaken include:

- to compare materials under standard conditions as a basis of material development or material selection;
- to obtain design data relevant to particular service applications;
- to investigate the mechanisms of failure resulting in degradation and ultimate failure;
- to ensure that the fatigue life is greater than required, and/or the replacement life is identified.

The data measured should give an adequate representation of the performance over the required lifetimes. This is most easily achieved by obtaining a full $S–N$ diagram (i.e. applied stress versus the number of cycles applied prior to failure) or Wohler curve over several cycles of lifetime. This normally covers the range of lifetimes from 100 or 1000 cycles to one million cycles due to the low test frequencies used as discussed later.

In all testing there is a need to define the failure criterion in use. This is particularly difficult for fibre reinforced plastics, compared to most metals, because non-catastrophic damage (e.g. microcracking, fibre debonding, fibre fractures) can occur throughout the stressed volume. This micro-damage may itself define the failure conditions. However, in some cases there will be propagation of a macro-crack along planes of lamination (i.e. delamination crack growth), in matrix dominated directions (e.g. 90° ply) or when the material is more nearly isotropic (e.g. short fibre-reinforced moulding compounds). Macro-crack propagation perpendicular to a high volume fraction of aligned fibres is difficult and not a preferred mode of failure. The distributed damage can, depending on the applied load or strain level, occur on the first and subsequent loading cycle leading to a reduction in the specimen stiffness. The data collected are normally for the primary high strength direction. Whereas, in several applications the weaker transverse and shear strengths can be more critical due to the presence of a lower-level secondary stress, which are a higher proportion of the relevant strength in those directions.

The failure criteria used must allow for the different service applications envisaged, and for the difference between displacement (often used in flexural tests) and load or strain (normally used for axial tests) controlled tests. For tests conducted under load control, final failure will result in a separation failure of the specimen into two or more parts. Under displacement control any damage occurring causes the specimen to 'soften', thereby reducing the applied load, but normally does not lead to failure by a specimen separation fracture. Hence, it is necessary to develop failure criteria based on loss of stiffness.[1] The continuous monitoring of the specimen condition throughout the test is now well estab-lished, having been highlighted several years ago[2] and is recommended in the ISO 13003 standard.[1] The monitored data are valuable for detecting damage or, as measures of dynamic properties for stiffness limited designs. It could also possibly be used as a measure of residual strength using a 'calibration' curve from prior tests based on measuring the residual strength of a series of specimens as a function of reduced stiffness, but the relationship would need proving for each material and loading situation.

The actual type of damage and its accumulation depend critically on the type of fibre, matrix, fibre interface, fibre geometry, specimen shape; and the level, type and direction of the applied stress. In addition these materials are often sensitive to the test temperature and/or the applied environment (e.g. water, acid, etc.). Consequentially, it is essential that full details are given of the materials, fabrication route, specimen conditioning and test method used if the available data are to be of highest and lasting value. Suitable material characteri-zation standards include:

- Measurement of fibre volume fraction
  - ISO 1172 – glass-fibre-based systems,[3]
  - ISO/DIS 14127 – carbon fibre-based system,[4]
- Assessment of cure by measurement of the glass-transition temperature
  - ISO 6721-11 – dynamic mechanical properties (DMA),[5]
  - ISO 11357 – differential scanning calorimetry (DSC).[6]

An appropriate standard for test plate manufacture is ISO 1268,[7] which covers in 10 parts most fabrication routes (e.g. filament winding, pultrusion, prepreg manufacture). These test plates are then machined to give the required test specimens. Most machining operations are conducted using diamond slitting or grinding tools, as outlined in a NPL Measurement Good Practice Guide.[8]

2.3   Fatigue testing requirements

In many applications the load cycles applied to a component in service vary in both the magnitude and the time history. In some cases for product testing load–time data are obtained by monitoring and recording actual or simulated service conditions. These load–time histories are captured electronically. The captured load cycle is then used to control a suitable test facility, such as a servo-hydraulic test machine. It is also possible to apply a strain or displacement history rather than a load (stress) history in the same manner.

However, the majority of laboratory fatigue studies are conducted under the conditions of constant frequency and constant amplitude profile (i.e. between constant maximum and minimum loads). Normally, a constant ratio of minimum and maximum load, etc. is applied, that is known as the stress ratio R, for different values of the peak load. That is,

$$R = \mathrm{load}_{min}/\mathrm{load}_{max} \hspace{4cm} [2.1]$$

The relationship of maximum, minimum and mean loads etc. is shown in Fig. 2.1.

Different R values scenarios can be identified as in the ISO standard ISO 13003, see Fig. 2.2. These encompass fully and partly reversed loading cycles as well as fully tensile or compression cycles. Most data exists for fully tension loaded specimens, where an R ratio of 0.1 is used. By returning to a minimum value greater than zero, the loading train is kept in tension to avoid unloading artefacts (e.g. release of wedge action grips).

The test duration or 'life' is determined by the number of cycles survived prior to failure under the applied conditions. The definition of failure also needs special consideration for composite materials, as described above.

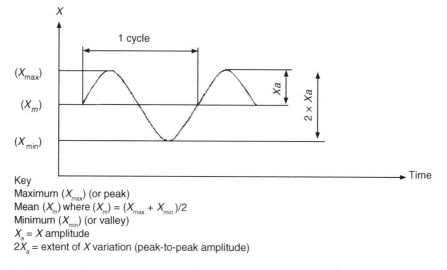

Key
Maximum (X_{max}) (or peak)
Mean (X_m) where $(X_m) = (X_{max} + X_{min})/2$
Minimum (X_{min}) (or valley)
$X_a = X$ amplitude
$2X_a$ = extent of X variation (peak-to-peak amplitude)

Fig. 2.1   Example of sine waveform cycle (X may be stress, strain or displacement) (see also ISO 13003).

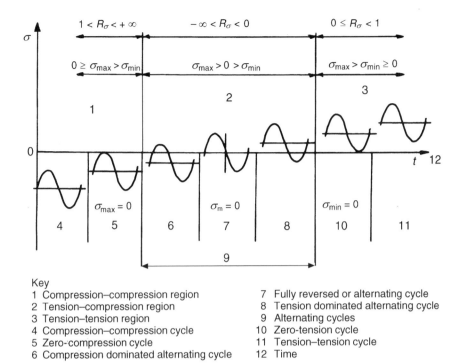

Key
1 Compression–compression region
2 Tension–compression region
3 Tension–tension region
4 Compression–compression cycle
5 Zero-compression cycle
6 Compression dominated alternating cycle

7 Fully reversed or alternating cycle
8 Tension dominated alternating cycle
9 Alternating cycles
10 Zero-tension cycle
11 Tension–tension cycle
12 Time

Fig. 2.2   Example of cycle types shown for stress (σ) (see also ISO 13003).

Tests are repeated at different combinations of maximum loads, or amplitudes, to obtain the life (number of cycles) under a range of conditions encompassing the required life times. The data are plotted normally as the applied maximum stress (strain, displacement) vs. number of cycles to failure, as shown in later sections.

2.4   Fatigue test equipment

The main requirement for the fatigue test machine is that it is suitable for the chosen test mode selected (e.g. tension, compression, flexure or shear) and can apply a high number of cycles ($\geq 10^8$), in the required waveform(s) (e.g. sine, square, triangular, saw-tooth). The machine should have adequate mechanical stiffness and stability to avoid excessive deflections. Any resonant frequency in the machine or loading train should be well above the applied test frequency.

Reliability of the equipment is important as breakdown results in lost specimens that have already involved a manufacturing and testing time and cost due to concern over re-loading a specimen even if the specimen is 'protected' from over-loading when the machine loses power. The main types of test machine available are:

- hydraulic or pneumatic powered ram driven machines that can apply constant or varying waveforms,
- mechanically driven equipment that use levers, cams etc. to apply the fatigue loads, normally applying constant sine waveforms,
- electric actuators, normally for applying low frequency displacement conditions,
- hydraulic or pneumatic pressure loading – including via bladders,
- vibroforms, resonant high frequency machines.

Fig. 2.3   Typical servo-hydraulic test machine, showing hydraulic grips.

A typical servo-hydraulic test machine is shown in Fig. 2.3, together with fatigue rated hydraulic grips.

The majority of research fatigue test equipment for high performance materials are servo controlled, hydraulically driven allowing higher loads and variable loading waveforms. These test machines are particularly suitable due to their high load capacity for uniaxial tensile and compression specimens. In contrast, industrial materials evaluation, selection or quality control may use cheaper mechanically driven lever or cam based systems based on displacement control.

Load cells are normally based on strain-gauged sensing elements designed for high fatigue lives. At high frequencies there may be a need to ensure that the load cell calibration is corrected for dynamic inertial effects as will be covered in a forthcoming standard. During the fatigue cycles the elements of the system are subject to acceleration. As a result, in addition to the force applied to the specimen, the load cell also reads forces resulting from its own movement and the mass of the grips and fixtures attached to it. At normally used frequencies for composite materials, this will not be a significant problem. In addition, the manufacturers now provide in-built inertia compensation to their load cells. Displacement measurements depend on type of fatigue machine used. For hydraulic ram machines, a displacement transducer (e.g. LVDT – linearly variable displacement transducer) is in-built into the ram. Strain measurements are normally via strain gauges or extensometer clip-on gauges attached to the specimen for axial tests, or from displacement measurements for flexure tests.

For servo-test machines, machine control is easiest under displacement control as the in-built displacement transducer in the hydraulic ram provides feedback on its position. Next easiest to undertake is load control, which requires a continuous specimen in the loading train to apply a displacement to the load cell, in order to generate the load reading. On specimen failure, and consequent loss of the load signal, the test machine will revert to displacement control. Under load control the stiffness of the specimen forms part of the electronic tuning of the gain control of the system to ensure the ram movement closely follows the control signal. As the stiffness of the specimen decreases due to fatigue damage the system gain will need to be increased. In modern test machines this occurs automatically. The most difficult control mode is strain as applied strain gauges or clip gauges can become detached with resultant loss of strain control. The machine safety limits will then take over and return the machine, and specimen, to the safer displacement control mode. Tensile fatigue data can be presented as applied strain rather than applied stress due to the fairly linear-elastic response of many composite materials, so that load control can be used in most cases. The number of cycles applied is measured directly or obtained from a knowledge of the applied frequency and test duration. An accuracy of ± 2% is normally required.

Most modern fatigue test machines use desktop computers for both machine control and data processing. The basic control facilities provide the opportunity to select test frequency, waveform shape, mean condition and applied amplitude, or alternatively minimum and maximum values. These controllers also allow block loading programmes to be specified which may contain blocks of cycles with different frequency or maximum/minimum values. Generally, continuous sine wave waveforms are used as being easiest to apply due to the absence of abrupt changes found in the input signals for triangular, saw-tooth or square waveforms. Sine waveforms are also generated most easily by test machines based on mechanical methods (e.g. cams, levers), including the original rotating beam machines used for metal fatigue (n.b. this mode of testing is usually not suitable for composite materials). Some data for a glass-fibre/epoxy used as a reference material tested for three waveforms (i.e. sine, triangular and square) shows that at longer lives there was no difference, see Fig. 2.4. The difference at shorter lives may be related to the mean load applied in each type of cycle, with the highest mean load for the square wave and lowest for the triangular.[9]

For data processing, a minimum requirement is to record the peak and trough values of the control parameter (e.g. load) and similarly associated displacement values. In practice, the data are frequently captured continuously. This can then be used to determine the storage and loss modulus, or damping factor – tan delta, of the specimen as a function of time, in a manner similar to the measurement of dynamic mechanical properties (see ISO 6721). Although these values are suitable for following damage development in a specimen, they should not be taken as absolute values (i.e. include test system hysteresis). Some typical data are shown in Fig. 2.5.

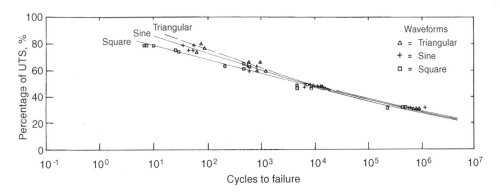

Fig. 2.4   Effect of waveform type on fatigue performance.

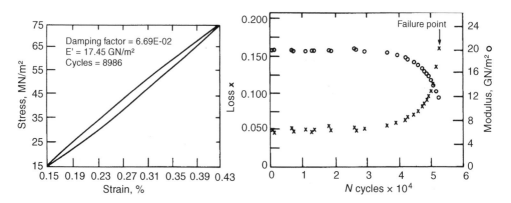

Fig. 2.5   (a) Typical hysteresis loop. (b) Storage modulus and damping changes.

Other techniques for following degradation include specimen temperature, acoustic emission, optical microscopy, *in situ* ultrasonic scanning. A specimen showing a range of transducers (e.g. acoustic emission sensor, thermocouple and clip-on strain gauge is shown in Fig. 2.6. Not all these monitors are normally required. Thermography used at NPL to monitor moulding compounds detected several hot-spots within individual specimens indicating precusor failure sites, one of which developed into the final failure site.

2.5   Artefacts in fatigue testing

This section reviews artefacts that are encountered in fatigue testing and shows the importance of minimizing their effects using the approaches identified. Several of these artefacts are illustrated using results obtained for a commercially produced glass-fibre fabric epoxy laminate with a low scatter in the ultimate tensile strength (i.e. coefficient of variation equal to 2.5%). Some of the effects are reduced for carbon-fibre-based systems.

Fig. 2.6   Dumbbell specimen with attached thermocouple, stress wave emission transducer and extensometer clip gauge.

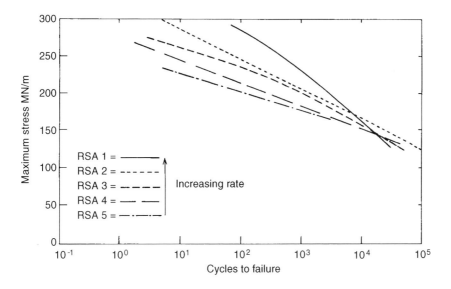

Fig. 2.7   Fatigue data at different rates of stress application (RSA) for a glass-fibre fabric epoxy.

2.5.1   Rate dependence effects

Fatigue tests are undertaken normally at the highest frequency possible in order to minimize the time and cost of undertaking a fatigue programme. There are two issues that must be considered, one is that because of the low thermal conductivity of reinforced plastics and the high damping factor (compared to metallic materials, that increases further as microdamage occurs in the specimen) autogenous or self-generated heating occurs as discussed below. The second effect is the rate dependence of the material properties themselves in the absence of the temperature effects.

In Fig. 2.7 is shown the fatigue properties at a series of loading rates.[9] A triangular waveform is used so that a constant loading or stressing rate is used, as indicated in Table 2.1. Figure 2.8 compares the case of constant frequency with constant rate of stress application, including for the ultimate strength test. This approach results in the test frequency increasing as the applied stress is reduced (i.e. 2 Hz at 80% to 5 Hz at 20% peak stress as a function of the ultimate stress). Also shown in Fig. 2.9 is the ultimate tensile strength of a glass-fibre/epoxy material at the same loading rates.

Table 2.1   Loading rates and equivalent frequencies

	Loading rate (N/s)	Rate of stressing (N/m²/s)	Typical frequency range (Hz)
RSA 1	10^6	1.25×10^{10}	20–80
RSA 2	10^5	1.25×10^9	2–8
RSA 3	10^4	1.25×10^8	0.2–0.8
RSA 4	10^3	1.25×10^7	0.02–0.08
RSA 5	10^2	1.25×10^6	0.002–0.008

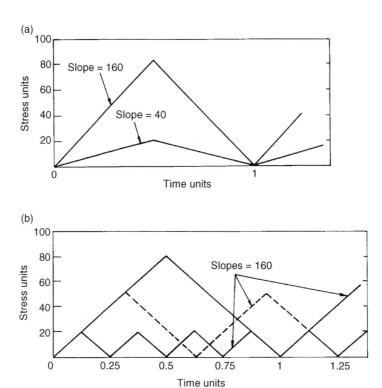

Fig. 2.8   Comparison of constant frequency and constant rate of stressing approach. (a) Fatigue tests conducted at constant frequency. (b) Fatigue tests conducted at constant rates of stress application (RSA).

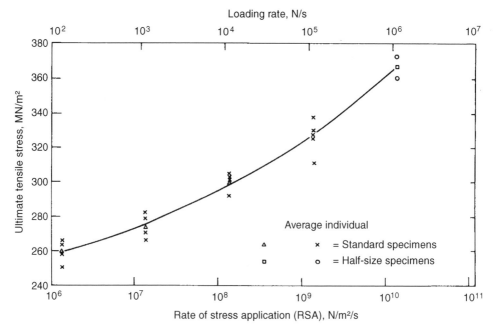

Fig. 2.9   Ultimate tensile strength as a function of rate of stress application (RSA).

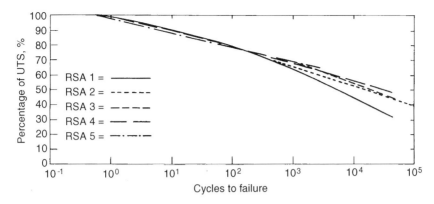

Fig. 2.10   Fatigue data normalized by ultimate strength for each rate for a glass-fibre fabric epoxy.

Normalization of the fatigue data with respect to the relevant tensile strength properties gives the normalized data shown in Fig. 2.10. This graph indicates that, excluding the highest loading rate, the normalized data are consistent for all loading rates. At the highest rate it is noted that there are temperature effects shown by the temperature surface rises in degrees C, shown in Fig. 2.11. The effect of these temperature rises is discussed in the following sub-section.

2.5.2   Autogenous heating

Plastics, in particular unreinforced plastics, can generate extensive rises in temperature during fatigue due to autogenous (self-generated) heating if the loading frequency is excessive. The temperature rise will result in reduced material properties and fatigue performance. Consequently, although the test frequency is normally taken as the maximum possible in order to reduce the test duration, the frequency must be chosen to avoid an excessive rise in the specimen temperature through this effect. Figure 2.11 shows data obtained for a glass-fibre fabric loaded in tension at test frequencies of 20 to 80 Hz. The values alongside the failure data points show the surface temperature rise in degrees Centigrade at failure.[9]

Using a procedure published by Heywood[10] the calculated internal temperatures for each measured surface temperature were determined to be even higher. These temperature rises can be compared with the data in Table 2.2 showing the tensile strength as a function of temperature.

It can be shown that these temperature rises directly affect the results by either stopping the tests when a fixed maximum temperature rise is reached and the specimen allowed to cool to ambient before continuing the test. It was found that the total life increased as the limiting temperature rise was reduced. In addition, normalizing each data point as a percentage of the reduced tensile strengths as a function of the predicted specimen internal temperature, based on surface measurements, gives the data values shown by 'x' in Fig. 2.11. These temperature corrected data points agree well with data collected at RSA 3 when heating effects were absent.

Table 2.2   Ultimate tensile strength as a function of test temperature

Temperature °C	−150	−100	−6	−20	23	60	100	150
UTS (MN/m²)	470	420	387	350	325	286	234	122

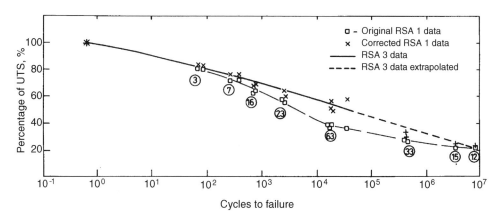

Fig. 2.11   Fatigue data measured at RSA 1 and RSA 3 showing effect of temperature correction.

Test frequencies can normally be higher for flexural tests than for tensile tests on the same material as the autogenous heating is less due to the smaller volume of material within the specimen at the maximum stress. The higher thermal conductivity of carbon-fibre bases systems allows higher test frequencies to be used compared with glass-fibre and aramid-fibre-based systems. A check should be made of the specimen temperature at each load/stress level. The acceptable level of temperature rise depends on the temperature dependence of the ultimate properties of the material under test, but a limiting value of 10 °C is recommended in ISO 13003[1]. The frequencies are therefore normally within the range from 1 Hz to 25 Hz but for loading rate-dependent materials the results can be sensitive to the frequency used (see Section 2.5.1).

Care must still be taken even when satisfactory conditions are determined for one case when a change is made. For example, if the test conditions giving rise to the 'accepted' data for the 0°/90° orientation are then used for tests on ±45≡ orientation of the same material, the data (see Fig. 2.12) were again unacceptable due to the temperature rises obtained. The frequency has to be reduced further, to 0.02–0.05 Hz, to measure the properties under acceptable conditions. When normalized with respect to the tensile strength, as shown in Fig. 2.13, the two ± 45≡ orientation data sets agree when heating is absent or low; and interestingly agree with 0°/90° orientation data. This suggests that the fatigue strength is controlled by the need to fail the fibres in each case for this fabric reinforced material. The result for ± 45≡ made from UD plies may not follow this trend as failure can occur without fibres failing in standard 25 mm wide coupons.

Forced cooling of specimens has been shown to be not fully effective as although the surface may be cooled the specimen internal volume is not.

2.5.3   Buckling of specimens under compression loads

The majority of composites, particularly for high performance versions, are available as thin sheets or plates. Consequently, testing in compression for short term properties itself has required careful consideration in order to avoid buckling failures prior to material fracture failures. This has led to numerous designs of support for compression testing. In some designs of loading jigs the approach relies on a short gauge length that will not buckle before the maximum failure load is reached. Equation (1) in ASTM D 3410[11] gives the relationship between the specimen thickness h, the gauge length l, and the material properties in order to avoid a buckling failure.

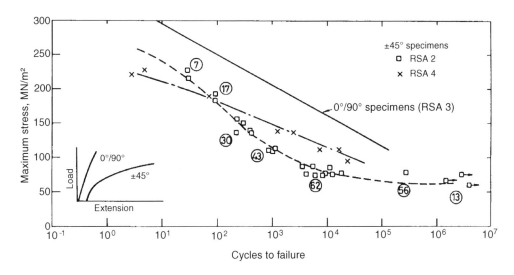

Fig. 2.12   Fatigue data for glass-fibre fabric/epoxy weave orientated at ± 45°.

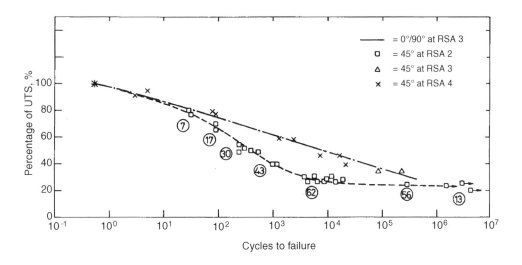

Fig. 2.13   Fatigue data for glass-fibre fabric/epoxy weave at ± 45° normalized with respect to the ultimate tensile strength at the correct frequency.

$$h \geq 1/(0.9069x\ \{(1 - (1.2\ F/G_{13})\ (E_{11}/F\ )\}^{0.5})$$ [2.2]

where G_{13} is through-thickness shear modulus, E_{11} is longitudinal Young's modulus and F is the maximum compressive stress to be applied (i.e. at the maximum equal to the ultimate compressive stress).

EN ISO 14126[12] for the static compression test gives two generic methods for the design of loading jigs based on the load application method (i.e. end or shear loaded), but both use a short gauge length in spite of concerns regarding a non-uniform stress distribution.

Recommended sizes are given for both unidirectionally and multidirectionally reinforced specimens. An innovation in EN ISO 14126, is the requirement for the bending strain in the specimen to be less than 10% of the applied axial strain as measured by strain or clip gauges on opposite faces. This good practice should also be applied to fatigue loaded compression tests, although, the maximum loads applied are lower than in the ultimate strength test.

These short gauge-length designs are suitable for fatigue loading in compression but obviously do not agree well with the design of the tensile specimens, which are generally long thin strips as described in EN ISO 527–4[13] and –5.[14] The long thin tensile specimens restrict the load that can be applied under partial or fully reversed loading without buckling occurring. Because of this, there is a requirement to ensure buckling will not occur in longer gauge length specimens when loaded in compression through the use of anti-buckling jigs.

2.5.4   Tensile testing – grip failures

Grip failures can occur in tensile specimens during fatigue as in static tests. To reduce these undesirable effects, the grip pressure should be as low as possible, a recommendation made also for the static test specimens, as in EN ISO 527–4 and 5. For some materials, such as moulding compounds, it may be possible to avoid the use of tabs as failures will mainly occur within the gauge length due to the material variability. For materials that are uniform in their properties, failures for plain strip specimens are likely in the grips.

Other specimen types, such as shear and tensile through-thickness (TT) have also been used successfully by Broughton et al.,[15] as shown in Fig. 2.14.

2.5.5   Flexure tests – loading point stress concentrations and fretting

Flexure tests, although simple in principle to undertake, have difficulties of their own. The most significant are the compression stress concentration at the centre loading point and fretting wear at the outer loading points. The wear at the outer loading points is particularly important when displacement control is used, as the required reference points of displacement, the tensile face of the specimen, are lost. Four point tests are used to reduce the stress concentrations at the centre loading points. In the static flexure tests, EN ISO 14125[18], an option based on Japanese work[19] allows a 0.2 mm thick polypropylene shim to be placed below the centre loading point. Although, no published work has used this approach in fatigue, it would appear to be suitable for reducing detrimental stress concentration effects at the loading point(s).

2.5.6   Effect of applied test temperature

In many cases the fatigue performance will be required at a non-ambient test temperature or as a function of a temperature range. In Fig. 2.15 are shown data obtained for the reference material (i.e. glass-fibre fabric/epoxy) at different test temperatures[20] from 150 °C to –150 °C, using the constant loading rate approach described above. Care was taken that no additional autogenous heating occurred. These S–N curves have been normalized in Fig. 2.16 with respect to the ultimate tensile strength at the fatigue loading rate. The ultimate strength varies by a factor of 4 for this temperature range (i.e. from 470 MPa to 122 MPa), with a significant increase in strength at temperatures below ambient. It is apparent that a good correlation is obtained. This result suggests that the fatigue strength has the same temperature dependence as the ultimate tensile strength for this material.

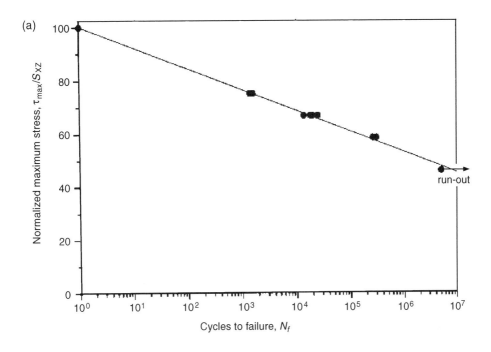

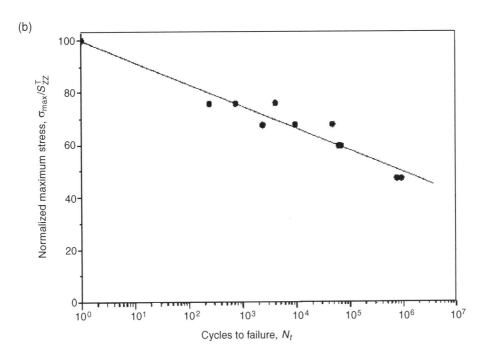

Fig. 2.14   Fatigue data for non-fibre controlled properties. (a) Normalized in-plane shear fatigue tests using V-notched beam (ASTM D 5379 [16]). (b) Normalized through-thickness fatigue tensile tests (NPL draft method [17]).

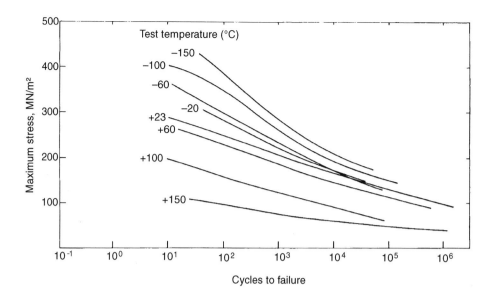

Fig. 2.15   *S–N* data at different applied temperatures for a glass-fibre fabric/epoxy.

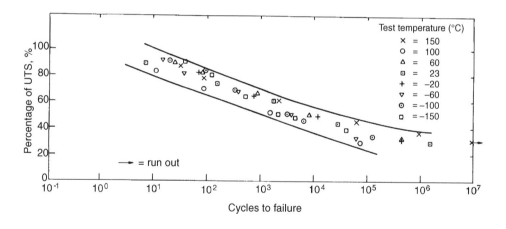

Fig. 2.16   Normalized *S–N* data for different test temperatures for a glass-fibre fabric/epoxy.

2.5.7   Effect of stress concentrations

Fatigue data has also been obtained for the stress concentrations specimen designs shown in Fig. 2.17, which include double-edge notched, centre-holed and a control glass-fibre fabric epoxy specimens.[21] The centre-notched specimen has become established for static tests with an aspect ratio of 6:1 for hole diameter to specimen width.[22]

The absolute data for these three specimen types are shown in Fig. 2.18. In Fig. 2.19 the data has been normalized with respect to the ultimate strength of the identical specimen, at the fatigue loading rate. The *S–N* curves are shown to be in agreement, suggesting that there is no additional degradation due to the notch or hole in the fatigue properties, other than the initial decrease in the ultimate strength.

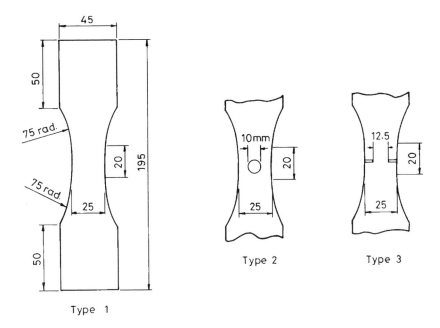

Fig. 2.17 Design of control, centre-holed and double-edge notched glass-fibre fabric epoxy specimens.

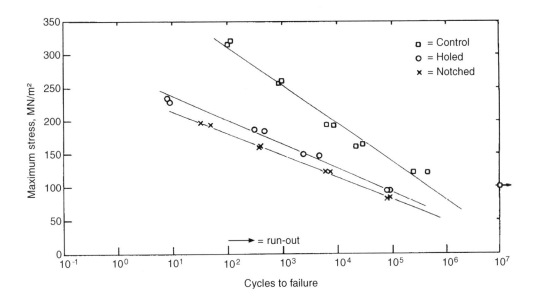

Fig. 2.18 Fatigue data for double-edge notched, centre-holed and control glass-fibre fabric epoxy specimens.

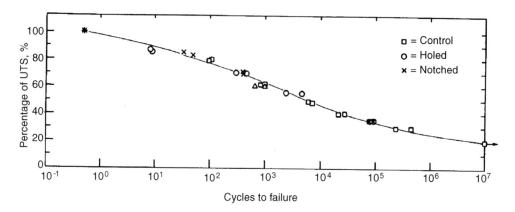

Fig. 2.19   Normalized fatigue data for double-edge notched, centre-holed and control glass-fibre fabric epoxy specimens.

2.6   Standardized test methods

2.6.1   Standardization bodies

The major international standards are produced by ISO (International Standardization Organisation) and CEN (Comité Européen de Normalisation). The CEN standards covering Europe, including countries outside the European Union, have a higher 'legal' profile than previously accorded to ISO standards and are encouraging increased attention to precision statements. The Vienna agreement between ISO and CEN ensures that work is not duplicated and allows a fast approval by CEN of existing ISO standards (UAP ballot – Unique Approval Procedure – yes/no without comment). Standards approved by CEN must be published by national committees, and national standards of the same scope withdrawn.

Other bodies involved with standards development include national standards organizations (e.g. ANSI, AFNOR, BSI, DIN, JIS), regulatory bodies such as the CAA and FAA, trade groupings and societies (e.g. ASTM). The ASTM (USA) has a specialized group, D-30, that has developed composite standards for many years and has made strong input into international standardization.

The Versailles Project on Advanced Materials and Standards (VAMAS) aims to aid the introduction and use of advanced materials through international pre-normalization research. The VAMAS is led by G7 countries (e.g. Canada, France, Germany, Italy, Japan, UK, USA and European Union) with other countries encouraged to participate in individual projects. The project aims to encourage technical agreement on the optimum practices for implementation standards through the normal procedures via national bodies. The VAMAS has high-level agreements with all standards development bodies.

VAMAS fatigue projects considered both tensile and flexure loading. Experiences gained in these round-robins were incorporated into the new ISO 13003 fatigue standard. Data from the VAMAS programme are shown in Section 2.7.

Table 2.3   Available EN ISO standard 'static' test methods and ASTM equivalents

Property	International European Standards	ASTM Standard
Tension – 'isotropic' (nominally)	EN ISO 527-4	D 3930
Tension – unidirectional (anisotropic)	EN ISO 527-5	D 3930
Flexure	EN ISO 14125	D 695
Compression	EN ISO 14126	D 3410
Shear – ±45° tension	EN ISO 14129	D 3815
Shear – interlaminar by short beam flexure	EN ISO 14130	D 2344
Shear – double V notch		D 5379
Mode I Fracture energy	EN ISO 15024	D 5528

2.6.2   Standards for coupon fatigue testing

2.6.2.1   EN ISO 13003, 'Fibre Reinforced Plastic Composites – Determination of Fatigue Properties Under Cyclic Loading Conditions'[1]
The latest fatigue standard published is EN ISO 13003, which is one of the few standards available for testing the fatigue properties of composites. This standard gives general principles for fatigue testing that can be applied, with care, to all modes of testing. This approach is necessary as fatigue tests have been undertaken on most if not all test geometries and stress modes. For example, following the development of static through-thickness test methods to measure the acknowledged weakness for all laminated composite materials, there has now been considerable fatigue testing undertaken using these geometries.[15]

The ISO standard sets out the prime requirements in the main text with recommendations for the two most frequent modes, tension and flexure, covered in two annexes. The general aspects are generally applicable to all testing modes and types of composite materials. It is recommended that, when available, the equivalent static test methods should be used. Some relevant static test methods are given in Table 2.3.

Several of these artefacts covered in Section 5 are covered in this standard. For example,

Effect of rate dependence – user required to undertake short-term ultimate strength tests at both the normal loading rate (i.e. 1–5 mm/min. crosshead displacement) and at a rate equivalent to the fatigue loading rate for rate dependent materials, such as glass-fibre based systems (i.e. test duration assumed equal to $1/(2 \times frequency)$ seconds),

Autogenous heating – user required to limit the fatigue frequencies so that autogenous heating is limited to a 10 °C temperature rise, or to record the specimen temperature throughout the test,

Failure criteria – importance of using an appropriate definition of failure (e.g. a percentage loss in stiffness) for cases when specimen fracture is not obtained. Monitoring specimen stiffness also provides continuous information to the operator on the state of the specimen throughout the test.

Other important aspects covered in the standard are:

- choosing a standard static test method for the stress mode of interest, if possible,
- importance of maintaining any non-ambient pre-conditioning during the fatigue test (e.g. pre-treatment at a defined relative humidity),
- need to avoid low quality specimens (e.g. ensure no machining marks),
- recommended percentages of the ultimate strength for a typical test programme (e.g. 80, 65, 55 and 40 for glass-fibre-based material, with higher values for flexure or for carbon-fibre-based systems).

Table 2.4   Recommended test specimen numbers for different data requirements[1]

Data requirement	Exploratory	Materials research	Design allowables/ full S–N curves
Number of specimens	6	12	24–30

2.6.2.2   ASTM D 3479, 'Standard test method for tension–tension fatigue of polymer matrix composite materials'[23]

This standard is restricted to tensile testing of unnotched coupons. It has a similar philosophy to the ISO standard in that it is based on the equivalent static test method, but in this case limited to tensile mode only. The ASTM standard is split into two methods, A and B, according to whether the control parameter is load (stress) or strain, respectively. Other aspects are similar to EN ISO 13003, for example, the cross-reference to the ultimate short term strength, but in the ASTM series (i.e. ASTM 3039 for tensile tests). Points highlighted include:

• test machine alignment,
• load cell and extensometry performance,
• specimen quality,
• within tab failures.

It is suggested that drift of more than 2% in the load due to a reduction in stiffness of the specimen due to micro-damage should be reported. The standard also includes a useful table, see Table 2.4, indicating the number of specimens recommended for different data requirements. These recommendations were also incorporated into EN ISO 13003.[1]

2.6.2.3   ASTM D 6115,[24] 'Standard test method for mode I fatigue delamination growth onset of unidirectional fibre reinforced polymer matrix composites'

This standard builds on the static or short-term Mode 1 fracture energy test methods for crack growth along the lamination plane as covered by the equivalent standards, ASTM D 5528[25] and EN ISO 15024.[26] The test method is conducted in a manner similar to other fatigue tests, except that the control mode relates to different energy levels rather than stress or strain levels. So that, the tests are conducted at displacements, δ_{max} and δ_{min}, equivalent to critical strain energy release rates $G_{IC_{max}}$ and $G_{IC_{min}}$. The failure criteria in this case is the number of cycles to onset of delamination crack growth.

However, observing the onset of crack growth is not easily accomplished, in common with the static Mode I fracture energy test method (e.g. EN ISO 15024). In a validation round-robin organized to validate this standard, three methods were used to observe crack growth initiation. These were visual observation, compliance increase by 1% (approximates to 1% loss in peak load) and the increase in compliance by 5% (approximates to 5% loss in peak load). The 1% increase gave the lowest result and is recommended in the standard for generating a conservative failure criteria. The visual method was not included in the standard due to the difficulties associated with this method.

The growth of the delamination is not measured in this method due to the fact that fibre bridging across the crack, which often occurs with crack growth, has a large effect on the threshold energy values. A linear elastic response is assumed as non-linearities in the response require the more complicated test analysis in the equivalent static test to be used. However, the basic test method has been used by researchers studying crack growth.

2.6.2.4   Mode II fatigue delamination crack growth

Work has been undertaken under a VAMAS programme that has not yet reached the stage of standardization. This also applies to the equivalent static test method. A recent VAMAS project has reviewed the different static methods available and recommended the four-point, end-notched flexure test. The VAMAS Mode II fracture energy project was undertaken on the earlier three-point version of the test.[27,28] Differences between the methods are probably least for onset, compared to crack propagation tests, where frictional effects are of concern. The four-point test is thought to be more stable than the three-point version.

2.6.2.5   Bearing fatigue – new ASTM work item[29]

A standard is also in preparation covering the specialist area of bearing fatigue. In common with the ASTM tensile test above, this standard also refers to the corresponding static bearing test, D5961.[30] The test covers tension, compression and reversed loading situations. The test is conducted under load control. It is recommended that at selected cyclic intervals the hole elongation is measured directly or from a load vs. deformation static loading for a single static tension–compression cycle. Warnings are included on both all the issues associated with bolted joints and the debris build-up that may mask the degree of hole elongation. It is recommended that the debris be removed before the hole elongation is measured.

2.6.3   Standards for component fatigue testing

These two following product standards contain requirements for fatigue testing of final components or products. This type of testing exists in other product areas, even though it may not be formalized in publicly available documents, such as national or international standards.

2.6.3.1   GRP piping offshore – ISO 14269[31]

This standard covers the design of glass-fibre reinforced plastic piping for use in the off-shore petroleum industry. Cyclic qualification is an optional property. It is conducted for two specimens at a preferred frequency of 25 cycles per minute (equivalent to 0.4 Hz), between 10% or less and 90% or more of the qualified pressure for the pipe in question. Failure within 7000 cycles is unacceptable. Water can be used as the test fluid and only two repeat tests are needed.

2.6.3.2   Fibre wrapped gas cylinders – EN 12245[32]

Required to undertake an 'environmental cycle' test after conditioning at 60 °C and 95% RH for 45 hrs. Fatigue test consists of 5000 cycles between atmospheric pressure and two-thirds of hydraulic pressure, followed by stabilization under ambient conditions, conditioning at 50 °C, further cycling for 5000 cycles, re-stabilization under ambient conditions and 30 cycles at ambient. The two 'fatigued' cylinders are then burst tested, when the pass is a failure pressure of 1.6 × the hydraulic test pressure. The damage tolerance test requires two cuts (one longitudinal, one transverse) to be machined by a 1 mm thick, ~ 20 mm diameter cutter. Each cut should be half the wall thickness with the length of the base of the cut or 'gouge' five times the wall thickness. One cylinder is burst tested, with a 2 × operating pressure pass requirement, and one cylinder pressurised, cycled to survive 1000 cycles between the ambient pressure and the operating pressure.

Table 2.5 Precision definitions from ISO 5725

Repeatability conditions	Reproducibility conditions
Same method	Same method
Identical material	Identical material
Same laboratory	Different laboratories
Same operator	Different operators
Same equipment	Different equipment
Short interval of time	

Precision is defined as 'the closeness of agreement between mutually independent test results obtained under stipulated conditions'. Two measures of precision, 'repeatability – r' and 'reproducibility – R', are necessary to describe the variability of a test method.

The repeatability value is defined as the value below which the absolute difference between two single test results obtained under repeatability conditions may be expected to lie within a probability of 95%. Similarly, the reproducibility value R refers to a 95% probability level.

2.7   Precision data

Increasingly, there is a requirement to supply the precision of measured data. Some of the variability reported can be due to material batch to batch variability. Other sources of variability relate to testing by different operators, on different machines at different times. In addition there are uncertainties associated with all test methods associated with the tolerances such as the accuracy of load or dimensional measurements.[33] The precision of a test method is normally determined through an experimental validation exercise and is reported as repeatability (i.e. within site variations) and reproducibility (i.e. between site variations). The relevant definitions are given in Table 2.5.

It is important that the repeatability and reproducibility of the test method are known for both free trade and liability uses of the standard.

The work involved in validation is very expensive and time-consuming for all materials. The advantage of being able to 'design' the material with composites, leads to potentially endless permutations of material to be tested in order to ensure validation of the test method. A minimum of six or seven materials is needed to represent the most commonly available materials, with testing at eight or more sites depending on the number of levels (materials) used (i.e. more sites needed if only one or two levels). ISO 5725[34] describes the procedure to be followed in validation exercises and is equivalent to ASTM E 691,[35] except that the latter is slightly stricter on the removal of outlying data.

The results are shown in Figs. 2.20 and 2.21 of the VAMAS round-robin for both a glass-fibre and carbon-fibre epoxy system, respectively. The data at recommended percentages of individually measured ultimate strengths can be identified by being in flat lines at set stress levels. There is no rate dependence noted for the small range of test frequencies used due to the available test equipment at different test sites for the carbon fibre system. An effect is shown for the glass-fibre system with the longest lives obtained for the 10 Hz tested data. Overall, the S–N fatigue data shows relatively low scatter. Data plotted at 0.5 cycles is the ultimate strength normally measured at the 'fatigue' rate, except for the lower values in Fig. 2.19 where only slow rate testing was possible.

In Fig. 2.22 is shown the high degree of agreement for four sets of glass-fibre fabric/epoxy with the stated ultimate strengths. In spite of the range of ultimate strengths, the normalized S–N curves agree well with each other and with scatter bands based on the ultimate strength scatter range and a single rate of degradation. The wider scatter bands illustrate the expected and actual dispersion in S-N data for a chopped-strand mat material.

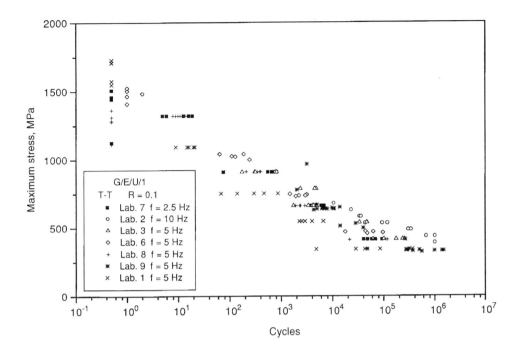

Fig. 2.20   *S–N* fatigue data from VAMAS RR for a glass-fibre epoxy system.

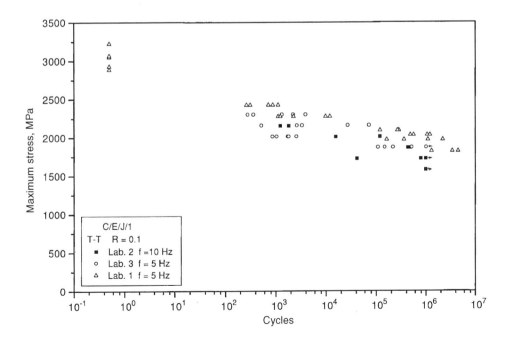

Fig. 2.21   *S–N* fatigue data from VAMAS RR for a carbon-fibre epoxy system.

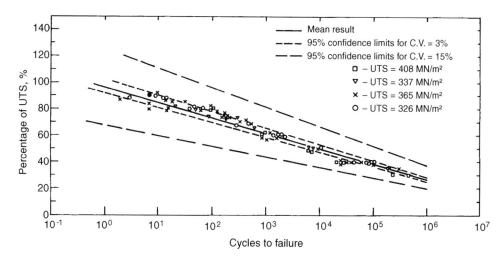

Fig. 2.22   Several sets of S–N data normalized in each case by the relevant ultimate tensile strength for different plates of glass-fibre fabric epoxy.

2.8   Data presentation

2.8.1   Plotting fatigue data

The results are expressed normally by plotting on a graph (Fig. 2.23) with:

on the y-axis (decimal scale):   the peak loads (stresses) or strains (i.e. S)
on the x-axis (log scale):   the number of cycles (i.e. N)

This method of representation leads to the well-known S–N plot or Wöhler curve. If the ultimate strength data are plotted on the same curve, the strength obtained at the fatigue loading rate data should be used for loading rate-dependent materials. The ultimate strength data point is normally plotted at 0.5 cycle.

2.8.2   Analysis of results

2.8.2.1   Curve fitting log N cycles
All the individual results obtained from the tests carried out are plotted as shown in Fig. 2.18. The data can be fitted using standard curve fitting procedures, such as the least square method (particularly if the data approximates to a straight line) to show the trend of the data. In order to retain full information on the test data, it is recommended to leave the experimental data points in the test report (see Fig. 2.20).

2.8.2.2   Statistical analysis of results
Statistical analysis can be applied to all of the results measured at each level of stress (Fig. 2.24). This method is imprecise in the vicinity of the limit of endurance (asymptotic curve), because for identical stress levels the lifetimes can have a large spread. A large number of tests for each well-defined stress level and a good repeatability of this stress is required for this analysis method.

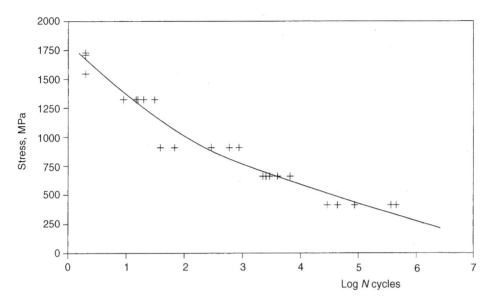

Fig. 2.23   S–N fatigue data diagram.

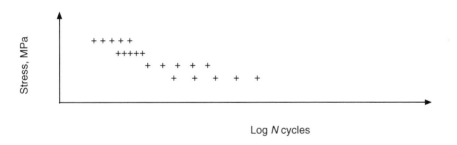

Fig. 2.24   Statistical analysis of the results.

2.9   Concluding comments

From the many factors discussed related to fatigue testing, it appears that there are three prime issues in the choice of any fatigue programme. These are:

- the stress state to be applied (e.g. multi-axial, uniaxial),
- the failure criteria to be applied (e.g. fracture, stiffness loss),
- the control mode to be applied (e.g. load, displacement).

The other factors involved, such as R ratio, specimen shape, grip design, etc. are all subsidiary to these initial choices, although important in their own right in ensuring valid and relevant data are obtained. This hierarchy is shown in Table 2.6.

Table 2.6 Hierarchy of test condition considerations

```
                    ┌─────────────────────────────────────────┐
                    │     Fatigue test programme requirements   │
                    └─────────────────────────────────────────┘
```

Control mode	Failure criteria	Stress mode

Load	Strain		Fracture	Stiffness loss		Uniaxial	Multiaxial

Displacement

Stress ratio, Frequency, Required lifetimes, Test machine capabilities	Automatic machine cut-off	Stiffness monitoring, (peak or full hystersis	Tension, Compression, Shear Torsion, In-plane, Through-thickness	Variable, Biaxial, Triaxial

Available static (slow rate) test method
Material type, properties and failure characteristics
Environmental conditioning and control
Temperature and other monitoring (e.g. acoustic emission)
Fixture design (e.g. buckling, fretting, grip failures)
Data logging and recording

There are few published standards to guide the user, but ISO 13003 provides a generic approach to fatigue that can be applied to most test geometries and materials. For tensile tests only, the ASTM D 3479 provides similar guidance.

For polymer matrix composites it is important to:

- avoid autogenous heating (i.e. use reduced test frequencies to avoid heating effects – note that cooling normally only cools surface of specimen and not centre),
- monitor specimen property changes, such as stiffness and damping properties, or specimen temperature (also see above),
- avoid buckling situations for compression loads,
- avoid fretting – particularly for flexure tests,
- limit tensile grip pressures to avoid grip failures.

A pronounced S-shape can result from artefacts that may be present. For a rate-dependent material, the ultimate data point will be plotted too low. Also, autogenous heating can depress the centre area of the S–N data at stress close to half that ultimate stress as shown previously (see Figs. 2.11 and 2.12). The result of extrapolating the S-shaped curve is to suggest a fatigue limit has been reached, whereas, the corrected curve and tests resulting in longer than normal fatigue lives (e.g. > 10^8) suggest that no limit has been reached.

In Fig. 2.25 are shown the effects of the test used for the ultimate strength measurement (Correction A) and the depression of the central area of the S–N curve due to heating effects (Correction B). The effect of these two artefacts is to give an S-shaped curve suggesting an apparent fatigue stress limit below which fatigue does not occur. In contrast the corrected curve suggests no fatigue limit. Further testing is needed for lives greater than 10^6 cycles to

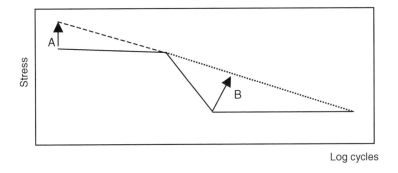

Fig. 2.25   *S–N* plot showing corrections A (stress rate) and B (temperature rise).

establish the true situation. Carbon-fibre-based systems, tested in the fibre direction, are generally considered not to show rate dependence and autogenous heating effects are less. The rate dependence appears to be related to the fibre as the resin is common to both systems.

2.10   Future trends

The wide range of composites together with low (2–5 Hz) test frequencies used have limited the fatigue data available on well characterized materials, particularly at lives greater than 10^6 cycles. In future, the use of higher frequencies, at low stresses, could enable progress on:

*   establishing larger database at long lifetimes (i.e. > 10^6 cycles),
*   establishing, if it is present, a fatigue limit stress level,
*   validating predictive methods for long lifetime data (i.e. > 10^6 cycles).

While some individual application requirements are being met by fatigue tests at the low stresses involved using frequencies of 60 Hz, the full *S–N* curve cannot be obtained at this frequency. For a major fatigue test programme, it would be worthwhile determining the optimum test frequency for each stress level. Although not within the current ISO 13003 standard, the use of a constant loading rate approach (cf. constant frequency) has been used by others and is recommended in the textbook based on the Imperial College/National Physical Laboratory/Queen Mary and Westfield testing course.[36] Further validation is required before this approach can be considered for standardization.

Ultimately, there may be a requirement to decide between the alternative philosophies of, firstly, only testing final or prototype components under service or simulated service conditions with limited fundamental understanding or carry-over to a different set of circumstances, and secondly, testing representative units (e.g. fully aligned material) and extrapolating through failure models and empirical frameworks to materials of different lay-ups and loading situations. The latter approach seems more likely to manage the range of composite materials (e.g. fibre type including hybrids, fibre format and matrix material), different manufacturers and loading conditions.

2.11   Acknowledgements

The author is pleased to recognise the support of many co-workers over the last 35 years, especially the late Den Gladman.

2.12   References

1. ISO 13003, Fibre reinforced plastics: determination of fatigue properties under cyclic loading.
2. SIMS G D and BASCOMBE D (1998), 'Continuous monitoring of degradation during fatigue testing', 6th ICCM/2nd ECCM, **3**, pp. 161–171, London.
3. ISO 1172, Textile glass reinforced plastics – determination of loss on ignition.
4. ISO/DIS 14127, Composites – determination of resin, fibre and void content of composites reinforced with carbon fibre.
5. ISO 6721–11, Plastics – dynamic mechanical properties, determination of glass transition temperature.
6. ISO 11357, Plastics – differential scanning calorimetry.
7. EN ISO 1268, Fibre reinforced plastics – test plate fabrication methods.
8. FOREMAN A, DAVIES A, SIMS G D and SHAW R (2001), 'Composites machining and specimen preparation', NPL Measurement Good Practice Guide No. 38.
9. SIMS G D and GLADMAN D G (1978), 'Effect of Test Conditions on the Fatigue Strength of Glass Fabric Laminate – Part A, Frequency', *Plastics and Rubber: Materials and Applications*, **1**, pp. 41–48.
10. HEYWOOD R B (1958), 'Present and potential fatigue and creep strengths of reinforced plastics', RAE Technical Note Chem. 1337.
11. ASTM D 3410, 'Standard test method for compressive properties of polymer matrix composites with unsupported gage section by shear loading'.
12. EN ISO 14126, Fibre-reinforced plastic composites – determination of the in-plane compression strength.
13. EN ISO 527–4, 'Plastics – determination of tensile properties – Part 4: Test conditions for isotropic and orthotropic fibre reinforced plastic composites'.
14. EN ISO 527–5, 'Plastics – determination of tensile properties – Part 5: Test conditions for unidirectional fibre reinforced plastic composites'.
15. BROUGHTON W R, GOWER M R L, LODEIRO M J and SHAW R M, 'Through-thickness fatigue testing of polymer matrix composites'.
16. ASTM D5379, Standard test method for shear properties of composite materials by the V-notched beam method.
17. NPL drafts for through-thickness tension and compression specimen drafts, 1999.
18. EN ISO 14125, 'Fibre reinforced plastic composites – determination of flexural properties'.
19. Japanese flexural PP spacer.
20. SIMS G D and GLADMAN D G (1982), 'A framework for specifying the fatigue performance of glass-fire reinforced plastics', NPL Report DMA(A) 59.
21. SIMS G D and GLADMAN D G (1980), 'Effect of test conditions on the fatigue strength of glass fabric laminate: Part B, Specimen condition', *Plastics and Rubber: Materials and Applications*, **3**, pp. 122–128.
22. NPL draft methods for open hole tension and open hole compression, 1999.
23. ASTM D 3479, 'Standard Test Method for Tension-Tension Fatigue of Polymer Matrix Composite Materials'.
24. ASTM D 6115, 'Standard Test Method for Mode I Fatigue Delamination Growth Onset of Unidirectional Fiber-Reinforced Polymer Matrix Composites'.
25. ASTM D 5528 'Standard Test Method for Mode I Interlaminar Fracture Toughness of Unidirectional Fiber-Reinforced Polymer Matrix Composites'.
26. EN ISO 15024, Determination of Mode I delamination resistance of unidirectional fibre-reinforced polymer laminates using the double cantilever beam.
27. DAVIES P (1999), 'Comparison of test configurations for the determination of Mode 2 G_{II} – an international round-robin', P Davies *et al. Plastics, Composites and Rubber*, November.
28. MARTIN R H, ELMS T and BOWRON S (1998), 'Characterisation of Mode II delamination using the 4ENF', Composites: Testing and Standardisation Conference 5, Lisbon.
29. ASTM work item draft on 'bearing fatigue testing', 2001.
30. ASTM D5961, 'Standard practice for testing of bolted bearings.
31. ISO 14269, Petroleum and natural gas industries – Glass Reinforced Plastic Piping (4 Parts).
32. EN 12245, Fibre wrapped gas cylinders.
33. ISO Guide to uncertainties of measurement.
34. ISO 5725, 'Accuracy (trueness and precision) of measurement methods and results'.
35. ASTM E 691, 'Standard practice for conducting an interlaboratory study to determine the precision for specimen preparation'.
36. *Mechanical Testing of Advanced Fibre Composites*, ed. J M Hodgkinson, Woodhead Publishing Ltd., 2000.

3

Fatigue under multiaxial stress systems

M. M. Shokrieh, Iran University of Science and Technology, Tehran, Iran, and L. B. Lessard, McGill University, Montreal, Canada

3.1   Introduction

Although there is an extensive amount of research on biaxial/multiaxial fatigue of metals,[1] research in the same field on composite materials is less complete. Literature reviews and results of research of multiaxial and biaxial fatigue loading of composite materials have been presented by Shokrieh,[2,3] Degrieck,[4] Quaresimin,[5] Philippidis,[6] Found,[7] and Chen and Matthews,[8] and these papers state that further research is needed. The idea of using polynomial failure criteria for predicting fatigue failure of composite laminates has been used by many authors;[9–20] however, the application of this idea, due to experimental difficulties, is limited to special cases. A deep understanding of the behaviour of a composite lamina under multiaxial fatigue loading, with arbitrary stress ratios, is a key point for studying the behaviour of a complicated problem.

3.2   Fatigue failure criteria

Under fatigue loading conditions, the material is loaded by a stress state which is less than the maximum strength of the material, therefore there is no static mode of failure. However, by increasing the number of cycles, the material properties degrade and eventually lower to the level of the stress state and, at this point, catastrophic failure occurs. The idea of using polynomial failure criteria to predict the life of a composite ply under multiaxial fatigue loading has been utilized by many investigators.[9–20] They used the fatigue strength, as a function of number of cycles, in the denominators of failure criteria instead of the static strength of the material. This strategy is potentially beneficial; however, in practice, the application of their models are restricted to very specific conditions.

   To show the restriction of application of fatigue failure criteria in traditional forms, consider the following fatigue failure criterion introduced by Hashin[11] for fibre tension fatigue failure mode of a unidirectional ply under a two-dimensional state of stress (biaxial fatigue),

$$\left(\frac{\sigma_{xx}}{X_t(n,\sigma,\kappa)}\right)^2 + \left(\frac{\sigma_{xy}}{S_{xy}(n,\sigma,\kappa)}\right)^2 = g_{f^+}^2 \quad \text{(if } g_{f^+} > 1, \text{ then failure)} \qquad [3.1]$$

where $X_t(n, \sigma, \kappa)$ is the residual longitudinal tensile strength of a unidirectional ply under uniaxial fatigue loading, and $S_{xy}(n, \sigma, \kappa)$ is the residual in-plane shear strength of a unidirectional ply under uniaxial shear fatigue loading conditions. Both X_t and S_{xy} are functions of n, σ, κ which are number of cycles, stress state and stress ratio, respectively.

The fatigue behaviour of a composite lamina varies under different states of stress. For instance, under high level state of stress, the residual strength as a function of number of cycles is nearly constant and it decreases drastically at the number of cycles to failure (Fig. 3.1). The *sudden death model*[94,95] is a suitable technique to describe this behaviour. However, at low level state of stress, the residual strength of the lamina, as a function of number of cycles, degrades gradually (Fig. 3.1). The *wear out model*[96] is a suitable technique to present this behaviour. It should be mentioned that for each state of stress, the *S–N* curve passes through the point (catastrophic failure point) of the residual strength curve, as shown in Fig. 3.1.

In practice, designers must deal with a wide range of states of stress, varying from low to high. Therefore, in order to apply equation [3.1], the residual longitudinal tensile fatigue strength and residual in-plane shear fatigue strength of a unidirectional ply ($X_t(n, \sigma, \kappa)$ and $S_{xy}(n, \sigma, \kappa)$) must be fully characterized under different stress levels and stress ratios. This requires a large quantity of experiments just to predict the fibre in tension fatigue failure mode of a unidirectional ply under simple biaxial fatigue loading conditions. By considering the other modes of failure and the multiaxial states of stress which are encountered in the real fatigue design of composite structures, the proposed method is faced with severe difficulties.

To overcome the difficulties arising from the large quantity of experiments required at different stress states and stress ratios to characterize the material, many investigators[9–20] restricted their models to specific stress ratios. A summary of different stress ratios utilized by authors is presented in Table 3.1. This assumption is too restrictive for general cases. For

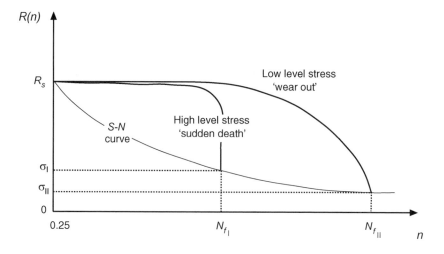

Fig. 3.1   Strength degradation under different states of stress.

Table 3.1 A summary of different load ratios utilized by authors

References	Utilized stress ratios (κ)
Sims and Brogdon[9]	0.818, 0.5 and 0.313
Hahn[10]	0 and 0.1
Hashin[11,12]	−1 to establish failure criteria
	0.1 for experiments
Rotem & Hashin[13]	0.1
Ellyin and El-Kadi[16]	
Wu[19]	
Ryder and Crossman[21]	
Tennyson et al.[18]	0.05 in tension
	(20 in compression)

example, in the analysis of a pin/bolt fatigue loaded composite laminate, using a constant stress ratio leads to incorrect results. Clearly, for this problem there are different states of stress at different points in the material. Also, after applying fatigue load on a notched composite laminate, failure initiates near the stress concentrations and the material property degrades, therefore the stress ratio and the state of stress are not constant at different points. This means that, in practice, stresses redistribute during the fatigue loading. By considering the different behaviour of a unidirectional ply for each combination of the stress state and stress ratio, an infinite number of experiments would be required in order to fully characterize the residual properties of a unidirectional ply under arbitrary state of stress and stress ratio.

To eliminate the aforementioned obstacle of using the quadratic polynomial failure criteria for a wide range of stress state and stress ratio, a technique is established in this study which will be explained in detail in the next section. In the following, a set of quadratic polynomial fatigue failure criteria capable of distinction of different modes of failure of a unidirectional ply under multiaxial fatigue loading conditions are established. The fatigue failure criteria for different modes of failure are similar to static failure criteria, except that the material properties are not constants but functions of number of cycles, stress state and stress ratios. It should be added that the effects of material nonlinearity on the fatigue failure criteria are also considered similar to the static loading conditions.

3.2.1 Fibre tension fatigue failure mode

For fibre tension fatigue failure mode ($\sigma_{xx} > 0$) of a unidirectional ply under a multiaxial state of fatigue stress, the following criterion is used:

$$\left(\frac{\sigma_{xx}}{X_t(n,\sigma,\kappa)}\right)^2 + \left(\frac{\dfrac{\sigma_{xy}^2}{2E_{xy}(n,\sigma,\kappa)} + \dfrac{3}{4}\delta\sigma_{xy}^4}{\dfrac{S_{xy}^2(n,\sigma,\kappa)}{2E_{xy}(n,\sigma,\kappa)} + \dfrac{3}{4}\delta S_{xy}^4(n,\sigma,\kappa)}\right) + \left(\frac{\dfrac{\sigma_{xz}^2}{2E_{xz}(n,\sigma,\kappa)} + \dfrac{3}{4}\delta\sigma_{xz}^4}{\dfrac{S_{xz}^2(n,\sigma,\kappa)}{2E_{xz}(n,\sigma,\kappa)} + \dfrac{3}{4}\delta S_{xz}^4(n,\sigma,\kappa)}\right) = g_{F^+}^2$$

(if $g_{F^+} > 1$, then failure)   [3.2]

where $X_t(n, \sigma, \kappa)$ is the longitudinal tensile residual fatigue strength of a unidirectional ply under uniaxial fatigue loading, $S_{xy}(n, \sigma, \kappa)$ is the in-plane shear residual fatigue strength of a unidirectional ply under uniaxial shear fatigue loading, $E_{xy}(n, \sigma, \kappa)$ is the in-plane shear residual fatigue stiffness of a unidirectional ply under uniaxial shear fatigue loading, $S_{xz}(n,$

σ, κ) is the out-of-plane shear (in x–z plane) residual fatigue strength of a unidirectional ply under uniaxial shear fatigue loading and $E_{xz}(n, \sigma, \kappa)$ is the out-of-plane shear residual fatigue stiffness of a unidirectional ply under uniaxial shear fatigue loading conditions. Also n, σ, κ and α are number of cycles, stress state, stress ratio and parameter of material nonlinearity, respectively. It should be mentioned that the parameter of material nonlinearity (α) is assumed to be a constant, not a function of number of cycles, stress state and stress ratio. In order to express the relationship between the parameter of material nonlinearity and number of cycles for various stress states and stress ratios, further research is needed.

3.2.2   Fibre compression fatigue failure mode

For fibre compression fatigue failure mode ($\sigma_{xx} < 0$), of a unidirectional ply under a multiaxial state of fatigue stress, the following criterion is used:

$$\left(\frac{\sigma_{xx}}{X_c(n, \sigma, \kappa)} \right) = g_{F^-} \quad \text{(if } g_{F^-} > 1 \text{, then failure)} \tag{3.3}$$

where $X_c(n, \sigma, \kappa)$ is the longitudinal compressive residual fatigue strength of a unidirectional ply under uniaxial fatigue loading conditions. Similar to the static loading conditions, the effect of shear stresses on the compressive fatigue behaviour of a unidirectional ply is not clear. Therefore, the interaction terms of shear stresses are not considered in the proposed criterion.

3.2.3   Fibre-matrix shearing fatigue failure mode

For fibre-matrix shearing fatigue failure mode ($\sigma_{xx} < 0$), of a unidirectional ply under a multiaxial state of fatigue stress, the following criterion is used:

$$\left(\frac{\sigma_{xx}}{X_c(n, \sigma, \kappa)} \right)^2 + \left(\frac{\dfrac{\sigma_{xy}^2}{2E_{xy}(n, \sigma, \kappa)} + \dfrac{3}{4}\delta\sigma_{xy}^4}{\dfrac{S_{xy}^2(n, \sigma, \kappa)}{2E_{xy}(n, \sigma, \kappa)} + \dfrac{3}{4}\delta S_{xy}^4(n, \sigma, \kappa)} \right) + \left(\frac{\dfrac{\sigma_{xz}^2}{2E_{xz}(n, \sigma, \kappa)} + \dfrac{3}{4}\delta\sigma_{xz}^4}{\dfrac{S_{xz}^2(n, \sigma, \kappa)}{2E_{xz}(n, \sigma, \kappa)} + \dfrac{3}{4}\delta S_{xz}^4(n, \sigma, \kappa)} \right) = g_{FM}^2$$

$$\text{(if } g_{FM} > 1 \text{, then failure)} \tag{3.4}$$

3.2.4   Matrix tension fatigue failure mode

For matrix tension fatigue failure mode ($\sigma_{yy} > 0$), of a unidirectional ply under a multiaxial state of fatigue stress, the following criterion is used:

$$\left(\frac{\sigma_{yy}}{Y_t(n, \sigma, \kappa)} \right)^2 + \left(\frac{\dfrac{\sigma_{xy}^2}{2E_{xy}(n, \sigma, \kappa)} + \dfrac{3}{4}\delta\sigma_{xy}^4}{\dfrac{S_{xy}^2(n, \sigma, \kappa)}{2E_{xy}(n, \sigma, \kappa)} + \dfrac{3}{4}\delta S_{xy}^4(n, \sigma, \kappa)} \right) + \left(\frac{\sigma_{yz}}{S_{yz}(n, \sigma, \kappa)} \right)^2 = g_{M^+}^2$$

$$\text{(if } g_{M^+} > 1 \text{, then failure)} \tag{3.5}$$

where $Y_t(n, \sigma, \kappa)$ is the transverse tensile residual fatigue strength of a unidirectional ply under uniaxial fatigue loading and $S_{yz}(n, \sigma, \kappa)$ is the out-of-plane shear (in y–z plane) residual fatigue strength of a unidirectional ply under uniaxial shear fatigue loading conditions.

3.2.5 Matrix compression fatigue failure mode

Similarly, for matrix compression static failure mode ($\sigma_{yy} < 0$), of a unidirectional ply under a multiaxial state of fatigue stress, the following equation can be derived:

$$\left(\frac{\sigma_{yy}}{Y_c(n,\sigma,\kappa)} \right)^2 + \left(\frac{\dfrac{\sigma_{xy}^2}{2E_{xy}(n,\sigma,\kappa)} + \dfrac{3}{4}\delta\sigma_{xy}^4}{\dfrac{S_{xy}^2(n,\sigma,\kappa)}{2E_{xy}(n,\sigma,\kappa)} + \dfrac{3}{4}\delta S_{xy}^4(n,\sigma,\kappa)} \right) + \left(\frac{\sigma_{yz}}{S_{yz}(n,\sigma,\kappa)} \right)^2 = g_{M^-}^2$$

(if $g_{M^-} > 1$, then failure)   [3.6]

where $Y_c(n, \sigma, \kappa)$ is the transverse compressive residual fatigue strength of a unidirectional ply under uniaxial fatigue loading conditions.

3.2.6 Normal tension fatigue failure mode

For normal tension fatigue failure mode ($\sigma_{zz} > 0$), of a unidirectional ply under a multiaxial state of fatigue stress, the following criterion is used:

$$\left(\frac{\sigma_{zz}}{Z_t(n,\sigma,\kappa)} \right)^2 + \left(\frac{\dfrac{\sigma_{xz}^2}{2E_{xz}(n,\sigma,\kappa)} + \dfrac{3}{4}\delta\sigma_{xz}^4}{\dfrac{S_{xz}^2(n,\sigma,\kappa)}{2E_{xz}(n,\sigma,\kappa)} + \dfrac{3}{4}\delta S_{xz}^4(n,\sigma,\kappa)} \right) + \left(\frac{\sigma_{yz}}{S_{yz}(n,\sigma,\kappa)} \right)^2 = g_{N^+}^2$$

(if $g_{N^+} > 1$, then failure)   [3.7]

where $Z_t(n, \sigma, \kappa)$ is the normal tensile residual fatigue strength of a unidirectional ply under uniaxial fatigue loading conditions.

3.2.7 Normal compression fatigue failure mode

For normal compression fatigue failure mode ($\sigma_{zz} < 0$), of a unidirectional ply under a multiaxial state of fatigue stress, the following criterion is used:

$$\left(\frac{\sigma_{zz}}{Z_c(n,\sigma,\kappa)} \right)^2 + \left(\frac{\dfrac{\sigma_{xz}^2}{2E_{xz}(n,\sigma,\kappa)} + \dfrac{3}{4}\delta\sigma_{xz}^4}{\dfrac{S_{xz}^2(n,\sigma,\kappa)}{2E_{xz}(n,\sigma,\kappa)} + \dfrac{3}{4}\delta S_{xz}^4(n,\sigma,\kappa)} \right) + \left(\frac{\sigma_{yz}}{S_{yz}(n,\sigma,\kappa)} \right)^2 = g_{N^-}^2$$

(if $g_{N^-} > 1$, then failure)   [3.8]

where $Z_c(n, \sigma, \kappa)$ is the normal compressive residual fatigue strength of a unidirectional ply under uniaxial fatigue loading conditions.

After failure detection by any of the fatigue failure criteria, the material properties of the failed material must be changed by suitable material property degradation rules, which will be explained in the next section.

3.3   Material properties degradation

As failure occurs in a ply of a laminate, material properties of that failed ply are changed by a set of sudden material property degradation rules. Some of the failure modes are catastrophic and some of them are not. Therefore, for a unidirectional ply failed under each mode of static or fatigue failure, there exists an appropriate *sudden* material property degradation rule.

The scenario of material degradation of a unidirectional ply failed under static and fatigue loading conditions before occurrence of sudden failure is different. For a unidirectional ply under a multiaxial state of static stress before sudden failure initiation, detected by the set of static failure criteria, there is no material degradation. However, for a unidirectional ply under a multiaxial state of fatigue stress before sudden failure initiation, detected by the set of fatigue failure criteria, there is gradual material property degradation. To explain this difference more clearly, consider a laminated composite under static loading conditions. The load is increased monotonically and at a certain load level, failure initiation in a ply of the laminate is detected by the static failure criteria. At this stage, the mechanical properties of the failed region of the unidirectional ply of the laminate must be changed. This type of degradation is called *sudden material property degradation*. For a laminated composite under fatigue loading conditions, in the first cycles, the strength of the plies can be higher than the stress state. Therefore, during the first cycles, the proposed fatigue failure criteria (equations [3.2] to [3.8]) do not detect any sudden mode of fatigue failure. However, by increasing the cyclic loading of the laminate, material properties of each ply are degraded. This type of degradation is called *gradual material property degradation*. By further increasing the number of cycles, mechanical properties of the plies eventually reach to a level where different modes of failure can be detected by the proposed fatigue failure criteria (equations [3.2] to [3.8]). At this stage, the mechanical properties of the failed material are changed by *sudden material property degradation rules*. The *sudden material property degradation rules* for some failure modes of a unidirectional ply under a biaxial state of static stress are available in the literature.[21–24] A complete set of sudden material property degradation rules for all the various failure modes of a unidirectional ply under a multiaxial state of static and fatigue stress is developed in this study and explained in the following section.

3.3.1   Sudden material property degradation rules

In the following, a complete set of sudden material property degradation rules is established for each mode of failure of a unidirectional ply under a multiaxial state of static or fatigue stress detected by the static or fatigue failure criteria.

Conventional finite element techniques are by definition limited to an intact continuum. Thus, after failure occurrence in a ply, instead of inducing a real crack, the failed region of the ply is replaced by an intact ply of lower material properties (Fig. 3.2). Therefore, conventional finite element techniques can be applied for stress analysis even after failure initiation.

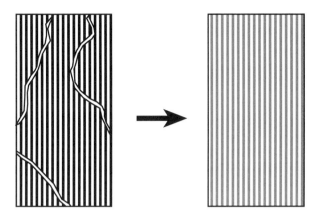

Fig. 3.2   Degraded ply is modelled by an intact ply of lower material properties.

3.3.1.1   Fibre tension property degradation

Fibre tension failure mode of a unidirectional ply is a catastrophic mode of failure and when it occurs, the failed material cannot sustain any type or combination of stresses. Thus, all material properties of the failed ply are reduced to zero.

As mentioned, this mode of failure is catastrophic, therefore if it occurs, the other modes of failure do not need to also be verified. During numerical computations by the computer program, reducing material properties to zero creates numerical instabilities. To avoid this difficulty, for the case of failure, the material properties are reduced to very small values.

3.3.1.2   Fibre compression property degradation

Fibre compression failure mode of a unidirectional ply is a catastrophic mode of failure and when it occurs, the failed material cannot sustain any type or combination of stresses. Thus, all material properties of the failed ply are reduced to zero.

As mentioned, this mode of failure is catastrophic, therefore if it occurs, the other modes of failure do not need to also be verified.

3.3.1.3   Fibre-matrix shearing property degradation

In fibre-matrix shearing failure mode of a unidirectional ply, the material can still carry load in the fibre, matrix and normal directions, but in-plane shear stress can no longer be carried. This is modelled by reducing the in-plane shear material properties of the failed ply to zero, as follows:

$$\left[E_{xy}, v_{xy}, v_{yx}, S_{xy} \right] \rightarrow \left[0 \right] \qquad\qquad [3.9]$$

3.3.1.4   Matrix tension property degradation

For matrix tension failure mode of a unidirectional ply, the transverse modulus E_{yy}, the transverse tensile strength Y_t, and Poisson's ratios v_{yx} and v_{yz} are reduced to zero. This mode of failure is not catastrophic, and affects only matrix direction properties, therefore other material properties are left unchanged.

$$\left[E_{yy}, Y_t, v_{yz}, v_{yx} \right] \rightarrow \left[0 \right] \qquad\qquad [3.10]$$

3.3.1.5   Matrix compression property degradation

Matrix compression failure mode results in the same type of damage to the composite ply as the matrix tension failure mode. Thus, the transverse modulus E_{yy}, the transverse compressive strength Y_c, and Poisson's ratios v_{yz} and v_{yx} are reduced to zero. This mode of failure is not catastrophic, therefore, other material properties are left unchanged.

$$\left[E_{yy}, Y_C, v_{yz}, v_{yx}\right] \rightarrow [0]$$ [3.11]

3.3.1.6   Normal tension property degradation

For normal tension failure mode of a unidirectional ply, the normal modulus E_{zz}, the normal tensile strength Z_t, and Poisson's ratios v_{zx} and v_{zy} are reduced to zero. This mode of failure is not catastrophic, therefore, other material properties are left unchanged. This is essentially the same type of failure as matrix tension failure mode.

$$\left[E_{zz}, Z_t, v_{zx}, v_{zy}\right] \rightarrow [0]$$ [3.12]

3.3.1.7   Normal compression property degradation

For normal compression failure mode of a unidirectional ply, the normal modulus E_{zz}, the normal compressive strength Z_c, and Poisson's ratios v_{zx} and v_{zy} are reduced to zero. This mode of failure is not catastrophic, therefore, other material properties are left unchanged. This is essentially the same type of failure as matrix compression failure mode.

$$\left[E_{zz}, Z_C, v_{zx}, v_{zy}\right] \rightarrow [0]$$ [3.13]

3.3.2   Gradual material property degradation rules

To apply the fatigue failure criteria (equations [3.2] to [3.8]), the residual material properties of a unidirectional ply under arbitrary multiaxial state of fatigue stress and stress ratio must be modelled. For this purpose, the *generalized material property degradation technique* is established, which simulates the fatigue behaviour of a unidirectional ply under multiaxial state of fatigue stress and arbitrary stress ratio by using the results of uniaxial fatigue experiments. In this way, the severe limitation of application of the fatigue failure criteria in traditional forms, mentioned in the previous section, is overcome.

3.3.2.1   Normalized strength degradation model

Harris *et al.*[25,26] presented a normalized equation consisting of two curve fitting parameters. They showed that these are stress independent curve fitting parameters which must be found experimentally. They emphasized that stress-independent models, like the model proposed by Fong,[27] which is based on the assumption that the fatigue process is controlled by a single primary damage mechanism, is not realistic. They postulated that their model permitted the incorporation of all modes of damage accumulation, from *wear out* to *sudden death*, by the adjustment of the curve fitting parameters α and β. In their studies, the equivalent number of fatigue cycles for a static loading condition is assumed to be 0.5, however, by considering that a static loading is really a quarter of a cycle, the equivalent number of cycles should be changed to 0.25.

By using the normalization technique, all different curves for different states of stress, in Fig. 3.1 collapse to a single curve (Fig. 3.3). For use in this research, the equation presented by Harris *et al.*[25,26] is changed to the following form (with the equivalent number of fatigue cycles for a static loading condition changed from 0.5 to 0.25):

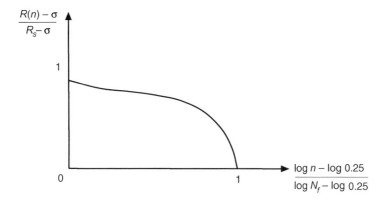

Fig. 3.3   Normalized strength degradation curve.

$$R(n,\sigma) = \left[1 - \left(\frac{\log(n) - \log(0.25)}{\log(N_f) - \log(0.25)}\right)^{\beta}\right]^{\frac{1}{\alpha}} (R_s - \sigma) + \sigma \qquad [3.14]$$

By having static strength R_s, state of stress σ, number of cycles to failure N_f related to the state of stress, and the curve fitting parameters α and β, residual strength $R(n,\sigma)$, as a function of number of cycles n and the state of stress σ, is found.

Since in equation [3.14], α and β are stress-independent parameters, this model is called the *normalized strength degradation model*. However, number of cycles to failure N_f is a function of the state of stress σ and the stress ratio $\kappa = \sigma_{min}/\sigma_{max}$. Therefore, to simulate the residual strength of a unidirectional ply under a general uniaxial fatigue loading (arbitrary state of stress and stress ratio), a suitable relationship between the fatigue life N_f, state of stress and stress ratio is needed. For the general case, i.e. arbitrary stress ratio, equation [3.14] is changed to the following form:

$$R(n,\sigma,\kappa) = \left[1 - \left(\frac{\log(n) - \log(0.25)}{\log(N_f) - \log(0.25)}\right)^{\beta}\right]^{\frac{1}{\alpha}} (R_s - \sigma) + \sigma \qquad [3.15]$$

By considering that for each combination of the state of stress and stress ratio, there is a fatigue life for a unidirectional ply, to characterize the residual strength of a unidirectional ply under arbitrary state of stress and stress ratio, an infinite number of experiments must still be performed. As mentioned in the previous section, many authors restricted their failure criteria to a certain stress ratio to overcome this difficulty. However, as previously discussed, assuming a certain stress ratio for the fatigue analysis of composite laminates is not always a realistic assumption. Before removing this obstacle by introducing the *normalized fatigue life model*, the *normalized stiffness degradation model* for a unidirectional ply in a normalized form is explained in the following.

3.3.2.2   Normalized stiffness degradation model
The residual stiffness of the material is also a function of state of stress and number of cycles. As discussed in the previous section, there are various number of strength degradation models. Similarly, there is much research in stiffness degradation[28–39] of composite materials.

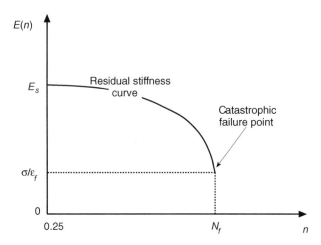

Fig. 3.4   Stiffness degradation of a unidirectional lamina under a constant uniaxial fatigue loading.

The stiffness degradation models are attractive to many investigators, because the residual stiffness can be used as a nondestructive measure for damage evaluation. By performing a similar procedure used as that for normalizing the residual strength, a suitable equation for residual stiffness of a unidirectional ply can be obtained. By using the normalization technique, all different curves for different states of stress can be shown by a single master curve. The idea of normalizing the residual stiffness curves and establishing a master curve has been used by many authors.[40–42] In this study, a new method of normalization is developed.

Consider a unidirectional lamina under a constant uniaxial fatigue loading. Under static loading, or equivalently at $n = 0.25$ cycles (quarter of a cycle) in fatigue, the static stiffness of the unidirectional lamina is E_s (Fig. 3.4). It should be mentioned that the character 'E' is used as a representative symbol for the stiffness of a unidirectional ply which has different magnitudes in different directions such as, E_{xx}, E_{yy}, etc.

By increasing the number of cycles, under a constant applied stress σ, the fatigue stiffness $E(n)$ decreases. Finally, after a certain number of cycles, which is called number of cycles to failure N_f, the magnitude of the stiffness decreases to a critical magnitude E_f. At this point, the composite lamina fails catastrophically. The stiffness degradation of a unidirectional ply is shown in Fig. 3.4. The aforementioned critical value for stiffness E_f can be expressed by the following equation,

$$E_f = \frac{\sigma}{\varepsilon_f} \qquad\qquad [3.16]$$

The average strain to failure ε_f is assumed to be a constant and independent on the state of stress and number of cycles. This assumption is used by many authors[28–31] and verified experimentally in this study. It should be mentioned that for different states of stress, the stiffness degradation of the unidirectional ply is different. The same as for the residual strength case, under high level state of stress, the residual stiffness as a function of number of cycles is nearly constant and it decreases drastically at the number of cycles to failure (Fig. 3.5). However at low level state of stress the residual stiffness of the lamina, as a function of number of cycles, degrades gradually. In practice, designers must deal with a wide range of states of stress varying from low to high. Therefore similar to strength degradation case, a

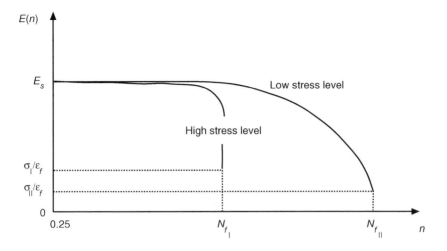

Fig. 3.5   Stiffness degradation under different states of stress.

model to present the residual stiffness behaviour of composite materials under a general state of stress is essential.

To present the residual stiffness as a function of number of cycles in a normalized form, the following equation is developed, based on a similar idea to that used for residual strength,

$$E(n,\sigma,\kappa) = \left[1 - \left(\frac{\log(n) - \log(0.25)}{\log(N_f) - \log(0.25)} \right)^{\lambda} \right]^{\frac{1}{\gamma}} (E_s - \frac{\sigma}{\varepsilon_f}) + \frac{\sigma}{\varepsilon_f} \qquad [3.17]$$

where $E(n, \sigma, \kappa)$ = residual stiffness, E_s = static stiffness, σ = magnitude of applied maximum stress, ε_f = average strain to failure, n = number of applied cycles, N_f = fatigue life at σ, and λ and γ = experimental curve fitting parameters

By using this normalization technique, all different curves for different states of stress in Fig. 3.5, collapse to a single curve (Fig. 3.6).

3.3.3   Normalized fatigue life model

The effect of mean stress $(\sigma_{max} + \sigma_{min})/2$ on fatigue life, can be presented efficiently by using constant life (Goodman-type) diagrams.[42] Establishing and interpolation of constant life diagram data in traditional form is a tedious task. However, there are some analytical methods[43–47] for predicting the effect of mean stress on fatigue life based on a limited number of experiments. In a paper by Adam *et al.*,[43] an analytical method has been proposed to convert and present all data from a constant life diagram in a single two-parameter fatigue curve, which can reduce the number of needed experiments drastically. In this study, this model is called the *normalized fatigue life model*. Recently, the normalized fatigue life model was modified by Harris and his co-workers[46,47] for more general cases. In the following, this model is explained in detail.

Introducing non-dimensional stresses by division of the mean stress σ_m, the alternating stress σ_a and the compressive strength σ_c by the tensile strength σ_t, where $q = \sigma_m/\sigma_t$, $a = \sigma_a/\sigma_t$, and $c = \sigma_c/\sigma_t$, an empirical interaction curve may be derived:[46,47]

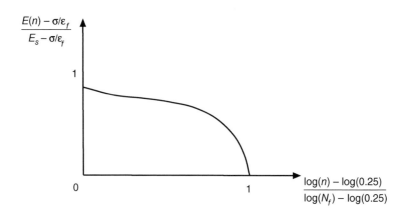

Fig. 3.6   Normalized stiffness degradation curve.

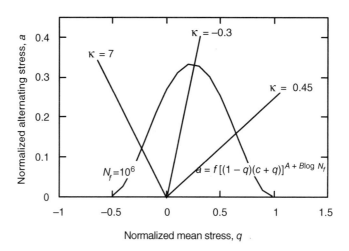

Fig. 3.7   Typical constant life diagram.

$$a=f(1-q)^u+(c+q)^v \qquad\qquad\qquad [3.18]$$

where f, u, and v = curve fitting constants, $\sigma_a = (\sigma_{max} - \sigma_{min})/2$ = alternating stress, $\sigma_m = (\sigma_{max} + \sigma_{min})/2$ = mean stress, $q = \sigma_m/\sigma_t$, $a = \sigma_a/\sigma_t$, and $c = \sigma_c/\sigma_t$.

A typical curve for a fatigue life of 10^6 cycles is shown in Fig. 3.7. The bell-shaped curve is the fatigue life curve. Experimental results by Gathercole et al.,[47] showed that their previous quadratic model[44] is inappropriate for the constant life curve especially in both low and high mean stress regions (Fig. 3.7). Therefore, they introduced a power law model (equation [3.18]) that produces a bell-shaped curve, which corresponds closer to the material behaviour under fatigue loading. In a paper by Gathercole et al.,[47] it was shown that the exponents u and v determine the shapes of the left and right wings of the bell-shaped curve. However, it was also shown[47] that the degree of curve-shape asymmetry was not very great, therefore they assumed u and v are equal and are linear functions of fatigue life N_f.

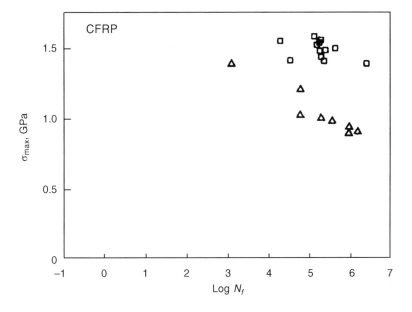

Fig. 3.8   *S*-log N_f curve, σ_t=1.91 (GPa), and σ_c=1.08 (GPa).[43]

$$u=v=A+B\log N_f \hspace{4cm} [3.19]$$

where *A* and *B* are the curve fitting constants. By substituting equation [3.19] into equation [3.18], the following equation is obtained:

$$a=f[(1-q)+(c+q)]^{A+B\log N_f} \hspace{3cm} [3.20]$$

The following example helps to explain the *normalized fatigue life model*. To predict the fatigue life, the following steps must be performed. First, a σ-log N_f curve for different stress ratios should be established experimentally (Fig. 3.8). Different symbols in Fig. 3.8 represent different applied stress ratios. It is obvious that testing at more states of stress will result in more accuracy. Then by rearranging equation [3.20], the following equation is derived and shown graphically in Fig. 3.9.

$$u = \frac{\ln(a/f)}{\ln[(1-q)(c+q)]} = A + B\log N_f \hspace{3cm} [3.21]$$

In Figs. 3.8 to 3.10, this procedure has been applied to numerical data from the paper by Adam *et al.*[43] In Fig. 3.8, original fatigue data is presented. Then, based on the data from Fig. 3.9, setting *f* = 1.06 (suggested by Gathercole *et al.*[47]) and equation [3.21], the *u* = ln(*a*/*f*)/ ln[(1 − *q*)(*c* + *q*)] vs. log N_f curve is extracted (Fig. 3.9), from which *A* and *B* are found. In Fig. 3.10, based on all previous information, the constant life diagram for different number of cycles to failure is predicted. Figure 3.10 is generated by knowing *A*, *B* and *f*, three constants which can be determined from a relatively small quantity of tests, as demonstrated in this example. Thus, the method is very useful for reducing the number of experiments for characterization of materials.

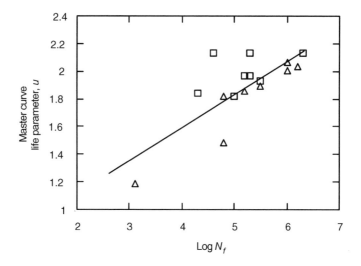

Fig. 3.9 u vs. log N_f curve.

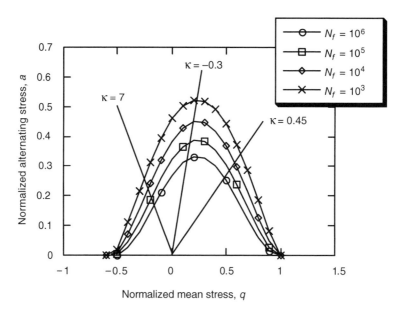

Fig. 3.10   Predicted constant life diagram.

3.3.4   Modification of the life model for shear fatigue conditions

For the simulation of the fatigue life of the unidirectional ply under shear fatigue loading conditions, the method explained by equations [3.18] to [3.21] must be modified. For a unidirectional ply under shear, the definitions of tensile strength and compression strength are meaningless, i.e. there is no difference between positive and negative shear. Therefore,

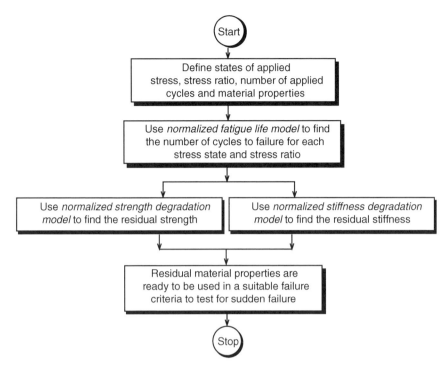

Fig. 3.11   Flowchart of *generalized material property degradation technique* at the ply level.

the word strength is used instead. By considering this, the parameter c in equation [3.21] is equal to one $(c = 1)$ for shear fatigue conditions. Also, the experimental results for unidirectional plies under in-plane shear loading conditions show that a better curve fitting is achieved by adding a '$\log_{10}$' to the left-hand side of equation [3.21]. Therefore, equation [3.21] is changed to the following form for the simulation of fatigue life of the unidirectional ply under shear loading conditions. The left-hand side of equation [3.22] is still denoted by 'u' for briefness.

$$u = \frac{\ln(a/f)}{\ln[(1-q)(1+q)]} = A + B \log N_f \qquad [3.22]$$

3.3.5   Generalized material property degradation technique
At this stage, the *normalized strength degradation* (equation [3.15[), *the normalized residual stiffness* (equation [3.17]), and the *normalized fatigue life models* in the form of equations [3.21] (and [3.22] for shear), are established and available. By coupling these models, the *generalized material property degradation technique* is established. By using this *technique*, polynomial fatigue failure criteria can be applied for failure analysis of unidirectional plies under arbitrary stress state and stress ratios. This *technique* is explained by the flowchart shown in Fig. 3.11.

To explain the model, consider a unidirectional ply under a multiaxial state of stress. Also, suppose that one of the modes of fatigue failure, e.g. the fibre tension fatigue failure mode (equation [3.2]) is to be verified. As shown in the flowchart (Fig. 3.11), the state of stress (σ), stress ratio (κ), number of applied cycles (n) and the static material properties must be defined at the beginning. For the aforementioned mode of failure, the static properties of the unidirectional ply in fibre direction (X_t) and in-plane shear S_{xy} and E_{xy} and out-of-plane shear S_{xz} and E_{xz} loading conditions must be known (see equation [3.2]). Then by using the *normalized fatigue life model* (equations [3.21] and [3.22]), the number of cycles to failure for each stress state (N_{fxx}, N_{fxy} and N_{fxz}) is calculated. By having this information and using the residual stiffness and strength degradation models (equations [3.15] and [3.17]), the residual material properties of the unidirectional ply under longitudinal stress, in-plane and out-of-plane shear stresses can be calculated. It should be mentioned here that the experimental parameters (α, β, γ, λ, A, B and f) must be fully characterized in advance for each of the three states of stress in this example. At this stage, all previous results are substituted into equation [3.2] to detect the fibre failure mode for the unidirectional ply under multiaxial state of stress. If sudden fibre tension failure is detected, the material properties of the failed region of the unidirectional ply must be changed by sudden material property degradation rule (equation [3.9]). This simple example shows that the model is capable of considering arbitrary state of stress and stress ratio. Therefore, by establishing the *generalized material property degradation technique*, the severe obstacle of application of quadratic failure criteria for arbitrary stress ratios is overcome.

3.4   Progressive fatigue damage modelling

The *model* is an integration of the three important components: stress analysis, failure analysis and material property degradation. The *model* is capable of simulating the residual strength, fatigue life and final failure mechanism of composite laminates with arbitrary geometry, stress ratio and stacking sequence under complicated fatigue loading conditions using the results of various types of uniaxial fatigue experiments on unidirectional plies. The generality and capabilities of the *model* are discussed in detail. Based on the *model*, a computer code is developed which simulates the cycle-by-cycle behaviour of composite laminates under fatigue loading conditions.

3.4.1   Framework of progressive fatigue damage modelling

The major difference between the *progressive fatigue damage model* and the traditional progressive damage model used for static loading conditions is the existence of the gradual material property degradation which occurs during fatigue loading. In the previous section, the *generalized material property degradation technique* is established. This technique simulates the material property (stiffness and strength) degradation and fatigue life of a unidirectional ply under a multiaxial state of stress and arbitrary stress ratio. By adding this technique to the traditional progressive damage model and necessary modification of the algorithm, the *progressive fatigue damage model* is established and explained by means of the flowchart shown in Fig. 3.12.

As shown in Fig. 3.12, the finite element model must first be prepared. In this step, material properties, geometry, boundary conditions, maximum and minimum fatigue loads, maximum number of cycles, incremental number of cycles, etc. are defined. Then the stress analysis, based on the maximum and minimum fatigue load, is performed. Consequently, the maximum and minimum induced on-axis stresses of all elements are calculated. It should be emphasized that on-axis stresses for each ply of each laminate of each element at Gauss points are calculated and averaged. Therefore, the stress ratio ($\kappa = \sigma_{min}/\sigma_{max}$) for each

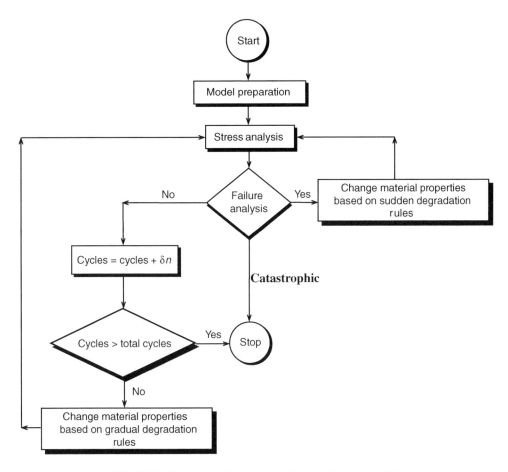

Fig. 3.12   Flowchart of *progressive fatigue damage model.*

element is determined. In the next step, failure analysis is performed and the maximum stresses are examined by the set of fatigue failure criteria (equations [3.2] to [3.8]). If there is a sudden mode of failure, then the material properties of the failed plies are changed according to appropriate *sudden* material property degradation rules. The stiffness matrix of the finite element model is rebuilt and the stress analysis is performed again. New stresses are examined by the set of fatigue failure criteria. In this step, if there is no sudden mode of failure, an incremental number of cycles are applied (e.g. $\delta n = 100$). If the number of cycles is greater than a preset total number of cycles, then the computer program stops. Otherwise, material properties of all plies of all elements are changed according to *gradual* material property degradation rules using the *generalized material property degradation technique* (see Fig. 3.11). Then stress analysis is performed again and the above loop is repeated until catastrophic failure occurs, or the maximum number of cycles (pre-defined by the user) is reached. If catastrophic failure is reached, then fatigue life and the mechanisms of failure due to fatigue loading have been achieved. It should be noted that, if the maximum number of cycles is selected as a large number, such as 10^9, the fatigue life of the problem can be obtained by the algorithm. If the computer program stops because the user-chosen maximum number of cycles is reached, the mechanisms of failure due to fatigue loading are found by examining the final state of damage. Furthermore, in the latter case, residual strength of the composite laminate is obtainable by performing a progressive static damage modelling on the final results of *progressive fatigue damage model*.

A user-friendly computer code is developed. The computer code developed in this study is published by the authors elsewhere.[48] The computer code is able to simulate the cycle-by-cycle behaviour of a laminated composite under general fatigue loading conditions and predict the residual strength and the fatigue life of the problem.

3.5   Material characterization

The material properties (strength, stiffness, residual strength, residual stiffness and fatigue life) of unidirectional AS4/3501-6 carbon/epoxy material are fully characterized under tension and compression, for fibre and matrix directions, and under in-plane and out-of-plane shear, in static and fatigue loading conditions. The information provided by this series of experiments is used as input data for the *progressive fatigue damage model*. To avoid performing infinite numbers of experiments under various stress states and stress ratios in fatigue loading conditions, the normalization techniques explained in the previous sections are utilized here. Some of the existing testing methods for characterization of composites are necessarily modified and improved during the experimental studies in this research.

3.5.1   Required experiments
The experiments are designed to determine the experimental parameters needed by the model explained in previous sections. As a first step, all material properties of a unidirectional ply (stiffness and strength) under static loading conditions are measured to establish initial strengths and stiffnesses. Using the results from static tests as normalizing parameters, material properties of a unidirectional ply (stiffness, strength, and life) under fatigue loading are characterized experimentally. From the experiments conducted in fatigue, residual strength, residual stiffness and fatigue life of the unidirectional ply under uniaxial loading are fully determined. The static and fatigue tests, required for full characterization of the material properties of a unidirectional ply, are shown in Fig. 3.13.

It must be noted that the series of tests are designed based on the transversely isotropic material property assumption. Consequently, the material properties of the unidirectional ply in normal and transverse directions are assumed to be the same. This assumption decreases the number of required experiments.

3.5.2 Specifications of test specimens
The specifications (dimensions, standards, and modifications) of the test specimens in static and fatigue loading conditions, for full characterization of unidirectional plies, are explained in Table 3.2.

3.5.2.1   Longitudinal tensile tests
In this section, the results of static and fatigue experiments for characterizing the material properties of a unidirectional ply $[0]_{16}$, in the fibre direction under tensile loading are summarized. The specimens for fibre in tension tests are manufactured based on ASTM D 3039–76[49] and ASTM D 3479–76[50] standards. The specimen and the dimensions are shown in Fig. 3.14.

The results of experiments for measuring the residual stiffness and residual strength of

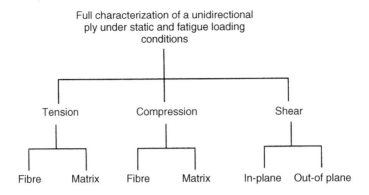

Fig. 3.13   Tests needed to fully characterize material properties of a unidirectional ply under static and fatigue loading.

Table 3.2   Specifications of test specimens

Type of test (static or fatigue)	Test specimens	Standards	Notes
Fibre tension		D 3039-76 D 3479-76	With hydraulic grips
Fibre compression		——	With hydraulic grips
Matrix tension		D 3039-76 D 3479-76	With hydraulic grips
Matrix compression		D 3410-87	With hydraulic grips
In-plane shear		D 4255-83	Modified notched specimen
Out-of-plane shear		D 2733-70 D 2344-84	With clamp

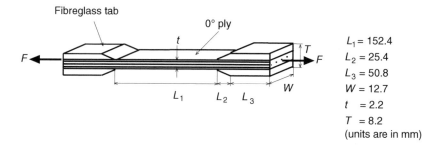

Fig. 3.14   Fibre in tension specimen.

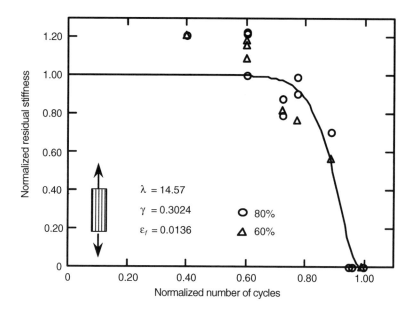

Fig. 3.15   Normalized residual stiffness of a unidirectional 0° ply under longitudinal tensile
fatigue loading conditions (using equation [3.14]).

unidirectional 0° plies under tension-tension fatigue are presented here. To measure the residual stiffness and residual strength, two different states of stress (80% and 60% of the longitudinal tensile static strength) are selected. By selecting these two different states of stress, the high and low stress levels are applied. A stress ratio equal to 0.1 and a frequency below 10 Hz are applied. The results of residual stiffness and strength experiments are shown in Figs. 3.15 and 3.16, respectively. A least square curve fitting method is used and the curve fitting parameters using equations [3.15] and [3.17] are also calculated and mentioned in Figs. 3.15 and 3.16. An interesting increase in residual stiffness and in residual strength (about 8 to 13% of the static stiffness and strength) for the first few cycles is observed experimentally. The increase in residual stiffness is perhaps due to realignment of some of the 0° fibres. The phenomenon of increasing residual fatigue stiffness and

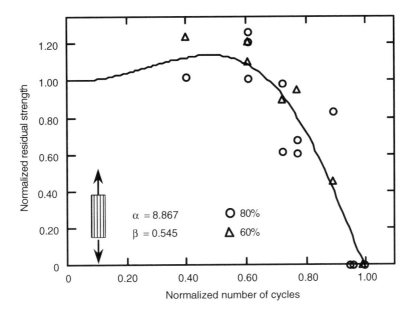

Fig. 3.16   Normalized residual strength of a unidirectional 0° ply under longitudinal tensile fatigue loading conditions (using equation [3.15]).

strength for unidirectional plies has also been observed by Awerbuch and Hahn.[51] As clearly shown in Figs. 3.15 and 3.16, while the curve fitting using equations [3.15] and [3.17] is able to fit the decreasing parts of the curves very well, it is not able to consider the increase in residual stiffness and strength in the first few cycles. As will be shown in the next section, these results in the present forms can be used for simulation of decreasing of the residual strength of notched composite laminates. However, by ignoring the increasing parts of the residual stiffness and strength curves of the unidirectional ply, simulation of increasing of the residual strength of notched composites for the first few fatigue cycles, which is a frequently observed phenomenon,[40,59–69] is not possible. A new strategy for curve fitting and more details about this subject will be discussed in the next section.

3.5.2.2   Longitudinal compressive tests

In this section, the results of static and fatigue experiments for characterizing the material properties of a unidirectional ply $[0]_{24}$, in the fibre direction under compressive loading are summarized. The specimen and the dimensions are shown in Fig. 3.17.

The results of experiments for measuring the residual strength of unidirectional 0° plies under compression–compression fatigue are presented here. To measure residual strength under fatigue loading, two different states of stress (80% and 60% of the longitudinal compressive static strength) are selected. Again, by selecting these two different states of stress, high and low stress levels are applied. A stress ratio equal to 10 and a frequency below 10 Hz are applied. The results of residual strength experiments are shown in Fig. 3.18. The residual stiffness of the unidirectional 0° ply under compressive fatigue loading is also experimentally characterized in this study but published by the authors elsewhere.[70] However, similar to the static case, the residual stiffness under tension and compression fatigue loading conditions are assumed to be equal. Also, similar to the fibre in tension case, an increase in residual strength of 8 to 10% of the static strength is observed experimentally. As

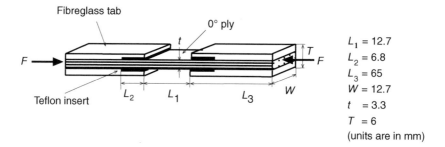

Fig. 3.17   Fibre compression specimen.

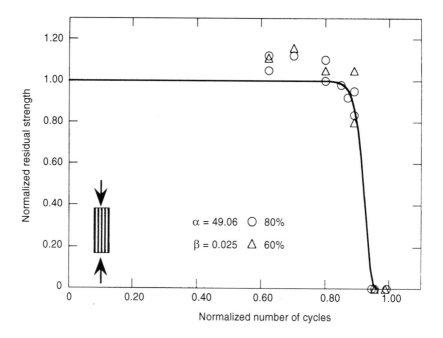

Fig. 3.18   Normalized residual strength of a unidirectional 0° ply under longitudinal compressive
fatigue loading conditions (using equation [3.15]).

is clearly shown in Fig. 3.18, equation [3.15] is not able to account for the increase in the
residual strength. This subject was explained for fibre in the tension case and is valid here,
and will be discussed further in the next section.

As mentioned earlier, in this section the results of fatigue life experiments for the
unidirectional 0° ply under longitudinal tensile and compressive fatigue loading conditions
are coupled and presented in a normalized form. Two different stress ratios ($\kappa = \sigma_{min}/\sigma_{max} =$
0.1 and 10) and different percentages of the static strength (selected as the maximum stress)
are applied to find the fatigue life of a unidirectional 0° ply under longitudinal tension–
tension and compression–compression fatigue loading conditions. In Fig. 3.19, the master
curve for the fatigue life of the unidirectional 0° ply under longitudinal tensile and

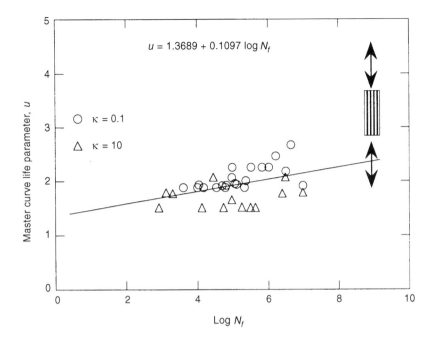

Fig. 3.19   Master curve for fatigue life of unidirectional 0° ply under longitudinal tensile and compressive fatigue loading conditions (using equation [3.20]).

compressive fatigue loading conditions is presented in a normalized form. By using equation [3.21], the curve fitting parameters (A and B) are found and mentioned in Fig. 3.19. Although the parameter f (in [3.21]) seems to be a function of the strength of laminated composite materials, however, in this study, a constant magnitude for this parameter ($f = 1.06$) appears to provide a proper curve fit.

3.5.2.3 Transverse tensile tests

In the following, the results of static and fatigue experiments for characterizing the material properties of a unidirectional ply $[90]_{16}$, in the matrix direction under tensile loading are summarized. The specimens for matrix in tension tests are manufactured based on ASTM D 3039-76[49] and ASTM D 3479-76[50] standards. The specimen and the dimensions are shown in Fig. 3.20. The specimen is equipped with flat metallic tabs.

The results of experiments for measuring the residual stiffness and residual strength of a unidirectional 90° ply under tension–tension fatigue are presented in this section. To measure the residual stiffness and strength under fatigue loading, two different states of stress (60% and 40% of the tensile transverse static strength) are selected. By selecting these two different states of stress, high and low stress levels are applied. A stress ratio equal to 0.1 and a frequency below 10 Hz are applied. The results of residual stiffness and strength experiments of a unidirectional 90° ply under tension–tension fatigue are shown in Figs. 3.21 and 3.22, respectively.

3.5.2.4 Transverse compressive tests

In this section, the results of static and fatigue experiments for characterizing the material properties of a unidirectional ply $[90]_{24}$, in the matrix direction under compressive loading

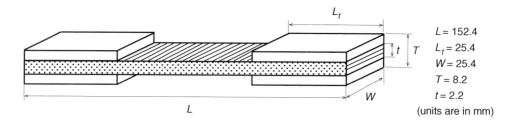

Fig. 3.20   Matrix tensile specimen.

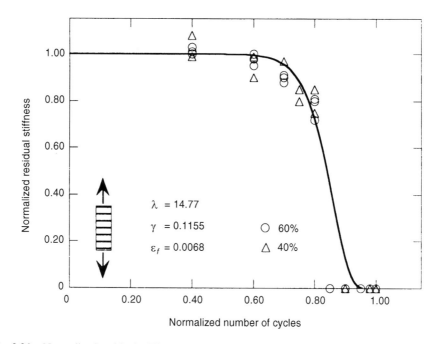

Fig. 3.21   Normalized residual stiffness of a unidirectional 90° ply under transverse tensile fatigue loading conditions (using equation [3.17]).

are summarized. The specimens for matrix in compression tests are manufactured based on ASTM D 3410–87[71] standard. The specimen and the dimensions are shown in Fig. 3.23. The specimen is equipped with flat metallic tabs and no fixture is required to perform the static and fatigue tests.

The results of experiments for measuring the residual strength of a unidirectional 90° ply under compression–compression fatigue are presented here. To measure the residual strength of the material under fatigue loading, two different states of stress (70% and 50% of the compressive transverse static strength) are selected. Again, by selecting these two different states of stress, high and low stress levels are applied. A stress ratio equal to 10 and a frequency below 10 Hz are applied. The residual stiffness of unidirectional 90° plies under compressive fatigue loading is also experimentally characterized in this study but published by the authors elsewhere.[48] However, similar to the static case, the residual stiffness under tension and compression fatigue loading conditions are assumed to be equal. The results of residual strength experiments of a unidirectional 90° ply under compression–compression fatigue are shown in Fig. 3.24.

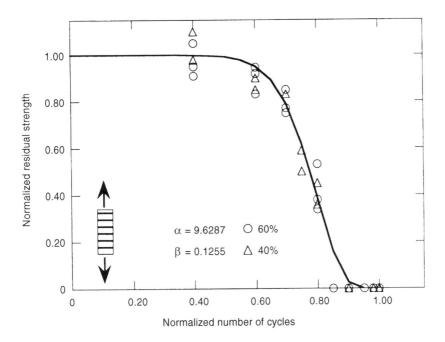

Fig. 3.22   Normalized residual strength of a unidirectional 90° ply under transverse tensile fatigue loading conditions (using equation [3.15]).

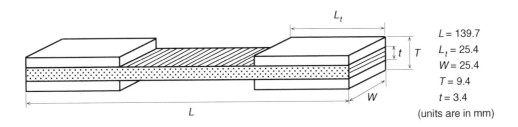

Fig. 3.23   Matrix in compression specimen.

As mentioned earlier, in this section the results of fatigue life experiments for the unidirectional 90° ply under transverse tensile and compressive fatigue loading conditions are coupled and presented in a normalized form. Two different stress ratios ($\sigma = \sigma_{min}/\sigma_{max} =$ 0.1 and 10) and different percentages of the static strength (selected as the maximum stress) are applied to find the fatigue life of a unidirectional 90° ply under transverse tension–tension and compression–compression fatigue loading conditions. In Fig. 3.25, the master curve for the fatigue life of the unidirectional 90° ply under transverse tensile and compressive fatigue loading conditions is presented in a normalized form. By using equation [3.21], the curve fitting parameters (A and B) are found and mentioned in Fig. 3.25.

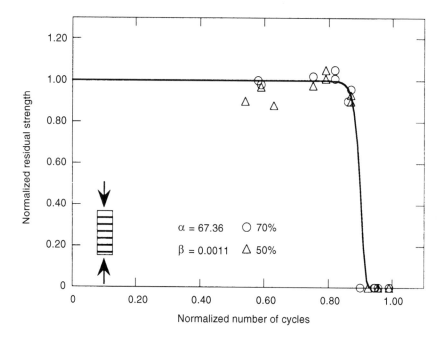

Fig. 3.24   Normalized residual strength of a unidirectional 90° ply under transverse compressive fatigue loading conditions (using equation [3.15]).

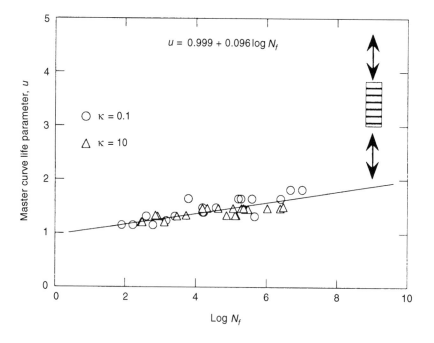

Fig. 3.25   Master curve for fatigue life of unidirectional 90° ply under transverse tensile and compressive fatigue loading conditions (using equation [3.21]).

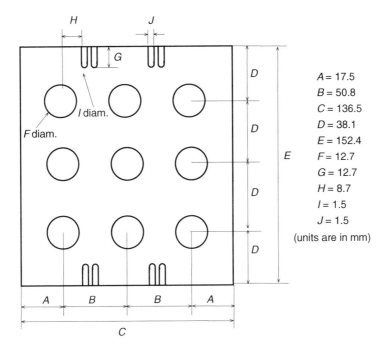

A = 17.5
B = 50.8
C = 136.5
D = 38.1
E = 152.4
F = 12.7
G = 12.7
H = 8.7
I = 1.5
J = 1.5
(units are in mm)

Fig. 3.26   Modified in-plane shear specimen.

3.5.2.5   In-plane shear tests

The specimen configuration and the dimensions are shown in Figure 3.26.

The results of the experiments for measuring the residual stiffness and residual strength of the notched samples under in-plane shear fatigue are presented in this section. To measure the residual stiffness and residual strength of the material, two different states of stress (59% and 40% of the in-plane shear static strength of the material) are selected. By selecting these two different states of stress, high and low stress levels are applied. A stress ratio equal to 0.1 and a frequency equal to 2 Hz are applied. The results of residual stiffness and strength experiments of the notched samples under in-plane shear fatigue are shown in Figs. 3.27 and 3.28, respectively. The curve fitting parameters for equations [3.15] and [3.17] and are also mentioned in the figures.

Although the parameter of material nonlinearity (δ) seems to be a function of number of fatigue cycles (for more details refer to[72,73]), however, in this study, this parameter is assumed to be a constant.

In this section, the results of fatigue life experiments for the notched samples under in-plane shear fatigue loading conditions are presented in a normalized form. Two different stress ratios ($\kappa = \sigma_{min}/\sigma_{max} = 0.1$ and 0.0) and different percentages of the static strength (selected as the maximum stress) are applied to find the fatigue life of the notched samples under in-plane shear fatigue loading conditions. In Fig. 3.29, the master curve for the fatigue life of the notched samples under in-plane shear fatigue loading conditions is presented in a normalized form. By using equation [3.22], the curve fitting parameters (A and B) are found and mentioned in Fig. 3.29.

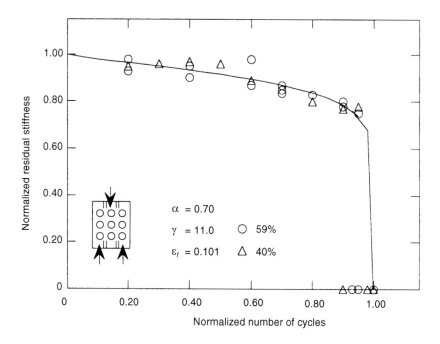

Fig. 3.27   Normalized residual stiffness of a unidirectional material under in-plane shear fatigue
loading conditions (using equation [3.17]).

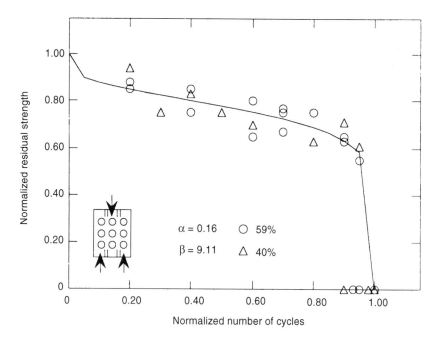

Fig. 3.28   Normalized residual strength of a unidirectional material under in-plane shear fatigue
loading conditions (using equation [3.15]).

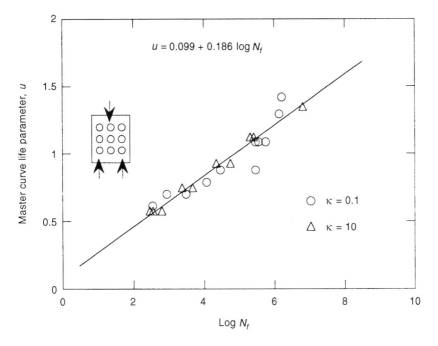

Fig. 3.29   Master curve for fatigue life of notched samples under in-plane shear fatigue loading conditions (using equation [3.22]).

3.5.2.6   Out-of-plane shear tests

The double-notch specimen test method, as described by the ASTM D 2733–70[74] and ASTM D 3846–93[75] standards, was used for characterizing the out-of-plane shear properties of the material. The specimen configuration and the dimensions are shown in Fig. 3.30. The analytical and experimental study of the modified specimen is published by the authors elsewhere,[76] and due to space limitations, is not repeated here. The out-of-plane shear strength of the unidirectional ply can be measured by the present method. The method is not capable of measuring the out-of-plane modulus of the unidirectional ply, however it can be easily calculated by transversely isotropic assumption (equation [3.6]).

In order to induce interlaminar shear (σ_{yz}) in the gauge area of a double notched specimen, a 90-degree lay-up must be used. Since the material is weaker in matrix tension than in interlaminar shear loading, a tensile load applied to a double notch specimen with 90-degree lay-up results in a matrix failure prior to failure in interlaminar shear. There are two solutions to this problem. The first solution is to use [0/90]$_s$ laminate instead of a 90-degree lay-up. Also, it is known that the strength of the material in matrix compression loading is higher than in matrix tension. Therefore, the second solution is to apply a compressive load instead of a tensile load on a 90-degree lay-up. Improbability of failure between the 0 and 90-degree plies is the disadvantage of using [0/90]$_s$ laminate (first method). The disadvantage of the second method is the possibility of buckling, which can be avoided by using anti-buckling clamps. In this study, the second solution is selected. The clamp and dimensions are shown in Fig. 3.31.

To measure the residual strength of the material, two different states of stress (80% and 60% of the out-of-plane shear static strength of the material) are selected. By selecting these two different states of stress, high and low stress levels are applied. A stress ratio equal to 0.1

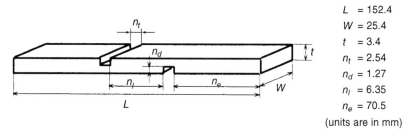

$$
\begin{aligned}
L &= 152.4 \\
W &= 25.4 \\
t &= 3.4 \\
n_t &= 2.54 \\
n_d &= 1.27 \\
n_l &= 6.35 \\
n_e &= 70.5
\end{aligned}
$$

(units are in mm)

Fig. 3.30   Out-of-plane double-notched shear specimen.

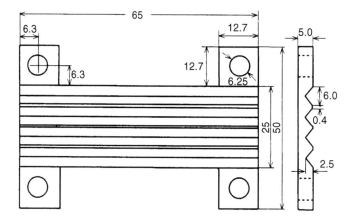

Fig. 3.31   Clamp used to eliminate the out-of-plane buckling (all units are in mm).

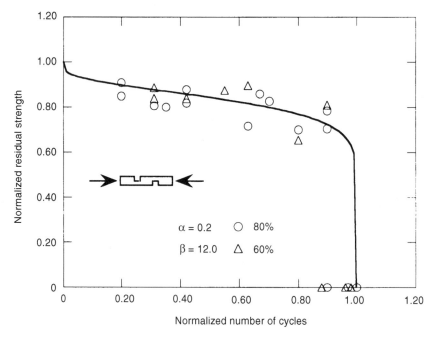

Fig. 3.32   Normalized residual strength of double-notched samples under out-of-plane shear fatigue loading conditions (using equation [3.17]).

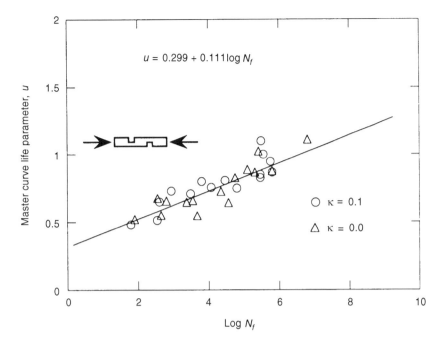

Fig. 3.33   Master curve for fatigue life of double-notched samples under out-of-plane shear fatigue loading conditions (using equation [3.22]).

and a frequency below 10 Hz are applied. The results of residual strength experiments of a unidirectional ply under out-of-plane shear fatigue are shown in Fig. 3.32. The curve fitting parameters for equation [3.17] are also mentioned in the figure. Furthermore, to calculate the residual out-of-plane shear stiffness of the unidirectional ply under fatigue loading conditions, the transversely isotropic assumption must be used.

Two different stress ratios ($\kappa = \sigma_{min}/\sigma_{max} = 0.1$ and 0.0) and different percentages of the static strength (selected as the maximum stress) are applied to find the fatigue life of double-notched samples under out-of-plane shear fatigue loading conditions. In Fig. 3.33, the master curve for the fatigue life of the double-notched samples under out-of-plane shear is presented in a normalized form. By using equation [3.22], the curve fitting parameters (A and B) are found and mentioned in Fig. 3.33.

3.6   Experimental evaluation of the model

This section is devoted to experimental evaluation of the *progressive fatigue damage model* and some of its components.

3.6.1   Evaluation of generalized residual material property degradation technique

Because of its simplicity, the off-axis specimen test method is used by many authors for experimental evaluation of polynomial failure criteria[77–83] for characterization of in-plane-shear properties of composites[84–86] and for fatigue analysis of off-axis composites.[64]

3.6.1.1   Off-axis specimen experiments and results

Tests are performed using an MTS 810 material testing system, equipped with hydraulic grips. A computer was connected to the MTS for data acquisition. Displacement and load are monitored for static experiments. During fatigue tests, maximum and minimum displacements and loads as well as number of cycles are monitored. Static tests are performed under displacement control, while the fatigue tests are carried out under load control conditions. The fatigue load is applied in a sinusoidal form. To avoid temperature effects, which could degrade the material properties, fatigue tests are performed at frequencies less than 10 Hz. All tests are performed in ambient temperature. The specimens are manufactured, cut and polished using standard techniques. To reduce the gripping effects, oblique aluminium tabs[87] are used.

At first, a series of static experiments are performed to measure the magnitude of static strength of the off-axis specimen and to evaluate the static failure criteria. The magnitude of the off-axis failure stress for the $[30_{16}]$ off-axis specimen is calculated and compared with the experimental results in Fig. 3.34. As shown, the static failure load calculated by polynomial failure criterion overestimates the static strength of off-axis specimen by about 5%, which is quite satisfactory.

Tension–tension fatigue tests are performed under load control conditions and the load ratio (F_{min}/F_{max}) equal to 0.1 is applied to off-axis specimens. Different percentages of the maximum static failure load, such as 40, 50, 60, 70 and 80% are selected as the maximum load. The fatigue tests are continued until catastrophic failure is achieved and the maximum number of cycles to failure is monitored. The experimental results of fatigue life of the $[30_{16}]$ off-axis specimen are shown in Fig. 3.35. A linear curve fitting approach is utilized and the experimental S–N curve is shown by a solid line in Fig. 3.35.

Now, by using the experimental curve fitting parameters, the number of cycles to failure for the $[30_{16}]$ off-axis specimen under various applied stress conditions and stress ratios are calculated by using the Newton–Raphson technique. The results calculated by the *technique* are compared with the experimental results and are shown in Fig. 3.35. By comparing the S–N curves (experimental data points curve-fitted mathematically and simulated by the *technique*), it seems the S–N curve simulated by the *technique* overestimates the fatigue life of the 30-degrees off-axis specimen. However, as shown in Fig. 3.35, the simulated S–N curve is located inside the experimental scatter range. Therefore, it can be concluded that the deterministic *technique* is reasonably simulating the behaviour of the unidirectional ply under biaxial state of stress.

A summary of selected fatigue life results from the experiments and the *technique* is presented in numerical form in Table 3.3. In fatigue loading conditions, applying the biaxial load decreases the fatigue life of the unidirectional ply drastically. For instance, consider the $[30_{16}]$ off-axis specimen under uniaxial tensile fatigue loading conditions, with the maximum stress equal to 80% of its maximum static strength as shown in Table 3.3. By ignoring the longitudinal stress (σ_{xx}), it is clear that this case is equivalent to a unidirectional ply under transverse loading combined with in-plane shear loading, where the σ_{yy} (maximum transverse stress) is equal to 66.0% of Y_t (maximum transverse tensile static strength) and the σ_{xy} (maximum in-plane shear stress) is equal to 45.3% of S_{xy} (maximum in-plane static shear strength). The fatigue life of the unidirectional ply under uniaxial transverse tensile loading with 66.0% of Y_t as the maximum stress is about 11 380 cycles. Moreover, the fatigue life of the unidirectional ply under uniaxial in-plane shear loading with 45.3% of S_{xy} as the maximum stress, is about 10 920 000 cycles. By coupling the two states of stress ($[30_{16}]$ off-axis specimen under 80% of its maximum strength) the fatigue life of the unidirectional ply, found experimentally, is decreased to about 1202 cycles and the *technique* simulated 1494

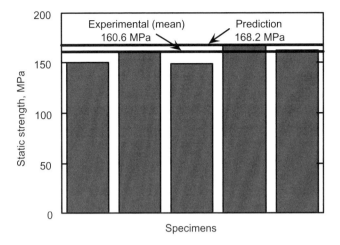

Fig. 3.34 Comparison of calculated static failure load with experimental results for $[30_{16}]$ off-axis specimens.

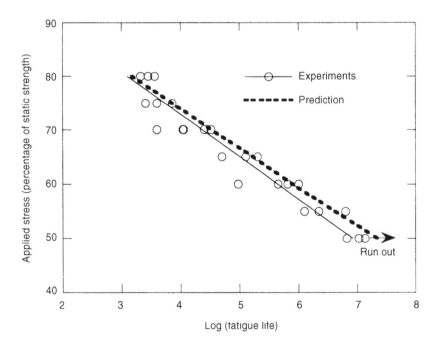

Fig. 3.35 Fatigue life (*S–N*) curve of the $[30_{16}]$ off-axis specimens (experiments and prediction).

cycles. It shows that the fatigue life of the off-axis specimen measured experimentally and simulated by the *technique* are in a very good agreement. For the other stress levels, the difference between the experimental and simulated results seems to be considerable, however, on a logarithmic scale (Fig. 3.35) very good agreement is achieved. The effect of the interaction of the transverse and in-plane shear stresses is apparent from the results.

Table 3.3   Fatigue life results from the experiments and the *technique*

Applied stress (off-axis) specimen)	Induced stress (σ_{yy}/Y_t)	Uniaxial life Nf_{yy} (cycles)	Induced stress (σ_{xy}/S_{xy})	Uniaxial life Nf_{xy} (cycles)	Experimental biaxial life (cycles)	Simulated biaxial life (cycles)
80%	66.0%	11 380	45.3%	10 920 000	1 202	1 494
75%	61.8%	57 507	42.4%	27 393 000	5 012	6 972
70%	57.7%	292 630	39.6%	72 361 000	23 422	33 060
65%	53.6%	1 502 400	36.8%	203 000 000	˙ 104 713	160 000
60%	49.5%	7 818 100	33.9%	610 850 000	441 570	794 700
55%	43.3%	41 584 000	31.1%	1 996 500 000	1 995 292	4 085 000

Before ending this section, there are some critical points which should be mentioned. As shown in Table 3.3, by decreasing the applied stress level, the difference between the results simulated by the *technique* and the experimental results increases. It should be mentioned that by decreasing the applied fatigue stress level for the off-axis specimen, the unidirectional material is under very low level states of stress. From the previous section, remember that the unidirectional material was characterized at high and low states of stress but not at very low stress levels. Therefore, the material properties of the unidirectional ply under very low level states of stress are extrapolated from the real experimental results. This is the main reason for the increased difference between the fatigue life simulated by the *technique* and measured experimentally at very low levels of applied stress.

Moreover, the magnitudes and proportions of the on-axis stresses induced in the off-axis specimen cannot be selected arbitrarily. The magnitudes of these stresses depend on the off-axis applied stress and the angle of orientation of fibres. This should be noted as a limitation of the off-axis specimen method as a biaxial testing technique. Nonetheless, the simplicity of this method makes it attractive as a biaxial loading technique.

Also, it is clear that by using the *generalized residual material property degradation technique*, which is a deterministic method, a single curve is simulated as the fatigue life curve of the off-axis specimen. It is well known that experimental scatter is inherent to the fatigue properties of the material. Therefore, instead of having a single curve for the fatigue life of the off-axis specimen, a range of scattered data points are found by the experimental techniques in the laboratory. This limitation could be eliminated by coupling a probabilistic model to the *technique* which is not considered in this study.

3.6.2   Evaluation of progressive fatigue damage model
The evaluation of the *progressive fatigue damage model* is performed in different ways. The capabilities of the *model* to simulate the fatigue life and the residual strength of composite laminates are examined. To study the stacking sequence, three different ply configurations $([0_4/90_4]_s, [90_4/0_4]_s$ and $[+45_4/-45_4]_s)$ are utilized. For the purpose of comparing results, all tests are performed at load ratio (F_{min}/F_{max}) equal to 0.1 and a frequency less than 10 Hz.

3.6.3   Fatigue life simulation
A series of fatigue tests is performed to measure the fatigue life of the pin or bolt-loaded composite laminates with different lay-ups. Based on the maximum static strength of each case, presented in the previous section, the fatigue experiments were accomplished under load control conditions.

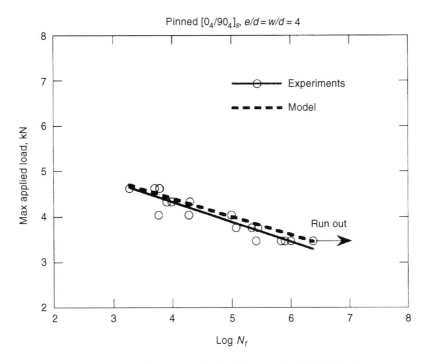

Fig. 3.36   Fatigue life curve of pin-loaded cross-ply $[0_4/90_4]_s$ laminates.

3.6.3.1   Cross-ply $[0_4/90_4]_s$

A series of fatigue life tests is performed at different percentages of the maximum strength of the pin-loaded cross-ply $[0_4/90_4]_s$ laminate with $e/d = w/d = 4$. The maximum applied load versus number of cycles for the pin-loaded cross-ply $[0_4/90_4]_s$ laminate is shown in Fig. 3.36. The solid line shows the experimental fatigue life curve, fitted by using a least square method. Also, the dotted line shows the simulated fatigue life using the *progressive fatigue damage model*. As shown in Fig. 3.36, very good agreement between the experimental and simulated results is achieved which shows that the model is performing successfully. For instance, at 4.335 kN which is 80% of the maximum static strength of the pin-loaded cross-ply $[0_4/90_4]_s$ laminate, the experimental fatigue life is about 9910 cycles and the fatigue life simulated by the *model* is 15 400 cycles, which is in the scatter range of the experimental results. As explained earlier, the main reason for the greater difference between the fatigue life prediction and the experiments in Fig. 3.36, at very low load levels, is that material characterization of the unidirectional ply is performed at high and low states of stress but not at very low stress levels.

A series of fatigue life tests is performed at different percentages of the maximum strength of the bolt-loaded cross-ply $[0_4/90_4]_s$ laminate with $e/d = w/d = 4$. The maximum applied load versus number of cycles for the bolt-loaded $[0_4/90_4]_s$ laminate is shown in Fig. 3.37. Again, the solid line shows the experimental fatigue life curve, fitted by using a least square method. Also, the dotted line shows the simulated fatigue life using the *progressive fatigue damage model*. As shown in Fig. 3.37, very good agreement between the experimental and simulated results is achieved.

By comparing the pin- and bolt-loaded cases for the cross-ply $[0_4/90_4]_s$ laminate (Figs. 3.36 and 3.37), it is clear that the bolt load increases the fatigue life by decreasing the edge

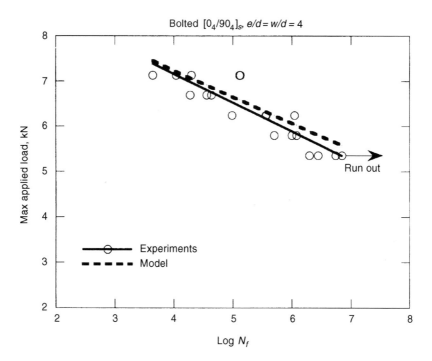

Fig. 3.37   Fatigue life curve of bolt-loaded cross-ply $[0_4/90_4]_s$ laminates.

effects. The effects of bolt load on the states of stress is greatest near the edge of the hole between plies with different orientations, which is the location of stress singularity. The predicted results show that the *model* is clearly capable of simulating this behaviour.

3.6.3.2   Cross-ply $[90_4/0_4]_s$

Another series of fatigue life tests is performed at different percentages of the maximum strength of the pin-loaded cross-ply $[90_4/0_4]_s$ laminate with $e/d = w/d = 4$. The maximum applied load versus number of cycles for the pin-loaded cross-ply $[90_4/0_4]_s$ laminate is shown in Fig. 3.38. Again, the solid line shows the experimental fatigue life curve, fitted by using a least square method. Also, the dotted line shows the simulated fatigue life using the *progressive fatigue damage model*. As shown in Fig. 3.38, very good agreement between the experimental and simulated results is also achieved for this case.

In order to compare the results of the fatigue life of pin-loaded $[0_4/90_4]_s$ and $[90_4/0_4]_s$ cross-ply laminates, Figs. 3.37 and 3.38 are shown in one graph (Fig. 3.39). As shown, similar to the static strength behaviour, the pin-loaded $[90_4/0_4]_s$ laminate shows a higher fatigue life than the $[0_4/90_4]_s$ cross-ply laminate for the same fatigue loading conditions. The main reason for this behaviour is explained by the lower singular stress state for the $[90_4/0_4]_s$ cross-ply laminate near the edge of the hole.

3.6.3.3   Angle-ply $[+45_4/-45_4]_s$

Another series of fatigue life tests is performed at different percentages of the maximum strength of the pin-loaded angle-ply $[+45_4/-45_4]_s$ laminate with $e/d = w/d = 4$. The maximum applied load versus number of cycles for the pin-loaded angle-ply laminate is shown in Fig. 3.40. Again, the solid line shows the experimental fatigue life curve, fitted by using a least square method. Also, the dotted line shows the simulated fatigue life using the *progressive*

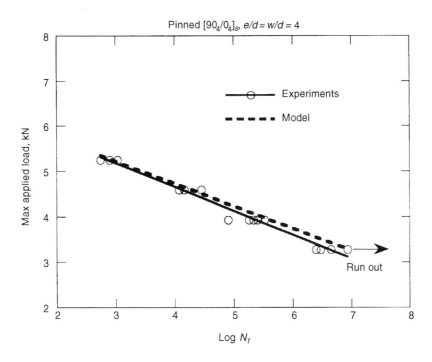

Fig. 3.38 Fatigue life curve of pin-loaded cross-ply $[90_4/0_4]_s$ laminates.

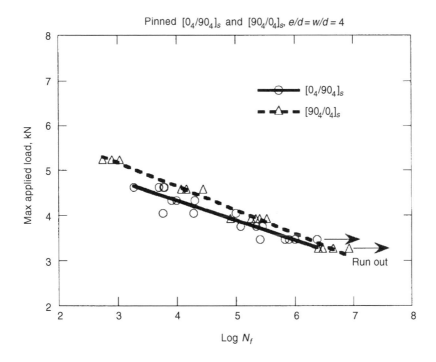

Fig. 3.39 Fatigue life curves of pin-loaded $[0_4/90_4]_s$ and $[90_4/0_4]_s$ laminates.

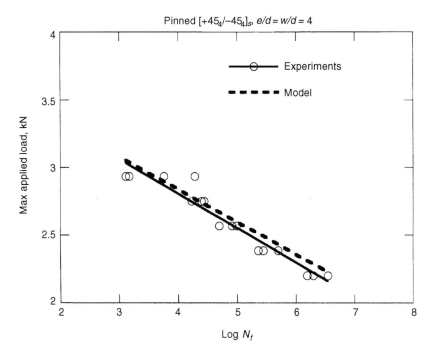

Fig. 3.40   Fatigue life curve of pin-loaded angle-ply [+45₄/-45₄]ₛ laminates.

fatigue damage model. As shown in Fig. 3.40, good agreement between the experimental and simulated results is also achieved for this case.

It should be mentioned that the final failure mechanisms of the mechanical joints under static and fatigue loading conditions are similar. Typical final failure mechanisms of the pin-loaded $[0_4/90_4]_s$ and $[90_4/0_4]_s$ cross-ply laminates and $[+45_4/-45_4]_s$ angle-ply laminate are shown in Fig. 3.41.

3.6.4   Residual strength simulation

To evaluate the residual strength simulation capability of the *progressive fatigue damage model,* a pin-loaded $[90_4/0_4]_s$ cross-ply laminate is selected as an example. The maximum fatigue load is selected as 80% of the maximum static strength of the pin-loaded $[90_4/0_4]_s$ cross-ply composite laminate measured by experiments and the load ratio is chosen to be equal to 0.1. Although the load ratio is constant, the stress ratio at different points of the pin-loaded $[90_4/0_4]_s$ cross-ply laminate and at different numbers of cycles is obviously not constant. The specimens, after being subjected to a certain number of cycles (e.g. 10^2, 10^3, etc.) under fatigue loading conditions, are tested under static loading conditions to measure the residual strength. For modelling purposes, first the fatigue behaviour of the specimen is simulated by the *progressive fatigue damage model* and after a certain number of cycles the computer program is stopped. Thereafter, the behaviour of the specimen, with the new residual stiffness and strength properties, is simulated under static loading by the progressive static damage model. The results of experiments and simulation of the residual strength of the pin-loaded $[90_4/0_4]_s$ cross-ply laminate with $e/d = w/d = 4$ as a function of number of cycles are shown in Fig. 3.42.

As shown in Fig. 3.42, an increase in the residual strength at 10^2 and 10^3 cycles is

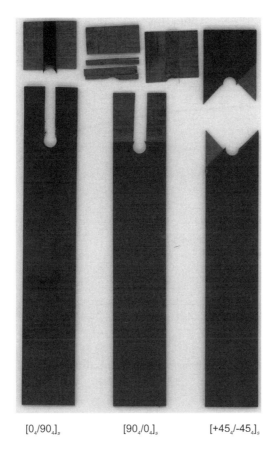

$[0_4/90_4]_s$ $[90_4/0_4]_s$ $[+45_4/-45_4]_s$

Fig. 3.41   Typical final failure mechanisms of the pin-loaded $[0_4/90_4]_s$ and $[90_4/0_4]_s$ cross-ply and $[+45_4/-45_4]_s$ angle-ply laminates.

observed experimentally. However, as shown in Fig. 3.42, while the *model* is simulating the decreasing part of the residual strength curve very well, it is not able to simulate the initial increase. The increase in the residual fatigue strength of notched composites, which sometimes is referred to as *wear-in*, has been frequently observed by various authors.[40,59–69] Some of the authors[40, 46, 52, 53] postulated that the redistribution and relaxation of the stresses around the notch area are the responsible mechanisms for causing such a phenomenon.

By referring to the basic concepts of the *progressive fatigue damage model*, it is clear that the redistribution and relaxation of the stresses have been considered and the *model* is able to simulate the stress distribution at different points of the specimen as a function of number of cycles. However, the *model* is still not able to simulate the increasing part of the residual fatigue strength curve shown in Fig. 3.42. Therefore, this observation shows that it is not possible to simulate this phenomenon just by redistribution and relaxation of stresses. The main reason for this deficiency lies in the existence of experimentally observed increases in residual stiffness and strength of the unidirectional ply under uniaxial tension and compression in the first cycles (Figs. 3.15, 3.16 and 3.18). The increase is ignored intentionally so far by the utilized curve fitting strategy. Hence, to establish a model capable of simulating this interesting phenomenon, the realistic fatigue degradation of the material properties of a unidirectional ply as well as the ability of considering the redistribution of stresses should

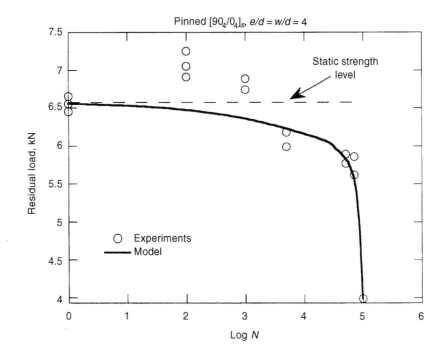

Fig. 3.42   Residual fatigue strength curve of pin-loaded cross-ply $[90_4/0_4]_s$ laminates (simulation and experiments).

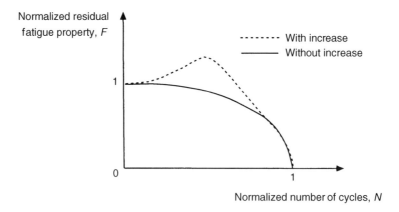

Fig. 3.43   Typical normalized residual fatigue property (stiffness or strength) of a unidirectional ply under uniaxial fatigue loading conditions (not to scale).

be considered. To eliminate this problem, a new strategy is established for curve fitting and explained in the following.

The typical residual fatigue property (stiffness or strength) of a unidirectional ply with and without considering the initial increase, under uniaxial fatigue loading conditions in a normalized form is shown in Fig. 3.43. For simplicity the x-axis (normalized number of cycles) and the y-axis (normalized residual fatigue property) are denoted by N and F, respectively.

As defined earlier, the normalized number of cycles (the x-axis in Fig. 3.43) and the normalized residual property (the y-axis in Fig. 3.43) were related by the following equation:

$$F = \left(1 - N^a\right)^{\frac{1}{b}}$$ [3.23]

which for the residual fatigue strength F is,

$$F = \frac{R(n, \sigma, \kappa) - \sigma}{R_s - \sigma}$$ [3.24]

and for the residual fatigue stiffness F is,

$$F = \frac{E(n, \sigma, \kappa) - \dfrac{\sigma}{\varepsilon_f}}{E_s - \dfrac{\sigma}{\varepsilon_f}}$$ [3.25]

and N denotes,

$$N = \frac{\log(n) - \log(0.25)}{\log(N_f) - \log(0.25)}$$ [3.26]

Equation [3.24], using two curve fitting parameters a and b, is able to curve fit the solid line in Fig. 3.43. However, this strategy cannot show the initial increase in the residual fatigue property (dotted line). To curve fit the dotted line, the following equation is a good candidate.

$$F = \left[1 - N^a + cN^d \left(1 - N\right)^e\right]^{\frac{1}{b}}$$ [3.27]

This equation (equation [3.27]) contains five curve fitting parameters (a, b, c, d and e) which must be found experimentally, therefore is not as simple as equation [3.28].

As explained in the previous section, during the characterization of the unidirectional ply, an increase in the residual fatigue stiffness and strength of fibre direction in tension and compression is observed. Using this newly developed curve fitting strategy (equation [3.27]), residual fatigue properties of the unidirectional ply under tension and compression fatigue loading (Figs. 3.15, 3.16 and 3.18), are characterized and shown in Figs. 3.44, 3.45 and 3.46). As shown, the new strategy for curve fitting is able to simulate the residual fatigue behaviour very well.

In this step, the effect of increase in the residual fatigue properties of the unidirectional ply on the fatigue behaviour of notched composites is studied. Using the new experimental curve fitting parameters in the *progressive fatigue damage model*, the residual fatigue strength of the pin-loaded [90₄/0₄]ₛ cross-ply with e/d = w/d = 4 as a function of number of cycles is simulated by the *model* and compared with the experimental results (Fig. 3.47).

As shown in Fig. 3.47, the new strategy of curve fitting enables the *progressive fatigue damage model* to simulate the residual fatigue strength of the pin-loaded [90₄/0₄]ₛ cross-ply laminate at low and high numbers of cycles (less than 10³ cycles). A comparison between the simulated residual fatigue strength curves by modified and original models in Fig. 3.47 reveals that while the original *model* is not able to simulate the behaviour in the first cycles (less than 10³ cycles), it is able to simulate the residual fatigue behaviour of the notched composites at high numbers of cycles (bigger than 10³ cycles). To perform a better

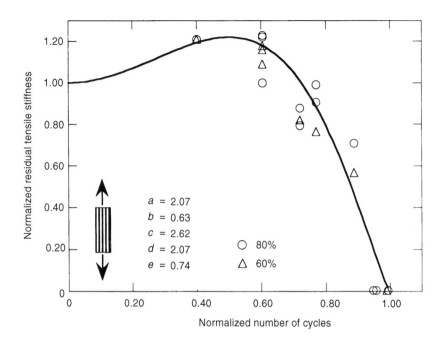

Fig. 3.44   Normalized residual stiffness of a unidirectional 0° ply under longitudinal tensile fatigue loading conditions (using equation [3.27]).

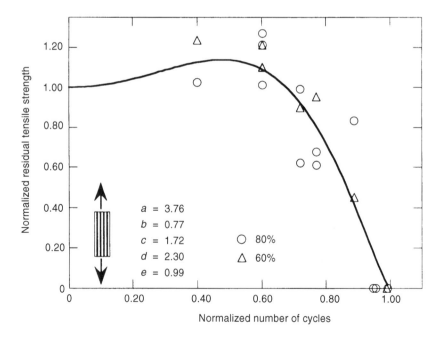

Fig. 3.45   Normalized residual strength of a unidirectional 0° ply under longitudinal tensile fatigue loading conditions (using equation [3.27]).

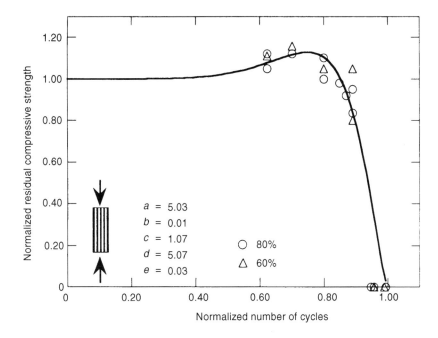

Fig. 3.46 Normalized residual strength of a unidirectional 0° ply under longitudinal compressive fatigue loading conditions (using equation [3.27]).

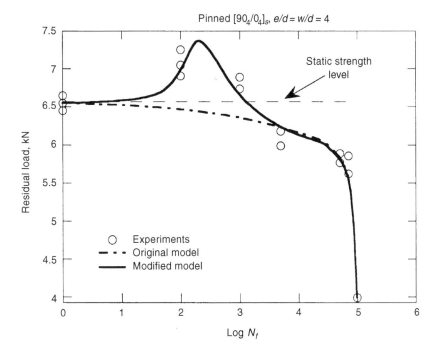

Fig. 3.47 Residual fatigue strength curve of pin-loaded cross-ply $[90_4/0_4]_s$ laminates (modified, simulation and experiments).

simulation, more experiments are needed for the material characterization of the unidirectional 0° ply in tension and compression which of course demands more time and expense.

3.6.5   Residual life simulation

Another interesting outcome of the *model* is its ability to simulate the fatigue behaviour of composite laminates under two or more consecutive load levels. Although the *model* is not limited to the number of the consecutive load levels, for simplicity, the study is performed in two stages. A traditional method of predicting this behaviour is by using the Palmgren-Miner's Rule[88] (sometimes called the Miner's Rule). The main procedure is that the composite laminate is under a fatigue load level for a certain number of cycles and then the load level is changed and the composite laminate is fatigue loaded under the second load level until final failure is achieved. The load levels for both cases and the number of fatigue cycles under the first load level are known and the number of cycles under the second load level (residual life) must be calculated. As an example, consider the behaviour of a composite laminate under two different stress levels as shown in Fig. 3.48. Suppose the composite laminate is under n_1 number of cycles at σ_1 state of stress and then the stress level is changed to σ_2 and the composite laminate is fatigued until catastrophic failure is achieved.

The simple Miner's Rule (for two consecutive stress levels) states that the following equation can be used to calculate the residual life. By knowing the σ_1, σ_2, n_1, N_{f_1} and N_{f_2}, the residual life (n_2) under σ_2 is calculated using equation [3.28], known as Miner's rule.[88]

$$\sum \frac{n}{N_f} = \frac{n_1}{N_{f_1}} + \frac{n_2}{N_{f_2}} = 1$$ [3.28]

where, n_1 = applied number of cycles at σ_1, N_{f_1} = fatigue life at σ_1, n_2 = residual number of cycles at σ_2, and N_{f_2} = fatigue life at σ_2.

Although the Miner's Rule is a simple and useful method, however, experimental evidence[89–93] reveals that it is not able to predict residual life in general. Also, experimental evidence shows that the sequence of applying stress levels (high-to-low or low-to-high) is important, while the Miner's Rule is not able to distinguish the difference. For instance, consider that the n_1 number of cycles under σ_1 stress level is applied first, and then the stress level is changed to σ_2 and the residual life (n_2) is calculated by equation [3.28]. Now, suppose if the n_2 number of cycles under σ_2 state of stress is applied first (n_2 is calculated previously), and the stress level is changed to σ_1. Then, the residual life (n_1) under σ_1 as calculated by Miner's Rule is the same as before, while experimental evidence does not confirm this result. This is another shortcoming of Miner's Rule which the *model* should be also checked for. From Fig. 3.48, it can be inferred that changing the loading sequence affects the residual fatigue life of the composite laminate. Therefore, considering the mechanics of the residual fatigue strength is a vital step in fatigue modelling which is considered by the *model*, while the Miner's Rule does not account for it.

To evaluate the *model* under two consecutive load levels, the pin-loaded $[+45_4/-45_4]_s$ angle-ply laminate with $e/d = w/d = 4$ under two consecutive load levels (80% and 60% of the maximum static strength) is selected as an experiment. The load ratio of 0.1 and frequency equal to 10 Hz are selected. From Fig. 3.40, the average number of cycles to failure for the pin-loaded $[+45_4/-45_4]_s$ angle-ply laminate at the load level equal to 80% and 60% of its maximum static strength is 3100 and 2 400 000 cycles, respectively. Two sets of tests are performed at the two consecutive stress levels (high-to-low and low-to-high) and for each set of experiments, three samples are tested. The results of the experiments, the prediction by Miner's Rule and the *model* are summarized in Table 3.4.

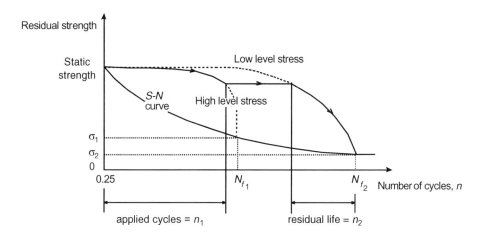

Fig. 3.48   Behaviour of a composite laminate under two different stress levels.

For the first set of experiments (high-to-low), 1000 cycles are applied at the load level equal to 80% of the maximum static strength of the pin-loaded $[+45_4/-45_4]_s$ angle-ply laminate. Thereafter, the load level is changed to 60% of the maximum static strength and the residual fatigue life is measured experimentally. The average residual fatigue life for three specimens, tested under the same conditions, is 725 000 cycles. The residual fatigue life predicted by Miner's Rule is 1 626 000 cycles, which shows 124% error with respect to the experimental results. The predicted residual fatigue life by the *model* is 910 000 cycles which is 25% different from the experimental results. The Miner's Rule and the *model* both overestimate the residual fatigue life, however, the acceptable percentage of error produced by the *model* shows a fairly good agreement between the simulation and the experiments. The next set of experiments (high-to-low) is performed by applying 1 626 000 cycles (calculated for the previous set of experiments by Miner's Rule) at the load level equal to 60% of the maximum static strength. Thereafter, the load level is changed to 80% of the maximum static strength and the residual fatigue life is measured experimentally. The average residual fatigue life for three specimens, tested under the same conditions, is 2200 cycles. While the Miner's Rule cannot distinguish the changing of the loading sequence, the *model* predicts the residual fatigue life equal to 1700 cycles, which is 23% different from the experimental results. Clearly, from equation [3.28], the mechanics of failure are not considered by the simple Miner's Rule, therefore it is not surprising that the prediction of the residual life by this equation for the examined cases is not accurate. The more successful simulation of the residual fatigue life results from the progressive nature of the *model* and considering the mechanics of failure.

Table 3.4   Residual fatigue life of pin-loaded $[+45_4/-45_4]_s$ angle-ply laminates, measured by experiments and predicted by Miner's Rule and *model*

		Residual fatigue life (n_2)		
Applied stresses at σ_1	Applied cycles (n_1)	Miner's Rule (error %)	Model (error %)	Experiment
High to low	1 000	1 626 000 (124%)	910 000 (25%)	725 000
Low to high	1 626 000	1 000 (54%)	1 700 (23%)	2 200

3.7   Conclusions

By performing several different series of experiments and using available independent experimental results by other authors, the validity of the *progressive fatigue damage model* and some of its capabilities are examined.

Although the *generalized residual material property degradation technique* is capable of simulating the fatigue behaviour of a unidirectional ply under multiaxial state of stress, experimental evaluation of the established technique under multiaxial state of fatigue stress is not a simple task. Therefore, the technique is evaluated under biaxial state of fatigue stress, using the 30° off-axis specimen. A very good agreement between the experimental and simulated results is achieved which validates the *generalized residual material property degradation technique*.

Before evaluating the fatigue simulation capability of the *model*, the progressive static damage model, which is another important part of the *progressive fatigue damage model*, is verified. Different ply configurations ($[0_4/90_4]_s$, $[90_4/0_4]_s$ and $[+45_4/-45_4]_s$) with different geometries (*e/d* and *w/d*) under static pin- and bolt-loading conditions are studied. The failure initiation and final failure load for different cases are simulated and compared with the experimental results. Excellent agreement between the experimental and simulated results is obtained.

To evaluate the capabilities of the *progressive fatigue damage model* for simulating the fatigue life and residual strength of the notched composites laminates, a series of experiments is performed. To show the fatigue life simulation capability of notched composites by the *model*, different pin/bolt-loaded composite laminates with different ply lay-ups ($[0_4/90_4]_s$, $[90_4/0_4]_s$ and $[+45_4/-45_4]_s$) are studied. A good agreement between the results of experiments and simulation is obtained which shows the successful fatigue life simulation capability of the *model*. Moreover, the residual strength simulation capability of the *model* is evaluated by performing experiments on the pin-loaded $[90_4/0_4]_s$ cross-ply laminates. The experimental results of the residual fatigue strength of the pin-loaded $[90_4/0_4]_s$ cross-ply laminates show an increase for the first few cycles followed by a subsequent decrease. The *model*, using the experimental curve fitting parameter in the previous section, is able to simulate the decreasing part of the residual fatigue strength curve as a function of number of cycles very well. However, to simulate the increasing part of the residual fatigue strength of the notched composite, the experimentally observed increase in the residual fatigue strength of the unidirectional ply in the fibre direction under tension and compression fatigue loading must be considered. It should be mentioned that this behaviour was ignored intentionally in the previous section to show the effect on the residual fatigue strength prediction of the notched composite laminates. By using a new curve fitting strategy and considering the initial increase of the residual fatigue properties of the unidirectional ply in the fibre direction under tension and compression, a successful simulation of the residual fatigue strength of the pin-loaded $[90_4/0_4]_s$ cross-ply laminate is achieved. It is concluded that, although the redistribution and relaxation of the stress field around the notch area are important factors, however, without considering the proper behaviour of the unidirectional ply under fatigue loading, the simulation of the residual fatigue strength behaviour of notched composites is difficult.

To evaluate another capability of the *model*, which is the fatigue behaviour simulation of composite laminates under two or more consecutive load levels, the pin-loaded $[+45_4/-45_4]_s$ angle-ply laminate with $e/d = w/d = 4$ under two consecutive load levels (80% and 60% of the maximum static strength) is selected as an example. The shortcoming of the Miner's

Rule to simulate this problem is shown and discussed. A very good agreement between the simulated and experimental results is achieved.

An extensive research is performed on the fatigue behaviour of composite materials under multiaxial loading during the past decades. However, due to the complexity of the fatigue phenomenon, more research is needed. Parameters such as load frequency, viscoelastic behaviour of composites, scatter in experimental data, etc. necessitate more challenges.

3.8   References

1. AMERICAN SOCIETY FOR METALS (ASM) (1986), Failure Analysis and Prevention, *Metals Handbook*, 9th Edn, Vol. 11.
2. SHOKRIEH M M and LESSARD L B (2000), 'Progressive fatigue damage modeling of composite materials, Part I: Modeling,' *Journal of Composite Materials*, **34**(13), 1056–1080.
3. SHOKRIEH M M and LESSARD L B (2000), 'Progressive fatigue damage modeling of composite materials, Part II: Material characterization and model verification,' *Journal of Composite Materials*, **34**(13), 1081–1116.
4. DEGRIECK J and PAEPEGEM W V (2001), 'Fatigue damage modeling of fiber-reinforced composite materials: review,' *Appl. Mech. Rev.*, **54**(4), 279–300, July, American Society of Mechanical Engineers.
5. QUARESIMIN M and SUSMEL L (2002), 'Multiaxial fatigue behavior of composite laminates,' *Key Engineering Materials*, **221–222**, 71–80.
6. PHILIPPIDIS T P and VASSILOPOULOS A P (1999), 'Fatigue of composite laminates under off-axis loading,' *International Journal of Fatigue*, **21**, 253–262.
7. FOUND M S (1985), 'A review of the multiaxial fatigue testing of fiber reinforced plastics,' *Multiaxial Fatigue*, ASTM STP 853, K J Miller and M W Brown, Eds., pp. 381–395.
8. CHEN A S and MATTHEWS F L (1993), 'A review of multiaxial biaxial loading tests for composite materials,' *Composites*, **24**(5), 395–406.
9. SIMS D F and BROGDON V H (1977), 'Fatigue Behavior of Composites under Different Loading Modes,' *Fatigue of Filamentary Materials*, ASTM STP 636, K L Reifsnider and K N Lauraitis, Eds., (1977), pp. 185–205.
10. HAHN H T (1979), 'Fatigue behavior and life prediction of composite laminates,' *Composite Materials: Testing and Design (Fifth Conference)*, ASTM STP 674, S. W. Tsai, Ed., pp. 383–417.
11. HASHIN Z (1981), 'Fatigue failure criteria for unidirectional fiber composites,' *Journal of Applied Mechanics*, **48**, 846–852, Dec.
12. HASHIN Z (1981), 'Fatigue failure criteria for combined cyclic stress,' *International Journal of Fracture*, **17**(2), 101–109, April.
13. ROTEM A and HASHIN Z (1976), 'Fatigue failure of angle ply laminates,' *AIAA Journal*, **14**(7), 868–872, July.
14. ROTEM A (1982), 'Fatigue failure mechanism of composite laminates,' IUTAM Symposium on Mechanics of Composite Materials, Mechanics of Composite Materials, Recent Advances, Z. Hashin and C. T. Herakovich, Eds., Blacksburg, VA, pp. 421–435.
15. ROTEM A and NELSON H G (1981), 'Fatigue behavior of graphite-epoxy laminates at elevated temperatures,' *Fatigue of Fibrous Composite Materials*, ASTM STP 723, pp. 152–173.
16. ELLYIN F and EL-KADI H (1990), 'A fatigue failure criterion for fiber reinforced composite laminae,' *Composite Structures*, **15**, 61–74.
17. TENNYSON R C, HANSEN J S, HEPPLER G R, MABSON G, WHARRAM G and STREET K N (1983), 'Computation of influence of defects on static and fatigue strength of composites,' AGARD-CP-355, pp. 14-1–14-17.
18. TENNYSON R C, TRATT M, MABSON G and WHARRAM G (1983), 'Development of general failure model for CF-18 graphite/epoxy laminates,' Proc. DND Composite Workshop, Victoria, B. C., pp. 13-1–13-35, July.
19. WU C M L (1993), 'Thermal and mechanical fatigue analysis of angle-ply CFRP laminates,' Second International Composites Conference and Exhibition, Ottawa, Ontario, Canada, pp. 631–638.
20. ROTEM A and NELSON H G (1981), 'Fatigue behavior of graphite-epoxy laminates at elevated temperatures,' *Fatigue of Fibrous Composite Materials*, ASTM STP 723, pp. 152–173.

21. RYDER J T and CROSSMAN F W (1983), 'A study of stiffness, residual strength and fatigue life relationships for composite laminates,' NASA Contract Report CR-172211.
22. SHOKRIEH M M (1991), Failure of laminated composites pinned connections, Master's Thesis, Department of Mechanical Engineering, McGill University, Montreal, Canada.
23. LESSARD L B and SHOKRIEH M M (1991), 'Pinned joint failure mechanisms, Part I – Two dimensional modeling,' CANCOM 91, First Canadian International Composites Conference and Exhibition, Montréal, Québec, Canada, pp. 1D51–1D58, September 4–6.
24. CHANG F K and CHANG K Y (1987), 'Post-failure analysis of bolted composite joints in tension or shear-out mode failure,' Journal of Composite Materials, 809–833.
25. ADAM T, DICKSON R F, FERNANDO G, HARRIS B and REITER H (1986), 'The fatigue behaviour of Kevlar/carbon hybrid composites,' IMechE Conference Publications (Institute of Mechanical Engineers), 2, 329–335.
26. ADAM T, DICKSON R F, JONES C J, REITER H and HARRIS B (1986), 'A power law fatigue damage model for fiber-reinforced plastic laminates,' Proceedings of the Institution of Mechanical Engineers, Part C: Mechanical Engineering Science, V. 200, n C3, pp. 155–166.
27. FONG J T (1982), 'What is fatigue damage?,' Damage in Composite Materials, ASTM STP 775, K. L. Reifsnider, Ed., pp. 243–266.
28. HWANG W and HAN K S (1986), 'Fatigue of composites – fatigue modulus concept and life prediction,' Journal of Composite Materials, 20, 154–165.
29. POURSARTIP A, ASHBY M F and BEAUMONT P W R (1986), 'The fatigue damage mechanics of a carbon fiber composite laminate: I – development of the model,' Composites Science and Technology, 25, 193–218.
30. WHITWORTH H W (1987), 'Modeling stiffness reduction of graphite/epoxy composite laminates,' Journal of Composite Materials, 21, 362–372.
31. HWANG W and HAN K S (1989), 'Fatigue of composite materials – damage model and life prediction,' Composite Materials: Fatigue and Fracture, Second Volume, ASTM STP 1012, P. A. Lagace, Ed., pp. 87–102.
32. NEVADUNSKY J J, LUCAS J J and SALKIND M J (1975), 'Early fatigue damage detection in composite materials,' Journal of Composite Materials, 9, 394–408.
33. POURSARTIP A and BEAUMONT P W R (1982), 'A damage approach to the fatigue of composite materials,' IUTAM Symposium on Mechanics of Composite Materials, Mechanics of Composite Materials, Recent Advances, Z Hashin and C T Herakovich, Eds., Blacksburg, VA, pp. 449–456.
34. HIGHSMITH A L and REIFSNIDER K L (1982), 'Stiffness-reduction mechanisms in composite laminates,' Damage in Composite Materials, ASTM STP 775, K L Reifsnider, Ed., pp. 103–117.
35. HIGHSMITH A L, STINCHCOMB W W and REIFSNIDER K L (1984), 'Effect of fatigue-induced defects on the residual response of composite laminates,' Effects of Defects in Composite Materials, ASTM STP 836, pp. 194–216.
36. JEN M H R, HSU J M and HWANG D G (1990), 'Fatigue degradation in centrally notched quasi-isotropic laminates,' Journal of Composite Materials, 823–837.
37. LEE L J, YANG J N and SHEU D Y (1991), 'Prediction of fatigue life for matrix dominated composite laminates,' ICCM/VIII, International Conference on Composite Materials, Honolulu, Hawaii, pp. 38-L-1–38-L-9.
38. YANG J N, LEE L J and SHEU D Y (1992), 'Modulus reduction and fatigue damage of matrix dominated composite laminates,' Composite Structures, 21, 91–100.
39. JONES D L, YANG S H, LEE J H and WITHWORTH H A (1994), 'Development of a stiffness degradation model for graphite epoxy laminates under fatigue loading,' Proceedings of International Conference on Composite Engineering ICCE/1, Ed. D. Hui, pp. 243–244.
40. STINCHCOMB W W and BAKIS C B (1990), 'Fatigue behavior of composite laminates,' Fatigue of Composite Materials, Ed. by K L Reifsnider, pp. 105–180.
41. SHIMOKAWA T and HAMAGUCHI Y (1983), 'Distributions of fatigue life and fatigue strength in notched specimens of a carbon eight-harness-stain laminate,' Journal of Composite Materials, 17, 64–76, Jan.
42. BOLLER K H (1957), 'Fatigue properties of fibrous glass-reinforced plastics laminates subjected to various conditions,' Modern Plastics, 163–293, June.
43. ADAM T, FERNANDO G, DICKSON R F, REITER H and HARRIS B (1989), 'Fatigue life prediction for hybrid composites,' International Journal of Fatigue, 11(4), 233–237.
44. HARRIS B, REITER H, ADAM R, DICKSON R F and FERNANDO G (1990), 'Fatigue behaviour of carbon fibre reinforced plastics,' Composites, 21(3), 232–242, May.

45. GATHERCOLE N, ADAM T, HARRIS B and REITER H (1992), 'A unified model for fatigue life prediction of carbon fibre/resin composites,' Developments in the Science and Technology of Composite Materials, ECCM 5th. European Conference on Composite Materials, Bordeaux, France, pp. 89–94, June 9–12.

46. ADAM T, GATHERCOLE N, REITER H and HARRIS B (1992), 'Fatigue life prediction for carbon fibre composites', Advanced Composites Letters, **1**, 23–26.

47. GATHERCOLE N, REITER H, ADAM T and HARRIS B (1994), 'Life prediction for fatigue of T800/524 carbon-fibre composites: I Constant-amplitude loading,' International Journal of Fatigue, **16**, 523–532, November.

48. LESSARD L B and SHOKRIEH M M (1995), Fatigue behaviour of composite pinned/bolted joints, Final Report, NRC #32171 and IAR-CR-29, Structure and Material Laboratory, Institute for Aerospace Research, National Research Council, Canada.

49. ASTM D 3039-76 (1989), (Reapproved 1989), Standard test method for tensile properties of fiber-resin composites, ASTM Designation, pp. 118–122.

50. ASTM D 3479-76 (1990), (Reapproved 1990), Standard test methods for tension-tension fatigue of oriented fiber-resin matrix composites, ASTM Designation, pp. 142–144.

51. AWERBUCH J and HAHN H T (1977), 'Fatigue and proof-testing of unidirectional graphite/epoxy composites,' Fatigue of Filamentary Materials, ASTM STP 636, K L Reifsnider and K N Lauraitis, Eds., pp. 248–266.

52. REIFSNIDER K L (1986), 'The critical element model: a modeling philosophy,' Engineering Fracture Mechanics, **25**(5/6), 739–749.

53. SPEARING S M and BEAUMONT P W R (1992), 'Fatigue damage mechanics of composite materials. III: Prediction of post fatigue strength,' Composites Science and Technology, **44**, 299–307.

54. STINCHCOMB W W and REIFSNIDER K L (1979), 'Fatigue damage mechanisms in composite materials: a review,' Fatigue Mechanisms, Proceedings of an ASTM-NBS-NSF Symposium, J. T. Fong, Ed., ASTM STP 675, pp. 762–787.

55. CHANG F H, GORDON D E, RODINI B T and MCDANEIL R H (1976), 'Real time characterization of damage growth in graphite/epoxy laminates,' Journal of Composite Materials, **10**, 182–192, July.

56. SENDECKYJ G P, STALNAKER H D and KLEISMIT R A (1977), 'Effect of temperature on fatigue response of surface-notches $[(0/\pm45/0)_s]_3$ graphite/epoxy laminate,' Fatigue of Filamentary Materials, ASTM STP 636, K L Reifsnider and K N Lauraitis, Eds., pp. 73–88.

57. KELLAS S, MORTON J and BISHOP S M (1986), 'Fatigue damage development in a notched carbon fiber composite,' Composites Science and Technology, **25**, 311–323.

58. BAKIS C E and STINCHCOMB W W (1986), 'Response of thick, notched laminates subjected to tension-compression cyclic loads,' Composite Materials: Fatigue and Fracture, ASTM STP 907, H T Hahn, Ed., pp. 314–334.

59. SIMONDS R A and STINCHCOMB W W (1989), 'Response of notched AS4/PEEK laminates to tension/compression loading,' Advances in Thermoplastic Matrix Composite Materials, ASTM STP 1044, G M Newaz, Ed., pp. 133–145.

60. BAKIS E, SIMONDS R A and STINCHCOMB W W (1989), 'A test method to measure the response of composite materials under reversed cyclic loads,' Test Methods for Design Allowables for Fibrous Composites, ASTM STP 1003, C C Chamis and K L Reifsnider, Eds., pp. 93–110.

61. WHITCOMB J D (1981), 'Experimental and analytical study of fatigue damage in notched graphite/epoxy laminates,' Fatigue of Fibrous Composite Materials, ASTM STP 723, pp. 46–63.

62. KULKARNI S V, MCLAUGHLIN JR. P V, PIPES R B and ROSEN B W (1977), 'Fatigue of notched fiber composite laminates: analytical and experimental evaluation,' Composite Materials: Testing and Design (Fourth Conference), ASTM STP 617, pp. 70–92.

63. WEBB J N and SMITH W A (1978), 'The fatigue and residual tensile strength of a multi-bolt joint between metal and carbon fiber composite,' Symposium: Joining in Fiber Reinforced Plastics, pp. 116–126, 4–5 September.

64. AWERBUCH J and HAHN H T (1981), 'Off-axis fatigue of graphite/epoxy composite,' Fatigue of Fibrous Composite Materials, ASTM STP 723, ASTM, pp. 243–273.

65. FRANCIS P H, WALRATH D E, SIMS D F and WEED D N (1977), 'Biaxial fatigue loading of notched composites,' Journal of Composite Materials, 488–501.

66. REIFSNIDER K L, STINCHCOMB W W and O'BRIEN T K (1977), 'Frequency effects on a stiffness-based fatigue failure criterion in flawed composite specimens,' Fatigue of Filamentary Composite Materials, ASTM STP 636, K L Reifsnider and K N Lauraitis, Eds., pp. 171–184.

67. KRESS G R and STINCHCOMB W W (1985), 'Fatigue response of notched graphite/epoxy laminates,'

Recent Advances in Composites in United States and Japan, ASTM STP 864, J R Vinson and M Taya, Eds., pp. 173–196.

68. LAGACE P A and NOLET S C (1986), 'Effect of ply thickness on longitudinal splitting and delamination in graphite/epoxy under compressive cyclic load,' *Composite Materials, Fatigue and Fracture*, ASTM STP 907, H T Hahn, Ed., pp. 335–360.

69. BAKIS C E, YIH H R, STINCHCOMB W W and REIFSNIDER K L (1989), 'Damage initiation and growth in notched laminates under reversed cycling loading,' *Composite Materials: Fatigue and Fracture*, Second Volume, ASTM STP 1012, P A Lagace, Ed., pp. 66–83.

70. MILETTE J F, SHOKRIEH M M and LESSARD L B (1995), 'Static and fatigue behaviour of unidirectional composites in compression,' ICCM-10 International Conference on Composite Materials, Whistler, B. C., Canada, pp. I-617–I-624.

71. ASTM D 3410-87 (1987), *Standard test method for compressive properties of unidirectional or crossply fiber-resin composites*, ASTM Designation, pp. 132–141.

72. LESSARD L B, EILERS O P and SHOKRIEH M M (1995), 'Testing of in-plane shear properties under fatigue loading,' *Journal of Reinforced Plastics and Composites*, **14**(9), 965–987, September.

73. SHOKRIEH M M, EILERS O P and LESSARD L B (1997), 'Characterization of a graphite/epoxy composite under in-plane shear fatigue loading,' High Temperature & Environmental Effects on Polymeric Composites: Second Symposium, STP 1302, pp. 133–148.

74. ASTM D 2733-70 (1970), *Standard methods of test for interlaminar shear strength of structural reinforced plastics at elevated temperatures*, ASTM Designation, pp. 773–776.

75. ASTM D 3846-93 (1993), *Standard test method for in-plane shear strength of reinforced plastics*, ASTM Designation, pp. 435–437.

76. SHOKRIEH M M, EILERS O P, KOTSIOPRIFTIS P and LESSARD L B (1995), 'Determination of interlaminar shear strength of graphite/epoxy composite materials in static and fatigue loading,' ICCM-10 International Conference on Composite Materials, Whistler, B. C., Canada, pp. IV-81–IV-88.

77. SCHNEIDER G J (1972), 'Evaluation of lamina strength criteria by off-axis tensile coupon tests,' *Fibre Science and Technology*, **5**, 29–35.

78. WU E M (1972), 'Optimal experimental measurements of anisotropic failure tensors,' *Journal of Composite Materials*, **6**, 472–489.

79. PIPES R B and COLE B W (1973), 'On the off-axis strength test for anisotropic materials,' *Journal of Composite Materials*, **7**, 246–256.

80. OWEN M J and FOUND M S (1975), 'The fatigue behaviour of a glass-fabric-reinforced polyester resin under off-axis loading,' *J. Phys. D: Appl. Phys.*, **8**, 480–4978.

81. OWEN M J and GRIFFITHS J R (1978), 'Evaluation of biaxial stress failure surfaces for a glass fabric reinforced polyester resin under static and fatigue loading,' *Journal of Material Science*, **13**, 1521–1537.

82. THEOCARIS P S and PHILLIPPIDIS T P (1991), 'On the validity of the tensor polynomial failure theory with stress interaction terms omitted,' *Composites Science and Technology*, **40**, 181–191.

83. TAN S C and CHENG S (1993), 'Failure criteria for fibrous anisotropic materials,' *Materials in Civil Engineering*, **5**(2), 198–211, May.

84. ROSEN B W (1972), 'A simple procedure for experimental determination of the longitudinal shear modulus of unidirectional composites,' *Journal of Composite Materials*, **6**, 552–554.

85. PINDERA M-J and HERAKOVICH C T (1986), 'Shear characterization of unidirectional composites with the off-axis tension test,' *Experimental Mechanics*, 103–112.

86. BROWNE C M (1988), 'Alternative methods for the determination of shear modulus in a composite material,' *Composite Materials: Testing Technology of Metal Matrix Composites*, ASTM STP 964, ASTM, P R Digiovanni and N R Adist, Eds., pp. 259–274.

87. SUN C T and BERRETH S P (1988), 'A new end tab design for off-axis tension test of composite materials,' *Journal of Composite Materials*, **22**, 766–779.

88. MINER M A and CALIF S M (1945), 'Cumulative damage in fatigue,' *Journal of Applied Mechanics*, A-159–A-164, September.

89. HASHIN Z and ROTEM A (1978), 'A cumulative damage theory of fatigue failure,' *Materials Science and Engineering*, **34**, 147–160.

90. HASHIN Z (1980), 'A reinterpretation of the Palmgren-Miner Rule for fatigue life prediction,' *Journal of Applied Mechanics*, **47**, 324–328, June.

91. HASHIN Z (1981), 'A reinterpration of the Palmgren-Miner Rule for fatigue life prediction,' *Journal of Applied Mechanics*, Discussion, **48**, 446–448, June.

92. GOLOS K and ELLYIN F (1987), 'Generalization of cumulative damage criterion to multilevel cyclic loading,' *Theoretical and Applied Fracture Mechanics*, **7**, 169–176.
93. BUCH A (1988), *Fatigue strength calculation, Materials Science Surveys* No. 6, Trans Tech. Publications, Switzerland.
94. CHOU P C and CROMAN R (1978), 'Residual strength in fatigue based on the strength-life equal rank assumption,' *Journal of Composite Materials*, **12**, 177–194.
95. CHOU P C and CROMAN R (1979), 'Degradation and sudden-death models of fatigue of graphite/epoxy composites,' *Composite Materials: Testing and Design (Fifth Conference)*, ASTM STP 674, S. W. Tsai, Ed., pp. 431–454.
96. HALPIN J C, JERINA K L and JOHNSON T A (1973), 'Characterization of composites for the purpose of reliability evaluation,' *Analysis of the Test Methods for High Modulus Fibers and Composites*, ASTM STP 521, (1973), pp. 5–64.

Part II

Micromechanical aspects of fatigue in composites

4

The effects of aggressive environments on long-term behaviour

F. R. Jones, University of Sheffield, UK

4.1   Introduction

The durability of a polymer–matrix composite is a complex issue because so many variables contribute to the long-term life under a static or dynamic load. The principal components of a fibre composite are the reinforcing fibre and the matrix. However, a composite may be made more complex by the incorporation of a particulate reinforcement or filler in some applications and by the fact that the matrix may contain a phase-separated toughening agent (either thermoplastic or rubber). Another factor is the orientation and length of the fibres. Both of these reduce the maximum stress to which the fibres can be loaded, prior to fracture.

For a simple system consisting of continuous fibres in a polymer matrix an interphase can form between the fibre and the matrix. 'Interphase' is a term used to describe a region of the matrix of different mechanical properties at the fibre interface. Normally, the interphase will have a gradation in properties but with so-called hard-sized fibres it can be more distinct in nature. This leads to more than one interfacial region subject to environmental degradation. It is therefore necessary to consider the role of the individual phases on the environmental durability of the composite material.

In order to provide some general rules, the effect of an environment on the major component-fibres and matrix need to be considered separately. Furthermore, different mechanisms operate in aqueous and non-aqueous environments.

4.2   Aqueous environments

Moisture diffuses into organic matrix composites to differing degrees and at different rates depending on a number of factors. These lead to changes in the thermomechanical properties of the resin through plasticization or to hydrolytic or chemical degradation of the resin network. It is important to identify the rate at which the moisture diffuses into the material since this will often have a major effect on the long-term life of the component or on the maximum service temperature which the material can withstand.

Many composite materials are either anisotropic or consist of laminated plies which are individually anisotropic. The properties in the fibre direction are dominated by the strength and modulus of the reinforcement, whereas properties transverse or at 90° to the fibres are strongly dominated by the properties of the matrix. Therefore, on diffusion of moisture, the properties transverse to the fibres are more likely to be significantly modified. The time-scale over which diffusion occurs is strongly determined by the relative humidity of the environment and the temperature. Whereas the relative humidity, which is a thermodynamic property, determines the maximum moisture concentration that can be achieved under these conditions, the temperature determines the rate at which the equilibrium moisture content is reached. This can have a profound influence on the durability of materials subjected to thermal excursions during service life. Higher temperatures can therefore be used to accelerate the ageing phenomenon and enable us to make predictions about durability. However, because plasticization of the matrix can lead to a reduction in the service temperature of the composite, the choice of temperature for acceleration is very important and must be kept well below the lowest service temperature. It is therefore necessary to predict the time it takes for a structure to become equilibrated. This is normally done through the use of Fickian diffusion kinetics. The Fickian laws were developed on the basis of thermal equilibration. Of interest are the relative rates of thermal and moisture diffusion. Typically, thermal diffusion occurs 10^6 times more rapidly than moisture diffusion. It can be estimated, therefore, that a structure 12 mm thick at 350 K can take 13 years for equilibration of moisture content whereas it takes only 15 seconds for thermal equilibration. This is a major issue in understanding composite performance. In many structures, therefore, the material will be subjected to a moisture gradient over significant proportions of its life. However, in many instances, thermal excursions are encountered which accelerate the moisture diffusion process. On increasing the temperature, the moisture will tend to diffuse both into the centre of the material and out of the material through the faces. Experience seems to suggest that the surface of the material can resorb water relatively easily when it is replaced in an appropriate humid environment. In this way the distribution throughout the material will be subjected to a series of moisture profiles which average out with time. The solution to Fick's second law provides equation [4.1] which defines the diffusion constant D with respect to the moisture uptake.

$$D = \frac{\pi d^2}{16 M_\infty^2} \left(\frac{M_2 - M_1}{t_2^{1/2} - t_1^{1/2}} \right)^2$$

[4.1]

where M_1 and M_2 are the moisture contents at times t_1 and t_2, d is the thickness of the specimen. From coupon tests a true one-dimensional diffusion constant can be obtained through an edge correction for diffusion through all the faces.[1,2]

To predict time-to-equilibrium for a known structure, it is necessary to know the diffusion constant D. However, to estimate D the equilibrium moisture content M_∞ needs to be measured in long-term tests. As with other kinetic processes, D is related to the absolute temperature T according to the Arrhenius equation.

$$D = A_{\exp} \left(-\frac{E_a}{RT} \right)$$

[4.2]

where E_a is the activation energy for moisture transport, A is the pre-exponential factor.

Some resin systems exhibit Fickian diffusion curves whereas other systems show non-Fickian diffusion. The definition of Fickian diffusion is shown in Fig. 4.1. The diffusion

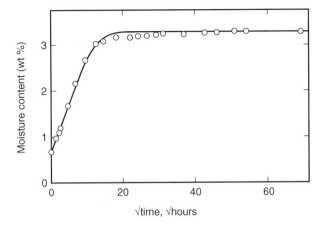

Fig. 4.1   Typical Fickian moisture diffusion curve for an equilibrated resin casting of a bismaleimide modified epoxy resin, which had previously been subject to thermally enhanced moisture absorption, followed by desorption prior to reabsorption. The sorption shown does not begin at zero because of a small residual quantity of absorbed moisture from the first conditioning cycle.[3] O, experimental; —, Fickian model.

curve exhibits a smooth process in which the curve is linear over the first 60% of the process and reaches an equilibrium value. In this particular case, in order to achieve Fickian diffusion, the resin has been subjected to preconditioning with moisture followed by desorption and reabsorption. Often in the early stages the diffusion appears to obey Fickian behaviour but tends to deviate in the long term. This can lead to difficulty in calculating the precise diffusion constant. It is believed that the tendency to non-Fickian behaviour results from the reorganization of the network as the material becomes plasticized.[4,5]

With an anisotropic composite material, the diffusion constant for the material parallel to the fibre and at 90° to the fibres can differ. These are related to each other through equation [4.3].

$$D = D_x \left[1 + \frac{d}{l} \left(\frac{D_y}{D_x} \right)^{\frac{1}{2}} + \frac{d}{b} \left(\frac{D_z}{D_x} \right)^{\frac{1}{2}} \right]^2 \qquad [4.3]$$

where D_x, D_y and D_z are diffusion constants through the thickness d along the length l and across the breadth b.

For a unidirectionally reinforced 0° ply, D_z and D_x are equivalent, both occurring at 90° to the fibres. Therefore, equation [4.3] becomes:

$$D = D_x \left[1 + \frac{d}{b} + \frac{d}{l} \left(\frac{D_y}{D_x} \right)^{\frac{1}{2}} \right]^2 \qquad [4.4]$$

It is therefore possible to measure the influence of the fibres on the diffusion process since, clearly, a poor interfacial bond between the fibre and the resin will lead to rapid transport at the interface. This can be differentiated from the resin-dominated diffusion constant at 90° to the fibres. If D_y is greater that D_x, then capillary diffusion at a poor interfacial bond must be occurring. For perfectly bonded fibres, D_x will be significantly larger than D_y because of the relatively higher surface area of resin in the 90° direction. Typical values of the diffusion constant are 10^{-6} mm^2/s for a resin and 10^{-7} mm^2/s for a composite.

4.3   Moisture sensitivity of resins

Moisture diffuses into polymers to differing extents depending on a number of molecular and microstructural aspects.

(i)   The polarity of the molecular structure
(ii)   The degree of crosslinking
(iii) The degree of crystallinity in the case of a thermoplastic matrix
(iv) The presence of residuals in the material.

While (i)–(iii) are clearly variables of the matrix, the presence of residuals (iv) is not so obvious, since these refer to unreacted hardeners and other impurities. The impurities of interest might well be calcium, sodium or potassium inclusions in fillers or, in the case of E-glass, a small surface sodium concentration.

Table 4.1 gives typical values of the diffusion constants, showing the effect of polarity of the resin at equilibrium on moisture concentration. There is a large difference between the moisture concentration at equilibrium for the differing resin systems used for composite materials. Epoxy resins are the network products of the reaction of a monomeric multifunctional epoxide and hardener, which forms during manufacture of a component. Thus the material is synthesized at the same time as component manufacture. The actual chemistry of the final network is a function of (a) the chemical structures of the epoxide and hardener and (b) the mechanism of cure. In this way the cured resins can have differing polarities. For example the reaction of an epoxy resin with an anhydride hardener gives rise to a 'polyester' type of structure of low polarity, whereas an amine hardener will form a β-hydroxy amine network of high polarity. The potential for hydrogen bonding of water molecules enhances the concentration of moisture which can be absorbed. With catalytic curing agents, polyether structures of relatively low polarity will form. However, it is quite common to use mixed hardeners in curing systems for composite matrices. In this case the cured network, will have a complex structure making the polarity strongly dependent on the degree of incorporation of the individual components.

Table 4.1   Typical values of moisture diffusion coefficients for resins[3]

Resin or composite	M_∞ (wt%)	D (10^{-3} mm^2 s^{-1})	RH (%)	T (°C)
Resins: unsaturated polyester	1.6	32	100	50
– isophthalic	1.4		90	50
	0.9		75	50
– orthophthalic	2.0	30	100	50
Epoxy	6.9	2.8	96	50
Advanced epoxy resin: Narmco 5245	1.96	11.0	96	45
	1.38	14.7	75	45
	0.80	19.4	46	45
	0.54	17.2	31	45
Aromatic cyanate ester (Primaset PT30	2.96	3.62	96	50
Epoxy (DEN431)) resin	0.48	5.99	11	50

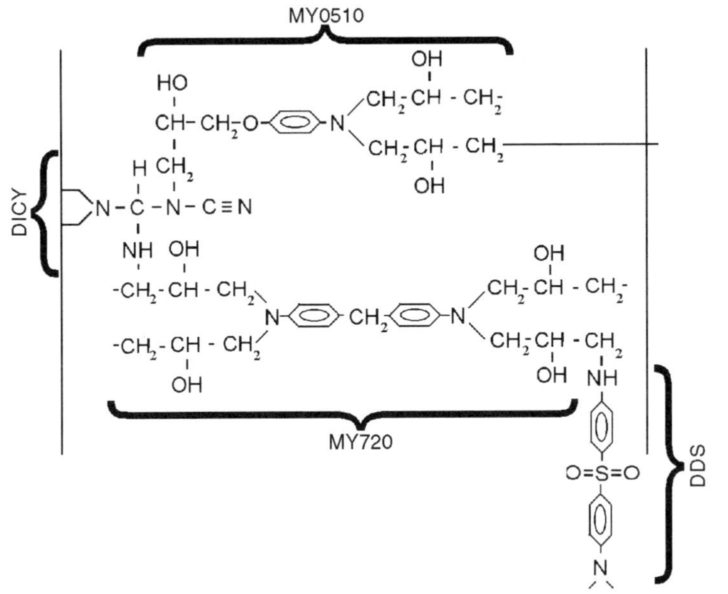

Fig. 4.2 Approximate chemical structure of a cured resin illustrating the use of a blend of two epoxy resins (MY720 and MY0510) and two types of hardener (DICY and DDS).[7]

Figure 4.2 gives a model for the structure of a cured resin employing two epoxide monomers of two differing functionalities (3 and 4) and two hardeners 1,4-diamino diphenyl sulphone (DDS) and dicyandiamide (DICY). It is apparent that the extent of the incorporation of each hardener and epoxide into the network will have a strong influence on the overall polarity of the cured resin, and hence moisture absorption.[7]

4.3.1   Advanced resin systems

As shown in Table 4.2 thermoplastic matrices also absorb much less moisture than the advanced epoxies. Polyetheretherketone (PEEK) is an example of a partially crystalline linear polymer with very low moisture absorption. Thermoplastics such as polyethersulphone (PES), which are relatively non-polar and absorb low concentrations of moisture are also used as 'flow-control' additives and/or toughening agents in advanced epoxy resins. These therefore have a reduced moisture sensitivity.

Table 4.2   Effect of thermosetting and thermoplastic modifiers on the moisture content of carbon fibre composites based on epoxy resins in comparison with the advanced thermoplastic (PEEK) and thermoset (BMI) resin matrices[3]

	Modified epoxide resins				PEEK	PMR-15
Resin system	924E	924C	927C	5255C	APC-2	BMI
Modifier	None	PES	Cyanate/PI	BMI	–	–
Moisture content (%)[d]	2.44[a]	1.72	0.98	0.82	0.02[b] 0.23[c]	0.32

PES = polyethersulfone, PI = polyimide, BMI = bismaleimide
[a] Estimated from data on cast resins (6.95%); [b] 23 °C/50% RH/350 h; [c] Immersion/100 °C/360 h; [d] 50 °C/96% RH

In recent times, thermoplastic composites based on commodity thermoplastics have become significant contenders as matrices for glass-fibre composites where environmental resistance is sought. For example, polypropylene is now available in a pre-preg form for fusion bonding. Since it has low polarity and is also partially crystalline, moisture absorption is very low.

4.3.2 Styrenated resins

Within the corrosion-resistant-composites industry both unsaturated polyester and vinyl ester resins are used. These invariably use styrene as the reactive diluent and moisture absorption is therefore at a low level. However, polyester resins may have polar end-groups or contain unreacted monomers which tend to enhance its sensitivity to water. The equilibrium moisture content of a cured, unsaturated polyester resin is likely to be similar to that of an anhydride-cured epoxy because of a similarity in structure. Typically, this is < 1% whereas for a general purpose epoxy it can be approximately 7–10%. The moisture absorption of polyester resins is often dominated by residuals from the synthesis which can cause an osmotic effect.

4.3.3 Effects of unreacted components

Osmosis occurs when the resin acts as a semi-impermeable membrane allowing only water to diffuse. Therefore, if the resin contains water-soluble impurities, thermodynamics will drive the water into the resin. Osmotic pressure (π) is a colligative property and is directly proportional to the molal concentration of the impurity. As shown in equation [4.5].

$$\pi = RTc \qquad\qquad\qquad [4.5]$$

where c is the molal concentration of solubilized inclusions, T is the absolute temperature and R is the gas constant.

Since the moisture can plasticize the resin, eventually the pressure which develops at an inclusion will lead to a blister. In the case of glass-fibre-reinforced materials, this has been referred to as 'boat pox'. This is especially prevalent in freshwater areas as opposed to sea environments because c in equation [4.5] will be the difference between the concentrations of impurities in the 'resin' and the environment. In unsaturated polyester resins, the impurities leading to osmosis are likely to be residual acids and anhydrides or glycols. In the case of glass-fibre composites, some aqueous-based sizings can also cause osmosis at the interface. Therefore, the selection of fibre 'finish' is very important in the manufacture of a composite destined for use in aqueous environments such as chemical plant or marine applications. With advanced composite materials, osmosis is less of a problem but can still occur. Dicyandiamide (DICY) is commonly used as a latent curing agent for epoxy resins. Since DICY has a melting point of 160 °C, it can be dispersed as a solid phase into the liquid resin. Curing will only begin when the DICY melts. Accelerators are available which reduce the cure temperature. However, to achieve a satisfactory cure, without the formation of encapsulated DICY particles, it is essential to disperse them finely throughout the pre-preg material, often referred to as micronisation. If this is not done efficiently, enhanced moisture absorption can be observed. In some cases this can lead to blistering. Furthermore, the hydrolysis products can provide an alkaline environment which can degrade glass fibres.

Blisters can also occur at the interface between gel-coats and structural resins as a result of localised residual stresses. This has been discussed in detail by Chen and Birley.[8,9] To achieve blister-resistant composites, it is important to minimize the presence of impurities

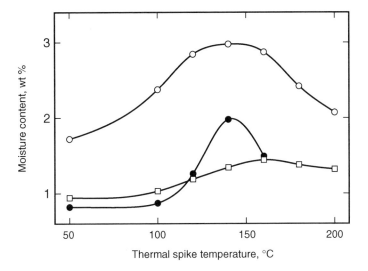

Fig. 4.3   Moisture enhancement after thermal spiking of a series of carbon fibre unidirectional laminates conditioned for 5000 h at 50 °C and 96% RH with 22 thermal spikes. Narmco Rigidite 5245C (●); Fibredux 927C (□) and, Fibredux 924C (○).[10]

which can act as osmotic centres and match the properties of the gel-coat to that of the structural resins (especially for the styrenated resins).

4.4   Thermal spiking

Another factor associated with moisture absorption by resin systems is the enhancement that can occur as a result of thermal excursions, normally of relatively short duration. So-called thermal spikes, acting for only a minute, can lead to a significant increase in moisture content. Figure 4.3 shows that there is a maximum enhancement temperature.[4] By comparing this data with that in Fig. 4.4 it can be seen that the 'thermal spiking' phenomenon is associated with the matrix and is not a consequence of combining the reinforcement with the resin.

4.5   Thermomechanical response of matrix resins

The most important response of a resin to moisture is its effect in reducing the glass-transition temperature T_g, this is known as plasticization and is observed for all polymers. The effect is illustrated in Fig. 4.5[3] and is particularly relevant to fibre-reinforced plastics because it determines the softening point of the resin. Moisture absorption will reduce the glass-transition temperature significantly. For example, with epoxy resins a rule of thumb exists that the glass-transition temperature is reduced on average by 20 K for each 1% moisture absorption.[11] Thus a resin which absorbs 7% moisture at saturation could have its glass transition temperature reduced by 140 K. A typical aerospace epoxy resin utilizes a high crosslink density and blends of non-polar thermoplastic or thermosetting resins to limit the moisture absorption (see Fig. 4.3) and the reduction in T_g. More advanced systems, such as an epoxy/cyanate ester blend have slightly lower values of M_∞. Figure 4.6 shows the

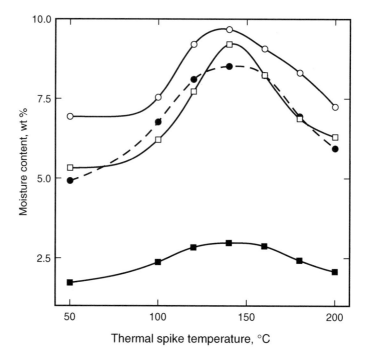

Fig. 4.4   Moisture enhancement on thermal spiking for a range of matrix resins; base-epoxy resin-924E (○); thermoplastic modified epoxy matrix resin-924T (□); matrix estimated from composite (●) and 924C composite (■).[10]

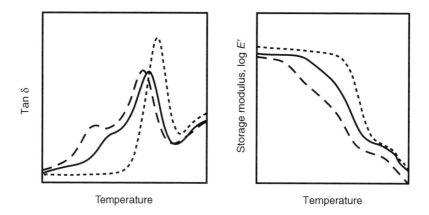

Fig. 4.5   Schematic showing the effect of moisture absorption on the thermomechanical response (DMTA, dynamic mechanical thermal analysis) of a resin, dry/as-cured resin (-----); wet from isothermal conditioning at 50 °C (——), comparative wet sample from thermal spiking experiment (– –). T_g is given by a maximum in tan δ, E' is the storage modulus.

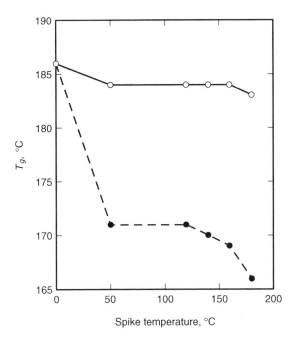

Fig. 4.6(a)   Effect of moisture absorption during thermal spiking on T_g (wet, ●, re-dried, ○). The resin is a thermally co-cured cyanate ester/epoxy resin blend/30% AroCy L10 (1,1-*bis*/4-cyanatophenyl ethane)/70% Novolac Epoxy (DEN 431).[12]

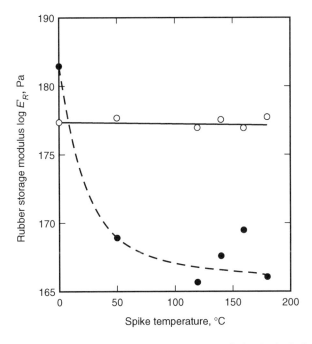

Fig. 4.6(b)   A comparison of the storage moduli above T_g (E_R') for the hydrolytically stable copolymer cyanate ester (○) (see Fig. 4.6(a)) with a non-hydrolytically stable thermally cured homopolymer. Cyanate ester (AroCy L10) (●) subjected to moisture absorption under thermal spiking, showing evidence of network degradation.[12]

reversibility associated with ~2% moisture absorption through thermal spiking. Typically, this might be 50 K so that the maximum service temperature needs to be at least 50 °C below T_g (as-cured) and include a further safety margin. As with many thermosets, the T_g, when dry, will be approximately equal to the cure or post-cure temperature so that a 150 °C-cured resin may have a maximum useful temperature in the long term of only 100 °C. This represents the design service temperature of the structure although equilibrium will need several years.

A small reduction in the modulus of the matrix in the glassy region may also occur although the effect on the modulus of the composite may not be significant. This arises from the hydrogen bonding of water molecules to the molecular chains in the network causing swelling and a slight reduction in density. Above the glass-transition temperature in the rubbery region, there should be no effect on modulus providing hydrolysis has not occurred. Any change in the modulus above the glass-transition temperature can be attributed to a hydrolytic effect as shown in Fig. 4.6(b).[12] The thermally cured cyanate ester, AroCy L10, is clearly susceptible to hydrolysis at temperatures above 50 °C in humid environments because the storage modulus E' decreases. The shear modulus of a rubber is inversely proportional to the average network chain length, according to the Gaussian theory of rubber elasticity[13] confirming the scission of network bonds. Furthermore, in comparison, the thermally co-cured epoxy cyanate ester is shown to be stable.[4]

Moisture absorption may also lead to a differential plasticization of the material. This may lead to a broadening of the glass-transition region, as shown in Fig. 4.5. It is for this reason that the choice of definition of glass transition can differ between industries. Typically, the aerospace industry may use the onset of a reduction in modulus rather than the maximum in tan δ from dynamic mechanical thermal analysis (DMTA) as a definition of the glass transition temperature. It is worth pointing out that the glass-transition temperature is not a thermodynamic parameter and values can vary depending on the technique employed.

Under non-isothermal conditions, such as during thermal spiking, the broadening can develop into a secondary relaxation peak below the glass transition. This has been attributed to the differential plasticization of the molecular structures within the cured network and/or the different phases in rubber or thermoplastic toughened matrices. Even cured unsaturated polyester resins exhibit a nanostructure as a result of the curing mechanism becoming diffusion controlled at intermediate stages of the cure.[14]

4.6   Effect of moisture on composite performance

4.6.1   Thermal stresses

In an angle-plied laminate, the expansion coefficients of the individual plies will differ. An example of an angle-ply laminate is a cross-ply or 0°/90°/0° laminate. In the latter example the expansion coefficient parallel to the fibres α_l is significantly less than the expansion coefficient transversely to the fibres α_t. The modulus of longitudinal ply E_l is also significantly higher than the modulus of the transverse ply E_t so that the differential shrinkage on cooling is constrained. Tensile thermal stress will develop in the plies transverse to the fibres and compressive stresses in the longitudinal or fibre direction. The magnitude of the residual thermal stress is determined by stress free temperature T_1, which is a function of the matrix glass transition temperature, and/or the cure or post-cure temperature. The tensile thermal strain in the longitudinal direction of the transverse ply (ε_{tl}^{th}) at temperature T_2 is given by equation [4.6].

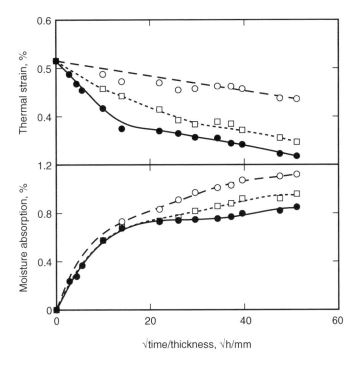

Fig. 4.7 Effect of moisture absorption at 50 °C and 96% RH on the thermal strain in a balanced 0°/90°/0° 927C laminate estimated from the curvature of an unbalanced 0°/90° beam.[3, 15] ●, control; □, 120 °C spike, ○, 140 °C spike.

$$\varepsilon_{tl}^{th} = \frac{E_l b(\alpha_t - \alpha_l)(T_1 - T_2)}{E_l b + E_t d} \qquad [4.6]$$

where b and d are 0° ply thickness and semi-90° ply thickness.

The first failure of a laminate structure such as a 0°/90°/0° composite will be by transverse or matrix cracking of the 90° or transverse ply. Since the residual thermal stress is tensile, the first-ply failure will occur at a lower applied stress. Analogously, the 0° plies will fail at a slightly higher stress because of a residual compressive stress in the fibres.

4.6.2 Thermal fatigue

Thermal fatigue is the phenomenon whereby the material exhibits damage resulting from multiple excursions to differing thermal environments. The stresses will also be multi-directional and in a composite laminate the tensile stresses at 90° to the fibres in all plies will vary during the heating cycles. Providing there are no changes in the expansion coefficients of the two plies, the material will be stable and transverse cracks will not form. However, if α_t is sensitive to temperature, there is potential for thermal cracking at 90° to the fibres, in all plies. Thermal cycling of dry composite materials to temperatures below the cure temperature would not normally lead to thermal cracking. However, in the presence of moisture, variations in concentration and temperature complicate the degree of constrained shrinkage. As shown in Fig. 4.7,[15] moisture absorbed by the resin within the composite causes a

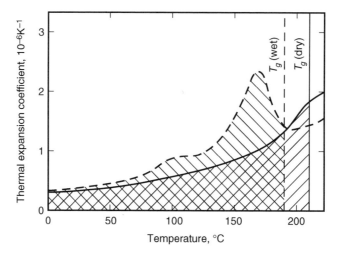

Fig. 4.8   Temperature dependence of the transverse thermal expansion coefficients of a bismaleimide modified epoxy resin-based carbon fibre composite (Narmco Rigidite 5245C); dry (continuous curve) and wet (dashed curve).[16,17] The hatching illustrates the differing constrained shrinkages (and hence thermal strain) for wet and dry laminates.

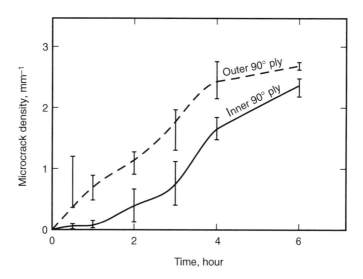

Fig. 4.9   Thermal transverse cracking of a 0°/90°/0° laminate from PMR-15 during ageing at 390 °C.[18]

constrained swelling in opposition to the constrained contraction responsible for the thermal strain. As a result, the thermal strain in the composite will be reduced on moisture diffusion. In some cases this may approach zero, but in others the reduction in thermal strain may be quite small. However, the presence of moisture in the material can modify the expansion coefficient of the matrix. In particular, the thermal response will mirror any changes occurring in the DMTA spectrum. It is more likely to lead to a higher degree of contraction (which will be constrained) because a secondary relaxation peak can appear in the expansion coefficient temperature profile. However, the reduction in T_g may lower T_1 but this is not usually exceeded in a thermal excursion. That means that during a thermal excursion, even to temperatures below the glass-transition temperature or post-cure temperature of the material, the higher constrained contraction on subsequent cooling will induce a higher residual thermal strain.[16,17] In Fig. 4.8 the additional contraction which is converted into a residual strain is represented by the difference between the areas under the two curves. In the next cycle, moisture absorption may lead to a further swelling of the material and a reduction in the thermal strain. However, after a subsequent thermal cycle, the thermal strain will again be enhanced. If the thermal stresses which are induced into the material exceed the transverse cracking strain of the individual ply, then thermal cracks will form. Because of the three-dimensional nature of the thermal stresses, thermal cracking occurs in every ply. As shown in Fig. 4.9, thermal cracking of the plies will occur differentially because the moisture absorption will not be uniformly distributed throughout the material. In Fig. 4.9 the thermal cracking occurred more rapidly in the outer ply. However, in this PMR-15 system the curing mechanism also involved loss of volatiles with enhanced potential for constrained shrinkage.[19]

Thermal fatigue is usually dominated by matrix cracking, but this can throw a load on the 0° fibres leading to reduced mechanical strength in the fibre direction.

4.7   Fibre-dominated properties

4.7.1   Static fatigue of glass fibres

The strength of a glass or other brittle material is determined by the presence of Griffith flaws.[20] Fibres represent a means of reducing the population of flaws of critical dimension. Therefore, glass fibres, like other reinforcing fibres, have a statistical distribution of strengths which can be characterised using Weibull statistics. Bartenev[21] and Metcalfe and Schmitz[22] have shown that fibres have three populations of flaws of differing dimension which are responsible for their strength.

* Severe surface flaws at a spacing of 20 mm provide an average strength of 3 GPa.
* Mild surface flaws (or internal defects[21]) at 0.1 mm spacing lead to an average strength of 3.5 GPa.
* Internal defects of 10^{-4} mm spacing provide an average strength of 5 GPa, which is considered to be characteristic of a defect-free filament with an uninterrupted surface layer. The origin of these flaws is discussed by Hand and Seddon.[23]

Thus, commercial E-glass fibres typically have an average strength of 3 GPa with a wide distribution as indicated by a Weibull modulus of ~4. It is very important to recognize the role of surface finish on the glass fibres, which protects them from damage during the manufacture of a composite. Individual filaments will have a range of strengths, so that in a composite under load, some fibres will fracture early and others late in the load cycle. Fortunately, composite behaviour is typified by the stress transfer of the additional matrix load back to the fibre through shear at the interface. The transfer length over which this occurs is often referred to as an ineffective length and dictates the fracture behaviour in the longitudinal direction by influencing the stress concentration experienced by neighbouring fibres in the composite. With a perfect bond the matrix can fail simultaneously with a fibre break leading to a brittle failure at low load. This is an important aspect of premature failure under static and dynamic loads.

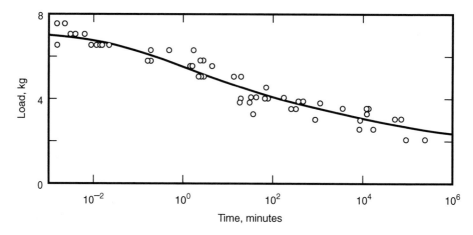

Fig. 4.10   Static fatigue of E-glass strands in distilled water. A load of 2 kg caused an applied
strain of 0.5%. Redrawn from Aveston *et al.*[24]

Glass fibres are also subject to time-dependent fracture under a static load. This, of
course, will also have a statistical component but is generally recognised to be the result of
a stress corrosion phenomenon involving 'condensed' water. Typical data for static fatigue
on E-glass fibre bundles in water are shown in Fig. 4.10.[24] The data show three different
regions of time-dependent fracture, which is amplified when composites are subjected to
corrosive environments because of the matrix cracks.[25]
   A trend similar to that shown in Fig. 4.10 is observed for loading in air. Since, there is no
time-dependence of strength in a vacuum, it is considered that the reduction in strength
results from a stress-corrosion mechanism in water. The chemical reactions associated with
this process are given below:

$$\equiv Si - O^- Na^+ + H_2O \quad \rightarrow \quad \equiv Si - OH + Na^+ + OH^-$$

$$\equiv Si - O - Si \equiv + OH^- \quad \rightarrow \quad \equiv Si - O^- + HO - Si \equiv \qquad [4.7]$$

$$\equiv Si - O^- + H_2O \quad \rightarrow \quad \equiv Si - OH + OH^-$$

Thus, the sodium ions present in E-glass act as a catalyst for the degradation of the silica
network which is propagated by hydroxyl ions. The three stages which appear to be
exhibited in the static fatigue of glass fibres can be attributed to the Charles mechanism.[26]
   Stage I is a stress-dominated region at high stresses where crack propagation is fast
compared to the rate of reaction with water, i.e. fibre corrosion at the crack or flaw tip. The
rate of diffusion of sodium ions to the surface is rate determining and the fracture is
dominated by the mechanical loading.
   Stage II is a stress-corrosion region. Here the rate of corrosion is similar to the rate of
crack propagation. Therefore the crack remains sharp and propagates into weakened glass.
   Stage III is the stress-assisted corrosion region where the effect of stress on the failure
time is much less significant because the rate of hydrolysis of the silica network is higher

than the rate of crack growth. The corrosive effect leads to a rounding of the crack-tip. This reduces the potential for crack propagation according to the Irwin equation:

$$\sigma_{max} = 2\sigma_a \left(\frac{x}{\rho}\right)^{\frac{1}{2}}$$ [4.8]

where σ_a = applied stress, σ_{max} = stress at a crack tip of depth x and radius ρ.

A typical bundle of E-glass fibres, as shown in Fig 4.10, can have a typical lifetime of 10^6–10^7 minutes at an applied strain of $\approx 0.5\%$. This provides a lifetime of 2–20 years. Therefore, provided the fibres are protected both from mechanical damage and moisture diffusion, a composite could be expected to have a minimum lifetime, at 0.5% strain in the fibres, of approximately 20 years. From equation [4.1], one-sided exposure to water would extend the life of a 10 mm thick composite to ≈ 120 years and two-sided diffusion ≈ 30 years. Poor interfacial integrity will cause a more rapid diffusion of the environment and will accelerate the degradation

4.7.2 Prediction of lifetime of fibre bundles under static fatigue

Kelly and McCartney[27] have analysed the data of Aveston et al.[24] by including the statistics of fibre strength into a conventional power law for crack growth. The number of fibres N surviving in a population of N_0 at a stress of σ, is given by a Weibull distribution:[28]

$$N = N_0 \exp\left[-\left(\frac{\sigma}{\sigma_0}\right)^m\right]$$ [4.9]

where σ_0 is the characteristic ratio, and m is the Weibull modulus.

For a bundle of fibres, the load on the surviving filaments will be distributed according to equation [4.10].

$$F = NA\sigma$$ [4.10]

where A is the cross-sectional area of a fibre.

Failure will occur when N decreases to the point when the remaining fibres can no longer support the load and the bundle fails. Since the fibres are characterized by a critical stress-intensity factor K_{1c}, it is the dimension of the flaws which determines the strength of an individual filament. A flaw of length a will grow until it reaches a critical length a_c at failure. Therefore all of the fibres with flaws longer than a_c will fail.

$$a_c = \left(\frac{K_{1c}}{y\sigma}\right)^2$$ [4.11]

where y is a constant.

Therefore, at a constant tensile stress, flaws with $a < a_c$ will grow with time until $a = a_c$ when the filaments will fail. The crack growth rate, da/dt, can be described by a power law.

$$\frac{da}{dt} = \alpha K_1^n$$ [4.12]

Equation [4.9] can therefore be rewritten in the form of equation [4.13] to describe the number of fibres in a population N_0 having flaws of initial length $< a$:

$$N = N_0 \exp\left[-\left(\frac{a_0}{a}\right)^{m/2}\right]$$

[4.13]

where $a_0^{1/2} = \dfrac{K_{1c}}{y\sigma_0}$.

Kelly and McCartney[27] combined equations [4.9] and [4.10] to recalculate the number of fibres surviving the application of load F:

$$\frac{N}{N_0} = \exp\left[-\left(\frac{F}{N_0\sigma_0 A}\right)^m \left(\frac{N_0}{N}\right)^m\right]$$

[4.14]

Time dependence can be incorporated through equations [4.12] and [4.10].

$$N(t) = F/A\sigma(t)$$

[4.15]

where $N(t)$ and $\sigma(t)$ are the number of surviving fibres and fibre stress at time t.

As F approaches the maximum load which can be supported by the bundle F_m, the following equation is obtained:

$$t_f \approx \frac{m^{2/m}\left[1 - F/F_m\right]}{\dfrac{1}{2}\alpha K_{1c}^{n-2} y^2 \sigma_0^2}$$

[4.16]

The theory was used to examine the data for the static fatigue of a glass fibre bundle.[24] The theoretical line was calculated from the more precise version of equation [4.16]. Figure 4.11 shows the fraction of E-glass fibres broken with time. These authors have discussed in detail the effect of fibre strength distribution on the relative failure times of the bundle. For example, one of the interesting outcomes of the theory is that it shows that for E-glass fibres, typically, 70% fibres survive for 90% life of the bundles. For carbon fibres where $m > 4$, 80% of fibres survive for 90% of the life. This explains the typical form of fatigue-life diagrams for composites where the life drops off rapidly after long loading times. Recent fatigue data in Fig. 4.12 from Shan and Liao[29] illustrate this aspect for wet and dry filament-wound hot-pressed composites. This also helps to explain the rapid fracture when the fibres are weakened under corrosive conditions.

4.7.2.1 Lifetimes of composites under load in aqueous environments
Aveston and Sillwood[30] applied this theory to composite materials to give equation [4.17].

$$t_c = \frac{2}{A\sigma^2 y^2}\left(\frac{1}{K_1} - \frac{1}{K_{1c}}\right)$$

$$= \frac{2}{A\sigma^3 y^3 a_i}\left(1 - \frac{\sigma_a}{\sigma_{max}}\right)$$

[4.17]

a_i is the initial flaw size which is unknown but can be used to fit the experimental data. The environmental stress corrosion cracking of a unidirectional E-glass fibre composite in acidic environments under static and fatigue loads, is shown in Fig. 4.13.

The above theory illustrates the role of statistical fibre fracture on the time-dependent

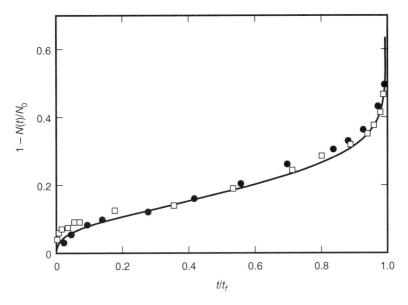

Fig. 4.11 Experimentally determined fraction of fibres broken as a function of time compared with a theoretical prediction from equation [4.16] with $m = 4$, $n = 15$ and $F/F_m = 0.6$. Experimental results are from Aveston and Silverwood[30] for E-glass in water ($F_m = 59 \pm 10$ N); $\square$, $F = 34$ N; $\bullet$, $F = 39$ N.[27]

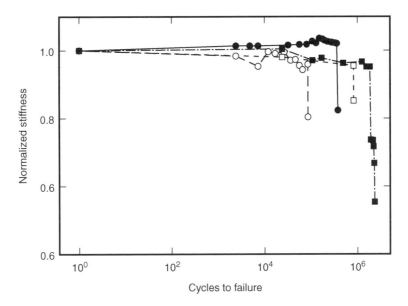

Fig. 4.12 Typical stiffness reduction curves for samples cyclically loaded at 65% UTS, for both all-glass-fibre and hybrid samples tested under dry and wet conditions. Unidirectional E-glass composites ($\bullet$ (dry), $\circ$ (wet)) are compared to hybrid composites with 25% of the fibres by volume of Type A carbon fibres (PAN HTA 6000 (Asahi Nippon) ($\blacksquare$ (dry), $\square$ (wet)). V_f was 30%.[29]

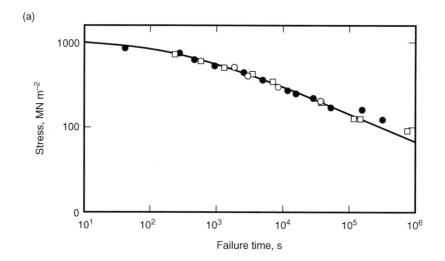

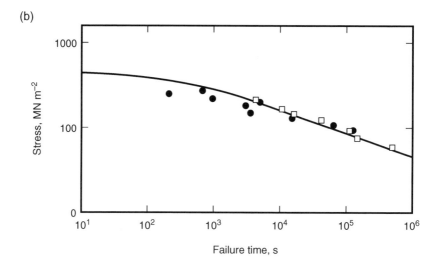

Fig. 4.13 Static and fatigue loading of (a) unidirectional and (b) cross-ply E-glass polyester composites in 0.5 M H_2SO_4 static load (●), static load with pre-soak for 1.8×10^6 s (○) fatigue at 0.1 Hz (□).[30]

behaviour of composites when loaded in the fibre direction. Thus the residual strength will follow a simple logarithmic model for ≈ 80% of life of the material.

$$\sigma_a = \sigma_{uc} - B \log t_f$$

$$\sigma_a = \sigma_{uc} - b \log N_f \qquad\qquad [4.18]$$

where σ_a is applied stress amplitude, σ_{uc} is the initial strength of the composite, where N_f is the number of cycles to failure, b and B are constants.

Lavoie *et al.*[31] have applied the critical-element model of Reifsnider[32] which introduces a power law of the form:

$$\frac{\sigma_a}{\sigma_{uc}} = A + B\left(\log t_f\right)^P$$

where A, B and P are constants to account for the complete data set. These models ignore the possibility of a limiting strain[33] for stress corrosion.

When significant off-axis material is included in the lay-up then matrix effects become critical and prediction will be more difficult and require a stiffness degradation model based on damage accumulation which includes a contribution from matrix plasticization. (See Section 4.5).

4.8   Role of the matrix and interface

Figure 4.14(a) shows that the nucleation and growth of stress corrosion cracks in the surface of a 0° E-glass/epoxy composite in 0.5 M H_2SO_4 occurs at single filaments.[34] The fracture of a unidirectional composite is illustrated in Fig 4.14(b). Hogg and Hull[34,35] discussed the role of the matrix in environmental stress-corrosion cracking (ESCC), whereby a fibre break leads to fracture of the adjacent resin. The ease of propagation of the crack into the resin will determine the failure of the composite. In the absence of water (or other environment) the first fibre will fracture at a significantly high strain so that the shear stresses which develop at the interface cause debonding or yielding within an interphase region.[37] However, when the fibres are weakened through the corrosive action of the water or aqueous acids, the shear stresses at the interface arising from a fibre break will be insufficient for debonding, unless chemical degradation of the interfacial bonds has occurred.

Therefore, when the interface remains intact, i.e. for a perfect bond, the matrix fractures at a fibre break. In this way, the adjacent or nearest-neighbour fibre will experience a high stress concentration with an increased probability to fracture. As shown in Table 4.3[38] the fracture toughness (K_{1c} or G_{1c}) of the resin will have a major influence on the propagation of a matrix crack from a fibre break.

Table 4.3   Fracture toughness (K_{1c}) of chemically resistant polyester and vinyl ester resins[37]

Resin	Type	Environment	K_{1c} (MNm$^{-3/2}$)
Crystic 272	Isophthalic/propylene glycol	Dry	0.79
		Moist (~0.2%H_2O)	0.61
		Wet (1.5%H_2O) – tested dry	0.55
		Wet (1.5%H_2O) – tested wet	0.89
		Dry – tested wet	0.85
Crystic 272/30% Crystic 586	Flexibilized isophthalic/propylene glycol	Laboratory environment, moisture present	0.77
Derakane 411-45	Vinyl ester	Laboratory environment, moisture present	0.75
Crystic 600 PA	Bisphenol polyester	Laboratory environment, moisture present	0.49
Beetle 870	Chemical resistant	Laboratory environment, moisture present	0.46
Atlac 382-05A	Urethane-bisphenol vinyl ester	Laboratory environment, moisture present	0.45

(a)

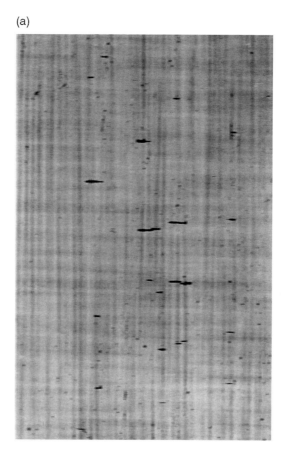

(b)

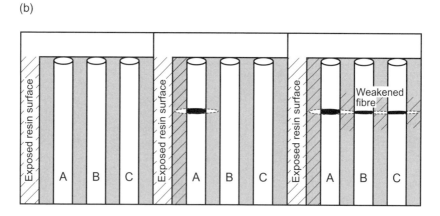

Fig. 4.14   The mechanism of environmental stress corrosion cracking of a 0° E-glass/epoxy resin composite. (a) Nucleation and growth of cracks at single filament breaks,[34] (b) schematic of the mechanism; the 'acid' diffuses through the surface resin causing Filament A to fracture and propagate into the adjacent matrix resin which facilitates environmental ingress and further fracture of weakened fibres B and C and adjacent resin.

Table 4.4   The effect of moisture absorption at 50 °C and desorption on the room-temperature fracture toughness (K_{1c}) of Crestomer 1080/Crystic 272 Blended Resin Castings (K_{1c} in MN m$^{-3/2}$ and M_∞ in %)[38]

Resin 272/1080	272		90/10		80/20		70/30		60/40	
Environment:	M_∞	K_{1c}	M_∞	K_{1c}	M_∞	K_{1c}	M_∞	K_{1c}	M_∞	K_{1c}
As cast, dried	–	0.72	–	1.1	–	1.54	–	1.76	–	1.85
Wet (31% RH)	0.32	–	0.3	–	0.35	1.53	0.34	1.68	0.33	1.61
Redried	–	–	–	–	–	1.3	–	1.46	–	1.37
Wet (96% RH)	1.42	0.55	1.7	0.91	2.2	0.71	2.3	0.81	2.5	0.93
Redried	0	0.6	–	0.99	–	0.74	–	0.54	–	0.65

When the effect of water on the fracture toughness of the resin (Table 4.4)[39] and the reduced strength of the fibre from static fatigue (or acidic corrosion) are coupled, the composite will exhibit a more brittle failure In plane mirror-like fractures are typical of environmental stress-corrosion cracking of GRP.[33,34] Sekine and Beaumont[40] have quantified these aspects of fractographs of composite failure to produce a micromechanical failure model.

The resistance to crack growth through the resin filet adjacent to a fibre break will determine whether an environmental stress crack will form. As shown in Table 4.3, the low value of K_{1c} for so called 'chemically resistant resins' can lead to lower resistance to ESCC. However, Table 4.4 shows that even in the presence of moisture, the fracture toughness of the resin matrix may be lower. Therefore, it is essential to utilize resins with high fracture toughness, especially under service conditions. For resistance to brittle fracture resulting from a single fibre break, the resin adjacent to the fibre needs to have a high resistance to fracture. Since the fibres are invariably coated with a resin size for protection and adhesion promotion, it is the fracture toughness of an interphase which invariably forms that is important in the design. This helps to explain the need for careful selection of fibre 'finish' or sizing.

4.9   Environmental stress-corrosion cracking (ESCC) of GRP

4.9.1   Glass fibres

As shown in Fig. 4.10, E-glass fibres have a reduced lifetime under load in the presence of moisture but this is even more severe in a corrosive environment. Figure 4.15 shows how pH affects the strength of unloaded E-glass fibres.[41] With a pH close to zero as achieved in dilute aqueous mineral acids the rate of strength degradation is maximized. Only in highly alkaline environments (pH ≈ 13) is a similar reduction in strength encountered. Under load, ESCC of E-glass filaments also has a maximum degradation rate at pH of 0.2 (0.5 M H$_2$SO$_4$).[42] ESCC occurs in acidic environments because the network modifiers (Ca, Na, Al, K, Fe) are leached from E-glass to leave the silica network largely intact. Therefore, for the fibre to fracture a crack needs to propagate through the weakened glass sheaf which retains a covalently bonded structure. The degradation mechanism in equation [4.7] is no longer available for the chemical rupture of these bonds because of the neutralization and extraction of the alkali catalyst. In alkaline environments, hydrolysis of the silica network occurs sequentially with pH.[43]

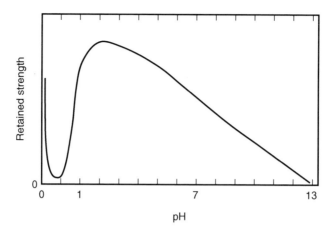

Fig. 4.15   Schematic of the retained strength of unloaded E-glass fibres in environments of differing acidity and alkalinity.[41]

$$SiO_2 + H_2O \underset{\longleftarrow}{\overset{K_1}{\rightleftharpoons}} H_2SiO_3 \underset{\longleftarrow}{\overset{K_2}{\rightleftharpoons}} H^+ + H\,SiO_3^- \underset{\longleftarrow}{\overset{K_3}{\rightleftharpoons}} 2H^+ + SiO_2^- \qquad [4.19]$$

Thermodynamically, step 1 with equilibrium constant K_1 occurs at a pH $\approx$ 10 and step 2 K_2 at pH $\approx$ 12.5.

Therefore, at high pH, found with aqueous alkalis, rapid hydrolysis of the silica network occurs. Any cracks can be blunted through corrosive mechanisms or ion precipitation. Weakening of the fibres is therefore more important in alkaline environments and brittle ESCC fractures are not normally observed (except when stress concentrations occur as a result of a crystallization pressure at the boundary between parts of the composite with a degraded and non-degraded interface).[44]

4.9.2 Composites

Figure 4.16 gives data for a commercial filament-wound pipe in aqueous acidic environments.[25] Its shape is similar to that shown in Fig. 4.10 for fibres alone because the mechanisms are similar. Figure 4.17 is a schematic illustration of the role of the various composite variables.

Stage I is the stress-dominated failure where crack propagation is dominant.

Stage II is the ESCC region where the rate of corrosion of E-glass fibres is similar to the rate of propagation of cracks through the material so that a synergistic effect occurs as described above.

Stage III is the stress-assisted corrosion and diffusion-dominated failure region, where the rate of corrosion of the E-glass fibre is larger than the rate of crack propagation so that the crack tip does not remain sharp.

As discussed above, stage III is determined by the integrity of the interface and the barrier properties of the matrix. For composites subject to low strains, highly cross-linked aromatic resins provide the best barrier properties because of their low diffusion constants. Furthermore, they have highest chemical resistance giving long-term durability to these materials.

However, in stage II the failure occurs because of the synergism between load and the

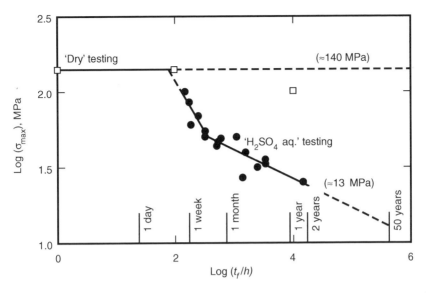

Fig. 4.16   Environmental stress–corrosion failure times (t_f) for circumferentially cut coupons from type B GRP sewer lining in 0.5 M H_2SO_4. The numbers in brackets represent the maximum stress for 50-year lifetime.[25]

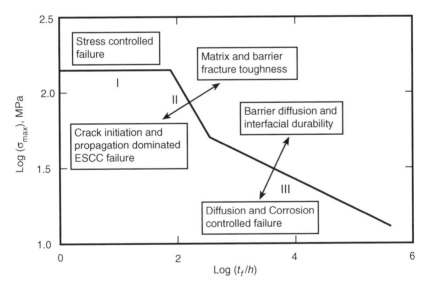

Fig. 4.17   Schematic description of environmental (acidic) stress corrosion (ESCC) failure times of E-glass composite under stress (σ_{max}) showing effects of composite design.

environment, which is described in Section 4.7.1. For unidirectional composites, the individual site of the failure will probably be the weakest fibre in the population and probably with the thinnest layer of protective matrix resin. The individual fibre break can initiate a stress-corrosion crack through propagation through the matrix in both directions to the component surface and the adjacent fibres, which will fail under the combined action of the corrodent and additional mechanical load. As illustrated in Fig. 4.13, there does not

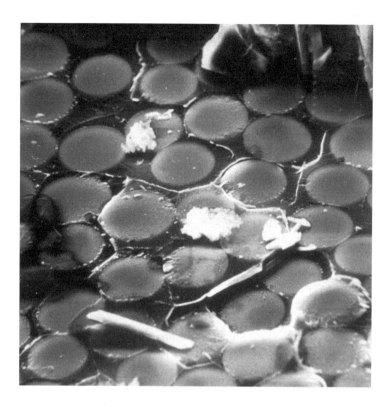

Fig. 4.18 Environmental stress corrosion fracture surface of a 0°/90°/0° E-glass epoxy resin composite in 0.5 M H_2SO_4 at an applied strain of 0.1%. The fibres have a diameter of 12 μm.[34]

appear to be a major difference between static and dynamic loading because it is the rate of propagation of matrix cracks which leads to the formation of a flaw of critical dimensions. As a result, the fracture surface will exhibit 'mirror' regions typical of ESCC (Fig 4.18), and hackle regions more typical of the fast fracture which follows the formation of a crack of critical dimensions. As a result the fracture surface exhibits a more fibrous character, usually in blocks.

This also means that the presence of notches, transverse or gel-coat cracks can all promote stress-corrosion failure. Notched samples invariably have significantly lower failure times. The role of precracks is illustrated in Fig 4.19.[35] However, the stress concentration associated with these flaws is clearly demonstrated in Fig. 4.20 where a precrack in the gel-coat is much more damaging than a mechanical notch.[45] Thus an individual fibre fracture can be considered to be a sharp flaw. This is illustrated in Fig 4.14(b) where stress corrosion cracks are seen to nucleate and grow in the surface of a 0° material. Jones and Rock[46] applied linear elastic fracture mechanics to the propagation of these ESCC cracks from single filament breaks to obtain a K_{1C} value. Resins with a high value of K_{1C} should therefore give the best durability. However, Hogg[35] showed that as the ductility of the resin increased, the stress corrosion resistance reached a maximum and then decayed. He attributed this to the fact that the acid could diffuse more easily through the less cross-linked resin to reach the adjacent fibre without the need for a resin crack, fracture occurring via coalescence of individual fibre fractures. However, Caddock *et al.*[47] could not demonstrate diffusion of acid through resins. An alternative explanation is that the fracture toughness of plasticized polyester resins is lower in the presence of aqueous environments

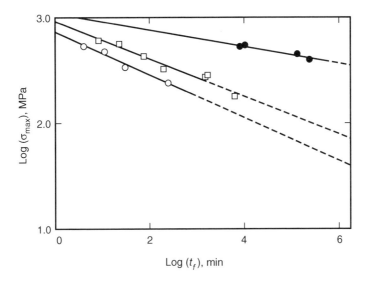

Fig. 4.19   Role of gel-coat cracks on the stress corrosion failure time (t_f) for hoop wound pipes in 0.65 M HCl at 20 °C, with the stress applied (σ_{max}) parallel to the fibres; with gel-coat (●); cracked gel-coat (○); without gel-coat (□).[35]

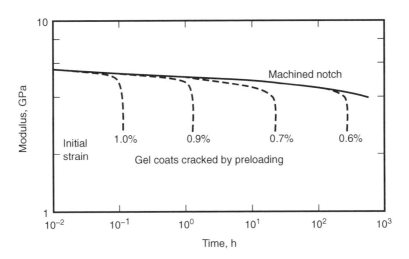

Fig. 4.20   Creep failure of chopped strand (CSM) laminates from a vinyl ester resin (Derakane 411.45) in 1 M HCl showing the effect of a pre-cracked gel-coat (redrawn from Ref. 45).

(see Table 4.4). With lower cross-link density, the chemical resistance is likely to be reduced and a small degree of hydrolysis could be responsible for microcracking of the resin.[38,39]

4.9.3   Phenomena associated with interfacial degradation

Stress-corrosion failures have been observed in the unexposed part of epoxy[33,34] and polyester composites[33,34,48] in aqueous sulphuric acid often at significantly lower applied strains. This mechanism has been referred to as Type II or Type B failure. This phenomenon occurs when the corrosion products can crystallize at the junction of the dry and wet material resulting from capillary transport along degraded interfaces. Stress-assisted damage accumulation or Type III or Type C failure has also been observed for unloaded specimens. Interfacial degradation provides the pathway for the corrodent while crystallization pressure causes transverse cracking of the material. However, within a composite, the fibres will be in thermal compression so that fracture cannot occur without a small external tensile load. This phenomenon is also observed in alkaline environments.

4.10   Designing for stress-corrosion resistance

4.10.1   Fibre choice

For industrial composites, E-glass is chosen because of its low cost. Therefore, the composite structure has a lay-up designed to prevent the formation of a damaging stress-corrosion crack. However, ECR (chemically resistant E-glass) provides a higher resistance to static fatigue and stress corrosion. C-glass (chemically resistant glass in veil form) is used for reinforcing barrier resins. As shown by Aveston et al.[24] carbon fibres do not suffer from static fatigue and are generally inert to all but highly oxidizing acids. They are inert at high temperatures except in air, where oxidation becomes significant at around 350 °C.

Aramid fibres have been shown to exhibit a time-dependent loss of strength and static fatigue in aqueous environments.[24,49] These fibres absorb approximately 5% moisture so that the mechanism may be through plasticization and a reduction in modulus or partial hydrolysis. They are highly susceptible to hydrolysis in alkalis.[50,51] Aramid fibres also oxidize in UV conditions. Fortunately, the degradation products act as a screen against further oxidation. However, it is important to ensure these fibres are coated in appropriate UV opaque resins for maximum protection. The strength retention of aramid fibres under oxidising (UV), acidic and alkaline conditions has been compared by van Dingenen.[51]

S and R glasses are used for high strength glass fibres, mostly for high-performance aerospace applications. However, they also have superior performance in chemical environments.

One of the crucial selection issues for high durability is the correct 'fibre sizing' since this will optimize interfacial integrity of the material. For example, powder-bound chopped strand mat rather than emulsion-bound material should always be used for exposure to aqueous environments.

4.10.2   Resin choice

As discussed above, the most important consideration is to balance the highest fracture toughness with optimum chemical resistance. This is because of the need to prevent a stress-corrosion crack from forming at a filament fracture or transverse crack (in cross-ply laminates). It is quite common to use a ductile resin at the surface in contact with the environment at a lower fibre volume fraction than in the structural material, to give a resin-rich barrier layer. Often C-glass veil is used to reinforce a gel coat or resin rich barrier layer. However, for most applications an E-glass is used for structural composites, and is protected from degradation by the use of a barrier layer. This is designed to prevent the formation of a single crack with a high stress intensity, and prevent the nucleation of a stress corrosion crack.

The resin-rich liner will consist of a surface layer of surface-tissue-reinforced resin or an unreinforced flexible resin. The barrier layer will employ chopped fibres or woven rovings. Should a filament fracture in the barrier layer the probability of a stress-corrosion crack is reduced because the damage will be spread over a 'large' volume as a result of micromechanisms associated with off-axis short fibres. The structural material is therefore protected and can be constructed of E-glass fibre. The construction of durable pipes and containers is described elsewhere.[3,9,52]

4.11   Non-aqueous environments

Durability towards organic solvents can be discussed from a consideration of solubility. Although crosslinked resins do not dissolve, swelling will be maximized in contact with fluids with the same solubility parameter as the polymer matrix. The solubility parameter of the matrix can be estimated using simple additive principles.[53] When:

$$\delta_{solvent} = \delta_{polymer}$$

where $\delta_{solvent}$, $\delta_{polymer}$ are the solubility parameters, maximum swelling will occur. This gives maximum plasticization of the matrix causing a high potential to creep under off-axis loads. The residual stress state is also significantly modified in a manner similar to that described in Section 4.6. The results given in Fig. 4.21 demonstrate how these environments can affect the matrix-dominant properties in flexural fatigue experiments on ± 45 laminates.

These results can be explained by the plasticization of polyether imide (PEI) matrix with the fluid. The reduction in matrix modulus reduces the shear strength of the matrix causing failure in flexure to change from fracture to delamination.

Swelling stresses have also contributed to the loss of durability. In Fig. 4.22, flexural fatigue of 0° PEI composites is described. In this case, the extent of plasticization leads to buckling in the compressive face of the coupon.[54,55]

This occurs because in compression, the matrix has to support the reinforcement. PEI is an amorphous polymer and is much more susceptible to solvents than partially crystalline polymers such as polyetheretherketone (PEEK).

In principle, these effects can be predicted by combining a diffusion profile with a calculation of relative 'solubility' summarizing partial polarities, and assuming that, with partially crystalline matrices, only the amorphous component is involved unless the interaction between the solvent and matrix is so strong that the crystallites are disrupted.

Weatherhead[56] and Jones[3] provide a survey of the durability of resins in a range of environments.

4.11.1   Microcracking during fatigue

Most composite laminates designed for fatigue resistance utilize the constraint on transverse cracking offered by the use of plies of low thickness.[57] In this way, the strain to first-ply failure is significantly increased above the isolated ply failure strain ε_{tu} because of the reduced potential energy in a thin ply. From a simplistic point of view, the transverse plies can be considered to be 'metastable' and cracks will form slowly with the number of load cycles. Ogin and Smith[58] have used fracture mechanics to describe this phenomenon. They derived equation [4.20].

$$\varepsilon_{tu} = \sqrt{\frac{G_c}{2d E_t}}$$

[4.20]

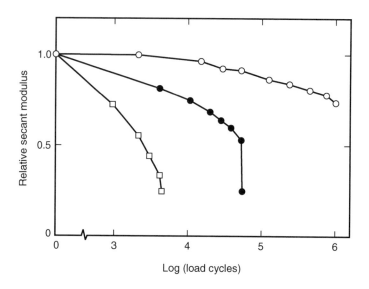

Fig. 4.21   Influence of aggressive fluids on the secant modulus of a PEI composite during fatigue (45° orientation, σ_{max} = 95 MPa). ○, in air; ●, in hydraulic fluid; □, in MEK (redrawn from Ref. 54).

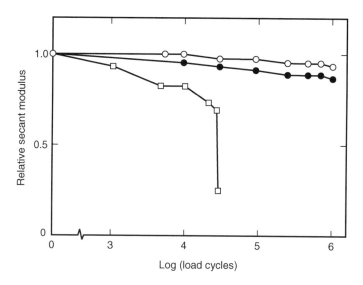

Fig. 4.22   Influence of aggressive fluids on the secant modulus of a PEI composite during flexural fatigue (0° orientation, σ_{max} = 120 MPa, ○, in air; ●, in hydraulic fluid; □, in MEK.[54]

where G_c is the critical-strain energy release rate for cracks growing in the transverse ply of thickness 2d and modulus $E_t \cdot \varepsilon_{tlu}$ is the first ply failure strain.

Examination of this equation shows that as a solvent or moisture diffuses into the laminate E_t will decrease. If G_c remains constant, then the first-ply failure strain will increase.

Since G_c is related to K_c, the fracture toughness of the matrix or interphase according to equation [4.21] (since transverse cracks tend to propagate in the matrix adjacent to the fibre).

$$G_c = \frac{K_c^2}{E_t}$$
[4.21]

we can see how the environment can influence the accumulation of transverse cracks in a complex manner, since K_c and E_t will tend to be reduced but with opposing effects. Add to this the fact that the thermal strain will also be modified as:

$$\varepsilon_{tlu} = \varepsilon_{tu} - \varepsilon_{tl}^{th}$$
[4.22]

and the prediction of the effect of solvent ingress on damage accumulation is complex. Further research is required to address this phenomenon.

4.12   Conclusions

The environmental effects on the static and dynamic fatigue of composite materials have been discussed. Of importance are the roles of the fibres, matrix and interface. E-glass fibres dominate the discussion because they are highly susceptible to ESCC, leading to time-dependent brittle failure even at low applied strains. However, technological solutions to the problem exist, making GRP the appropriate material choice for application in corrosive environments such as chemical plant.

Different phenomena operate in aerospace laminates where matrix and interfacial effects dominate. These are difficult to quantify because of the complexity of the mechanisms which operate. However, simple 'rules-of-thumb' are available, which provide confidence in their application.

4.13   References

1. SPRINGER G S (1981), *Environmental Effects on Composite Materials*, ed. G S Springer, Westport, USA, Technomic, Vol. 1.
2. SHEN C H and SPRINGER G S (1976), *J. Compos. Mater.*, **10**, 2–20.
3. JONES F R (1999), *Durability of Reinforced Plastics in Liquid Environments, in Reinforced Plastics Durability*, ed. G Prichard, Cambridge, UK, Woodhead, Ch. 3, 70–110.
4. XIANG Z D and JONES F R (1997), *Compos. Sci. Technol.*, **57**, 451.
5. KARAD S K, JONES F R and ATTWOOD D (2002), *Polymer*, **43**, 5209–5218.
6. KARAD S K, JONES F R and ATTWOOD D (2002), *Polymer*, **42**, 5643–5649.
7. GUMEN V R, JONES F R and ATTWOOD D (2001), *Polymer*, **42**, 5717–5725.
8. CHEN F and BIRLEY A W (1991), *Plastics Rubber Compos. Proc. Appl.*, **15**, 161.
9. CHEN F and BIRLEY A W (1991), *Plastics Rubber Compos. Proc. Appl.*, **15**, 169.
10. HOUGH J A, JONES F R and XIANG Z D (1997), in *Proc. 4th Int. Conf. Deformation and Fracture of Composites*, London, Institute of Materials, pp 181–190.
11. WRIGHT W W (1981), *Composites*, **12**, 201.
12. KARAD S K, ATTWOOD D and JONES F R (2002), *Composites A*, **33A**, 1665–1675.
13. TRELOAR L R G (1975), *The Physics of Rubber Elasticity*, 3rd edn, Oxford, Clarendon Press.
14. BERGMANN K and DEMMLER K (1974), *Koll. ZZ. Polym.*, **252**, 204.
15. CALOTA E and JONES F R (1997), unpublished data.
16. JONES F R (1994), in *Handbook of Polymer-Fibre Composites*, ed. FR Jones, Harlow, UK, Longman, pp. 379–391.
17. JACOBS P M and JONES F R (1991), in *Composite Design, Manufacture and Application* (ICCM VIII), eds. S W Tsai and G Springer, Corina, CA, USA, SAMPE 1991 Vol 2, Ch 16 paper G.
18. XIANG Z D and JONES F R (1995), Effect of isothermal ageing on thermomechanical stability of carbon fibre reinforced PMR-15 resin matrix composites. in *Proc. Seminar on Exptl. Techniques and Design in Composites Materials*, ed. M S Found, Sheffield Academic Press, Sheffield, pp. 406–420.

19. SIMPSON M, JACOBS P M and JONES F R (1991), *Composites*, **22**, 105.
20. GRIFFITHS A A (1920), *Phil Trans R. Soc.*, London, **A221**, 163.
21. BARTENEV G M (1970), *The Structure and Mechanical Properties of Inorganic Glasses*, Groningen, Walters-Noordhoff.
22. METCALFE A G and SCHMITZ G K (1972), *Glass Tech.*, **13**, 5.
23. HAND R J and SEDDON A B (1997), *Phys. Chem. Glasses*, **381**, 11.
24. AVESTON J, KELLY A and SILLWOOD J M (1980), Long-term strength of glass reinforced plastics in wet environments, in *Advances in Composite Materials*, vol 1, eds Bunsel *et al.*, Paris, Pergamon, pp. 556–568.
25. TSUI S-W and JONES F R (1989), *Plastics, Rubber, Process Applications*, **11**, 141–146.
26. CHARLES R J (1958), *J. Appl. Phys.*, **29**, 1549.
27. KELLY A and MCCARTNEY L N (1981), *Proc. R. Soc. Lond.*, **A374**, 475–489.
28. WEIBULL W (1951), *J. Appl. Mech.*, **18**, 293–297.
29. SHAN Y and LIAO K (2001), *Composites B*, **32B**, 355–363.
30. AVESTON J and SILLWOOD J M (1982), *J. Mater. Sci.*, **17**, 3491–3498.
31. LAVOIE J A, REIFSNIDER K L, RENSHAW A J and MITTEN W A (2000), *Int. J. Fatigue*, **22**, 467–480.
32. REIFSNIDER K L (1992), Use of mechanistic life prediction methods for the design of damage tolerant composite material systems ASTM STP 1157, Philadelphia, PA, 205–223.
33. JONES F R, ROCK J W and WHEATLEY A R (1983), *Composites*, **14**, 262.
34. JONES F R, ROCK J W and BAILEY J E (1983), *J. Mater. Sci.*, **18**, 1059.
35. HOGG P J (1983), *Composites*, **14**, 254–261.
36. HOGG P J and HULL (1989), *Progress in Rubber and Plastics Technology*, **5**, 136–137.
37. CHENG T H, WANG D and JONES F R (1993), *Composites Science Technology*, **48**, 89–96.
38. JONES F R (1989), *J. Strain Analysis*, **24**, 223.
39. JONES F R (1998), Designing composites for durability in aqueous and corrosive environments, in *Proc. of Conf. on Designing Cost Effective Composites*, London, I Mech Eng, pp. 65–82.
40. SEKINE H and BEAUMONT P W R (1998), *Compos. Sci. Tech.*, **58**, 1659–1665.
41. COCKRAM D R (1981), *Glass Tech.*, **22**, 211–214.
42. JONES F R and ROCK J W (1983), *J. Mater. Sci. Lett.*, **2**, 415–418.
43. FOX P G (1977), Mechanisms of environmentally sensitive cracking in glasses, in *Proc. Congr. on Mechanisms of Environmental Stress Cracking, Metals Soc.*, London, pp. 268–282.
44. SHEARD P A (1986), PhD Thesis, Surrey University, UK.
45. MARSHALL G P and HARRISON D (1982), *Plastics, Rubber, Proc. Applic.*, **2**, 269.
46. ROCK J W and JONES F R (1985), Nucleation and growth of cracks in GRP under stress corrosion conditions. *Proc. 5th International Conference on Composite Materials (ICCM5)*, ed. Harrigan *et al.*, AIME, Philadelphia, pp. 1453–1462.
47. CADDOCK B D, EVANS K E and HULL D (1983), *J. Mater. Sci.*, **22**, 3368–3372.
48. JONES F R, ROCK J W and WHEATLEY A R (1983), *J. Mater. Sci. Lett.*, **2**, 519.
49. HOWARD A and PARRATT N J (1985), *Life Prediction for Aromatic Polyamide Reinforcements, in ICCM5*, ed. W Harrington *et al.* The Metallurgical Society, Warrendale, PA, USA, pp. 277–292.
50. HORIO M, KANEDA T, ISHIKANA S and SHIMAMURA K (1984), *J. Fibre Sci. Tech. (Japan)*, **40**, 1285.
51. VAN DINGENEN J L J, *Gel spun High-Performance Polyethylene Fibres in High-performance Fibres*, ed. J W S Hearle, Woodhead, Cambridge UK, Ch. 3, pp. 62–92.
52. *Proceedings of Plastics for Pipeline Renovation and Corrosion Protection*, Plastics and Rubber Institute, London, 1985 (Various authors).
53. BRYDSON J A (1988), *Plastics Materials*, 5th Edn, London, Butterworth.
54. SCHULTE K L (1999), *Cyclic Mechanical Loading on Reinforced Plastics Durability*, ed. G Pritchard, Woodhead, Cambridge, UK, Ch 5, pp. 151–185.
55. SCHULTE K, MULKERS A, BERG H D and SCHOKE H (1997), Environmental influence on the fatigue behaviour of amorphous glass/thermoplastic matrix composites, in *International Conf. on Fatigue of Composites*, Paper. Eds S Degallaix, C Bathias and R Fongeres, pp. 339–346.
56. WEATHERHEAD R G (1980), *FRP Technology, Fibre Reinforced Resin Systems*, London, Applied Science.
57. BAILEY J E, CURTIS P T and PARVIZI A (1979), *Proc. Roy. Soc., Lond., A*, **366**, 599.
58. OGIN S L and SMITH P A (1987), *ESA Journal*, **11**, 45–60.

5

The effect of the interface on the fatigue performance of fibre composites

C. Galiotis and C. Koimtzoglou, Institute of Chemical Engineering and High Temperature Processes, Foundation for Research and Technology, Greece and Materials Department, University of Patras, Greece

5.1   Introduction

The effect of interface on the fatigue performance of fibre-reinforced composites, as well as the effect of fatigue loading on the interface integrity is reviewed in this chapter. Specific factors that affect the fibre/matrix interface characteristics like the fibre surface treatment, the fibre sizing and the presence of interface modifiers are discussed in the light of fatigue performance. In general terms, it can be argued that any improvement of the fibre/matrix adhesion brought about by modification of one or more of the parameters mentioned above results in the enhancement of the fatigue performance of a broad range of composite materials. However, this overall improvement has not been adequately quantified and very few analytical models exist that relate certain interface characteristics with one or more fatigue parameters. It is also shown that environmental ageing has a detrimental effect on the fatigue performance due primarily to the deterioration of the properties of constituent materials, as well as to interfacial weakening. Finally, there is very little information as to how the fatigue loading itself affects the interface integrity prior to catastrophic failure of the composite component, and additional research in this area is required.

5.2   Effect of interface parameters on fatigue performance

To assess the effect of interface parameters upon the fatigue performance, one needs to have a good understanding of how the same parameters affect the static mechanical properties. Unfortunately, in spite of a significant volume of work reported in this area over the last 30 years, the link between interface parameters and specific mechanical properties or damage characteristics is not, as yet, clear (Kim and Mai, 1998). Hashin (1990) introduced the very important concept of the 'imperfect interface' and showed that its presence has negligible effect on the axial Young's modulus and moderate effect on axial Poisson's ratio, whereas, it can affect significantly the shear and transverse moduli. Furthermore, Mahiou and Beakou

(1998) showed by means of modelling that an imperfect interface in unidirectional glass/epoxy composites has a significant effect upon the angle at which the change of the failure mode occurs. It is reasonable therefore to assume that any deterioration of the integrity of the interface under dynamic conditions will mainly affect the off-axis and shear properties and corresponding damage development. There is also experimental evidence that debonding along the fibre is an active fatigue damage mechanism in unidirectional 0° carbon fibre-reinforced epoxy composites but it is of subcritical nature as if triggered by fibre fracture (Gamstedt, 2000). The interaction between the fibre strength distribution and debond rate can affect the fracture behaviour under dynamic loading and in some cases can increase the tensile fracture toughness (Gamstedt, 2000). In cross-ply carbon fibre/epoxy composite laminates, however, Song and Otani (1997) came to the conclusion that high fibre/matrix interface strength is needed for effective prevention of crack initiation and propagation in fatigue.

5.2.1   Fibre surface treatment/modification

It is well known that adhesion can be attributed to five main mechanisms that can occur at the interface either in isolation or in combination, to produce a fibre/matrix 'bond': adsorption and wetting, inter-diffusion, electrostatic attraction, chemical bonding, and mechanical adhesion (Hull and Clyne, 1996). One of the most direct ways to change the interfacial properties is by fibre surface treatment/modification, which has a minimal effect upon the mechanical integrity of fibres.

5.2.1.1   Carbon fibre composites

The electrolytic anodization process adds surface oxygens and other species to the carbon fibre surface. In fact, the external highly graphitized fibre surface is normally removed by the surface treatment (Kelly and Zweben, 2000) and this allows a more effective grafting of chemically bound oxygen. Drzal and Madhukar (1993) examined the failure path before and after surface treatment on model composites by means of post-interfacial failure ultra-microtome sectioning and TEM observation. The results showed that in the 'as-received' fibres, cohesive interface failure through the outer layer is present whereas pure interfacial failure results after surface treatment. Thus, in addition to promoting chemical bonding, the fibre surface treatment also removes the initial defect-laden surface and leaves behind a structurally sound surface, i.e. one which is capable of sustaining high mechanical loads without failure (Drzal and Madhukar, 1993). The same authors examined experimentally the effect of surface treatment on the mechanical properties of full carbon fibre composites and concluded that the fibre/matrix adhesion affects composite properties in different ways depending on the state of stress created at the fibre/matrix interface. For example, regarding on-axis properties, the tensile strength increases with increasing interfacial shear strength only as long as the failure is interfacial. If the interfacial strength is low, the composite fails prematurely because of cumulative weakening of the material. On the other hand, when the interfacial bond strength is high, the failure mode changes from fibre/matrix debonding to matrix cracking and the composite behaves like a brittle material, i.e. it becomes 'notch-sensitive' which may have a detrimental effect on its longitudinal tensile strength (Drzal and Madhukar, 1993).

In addition to the tensile loading, Drzal and Madhukar (1993) examined also other modes of composite loading. They found that the compressive strength increases with increasing fibre/matrix adhesion (Drzal and Madhukar, 1993) due primarily to (i) the prevention of local microbuckling due to the high adhesion, (ii) the presence of the brittle interface layer which provides additional lateral support to the graphite fibres, and (iii) the prevention of local delamination due to the high transverse strength resulting from Poisson's effects (Drzal and Madhukar, 1993). Regarding off-axis properties, the transverse tensile strength increases with increasing fibre/matrix adhesion. The transverse flexural test results indicated that fibre/matrix adhesion has a stronger influence on the transverse flexural strength than on the transverse tensile strength. The effect of fibre/matrix adhesion on the G_{IIc} and the observed failure modes was shown to be a primary failure mode change from interfacial failure to the matrix failure. When the interfacial strength approaches the matrix strength, the additional increase in the ISS may not yield much improvement in the fracture toughness of the composite (Drzal and Madhukar, 1993).

Lesko et al. (1994) have reported the effect of fibre surface treatment on the static and fatigue mechanical performance of notched cross-ply carbon/epoxy composites. The results concerning the effect of fibre/matrix adhesion on the mechanical properties (Lesko et al., 1994) are in agreement with those reported by Drzal and Madhukar (1993), while the additional surface treatment brings about a slight increase in life under dynamic tension–compression loading (Lesko et al., 1994).

Deng and Ye (1999) have reported tension–tension results on unidirectional carbon/epoxy composites with a strong fibre/matrix adhesion. At high applied stresses there is a marked improvement in the fatigue life as compared to untreated fibre composites, whereas at low applied fatigue stresses the effect of fibre/matrix adhesion on the fatigue life appears less pronounced (Deng and Ye, 1999). In other words, the S–N curve of the specimens with surface treated fibres is shifted to higher values of applied stress but with an additional slight increase in the slope as compared to the untreated fibre case, which confirms the dependence of the fatigue behaviour to the fibre surface treatment (Deng and Ye, 1999).

Goutianos and Peijs (2001) investigated the effect of fibre surface treatment on the fatigue damage mechanisms of model carbon/epoxy composites. In contrast to treated fibre composites, untreated fibres show significant debonding and a less fibre–fibre interaction. In corresponding full composites such a deflected fracture path is indicative for a brush-like failure process, while in the case of treated fibres with strong fibre–fibre interaction, a brittle mode of failure is expected (Goutianos and Peijs, 2001). These results come to strengthen those reported earlier by Gamstedt (2000).

5.2.1.2   Glass fibre composites

In contrast to the volume of work reported on carbon fibre composites, there is not much work concerning the effect of surface treatment on the fatigue performance of glass fibre composites. Hachiya et al. (1999) reported an average fatigue life increase by 5 times for the modified glass/PPE as compared to the unmodified glass/PPE. The modification of the glass/PPE interface involved chemical treatment of both fibres and matrix. In particular, the glass fibres were treated with an aminotrimethylsilane coupling agent and therefore their surface was covered by amino groups as shown in Fig. 5.1 (Hachiya et al., 1999). On the other hand, PPE has two end groups one of which is hydroxy and the other a methyl end group as shown in Fig. 5.1 (Hachiya et al., 1999). By aminating the methyl radical end group and by reacting it with maleic anhydride, an anhydrite end group forms in PPE as shown in Fig. 5.2 (Hachiya et al., 1999). As a consequence, a chemical bond between the amino group on the surface of glass fibres and the anhydride on the end of PPE is created (Hachiya et al., 1999).

Work done on undamaged and impact damaged cross-ply glass epoxy laminates by Kessler and Bledzki (2000) showed once more that good fibre/matrix adhesion results in more damage tolerant materials. The glass fibres used for this work had three different

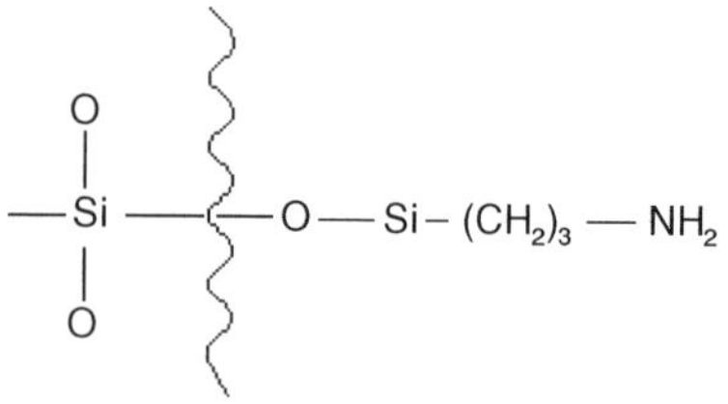

Fig. 5.1   Surface chemical structure of modified glass fibre.

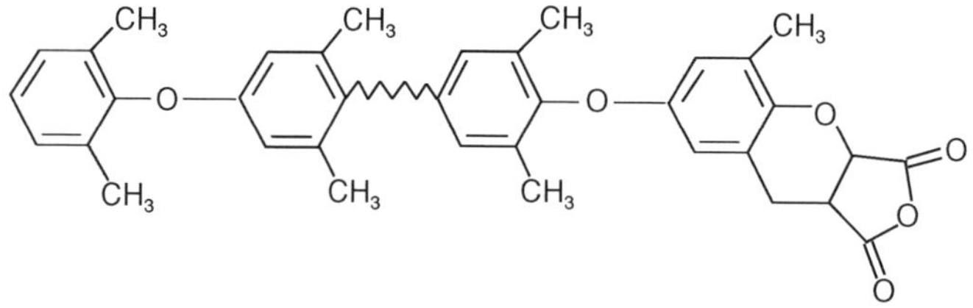

Fig. 5.2   End group chemical structure of modified PPE.

surface treatments: (i) an epoxy dispersion on the base of bisphenol A as binder and a γ-aminopropyltriethoxy silane coupling agent for good fibre/matrix adhesion, (ii) as in (i), but the epoxy binder was substituted by a polyurethane dispersion for medium adhesion, and (iii) a high molecular polyethylene (PE) dispersion for poor adhesion. The results from cyclic loading showed that the strength of the undamaged laminates with PE-treated fibres is lower compared to the other materials. Taking into account the dynamic modulus, the laminates with poor fibre/matrix adhesion show an early stiffness reduction with increasing cycle number. This indicates the high rate of damage growth for PE-treated fibre plates that confirms the low damage tolerance of these materials. Also using the temperature rise during the test as an indirect measurement for the energy absorption, it was shown that the temperature increases faster in the laminates with the PE-treated fibres corresponding to the higher accumulated dissipated energy (Kessler and Bledzki, 2000).

5.2.1.3   Natural fibre composites

In composites with natural fibres like jute and flax the main problem is their high level of moisture absorption, poor wettability, and insufficient adhesion between untreated fibres and polymer matrix (Gassan and Bledzki, 1997). Regarding mechanical behaviour, the tensile strength of these fibres is only 20–50% of that of E-glass fibres (Table 5.1) (Gassan, 1999). For this class of material, the work done over the years to improve the interfacial adhesion to common matrices has resulted in surface treatment processes which in some cases have an effect upon the fibre strength itself (Gassan & Bledzki, 1997, 1999). For example, treating jute fibres with a NaOH solution improves the mechanical properties of the fibres, although the creation of a rough fibre surface does not promote the fibre/matrix adhesion (Gassan & Bledzki, 1999).

Table 5.1   Physical properties of some natural fibres (Gassan and Bledzki, 1999)

	Jute	Flax	Sisal	Ramie	Cotton
Density (g/cm³)	1.3	1.5	1.5	–	1.5–1.6
Elongation at break (%)	1.5–1.8	2.7–3.2	2.0–2.5	3.6–3.8	7.0–8.0
Tensile strength (MPa)	393–773	343–1035	511–635	400–938	287–597
Young's modulus (GPa)	26.5	27.6	9.4–22.0	–	5.5–12.6

Gassan and Bledzki (1997) attempted to strengthen the jute/polypropylene (PP) interface by treating the jute fibre with a maleic anhydride (MAH) coupling agent. The acidic anhydride groups of the MAH coupling agent can form secondary (hydrogen), as well as primary chemical bonds with the hydroxyl groups of the flax fibre. Furthermore, the long PP chains of the MAH-PP coupling agent promote the thermodynamic wetting of the fibre by the viscous polymer and this can increase the adhesion strength by increasing the work of adhesion (Gassan and Bledzki, 1997). Under dynamic loading the improved fibre/matrix adhesion gave rise to a higher damage resistance. This was demonstrated by a shift in the initiation of damage towards higher values of maximal stress and by a decrease of the progress of damage with increasing load cycles. Without the coupling agent the same jute/polypropylene composites showed a virtually identical behaviour as regards dynamic strength, independent of the fibre volume fraction (Gassan and Bledzki, 1997). Further experimental results published by Gassan and Bledzki (2000) showed that in tension–tension fatigue tests ($R = 0.1$) a strong interface leads to a higher dynamic modulus and to a reduction in stiffness degradation with increasing load cycles. However, the specific damping capacity is found to be higher for the composites with poorly bonded fibres (Gassan and Bledzki, 2000) through the promotion of extensive interfacial slippage in the case of the untreated fibres.

The effect of natural fibre type has also been investigated recently by Gassan (2002). The fibres used were jute and flax embedded in three different types of matrix: epoxy resin, unsaturated polyester and polypropylene matrix. Also, in order to alter the interfacial adhesion different surface treatments were employed depending on the matrix material. In short, MAH-PP treatment was used for the PP-based composites, and silane treatment for the unsaturated polyester composites. For the epoxy-based composites the influence of fibre strength and modulus were studied instead. The quality of fibre/matrix adhesion was shown to have a significant effect on the fatigue behaviour of brittle polyester and ductile polypropylene composites. For example, in the case of untreated woven jute/polyester or polypropylene composites the critical load for damage initiation is lower and the rate of damage propagation is higher than the corresponding treated materials (Gassan, 2002).

5.2.1.4   Polyethylene (PE) fibre composites

High performance (HP) polyethylene fibres (PE) have been employed as reinforcement over the last 15 years. Applications include biomedical acrylic resin composites (Andreopoulos et al., 1991), or hybrid PE-carbon composites for applications requiring enhanced damage tolerance particularly under impact conditions (Peijs and de Kok, 1993). The poor PE fibre/matrix adhesion is quite often responsible for the rather inferior performance of these composites (Andreopoulos et al., 1991).

The hybrid composites, HP–PE and carbon fibres embedded in epoxy resin, developed by Peijs and de Kok (1993), have also been studied under fatigue conditions. In order to study the influence of HP–PE adhesion on the performance of the hybrids, composites incorporating untreated and chromic-acid treated PE fibres were used. The improved adhesion of polyolefins to epoxy resin after acid etching is related to a number of factors such as (a) fibre surface roughening, (b) increase of surface free energy, which promotes resin wetability and (c) the introduction of specific functional groups, giving rise to enhanced chemical/physical interactions at the interface (Mercx *et al.*, 1993). The results indicated that the existence of synergistic or hybrid effects depends on both hybrid design and the interfacial bond strength of the HP–PE fibres. After surface treatment, the fatigue performance of HP–PE composites becomes more fibre-dominated than interface-dominated. The *S–N* slopes for all the hybrids are lower than those of the corresponding plain carbon fibre composites whereas the slopes of the various types of hybrids are all identical. Moreover, the fatigue life of all hybrids examined by Peijs and de Kok is shorter compared to that of carbon fibre composites. A notable exception is presented in the case of the intermingled hybrid incorporating treated HP–PE fibres; the *S–N* slope is even lower than the other hybrid composites while, compared to carbon fibre composites, the fatigue life is lower for high levels of applied stress (low cycle fatigue) and higher for low levels of applied stress (high cycle fatigue) (Peijs and de Kok, 1993).

5.2.2   Fibre sizing/coating

While oxidative fibre surface treatments offer improved composite strength over non-surface-treated systems, the improvements are limited to particular levels of applied treatment (Drzal *et al.*, 1992). Moreover, there exists no *a priori* knowledge of appropriate surface-treatment levels and their effects on composite properties. Sizing or coating the fibres with a material, usually a polymer, presents a potentially more precise method of controlling/designing the interface properties of a composite. Here one can add a known volume of a third material with specific properties to bridge the fibre and the matrix, the so-called interphase, thus ridding one of the unknowns of oxidative surface treatments. Many questions remain regarding the critical properties and dimensions of the interphase that are necessary to bring about the optimum laminate performance for all states of deformation (static and dynamic) (Lesko *et al.*, 1994).

As in the case of fibre surface treatment, modelling work can provide some clues regarding the effect of fibre coating on the composite fatigue performance. Zhifei and Limin in 2000 modelled the interfacial debonding of coated-fibre-reinforced composites under tension–tension cyclic loading. The results showed that the higher the strength of coating materials, the faster the debond rate dl/dN and the longer the debond length. Also, the debond rate dl/dN increases with the increase of coating thickness t, when the strength of the coating is higher than that of the matrix material. Conversely, the debond rate dl/dN decreases with the increase in the coating thickness t when the strength of the coating is lower than that of the matrix material (Zhifei and Limin, 2000).

5.2.2.1   Carbon fibre composites

Lesko *et al.* in 1994 reported the effect of a diglicidyl ether of *bis*phenol-A, named as sizing 'A', and the effect of a thermoplastic poly(*N*-vinyl pyrrolidone), named as sizing 'O', on the mechanical properties and dynamic response of circular-notched cross-ply carbon/epoxy composites. The presence of the thermoplastic poly(*N*-vinylpyrrolidone) 'O' sizing gives rise to a more ductile interphase as compared to that of sizing 'A' and improves the compressive performance of the sized 'O' Apollo fibre/HC 9106-3 epoxy composites. The poly(*N*-vinyl pyrrolidone) sizing produces interphase morphology distinct from, and of greater extent than, that of the epoxy size. It is believed that these morphological differences are responsible for the more ductile response in compression as illustrated by the increased failure strains observed in interphase characterization and laminate tests (Lesko *et al.*, 1994). Under tension–compression cyclic loading, the use of the 'O' sizing brings about an improvement of two orders of magnitude in fatigue life as compared to the 'A' sized fibre composites. Failure initiation manifested itself with the development of longitudinal splits emanating from the edges of the hole, yet no evidence of fibre buckling is observed at the same location where the stress concentrations are highest. Higher resistance to fibre buckling is observed compared to the system with the 'A' sizing, while the onset of compressive failure of the system with the 'O' sizing is delayed during cyclic loading. One should take away from the evidence presented that high static interface strength, reached in this case by using the 'A' sizing, may not be translated to improved long term performance (Lesko *et al.*, 1994).

The effect of a tough polymer, phenoxy poly(hydroxyether), and that of an extremely brittle polymer, poly(vinyl pyrrolidone), as sizing agents on the tension–compression fatigue performance of carbon/vinyl ester matrix composites was investigated by Broyles *et al.* (1998). The results showed that the slopes of S–N curves are reduced for both sized systems relative to the unsized fibre case whereas large differences are observed at the fatigue limit of the composites. The poly(hydroxyether) sizing (tough polymer) brought about a 60% improvement in the fatigue limit compared to the unsized composite, while the use of poly(vinyl pyrrolidone) (extremely brittle polymer) results only in a 20% corresponding increase of the fatigue limit (Broyles *et al.*, 1998).

Even though sizing seems to affect positively the dynamic response of composites, the sizing may or may not diffuse into the matrix resin during the cure reaction and this may or may not result in a gradient in the chemical composition at the vicinity of the fibre surface. Robertson *et al.* (1999) used a series of ductile poly(hydroxyether) sizings which exhibited different levels of diffusion into the matrix material. The effect of an unmodified poly(hydroxyether), a carboxy-modified poly(hydroxyether) which is less soluble in the resin than the unmodified poly(hydroxyether), and a poly(hydroxyether ethanolamine), a sizing which does not diffuse in the matrix during cure, on the dynamic response of carbon fibre/vinyl ester matrix composites was investigated (Robertson *et al.*, 1999). Cross-ply notched composites with unsized and sized fibres with a carboxy-modified poly(hydroxyether) and poly(hydroxyether ethanolamine) were tested under fully-reversed ($R = -1$) fatigue tests. The slopes of the S–N curves decrease for both sized systems relative to the unsized fibre systems. Addition of poly(hydroxyether ethanolamine) to the composite improves the fatigue durability by about 25%. However, at low cycle fatigue, and consequently higher stress levels, these composites do not outperform those produced with unsized fibres. It may be possible that, at lower stress levels, the weak interface of the sized system facilitates the growth of splits at the notch, which dilute the effects of stress concentration and, therefore, the stress levels in the material are not high enough to precipitate compression failure. In contrast, the addition of a very small amount of carboxy-modified poly(hydroxyether) sizing in the composite, improves by about 50% the fatigue limit over the unsized fibre case (Robertson *et al.*, 1999).

5.2.2.2   Glass fibre composites

Keush *et al.* (1998) working with glass fibre composites investigated the effect of six different sizing systems on the mechanical properties of unidirectional composites. The effect of two of them that exhibited 'good' (type I) and 'reduced' (type II) fibre/matrix adhesion on the tension–tension fatigue performance of cross-ply composites loaded parallel to the 0° fibres, was also examined. Each ply was treated preferentially with different types of sizing and the results in terms of fatigue life performance were ranked as follows (a) all plies with fibres sized with the system I, (b) 0° plies with sizing I and 90° plies with sizing II (c) 0° plies with sizing II and 90° plies with sizing I, and (d) all plies with sizing II (Keush *et al.*, 1998). These results also come in agreement with Andersen *et al.* (1996) who states that in fatigue of multidirectional laminates, the 0° ply controls the fatigue life of the entire laminate when interpreted in terms of the initial peak strain (Andersen *et al.*, 1996).

Gassan (2000) also examined the effect of sizing upon tension–tension fatigue performance of cross-ply glass/epoxy laminates. Three different types of polymeric sizing were employed: a specially developed epoxy compatible sizing (EP) for strong fibre/matrix adhesion, a polyethylene sizing (PE) for weak adhesion and a commercial epoxy-compatible sizing. The epoxy sizing developed by the authors was based on an uncured *bis*phenol A epoxy binder which contains γ-aminopropyltriethoxysilane, while the polyethylene sizing was pure high molecular weight polyethylene (Gassan, 2000). The *S–N* curve for the 'EP' sized fibre composites is shifted to approx. 30% higher applied maximum loads for a given load cycle compared to the corresponding 'PE' sized composites, while the slope remains unaffected. The damage, as measured by stiffness reduction in the laminates after 4000 load cycles, is more significant for the composites with 'PE' and commercial epoxy-sized fibres than found for the 'EP' sized composites. The loss energy for composites with poor fibre/matrix adhesion results in significantly higher amounts of consumed energy during a single stress–strain loop (compared at 4000 load cycles) than those composites containing well-bonded fibres (Gassan, 2000).

5.2.3   Interface modifiers

A clear disadvantage of PP as a matrix material for composite applications is its apolar character, which leads to limited wettability and poor fibre/matrix adhesion. Generally, silane coupling agents are successfully used as adhesion promoters between glass fibres and thermosets or polar polymers such as polyamides. Because of their low polarity and lack of reactive groups these coupling agents have, however, limited interaction with polyolefin matrices. Modification of the matrix, through functionalization of the polymer has proven to be very effective in enhancing interfacial bonding in both short- and continuous-fibre-reinforced PP composites. Because of their increased polarity and reactivity, maleic-anhydride or acrylic acid grafted polyolefins are absorbed at the polar fibre surface if an appropriate sizing, e.g. γ-aminopropyltriethoxysilane, is applied. Generally, only small amount of these polar PPs are needed to achieve significant improvements in interfacial bonding (van den Oever and Peijs, 1998). Figure 5.3 (Gamstedt *et al.*, 1999) illustrates possible interfacial bonding after maleic anhydride modification (Gamstedt *et al.*, 1999).

Van den Oever and Peijs studying the influence of maleic-anhydride modified polypropylene (MA–PP) on fatigue behaviour of glass fibre/PP composites showed that, in the case of longitudinal tension–tension fatigue, the incurred improved interfacial bonding results only in a slightly higher absolute fatigue strength. Moreover, the slopes of *S–N* curves for both the PP and the MA–PP composite are similar, meaning that the use of MA–PP has no significant effect on the fatigue sensitivity of these materials. In the case of off-axis (shear or transverse) fatigue, improved adhesion as a result of the use of MA–PP does result in a significantly higher fatigue strength. However, although the absolute fatigue stresses are markedly improved by chemical modification of the matrix, again the fatigue sensitivity, i.e. the slope of *S–N* curve, is not significantly affected. Improved adhesion also played an important role in controlling the damage during fatigue life. For all MA–PP base composites no significant modulus reduction during life was measured and the stiffness decreased only

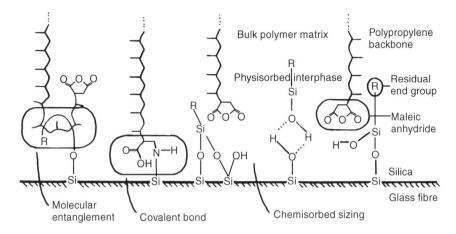

Fig. 5.3   Possible interfacial bonding after maleic anhydride modification.

just prior to failure. On the other hand, for PP-based specimens, a modulus decay is observed for all fibre orientations, indicating that these composites accumulate a significant amount of damage before final failure (van den Oever and Peijs, 1998). A schematic illustration of micro- to macro-relation for these composites proposed by Gamstedt *et al.* (1999) is shown in Fig. 5.4 (Gamstedt *et al.*, 1999) whereas Fig. 5.5 (Gamstedt *et al.*, 1999) shows the adhesive and cohesive failure types attributed to poor and good fibre/matrix adhesion respectively (Gamstedt *et al.*, 1999).

5.3   Effect of other parameters that indirectly affect the interface on fatigue performance

Until now, we have reported as to how the fatigue performance of composites can be dependent on all those parameters that directly affect the interface integrity. However, other secondary parameters such as the curing temperature and time of cure, the cooling rate and the post-curing process can also alter the interfacial efficiency and, hence, possibly the fatigue characteristics. Also, environmental parameters such as the level of humidity, the temperature of operation, the amount of UV radiation, possible solvent attack, etc. or combination of these, can affect severely the overall performance and, of course, the interface integrity. Unfortunately, it is not always clear how to distinguish between interface-induced deterioration of the fatigue performance from that caused by material degradation. In the section below, we will report on all related studies for which the interface has been singled out as a possible parameter that can affect the fatigue performance.

5.3.1   Effect of curing process

The effect of degree of post-curing on the mechanical properties and the fatigue perform-ance of woven glass/polyester composites has been studied by Elleuch *et al.* (1999). Microindentation experiments showed that a rigid interface (brittle failure) is obtained in the case of post-cured materials while weak interface (progressive failure) is obtained in the case of non-post-cured materials. The fatigue life of post-cured composite is clearly higher

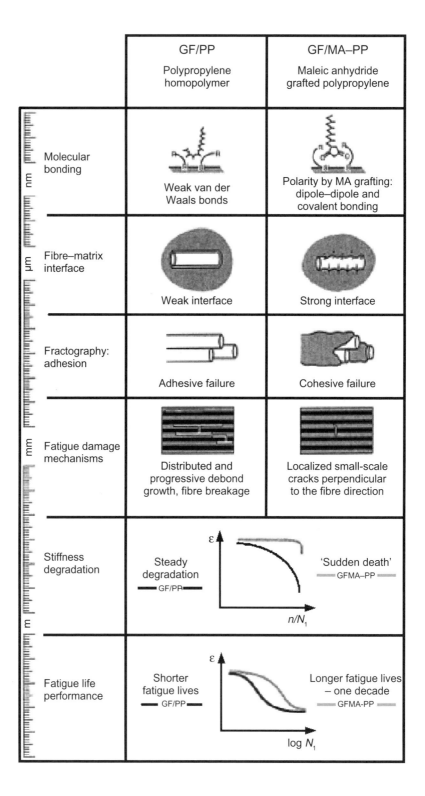

Fig. 5.4   Schematic illustration of micro-macro relation.

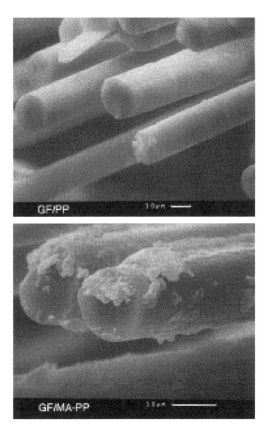

Fig. 5.5   Fractographic scanning electron micrographs for glass-fibre/PP and glass-fibre/MA-PP.

than those that have not been subjected to post-curing. It was therefore assumed that the post-curing improves the resistance of interface and hence the fatigue life even though the optimization of interface characteristics by post-curing is very difficult (Elleuch *et al.*, 1999). A strong interface in the case of post-cured composites results in limited debonding and quite high local stress concentration near the ends. Thus cracks are propagated rapidly and, as a result, brittle fracture is observed. On the other hand, a weak interface in the case of non-post-cured composites results in stress redistribution over a larger region around longitudinal bundles. This constitutes a kind of barrier against crack propagation and leads to a more progressive failure (Elleuch *et al.*, 1999).

Regarding process parameters such as moulding temperature, residence time at melt temperature, and cooling rate, it has been shown that they strongly affect the matrix morphology as well as the fibre/matrix interface properties of the end product (Vu-Khanh and Denault, 1991 and 1993). El Kadi and Denault, studying the effects of processing conditions on the mechanical properties of carbon fibre/PEEK composites found no definite effect of the various moulding parameters on the fatigue life of the laminates (El Kadi and Denault, 2001). Even though his results were preliminary, they are in agreement with those presented by Trotignon and Verdu, who showed that the variation in the matrix properties seem to play no major role in the fatigue life of the composite (Trotignon and Verdu, 1993). On the other hand, Bureau *et al.* (2002) studying the interlaminar fatigue crack propagation in glass fibre/polypropylene composites under dynamic loading found a major influence of the fibre/matrix interface and of the matrix morphology on the crack propagation resistance. Three different moulding conditions are used for the preparation of the composites: (a) a mould condition that bears 'normal' designation, (b) a moulding process which retains moulding temperature and holding time same as in case (a) but with a 20 times slower cooling rate and, finally, (c) a low temperature process with four times greater holding time compared to the others but with a cooling rate same as in case (a). The distribution of the soft amorphous PP phase in the semi-crystalline PP matrix appears to be the controlling parameter determining the fracture and fatigue resistance of the composite since interlaminar fatigue crack propagation occurred in the ductile amorphous-phase-rich regions (Bureau *et al.*, 2002). Under the 'normal' moulding condition, interspherulitic regions with strong amorphous material, strong fibre/matrix interactions due to the concentration of the amorphous phase near the fibre/matrix interface and good fibre dispersion are obtained. Fatigue cracks propagate in the matrix very close to the fibre/matrix interface while the interlaminar fatigue crack propagation resistance is at its maximum (Fig. 5.6, Bureau *et al.*, 2002). Under slow cooling, the presence of amorphous and hence weaker interspherulitic regions lead to crack propagation through these regions and therefore the interlaminar fatigue crack propagation resistance is considerably lower. Finally, in the low temperature condition, a very fine crystalline structure of the PP matrix and a poor fibre dispersion are obtained, resulting in the lowest flexural and interlaminar shear strength compared to the other curing conditions. Here, the cracks propagate also in the matrix very close to the fibre/matrix interface but with considerably less matrix visible on the fracture surface. In this case, the interlaminar fatigue crack propagation resistance is – not unexpectedly – the lowest among all three conditions tested (Fig. 5.7, Bureau *et al.*, 2002).

5.3.2   Effect of environment

Besides the advantages of high stiffness-to-weight and strength-to-weight ratios over conventional structural materials, composites also offer excellent corrosion resistance to environmental agents. There are numerous applications of these materials in the construction industry and a large volume of work has been reported concerning the environmental degradation of composites under elevated temperature, humidity, UV exposure, etc. In general, the combined environmental effects tend to shorten the fatigue life of composites compared to those that have not been environmentally aged. The observed shortening of life is primarily due to the deterioration in the properties of the constituents, as well as to interfacial weakening (Liao *et al.*, 1998).

A considerable volume of work has examined the effect of immersion in fluids probably due to the extensive use of fibre reinforced plastics in marine and offshore applications. The sorption behaviour of fluid into a polymer composite depends on the type of fluid (i.e. water, acid or base, etc.), the fluid concentration, the chemical structure of the polymer, the temperature, the stress state and the strength of the fibre/matrix interface. Numerous studies have confirmed that the fibre/matrix interface region or interphase plays a crucial role in composite durability in aqueous environments. Improved bonding between the fibre and the matrix (e.g. with the use of coupling agents) tends to delay the corrosion process and minimize the reduction in the mechanical properties. The detrimental effect of fluid absorption on composite matrix seems to be only secondary compared to the damage in the fibres and the fibre/matrix interphase (Liao *et al.*, 1998). In summary, it is evident that fluids can significantly accelerate the degradation process during fatigue and that a more environment-resistant fibre/matrix interphase will result in a material with better fatigue performance (Liao *et al.*, 1998).

Fig. 5.6   SEM micrographs of mode II interlaminar fatigue surfaces obtained for PP/GF composite: (a) at low magnification and (b) high magnification for the NM condition ($da/dN = 1.1 \times 10^{-5}$
mm/cycle, $\Delta G_{//} = 420$ J/m^2). The crack propagation direction is from left to right. Examples of
shear cusp (C) and debris (D) are indicated.

Hancox in 1998 published a review article on the effects of temperature and environment
on the performance of polymer matrix composites. The degradation of fibre/resin interface
due to hygrothermal effects was commonly observed in many papers covered by this
review. In general, fluids can travel along the fibre/matrix interface, preferentially by
capillary attraction, disrupting the bonding between the two components and possibly
causing chemical attack. The damage gives a greater area over which diffusion can occur
and may allow transport of moisture through internal microcracks. Simple interfacial

(a)

(b)

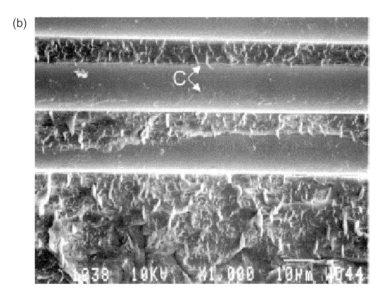

Fig. 5.7   SEM micrographs of mode II interlaminar fatigue surfaces obtained for PP/GF composite: (a) at low magnification and (b) high magnification for the LT condition ($da/dN = 9.1 \times 10^{-4}$ mm/cycle, ΔG_{II}=500 J/m^2). The crack propagation direction is from left to right. Examples of shear cusp (C) are indicated.

damage due to disruption of bonding between the two components may be reversible on drying out. All these processes are enhanced by increasing the temperature as this increases the diffusion rate and rapidity of any chemical attack (Hancox, 1998).

The effect of hygrothermal ageing on fatigue damage in unidirectional glass/epoxy composites has been reported by Vauthier *et al.* (1998). An environment with 60% relative humidity (RH) at two different temperatures, 50 °C and 70 °C, and immersion in distilled water at 60 °C and 90 °C are the different ageing conditions used. The fatigue results show that even with low moisture content in the test environment, a temperature rise has deleterious effects on the material lifetime. In fact, temperature and moisture together always influence the mechanical behaviour of glass reinforcement. The results also show a great discrepancy between ageing in immersion and ageing in conditions of RH. In fact, the latter does not seem to affect clearly the material fatigue behaviour. On the other hand, immersion induced a drastic reduction of properties. But the fact that, in the case of immersion, the critical density of broken fibres leading to macroscopic damage is higher than that of the non-aged composites, indicates better tolerance of the aged material to the first nucleated fibre breaks. This effect can be a consequence of interfacial degradation after ageing in immersion; for example, increased possibility of fibre/matrix debonding at the crack tip would allow stress redistribution at a larger volume. The process of broken fibre interaction will then be slowed down in tandem with the resulting macroscopic crack initiation and propagation. Nevertheless, the overall reduction of properties is linked to the drop in the statistical distribution of the fibre strength after ageing (Vauthier et al., 1998).

The long-term environmental fatigue of pultruded E-glass fibre/vinyl ester matrix composites under flexural loading has been reported by Liao et al. (1999). Four different ageing conditions are used for the specimens, immersion at two salt solutions, 5% and 10%, and immersion in de-ionized water at RT and 75 °C. Fatigue tests are also conducted at different conditions according to the precondition procedure followed for the specimen tested. The results show that, at cyclic loads above 45% of flexural strength (FS), the specimens exhibit the same behaviour when tested in air, in water or in salt solution. In this loading regime, the behaviour depends on load but is independent of environment. The fatigue lives are less than 10^6 cycles in all cases. At cyclic load of 30% FS, however, the results indicate that water and salt solution have a significant detrimental effect on the life of the coupons (a regime of stress and environment dependence). This regime is character-ized with fatigue life beyond 10^7 cycles for dry coupons and within 10^7 cycles for those tested in water environment. The effect of fibre/matrix interfacial damage on fatigue performance is evident in all immersed cases. Examination of the failure surfaces under SEM revealed differences on the fibre surface; typically, more matrix residue adheres to the fibre surface of specimens tested dry (Fig. 5.8, Liao et al., 1999), while 'cleaner' fibre surfaces with much less matrix adhering are seen from specimens failed under environ-mental fatigue (Fig. 5.9, Liao et al., 1999). This difference on the fracture surface indicates that fluid action degrades the adhesion between the fibres and the matrix (Liao et al., 1999). The same observation was also reported by Wanatabe (1979) and Sekine et al. (1988).

The effect of seawater on the fatigue performance of glass fibre/isophthalic polyester composites was studied by Kotsikos et al. (2000). They used acoustic emission (AE) to evaluate the damage accumulation under monotonic four-point bending loading and a significant reduction in strength and stiffness caused by pre-exposure to sea water was detected. Most AE events occur in the 40–60 dB range, associated with matrix cracking and fibre/matrix debonding in both exposed and unexposed specimens, but the number of events is about four times greater in the pre-exposed specimens. This indicated that matrix cracking, fibre/matrix debonding and delamination are strongly influenced by pre-exposure (Kotsikos et al., 2000).

Kotsikos et al. (2000) also carried out cyclic flexure tests on isophthalic polyester glass woven roving laminates combined with seawater exposure. Unexposed laminates show a stiffness plateau after an initial decrease in stiffness when tested with an initial surface strain amplitude. In contrast, pre-exposed laminates exhibit continuous damage accumulation with number of cycles at the same strain level. Furthermore, the damage accumulation rate

Fig. 5.8   Scanning electron micrograph of delamination surface for specimen failed by cycling testing in air.

Fig. 5.9   Scanning electron micrograph of delamination surface for specimen failed in environmental fatigue.

is higher for specimens exposed for 6 months than those exposed for 3 months. Consistent with the small number of AE events of high amplitude (>85 dB), there is little evidence of fibre fracture in unexposed or pre-exposed laminates during fatigue. The increase in intermediate amplitude events (50–80 dB) is related to delamination and debonding and this interpretation is also consistent with similar damage mechanisms observed in microsections of fatigued specimens (Kotsikos *et al.*, 2000).

Gibson *et al.* (2000) attributed the fatigue behaviour of glass/vinyl ester laminates conditioned in seawater to the strong and more hydrolysis resistant fibre/matrix interface. They carried out cyclic four-point bending tests on glass fibre composites that incorporated isophthalic polyester, vinyl ester, and phenolic resin matrices. All specimens are immersed in seawater (under conditions that accelerate water absorption and bring the surface layer close to that pertaining after 1–2 years in sea). Vinyl ester resin laminates show little sensitivity to water conditioning and exhibit the highest fatigue limit. Phenolic laminates are also insensitive to water, but show a lower fatigue limit, which is attributed to initially lower interfacial bond between the glass fibres and the phenolic matrix. Finally, the seawater weakens considerably the initially good interfacial bond of isophthalic polyester composites, the ultimate behaviour of which is found to be similar to that observed for the phenolic laminates in the wet state (Gibson et al., 2000).

Kawai et al. (2001) investigated the high temperature off-axis fatigue behaviour of unidirectional carbon fibre reinforced composites. Unidirectional laminates consisting of AS4/PEEK, T800H/polyimide and T800H-epoxy systems at several reinforcing angles are subjected to tension–tension cyclic loading at ambient and 100 °C temperatures. From the results obtained, the AS4/PEEK composite exhibits the highest fatigue strength of all off-axis angles – except 0° – whereas the fatigue resistance of T800H-polyimide is the lowest. Optical micrographs though of the cross-section of pristine specimens of T800H-polyimide reveal that such an inferior fatigue performance is due to the presence of huge resin-rich regions that are formed during the fabrication process (Kawai et al., 2001). Microscopic post-mortem examination of the failure surfaces of the T800H/Epoxy system revealed extensive debonding at the fibre/matrix interface and presence of matrix debris between fibres. For the AS4/PEEK, the AS4 fibres present at failure surface are mostly surrounded by the PEEK resin regardless of the off-axis angle. Fibre/matrix debonding is not clearly observed for the PEEK system. Considering these results together, it is speculated that the fatigue strength of the fibre/matrix interfaces for AS4/PEEK is higher than that of the T800H-Epoxy. On the other hand, less debris and more matrix residue on fibres can be observed in the T800H/Polyimide system for all off-axis angles, which implies that the fatigue strength of the fibre/matrix interface is higher than that of T800H/Epoxy particularly under off-axis loading conditions. Finally, failure surfaces of T800H/Epoxy at RT show more brittle nature compared with that observed at 100 °C, while this increase of temperature results in the reduction of the fibre/matrix interface strength (Kawai et al., 2001).

Most recently, Komai et al. (2002) examined the effect of dynamic stress waveform and water absorption in angle-ply aramid fibre/epoxy composites. The results show that water absorption decreases the static tensile and fatigue strength, whereas the influence of the stress waveform on the fatigue strength in wet specimens is smaller than in the dry case. The fatigue strength under the negative pulse waveform is slightly higher than that under the positive pulse waveform, for either wet or dry specimens. From SEM observations of the fracture surfaces the failure of dry specimens is attributed to fibre/matrix interfacial debonding (Fig. 5.10, Komai et al., 2002). For the wet specimens, fibre/matrix interfacial debonding is also predominantly present over the fracture surface area (Komai et al., 2002).

5.4   Effect of fatigue loading on interface

The effect of interface on the fatigue performance has already been reviewed in detail. From the information presented in the preceding sections, it is evident that the interface strength plays an important role in the overall performance of the composite material and in the way fatigue-induced damage propagates. In spite of that, there seems to be very little information

(a)

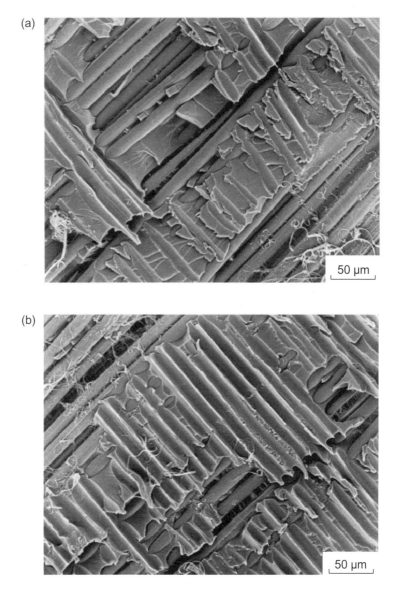

50 µm

(b)

50 µm

Fig. 5.10   Fracture surface of dry specimen (σ_{max} = 140 MPa, f = 1 Hz) (a) negative pulse waveform, (b) positive pulse waveform.

in the literature at to how fatigue loading itself affects the interface integrity prior to catastrophic failure of the composite component. This is in fact an area where additional research is required since, as reported recently by Gamstedt (2000) 'the evolution of stress transfer during fatigue debond growth and the resulting successive breakage of fibres are key mechanisms in polymer-matrix composites that are prone to debonding' (Gamstedt, 2000). Fatigue loading involves a number of parameters that can affect the life of the composite; the brief review that follows will be centred on fatigue variables (load/displacement control, frequency effects, mean stress and amplitude effects, etc.), loading direction

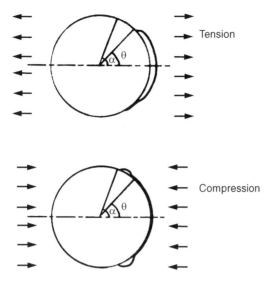

Fig. 5.11   Drawing of crack opening and contact zone for a transversely loaded fibre in tension and compression.

(tensile, compressive or mixed mode) and finally specimen geometry (long/short fibre composites, full/model composites).

Gao and Zhou (1998) reported a numerical analysis of the interface debonding process in fibre/matrix composites under cyclic loading. It is shown that the interface friction plays an important role in resisting debonding by crack growth, but the degradation of interface friction can reduce the friction stress. For the load-controlled case, after certain load cycles, the debonding can be considered as a steady state for which the rate of debonding remains constant. For the displacement-controlled case, after some cycles the debond speed slows down (Gao and Zhou, 1998).

Nayfeh and Abdelrahman (1999) developed a micromechanical model in order to study the effect of frequency on the stress distribution in fibrous composites as a function of induced damage. For the pristine material and for normal stresses acting along the fibres, it is seen that an increase in frequency under displacement control leads to a pronounced stiffening of the material and hence to an increase in the values of stress. This is in contrast to the interfacial shear stress, which seems to be rather insensitive to frequency variations. For the case of a matrix crack transverse to the fibre direction, all figures clearly show comparative increase in the stresses for increasing frequency. Also, all stresses are seen to be more or less similar to those corresponding to the undamaged case in the vicinity of the edge loads, whereas pronounced changes in the stress pattern take place close to the cracks due to the large transfer of load between the matrix and the fibre. Besides such a transfer between the normal stress components, a pronounced variation of the interfacial shear stress with the frequency takes place close to the break. In the case of a broken fibre, the stress transferred from the fibre to the matrix whereas in the case of cracked matrix the opposite occurred. Finally, the interfacial shear stress is more pronounced in the case of the broken fibre, almost double for each frequency, when compared to the case of a cracked matrix in the vicinity of the damage (Nayfeh and Abdelrahman, 1999).

Regarding the effect of the stress ratio R on the fatigue performance of composite

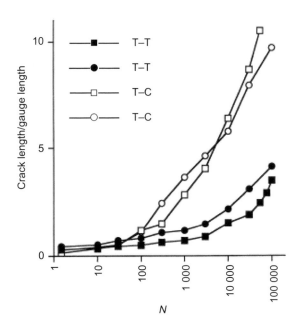

Fig. 5.12   Evolution of transverse crack length in fatigue in T–T and T–C loading with respect to number of elapsed load cycles.

materials, Gamstedt and Sjögren (1999) compared tension–tension (T–T) and tension–compression (T–C) loading modes. They explained why the T–C mode has been shown to be more deleterious than the T–T mode, why S–N curves show significantly steeper slopes for loading waveforms containing compressive load excursions. The experiments are conducted in cross-ply glass/epoxy and single fibre model composites with the fibre perpendicular to the loading direction. Composite laminates containing transverse plies degrade more rapidly in T–C compared to T–T fatigue loading. The reason for this is attributed to the more rapid debond growth around the transverse fibres in T–C loading, due to effective crack tip opening under global compression for sufficiently large debonds (Fig. 5.11, Gamstedt and Sjögren, 1999). Due to the presence of these debonds, transverse cracks initiate at an earlier stage for T–C loading and hence the premature appearance of multiple transverse cracking (Fig. 5.12, Gamstedt and Sjögren, 1999). Unidirectional transverse specimens fail immediately upon formation of the first transverse crack, whereas for multidirectional laminates, the transverse cracks have a detrimental effect on the fatigue performance. A schematic diagram of the link between microscopic to macroscopic fatigue behaviour is shown in Fig. 5.13 (Gamstedt and Sjögren, 1999).

Regarding specimen geometry, Horst et al. (1998) working with short glass fibre composites showed that a radial tensile stress is generated at the interface as a result of fatigue loading (Fig. 5.14, Horst et al., 1998). Corresponding experiments confirm that, in the case of fatigue loading, the fibres are debonded from the matrix, while in a static tensile test the failure occurs at the matrix as detected by a thin layer of matrix material that remains attached to the fibre. Additional finite element modelling (FEM) indicate that, for a purely elastic matrix, the shear stress at the interface is much higher than the tensile stress. However, when the matrix shows an elastic–plastic behaviour the generated tensile stress in the matrix is higher than the interfacial shear stress and can induce fibre/matrix debonding (Horst et al., 1998).

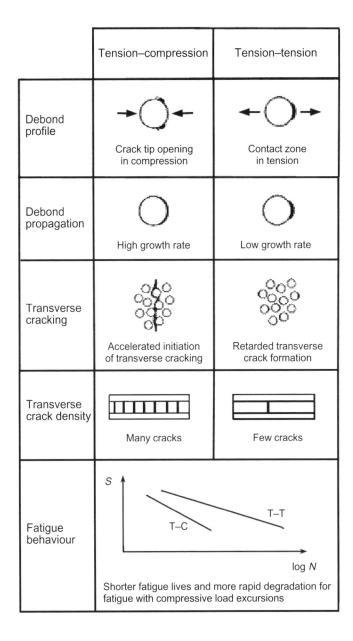

Fig. 5.13 Schematic diagram of link from micromechanics to macroscopic fatigue behaviour.

In 1995 Koimtzoglou *et al.* working with single fibre model composites made a comparative study on the effect of fatigue loading on the micromechanics of the interface. Long and discontinuous single filament composites are subjected to tensile cyclic loading below the matrix endurance fatigue limit. Fragmentation results show no alteration of the saturation level of fibre fractures with the fatigue history, which implies that the strength of the interfacial bond remains unaffected. The consistent increase of the speed of the fragmentation process observed with the number of cycles is attributed to resin hardening and consistent increase of the shear modulus G due to cyclic loading. Similar results are also

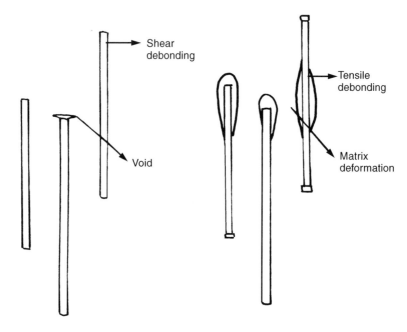

Fig. 5.14   Tensile debonding of the interface, due to the lateral contraction if the matrix is deformed. Left side: initiation of damage at fibre ends. Right side: development of damage of voids.

obtained for the discontinuous fibre model composites, but with a persistent 6% decrease of the saturation level compared to the continuous case. This decrease is attributed to an increase of the ineffective length due to the initial pre-strain procedure in order to introduce the observed discontinuities (Koimtzoglou *et al.*, 1995).

Most recently Koimtzoglou *et al.* presented a study of the stress transfer efficiency in model composites under tensile dynamic loading. The use of laser Raman spectroscopy makes possible the measurement of the axial fibre stress and the derivation of the interfacial shear stress distributions along the fibre length at different numbers of cyclic loads (Fig. 5.15, Koimtzoglou *et al.*, 2003). Regarding the model composites preparation, a procedure is followed in order to end with composites having embedded fibres under different tensile strains (Koimtzoglou *et al.*, 2001). Results from the cyclic loading of model composites with two different 'pre-strain' levels show no effect on the stress transfer efficiency and hence the interfacial properties, while any differences observed are attributed to either changes in the matrix material or the fibre fragmentation procedure that appeared in one of the cases (Koimtzoglou *et al.*, 2003).

5.5   Conclusions

The effect of interface characteristics on the fatigue performance of fibre reinforced composites, as well as the effect of fatigue loading on the interface integrity have been reviewed in this chapter. The interface characteristics that were examined were the fibre surface treatment, the fibre sizing, the presence of interface modifiers in the matrix material and other parameters that indirectly affect the interface integrity like the curing process and the environment. It is clear that any improvement of the fibre/matrix adhesion brought about

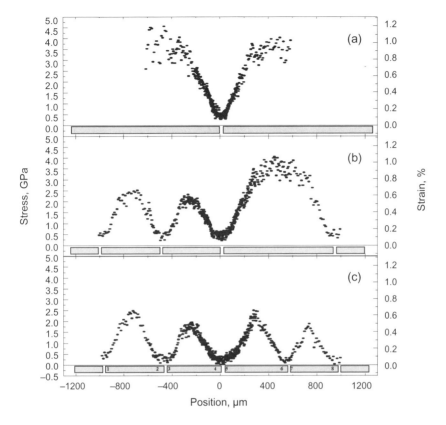

Fig. 5.15   Axial fibre stress (left) and fibre strain (right) along the fibre length after (a) 10^0 cycles, (b) 5×10^5 cycles and (c) 10^6 cycles for case B. The values of stress (strain) were calculated through the corresponding wavenumber dependence by means of LRS.

by modification of one or more of the parameters mentioned above, results in an overall improvement of the fatigue performance of composite materials. Certain limitations are, however, evident; for example, regarding fibre surface treatment, these improvements are only evident for particular levels of applied treatment (Drzal *et al.*, 1992). Moreover, there exists no *a priori* knowledge of the appropriate surface-treatment levels and their effects on composite properties (Lesko *et al.*, 1994). On the other hand, sizing or coating the fibres with an interface-tailored polymeric material, presents a potentially more precise method of controlling/designing the interface characteristics of a composite. Even in this case, certain questions remain regarding the critical properties and dimensions of the applied sizing layer that are necessary to bring about the optimum laminate performance for all states of deformation (static and dynamic) (Lesko *et al.*, 1994). Finally, even though the addition of interface modifiers to the matrix material does not affect significantly the fatigue performance of composites, the resulting improved adhesion played an important role in controlling the damage during fatigue life.

Regarding now the effect of other parameters such as the curing process and the effect of environment, it is not always clear to distinguish between interface-induced alteration of the fatigue performance from that caused by either material enhancement or degradation. For the curing process, the prevailing assumption is that adequate post-curing may contribute to improved fatigue behaviour through interface improvement. On the other hand, the combined environmental effects tend to shorten the fatigue life of composites compared to those that have not been environmentally aged, and this is primarily due to the deterioration in the properties of the constituents, as well as, to interfacial weakening (Liao *et al.*, 1998). Numerous studies have confirmed that the fibre/matrix interface region or interphase plays a crucial role in composite durability in aqueous environments, where improved bonding between the fibre and matrix (e.g. with the use of coupling agents) tends to delay the corrosion process and minimize any decrease in the mechanical properties. The detrimental effect of fluid absorption on the composite matrix seems to be only secondary compared to the damage in the fibres and the fibre/matrix interphase (Liao *et al.*, 1998). In addition, any increase of temperature results in the deterioration of the fatigue performance of composite materials presumably due to the reduction of the fibre/matrix interface strength (Kawai *et al.*, 2001).

Finally, regarding the way fatigue loading itself affects the interface integrity prior to catastrophic failure of the composite component, there seems to be very little information in the literature. This is in fact an area where additional research is required. It can, however, be said that the interface friction plays an important role in resisting debonding by crack growth, but the degradation of interface friction due to cyclic loading can reduce the friction stress. Furthermore, the interfacial shear stresses (ISS) seem to be insensitive to the increase of loading frequency in pristine materials, while the presence of stress induced matrix and fibre cracks can lead to pronounced changes of ISS with frequency (Nayfeh and Abdelrahman, 1999). The deleterious effect of compressive loads in the loading cycle of multidirectional composites is attributed to the more rapid debond growth around the transverse fibres in T–C loading (Gamstedt and Sjögren, 1999). In composites with short fibres, it has been shown that a radial tensile stress is generated at the interface as a result of fatigue loading which can be higher than the interfacial shear stress in matrices showing elastoplastic behaviour and can induce fibre/matrix debonding (Horst *et al.*, 1998). Finally, the use of laser Raman spectroscopy to observe the evolution of stress transfer during fatigue loading on single treated and sized carbon fibre model composites revealed no significant effects on the stress transfer efficiency and hence the interface characteristics (Koimtzoglou *et al.*, 2003).

5.6   References

ANDERSEN S I, LILHOLT H and LYSTRUP Å (1996), *Design of composite structures against fatigue*, Bury St Edmunds, Mechanical engineering publications.

ANDREOPOULOS A G, PAPASPYRIDES C D and TSILIBOUNIDIS S (1991), 'Surface treated polyethylene fibres as reinforcement for acrylic resins', *Biomaterials*, **12**, 83–87.

BROYLES N S, VERGHESE K N E, DAVIS S V, LI H, DAVIS R M, LESKO J J and RIFFLE J S (1998), 'Fatigue performance of carbon fibre/vinyl ester composites: the effect of two dissimilar polymeric sizing agents, *Polymer*, **39**(15), 3417–3424.

BUREAU M N, PERRIN F, DENAULT J and DICKSON J I (2002), Interlaminar fatigue crack propagation in continuous glass fiber/polypropylene composites, *Int. J. Fat*, **24**, 99–108.

DENG S and YE L (1999), 'Influence of fiber-matrix adhesion on mechanical properties of graphite/epoxy composites: I. Tensile, flexure, and fatigue properties', *J. Reinf. Plast. Comp.*, **18**(11), 1021–1040.

DRZAL L T and MADHUKAR M (1993), 'Fibre–matrix adhesion and its relationship to composite mechanical properties', *J. Mater. Sci.*, **28**, 569–610.

DRZAL L T, MADHUKAR M and WATERBURY M C (1992), 'Surface chemical and surface energetic alteration of IM6 carbon fiber surfaces and its effects on composite properties', Proceedings of the Adhesion Society, 15th Annual Meeting, 144–147.

EL KADI H and DENAULT J (2001), 'Effects of processing conditions on the mechanical behaviour of carbon-fiber-reinforced PEEK', *J. Therm. Comp. Mater.*, **14**, 34–53.

ELLEUCH R, ZIDI M and BRADAI C (1999), 'Effects of post-cure on the mechanical properties of woven glass-polyester composite by macro and micro-mechanical methods', *Sci. Eng. Comp. Mater.*, **8**(1), 25–34.

GAMSTEDT E K (2000), 'Effect of debonding and fiber strength distribution on fatigue-damage propagation in carbon fiber-reinforced epoxy', *J. Appl. Polym. Sci.*, **76**, 457–474.

GAMSTEDT E K and SJÖGREN B A (1999), 'Micromechanisms in tension-compression fatigue of composite laminates containing transverse plies', *Comp. Sci. Tech.*, **59**, 167–178.

GAMSTEDT E K, BERGLUND L A and PEIJS T (1999), 'Fatigue mechanisms in unidirectional glass-fibre-reinforced polypropylene', *Comp. Sci. Tech.*, **59**, 759–768.

GAO Y C and ZHOU L M (1998), 'Numerical analysis of interface fatigue of fiber reinforced composites', *Theor. Appl. Fract. Mech.*, **30**, 235–241.

GASSAN J (2000), 'Fatigue behaviour of cross-ply glass-fiber epoxy composites including the effect of fiber-matrix interphase', *Comp. Interf.*, **7**(4), 287–299.

GASSAN J (2002), 'A study of fibre and interface parameters affecting the fatigue behaviour of natural fibre composites', *Composites*, **33**A, 369–374.

GASSAN J and BLEDZKI A K (1997), 'The influence of fiber-surface treatment on the mechanical properties of jute-polypropylene composites', *Composites*, **28**A, 1001–1005.

GASSAN J and BLEDZKI A K (1999), 'Possibilities for improving the mechanical properties of jute/epoxy composites by alkali treatment of fibres', *Comp. Sci. Tech.*, **59**, 1303–1309.

GASSAN J and BLEDZKI A K (2000), 'Possibilities to improve the properties of natural fiber reinforced plastics by fiber modification – jute polypropylene composites', *Appl. Comp. Mater.*, **7**, 373–385.

GIBSON A G , EVANS J T, KOTSIKOS G, SPEAKE S D and HALE J M (2000), 'Fatigue of marine laminates in aqueous environments', *Plast. Rub. Comp.*, **29**(10), 533–538.

GOUTIANOS S and PEIJS T (2001), 'Fatigue damage mechanisms in carbon-epoxy multi-fibre model composites', *Adv. Comp. Lett.*, **10**(1), 21–32.

HACHIYA H, TAKAYAMA S and TAKEDA K (1999), 'Effect of interface entanglement on fatigue life of polymer alloy and composites', *Comp. Interf.*, **6**(3), 187–200.

HANCOX N L (1998), 'Overview of effects of temperature and environment on performance of polymer matrix composite properties', *Plast. Rub. Comp. Proc. Appl.*, **27**(3), 97–106.

HASHIN Z (1990), 'Thermoelastic properties of fiber composites with imperfect interface', *Mechanics of Materials*, **8**, 333–348.

HORST J J, SALIENKO N V and SPOORMAKER J L (1998), 'Fibre-matrix debonding stress analysis for short fibre-reinforced materials with matrix plasticity, finite element modelling and experimental verification', *Composites*, **29**A, 525–531.

HULL D and CLYNE T W (1996), *An introduction to composite materials (Second Edition)*, Cambridge, Cambridge University Press.

KAWAI M, YAJIMA S, HACHINOHE A and KAWASE Y (2001), 'High-temperature off-axis fatigue behaviour of unidirectional carbon-fibre-reinforced composites with different resin matrices', *Comp. Sci. Tech.*, **61**, 1285–1302.

KELLY A and ZWEBEN C (2000), *Comprehensive composite materials*, Pergamon.

KESSLER A and BLEDZKI A K (2000), 'Influence of the fiber/matrix-interphase on the post-impact properties of glass/epoxy-laminates', *Adv. Comp. Mater.*, **9**(2), 109–118.

KEUSH S, QUECK H and GLIESCHE K (1998), 'Influence of glass fibre/epoxy resin interface on static mechanical properties of unidirectional composites and on fatigue performance of cross ply composites', *Composites*, **29**A, 701–705.

KIM J-K and MAI Y-M (1998), *Engineered interfaces in fiber reinforced composites*, Amsterdam, Elsevier.

KOIMTZOGLOU C, KOSTOPOULOS V, MELANITIS N E and PAIPETIS S A (1995), 'The effect of cyclic loading on the micromechanics of the interface', *Adv. Comp. Lett.*, **4**(5), 151–155.

KOIMTZOGLOU C, KOSTOPOULOS V and GALIOTIS C (2001), 'Micromechanics of reinforcement and damage initiation in carbon fibre/epoxy under fatigue loading', *Composites*, **32**A, 457–471.

KOIMTZOGLOU C, KOSTOPOULOS V and GALIOTIS C (2003), 'Stress transfer efficiency in model composites under dynamic loading', *Appl. Phys. A*, **76**, 231–239, DOI: 10.1007/s003390201420.

KOMAI K, MINOSHIMA K, TANAKA K and TOKURA T (2002), 'Effects of stress waveform and water absorption on the fatigue strength of angle-ply aramid fiber/epoxy composites', *Int. J. Fat*, **24**, 339–348.

KOTSIKOS G, EVANS J T, GIBSON A G and HALE J M (2000), 'Environmentally enhanced fatigue damage in glass fibre reinforced composites characterised by acoustic emission', *Composites,* **31**A, 969–977.

LESKO J J, SWAIN R E, CARTWRIGHT J M, CHIN J W, REIFSNEIDER K L, DILLERD D A and WIGHTMAN J P (1994), 'Interphase developers from fiber sizings and their chemical-structural relationship to composite compressive performance', *J. Adhesion*, **45**, 43–57.

LIAO K, SCHULTHEISZ C R, HUNSTON D L and BRINSON L C (1998), 'Long-term durability of fiber-reinforced polymer-matrix composite materials for infrastructure applications: A review', *J. Adv. Mater.*, **30**(4), 3–40.

LIAO K, SCHULTHEISZ C R and HUNSTON D L (1999), 'Lont-term environmental fatigue of pultruded glass-fiber-reinforced composites under flexural loading', *Int. J. Fat*, **21**, 485–495.

MAHIOU H and BEAKOU A (1998), 'Modelling of interfacial effects on the mechanical properties of fibre-reinforced composites', *Composites*, **29**A, 1035–1048.

MERCX F P M, BENZINA A, VAN LANGEVELD A D and LEMSTRA P J (1993), 'Improved adhesive properties of high-modulus polyethylene structures', *J. Mater. Sci.*, **28**, 753–759.

NAYFEH A H and ABDELRAHMAN W G (1999), 'Dynamic stress transfer in fibrous composites with damage', *Composites*, **30**B, 233–243.

PEIJS A A J M and DE KOK J J M (1993), 'Hybrid composites based on polyethylene and carbon fibres', *Composites*, **24**(1), 19–32.

ROBERTSON M A F, BUMP M B, VERGHESE K E, MCCARTNEY S R, LESKO J J, RIFLE J S, KIM I-C and YOON T-H (1999), 'Designed interphase regions in carbon fiber reinforced vinyl ester matrix composites', *J. Adhesion*, **71**, 395–416.

SEKINE H, SHIMOMURA K and HAMANA N (1988), 'Strength deterioration and degradation mechanism of glass chopped reinforced plastics in water environment', *ISME Int. J. Series I*, **31**(3), 619–626.

SONG D-Y and OTANI N (1997), 'Fatigue life prediction of cross-ply composite laminates', *Mater. Sci. Eng.*, **238**A, 329–335.

TROTIGNON J P and VERDU J (1993), 'Comparative study of flexural fatigue properties on epoxy and PEEK composites and matrices', Int Conf *Advanced Composites*, T Chandra and A K Dhingra.

VAN DEN OEVER M and PEIJS T (1998), 'Continuous-glass-fibre-reinforced polypropylene composites II. Influence of maleic-anhydride modified polypropylene on fatigue behaviour'', *Composites*, **29**, 227–239.

VAUTHIER E, ABRY J C, BAILLIEZ T and CHATEAUMINOIS A (1998), 'Interactions between hygrothermal ageing and fatigue damage in unidirectional glass/epoxy composites', *Comp. Sci. Tech.*, **58**, 687–692.

VU-KHANH T and DENAULT J (1991), 'Processing-structure-property relations in PEEK/carbon composites made from comingled fabric and prepreg', *J. Therm. Comp. Mater.*, **4**, 363–376.

VU-KHANH T and DENAULT J (1993), 'Effect of molding parameters on the interfacial strength in PEEK/carbon composites', *J. Reinf. Plast. Comp.*, **12**, 916–931.

WANATABE M (1979), 'Effect of water environment on fatigue behaviour of fiberglass reinforced plastics', *ASTM STP*, **674**, 345–367.

ZHIFEI S and LIMIN Z (2000), 'Interfacial debonding of coated-fiber-reinforced composites under tension-tension cyclic loading', *ACTA MECHANICA SINICA*, **16**(4), 347–356.

6

Delamination fatigue

R. Martin, Materials Engineering Research Laboratory, UK

6.1   Introduction

The threat of delamination arising from in-service loading has been one of the factors in limiting the adoption of laminated composite materials in greater volume for primary structure.[1] The use of interlaminar fracture mechanics in the design phase will help to identify both the likelihood of a delamination arising and its criticality if present. Currently, the design of structures utilizing composite materials in primary load-bearing applications usually requires a 'building-block' approach to testing and design.[2] This approach involves increasing the testing complexity and size from coupon tests to full-scale structural tests. The tests involved in the building-block approach, particularly the larger structural tests, are expensive in terms of specimen production and test set-up, and only help to provide qualitative empirical data to aid in understanding the response of the structure. Should the application experience fatigue or repetitive loading, structural integrity must also be evaluated for the anticipated life of the part.

Evaluation of structural integrity includes the performance of the structural component when in a damaged state. Identifying the damage state first requires an understanding of the potential damage threats and the likely damage from each of those threats. These may include damage during:

- manufacture, e.g. bad lay-up, cure, consolidation, voids, etc.
- assembly, e.g. over-tightening of bolts, impact during moving, etc.
- in-service exposure, e.g. low-velocity impact damage, accidents, out-of envelope manoeuvres, etc.

Once the threat has been identified, the extent of damage, which may not always be detectable, should also be identified. The structural tests are then conducted with the expected damage under the expected operating limits, in terms of strain and fatigue cycles the component may experience. From these test data, component life limitations may be set along with inspection and maintenance intervals. Detectable and non-detectable damage is identified as requiring immediate repair, future repair, or no repair at all.

While the above scenario is a typical design and evaluation method, current design techniques are attempting to reduce the amount of testing by utilizing empirical and

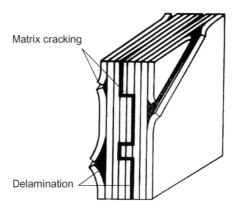

Fig. 6.1 Typical damage modes for a laminated composite.

computer-based models to predict the effect of damage or defects such as delaminations within the component.

Composite material components may be damaged and eventually fail in a progressive manner (Fig. 6.1). While other damage modes such as matrix cracks occur first, delaminations result is larger stiffness drop and reduction in load-bearing capabilities. Delaminations may occur from interlaminar stresses arising from geometric or material discontinuities from design features, such as an edge, a hole, a dropped ply.[3] However, they may also occur from matrix cracks or from interlaminar stresses caused by structural loading, such as in a curved laminate, or by foreign body impacts. The delamination, once initiated, will grow under fatigue loads. During delamination growth, the structural loads may be redistributed such that another delamination occurs in another location. The delaminations may continue to grow and accumulate until a structural failure occurs, such as buckling or fibre failure. Additionally, the delamination may be arrested and the structure may maintain some integrity.

This chapter addresses delamination growing under fatigue loads as it is potentially the more critical mode of damage. Although delamination may not cause total collapse of the load-bearing properties of the component, it is usually a precursor to such an event. Therefore, not only is knowledge of the composite's resistance to interlaminar fracture useful for product development and material screening, but a generic measurement of the interlaminar fracture toughness of the composite is useful for establishing design allowables for damage tolerance analyses of composite structures.

Efforts to predict the more dominant failure mode of delamination onset and growth have focused on interlaminar fracture mechanics.[4–7] This approach requires the determination of the change in strain energy for a unit area of delamination growth. This is termed the strain-energy release rate G. These calculated values of G are compared with the critical values to determine if the delamination will grow. This approach requires both computer modelling and experimental characterization under fatigue conditions.

Over the years both interlaminar fracture modelling and testing have been developed. The tests have been sufficiently refined to develop them into standards.[8–9] This chapter presents the means of incorporating delamination fatigue considerations into practice.

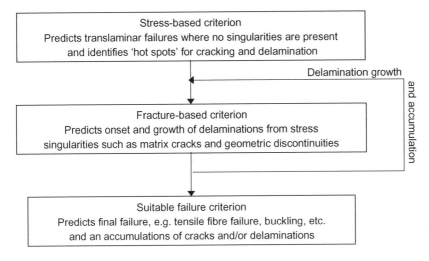

Fig. 6.2   A schematic of the fracture mechanics approach.

6.2   The interlaminar fracture mechanics approach for fatigue

A flow diagram showing the interlaminar fracture-mechanics approach for structural integrity is given in Fig. 6.2. The methodology begins by investigating 'areas of concern' or 'hot spots' with high interlaminar stresses and strains that result in the matrix being highly loaded. These interlaminar stresses may arise from geometry or from damage threats. Once identified, a fracture analysis is conducted to determine whether or not a delamination will initiate and grow. If a delamination does grow, the analysis should indicate how far it will grow and whether that will result in growth which may redistribute the load and cause structural failure.

Identification of the interlaminar stresses and of the fracture properties requires the accurate modelling of through-thickness properties. Often these models are a local model of the area of concern with either idealized boundary conditions applied, or the actual boundary conditions from the global model using global/local modelling techniques.[5,6] Selection of this 'area of concern' must often be done in the light of engineering judgement, especially if global finite-element models include two-dimensional shell elements that do not identify areas of high interlaminar stress.

The stress outputs from the local models will allow the interlaminar stresses away from any stress singularities associated with geometric discontinuities to be identified. These stresses or strains may be used with suitable failure criteria to determine if an interlaminar failure will occur with monotonic or fatigue loads. If an interlaminar failure does occur it will occur as a delamination and the extent to which it will grow should be determined. If a delamination is not predicted to initiate, then other structural discontinuities must be examined. Delaminations primarily occur when the interlaminar tension stresses are high. They may also grow where there is a high interlaminar shear stress. Therefore, these areas should be identified for fracture analysis. In a damaged structure, invariably the damage will be the region where further delaminations may grow and the type of damage should be modelled. For a damaged component and for a component where delamination is expected to initiate, a fracture analysis is conducted for a delamination growing either from the damage or from the potential initiation site.

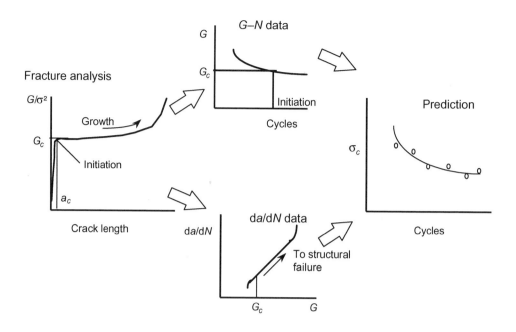

Fig. 6.3   The fracture mechanics life prediction steps.

Using delamination onset criteria and delamination onset data, it must then be established if the delamination will initiate during the life of the component. If the delamination will not grow, then the analysis may be stopped, or another potential delamination site examined. If a delamination is predicted to initiate, then it must be determined how far it will grow under fatigue loads and if this amount of growth is critical leading to component failure. Component failure is dependent on the loading in the area of interest and needs to be defined. In many situations failure may be deemed to be a significant reduction in stiffness for the component to be unserviceable. If component failure does not occur, then the analysis may be stopped, or, another potential delamination site examined. If the delamination is from a structural discontinuity, then that local area could be redesigned to prevent delamination initiation from that site. If the delamination will grow in a stable manner, then inspection intervals may be set up to ensure that the delamination has not grown beyond some expected extent.

The fracture-mechanics prediction procedure is summarized in Fig. 6.3.[10] There are essentially two steps: modelling the structure, and characterizing the materials delamination properties. These steps are described in more detail in this chapter. The first step is to analyse the model to obtain a relationship between strain-energy release rate G and delamination length a for a given stress or strain. For an initial delamination length, a critical value of G, G_c, is obtained. This G_c value is compared with the material's delamination data to give both a monotonic failure load and location and a number of cycles to initiate the delamination. From this value of G, the delamination growth rate, da/dN is obtained. For an incremental number of cycles, the increment in delamination length is determined. This gives a new value of G from the G–a relationship and a new value of da/dN. This continues until the delamination grows to a critical length or stops, leading to a number of fatigue cycles to failure at the given load.

Fig. 6.4   Multi-station machine for fracture specimens showing five DCBs being tested.

6.3   Characterizing delamination in fatigue

Delaminations will grow under a combination of tension or peel and shear stresses, defined as mode I (peel) and mode II and mode III (in-plane and transverse shear, respectively). Test methods have been developed for each of these modes along with some tests that provide mixed-mode testing, such as the mixed-mode bending test.[11] The more critical modes are mode I and mode II and these have received most attention in test development and materials characterization.[12–16] Therefore, this section focuses on the fatigue-test methods and the approach for characterizing these modes.

While most of the test-method development has focused on static delamination growth, the importance on delamination fatigue has also been well covered by some researchers. The test specimens to characterize delamination in fatigue are identical to those used for static characterization for all modes of fracture. In some instances when the delamination characterization is focused on threshold testing, the associated amplitudes may be small, particularly in the mode-II flexure tests. Therefore, it is often advisable to use thinner specimens than for the static tests so that the amplitudes are higher. This, in turn, results in lower loads requiring appropriate load cells.

Specimens may be tested on standard servo-hydraulic machines often with low-load load cells fitted. Alternatively, specialized test equipment exists to generate these materials data quickly and efficiently by testing six specimens at one time, Fig. 6.4.[17] The machines are operated either by an electric motor or by a small servo-hydraulic pump. Data acquisition is via a computer and the control. The specimens can be enclosed in an environmental chamber for hot/wet and cold conditions.

There are essentially two approaches for characterizing fatigue delamination. These methods are the delamination initiation method and the delamination growth method. Both methods are needed to accurately predict structural integrity of a component.

The specimens used to characterize delamination statically[9] are also used to characterize fatigue delamination by monitoring the delamination growth per fatigue cycle, da/dN. Expressions are given relating the applied cyclic strain energy release rate (G_{max} or ΔG) with da/dN as a power law, equation [6.1].[12,15,16] This equation may be further extended to incorporate the acceleration of delamination growth as G approaches the quasi-static value and the deceleration as the delamination growth rate reaches a threshold value, equation [6.2].[12]

$$\frac{da}{dN} = A(G_{max})^B \qquad\qquad [6.1]$$

$$\frac{da}{dN} = A(G_{max})^B \frac{\left[1-\left(\dfrac{G_{th}}{G_{max}}\right)^{D_1}\right]}{\left[1-\left(\dfrac{G_{max}}{G_c}\right)^{D_2}\right]} \qquad\qquad [6.2]$$

For composite materials, the values of the exponent B in these power laws are typically high. They can range from approximately 3 to values in excess of 15 (Fig. 6.5). Thus, by using just the fatigue growth part of the curve, any small deviation from the anticipated service load may lead to large errors in the predicted delamination growth rate. This is because G is proportional to the load squared and hence the delamination growth rate is proportional to the load to the power of $2B$. This potential error and the high rates of delamination growth have led to the adoption of a no-growth approach to design and damage-tolerance characterization of composite structures in fatigue. The no-growth approach requires the threshold value of strain-energy release rate G_{th} to be determined. Then, if a delamination is present, and the strain energy release rate is below the G_{th} value it will not grow.

For a threshold value, as in metals, the delamination is allowed to grow under cyclic loading and the delamination growth rate is decreased until the delamination growth arrests. However, this technique requires that the delamination be allowed to grow some distance before delamination arrest. As the delamination grows in fatigue, fibre bridging may occur as it does in monotonic tests, especially with the DCB specimen. Therefore, when the delamination eventually arrests during the fatigue test, the measured G will include the effects of fibre bridging and will give artificially high values of G_{Ith}. This may be accounted for by normalizing by the R curve as described below.

An alternative method of obtaining data for the no-growth approach, involves the characterization of delamination initiation.[12–14] This method involves determining the onset of delamination growth at the end of the delamination within the specimen by monitoring changes in the compliance associated with delamination growth. By testing several interlaminar fracture test specimens of one type at different G levels, a complete $G–N$ characterization can be obtained. Hence, by testing mode-I, mixed-mode and mode-II specimens, a complete $G–N$ characterization can be developed for all modes (Fig. 6.6). By choosing an appropriate number of cycles for the application N_a such as the cycles between inspection intervals or the life, a design value of G may be specified, such that the delamination will not grow within that number of cycles. The data in the $G–N$ plot are not strictly threshold values because delamination growth may occur after further cycles at lower loads. Therefore, it is necessary to extend the test data out to and beyond the number of cycles required for the application.

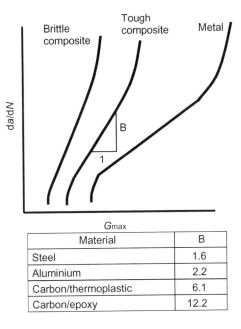

Material	B
Steel	1.6
Aluminium	2.2
Carbon/thermoplastic	6.1
Carbon/epoxy	12.2

Fig. 6.5   Schematic illustration of delamination growth curves with typical values of B.

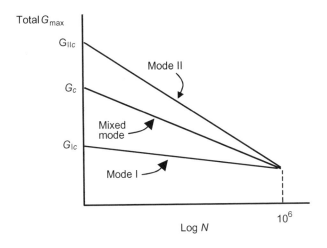

Fig. 6.6   Delamination onset for mixed modes.

6.3.1   The mode-I double-cantilever-beam test

The double-cantilever-beam specimen has been widely used to measure the mode-I interlaminar fracture toughness both statically and in fatigue.[8,9,12,14–16] The DCB specimen is a laminate with a non-adhesive insert placed at the mid-plane, at one end prior to curing or consolidation, to simulate a delamination. Both 0°, unidirectional and multidirectional[18] lay-ups have been suggested. However, if angle plies are used in a multidirectional lay-up these specimens may experience branching of the delamination away from the mid-plane through matrix cracks in off-axis plies. If the delamination branches away from the mid-plane, a pure mode-I fracture will not be achieved because of the coupling between extension and shear which may exist in the asymmetric sublaminates formed as the delamination grows. Typically, loads are applied to the DCB via loading blocks or hinges adhesively bonded to the surface of the DCB.

A unidirectional DCB specimen of uniform width subjected to displacement-controlled loading, usually experiences stable delamination growth during fatigue testing such that the G_{max} value decreases during the test as does the delamination growth rates. As discussed above, fibre bridging usually occurs as the delamination progresses along the length of the beam resulting in an increased value of G_{max}. Hence, the mode-I data can be normalized with respect to the static G_{Ic} value at the corresponding delamination length resulting in a delamination characterization curve without the effects of fibre bridging.[19] This can be expressed as:

$$\frac{da}{dN} = A \left(\frac{G_{Imax}}{G_{IR}}\right)^B \frac{\left[1 - \left(\dfrac{G_{Ith}}{G_{Imax}}\right)^{D_1}\right]}{\left[1 - \left(\dfrac{G_{Imax}}{G_{Ic}}\right)^{D_2}\right]} \qquad [6.3]$$

This issue does not arise for the delamination initiation method where delamination initiation is measured from the inserted delamination. However, this insert must be suffi-ciently thin not to affect initiation values. Typically, the thinnest insert commercially available ranges between a 7 and 13 μm film.[9] These thicknesses are approximately equivalent to one glass fibre diameter and are also the approximate thickness of the resin-rich layer that lies between plies of different orientation.[14]

The most commonly used data reduction technique for the DCB is the modified beam theory.[9] This involves adjusting the measured delamination length by a value Δ. Beam theory assumes that the cantilever beams are rigidly clamped at the delamination front. The value of Δ is used to account for any shear deformation and rotation at the delamination front. The fracture toughness is calculated by

$$G_{Imax} = \frac{3P_{max}\delta_{max}}{2b(a + \Delta)} \qquad [6.4]$$

where P_{max} and δ_{max} are the maximum cyclic load and displacement respectively, b is the width and a the current delamination length. The value Δ is determined experimentally during monotonic tests by fitting a least-squares curve to a plot of the cube root of the compliance, $C^{1/3}$, as a function of the delamination length. The value of Δ is the value of a at $C^{1/3} = 0$. A plot of representative mode-I data is given in Fig. 6.7.[4,12,17,18,24]

6.3.2   Mode-II tests

There are several mode-II tests which are used to characterize fatigue delamination growth. These methods essentially use the same specimen type: it is the loading of this specimen that varies. The principal methods are the end-notched flexure (ENF),[20] the four-point end-notched flexure (4ENF)[21] and the end-loaded split specimen (ELS).[22]

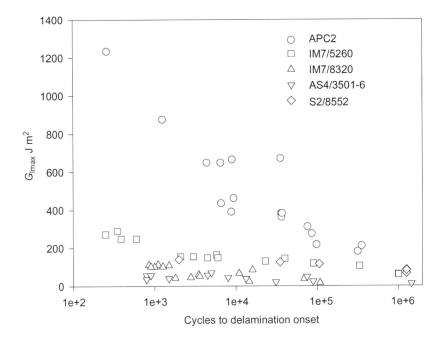

Fig. 6.7   Representative Mode-I delamination onset experimental data.

The specimen configurations for these methods are similar to that of the DCB in that the lay-up is unidirectional for the same reasons discussed for the DCB, and the sides are parallel. A non-adhesive insert is placed at the mid-plane at one end prior to curing. For the ENF, the shear loading arises from three-point bending. The loading fixture uses rollers to support the specimen and to allow it to rotate freely. Delamination growth in this specimen is unstable and the fatigue delamination growth rate increases as the test progresses. For the 4ENF the specimen is placed in four-point bending with the delamination between the centre loading rollers, which are free to rotate about their centre line to allow for the asymmetric deflection of the specimen. The delamination growth is then stable and the fatigue delamination growth rate decreases as the fatigue test progresses. Delamination growth is also stable for certain delamination lengths with the ELS specimen, which is loaded as a cantilever beam.

For all of these mode-II specimens, the displacements in the fatigue tests are small. It is often necessary to use an external displacement-measuring device to measure and control displacement, thus removing any additional displacements the machine experiences from the load train.

The data reduction for the ENF and the ELS can be found in Ref. 22. For the 4ENF the mode II values of strain-energy release rate is given as:[21]

$$G_{\text{Imax}} = \frac{C_1 P_{\text{max}}^2}{2b}$$ [6.5]

where C_1 is determined from a static compliance calibration straight-line fit relating the compliance to the delamination length cubed.[21] While there is a decreasing delamination growth rate with the 4ENF, the rate of decrease is often insufficient to produce a complete da/dN curve from one test. In this situation the applied displacement may also be reduced during the test. A plot of representative mode-II data is given in Fig. 6.8.[12,24]

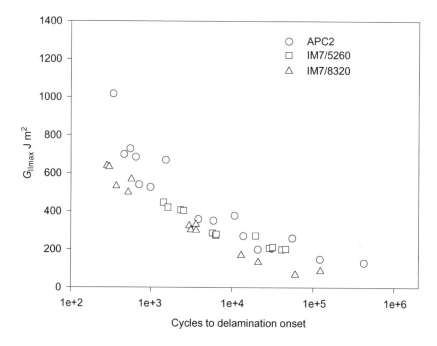

Fig. 6.8   Representative Mode-II delamination onset experimental data.

6.3.3   Factors affecting fatigue properties

There is a significant difference between the fatigue delamination growth properties in the different modes. Pure mode-I delaminations initiate and grow more rapidly than pure mode-II delaminations, this is shown schematically in Fig. 6.6. Similarly, a combination or mixed mode I/II delamination growth falls between the pure modes I and II data. The difference between pure mode-I and mode-II data is greater at high loads low cycles but this difference reduces at higher cycles.

Interlaminar fracture tests are an effective method of screening materials to determine their toughness and their resistance to damage growth. The toughness of the matrix has a significant effect on the static toughness and on initiation and growth values. This is shown schematically for delamination growth in Fig. 6.5. The tougher materials have longer cycles to initiation and a slower delamination growth rate.

The R ratio, $\delta_{min}/\delta_{max}$, also has an effect on the fatigue data as illustrated in Fig. 6.9 for delamination growth. For the range $0 \leq R \leq 0.5$, the higher the R ratio, the more cycles to delamination initiation and the lower the delamination growth rate.[2]

The effect on frequency has also been studied for delamination onset. Provided there are no heating effects from high-frequency testing, the frequency was shown not to have an effect on delamination initiation.[18]

As for other composite properties, environmental testing affects the fatigue delamination properties. For elevated-temperature testing, the resin softens and the fatigue delamination resistance is reduced. However, when the resin is saturated, the resin has a small degree of plasticization and increased fatigue delamination resistance can be observed.

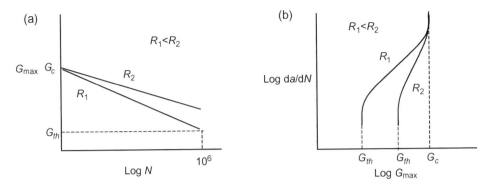

Fig. 6.9   Effect of R ratio on delamination data.

6.4   Modelling a delamination

Fracture analysis of a structure takes the form of the values of the strain-energy release rate for a given load at different delamination lengths. To model a crack or a delamination in a structure, it is often necessary to create duplicate nodes. In most finite-element codes this is achieved during the pre-processor stage by creating the mesh geometry on either side of the delamination and excluding those nodes during any 'merging of coincident nodes', a function available in most pre-processors. Often a delamination is modelled along the complete expected path of the delamination. The coincident nodes are then connected by using multi-point constraints (MPCs) or some form of link element. To model a delamination of a certain length, relevant MPCs are released or link elements removed. Thus, the variation of G with delamination length is obtained by solving the model with several different delamination lengths. The disadvantage with this approach is that it must be known *a priori* where the delamination will grow. A more efficient methodology is to automate the generation of a crack by using macros. The macros create the required number of duplicate nodes in a virgin uncracked model to form the delamination to a chosen length. This allows easier modelling of different potential delamination paths from the uncracked original model and more efficient solution times.

There is no ideal element size for modelling delaminations, although the element size may have an effect on the individual modes of G.[23,24] The smaller the size of element used, the more refined are the changes in G with delamination length that may be obtained if this information is required. This may be important close to the geometric discontinuity where the delamination may initiate, but is less important as the delamination grows. Thus, elements as small as one eighth of a ply thickness can be used in the regions where there are large changes in G over a short distance although elements of one ply thickness are adequate.[24]

6.4.1   Calculating strain-energy release rate

There are two common methods of calculating G. In most commercial finite-element codes calculation of G must be done as a separate post-processing function. First, a global energy balance between finite-element analysis solutions of different incremental delamination areas (A_i and A_{i+1}) may be used, such that:

$$G = -\frac{dU}{dA} = -\frac{U_{i+1} - U_i}{A_{i+1} - A_i}$$ [6.6]

where U is the strain energy and A is the delamination area for the ith solution. This gives a value for the total strain-energy release rate G_{tot}. The value of U is often an optional or mandatory output in FE codes.

Because a delamination may grow under a combination of mode I, tension or peel, mode II, in-plane shear, or mode III transverse shear, the value of G_{tot} can be broken into its component parts, G_I, G_{II}, and G_{III}. This can be achieved for linear analyses by using the virtual crack closure technique (VCCT).[25] This technique is based on the work done to close the crack tip. An assumption can be made with VCCT so that the values of G may be calculated from the results of one finite-element solution rather than two. If the increment of delamination growth Δ is small in comparison with the overall length of the delamination, then the forces ahead of the delamination may be assumed to be similar to those when the delamination has grown. Once again, the calculation of G may be done manually or, once the node and element identification is known, can be calculated by the use of suitable routines.

In two-dimensions using eight-noded quadrilateral elements, the values of G_I and G_{II} are calculated by using the following equations.

$$G_I = \frac{1}{2\Delta A}[F_y^F(V^B - V^C) + F_y^G(V^D - V^E)]$$ [6.7]

$$G_{II} = \frac{1}{2\Delta A}[F_x^F(U^B - U^C) + F_x^G(U^D - U^E)]$$ [6.8]

Where: ΔA is the element length

$F_x^F, F_x^G, F_y^E, F_y^G$ are x and y components of force at nodes F and G.

U^B, U^C, U^D, U^E are x components of displacement at nodes B, C, D and E

V^B, V^C, V^D, V^E are y components of displacement at nodes B, C, D and E

The x and y directions are in a local co-ordinate system. The locations of nodes B to D relative to the crack tip are shown in Fig. 6.10. For four-noded elements, the mid-side terms are omitted.

6.5   Using fracture mechanics analysis as a design tool

An example of a $G-a$ plot for a delamination under a stiffener is given in Fig. 6.11.[5] This plot shows the G_{tot} and G_I and G_{II} using VCCT in a two-dimensional plane-strain model. This type of plot gives three pieces of information that will help predict fatigue delamination initiation and growth in the component. First, the value of G_{tot} comprises approximately 60% G_I. In most materials, the mode-I interlaminar fracture toughness G_{Ic} is significantly less than the mode-II interlaminar fracture toughness G_{IIc}. Significant differences may also be seen in fatigue initiation and crack growth testing. Hence, if the geometry of the part, the lay-up, or the material can be altered to give a lower quantity of G_I, the panel will be more damage resistant and damage tolerant.

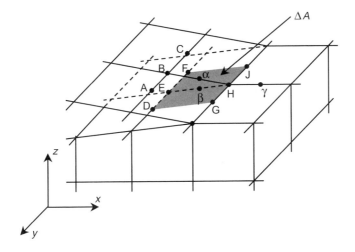

Fig. 6.10   Virtual crack closure technique (VCCT) notation.

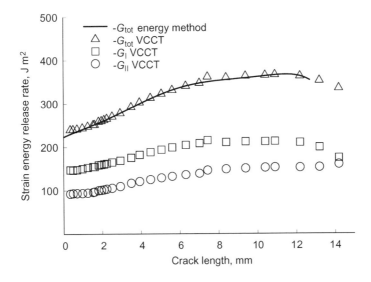

Fig. 6.11   Strain energy release rate versus crack length for stiffener debond on a compression panel.

The second piece of information from Fig. 6.11, is the general slope of the G–a plot. For all delamination lengths up to 12 mm, the slope is positive, indicating that delamination growth will be unstable, under quasi-static loading or that the fatigue delamination growth rate will increase as the delamination grows. Should the slope be negative, the delamination would grow under fatigue loads, but the rate would slow and delamination arrest may well occur depending on the values.

The third piece of information from Fig. 6.11 is the value of G to initiate the delamination. Because there is a sudden termination of the delamination at the start of the crack, a stress

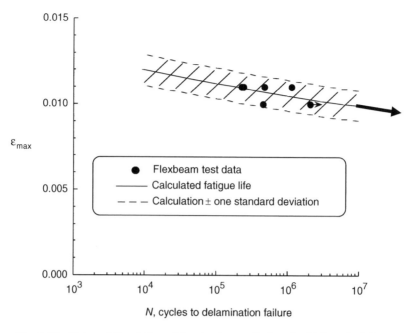

Fig. 6.12 Extrapolating fatigue delamination predictions for high cycle fatigue.

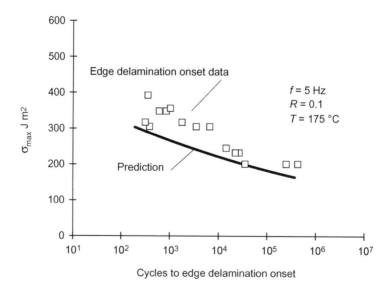

Fig. 6.13 Delamination prediction at elevated temperatures.

singularity exists. In the close vicinity of the stress singularity, the G-a curve probably turns towards zero sharply. However, if the G-a curve is extrapolated to a zero crack length ignoring this sharp turn it is possible to use this extrapolated value of G to compare to the material's interlaminar fracture toughness G_c.

This methodology has been validated against many different configurations including: Edge delamination in a flat multidirectional laminate,[1] a tapered laminate[3] and a curved laminate.[4] In Reference 5, the extrapolated value was used to predict stringer debond and failure in a stiffened compression panel.

6.6   Structural integrity prediction

With the analysis and the materials data obtained, structural integrity predictions are made by utilizing Fig. 6.3. From the analysis a critical value of G_{init} is obtained for delamination initiation. This value is then compared with the G–N curve for that material at the appropriate parameters (such as R ratio, mixed mode ratio and frequency) to obtain the number of cycles to initiate a delamination or further grow a delamination within that component N_{init}. If the full mixed-mode delamination characterization is not available the possibility of using the data from the DCB test (i.e. pure mode) is an option. This is a conservative approach for delaminations that have a high mode II component because the mode-II toughness of the composite is higher than the mode I.

If the number of cycles for initiation is less than the expected or required number of cycles, then the extent of delamination growth must be determined. If no delamination is permitted, the component must be redesigned at this local region. Because of the rapid rate of delamination growth as discussed above, one assumption is that delamination growth can be considered to be instantaneous along the path of interest. For G–a plots that show increasing values of G with a, this is a reasonable assumption. Once the delamination has initiated the effect of both the ever-increasing G and the high exponent B, there is only a short period of delamination growth. This period is too short to plan inspection intervals or repair. However, if the G–a plot has a decreasing G value with a, the delamination will grow a little way and then stop growing because of the decreasing G. Therefore, if the resulting delamination length is small and does not have the effect of a structural response, it can be ignored.

For validation of the structural integrity methodology testing of sub-elements and components is recommended. These tests should be taken to failure identifying delamination initiation and growth using NDE methods wherever possible. Because of the expense and duration of the high-cycle fatigue tests, lower fatigue cycle tests should be obtained. The prediction methodology should be validated at these lower lives. The methodology can then be extrapolated to the high-cycle fatigue regime as illustrated in Fig. 6.12.[26]

For other examples the effect of temperature on material properties needs to be accounted for and edge delamination in a laminate can be predicted under fatigue conditions by using analysis and DCB data (Fig. 6.13).[27] Once delamination initiates other damage modes need to be accounted for before complete component failure.[1] Delamination prediction for a radial delaminate in a curved laminate was given in Reference 4. Here fatigue delamination growth was virtually instantaneous after delamination initiation. Hence, prediction of fatigue delamination initiation is sufficient for predicting the life of the part.

6.7   References

1. O'BRIEN T K (1990), Towards a damage tolerance philosophy for composite materials and structures, in *Composite Materials: Testing and Design (Ninth Volume)*, ASTM STP 1059, S P Garbo, Editor. American Society for Testing and Materials: Philadelphia. pp. 7–33.
2. Mil-Hndbk-17 Volumes 1–3.
3. MURRI G B, O'BRIEN T K and ROUSSEAU, C Q (1998), Fatigue life methodology for tapered Composite flexbeam laminates, *J. American Helicopter Society,* **43**(2), 146–155, April.
4. MARTIN R H and JACKSON W C (1993), 'Damage prediction in curved cross-plied composite laminates,' *Composite Materials: Fatigue and Fracture, Fourth Volume*, ASTM STP 1156, W W

Stinchcomb and N E Ashbaugh, eds., American Society for Testing and Materials, Philadelphia, pp.105–126. Also, NASA TM 104089, USAAVSCOM TR-91, B-009, July 1991.

5. MARTIN R H (1995), 'Local fracture mechanics analysis of stringer pull-off and delamination in a post-buckled compression panel,' MERL-CRR-94-002, November 28th, 1994, *Proceedings of the ICCM-10*, Whistler, British Columbia, August 14–18, VI–253.

6. MINGUET P J and O'BRIEN T K (1996), Analysis of test methods for characterizing skin/stringer debonding failures in reinforced composite panels, in *Composite Materials: Testing and Design, Twelfth Volume*, STP 1274, American Society for Testing and Materials August, pp 105–124.

7. KRUEGER R, CVITKOVICH M K, O'BRIEN T K and MINGUET P J (2000), Testing and analysis of composite skin/stringer debonding under multi-axial loading, *J. Composite Materials*, **34**(15), 1264–1300.

8. O'BRIEN T K (1998), Interlaminar fracture toughness: the long and winding road to standardization, *Composites, Part B: Engineering*, **29B**, 57–62.

9. O'BRIEN T K and MARTIN R H (1993), Round robin testing for mode I interlaminar fracture toughness of composite materials, *J. Comp. Tech. and Research*, **15**(4), 269–281, winter.

10. MARTIN R H (1998), 'Incorporating interlaminar fracture mechanics into design,' *International Conference on Designing Cost-Effective Composites, IMechE Conference Transactions*, London, 83–92, 15–16 September.

11. REEDER J R and CREWS J H, JR (1990), The mixed-mode bending method for delamination testing, *AIAA Journal*, **28**(7), 1270–1276, July.

12. MARTIN R H and MURRI G B (1990), Characterization of mode I and II delamination growth and thresholds in AS4/PEEK composites, in *Composite Materials: Testing and Design, Ninth Volume*, STP 1059, American Society for Testing and Materials, pp. 251–270.

13. O'BRIEN T K, MURRI G B and SALPEKAR S A (1989), Interlaminar shear fracture toughness and fatigue thresholds for composite materials, in *Composite Materials: Fatigue and Fracture, Second Volume*, STP 1012, American Society for Testing and Materials, pp 222–250, April.

14. MURRI G B and MARTIN R H (1993), Effect of initial delamination on mode I and mode II interlaminar fracture toughness and fatigue fracture thresholds, in *Composite Materials: Fatigue and Fracture, Fourth volume*, STP 1156, American Society for Testing and Materials, pp. 239–256, June.

15. BATHIAS C and LAKSIMI A (1985), *ASTM STP 876*, W.S. Johnson, Ed., ASTM, Philadelphia, pp. 217–237.

16. HOJO M *et al.* (1987), *Composites Science and Technology*, **29**, 273–292.

17. MARTIN R H (1998), 'Accelerated characterisation of delamination for rotorcraft applications,' 4th European Conference on Composites: Testing and Standardisation, 31st August–2nd September, European Society for Composite Materials, London, pp. 105–114.

18. BOWRON S and MARTIN R H (2000), Interlaminar fracture properties of hybrid laminates, American Society for Composites, 15th Annual Technical Conference, Texas A&M University, College Station, Texas, September 24–27.

19. MARTIN R H (1991), 'Characterizing mode I fatigue delamination of composite materials,' *Mechanics Computing in 1990s and Beyond*, **2**, 943–948, May.

20. RUSSELL A J (1982), On measurement of mode II interlaminar fracture energies, Defence Research Establishment Pacific, Victoria, British Columbia, Canada, Materials DREP Report, 82-0, Dec.

21. MARTIN R H and DAVIDSON B D (1999), Mode II fracture toughness evaluation using a four point bend end notched flexure test, *Plastics, Rubber and Composites,* **28**(8), 401–406.

22. DAVIES P *et al.* (1996), 'Development of a standard mode II shear fracture test procedure,' *Seventh European Conference on Composite Materials, The Institute of Materials,* London, pp. 9–16, 14–16 May.

23. SUN C T and JIH C J (1987), 'On the strain energy release rates for interfacial cracks in bi-material media,' *Engineering Fracture Mechanics*, **28**, 13–27.

24. MARTIN R H, SRIRAM P and HOOPER S J (1996), Using a mixed mode fatigue delamination, *Composite Materials: Testing and Design (Twelfth Volume)*, ASTM STP1274, ASTM, pp. 371–392.

25. SHIVAKUMAR K N, TAN P W and NEWMAN J C (1988), 'A virtual crack-closure technique for calculating stress intensity factors for cracked three dimensional bodies,' *Int. J. Fracture*, **36**, R43-R50.

26. MURRI G B *et al.* (1997)., 'Fatigue life prediction of tapered composite laminates', 53rd AHS Meeting, May.

27. MARTIN R H (1993), 'Delamination onset in polymeric composite laminates under thermal and mechanical loads,' *High Temperature and Environmental Effects on Polymeric Composites*, ASTM STP-1174, C E Harris and T S Gates, eds., pp. 39–65. Also NASA TM-189548, November 1991.

7

The fatigue of hybrid composites

G. F. Fernando[†] and F. A. A. Al-Khodairi[†*], Cranfield University, UK

7.1 Introduction

A number of techniques have been used previously to control the toughness and fracture behaviour of glass and carbon-fibre-reinforced composites: examples are hybridizing by using two or more reinforcing fibre types, and interleaving the primary resin with a tougher layer. This current article presents an overview of this subject area followed by a detailed report on the effect of hybridizing conventional unidirectional E-glass/epoxy-resin composites. The hybridizing fibres investigated in this study were short E-glass, short silicon carbide and continuous polyethylene. The resin systems investigated were commercially available epoxy/amine-based thermosets.

7.1.1 Organic-matrix hybrid composites

7.1.1.1 Classification
A schematic illustration of a classification system for hybrid composites is presented in Fig. 7.1. With reference to this figure, the definition of the various classes of hybrids is as follows.

Interply fibre hybrids
Here the individual plies or layers are composed of one fibre type. The preform is built up by stacking plies of different fibre types in the required sequence and relative fibre orientation. This class of hybrid can be further sub-divided into short and continuous-fibre hybrids.

Intraply fibre hybrids
This class of hybrid consists of two or more fibres in the same ply. It can be further sub-divided into intimately mixed fibre hybrids and tow-hybrids. Tow-hybrids are generally

---

*Present address: Saudi Basic Industries Corporation, Saudi Arabia
[†] Work performed whilst both the authors were at the Department of Materials Engineering, Brunel University, Uxbridge, UB8 3PH UK.

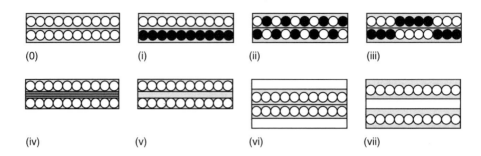

Fig. 7.1   Schematic illustration of a classification system for organic-matrix hybrid composites.
(0) Conventional unidirectional composite. (i) Interply hybrid. (ii) Intraply intimately mixed fibre
hybrid. (iii) Intraply tow mixed hybrid. (iv) Interply reinforced interface hybrid (the reinforcement
can be particulates, fibres, etc.) (v) Interply resin hybrid (the resin system can be different (interleaf) or similar). (vi) Skin/core hybrid. (vii) Fibre skin, non-fibre hybrid core hybrid.

available in the form of fabrics where the different fibre types are present in the form of tows
or fibre bundles with a specified number of individual filaments per bundle. Co-mingled
fibre bundles or tows are now commercially available.

Interply-reinforced interface hybrid: interply metal foil/sheet hybrids
In this class of hybrid composite, a thin metal sheet is placed at the ply interfaces and
processed with the matrix, binding the reinforcing fibres and the metal foils. Perforated
interlayers could form a sub-classification of this class of hybrid.

Interply-reinforced interface hybrid: interply interface particulate hybrids
Here a toughening agent in the form of small particles is added at the ply interface.

Interply-reinforced interface hybrid: interply interface short-fibre hybrids
This class of hybrid consists of short fibres of a similar or different composition from the
primary reinforcing fibres being present at the ply interfaces.

Interply–interface hybrid resin (interleaf) composite
In this case, a resin layer is introduced at the ply interface. The interleaf resin, in general,
tends to exhibit a higher failure strain and toughness when compared to the primary resin
matrix. Additional resin layers, identical to the primary resin matrix have also been used to
produce interply hybrid resin composites.

Fibre skin and core hybrids
These hybrids consists of outer skins of one or more types of fibre laminates applied to a core
made of another fibre laminate.

Fibre skin, non-fibre core hybrids
These consists of fibre skins applied to a core of foam, filled resin, honeycomb etc.

7.1.1.2   *Relevant background to hybrid composites*
Hybridization offers a route to the engineering of fibre-reinforced composites with properties
that cannot be realized in the un-hybridized counterparts. For example, the required thermal-
expansion coefficient, the strength and the stiffness can be tailored to comply with a broad
range of design requirements. As will be seen later, hybridization can be used to modify the
failure modes in FRCs.

Hybrid composites have generated significant interest since the 1970s and this has in part been due to the so called 'hybrid effect' (synergistic). There have been two schools of thought with regard to the definition of the hybrid effect. Some have defined the hybrid effect as the enhancement of the failure strain of a low-elongation fibre in a low/high elongation hybrid composite when compared with the low elongation un-hybridized composite. The percentage difference is generally referred to as the hybrid effect. The other school of thought has used any deviations from the rule of mixtures (RoM) as the basis for the presence of a positive or negative hybrid effect. Hayashi (1972) reported that the first fracture stress and strain for unidirectional carbon/glass hybrid composite were 37% and 45% higher, respectively, than that predicted by the RoM. He attributed this increase to the retardation in the fracture propagation of the carbon fibres as a result of them being surrounded by a material of greater ductility, i.e. the glass fibres.

Bunsell and Harris (1974) reconsidered Hayashi's work and reported that, for a carbon/glass hybrid, the initial modulus was in agreement with the RoM up to the fracture of the carbon fibres in the hybrid. They were in agreement with Hayashi in that the failure strain of the carbon fibres in the hybrid was higher than that obtained from the all-carbon fibre composite. They attributed the hybrid effect in part to the residual compressive stress induced in the carbon fibres during the manufacture of the hybrid composite. These residual stresses originate as a consequence of the mismatch in the coefficients of thermal expansion of the two reinforcing fibre types.

Other notable original work in the area of hybrid composites includes that reported by Beaumont et al. (1974), Aveston and Silwood (1976), Zweben (1977), Summerscales and Short (1978), Manders and Bader (1981a,b), Dorey (1982a,b), Fukuda (1983), Evans and Masters (1987), Johnston (1987), Curtis and Browne (1994) and Glenn et al. (1998). A brief review of selected works from these publications is presented below.

According to Aveston and Silwood (1976), the low-elongation fibre in the hybrid composite had to be present in small quantities and distributed evenly through the matrix for the hybrid effect to be realized. They also suggested that hybridization of carbon with glass fibres would retard the rate of catastrophic crack propagation when the carbon fibres failed. Zweben (1977) proposed a statistical model to describe the tensile strength of unidirectional hybrid composites consisting of two-dimensional arrays of alternating low and high-failure-strain fibres in a common matrix. His analysis suggested that it was possible to design hybrids with failure strains that are higher or lower than that of the all-low elongation fibre composite. Manders and Bader (1981a,b) carried out a systematic and detailed investigation into the monotonic strength and fracture characteristics of glass/carbon hybrids. They, too, adapted a statistical approach in trying to model the strength of hybrid composites. They defined two parameters for hybrid composites, namely, the hybrid ratio and the degree of dispersion. The hybrid ratio was defined as the proportion of a specified fibre type to the total amount of fibre in the hybrid composite. Dispersion was defined as the reciprocal of the smallest repeat unit of the laminates. They defined the hybrid effect as the apparent increase in the failure strain and hence the strength of the low-elongation fibres in the hybrid when compared to the all-low-elongation fibre composite. As with the findings of previous researchers, a greater hybrid effect was apparent in a carbon/glass hybrid composite when the carbon (lower failure-strain fibre) was more finely dispersed and when it occupied a lower proportion of the volume. An interesting observation from their work was that the all-carbon composites showed an apparent relationship between the thickness of the composite and the first failure strain. The thicker laminates failed at a higher strain; about 20% higher for each doubling of the laminate thickness up to 12 plies. They postulated that this may have been due to imperfect fibre alignment in the prepregs. This issue of fibre misalignment is discussed in detail in subsequent sections as its contribution to 'improved properties' in hybrid composites may have been underestimated and unappreciated by previous researchers.

In conclusion, the pioneering work of the above mentioned researchers has paved the way for the continued academic and commercial interest in organic-matrix hybrid composites.

7.1.2   Modifying the properties of composites

With reference to Fig. 7.1, a significant body of literature has been reported previously on techniques for improving and/or modifying the mechanical properties of fibre-reinforced composites. However, the majority of these activities have concentrated on improving the toughness of fibre-reinforced composites (FRC). For example, interleaving (Lagace *et al.*, 1986; Masters, 1989; Sela and Ishai, 1989; Sela *et al.*, 1989b; Altstadt *et al.*, 1993), employing rubber-toughened resins, and a general review of toughened epoxy resins (Garg and Mai, 1988), control of interfacial properties (Atkins, 1975; Kim and Mai, 1991; Rezaifard *et al.*, 1994; Pickering and Bader, 1994; Marston *et al.*, 1997), fibre architecture (Fernando *et al.*, 1987, Mignery *et al.*, 1985; Bibo and Hogg, 1998) and fibre hybridization (Hancox, 1981; Fernando *et al.*, 1988; Peijs and De Kok, 1993; Chaudhuri and Garala, 1995; Glenn *et al.*, 1998).

7.1.2.1   *Interleaving*

The hybrid resin composite can be produced by the technique of interleaving. The term interleaving is defined as the technique of inserting a tough resin film at the prepreg interfaces as an extra interlaminar layer. The technique of interleaving was implemented by American Cyanamid in the early 1980s (Krieger, 1987). It was suggested that the interleaf layer should be characterized by high toughness and ultimate failure strain (Sela and Ishai, 1989; Sela *et al.*, 1989). These properties of the interleaf layer are necessary since most epoxies used in composite materials are brittle and show relatively poor resistance to delamination. Two further requirements for the interleaf stated by Masters (1989) were: (i) the interleaf resins must be ductile and have a large ultimate shear strain-to-failure; and (ii) the interleaf thickness must be minimized to retain compression strength and to reduce interlaminar stresses.

Krieger (1987) noted that the shear load transfer in the interply is stiffness-driven and large shear forces are transferred between plies via the thin resin layer which lies between lamina. He also noted that an interleaf with low stiffness could reduce shear stress concentrations when used as strategic plies in structural composites. He concluded that, if the adhesive layer is miscible with the matrix resin and intermixing occurs, then the adhesive stiffness will increase and the shear stress rises and the hot–wet compression strength is reduced. Krieger (1987) also claimed that it is possible to obtain maximum reduction of local shear stress concentrations and minimize the loss of hot–wet compression strength by the use of an adhesive formulated so as not to mix with the matrix resin. Sela and Ishai (1989; Sela *et al.*, 1989) reported that interleaving can reduce the strength and stiffness of the composite material if the strength and stiffness of the interleaved layers are low. Chan (1986) showed that the use of adhesive strips had effectively acted as delamination arresters for both matrix-dominated and fibre-dominated composites. It was said that the delay in delamination growth resulted in a significant increase in fatigue life. The suppression of delamination was attributable to a reduction in the mode I component of the total strain-energy release rate. Joneja (1987) investigated the influence of polyester toughness on longitudinal fatigue behaviour of glass-fibre-reinforced composites. The polyester was toughened by the addition of a flexible isophthalic polyester resin as a modifier to a standard polyester resin. The fatigue results revealed that marginal improvement was obtained for composites utilizing a tougher polyester resin. No interpretation was given to explain the mechanisms involved in this improvement of fatigue performance. Chan (1991) reviewed the material and structural approaches to increase the resistance to delamination initiation and growth. In the materials-based approach, it was said that currently available toughened thermoset and thermoplastic composites could improve significantly the delamination resistance for monotonic, but not fatigue loading. In the structural approach, it was concluded that stitching and interleaving are effective ways of resisting delamination for both monotonic and fatigue loading.

Leaity *et al.* (1992) evaluated hybrid matrix composites in which modified matrices were used only in those plies susceptible to matrix damage. They added urethane resin in various ratios to the original matrix to increase the flexibility and toughness of the cured resin. They found that the incorporation of urethane resin within the epoxy matrix of the 90° ply in a cross-ply composite led to transverse-ply crack resistance. Additionally, it was noted that the Young's modulus was lowered and the toughness was increased in the transverse ply. They also reported that there was no reduction in the tensile strength of the composite compared to the conventional counterpart. Partridge *et al.* (1989) and Partridge (1993) investigated the influence of interleaving on the fatigue response of different unidirectional composites. The interleaf layers were always the same as the matrix resin in the prepreg. The interleaved composites were more resistant to delamination and exhibited lower fatigue crack growth rates. They reported that the effectiveness of interleaving was enhanced by using thicker and/or tougher resin layers. Singh and Partridge (1995) examined the influence of the film thickness on mode I and mode II interlaminar fracture toughness in unidirectional carbon (IMS)/epoxy (Fibredux 927) when interleaved with the same matrix resin. They found that the values of G_{Ic} and G_{IIc} increased with increase in the thickness of the interleaved film by 70% and 200%, respectively, over the reference material.

7.1.2.2 Hybrid short-fibre composites

Hybrid fibre composites are materials where two or more different fibres are mixed in one matrix resin. Kretsis (1987) presented an excellent review on the mechanical properties of hybrid fibre-reinforced composites. Garcia *et al.* (1987) fabricated a hybrid composite by adding 3 to 15 parts of randomly oriented silicon carbide whiskers as a supplementary reinforcement into the matrix prior to the composite impregnation process. The 90° tensile strengths and strains were significantly increased while in-plane fibre-dominated properties were all significantly reduced as a result of fibre damage. Apparently, fibre surface scratches were incurred during the whisker-resin impregnation process. The fibre damage can be minimized if it is applied at the ply interfaces during lay-up rather than during impregnation. Lin and Jang (1990) followed the procedure suggested by Garcia and his team. They concluded that the impact toughness and penetration resistance of a continuous-fibre composite can be improved by modifying the matrix resin with short fibres of Kevlar. It was also shown that the addition of a small amount of short fibres, such as carbon and Kevlar, led to significant improvements in mode I and mode II fracture toughness.

Yamashita *et al.* (1989) used oriented whiskers to reinforce in-plane carbon fibres which were prepared previously by filament winding. The short fibres (23 μm long and 0.39 μm in diameter) of silicon carbide were coated with ferromagnetic Ni–Fe–P alloy in order to orient the fibres in the direction of the plate thickness via the application of a magnetic field. Recently, they showed that mode-I interlaminar fracture toughness was improved whereas, mode-II interlaminar fracture toughness and interlaminar shear strength were not improved (Yamashita *et al.*, 1992).

Hitchen and Ogin (1993a,b; Hitchen *et al.*, 1995) investigated the effect of fibre length on the fatigue of a random-short-carbon-fibre/epoxy composite containing different fibre lengths (1, 5 or 15 mm). It was found that the fatigue life was independent of fibre length at any peak strain and the short-fibre composites failed in a sudden death mode. However, adding a greater quantity of flexibilizer to the epoxy matrix resulted in shorter fatigue lives for composites having the more flexible matrix.

7.1.2.3   Hybrid continuous fibre composites

An extensive programme of research was undertaken by Fernando (1989) and Dickson *et al.* (1989) to investigate the fatigue behaviour of inter-ply hybrid carbon/Kevlar and glass/carbon hybrid composites respectively. The fatigue behaviour in repeated tension of unidirectional hybrid laminates composed of XAS carbon and E-glass fibres in the same Fibredux 913 epoxy resin was studied (Dickson *et al.*, 1989). It was found that the fatigue stress for a given life was not a linear function of composition, showing a substantial positive deviation from the rule of mixtures. It was shown that the slopes of the hybrids are all nearly the same, but lower than that of the plain carbon composite. However, the data for the plain carbon and for the hybrid of 25% glass and 75% carbon overlap at long lives.

In the case of the carbon/Kevlar interply hybrid composites, Fernando (1989) reported on the quasi-static and fatigue behaviour of unidirectional carbon (XAS/Fibredux 914) and unidirectional Kevlar/Fibredux 914 interply composites. The all-carbon composite exhibited a non-linear stress/strain curve with the Young's modulus increasing with applied strain and stress. Longitudinal modulus increases in the range 6–21% were recorded. It was speculated that this may have been due to initial waviness of the fibre crystallites and subsequent straightening out with applied stress. The unidirectional Kevlar/Fibredux 914 composite exhibited a modulus increase of up to 5%.

Three interply hybrid compositions were investigated namely, 25%, 37.5% and 50% XAS/Kevlar. Comparison of the fatigue behaviour of the hybrids against the all-carbon and all-Kevlar composites by a simple rule-of-mixtures approach indicated that the fatigue performance of the hybrids tested at a stress ration of $R = 0.1$ was superior to that predicted at 10^5 and 10^6 fatigue cycles. The fatigue performance of the 25% and 37.5% hybrid was found to be marginally superior to the all-carbon composite at all stress ratios investigated ($R = 0.5, 0.1, 0.01, -0.3$ and -0.6. The 50% hybrid composite exhibited a superior fatigue performance compared to the all-carbon composite at 10^5 cycles for all the stress ratios investigated. However, at 10^6 cycles, a marginal decrease in the fatigue performance was observed for this hybrid when compared with the all-carbon composite.

The predominant failure mode observed for the unidirectional all-Kevlar subjected to monotonic tensile testing was longitudinal splitting, extensive intra-ply fibre defibrillation and inter-ply separation. Under tension/tension fatigue testing, the extent of longitudinal splitting, fibre defibrillation and fracture was found to increase. The predominance of these failure modes under tension/tension fatigue loading was found to be a function of the applied peak stress. The most obvious and predominant feature that was observed in the all-Kevlar composites subjected to tension/compression fatigue cycling was the development of extensive surface abrasion damage on the Kevlar fibres. Surface temperature increases up to 45 °C above ambient were recorded during the fatigue testing of the UD all-Kevlar composites. These high temperature excursions were always observed just prior to failure. The specimens which were subjected to comparatively high compressive stresses during tension/compression cycling exhibited a planar fracture surface. The macroscopic failure modes observed for the unidirectional all-carbon composite was transverse fracture followed by longitudinal splitting. Under tension/tension fatigue cycling, longitudinal splitting was observed to develop early in the fatigue life of the specimens. In general, the effect of these longitudinal cracks was to initiate delamination of the surface plies in the form of discrete strips. Under tension/compression loading, the rate of delamination development was observed to be greater when compared to the tension/tension tested specimens. Under tension/tension fatigue testing, no obvious differences were observed in the macroscopic failure modes for the hybrid composites when compared with the all-carbon composite. However, under tension/compression fatigue testing, patches of delaminations were seen to develop on the outer Kevlar plies.

Peijs *et al.* (1990) investigated the mechanical properties of unidirectional high-performance polyethylene (HP–PE)/carbon fibres in epoxy resin. The influence of composition and adhesion level of the HP–PE fibres on the mechanical properties of the hybrid was described. It was also found that the compressive strength and initial, dynamic and long-term modulus follow the rule of mixtures. Other properties, e.g. vibrational damping, tensile and shear strength were lower than predicted by the mixtures rule. They attributed the enhancement of the failure strain of the carbon component to a hybrid effect. The work of fracture of untreated HP–PE hybrids obtained by impact testing showed a strong positive deviation from the rule of mixtures. Peijs and De Kok (1993) investigated the tensile properties of unidirectional carbon–polyethylene/epoxy hybrid composites. They noted a positive hybrid effect with surface-treated polyethylene fibres.

In summary, a brief review has been presented of previous research on techniques to modify the mechanical and fatigue properties of fibre-reinforced composites. Whilst extensive research has been reported on techniques to improve the fracture toughness and impact response of composites, relatively little in comparison has been published on the fatigue, especially the tension/compression and compression/compression fatigue, of hybrid composites.

The following section presents a view on the difficulties of comparing fatigue data from different laboratories.

7.2   Comparison of fatigue data

With reference to certification of FRC components and structures, a defined fatigue loading test regime tends to form part of the requirements. Fatigue testing can be performed under tension, compression, shear, flexural loads or some combination of these methods (e.g. Curtis, 1989a,b). The fatigue behaviour of composites can be influenced by several factors including specimen size and geometry, grip pressure, specimen alignment, smoothness of the free edges, stress ratio, test frequency, temperature, environmental effects, the nature of the interfacial bond strength and processing method used to manufacture the composite. Therefore, it is often very difficult to perform meaningful cross-comparison of fatigue data generated by different research groups for a similar FRC. This is also the case where the composite is modified with additional resin layers or reinforcing fibres. The following section presents an overview of some of these issues.

7.2.1   Resin quality and interface issues

A factor that has received relatively little attention is the effect of the 'age' of the resin system on the fatigue sensitivity of FRCs. For example, the shelf-life of common high-performance prepreg systems is generally 18 months when stored at −18 °C. However, the cure schedule that is employed in practice does not take into account the number of times the prepreg is thawed and re-stored at −18 °C. Undoubtedly, this issue is regulated in a commercial production environment but it is hardly mentioned in published academic literature. Differential scanning calorimetry (DSC) is frequently used to assess the enthalpy of cure of thermosetting resin systems. Whilst DSC can yield valuable information on the total (bulk) enthalpy of cure, experiments have to be designed specifically to study the reactions at surfaces and interfaces. In other words, conventional analytical techniques may not be appropriate for assessing the chemical and physical ageing of resin systems, the migration of additives or their preferential adsorption or chemisorption on the surface of the fibres and interfaces. This issue was highlighted recently in an elegant study reported by Vickers et al. (2000), where time-of-flight surface ion mass spectrometry (SIMS) detected the presence of a common mould-release agent on the fracture surface of carbon-fibre composites that was fabricated from prepreg tape. The origin of the mould-release agent, polydimethylsiloxane, was said to be from the protective films on the surfaces of the prepreg tape. This then raises a number of other concerns about the influence of this mould release on previous research that involved the used of prepreg-based preforms. It is possible that the use of low-molecular-weight processing additives may be volatilized at the processing temperatures and vacuum.

In general, researchers do not have ready access to details of the specific nature of the fibre surface treatments and coupling agents used as this tends to be proprietary information. Furthermore, surface treated fibres may be stored for extended periods prior to resin impregnation. There is little information available on the integrity of the interfacial bond strength on the fatigue sensitivity of a fresh resin system compared to one that is nearing the end of its shelf-life. The use of low-molecular-weight processing additives in resin formulations was discussed previously but it is likely to play a prominent part in mechanical tests designed to study the nature of the interfaces. Although quasi-static tests such as interlaminar shear and hot–wet compression tests have a bearing on the matrix-dominated properties, they are not sensitive to the subtle changes in the interfacial bond strength. On the other hand, the low-load, high-cycle fatigue test is sensitive to these changes. However, on account of economic reasons and time constraints, fatigue tests are generally terminated at 10^6 cycles and the data are reported as run-outs.

7.2.2   Manufacturing method and quality control of FRC

A number of techniques are available for manufacturing flat-plate test specimens including autoclaving, hot-pressing, filament winding, resin-transfer moulding and associated variants, pultrusion and hand-lay-up. With reference to published literature in the public domain, the manufacturing and quality-control procedures are seldom in compliance with a common specification. Parameters such as the tension on the fibre during manufacture (for filament winding and pultrusion), residual fabrication strains, void content, and fibre waviness are seldom considered or quantified. The waviness or undulations in the reinforcing layers are important features when considering any form of compressive loading on the FRC. Also, it has been shown that voids can significantly reduce the mechanical properties and fatigue resistance of fibre-reinforced polymer composites (Thomason, 1995). Voids can be caused by degassing, incomplete wetting out or improper ply consolidation, which leads to the entrapment of air. Voids may also be caused by the entrapment of volatiles produced during the cure of the composite (Cable, 1991). In general, a common technique that is used to assess the macroscopic quality of the composite is ultrasonic C-scanning. Whilst significant advances have been made with regard to user-friendly software for data analysis and probe design, the minimum flaw size that can be detected using this technique is in the range 0.2–0.5 mm.

Practical issues such as the method used to cut out the test specimens from a large flat plate also need to be considered as the cutting methodology can induce damage in the FRC. Previous research by Fernando (1989) and Dickson *et al.* (1989) showed that polishing the edges of the composite test specimen resulted in a significant reduction in the scatter for unidirectional glass, carbon and Kevlar composites. This was attributed to the fact that polishing down to 0.5 μm removed surface scratches and damage caused by the cutting operation.

7.2.3 Fatigue machine

Parameters such as waveform control and amplitude control are important prerequisites in obtaining reliable and repeatable fatigue data. The mode of control of the loading regime can also have an important bearing on the apparent fatigue data. For example, data generated under position-control (actuator position control) could be suspect because it is difficult to guarantee that the specimen does not experience any slippage and the data will be invalid if the test specimen creeps. The majority of the fatigue data reported in the literature have been generated under load-control. For materials such as glass-fibre-reinforced composites, they can undergo significant stiffness reductions as a function of fatigue-induced damage. In such circumstances, the fatigue machine must be capable of detecting this reduction of the stiffness and the actuator must be capable of delivering the required load at the specified cyclic frequency. The new generation of fatigue machines perform this adjustment automatically, but in general, the older machines required a manual adjustment. Strain-controlled fatigue experiments may be ideal for multi-component FRC but the primary difficulties associated here tends to be delaminations of the outer plies. Surface-mounted extensometers can also cause friction-induced heating and indentation into the test specimen.

7.2.4 Test frequency and gripping

The use of high frequency in the fatigue test can result in increased heat generation in the test specimens. Furthermore, for rate-sensitive materials such as glass-fibre composites, it is necessary to carry out the fatigue tests at a constant rate of stress application (Sims and Gladman, 1978). This means that the cyclic frequency is a function of the peak stress used in the fatigue test. Therefore, to maintain a constant rate of loading for the tests, the samples tested at higher loads will have a correspondingly lower frequency compared to the tests carried out at lower peak stresses. It has been shown that end-tab failure can be caused by the hysteretic heating of the adhesive used to bond the end-tabs (Curtis and Moore, 1983).

The mode of gripping the test specimen can also have an influence on damage development, for example, longitudinal splitting and delaminations can originate in the vicinity of the gripped area. At present, it is not clear if the mode of gripping, i.e. parallel-action or wedge-action grips, can influence the rate and nature of damage initiation and propagation. In general, the clamping force for the test specimen is often not specified or standardized. The issue of the gripping-pressure was found to be significant in damage development in carbon/Kevlar hybrid composites when tested under tension/compression loading (Fernando, 1989).

7.2.5 Compressive loading

The introduction of a compressive element into the loading regime is not simple and can be difficult to achieve on a consistent basis. The preferred methodology involves the deployment of a jig to prevent the specimen from buckling or in some instances, specimens of short gauge length are used. There is evidence to suggest that the observed damage modes in the FRC when using anti-buckling jigs can influence the nature and rate of damage initiation and propagation (Fernando, 1989). Tension–compression fatigue has received little coverage compared to tension–tension fatigue with much less information being available. The test is often described as difficult to perform and complex to interpret (e.g. Rotem and Nelson, 1989).

With regard to the above discussion, it is readily apparent that cross-comparison of fatigue data from different studies is not straightforward and there is a need for standard-ization in fabrication, processing and test protocols. In conclusion, as regards fatigue experiments involving organic-matrix fibre-reinforced composites, there is a requirement for a full life-cycle analysis approach to be adopted. This means that, for a fundamental understanding of the fatigue properties of composites, the whole life history of the constituent materials, the processing routes used and the test methodology need to be considered in any modelling or experimental-based studies. In the meantime, empirical or semi-empirical-based approaches, although time consuming, material specific and rela-tively expensive to conduct, may offer the best way forward.

7.3   Materials and experimental procedures

7.3.1   Materials

7.3.1.1   Selection criteria
The selection criteria for the fibres and resin were based on: (i) reinforcing fibres with specified stiffness and failure strains; (ii) short fibres that were capable of acting as crack-arrestors and to reinforce the interleaf layers; (iii) continuous fibre with a high failure strain and ductility. The ease of fibre separation was also another requirement as these fibres were spread out and placed transverse to the primary reinforcing fibres. Thus fibres were to be deployed as crack-arrestors and also to 'pin' and restrict the extent of longitudinal splitting; and (iv) interleaf resin which had a significantly higher failure strain and toughness when compared to the primary matrix. Table 7.1 lists a selection of the properties of the fibres employed in this study.

7.3.1.2   Prepreg
The prepreg material chosen for this study was Fibredux 913G-E-5–30% (Ciba Geigy, UK). The prepreg was supplied as rolls of tape 300 mm wide. The prepreg was stored in a dry sealed container at –18 °C according to the manufacturer's recommendations. Prior to lay-

Table 7.1   Selected fibre properties for: E-glass (Hull, 1981); polyethylene (Dyneema® 1988), silicon carbide (Tyrano Fibre, 1992; Harris, 1991; Hiramatsu and Nishimura, 1989)

Fibre type	E-glass	Polyethylene	Silicon carbide
Fibre density (g cm^{-3})	2.56	0.97	2.3–2.4
Tensile strength (GPa)	3.65	2.7	3.18
Young's modulus (GPa)	76	87.0	177.0
Failure strain (%)	1.8–3.2	3.5	1.8–1.9
Fibre diameter (μm)	8.9–10.2	12	8.5

up, the prepreg was removed from the freezer and left to thaw at room temperatι removing it from sealed container (Ciba Geigy, 1988, 1991).

7.3.1.3   Fibres and resins used for hybridization

Polyethylene
Dyneema SK60 fibres were donated by DSM High-Performance Fibres B.V. The polyethylene tow fibres consisted of 665 filaments.

Short E-glass
The short E-glass fibres, 3 mm long, with an epoxy-compatible size were supplied by Fibreglass Ltd. The fibres were dried at 60 °C in an oven for one week and then stored in a dessicator until required.

Silicon carbide
The silicon carbide fibres were donated by Tyrano Fibre. The fibre bundle, which consisted of 800 filaments, was sized with an epoxy resin coupling agent.

Fibredux 913 and 920
Two kinds of resin films with different properties were used as the interleaf layers, namely, Fibredux 913 and 920. They were supplied in film-form from the manufacturer. Similar storage procedure to that used for the prepregs was used for the resin films.

7.3.2   Manufacture of composites

7.3.2.1   General lay-up procedure
After removing the prepregs from storage at −18 °C and allowing them to thaw-out, the prepregs were cut into sheets 300 mm × 280 mm using a guillotine. A vacuum-assisted hand lay-up template was designed and built to assist in the alignment of the prepregs during the laying-up stage.

Consolidation of one prepreg layer onto the previous layer was carried out by the use of a smooth roller. This method of consolidation was essential to expel entrapped air between the prepreg plies. The composites manufactured in this programme consisted of 16 plies of prepreg. The laminated prepregs were cured on a hot-press as soon as they were laid-up. Unidirectional glass and carbon-fibre composites (reference, i.e. unmodified) were laid-up using this procedure.

7.3.2.2   Manufacture of interleaved composites
The interleaved composites were manufactured by the following procedure. The first layer of the prepreg was secured to the lay-up table with a piece of double-sided masking-tape. The pre-cut resin film was then stacked and pressed onto another pre-cut prepreg sheet. The two layers were consolidated and the backing film on the resin side was carefully removed then stacked and consolidated on the prepreg which was secured on the laying-up table. The interleaf resin was introduced between each layer of the prepreg.

7.3.2.3   Manufacture of hybrid fibre composites
Continuous polyethylene fibre/glass hybrids: After securing the first layer of prepreg on the lay-up table, a tow of the polyethylene was secured at one-end with double-sided tape. The polyethylene fibres were separated with a fine-tooth comb. The separated fibres were then placed above two parallel metal rollers. Once a satisfactory level of fibre separation had been

achieved (visual estimation), the opposite ends of the fibres were secured with double-sided tape. A clean roller was then used to press the fibres onto the prepreg layer. This method allowed a degree of control of the alignment of the hybrid polyethylene fibre. Subsequent layers of prepregs and polyethylene fibres were then introduced in the same way as described previously.

Short E-Glass and SiC fibre/glass hybrid
Short E-Glass/E-Glass/Epoxy Composites: 2.5 g of short E-glass fibres were randomly distributed at each of the ply interfaces of the 16 ply composite. A fine brush was used in an attempt to distribute the short fibres in a uniform manner over the prepreg surface. However, it was not possible to control the relative orientation and distribution of the short E-glass fibres with any degree of consistency.

Short SiC/E-Glass/Epoxy composites
A similar procedure to that described above was used to manufacture the short SiC/E-glass/ epoxy composites. 0.8 to 0.9 g of SiC short fibres were randomly distributed at each ply interface. In both these cases, attention was paid in consolidating the prepregs to reducing the possibility of entrapped air. Care was also taken to avoid the contamination of the prepreg and fibre surfaces during lay-up.

7.3.2.4   Curing of the prepregs
All the laminated prepregs were cured in a hot-press. A custom-made aluminium mould, of dimensions 300 mm × 280 mm, was used to cure the prepregs. The laminated prepregs were cured according to the manufacturer's recommended cure schedule.

7.3.2.5   Coding of the composites
In order to identify the modified composites from each other, a code system was used, a complete description of which is given in Table 7.2.

7.3.2.6   Quality control of composites
The quality control of the composites was checked by ultrasonic C-scanning. Visual

Table 7.2   A description for the composite coding system used in this study

Composite system	Code
Glass fibre reinforced 913 epoxy resin (reference material)	G913
Glass fibre reinforced 913 epoxy resin and interleaved with 16 layers of 913 epoxy resin	G913/913
Glass fibre reinforced 913 epoxy resin and interleaved with 16 layers of 920 epoxy resin	G913/920
Glass fibre reinforced 913 epoxy resin and randomly reinforced with short silicon carbide fibres	G913/SiC
Glass fibre reinforced 913 epoxy resin and randomly reinforced with long polyethylene fibres oriented at 90° to glass fibres	G913/PE
Glass fibre reinforced 913 epoxy resin and randomly reinforced with short glass fibres	G913/G

In this table, the first alphabetic letter refers to the primary reinforcing fibre, ie., G = E-glass. This is followed by three digits representing the resin type, 913 = Fibredux 913. The modified composites are represented by a slash (/). The next three digits after the slash represent the interleaved composites, i.e. /913 = interleaved with Fibredux 913 resin and /920 = interleaved with Fibredux 920 resin. The hybrid fibre composites are represented by upper case letters, i.e. /SiC, /G and /PE for hybrids of short random SiC fibres at the interface, short random E-glass fibres at the interface and continuous polyethylene fibres introduced at 90° to the primary fibres.

inspection was also carried out by using an optical microscope on polished sections which were previously cut out from the composite panels. Two techniques were used to determine the fibre volume fraction: burn-off and image analysis. The former was used for laminates containing glass fibres whereas the latter was used for the hybrid fibre composites. In the burn-off method, the average from six specimens was used and for the image analysis, the average of 12 frames was used.

7.3.3 Tensile and fatigue tests

All tests were carried out in ambient laboratory conditions (temperature = 23 °C, relative humidity = 50%). The dimensions of the tensile and fatigue specimens were standardized at 200 mm long by 20 mm wide with a gauge length of 100 mm. The test specimens were end-tabbed with aluminium tabs by using conventional procedures. The tensile mechanical properties were measured in an Instron 1195 machine of 100 kN capacity at a cross-head speed of 2 mm/minute. The strain was measured with an extensometer over a 50 mm gauge length.

Fatigue tests were carried out under constant amplitude in a servo-hydraulic Instron testing machine model 8501. The tension–tension fatigue tests were carried out at a loading rate of 500 kN s^{-1}, however, the loading rate for the tension–compression fatigue was reduced to 250 kN s^{-1} because the fatigue machine could not maintain the required amplitude. Because of time constraints, all the fatigue tests were stopped at 10^6 cycles if the specimens had not failed. The fatigue data were logged via custom-written software (Badcock, 1993). An anti-buckling guide was necessary to support the specimen and stop it buckling during tension–compression fatigue. The jig design was based on that proposed by Curtis (1985). Preliminary tension–compression fatigue tests showed that the unidirectional test specimens slipped especially when high loads were applied. The anti-buckling jig was modified at the gripping area by machining slots 0.4 mm deep. A schematic diagram of the modified jig is given in Fig. 7.2.

7.3.4 Other mechanical characterization techniques

Flexural, interlaminar shear strength (ILSS), double cantilever beam tests for G_{Ic} determinations and end-notch flexure (Mode II) tests were also used to characterize the composites. The sample geometry of double cantilever beam specimens used was based on the standard proposed by the European Structural Integrity Society Polymer and Composites Task Group (Davies, 1992).

7.3.5 Thermal analysis

This study was undertaken in order to define a criterion for processing the hybrid resin composites. This was necessary as the cure schedules specified by the resin supplier were specific for a single resin system, and furthermore, the recommended processing parameters were different for the two resins used in this study. Differential thermal analysis (DSC) experiments were conducted in a Perkin-Elmer model DSC-7 which was previously calibrated with high-purity indium and tin. Sample masses between 5 and 10 mg were placed in open aluminium pans and cured in the DSC with either a constant temperature ramp rate or isothermal conditions. All the experiments were carried out in a nitrogen gas flow of 20 ml/minute.

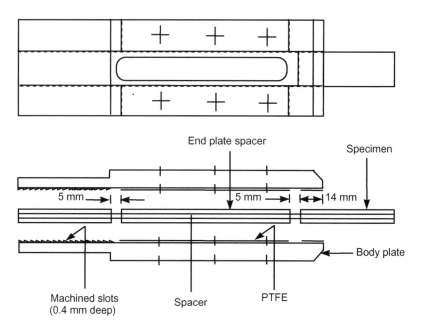

Fig. 7.2   Schematic illustration of the anti-buckling jigs used in the tension/compression fatigue
tests.

7.4   Results and discussion

7.4.1   Cure behaviour

A summary of the enthalpy of cure from isothermal DSC experiments for the various resins
and prepreg systems is presented in Table 7.3.

In DSC experiments where the epoxy resin is cured under isothermal conditions, a
relationship between the heat developed during the cure H_t and the extent of reaction α is
assumed (Prime, 1981; Dusi *et al.*, 1987): i.e.

$$\alpha = \frac{H_t}{H_{ult}} \qquad\qquad [7.1]$$

$$\frac{d\alpha}{dt} = \left(\frac{1}{H_{ult}}\right)\frac{dH}{dt} \qquad\qquad [7.2]$$

where H_{ult} is the total heat developed in the process at full conversion.

Table 7.3   The apparent heat cure (H_{iso}) for the isothermal tests obtained at different temperatures

Material system	90 °C	100 °C	110 °C	120 °C	130 °C	140 °C	150 °C
Fibredux 913	−349.2	−386.5	−396.0	−412.4	−441.5	−465.3	−497.0
Fibredux 920	−236.8	−257.5	−284.1	−326.2	−334.1	−344.6	−344.6
Hybrid resin system	−252.2	−259.5	−306.4	−345.8	−387.9	−404.5	−409.3
Glass/913 prepreg	−373.8	−378.0	−384.3	−420.5	−444.9	−460.1	−517.6
Glass/913-920 hybrid	−304.4	−317.5	−328.4	−372.7	−387.9	−404.5	−407.3

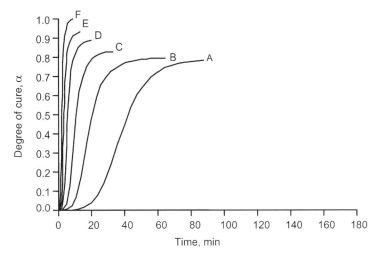

Fig. 7.3   The degree of cure for the Fibredux 913 measured by DSC as a function of time for six isothermal temperatures (A = 100 °C, B = 110 °C, C = 120 °C, D = 130 °C, E = 140 °C and F = 150 °C).

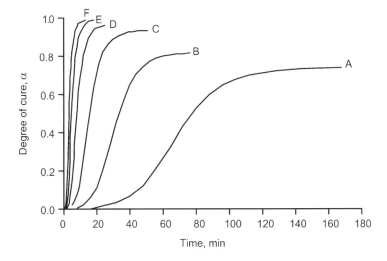

Fig. 7.4   The degree of cure for the Fibredux 920 measured by DSC as a function of time for six isothermal temperatures (A = 100 °C, B = 110 °C, C = 120 °C, D = 130 °C, E = 140 °C and F = 150 °C).

The isothermal reaction rate $d\alpha/dt$ for the two resin systems used in this current study was calculated from the DSC plots. The reaction rate was found to be proportional to the applied temperature, i.e., the rate is higher at high temperatures and vice versa. Typical plots of the extent of reaction versus cure time for the Fibredux 913 and 920 are illustrated in Figs. 7.3 and 7.4, respectively. The total enthalpy of the cure reaction and the reactions rates were found to be higher for the Fibredux 913 resin at each of the temperatures. Significant voiding was observed in the cured Fibredux 920 resin system and this may account for the trend observed in Table 7.3.

The cure of epoxy resins has been frequently considered as an autocatalytic reaction. The general kinetic equation that has been used to describe the autocatalytic reaction is as follows (Sourour and Kamal, 1976):

$$r = (k_1 + k_2\alpha^m)(1 - \alpha)^n \qquad\qquad [7.3]$$

where $r = d\alpha/dt$, k_1 and k_2 are the apparent rate constants, which represent the autocatalytic nature of the reaction, and m and n are constants related to the order of the reactions.

This model has been successfully applied to autocatalytic polymerization reactions where one of the by-products of the cure process acts as a catalyst for the reaction (Sourour and Kamal, 1976; Ryan and Dutta, 1979).

The applicability of equation [7.3] for the two resin systems was investigated by plotting the reduced reaction rate $[r/(1 - \alpha)^n]$ against conversion α: the reaction order n was assumed to be unity. With reference to Fig. 7.5, excellent agreement was observed between the experimental predicted cure behaviour for Fibredux 913. This agreement was observed for all the temperatures investigated in this study, including the cure behaviour of the glass-fibre prepregs. It is apparent from Fig. 7.6 that the cure characteristics of the Fibredux 920 resin showed some deviation from the predicted trend at the higher processing temperatures. This deviation was also observed in the prepreg with this resin system. The issue of voiding in the DSC samples was mentioned in the previous section for this resin. Although the actual reasons for this voiding were not investigated, the following factors may be contributing: (i) absorbed moisture; (ii) residual solvent; (iii) dissolved gases; and (iv) entrapped air during sample preparation.

In equation [7.3], the rate constants k_1 and k_2 were assumed to follow an Arrhenius relationship:

$$k_i = c_i \exp\left(\frac{-E_i}{RT}\right) \qquad\qquad [7.4]$$

$$i = 1, 2$$

where T is absolute temperature, R is the gas constant, c_i and E_i are the Arrhenius parameters to be estimated.

The activation energies corresponding to the autocatalytic and diffusion-controlled reactions E_i, as well as the pre-exponential factors (c_i) for the materials, were obtained from linear regression and are given in Table 7.4. These activation values can be utilized to describe the cure kinetics of the two resins and prepregs at the processing temperatures of interest. On the basis of the previous results and discussion, the following cure schedule for the hybrid epoxy resin and for E-glass/913-Fibredux 920 was used:

(i) apply 0.80 MPa pressure; (ii) heat from room temperature to 140 °C at a heating rate of 2 °C min^{-1}; (iii) hold for 30 minutes at 140 °C; and (iv) cool to room temperature before releasing pressure and removing component.

Table 7.4   Values for the activation energies and pre-exponential factors for the neat resin and prepeg systems investigated

Material system	Ea_0 (kJ mol^{-1})	Ea_1 (kJ mol^{-1})	Ea_2 (kJ mol^{-1})	C_0 (s^{-1})	C_1 (s^{-1})	C_2 (s^{-1})
Fibredux 913	205.9	78.3	69.9	56.2	23.7	21.3
Fibredux 920	96.6	77.0	63.9	25.0	22.8	18.8
913-920 hybrid resin system	144.5	87.0	72.4	38.4	25.9	21.6
Glass/913 prepreg	103.9	69.8	63.2	27.2	20.8	18.9
Glass/913/920 hybrid	178.8	83.1	75.7	48.6	24.8	22.5

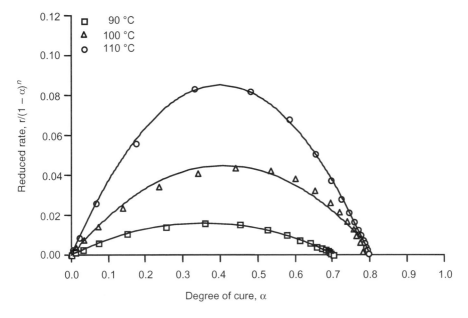

Fig. 7.5   Reduced reaction rate as a function of degree of cure for Fibredux 913 neat resin when $n = 1$. The solid lines represent the predicted behaviour.

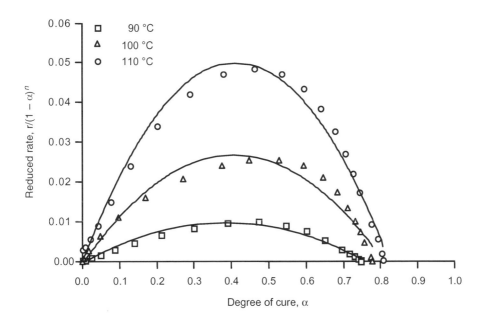

Fig. 7.6   Reduced reaction rate as a function of degree of cure for glass/913 prepreg-Fibredux 920 hybrid system when $n = 1$. The solid lines represent the predicted behaviour.

7.4.2   Quasi-static mechanical properties

A selection of the typical stress/strain curves for unidirectional Fibredux glass/epoxy, hybrid resin and hybrid fibre composites is shown in Fig. 7.7(a). A summary of the tensile test results is presented in Table 7.5.

7.4.2.1   Tensile properties

With reference to Fig. 7.7, a degree of non-linearity was observed for all the composites evaluated in this programme. The average strains at which the non-linearity was observed

Table 7.5   Summary of mechanical properties for the mono fibre and hybrid composites. The number in parentheses represents the standard deviation: (i) tensile strength; (ii) Young's modulus; (iii) modulus at failure; (iv) normalized modulus; (v) failure strain; (vi) strain at deviation; (vii) fibre volume fraction; (viii) void content; (ix) flexural strength; (x) flexural modulus; (xi) interlaminar shear strength (ILSS); (xii) G_{1c} initiation; (xiii) G_{1c} at propagation; (xiv)$G_{IIc\ C,\ D,\ E}$

Material	G913	G913/913	G913/920	G913/SiC	G913/PE	G913/G
Tensile strength (GPa)	1.16	0.96	0.74	1.19	1.22	1.16
	(0.04)	(0.05)	(0.03)	(0.04)	(0.03)	(0.03)
Young's Modulus (GPa)	43.69	39.75	36.74	45.85	44.71	45.51
	(5.2)	(3.9)	(4.7)	(4.2)	(3.5)	(3.2)
Modulus at failure (GPa)	39.42	36.01	34.15	42.11	40.24	42.81
	(1.1)	(0.5)	(0.2)	(0.6)	(0.5)	(0.9)
Normalized Young's Modulus (GPa)^A	41.4	43.0	40.2	43.1	44.2	43.6
Failure strain (%)	2.93	2.66	2.05	2.90	3.02	2.82
	(0.08)	(0.02)	(0.05)	(0.06)	(0.09)	(0.05)
Strain at deviation (%)^B	1.37	1.58	0.93	1.10	1.29	1.97
	(0.08)	(0.12)	(0.13)	(0.09)	(0.08)	(0.16)
Fibre volume fraction (%)	62.2	54.5	53.8	62.7	59.5	61.5
	(1.6)	(2.2)	(2.1)	(2.3)	(2.7)	(1.3)
Void content (%)	0.6	1.9	2.5	2.1	2.0	1.6
	(0.2)	(0.15)	(0.22)	(0.18)	(0.14)	(0.2)
Flexural strength (MPa)	1500.2	1159.7	958.6	1447.9	1501.1	1489.1
	(85.7)	(37.5)	(35.2)	(53.3)	(32.9)	(46.5)
Flexural modulus (GPa)	48.7	47.0	43.9	43.8	44.6	43.7
	(1.7)	(1.9)	(1.5)	(0.8)	(1.0)	(1.3)
ILSS (MPa)	83.0	83.7	82.6	82.3	80.6	81.4
	(4.0)	(2.4)	(2.2)	(2.7)	(1.9)	(2.8)
G_{1c} at initiation (J m^{-2})	319.0	358.0	557.4	276.0	407.5	232.6
	(36.7)	(43.6)	(60.2)	(14.1)	(25.2)	(51.8)
G_{1C} at propagation (J m^{-2})	396.5	553.1	614.9	390.0	903.1	339.0
	(36.2)	(43.6)	(57.0)	(4.0)	(18.1)	(23.4)
G_{IIc} (J m^{-2})^C	265.1	448.2	808.4	4117.8	465.5	458.9
	(28.3)	(35.1)	(42.6)	(23.5)	(26.2)	(21.9)
G_{IIc} (J m^{-2})^D	422.2	497.5	1211.0	1024.0	868.1	867.0
	(20.2)	(23.2)	(28.2)	(28.2)	(11.2)	(18.0)
G_{IIc} (J m^{-2})^E	554.4	662.9	1792.3	1324.0	2118.4	1622.0
	(19.1)	(24.6)	(25.3)	(12.0)	(14.4)	(18.5)

A = normalized to 58.9% fibre volume fractions.
B = deviation from linearity in the stress/strain diagram.
C = calculated from the point of deviation from linearity of the load/displacement (L/D) trace.
D = calculation based on the visually observed deviation from linearity of the L/D trace.
E = calculation based on the peak load.

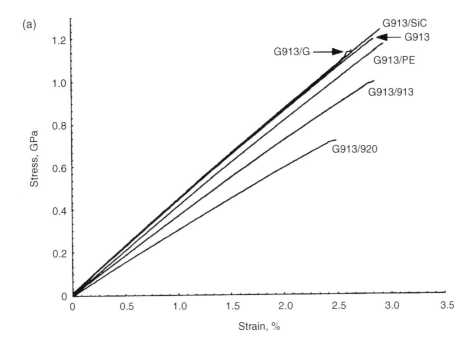

Fig. 7.7(a) Selection of typical stress–strain curves for the mono fibre and hybrid composites.

are also summarized in Table 7.5. No obvious correlation was found between the onset of deviation from linearity for the composites investigated in this study. However, the G913/920 composite exhibited deviation from linearity at an average of 0.93% strain. Possible reasons for the observed non-linearity in the various composites evaluated may be attributed to the following.

Non-linear behaviour of the matrix
Attempts to cast Fibredux 920 resin into plaques were not successful and hence it was not possible to establish the stress/strain behaviour for this resin. The failure strain reported by the manufacturer is in excess of 6%. It may be reasonable to expect a relatively small contribution from the non-linear stress/strain behaviour for the resin to be reflected in the unidirectional composite.

Introduction of the hybrid fibres
Another factor that could have contributed to the observed non-linear behaviour for the hybrid fibre composites is the presence of the hybrid fibres. In other words, the presence of the hybrid fibres may have caused localized undulations in the primary reinforcing fibres.

Non-linear behaviour of the reinforcing fibres

Fibre curvature and waviness
The composites manufactured in this programme were hot-pressed in a mould. Although the extent of resin leakage was kept to a minimum, it was not possible to control the leakage on a consistent basis. The consequence of this was a degree of induced fibre curvature. No attempt was made to quantify the extent of fibre curvature. Obviously, with increasing the resin volume fraction, as in the case with interleaving, the probability of fibre movement during the cure operation is much higher. Increasing the resin volume fraction by interleaving

Fig. 7.7(b)   Illustration of typical macroscopic failure modes observed for the composites investigated in this study.

may also increase the probability of entrapped air at the ply interface. Although not reported here, the viscosity profiles for the Fibredux 913 and 920 resins were different. For example, the resin viscosity at the gel-point for isothermal experiments conducted at 140 °C were 9.2 and 3.9 kPas for the Fibredux 913 and 920, respectively (Al-Khodairi, 1996). An issue that has not been considered here is the induced undulation of the reinforcing fibres as a consequence of the presence of the interleaf resin. In other words, the higher resin volume fraction gives the reinforcing fibres a degree of freedom to move during processing thus introducing waviness and undulation in the reinforcing fibres. Fibre waviness is also thought to contribute towards improvements in the G_{IC} and G_{IIC} values of FRCs (Hunston *et al.* (1987).

Tensile strength

The ultimate tensile strength for the G913 quoted by the manufacturer was 1.5 GPa. This is somewhat higher than the average value obtained in this study and the reason for this discrepancy was not established. The tensile strengths reported by other researchers for the G913 composite are as follows: 1.4 GPa (Dickson *et al.*, 1989), 1.32 GPa (Partridge *et al.*, 1989), 1.1 GPa (Barnard *et al.*, 1985) and 1.21 GPa (Manders and Bader, 1981a,b).

Modulus

As expected, the modulus at 0.5% strain was lower for the hybrid resin composites. In order to facilitate comparison of the different composites, the data were normalized to the average fibre volume fraction (58.9%). With reference to Table 7.5, the normalized initial modulus values for the hybrid resin composites are comparable to the reference unmodified G913 composite. A range of 43.7–49.9 GPa was cited by the supplier of the G913 prepreg and this range is similar to that obtained in this study.

Failure strain

The failure strain data presented in Table 7.5 gives an interesting insight into the effects of hybridization of the glass/913 prepreg system. Hybridization with polyethylene fibres resulted in an average failure strain of 3.02% compared to 2.93% which was obtained for the parent (unmodified) composite. As will be seen later, the hybridization with polyethylene fibres resulted in a transformation in the macroscopic failure of the GRP composite. The brush-like failure generally associated with GRP was not observed. The failure strains of the SiC and short-glass-fibre hybrids were within the experimental scatter of the unmodified parent composite. The failure strain of 2.05% for the systems interleaved with Fibredux 920 resin can be attributed to the relatively high void content (2.5%) and the difficulties associated with the manufacture of this interleaved composite. Fibre waviness may have also contributed to the relatively lower failure strains for the interleaved hybrid composites. With reference to the short-fibre hybrids, the large tow thickness could influence the perturbations caused to the primary reinforcing fibres and this warrants further investigation. Representative photographs of the macroscopic failure modes for the all-glass and hybrid glass-fibre composites are presented in Fig. 7.7(b). A discussion on these failure modes is considered in a subsequent section. However, the change in the macroscopic failure mode upon hybridization is readily apparent in Fig. 7.7(b).

Flexural properties

The flexural strength of the hybrid resin composites was reduced by 22.7% for the G913/913 composite and 36.1% for the G913/920 composite when compared to the reference G913 composites. The reduction in flexural modulus was 3.5% for the G913/913 composite and 9.9% for the G913/920 composite. Unlike the hybrid resin composites, the flexural strength of the hybrid fibre composites was similar to the reference G913 composite. The flexural modulus was lower by 10.1% for the G913/SiC composite, 8.4% for the G913/PE composite and 10.1% for the G913/G composite.

Inter-laminar shear strength (ILSS)

Although the fibre volume fractions differ between the glass composites, the ILSS results were almost the same. Unlike the tensile strength and flexural strength results, the ILSS results showed that the hybrid resin composites were not affected by lowering the fibre volume fraction. Similar ILSS results on glass/913 composite were reported by Cui *et al.* (1992).

G_{Ic}

On inspecting the strain-energy release rates summarized in Table 7.5, it is apparent that the Fibredux 920 resin successfully increased the G_{Ic} at initiation by 75% over the reference G913 composite: this is in spite of the relatively high void content present in this composite (2.5%). As mentioned previously, the voiding in the G913/920 composites was primarily associated with the difficulties encountered in transferring the resin film onto the prepregs. The observed improvement in the G_{Ic} at initiation may be attributed to the inherent toughness of the Fibredux 920 resin and its ability to undergo extensive plastic deformation as observed in the post-failed samples. The relative improvements in the G_{Ic} at initiation for the G913/913 and G913/PE were 12% and 27.7%, respectively. The incorporation of short fibre reinforcements in the form of glass and silicon carbide fibres did not contribute to an enhancement of the G_{Ic} at initiation. The observed damage modes were interfacial debonding and longitudinal splitting. In the hybrid resin composites, a higher concentration of fibre fractures and fibre pull-out than the G913 composites was observed due to a higher degree of fibre bridging. The fracture surfaces of the hybrid resin composites also showed matrix ductility, particularly, in the G913/920 composite. In the hybrid fibre composites the damage was extensive in the vicinity of the hybrid fibres.

In general, a variation of fibre volume fraction in the hybrid resin composites was not thought to be a major contributing factor to the variation of the G_{Ic} values. A similar observation was reported by Hunston et al. (1987). It is generally accepted that a single value for the G_{Ic} is insufficient to represent fully the composite behaviour under mode I fracture. Rather, it is believed that R curves give a better description of the material behaviour. R curves, which measure the relationship between crack length and G_{Ic}, are able to describe the change in toughness while a crack propagates at the mid-plane interface of laminated composites. Many authors have used R curves and showed their benefit in describing the behaviour of thin composites (for example, Berry, 1963; Davies and Benzeggagh, 1989). From Table 7.5, it can be seen that the G_{Ic} values at initiation were less than those obtained at propagation.

An improvement of 2.3 times was obtained for the G_{Ic} at propagation for the G913/PE composite over the unmodified material. The relative improvements for the G913/913 and G913/920 were 1.4 and 1.6 times that of the unmodified G913 composite, respectively. The observed improvement in the G_{Ic} at propagation for the G913/PE is impressive, and as will be shown later, this was achieved without any detectable deterioration in fatigue properties. A number of factors may have contributed to account for the observed improvement obtained for G913/PE. Firstly, it is possible that the PE fibres, located transverse to the reinforcing fibre direction acted as crack arrestors and/or offered additional mechanisms for crack blunting. The fibre manufacturers had previously subjected the PE fibres to corona surface treatment. In addition to the inherent toughness of the PE fibres, therefore, it is reasonable to assume (i) a degree of bonding between the PE fibres and the matrix because of the corona surface treatment and (ii) crack bridging and retardation of longitudinal crack propagation; the post-failure surface analysis, supports this point of view. Secondly, the cure temperature used in this study (140 °C) would have resulted in the melting and deformation of the thermoplastic PE fibres (128 °C). Inspection of the post-tested composites showed that the post-manufactured cross-section of the PE fibres resembled a ribbon with a width of approximately 15–20 μm. This method of hybridizing may offer a simple route to the production of composites with a periodically spaced interlayer with dimensions not too dissimilar to the primary reinforcing fibres. Another production method could be the use of co-mingled woven fabrics but the difference here will be that the toughening fibres cannot be spread out and separated, as was the case in the G913/PE.

With reference to Table 7.5, and ignoring any justifications for averaging the G_{Ic} values at initiation and propagation, the difference in the mean values for G913/PE and G913/920 is only about 11%. However, on inspecting the other mechanical properties cited in Table 7.5, the G913/PE is seen to exhibit superior properties, for example, the flexural properties are not compromised.

The composites reinforced with E-glass or silicon carbide short fibres did not show high values of fracture toughness when compared with the reference G913 composite. It is proposed that the high shear stress at the fibre-ends may have contributed to this behaviour. Lin and Jang (1990) hybridized G913/SiC and G913/G where the fibres were in the form of short fibre tows and their respective orientation in relation to the primary reinforcing fibres was random. Therefore, the random orientation and the relative thickness of the tows may have induced undulations in the glass fibres. However, it may have been less effective in acting as a crack arrestor inclusion in the prepreg. Although not investigated in this current study, it would be interesting to investigate the effect of reinforcing the G913/920 and G913/913 resin inter-layers with short and continuous fibres.

With reference to designations [C, D and E] in Table 7.5 of the G_{IIc} data, these represent three criteria which were used to compute the GI_{Ic} values: they were calculated at (i) the point of departure from linear behaviour [C], (ii) the point of visual observation of crack onset [D] and (iii) the point of peak load [E].

Improvements in interlaminar fracture toughness of the hybrid resin and the hybrid fibre composites were significantly higher under mode II shear loading than under mode I tensile loading. The general trends for the average G_{IIc} for the hybrid resin (G913/920) and hybrid fibre (G913/PE) were 3.1 and 2.8 times greater, respectively, than that obtained for the unmodified unidirectional G913 composite. Once again the implication here is that the dispersed, transverse and continuous polyethylene fibres offer a unique technique for enhancing the fracture toughness of glass-fibre reinforced composites. On comparing the relative average performance of the G913/913 composite under modes I and II loading conditions, the performance was observed to be lower than that of the G913/920 and G913/PE composites.

With respect to the current study, there are significant difficulties in attempting to rank the various hybrid composites in terms of their fracture toughness for the following reasons. (i) The composites were manufactured by hot-pressing and it was difficult to reproduce the applied pressure for various composites that were manufactured. This was a more significant issue with the hybrid resin composites as the higher resin content may have permitted a degree of fibre movement during processing. This may have part-contributed to the observed non-linear behaviour in the load/displacement traces. However, other researchers have reported non-linear behaviour for toughened resin systems, for example, Carlsson *et al.* (1986). Processing the hybrids in an autoclave rather than a hot-press will offer better control on the viscosity/pressure during processing. Although not reported here, the viscosity/temperature profiles were established for the individual resin and prepreg systems used in this study and the viscosity of the Fibredux 920 resin was significantly lower at 140 °C. (ii) The relative crack propagation paths for the modified composites are different and it is difficult to assign relative contributions towards the overall toughness from (a) the ductility of the matrix, (b) fibre bridging, (c) 'nesting', a term coined by Hunston *et al.* (1987) to describe the case where the fibres from adjacent ply interfaces tend to intermingle and (d) other contributing factors such as the complex stress fields at the crack front, extent of fibre pull-out and fracture.

In summary, this study has shown that the modes I and II fracture toughness of commercially available glass-fibre-reinforced epoxy composites can be enhanced by utilizing

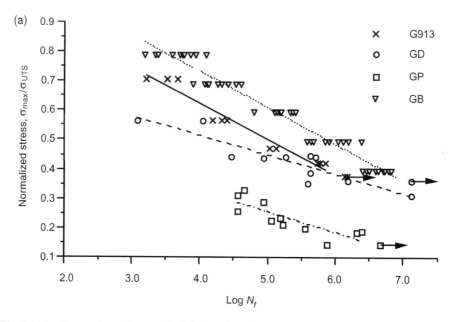

Fig. 7.8(a)   Comparison of normalized fatigue data from four different sources for E-glass/913; GD: (Dickson *et al.*, 1989); GB: (Barnard *et al.*, 1985); GP: (Partridge *et al.*, 1989); and G913 this book.

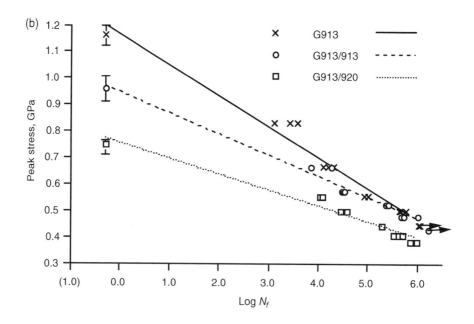

Fig. 7.8(b)   Comparison of the tension/tension fatigue results for the G913 and the hybrid resin composites. The linear best-fit lines were calculated including the UTS.

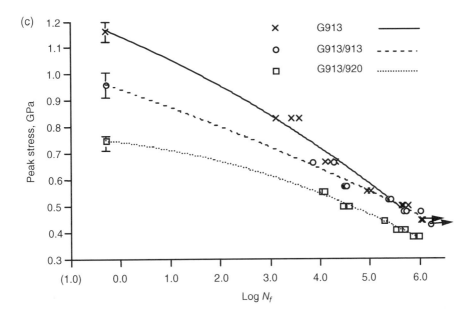

Fig. 7.8(c)   Comparison of the tension/tension fatigue results for the G913 and the hybrid resin composites. A second order fit was calculated including the UTS.

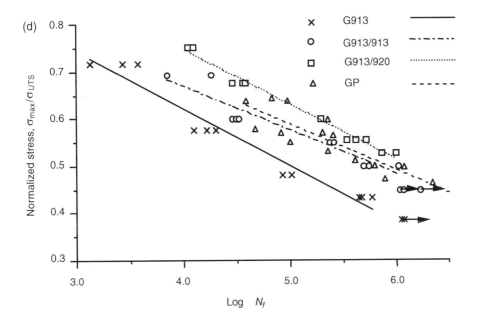

Fig. 7.8(d)   Comparison of the fatigue trends of G913, G913/913, G913/920 and GP composites (Partridge *et al.*, 1989) composite. The best fit lines were calculated excluding the UTS.

Table 7.6(a)   Details of fatigue testing conditions used in the current programmes and those reported by three previous researchers for the G913 composite

Material G913	Lay-up	Stress ratio (R)	UTS (GPa)	V_f (%)	Rate of stress application (kN s^{-1})
Current work	$[0]_{16}$	0.1	1.16	62.3	500
GD	$[0]_{16}$	0.1	1.40	N/A	500
GB	$[0]_{16}$	0.05	1.10	57.0	Fixed frequency 30 Hz
GP	$[0]_{8}$	0.05	1.34	69.0	Fixed frequency 30 Hz

Table 7.6(b)   S–N curve-fitting parameters using equation [7.6] for the G913 and the modified composites: both the hybrid resin and hybrid fibre data are presented

Material	Measured UTS	Equivalent UTS	b	c	b'	c'
G913	1.16	1.14	−0.081	−0.006	−0.069	−0.005
G913/913	0.96	0.94	−0.067	−0.002	−0.074	−0.002
G913/920	0.74	0.74	−0.024	−0.006	−0.027	−0.009
G913/SiC	1.19	1.17	−0.074	−0.008	−0.062	−0.006
G913/PE	1.22	1.20	−0.094	−0.005	−0.077	−0.004
G913/G	1.16	1.14	−0.114	−0.0002	−0.098	−0.0002

Table 7.6(c)   S–N curve-fitting parameter using the linear regression along with the reduction in fatigue strength for the G913 and the modified composites: both the hybrid resin and hybrid results are presented

Material	b	b/UTS (%)
G913	−0.140	10.9
G913/913	−0.089	9.0
G913/920	−0.087	9.7
G913/SiC	−0.148	11.0
G913/PE	−0.142	11.0
G913/G	−0.120	10.3

polyethylene hybrid fibres. This hybridization did not result in any significant deterioration in the tensile properties of the modified composite.

7.4.3   Fatigue

7.4.3.1   Tension/tension fatigue of G913 composite

Figure 7.8(a) shows a normalized S–N plot for the G913 composite along with three similar composite systems reported in the literature (Dickson *et al.*, 1989 (coded as GD); Partridge *et al.*, 1989 (coded as GP) and Barnard *et al.*, 1985 (coded as GB)). A summary of the lay-up sequence for the composites and the published data for the test procedure for the four essentially similar composites is presented in Table 7.6(b). The vertical axis in Fig. 7.8(a) represents the peak tensile stress normalized to the respective ultimate tensile strength for each of the composite systems. From Fig. 7.8(a) and Table 7.6(b), a number of features are readily apparent. Firstly, the scatter in data for the G913 and GB composites is significantly less than that seen in the GD and GP specimens. Secondly, the relative slopes for the G913 and GB data set are similar but are significantly different to those reported for the GD and GP composites. The GD and GP fatigue data seem to exhibit a similar slope. Finally, the variations in the fibre volume fractions alone cannot account for the observed differences in the quasi-static and fatigue performance.

From Fig. 7.8(a) and the above discussion, the differences in the fatigue response of G913 (unmodified GRP) may be due to one factor or a combination of factors. On comparing the G913 and GP fatigue results, it is seen that the fatigue lifetime of GP specimens was significantly shorter than the G913 samples at a given stress level. The fatigue behaviour of the GP samples may have been influenced by the high test frequency of 30 Hz which was used. In GP composite, a number of hot spots at approximately 100 °C were recorded on the surface of a few samples (Partridge, 1989). Early work by Sims and Gladman (1978) on a similar composite system showed that the internal temperature of the tested specimens was 28% greater than the surface temperature of the specimens. The glass transition temperature T_g of the G913 composites cured at 120 °C for 60 minutes is approximately 131 °C (Ciba-Geigy, 1988). With respect to the GB composite, no details were given regarding the heat generation and the composite quality. Therefore, it is difficult to explain the reasons behind the better fatigue performance of the GB composite compared with the GP composite. This is despite the fact that both composites were tested at the same frequency and stress ratio. However, it has to be pointed out that on comparing all the data presented in Fig. 7.8(a), the GB data set was generated from a significantly larger data set. The observed variation in the fatigue data may have been due to one or more of the factors that were discussed previously in relation to comparing fatigue data from different laboratories.

7.4.3.2   Tension/tension fatigue of hybrid resin composites

Figure 7.8(b) represents the S–N plots for the G913, G913/913 and G913/920 composites when the UTS is included in a linear-regression fit. The issue of whether the UTS should be included in the description of the fatigue data is debatable. It is customary to represent the quasi-static UTS at 0.5 cycles. In general, with reference to published data, the UTS is not generated at the same rate of loading as the fatigue data. Furthermore, it is often difficult to generate fatigue data in the low-cycle region as a consequence of specimens sometimes failing prior to the desired loading conditions being achieved. With reference to Fig. 7.8(b), a linear relationship is apparent in the high-cycle region, however, this has to be taken in the context of the limited data. This relationship was also previously noticed by Mandell (1982). He showed that when the number of cycles to failure lay between 10^2 and 10^6, the S–N curve can be approximated by a straight line of the form:

$$\sigma_{max} = \sigma_{UTS} + b \log N_f \qquad [7.5]$$

where σ_{max} is the maximum applied stress, σ_{UTS} is the ultimate tensile strength, N_f is the number of cycles to failure and b is a constant. The ratio of b/σ_{UTS} was defined as the fractional loss in tensile strength per decade of cycles, Mandell (1982).

Figure 7.8(c) shows that a quadratic relationship was found to give a better fit to the fatigue data. This equation was previously used by Daniel and Charewicz (1986) to fit the fatigue data of unidirectional and cross-ply graphite/epoxy (AS-4/3501-6) composites.

$$\sigma_{max} = \sigma_{equ} + b \log N_f + c (\log N_f)^2 \qquad [7.6]$$

where σ_{max} is the maximum applied stress, σ_{UTS} is the ultimate tensile strength, N_f is the number of cycles to failure and b and c are constants.

The curve-fitting parameters (b and c) and the calculated σ_{UTS} in the above equation [7.6] for the composites investigated in this study are given in Table 7.6(b). It is interesting that this equation gives a good approximation of the UTS, see Table 7.6(b). The term 'equivalent' UTS is used to describe the ultimate tensile strength value computed by this equation. Furthermore, this equation can be used to estimate the number of cycles to failure at any given stress level if it is rewritten in terms of number of cycles to failure N_f.

With reference to Fig. 7.8(c), the effect of interleaving on the UTS is readily apparent. The relative strength decay per decade (calculated by using linear regression and excluding the UTS) was 10.9%, 9.0%, 9.7% for the G913, G913/913 and G913/920 composites respectively, see Table 7.6(c). The fatigue data for the G913 and G913/913 composites were seen to merge after approximately $10^{5.5}$ cycles. It is probable that this is due to the fact that, at low stresses, the predominant failure modes were resin-dominated. Run-outs were not obtained at 10^6 cycles for the G913/920 composite.

In order to compare the fatigue data for the three composites, the data were normalized with respect to the UTS, see Fig. 7.8(d). Harris *et al.* (1990) have reported that when variations in strength and stiffness of different composites are present, comparison between the S–N curves is not straightforward. A procedure for normalization is suggested to eliminate the effects of different fibre strengths, volume fractions and lay-ups. In the current study, the normalized fatigue data suggest that interleaving the G913 composite has resulted in an improvement in the fatigue life for both the interleaved composites. Of the two interleaf resins, namely Fibredux 913 and 920, the 920 resin system was seen to be superior.

The parameters b' and c' obtained from the normalized S–N plot (calculated including the UTS) are presented in Table 7.6(b). For normalized stresses higher than 0.7, the improvements achieved in the fatigue life for the G913/913 and G913/920 composites were 2.4 and 10.7 times over the G913 composite. At normalized stresses less than 0.7, the improvements achieved in the fatigue life of the G913/913 and G913/920 composites were 6.6 and 11.5 times over the reference material, respectively.

7.4.3.3   Tension/tension fatigue of hybrid fibre composites

With reference to Fig. 7.9(a), the G913/SiC and G913/PE composites show a very marginal increase in the fatigue life when compared with the G913 composite. The fatigue performance of G913/G composite was found to be inferior to that of the reference material. The introduction of the hybrid fibre results in a small change in the fibre volume fraction. Although the variations in the fibre volume fractions were low with reference to the introduction of the hybrid fibre, the fatigue data were normalized to the UTS, see Fig. 7.9(b). The apparent constant parameters b' and c' obtained from the normalized S–N plot (calculated including the UTS) are presented in Table 7.6(a).

Although only a marginal improvement in the fatigue performance was obtained for the hybrid fibre composites, the G_{Ic} for the G913/PE and G_{IIc} results for all the hybrid fibre composites showed a significant increase. This is particularly true for the G913/SiC and G913/PE hybrid composites. Therefore, it is proposed that the hybridization technique developed in this programme offers a method of improving the toughness without any significant detrimental effect on the tensile fatigue properties.

7.4.3.4   An approach to estimate the number of cycles to failure

The relationship between the maximum stress and the number of cycles to failure is usually expressed in a linear equation, as shown previously in equation [7.5]. However, it was shown that equation [7.5] was not appropriate, especially if the ultimate tensile strengths are obtained at a loading rate different from that used for the fatigue tests. In fatigue experiments,

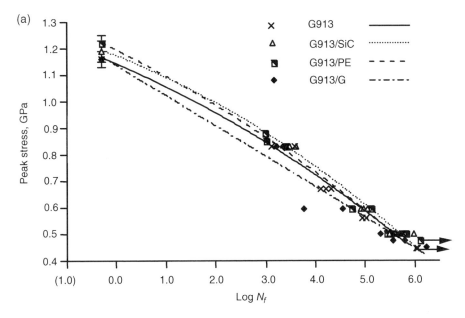

Fig. 7.9(a)   Comparison of the tension/tension fatigue results for the G913 and hybrid fibre composites. A second-order polynomial fit was used to fit the experimental data.

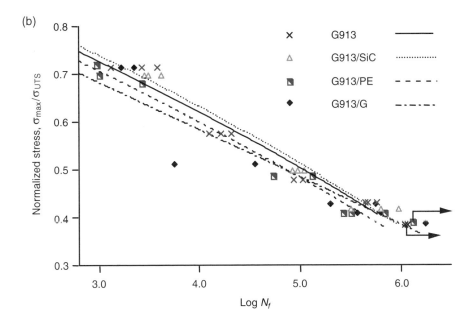

Fig. 7.9(b)   Comparison of the normalized tension/tension fatigue results for the G913 and the hybrid fibre composites. A second-order polynomial fit was used to fit the experimental data.

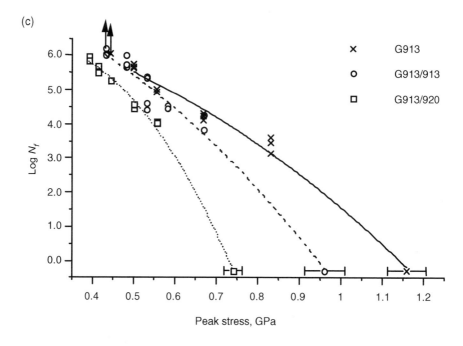

Fig. 7.9(c)   Tension/tension fatigue results for the G913 and the hybrid resin composites plotted according to equation [7.7]. A second-order fit was calculated including the UTS in the data set.

the independent variable was the maximum stress (σ_{max}) and the dependent variable was the number of cycles to failure N_f. In the experimental work, the maximum stress was determined first as an input and then the experiment was carried out until the failure of the specimen. The number of cycles to failure was then recorded. This means that the relationship between the number of cycles to failure and the maximum stress can be expressed in the following form:

$$\log N_f = c(\sigma_{max})^2 + b\,\sigma_{max} + a \qquad\qquad [7.7]$$

In order to check the validity of equation [7.7], Fig. 7.8(c) was plotted again by using equation [7.7], as shown in Fig. 7.9(c). The parameters a, b and c for all the composites investigated in this study are tabulated in Table 7.7. It was found that equation [7.7] gave an excellent approximation of the number of cycles to failure at any given stress level. However, empirical equations of this nature are adequate for a given class of material type, but their general applicability when the material is modified needs a further detailed study.

Table 7.7   Curve-fitting parameters calculated using equation [7.7] for the G913 and all the modified composites

Material	a	b	c
G913	7.14	−0.95	−4.62
G913/913	8.08	−1.72	−7.23
G913/920	3.98	16.27	−29.70
G913/SiC	6.78	0.36	−5.27
G913/PE	7.54	−2.29	−3.38
G913/G	8.37	−4.72	−2.25

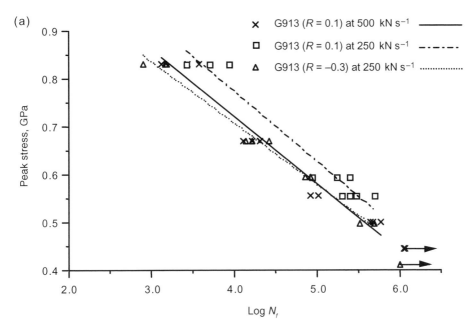

Fig. 7.10(a) Comparison between the *S–N* curves of G913 reference material at stress ratios of $R = 0.1$ and -0.3 and at loading rate of 250 kN s⁻¹ and 500 kN s⁻¹.

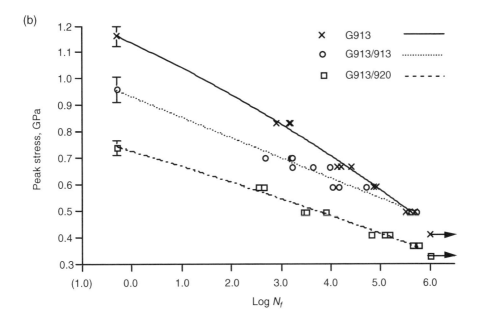

Fig. 7.10(b) Comparison of the tension/compression fatigue trends for G913, G913/913 and G913/920 composites. The UTS was included in the data-set.

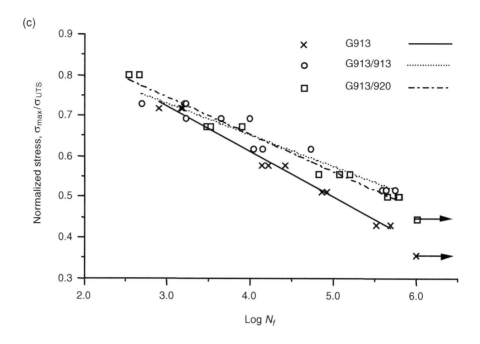

Fig. 7.10(c)   Comparison of the fatigue trends for the G913, G913/913 and G913/920 composites under tension/compression fatigue. The best fit lines were calculated excluding UTS.

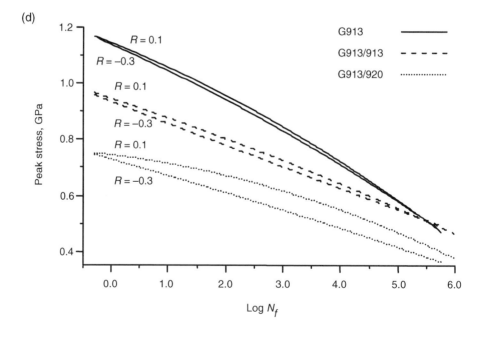

Fig. 7.10(d)   Comparison between the fatigue data for the G913 composite and the hybrid resin composites at stress ratios of $R = 0.1$ and R $= -0.3$.

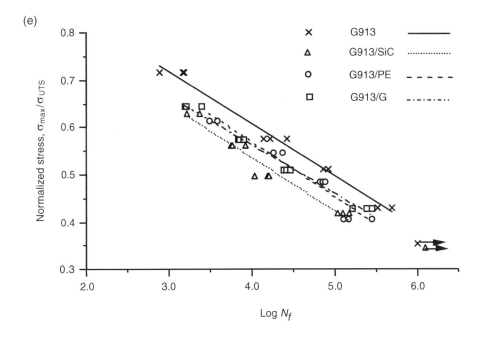

Fig. 7.10(e)   Comparison of the fatigue curves for the G913 and hybrid fibre composites under tension/compression loading ($R = -0.3$).

7.4.4   Tension/compression fatigue

7.4.4.1   Tension/compression fatigue behaviour of G913 composite
The tension/compression (T/C) fatigue tests were performed at a stress ratio of $R = -0.3$. A modified anti-buckling jig was used as described previously.

The T/C data for glass composites were generated at $250 \, \mathrm{kN \, s^{-1}}$ which is half the loading rate used for T/T fatigue. This was necessary because of the limitations imposed by the fatigue machine. Figure 7.10(a) represents the fatigue data for experiments carried out at $R = 0.1$ ($250 \, \mathrm{kN \, s^{-1}}$ and $500 \, \mathrm{kN \, s^{-1}}$) and $R = -0.3$ ($250 \, \mathrm{kN \, s^{-1}}$) for the reference G913 material. The S–N curves, which were plotted excluding the UTS, seem to merge after 10^5 cycles. With reference to Fig. 7.10(a), it is clear that the fatigue behaviour of G913 is weaker under T/C fatigue compared with T/T at a given loading rate. The calculated loss of strength per decade from Fig. 7.10(a) for the G913 composite tested at $R = -0.3$ was 10.6%.

7.4.4.2   Tension/compression fatigue of hybrid resin composites
The S–N curves for the G913 and the hybrid resin composites are illustrated in Fig. 7.10(b). The error bars at 0.5 cycles represent the monotonic tensile strength of the composites. Like the T/T fatigue results, a second-order polynomial curve fit was the most suitable way of representing the experimental data with the UTS being included in the data-set. Table 7.8(a) summarizes the fatigue parameters for all composite types evaluated in this programme along with the calculated σ_{UTS} (equivalent UTS) using equation [7.7]. With reference to Fig. 7.10(b), the fatigue data for the reference material and the G913/913 composite seem to merge after $10^{5.5}$ cycles. This behaviour was also observed for the T/T results. Comparison

Table 7.8(a)   *S–N* curve-fitting parameters of G913 and modified G913 composites under tension/compression fatigue

Material	Measured UTS	Equivalent UTS	b	c	b'	c'
G913	1.16	1.14	−0.089	−0.005	−0.076	−0.004
G913/913	0.96	0.93	−0.078	−0.0003	−0.078	−0.0003
G913/920	0.74	0.73	−0.056	−0.001	−0.089	−0.005
G913/SiC	1.19	1.15	−0.126	−0.001	−0.106	−0.001
G913/PE	1.22	1.19	−0.105	−0.004	−0.086	−0.004
G913/G	1.16	1.13	−0.118	−0.0001	−0.102	−0.0001

The UTS was included in the data-set

Table 7.8(b)   *S–N* curve-fitting parameter along with the reduction in fatigue strength of G913 and modified G913 laminates submitted to tension/compression fatigue

Material	b	b/UTS (%)
G913	−0.129	10.6
G913/913	−0.075	8.1
G913/920	−0.068	9.0
G913/SiC	−0.135	11.5
G913/PE	−0.142	11.2
G913/G	−0.120	10.6

The UTS was excluded from the data-set

between the G913 composite and G913/920 composite showed that the G913 composite was superior over the full range of lifetimes investigated. However, there was no superiority in fatigue performance of the reference material when the fatigue results were normalized with respect to the UTS for each composite system. The normalized fatigue trends for the G913 and the modified G913 composites under T/C fatigue are plotted in Fig. 7.10(c) excluding the UTS. With respect to Fig. 7.10(c), it is apparent that the hybrid resin composites show a slightly higher fatigue resistance than the reference material at lives greater than 10^3 cycles as characterized by less steep gradients. The constants, i.e., b' and c', obtained from Fig. 7.10(c) using equation [7.7] with the UTS being included are presented in Table 7.8(a). The experimental parameters with corresponding reduction in strength per decade, calculated from Fig. 7.10(c) by using linear regression, excluding the UTS, for the G913 and hybrid resin composites, are given in Table 7.8(b). The reduction of strength per decade of the hybrid resin composites was lower than the reference material, see Table 7.8(b). This was supported by the values of a *t* test which indicate that the hybrid resin composites have been improved significantly at the 0.1 per cent level over the G913 composite material in terms of fatigue strength loss per decade.

It is interesting to observe that, from previous results, the T/C fatigue data for the G913 and the hybrid resin composites are similar to that seen under T/T fatigue. Figure 7.10(d) shows the complete set of the *S–N* curves obtained at $R = 0.1$ and $R = -0.3$ for the G913 and the hybrid resin composites (including the UTS and using equation [7.6]). It can be seen that all the *S–N* curves intersect with each other at $10^{5.5}$ cycles. This suggests that, at this fatigue stress level, the failure modes in the composite are matrix dominated. Visual observations of failed samples showed that strips of the outer layers had delaminated from the specimens. At high cyclic stress, the reference material and the hybrid resin composites showed a greater difference between the S–N curves obtained at $R = 0.1$ and $R = -0.3$ than that at lower cyclic stresses. This suggests that failure modes were fibre dominated at higher loads. The small difference of the S–N curves at $R = 0.1$ and $R = -0.3$ for the reference material and G913/913 composite is attributed to the sequence of damage mechanisms in each system. In other words, interleaving with the same resin as the reinforcing matrix may not alter the damage mechanisms of the reference material significantly. However, the use of tough resins, such as Fibredux 920 resin, can influence damage development especially under low fatigue loads.

7.4.4.3   Tension/compression fatigue of hybrid fibre composites

Figure 7.10(e) shows the normalized fatigue results of the hybrid fibre composites, which are plotted without the UTS. The values of the strength reduction per decade confirm that the fatigue behaviour of the reference material is much better than that of the hybrid fibre composites. Contrary to the T/T fatigue data, the fatigue behaviour of the G913/SiC composite became poorer. This indicates that the fatigue response of the G913/SiC is more sensitive to the small compression portion of the fatigue cycle than other hybrid fibre composites. Generally, the hybrid fibre composites gave no indication of fatigue life enhancement. Differences in the fatigue responses for the reference and each hybrid fibre composite were statistically insignificant.

7.4.5   Fatigue damage development

7.4.5.1   Fatigue damage development under tension/tension loading

In the current work, the damage development induced by fatigue loading was studied for the G913 and the modified composites by non-destructive and destructive methods. The non-destructive techniques involved real-time monitoring of stiffness and surface temperature changes as a function of fatigue life. Visual inspection of failed specimens was also carried out. Dynamic strain measurements were obtained during the fatigue tests by a surface mounted extensometer for all composites. The strain and corresponding load measurements were used to calculate the stiffness reduction. Measurements of the surface temperature changes from ambient during fatigue were also utilized as an indicator of damage development. Many researchers have indicated that the stiffness changes are an excellent indicator of the damage development in composite materials when subjected to fatigue loading (e.g. Poursartip *et al.*, 1982; Wang and Chin, 1983; Hwang and Han, 1986).

The stiffness and temperature measurements were obtained for all the fatigue-tested specimens. However, only the measurements obtained at high and low fatigue stress levels are reported here.

G913 composite (reference material)
The starting point was the study of the stiffness and the surface temperature changes in the reference material. Figure 7.11 illustrates a selection of normalized stiffness and surface temperature data from the specimens during fatigue tests versus cycles to failure for the G913 composite.

In general, the stiffness decay was observed to show three-stage behaviour. This three-stage behaviour of the stiffness-decay under fatigue loading was also reported by other researchers (Reifsnider *et al.*, 1977; Rotem, 1989; Ye, 1988, 1989; Reifsnider 1991). At the start of the fatigue test, a small reduction in the stiffness was observed and this usually

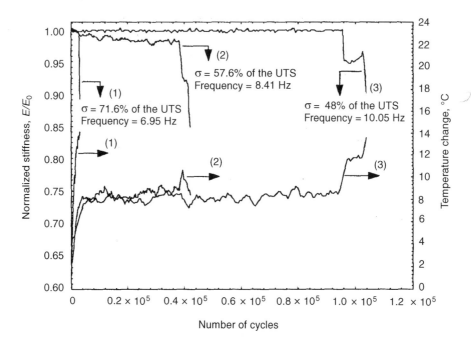

Fig. 7.11   Normalized stiffness and surface temperature changes (above ambient) in the G913 composite under tension/tension fatigue ($R = 0.1$).

corresponded to 5% of the fatigue life; this initial behaviour was defined as stage I. The stiffness was then observed to show a small rate of decrease up to approximately 90–95% of the fatigue life; this region was classified as stage II. Stage III for the unidirectional composites investigated in this programme was very short-lived and was characterized by a sudden catastrophic failure of the specimen. In Fig. 7.11, the sudden drop observed in some of the specimens was seen to correlate with the development of longitudinal splitting and delamination in the test specimens. Harris (1977) has stated that the damage in glass/epoxy composites is accompanied by fibre/resin debonding and the composite will often fail by splitting parallel to the fibres.

With respect to the surface temperature measurements during the fatigue tests, Fig. 7.11 also shows a three-stage behaviour, i.e. a rapid initial increase at the start of the test. This was followed by a very small increase in the measured temperature rise up to just prior to failure. At failure, a rapid surface-temperature increase was observed. The surface-temperature measurements were used as a cheaper alternative to an infra-red camera. However, the surface-mounted thermocouple technique suffers from a number of major limitations. For example, the location of the thermocouple with respect to the fracture zone influences the measured surface temperature. In other words, if the thermocouple happened to be located in the vicinity of a longitudinal split or internal delamination, then a high surface tempera- ture would be recorded. Delamination of the outer plies in some experiments resulted in the thermocouples becoming ineffective. The average surface peak temperature at failure increased with increasing loading rate.

Examination of polished sections for G913 samples that were suspended a few cycles prior to failure revealed that the accumulated damage was mainly interfacial debonding. It was also found that the density of the interfacial debonding was relatively higher for samples tested at high cyclic stress (71.6% of the UTS). Steif (1984) showed that fibre breakage, combined with interfacial debonding of the fibre/matrix interface, will lead to stiffness reductions. Furthermore, Horstemeyer and Staab (1990) have shown that unidirectional glass composites failed as a result of interface debonding under fatigue loading. However, in this current work, it was not possible to modify the fibre/matrix adhesion after receiving the prepreg from the manufacturer. Sih and Ebert (1986) studied interfacial effects on the fatigue performance of unidirectional E-glass/epoxy composites. The silane (Z-6020)-coated glass-fibre composite had a superior fatigue performance compared to the composite with uncoated fibres. Other researchers have also stated that improved interfacial adhesion would result in an improved fatigue performance (Harris, 1977; Dickson et al., 1985).

Hybrid resin composites
Figures 7.12(a) and (b) illustrate the stiffness change and the measured surface temperature increase at high and low stresses for the hybrid resin composites as a function of number of cycles to failure. The stiffness-decay data for the G913 have also been plotted for ease of comparison. In general, the G913/920 composite displayed a three-stage behaviour (similar to that observed for the G913) for the stiffness reduction and surface temperature increase during fatigue tests. However, for the G913/920 composite, the stiffness loss during stage II was seen to be slightly lower than that observed for the G913. This points out that the micro-damage initiation and or propagation in the G913/920 specimens was relatively delayed as a consequence of the tougher resin used for interleaving, i.e. Fibredux 920 resin. In general, stage III of the stiffness decay for the G913/920 was also significantly longer compared to the G913 reference material.

The surface temperature measurements showed similar behaviour to that seen for the reference material. However, the average peak temperature at failure was found to be less than that for the G913 specimens. This lower surface temperature may be attributed to a slower rate of damage development in the hybrid resin composites. The limitations of surface temperature measurements during fatigue testing was discussed previously.

With reference to Fig. 7.12(b), the stiffness behaviour at a peak applied stress corresponding to 51.9% of the UTS was similar to that for the G913/920 specimens cycled at low stress. Unlike the other composites, the duration of stage III was lower for the G913/913 composite. The rise in the measured temperature at failure was 9.0 °C above ambient.

Hybrid fibre composites
The stiffness decay and the surface temperature measurements for the hybrid fibre composites at high cyclic stress are presented in Fig. 7.13(a). For the G913/SiC composite tested at 69.8% of the UTS, the stiffness and surface temperature measurements show similar behaviour to the reference material. An exception to this is that the onset of stage III of the stiffness decay for the G913/SiC specimen occurred earlier. This has been attributed to the earlier initiation of delamination. The loss in stiffness at this stage was higher for the G913/SiC composite by about 1.5% whereas the surface temperature at failure showed no change. At low stress corresponding to 41.9% of the UTS, the stiffness decay for the G913/SiC specimens showed a very small change until final failure.

With reference to the G913/G composite, the extension of stage I of the stiffness decay, at 71.6% of the UTS, was much longer than for the reference material and the G913/SiC composite at corresponding stress levels, see Fig. 7.13(a). The stiffness decay at stages II and III resembled that for the G913/SiC composite. Figure 7.13(a) also shows that the surface temperature measurements increased gradually with cycling until failure. This is indicative of a higher damage development growth rate at higher fatigue stresses. Figure 7.13(c) shows the nature of damage accumulation prior to failure. The loss of stiffness at an early stage of the fatigue life (Figure 7.13a) is attributed to the observed debonding of the short

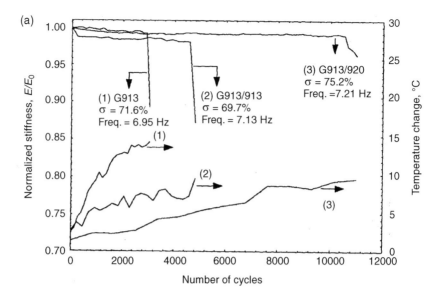

Fig. 7.12(a)   Normalized stiffness and surface temperature changes at high cyclic stress in the hybrid resin composites under tension/tension fatigue loading ($R = 0.1$). The corresponding behaviour for the reference material is also represented.

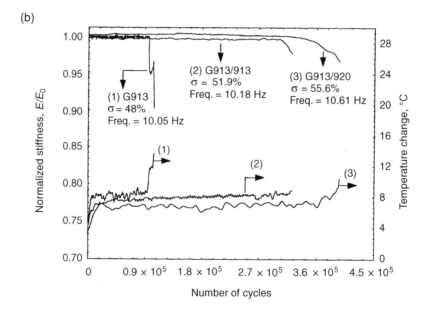

Fig. 7.12(b)   Normalized stiffness and surface temperature changes at low cyclic stress in the hybrid resin composites under tension/tension fatigue loading ($R = 0.1$). The corresponding behaviour for the reference material is also included.

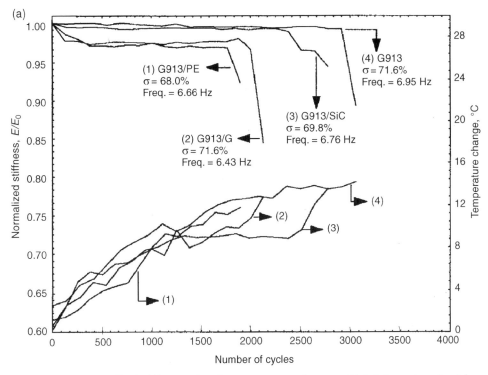

Fig. 7.13(a)   Normalized stiffness and surface temperature changes at high fatigue stress level for the hybrid fibre composites under tension/tension fatigue loading ($R = 0.1$). The corresponding behaviour for the reference material is also presented.

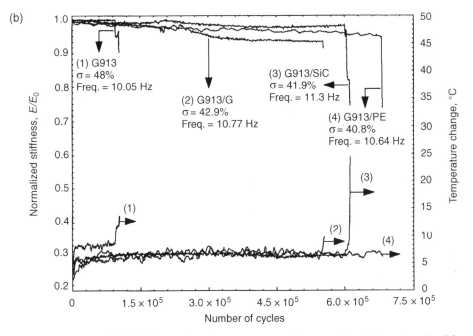

Fig. 7.13(b)   Normalized stiffness and surface temperature changes at low fatigue stress level for the hybrid fibre composites under tension/tension fatigue loading ($R = 0.1$). The corresponding behaviour for the reference material is also presented.

(c)

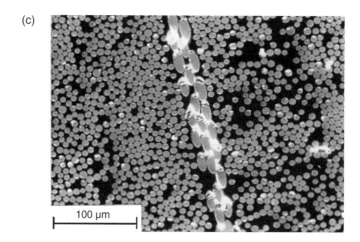

100 μm

Fig. 7.13(c)   Illustration of extensive deboning between the short E-glass fibres from the Fibredux 913 matrix in the G913/G composites: this test was terminated close to the predicted cycles-to-failure.

E-glass fibres from the surrounding matrix. Figure 7.13(b) shows that at low cyclic stress (42.9% of the UTS), the stiffness of the G913/G specimen continued to decrease with cycling until failure. The loss of stiffness prior to failure was about 7.1%. The peak surface temperature at failure was significantly less than that observed with the G913/SiC at low fatigue stress.

The final composite system investigated in this section is the G913/PE. At a stress level corresponding to 68.0% of the UTS, the stiffness decay at the end of stage I was about 2%, see Fig. 7.13(a). In stages I and II, the stiffness-decay was similar to that reported earlier for the G913/G composite at high cyclic stress level. At a low stress level (40.8% of the UTS), the stiffness continued to decrease with cycling until failure (Fig. 7.13(b)). The loss in stiffness prior to failure was about 4.8%.

7.4.5.2   Fatigue damage development under tension/compression loading

The stiffness decay and surface temperature change results showed that the general behaviour of the composites investigated in this programme at $R = -0.3$ resembles that obtained at $R = 0.1$. As described earlier, this is attributed to the introduction of the small compression component in the fatigue cycle. Therefore, the following discussion reports only the differences that were seen under T/C in order to avoid repetition.

G913 composite (reference material)
The normalized stiffness decay and the surface temperature changes for the G913 composite at fatigue stresses correspond to 71.6%, 57.6% and 42.9% and are presented in Fig. 7.14(a). As in T/T fatigue, the stiffness decay showed a three-stage behaviour. The stiffness loss at the end of stage I was greater than that noticed at $R = 0.1$ (1.1%). However, the total loss of stiffness at the end of stage II was extremely small, indicating ineffectual damage during most of the fatigue life. In Fig. 7.14(a), the temperature increased very quickly by 8 °C and then continued to increase at a small rate reaching 7.7 °C at failure.

Hybrid resin composites
The stiffness decay and the surface temperature behaviour at high and low cyclic stresses for the hybrid resin composites are illustrated in Figs. 7.14(b) and (c), respectively. With respect

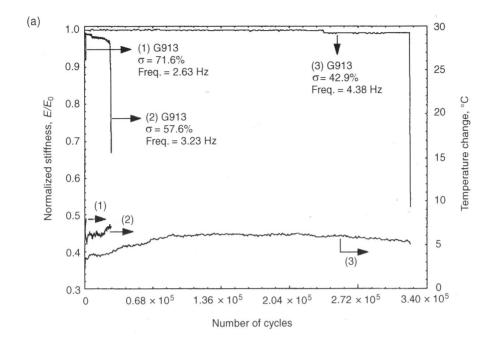

Fig. 7.14(a)   Stiffness and surface temperature changes in the G913 composite under tension/compression fatigue ($R = -0.3$).

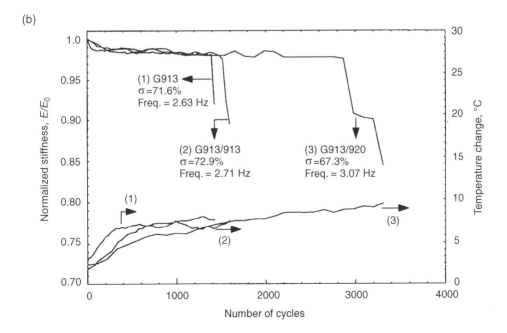

Fig. 7.14(b)   Stiffness and surface temperature changes for the hybrid resin composites at high cyclic stress and under tension/compression fatigue ($R = -0.3$).

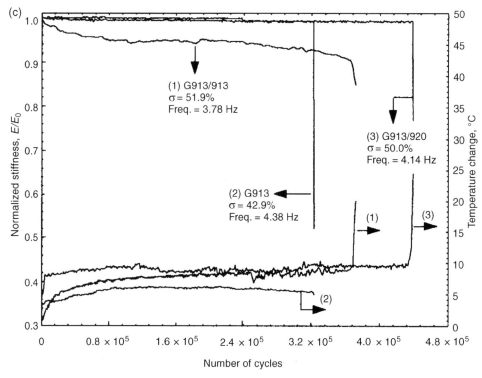

Fig. 7.14(c)   Stiffness and surface temperature changes for the hybrid resin composites at low cyclic stress and under tension/compression fatigue ($R = -0.3$).

to Fig. 7.14(b), the stiffness decay for the G913/913 composite at high cyclic stress (72.9% of the UTS) was identical to that obtained for the reference material. Stiffness-decay for the G913/913 specimens at 51.9% of the UTS was different to that observed for the G913 specimens at a corresponding stress level, see Fig. 7.14(c). The stiffness of the G913/913 specimens continued to decrease gradually throughout the fatigue life with a short stage II. A greater concentration of fibre/matrix debonding than the G913 composite was observed in the G913/913 composite. Consequently, the magnitude of the stiffness loss prior to failure was about 9%. The surface temperature showed a sharp increase (20 °C) at failure.

In Fig. 7.14(b), the stiffness loss for a G913/920 specimen cycled at 67.3% of the UTS was equivalent to 9.9%. At low cyclic stresses (50% of the UTS), the stiffness decay was negligible throughout the fatigue life, see Fig. 7.14(c). The overall loss of stiffness before failure was only 1.1%. The study of the damage accumulation after 95% of fatigue life did not reveal any damage in the matrix.

Hybrid fibre composites
The stiffness decay of the G913/SiC and G913/PE specimens cycled at high stress levels, corresponding to 63% and 61.5% of the UTS, respectively, suffered a significant reduction in stiffness at the end of stage I. A part of the stiffness decay was identical to the reference material. Figure 7.15(a) illustrates the stiffness decay and surface temperature changes at high fatigue stress levels. At low stress levels, the stiffness decay was seen to occur in a gradual fashion until failure for the G913/SiC and the G913/G specimens, see Fig. 7.15(b). In the G913/PE composite, the onset of stage III occurred earlier than with other hybrid fibre composites. The sudden drop in stiffness after 85% of fatigue life was due to the onset of delamination.

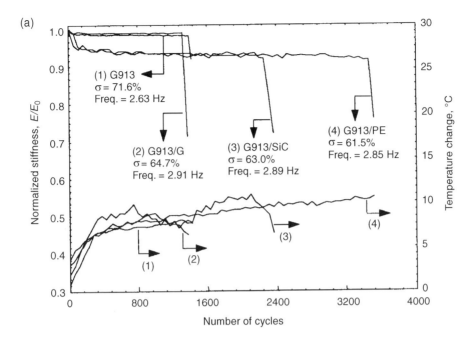

Fig. 7.15(a)   Stiffness and surface temperature changes for the hybrid fibre composites at high cyclic stress and under tension/compression fatigue loading ($R = -0.3$).

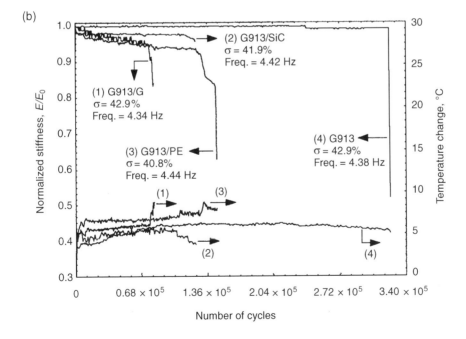

Fig. 7.15(b)   Stiffness and surface temperature changes for the hybrid fibre composites at low cyclic stress and under tension/compression fatigue ($R = -0.3$).

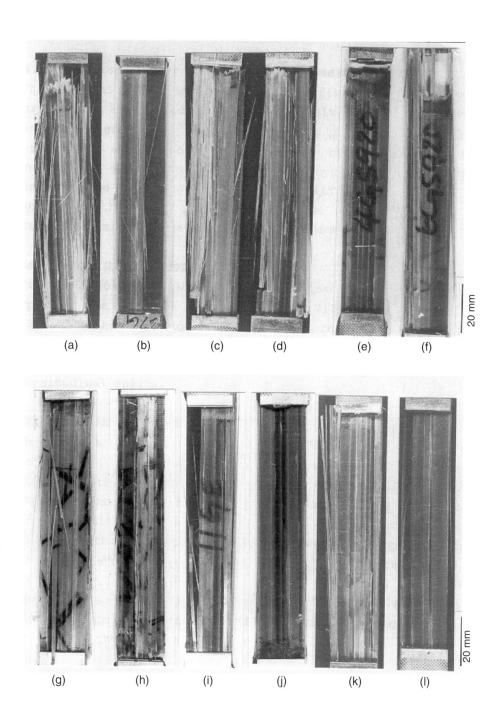

Fig. 7.16 Macrographs of failed G913 and modified G913 specimens fatigue tested at stress ratio, $R = 0.1$. (a) and (b) = G913, (c) and (d) = G913/913, (e) and (f) = G913/920, (g) and (h) = G913/SiC, (i) and (j) = G913/G and (k) and (l) = G913/PE.

7.5   Fractography

7.5.1   Tension/tension fatigue

Reference G913 composite
The failure of the G913 specimens tested at a stress level corresponding to 71.6% of the UTS was due to a significant number of longitudinal splits and transverse failure near the end-tab region (Fig. 7.16(a)). Similar damage modes for unidirectional glass/epoxy have been reported by Dharan (1975), Talreja (1981), Curtis and Moore (1983), and Newaz (1985). Curtis and Moore (1983) have reported that longitudinal splits may develop from the cut edges of the specimens. The longitudinal splits were seen to propagate along the whole gauge length of the specimens to the end-tab regions. This makes the specimens act as several samples gripped together at the end-tab regions. Therefore, the load transfer from one split bundle to another becomes limited. Fibre fracture was also observed in failed G913 samples with higher density of fibre fracture at the end-tab regions.

Conversely, the G913 samples which were tested at low cyclic stress (corresponding to 48.0% of the UTS), experienced a significant reduction in the concentration of longitudinal splits (Fig. 7.16(b)). The failure was combined with delamination. The onset of delamination was marked by a sudden drop of stiffness with a sudden rise in surface temperature from the ambient. The delaminations were seen on the outer layers on both sides of the specimens in the form of thin strips (consisting of 2–4 layers).

Hybrid resin composites
Typical failure appearance of the G913/913 specimens which were tested under T/T fatigue at high and low cyclic loads are shown in Fig. 7.16(c) and (d), respectively. The density of damage at both stress levels was found to be less than the reference G913 composite at corresponding stresses. This may be attributed to the increase of the resin volume fraction of the composite by interleaving with the same epoxy resin, i.e. Fibredux 913 resin. The effect of increasing the resin volume fraction of the Fibredux 913 resin was investigated by Barnard *et al.* (1985). The change in failure modes was attributed to the increase of the resin volume fraction. Similar observations were also reported by Partridge *et al.* (1989) on unidirectional glass-fibre/epoxy (Fibredux 913). The reduced longitudinal splitting in the interleaved glass/913 composite becomes more apparent as the thickness of the resin interleaf is increased.

With respect to the G913/920 composite, the damage under T/T fatigue (at cyclic stresses corresponding to 75.2% and 55.6% of the UTS) was significantly reduced compared to the G913 and G913/913 specimens, see Fig. 7.16(e) and (f). This is attributed to the inclusion of the tough Fibredux 920 resin layers. A study on the influence of tough interleaves on the damage mechanism shows that the use of a tough matrix leads to a relative slowing down of the growth of the longitudinal splitting (Partridge, 1993). In this study, it was also shown that the cracks are longer in brittle matrix composites than in composites having the tough matrix resin.

Hybrid fibre composites
Visual examination of the failed G913/SiC samples, tested at 69.8% of the UTS, showed extensive delamination with a lesser extent of longitudinal splits than the G913 specimens at an equivalent stress level Fig. 7.16(g). Figure 7.16(h) shows the macroscopic failure of a failed G913/SiC specimen at 41.9% of the UTS. The failure of the G913/SiC specimens at this low stress level was mainly due to delamination and transverse failure. The observed damage was seen to be slightly greater than for the G913 specimens at low stress level.

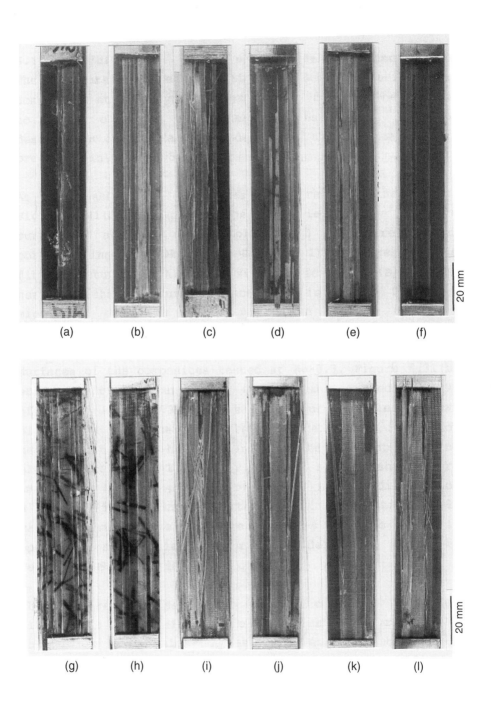

Fig. 7.17 Macrographs of failed G913 and modified G913 specimens fatigue tested at stress ratio, $R = -0.3$. (a) and (b) = G913, (c) and (d) = G913/913, (e) and (f) = G913/920, (g) and (h) = G913/SiC, (i) and (j) = G913/G and (k) and (l) = G913/PE.

However, the width of the delaminated areas for the G913/SiC specimens was less than that for the reference material.

Similar failure characteristics to the G913/SiC specimens were also observed in the G913/G at high and low cyclic stresses (Fig. 7.16(g)–(j)). The greater density of delamination in the hybrid fibre composites than the reference G913 composite is attributed to the higher shear stresses which were concentrated at the ends of the short fibres.

With respect to the G913/PE composite, Fig. 7.16(k) and (l) show the failure appearance of specimens tested at high (68.0% of the UTS) and low (40.8% of the UTS) stress levels. The density of damage at high stress level was substantially less than the reference material.

In general, the failure of all glass composites tested in this programme occurred suddenly in a catastrophic manner. The failure of the G913 and the modified G913 composites at high fatigue loads resembled that observed under tensile loading. Both the longitudinal splitting and delamination propagate under predominantly shear loading conditions (Partridge, 1993).

The failure of the composites can be divided into three groups on the basis of extent and type of damage.

(i) The first group includes the reference G913 composite. The predominant failure was the formation of longitudinal splitting due to the high normal tensile and shear stresses.

(ii) The second group includes the hybrid resin composites. The extent of longitudinal splitting and delamination was significantly reduced. This was attributed to the increase in the resin volume fraction and the toughness of the hybrid resin system. It was also noted that the higher the resin ductility the lower the delamination. Lagace (1986; Lagace et al., 1986) has attributed the suppression of delamination in interleaved composites to the fact that the interleaf layers substantially reduce the magnitude of the interlaminar shear stress. The interleaf film mitigates the contrast in ply elastic constants by redistributing the stresses over a larger area.

(iii) The final group includes the hybrid fibre composites. These composites showed greater delamination compared to other composites. This was attributed to the high shear stress at the ends of short fibres.

7.5.2   Macroscopic failure modes under tension/compression loading

The T/C fatigue loading produced a modified failure mode at high cyclic stresses due to the compressive stress component in the fatigue cycle. The most prominent macroscopic feature of failed samples of the G913 and the modified G913 composites tested at high and low cyclic stresses was delamination with less longitudinal splitting (Fig. 7.17). Strips of the outer plies were seen to delaminate with a greater density in the hybrid fibre specimens.

7.5.2.1   Reference G913 composite

Figures 7.17(a) and (b) show the appearance of failed G913 specimens at stresses corresponding to 71.6% of the UTS and 42.9% of the UTS under T/C loading. The effects of the loading conditions on the specimens are clear. At low cyclic stress, the failure was due to delamination with fewer longitudinal splits.

7.5.2.2   Hybrid resin composites

The failure appearance of the G913/913 specimens under T/C fatigue was also dependent on the magnitude of the peak stress of the cycle. At high cyclic stress (69.6% of the UTS), the damage density was greater than for the reference G913 composite (Fig. 7.17(c)). At a low cyclic stress level (51.9% of the UTS), the delamination was not suppressed to the degree which was seen under T/T loading (Fig. 7.17(d)). Furthermore, the failure of the G913/920 specimens under T/C loading was not influenced by the Fibredux 920 resin. Fig. 7.17(e) and (f) show that the extent of damage was similar to the reference G913 composite.

7.5.2.3   Hybrid fibre composites

As for hybrid resin composites, the extent of damage in the hybrid fibre composites under T/C fatigue loading was greater than that observed in the reference G913 specimens tested at corresponding stress levels (Fig. 7.17(g) to(l).

7.6   Conclusions

7.6.1   Kinetics of cure

Prior to producing the hybrid resin composites for this programme, it was necessary to investigate the cure kinetics of the hybrid resin system. The kinetic parameters and the prediction of the reaction rate of two aromatic epoxy resin systems and the hybrid resin system were calculated using a semi-empirical kinetic model. This model was found to be valid for the DSC data except when the curing temperature exceeded 140 °C for the Fibredux 920 resin and the hybrid resin system.

7.6.2   Static mechanical properties

The monotonic tensile properties of the hybrid resin composites were decreased as a result of lowering of the fibre volume fraction through interleaving. However, their normalized initial modulus values were found to be comparable to those of the reference materials. The hybrid fibres were found to be effective in improving the tensile properties of the hybrid fibre composites.

The macroscopic failure modes of the hybrid resin and hybrid fibre composites indicated that they were modified by comparison with the G913 composite. The formation of longitudinal splitting which distinguishes the unidirectional glass/epoxy composites was reduced significantly after the modifications. The reduction of the longitudinal splitting in the hybrid resin was due to the increase of the resin volume fraction and to the higher fracture toughness of the interleaving resin. The suppression of longitudinal splitting resulted in an increase in the other damage modes such as hackles and matrix ductility.

The mode I interlaminar fracture toughness of the hybrid resin and G913/PE composites were marginally improved compared with the G913 composite. The improvements of the G_{Ic} at crack initiation were 12%, 75% and 27.7%, whereas improvements at propagation were 39.5%, 55% and 128% for the G913/913, G913/920 and G913/PE composites respectively. This was attributed to the greater ductility of the Fibredux 920 resin and the PE fibres. In contrast, incorporation of the short SiC and E-glass fibres at the interfaces between plies did not contribute to the mode I interlaminar fracture toughness.

7.6.3   Fatigue behaviour of glass/epoxy composites

Normalized T/T fatigue data for the hybrid resin composites showed that their fatigue lives were improved by interleaving. This improvement was superior when the Fibredux 920 resin was used for interleaving. The improvements achieved in the fatigue life of the G913/ 913 and G913/920 composites were 6.6 and 11.5 times over the reference G913 composite, respectively. Statistically, it was found that each composite system belonged to a different population. The fatigue resistance of the G913/913 composite was found to be significant compared with the reference material at the 5% level, whereas the fatigue behaviour of the G913/920 composite was improved significantly over the reference material at the 1% level. The observed superiority of the hybrid resin composites under T/T fatigue was not present to the same degree under T/C fatigue. This was as expected since the compressive properties of the interleaved materials are poor. Generally, the fatigue behaviour of the hybrid resin composites under T/T and the T/C loading was much better at low stress levels. This indicates that, because the matrix properties become more influential at low fatigue loads, the damage mechanisms were altered. In contrast, the fatigue performance of the hybrid fibre results in a marginal increase compared to reference material whereas the G913/G composite was found to be inferior. Furthermore, no indication of fatigue-life enhancement was seen under T/C fatigue.

The reduction in the stiffness due to fatigue damage for the G913 and the modified G913 composites was found to show a three-stage behaviour with the second stage accounting for over 90% of fatigue life. The G913 and the modified G913 composites retained their modulus during T/T and T/C fatigue up to the final failure. Microscopic examination of fatigue specimens, which were suspended a few cycles prior to failure, revealed that the accumulated damage was mainly localized interfacial debonding. The Fibredux 920 resin was found to be more effective in delaying the initiation of micro-damage during fatigue than the Fibredux 913 resin. Interleaving with the Fibredux 913 resin led to a greater reduction in stiffness at the end of stage I. This was due to the formation of a significant number of transverse matrix cracks. The stiffness-decay of the hybrid fibre composites under T/T fatigue behaved similarly to the reference G913 composite. Conversely, under T/C fatigue they showed a high reduction in stiffness at the end of stage I.

The failure of the composites investigated here occurred suddenly and in a catastrophic manner. The failure of the reference G913 composites was due to longitudinal splitting and transverse fracture at high stress levels. However, at low fatigue loads, the G913 specimens failed by a combination of longitudinal splitting and delamination. In the hybrid resin composites, the longitudinal splitting and delamination were significantly reduced. In contrast, the extent of delamination in the hybrid fibre composites was greater than the reference material. The observed damage modes were found to be similar to those observed after tensile loading.

The general behaviour of the surface temperature trends were found to correlate well with the stiffness-decay behaviour. The rise of the surface temperature in the G913 and the hybrid composites during fatigue loading was within the acceptable limits. A sudden jump in surface temperature was observed prior to failure. Monitoring the surface temperature of unidirectional composites would seem to be a promising method for following damage development.

7.7   Acknowledgements

The authors wish to acknowledge the tremendous technical support and encouragement given by Professors Brian Ralph and Bryan Harris. This research was carried out at the Materials Engineering Department, Brunel University and was funded by the Saudi Arabian Government under the remit of a studentship for F. Al-Khodairi. The assistance given by Mr Norman Marks of GKN Westland Helicopters (UK) and Nornal October of Ciba Geigy (UK), George Ragbir, Rodney Badcock, Pam Robinson, Les Mellett, Prakash Dodia and

John Felgate of the Materials Engineering Department and Alan Reynolds of ETC at Brunel University are also duly acknowledged. This article is dedicated to the memory of Dominique Guruswamy.

7.8   References

AL-KHODAIRI F A (1996), Static and dynamic properties of unidirectional hybrid resin and hybrid fibre composites, PhD thesis, Brunel University, UK.

ALTSTADT V, GERTH D, STANGLE M and RECKER H J (1993), Interlaminar crack-growth in 3rd-generation thermoset prepreg systems, *Polymer*, **34**, 907–909.

ATKINS A G (1975), Intermittent bonding for high toughness/high strength composites. *Materials Science*, **10**, 819–832.

AVESTON J and SILWOOD J M (1976), *Journal of Materials Science*, **11**, 1877.

BADCOCK R (1993), PhD thesis, Department of Materials Technology, Brunel University.

BARNARD P M, BUTLER R J and CURTIS P T (1985), Fatigue scatter of unidirectional glass epoxy, a fact or fiction?, *Composite Structures*, 69–82.

BEAUMONT, P W R, RIEWALD P G and ZWEBEN C (1974), Methods for improving the impact resistance of composite materials. *Foreign Body Impact Damage to Composites*, ASTM STP, pp. 134–158.

BERNAY P (1993), Prepreg composites in the nautical industry, *Proceedings of the Ninth International Conference on Composite Materials* (ICCM/9), Antonio Miravete, ed., Vol. VI, pp. 327–330.

BERRY J B (1963), Determination of fracture surface energies by the cleavage technique, *Applied Physics*, **34**, 62–68.

BIBO G A and HOGG P J (1998), Damage tolerance of continuous fibre composites: Material and Environmental Effects. *Key Engineering Materials*, **141–142**, 93–126.

BUNSELL A R and HARRIS B (1974), *Composites*, 157.

CABLE C (1991), The effect of defects in glass-reinforced plastic (GRP), *Marine Technology and News*, **28**, 91–98.

CARLSSON L A, GILLESPIE J W and PIPES R B (1986), On the analysis and design of the end notched flexure (ENF) specimen for mode-II testing, *Journal of Composite Materials*, **20**, 594–604.

CHAN W (1986), Delamination arrester – an adhesive inner layer in laminated composites, *Composite Materials: Fatigue and Fracture*, ASTM STP 907, pp. 176–196.

CHAN W (1991), Design approaches for edge delamination resistance in laminated composites, *Composites Technology and Research*, **14**, 91–96.

CHAUDHURI R A and GARALA H J (1995), Analytical experimental evaluation of hybrid comingled carbon glass epoxy thick-section composite under compression, *Journal of Composite Materials*, **29**(13), 1695–1718.

CIBA-GEIGY (1988), Fibredux® 913.

CIBA-GEIGY (1991), Fibredux® 920.

CUI W C, WISNOM M R and JONES M (1992), Failure mechanism in 3-point and 4-point short beam bending tests of unidirectional glass epoxy, *Journal of Strain Anal Eng*, **27**(4), 235–243.

CURTIS P T (1985), Royal Aircraft Establishment Technical Report No. 85099.

CURTIS P T (1989a), The fatigue of organic matrix composite materials, *Advanced Composites*, Chapter 10, Partridge, I., ed., Elsevier Applied Science, pp. 331–367.

CURTIS P T (1989b), Fatigue behaviour of fibrous composite materials, *Journal of Strain Analysis For Engineering Design*, **24**, 235–244.

CURTIS P T and BROWNE M (1994), Cost-effective high-performance composites, *Composites*, **25**, 273–280.

CURTIS P T and MOORE B B (1983), A comparison of plain and double waisted coupons for static and fatigue tensile testing of unidirectional GRP and CFRC, *Composite Structures*, **2**, 383–398.

DANIEL I M and CHAREWICZ A (1986), Fatigue damage mechanisms and residual properties of graphite/ epoxy laminates, *Engineering Fracture Mechanics*, **25**(5–6), 793.

DAVIES P (1992), Protocols for Interlaminar Fracture testing of composites. European Structural Integrity Society Polymer and Composites Task Group.

DEW-HUGHES D and WAY J L (1973), Fatigue of fibre-reinforced plastics: a review, *Composites*, 167–173.

DHARAN C K H (1975), Fatigue failure in graphite fibre and glass fibre polymer composites, *Journal of Materials Science*, **10**, 1665–1670.

DICKSON R F, JONES C J, HARRIS B, LEACH D C and MOORE D R (1985), The environmental fatigue behavior of carbon-fibre-reinforced polyether ether ketone, *Journal of Materials Science*, **20**, 60–70.

DICKSON R F, FERNANDO G, ADAM T, REITER H and HARRIS B (1989), Fatigue behavior of hybrid composites. 2. carbon glass hybrids, *Journal of Materials Science*, **24**, 227–233.

DOREY G (1982a), Can hybrids improve composite reliability?, *Astronautics and Aeronautics*, **20**, 63–64.

DOREY G (1982b), Fracture and damage tolerance, *AGARD Lecture Series*, North Atlantic Organization, No 124, pp. 6–1.

DUSI M R, LEE W I, CIRISCIOLI P R and SPRINGER G S (1987), Cure kinetics and viscosity of Fiberite-976 resin, *Journal of Composite Materials*, **21**, 243–261.

DYNEEMA® (1988), Trade Literature, Dyneema® SK 60.

EVANS R E and MASTERS J E (1987), A new generation of epoxy composites for primary structural applications: materials and mechanics, *Toughened Composites*, ASTM STP 937, Johnston, N. J. ed., American Society for Testing and Materials, Philadelphia, pp. 413–436.

FERNANDO G F, ANSELL M P, GEORGALLIDES C and NEWTON A (1987), 'Design, fabrication and properties of composites with multi-layered and 3-D glass fabric reinforcement', *Composites Evaluation*, TEQC-87, University of Surrey, 96–104.

FERNANDO G, DICKSON R F, ADAM T, REITER H and HARRIS B (1988), Fatigue behavior of hybrid composites. 1. carbon Kevlar hybrids, *Journal of Materials Science*, **23**, 3732–3743.

FERNANDO G F (1989), The fatigue behaviour of mono-fibre and hybrid Kevlar/XAS/914 composites, PhD thesis, Bath University, UK.

GARCIA R, EVANS R E and PALMER R J (1987), Structural property improvements through hybridized composites, *Toughened Composites*, ASTM STP 937, Johnston, N. J. ed., American Society for Testing and Materials, Philadelphia, pp. 383–412.

GARG AND MAI (1988), Failure mechanisms in toughened epoxy-resins: A review, *Composites Science and Technology*, **31**(3), 179–223.

GLENN T A, CHEN J and SHERWOOD J A (1998), Carbon/glass hybridization: Another degree of design freedom for composite structures, *SAMPE Journal*, **34**(3), 22–31.

HAHN H T and KIM R Y (1976), Fatigue behaviour of composite laminate, *Composite Materials*, **10**, 156–180.

HANCOX N L (1981), Fibre Composite Hybrid Materials, Applied Science Publishers, London.

HARRIS B (1977), Fatigue and accumulation of damage in reinforced plastics, *Composites*, **8**, 214–220.

HARRIS B (1991), A perspective view of composite materials development, *Journal of Materials and Design*, **12**, 259–279.

HARRIS B, REITER H, ADAM T, DICKSON R F and FERNANDO G (1990), Fatigue behavior of carbon-fibre reinforced-plastics, *Composites*, **21**, 232–242.

HAYASHI (1972), Eighth International Reinforced Plastics Conference, British Plastics Federation, Brighton, UK. Paper 22, pp. 149.

HITCHEN S A and OGIN S L (1993a), Damage accumulation during the fatigue of an injection moulded glass/nylon composite, *Composites Science and Technology*, **47**, 83–89.

HITCHEN S A and OGIN S L (1993b), Matrix cracking and modulus reduction during the fatigue of an injection-moulded glass/nylon composite. *Composites Science and Technology*, **47**, 239–244.

HITCHEN S A, OGIN S L and SMITH P A (1995), Effect of fibre length on fatigue of short carbon fibre/epoxy composite, *Composites*, **26**, 303–308.

HORSTEMEYER M F and STAAB G H (1990), Interface debonding in fatigue cycling of glass reinforced-plastics, *Journal of Reinforced Plastics and Composites*, **9**, 446–455.

HUNSTON D L, MOULTON R J, JOHNSTON N J and BASCOM W D (1987), Matrix resin effects in composite delamination: Mode I fracture aspects, *Toughened Composites*, ASTM STP 937, Johnston, N. J. Ed., American Society for Testing and Materials, Philadelphia, pp. 74–94.

HWANG W and HAN K S (1986), Fatigue of composites – fatigue modulus concept and life prediction, *Journal of Composite Materials*, **20**, 154–165.

JOHNSTON H J, ED. (1987), *Toughened Composites*, ASTM STP 937, Philadelphia, USA.

JONEJA S K (1987), Matrix contribution to fatigue behaviour of glass reinforced polyester composites, *Reinforced Plastics and Composites*, **6**, 343–356.

KIM J and MAI Y (1991), High strength, high fracture toughness fibre composite with interface control – a review, *Composites Science and Technology*, **41**, 333–378.

KRETSIS G (1987), A review of the tensile, compressive, flexural and shear properties of hybrid fibre-reinforced plastics, *Composites*, **18**(1), 13–23.

KRIEGER R B (1987), An adhesive interleaf to reduce stress-concentrations between plies of structural composites, *SAMPE Journal of the Society for the Advancement of Material and Process Engineering*, **23**, 30–32.

KUJAWSKI D and ELLYIN F (1995), Rate/frequency-dependent behaviour of fibre glass/epoxy laminates in tensile and cyclic loading, *Composites*, **26**, 719–723.

LADIZESKY N H and WARD I M (1986), Ultra-high modulus polyethylene composites: III – An exploratory study of hybrid composites, *Composites Science and Technology*, **26**, 199–224.

LAGACE A (1986), Delamination in composites: Is toughness the key?, *SAMPE*, 53–60.

LAGACE P A, WEEMS D B and BREWER J C (1986), Suppression of delamination via an interply adhesive layer, *Proceedings of the 3rd Japan–USA Conference on Composite Materials*, pp. 323–328.

LEAITY M A, SMITH P A, BADER M G and CURTIS P T (1992), The behaviour of cross-ply hybrid matrix composite laminates – Part 1: Experimental, *Composites*, **23**, 387–395.

LEE S, SCOTT R F, GAUDERT P C, UBBINK W H and POON C (1988), Mechanical testing of toughened resin composite materials, *Composites*, **19**, 300–310.

LIN T L and JANG B Z (1990), Fracture behaviour of hybrid composites containing both short and continuous fibres, *Polymer Composites*, **11**, 291–300.

MANDELL J F (1982), Fatigue behaviour of fibre-resin composites, *Developments in Reinforced Plastics – 2*, G Pritchard, ed., Applied Science Publishers, pp. 67–107.

MANDERS P W and BADER M G (1981a), The strength of hybrid glass-carbon fibre composites. 1. Failure strain enhancement and failure mode. *Journal of Material Science*, **16**(8), 2232–2245.

MANDERS P W and BADER M G (1981b), The strength of hybrid glass-carbon composites. 2. A statistical-model. *Journal of Material Science*, **16**(8), 2246–2256.

MARSTON C, GABBITAS B and ADAMS J (1997), The effect of fibre sizing on fibres and bundle strength in hybrid glass carbon fibre composites, *Journal of Materials Science*, **32**(6), 1415–1423.

MASTERS J E (1989), Improved impact and delamination resistance through interleaving, *Key Engineering Materials*, **37**, 317–348.

MIGNERY L A, TAN T M and SUN C T (1985), Delaminations and Debonding, ASTM STP 876, Johnson, W. S. (ed.), pp. 371–385.

MIWA M AND HORIBA (1994), Effects of fibre length on tensile-strength of carbon glass-fibre hybrid composites, *Journal of Materials Science*, **29**(4), 973–977.

PARTRIDGE I (1993), Effects of resin-rich interply zones on fatigue of unidirectional and cross-ply laminates, *Second International Conference on Deformation and Fracture of Composites*, England, pp. 34–1.

PARTRIDGE I, VIRLOUVET P, CHUBB J and CURTIS P (1989), Effect of fibre volume fraction on tensile fatigue behaviour of unidirectional glass/epoxy composite, *Third European Conference on Composite Materials (ECCM 3)*, Bunsell, A. R., ed., France, pp. 451–456.

PEIJS A A J M, CATSMAN P, GOVAERTLE L E and LEMSTRA P J (1990), Hybrid composites based on polyethylene and carbon-fibre. 2. Influence of composition and adhesion level of polyethylene fibres on mechanical properties. *Composites*, **21**(6), 513–521.

PEIJS A A J M and DE KOK J M M (1993), Hybrid composites based on polyethylene and carbon fibres, *Composites*, **24**, 19–32.

PICKERING K L and BADER M G (1994), The effect of fibre surface-treatment on the failure of continuous carbon-fibre epoxy-resin composites. *Journal of Adhesion*, **45**(1–4), 161–172.

POURSARTIP A, ASHBY M F and BEAUMONT P W R (1982), Damage accumulation in composites during fatigue, *Proceedings of the Riso International Symposium on Metallurgy and Materials Science*, pp. 279–284.

PRIME R B (1981). *Thermal Characterization of Polymeric Materials*, Chapter 5, Turi, E. A. ed., Academic Press, New York.

REIFSNIDER K L (1991), *Fatigue of Composite Materials*, Chapter 2, Reifsnider, K., ed., Elsevier Science Publishers.

REIFSNIDER K L, STINCHCOMB W W and O'BRIEN T K (1977), Frequency effects on a stiffness-based fatigue failure criterion in flawed composite specimens, *American Society for Testing and Materials*, pp. 171–184.

REZAIFARD A H, BADER M G and SMITH P A (1994), Investigation of the transverse properties of a unidirectional carbon-epoxy laminate: 2. Laminate properties, *Composites Science and Technology*, **52**(2), 287–295.

ROTEM A (1989), Stiffness change of a graphite epoxy laminate under reverse fatigue loading, *Composites Research and Technology*, **11**, 59–64.

ROTEM A (1993), Load frequency effect on the fatigue strength of isotropic laminates, *Composites Science and Technology*, **46**, 129–138.

ROTEM A and NELSON H G (1989), Failure of a laminated composite under tension–compression fatigue loading, *Composites Science and Technology*, **36**, 45–62.

RYAN M E and DUTTA A (1979), Kinetics of epoxy cure: A rapid technique for kinetic parameter estimation, *Polymer*, **20**, 203–206.

SELA N and ISHAI O (1989), Interlaminar fracture-toughness and toughening of laminated composite-materials – a review, *Composites*, **20**, 423–435.

SELA N, ISHAI O and BANKSSILLS L (1989), The effect of adhesive thickness on interlaminar fracture-toughness of interleaved CFRP specimens, *Composites*, **20**, 257–264.

SIH G C and EBERT L J (1986), Flexural failure mechanisms and global stress plane for unidirectional composites subjected to 4-point bend tests, *Composites*, **17**(4), 309–320.

SIMS G D and GLADMAN D G (1978), Effect of test conditions on the fatigue strength of a glass-fabric laminate: Part A – frequency, *Plastics and Rubber: Materials and Applications*, May, pp. 41–48.

SINGH S and PARTRIDGE I K (1995), Mixed-mode fracture in an interleaved carbon-fibre epoxy composite, *Composites Science and Technology*, **55**, 319–327.

SOUROUR S and KAMAL M R (1976), Differential scanning calorimetry of epoxy cure: isothermal cure kinetics, *Thermochimica Acta*, **14**, 41–59.

STEIF P S (1984), Stiffness reduction due to fibre breakage, *Journal of Composite Materials*, **17**, 153–172.

SUMMERSCALES J and SHORT D (1978), Carbon fibre and glass fibre hybrid reinforced plastics, *Composites*, **9**, 157–166.

TALREJA R (1981), Fatigue of composite materials: Damage mechanisms and fatigue-life Diagrams, *Proceedings of the Royal Society of London, Series A: Mathematical and Physical Sciences*, **378**, 461–475.

THOMASON J L (1995), The interface region in glass-fibre-reinforced epoxy-resin composites. 1. Sample preparation, void content and interfacial strength, *Composites*, **26**, 467–475.

TYRANO FIBRE (1992), Ube Industries, Technical Data Sheet.

VICKERS P E, BONIFACE A, PRICKET J F and WATTS J F (2000), The effect of siloxane-type molecules on the interlaminar toughness of CFRO, *Composites: Part A*, 559–569.

WANG S S, CHIM E S M and ZAHLAN N M (1983), Fatigue crack propagation in random short fibre SMC composite, *Journal of Composite Materials*, **17**(3), 250–266.

YAMASHITA S, HATTA H, SUGANO T and MURAYAMA K (1989), Fibre orientation control of short fibre composites: experiment, *Journal of Composite Materials*, **23**(1), 32–41.

YAMASHITA S, HAHA H, TAKEI T and SUGANO T (1992), Interlaminar reinforcement of laminated composites by addition of oriented whiskers in the matrix, *Journal of Composite Materials*, **26**, 1254–1268.

YE L (1988), Role of matrix resin in delamination onset and growth in composite laminates, *Composites Science and Technology*, **33**, 257–277.

YE L (1989), On fatigue damage accumulation and material degradation in composite materials, *Composites Science and Technology*, **36**, 339–350.

ZWEBEN (1977), *Journal of Material Science*, **12**, 1325.

8

Non-destructive evaluation of damage accumulation

A. P. Mouritz, RMIT University, Australia

8.1 Introduction

The superior fatigue resistance of continuous fibre reinforced polymer (FRP) laminates compared to traditional engineering materials (such as steels and aluminium alloys) has been an important factor in the widespread application of composites in lightweight structures. The outstanding fatigue performance of composites has led to their use in a wide variety of components that must withstand extreme cyclic loads for long times. These components include aircraft propellers, wings, helicopter rotor blades, rotating machinery, yacht hulls, boat propellers and racing bicycle frames. High fatigue resistance is also a key factor supporting the future use of composites in new applications such as medical prosthesis (e.g. artificial limbs, hip joints, knee replacements) and automotive components (e.g. suspension springs).

Continuous fibre laminates are usually highly fatigue resistant under in-plane cyclic loading, although damage can occur under high in-plane fatigue loads as well as under modest out-of-plane and through-thickness dynamic loads. When composites are exposed to these fatigue load conditions then damage develops in the forms of matrix cracking, crack coupling, delamination initiation and growth, and fibre fracture.[1] In addition to these damage modes, other forms of fatigue damage can occur to sandwich composite materials, including skin-core debonding and core failure. Both laminates and sandwich composites are also susceptible to thermally-induced fatigue damage when exposed to an environment that experiences wide ranging and rapid fluctuations in temperature.[2-4] Fatigue damage caused by stress or thermal cycling can compromise the mechanical integrity and safety of a composite structure, and therefore it is essential that the damage is detected early using non-destructive evaluation (NDE) technologies.

The NDE for fatigue damage is an essential requirement when composites are used in structural applications. The NDE process should have two basic objectives:

- the reliable and repeatable characterization of the types, dimensions and locations of fatigue damage, and

- the accurate determination of changes to the mechanical properties (e.g. stiffness) due to fatigue damage.

These are challenging objectives because of the complexity of fatigue damage in composites. Detection of damage in composites has required the improvement of traditional NDE methods as well as fostered the development of a variety of new NDE technologies.

This chapter examines the capabilities of conventional and emerging NDE methods for the detection of stress-induced and thermal-induced fatigue damage in composite materials. The chapter reviews the mainstream NDE techniques that include the *acoustic methods* (e.g. ultrasonics, acousto-ultrasonics, Lamb waves and acoustic emission), *radiography, thermography* and *eddy currents*. Emerging techniques are also examined, including *acoustography, vibrothermography* and *Moiré interferometry*. Elementary NDE methods such as visual inspection and tap testing are not reviewed because of their inability to detect most types of fatigue damage. The main focus of this chapter is to examine the capabilities and limitations of the various NDE techniques for detecting and characterizing fatigue damage in laminates and sandwich composites. A detailed description of the operating principles of each NDE technique will not be given, but instead a brief outline will be provided. More detailed information on the principles of the various NDE methods is provided in numerous review articles.[5–8]

8.2   Acoustic NDE techniques

8.2.1   Ultrasonics

Ultrasonics is one of the most used techniques for the non-destructive detection of fatigue damage in composite structures used in aircraft, ships, civil infrastructure and many other applications. Ultrasonics is also a valuable research tool used in the study of fatigue damage mechanisms. Ultrasonics can be performed in various modes of operation, although the two most common are the pulse-echo (A-scan) technique and through-transmission (C-scan) technique. The principles of pulse-echo and through-transmission ultrasonics are described in detail in numerous reviews,[6,9,10] and therefore are only briefly outlined here.

With the pulse-echo method an ultrasonic transducer is coupled to the surface to transmit high frequency acoustic waves through the composite. The transducer is used to transmit planar waves in the direction normal to the surface, although angled transducer probes can be used to transmit waves in other directions. Ultrasound frequencies of 0.5 to 50 MHz can be used, with the ability to detect small defects improving while the wave penetration depth decreases with increasing frequency. In a pristine composite without fatigue damage, the acoustic waves propagate through the material and are back-reflected from the rear surface and then recorded by a sensor located within the emitting transducer. As the ultrasound waves travel through a composite they experience some attenuation due to scattering at fibre-resin interfaces and manufacturing defects, such as voids, which have acoustic impedance values different to the laminate.

During the ultrasonic inspection of a composite containing fatigue damage, the acoustic waves are attenuated by delaminations, matrix cracks and other defects. The amount of attenuation can be quantitatively defined by the attenuation coefficient, which is an effective parameter for evaluating the state and quality of a material. The attenuation coefficient is determined by comparing the peak values of successive reflected acoustic signals, and is calculated by:

$$\alpha = \frac{20 \log A_2/A_1}{d}$$

where A_1 and A_2 are the amplitudes of any two successive echoes and d is the distance travelled by the ultrasound wave.

Through-transmission ultrasonics basically consists of a transducer for emitting ultrasonic pulses that is placed at or near one surface and a receiver sensor that is located at the opposite surface. The transducer and receiver are coupled to the surfaces or they are immersed in water together with the composite. The ultrasound waves are attenuated by defects within the composite in the same way as with the pulse-echo method, and the acoustic attenuation is monitored using the receiver. A feature of the through-transmission method is that the damage distribution is mapped as a C-scan.

Modern ultrasonic systems have several advantages when inspecting composites for fatigue damage, including the ability to determine the three-dimensional positioning of damaged areas, the ability to inspect in real-time, the systems are simple to use, and the pulse-echo method is portable. A drawback of ultrasonics is that it is a point-by-point inspection method and therefore slow to perform over a large area. A problem with through-transmission ultrasonics is that when used as a research tool, the composite specimen must usually be removed from the fatigue test machine to perform the NDE analysis.

Ultrasonics can be used to non-destructively evaluate some of the mechanical properties of composites, including fatigue endurance. It is well known that the wave speed of the acoustic pulses can be used to determine the Young's modulus of a composite. Studies have shown that the ultrasound attenuation coefficient of composites can be related to their mechanical properties such as flexural strength,[11] interlaminar fracture toughness,[12] interlaminar shear strength,[13,14] tensile strength[15] and fatigue life.[11,16–19] Williams and Doll[16] were the first to report that the attenuation coefficient of composites measured immediately after fabrication correlates with their fatigue life. Figure 8.1 shows the relationship between the initial attenuation coefficient for carbon/epoxy composites against the number of compression–compression load cycles of failure. This data shows that the fatigue life is substantially lower for composites with a high attenuation coefficient. It is believed that laminates with a high initial attenuation coefficient have a greater amount of manufacturing defects (such as voids) that shorten the fatigue life. For a similar reason, Srivastava and Prakash[18] found that the initial attenuation coefficient of composites correlated with their fatigue resistance under repeated impact loading. This relationship is shown in Fig. 8.2 where the impact fatigue resistance is seen to decrease rapidly with an increase in the initial attenuation coefficient. While these studies demonstrate that the initial attenuation coefficient can be related to fatigue performance under cyclic compression or impact loading, the relationship has not yet been demonstrated for other fatigue load conditions such as cyclic tension, flexure or reversed tension-compression loading. More importantly, the relationship shown by Williams and Doll[16] and Srivastava and Prakash[18] is empirical, and therefore should not be considered a reliable predictor of fatigue life.

Ultrasonics is a more reliable technique for detecting damage incurred during fatigue loading. Pulse-echo ultrasonics[20,21] and through-transmission ultrasonics[16,22–31] have been used for many years to evaluate fatigue damage in composites, and the capabilities and limitations of the method are thoroughly understood.

Various properties of the ultrasound signals can be used to identify the formation and growth of fatigue damage. Reliable indicators of fatigue damage are a change to the amplitude or attenuation coefficient of the ultrasound signal.[16,20,21,23,24,28,32] For example,

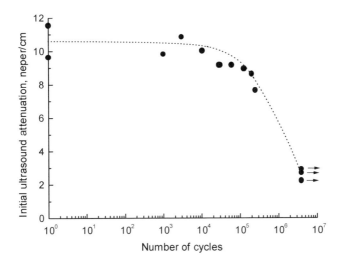

Fig. 8.1   Relationship between the initial attenuation coefficient of carbon/epoxy composites and the number of compression-compression load cycles to failure. (Data from Williams and Doll.[16])

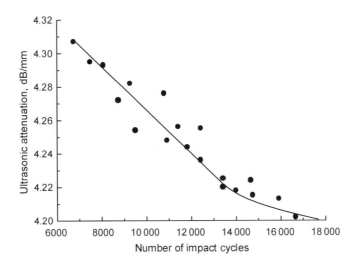

Fig. 8.2   Relationship between the initial attenuation coefficient and the number of impact events to failure. (Data from Srivastava and Prakash.[18])

Tsushima and Ono[20] used the amplitude of the pulse-echo signal to monitor the growth of damage in fibreglass composites caused by tensile fatigue loading. A steady reduction in the amplitude of the pulse-echo signal was measured with an increasing number of load cycles, as shown in Fig. 8.3. The progressive attenuation of the signal is a clear indication of the accumulation of damage. Microscopy revealed that the fatigue loading caused matrix cracking throughout the composite, and thereby Tsushima and Ono were able to correlate the reduction to the pulse-echo amplitude with an increase in the matrix crack density, as shown in Fig. 8.3(b).

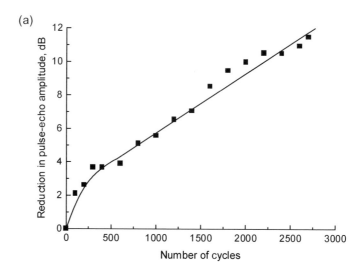

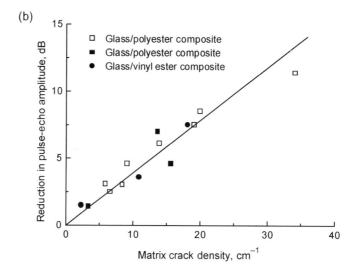

Fig. 8.3   (a) Reduction in the pulse-echo amplitude signal with increasing number of load cycles for a glass/polyester composite. (b) Relationship between the line density of matrix cracks and the reduction in the pulse-echo amplitude signal for glass/polyester and glass/vinyl ester composites subjected to fatigue loading. (Data from Tsushima and Ono.[20])

Other studies have also found that the increase in ultrasound attenuation closely parallels the accumulation of fatigue damage.[16,21,32] As a further example, Nayeb-Hashemi et al.[28] used the change to the attenuation coefficient to monitor the development of fatigue damage in a carbon/epoxy composite subjected to cyclic tensile loading. It was found that the attenuation coefficient increases with the number of load cycles, as shown in Fig. 8.4, and rises rapidly when the laminate nears the end of its life. Nayeb-Hashemi et al. therefore concluded that the rate of attenuation change is a good indicator of the residual fatigue life. However, the change to the attenuation coefficient does not provide information on the type, size or morphology of the fatigue damage. Despite the sensitivity of ultrasonics to the

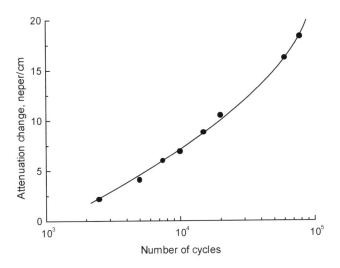

Fig. 8.4   Effect of number of load cycles on the attenuation coefficient of a carbon/epoxy composite. (Data from Nayeb-Hashemi et al.[28])

presence of fatigue damage, the method cannot reliably distinguish between different types of damage (e.g. matrix cracks from small delaminations), and therefore it is necessary to use microscopy or other NDE techniques to characterize the damage.

Without doubt, the most popular method for ultrasonically detecting fatigue damage is by C-scanning.[22,25–27,29–31] The ultrasonic C-scan technique is ideally suited to detecting delamination-type fractures in composites that develop at the later stages of fatigue, particularly when the cracks are transverse to the transmission path of the acoustic waves. However, it cannot be used to inspect sandwich composites because the ultrasound signal is completely attenuated by the core. Examples of C-scans measured by Scarponi and Briotti[29] at different stages of the fatigue life of a laminate are presented in Fig. 8.5, and it is seen that this method tracks the formation and spread of delamination damage. C-scan ultrasonics is a simple yet powerful technique for showing the morphology and size of delaminations to a high degree of resolution. This method is able to determine the size of defects to within 0.4–0.7 mm for composites that are several millimetres thick, although the resolution deteriorates with thicker materials. It is also noteworthy that the resolution is affected by whether the composite is under load when the ultrasonic inspection is made. Mouritz et al.[21] and Beghini et al.[22] found that fatigue-induced delaminations are more clearly resolved when the composite is loaded during the ultrasonic inspection. It appears that the common practice of removing the laminate from the fatigue test machine causes partial closure of the delaminations, particularly at the crack fronts, which makes the damage appear smaller than the actual size. However, in most composites this apparent reduction to the delamination size is small, and does not unduly affect the capability of ultrasonics for detecting delamination damage.

C-scan ultrasonics is often used to generate a two-dimensional map of fatigue damage (as shown in Fig. 8.5), and this has the disadvantage of not providing information on the distribution of damage in the through-thickness direction. It is possible to combine B-scans (through-thickness profiles of damage) with C-scans to generate a three-dimensional map of fatigue damage.

While ultrasonics can detect planar defects such as delaminations, it is not capable of

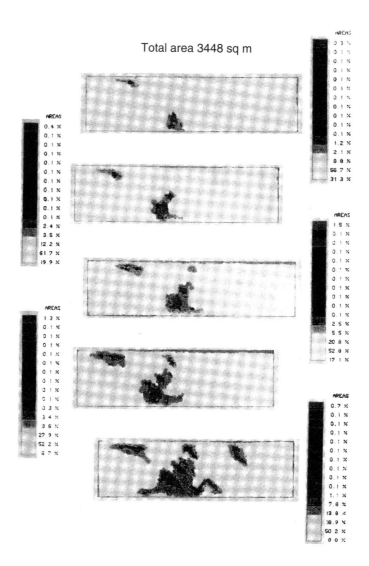

Fig. 8.5   C-scans showing delamination growth (which appears dark) in a carbon/epoxy composite after 4000, 5500, 7000, 9000 and 13 000 cycles. (Images from Scarponi and Briotti.[29])

resolving fine-scale fatigue damage, such as fibre splitting or broken fibres.[20,21,25,27] Ultrasonics is usually not capable of detecting damage such as matrix cracks and off-axis ply cracks that are aligned parallel to the transmission path of the ultrasound waves. Other NDE techniques such as acousto-ultrasonics or radiography must be used to detect these types of damage, and these methods are described later.

Ultrasonics can be an effective method for non-destructively detecting thermal fatigue damage in composites. Kasap *et al.*[3] and Forsyth *et al.*[4] evaluated the efficacy of through-transmission ultrasonics for detecting fatigue damage in composites following thermal cycling. It was found that the group velocity of the acoustic waves decreased and the signal attenuation increased with the number of thermal cycles, as shown in Fig. 8.6. The reduction

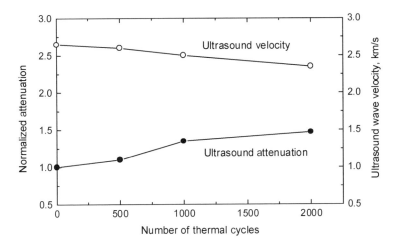

Fig. 8.6   Ultrasonic detection of thermal fatigue damage. Effect of thermal cycling of an E-glass/ polyester composite over the temperature range of 25 to 75 °C on the wave velocity and attenuation of the ultrasound signal. (Data from Kasap *et al.*[3])

in the wave velocity is the result of a reduction in the Young's modulus of the composite due to thermally induced fatigue damage. The rise in the signal attenuation is due to scattering of ultrasound waves from thermal fatigue defects such as fibre–matrix debonds and matrix cracks. While ultrasonics is a useful method for identifying the presence of thermal fatigue damage, it has the same limitation as when used for detecting stress fatigue damage of not being capable of distinguishing between the different types of damage.

In addition to A-scan and C-scan ultrasonics, fatigue damage in composites can be detected using an ultrasound technique known as phase-insensitive tone-burst spectroscopy. This technique basically involves transmitting ultrasound waves over a range of frequencies through a material, and then analysing the received signal for changes to the attenuation and frequency spectrum. This technique has been used to detect fatigue damage in composites, although it is rarely used.[33]

8.2.2   Acousto-ultrasonics

Acousto-ultrasonics was developed by Vary in the mid-1970s as a non-destructive method of inspecting metallic, ceramic and composite materials.[34,35] It is a versatile technique that can be used to identify the degree of resin cure, impact damage, damage caused by monotonic loading, and changes to the tensile modulus, tensile strength and interlaminar shear strength of composites.[34,36–38] It is also an effective method for detecting the onset and growth of fatigue damage in composites.

The acousto-ultrasonic technique involves transmitting broad-band acoustic waves in a series of repeating pulses along a material. A broad-band transducer coupled to the material surface generates ultrasound waves over a range of frequencies (typically from 0.1 to 5 MHz) in a series of discrete pulses. These pulses are reflected off the back and front surfaces as they propagate along the length of the material. The pulses are affected by internal defects such as matrix cracks and delaminations that attenuate the signal. One of the advantages of the acousto-ultrasonics technique is that the pulses propagate along the major fibre direction unlike normal incidence pulse-echo and through-transmission ultrasonics. A piezoelectric

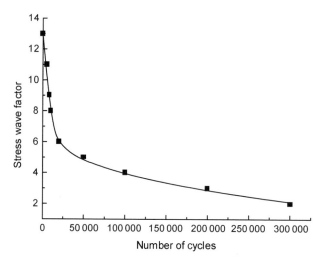

Fig. 8.7   Effect of tensile fatigue loading on the stress wave factor of a carbon/epoxy composite inspected using acousto-ultrasonics. (Data from Nayeb-Hashemi *et al.*[28])

acoustic emission sensor that is coupled to the front surface a fixed distance from the acoustic transducer records those pulses that are above a threshold intensity for a set period of time. The signal recorded by the sensor is analysed to assess the quality of the material and determine the presence of damage. The quality of a material is usually described by the 'stress wave factor', which is a measure of the attenuation of the ultrasound waves as they propagate through the material. The stress wave factor can be determined in various ways from the acoustic signal recorded by the receiving sensor. But regardless of how it is defined, a reduction to the stress wave factor is a strong indication of the presence of damage inside materials.

The efficacy of acousto-ultrasonics for the detection of fatigue damage in composites has been evaluated over the last 25 years.[19,28,39–42] The technique is able to monitor the initiation and growth of damage in laminates caused by fatigue loading. For example, Fig. 8.7 shows the reduction of the stress wave factor in a carbon/epoxy composite as a result of the accumulation of fatigue damage with increasing number of load cycles. The rapid reduction to the stress wave factor at the early stage of the fatigue life is almost certainly due to the formation of transverse matrix cracks. These cracks can be difficult to detect using normal-incident pulse-echo and through-transmission ultrasonics because the flaws are aligned in the transmission direction of the acoustic waves. With the acousto-ultrasonics technique, on the other hand, the waves propagate normal to the matrix cracks and therefore the damage is easily detected.

Studies by Duke *et al.*,[40] Talreja *et al.*[41] and Govoda *et al.*[42] have revealed that the stress wave factor is much more sensitive to the presence of fatigue damage than a change to the Young's modulus of a composite. Figure 8.8 shows the effect of increasing the number of load cycles on the Young's modulus and stress wave factor for a carbon/epoxy laminate. In this figure the normalized Young's modulus is the modulus of the fatigued laminate divided by the original modulus before fatigue loading. The stress wave factor is defined as the root mean square of the power spectral density of the acousto-ultrasonic signal. It is seen that the Young's modulus drops slightly within the first few load cycles due to the formation of transverse matrix cracks, and then decreases gradually with further cyclic loading until the

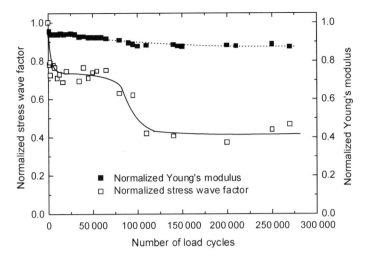

Fig. 8.8 Effect of number of load cycles on the normalized stress wave factor and normalized
Young's modulus of a carbon/epoxy composite. (Data from Talreja et al.[41])

modulus stabilizes at 88% of the original value after about 100 000 cycles. In comparison,
Fig. 8.8 shows that the stress wave factor drops sharply within the first few load cycles due
to the high sensitivity of acousto-ultrasonics to matrix cracks. The stress wave factor
continues to drop rapidly with further loading before stabilizing at about 40% of the original
value after 100 000 cycles. The profile of the curve for the stress wave factor closely follows
the modulus curve, showing it is a reliable measure of the presence of fatigue damage.
However, the reduction to the stress wave factor is much greater than for the Young's
modulus, indicating it is a more sensitive parameter to fatigue damage.

The capability of acousto-ultrasonics for monitoring the formation and growth of fatigue
damage caused by cyclic stress loading has been thoroughly evaluated. However, the
efficacy of the method for monitoring thermal fatigue damage in laminates as well as
thermal and stress fatigue damage in sandwich composites has not been widely reported.

8.2.3 Lamb waves

Ultrasonics technology can be adapted to generate Lamb waves for the large area non-
destructive inspection of materials.[6,43,44] The leaky Lamb wave technique involves using an
ultrasonic transducer to introduce Lamb waves that propagate along the plane of a material
plate for a long distance. Because the waves travel a long distance they can be used to
interrogate a composite over much larger areas than by single pulse-echo or through-
transmission inspections. The Lamb waves interact with microstructural features such as
fibre-resin interfaces, voids and other defects including damage caused by fatigue loading.
Lamb waves can detect matrix cracks and planar defects such as delaminations.[45–48] Sensors
are placed at various locations on the material, and these are used to measure any attenuation
of Lamb waves that 'leak' from the sides of the plate. The Lamb wave velocity is very
sensitive to a change to the Young's modulus of a material caused by damage, and therefore
sensors are also used to measure the exit speed of the leaky waves.

The Lamb wave technique has been used to detect defects in composites caused by poor
quality fabrication or monotonic loading.[45–47] However, the technique is not often used for

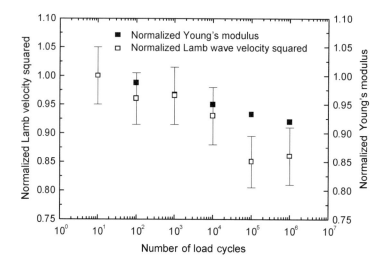

Fig. 8.9   Effect of number of tension–tension fatigue cycles on the normalized Lamb wave velocity squared and normalized Young's modulus for a carbon/epoxy composite. (Data from Seale et al.[49])

determining the presence of fatigue damage. Dayal et al.[45] and Seale et al.[49] evaluated the efficacy of Lamb waves for detecting fatigue damage in composites after cyclic loading. Seale et al.[49] measured a steady reduction in the Lamb wave speed (expressed as velocity^2) in a carbon/epoxy laminate with increasing number of the load cycles, as shown in Fig. 8.9. Using the velocity of the low frequency (S_o-mode) Lamb wave, it is possible to determine the Young's modulus of the fatigued composite using the simple expression:

$$E = \rho v^2$$

where ρ is the density of the material and v is the Lamb wave speed. Figure 8.9 shows the calculated reduction of the elastic modulus due to cyclic loading. A distinct advantage of the Lamb wave technique is that it can be used to non-destructively monitor changes to the stiffness of a composite over a large distance.

Seale et al.[49] found that the reduction to the Lamb wave speed and Young's modulus shown in Fig. 8.9 was due to the accumulation of transverse matrix cracks caused by fatigue. Figure 8.10 shows the effect of the matrix crack density on the Lamb wave speed (velocity^2) in the fatigued carbon/epoxy laminate. Despite some scatter in the values, it is apparent that a reduction to the Lamb wave velocity is related to the accumulation of matrix cracks caused by fatigue.

The studies by Dayal et al.[45] and Searle et al.[49] demonstrate that the Lamb wave technique is an effective NDE method for detecting transverse matrix cracks and monitoring changes to the Young's modulus of composites over a large area due to fatigue loading. Further research is needed to determine the capabilities of the technique for detecting other forms of stress-induced fatigue damage (e.g. shear cracks, splitting, delaminations, fibre fracture) and thermal fatigue damage in laminates as well as fatigue damage to sandwich composites.

8.2.4   Acoustography

Acoustography is an emerging NDE technology that was recently developed by Santec

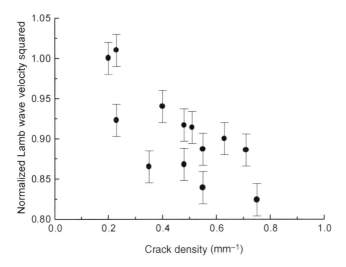

Fig. 8.10 Effect of the density of transverse matrix cracks on the normalized Lamb wave velocity squared for a carbon/epoxy laminate subjected to tension–tension fatigue. (Data from Seale *et al.*[49])

Systems Inc. (USA) for the near real-time, large area inspection of materials.[50,51] It is an ultrasonics-based technology that has the capability of inspecting materials much more rapidly than conventional point-by-point ultrasonic scanning as performed using the pulse-echo and through-transmission methods. Acoustography basically involves transmitting into a material a series of high frequency ultrasonic pulses that are randomly generated by a wide area piezoelectric transducer. These waves are spread over a large area and travel through the material where they are attenuated by microstructural features such as fibre-resin interfaces and defects.

The unique feature of the acoustography technique is the way the ultrasound waves are detected and analysed. When the waves exit the material they are analysed using a wide area, high resolution acousto-optic sensor.[52,53] The sensor is a large screen or film coated with a thin layer of liquid crystal molecules that are specially formulated to be sensitive to acoustic waves. Upon exposure to ultrasound, the molecules are excited and that causes them to change orientation on the screen/film (i.e. the molecular layer become birefringent). Attenuation of the ultrasound signal due to defects inside the material modifies the degree of excitation of the liquid crystal molecules, and this causes a change to the optical density (or visual contrast) of the film. The sensor can display a relatively large area (e.g. 150 mm × 150 mm) of a material in the near real-time with a single inspection, resulting in faster inspection times than conventional ultrasonics and many other NDE methods.

Acoustography can be performed in a reflective shadow (or pulse-echo) mode or through-transmission mode, depending on the position of the acousto-optic sensor. In the reflective shadow mode the pulse generator and acousto-optic sensor are on the same side of the material, and this is useful for inspecting components when there is access to one side only. With the through-transmission mode the sensor is placed on the opposite side of the material to the pulse generator.

Acoustography is capable of detecting planar defects within composites, such as delaminations and impact damage, and often to a higher degree of resolution than C-scan ultrasonics.[51] Recent research by Sandhu *et al.*[50] and Chen *et al.*[54–56] demonstrated the ability

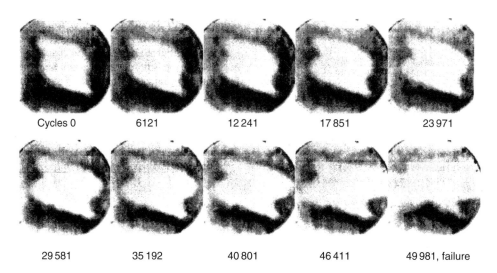

Cycles 0   6121   12 241   17 851   23 971

29 581   35 192   40 801   46 411   49 981, failure

Fig. 8.11   Acoustography images of fatigue damage in a carbon/epoxy composite taken at different numbers of load cycles. The central white region shows the damage. (Reprinted from *Composites Science and Technology*, Vol 61, A.S. Chen, D.P. Almond and B. Harris, 'In situ monitoring in real time of fatigue-induced damage growth in composite materials by acoustography', pp. 2437–2443, 2001, with permission from Elsevier Science.)

of acoustography to detect fatigue damage in the near real-time. Chen *et al.*[54–56] used acoustography to continuously monitor the growth of fatigue damage from an impact site in a carbon/epoxy laminate subjected to cyclic compressive loading. Figure 8.11 shows acoustographic images of the laminate taken while under cyclic loading at different stages of the fatigue life, and the damage region (which appears white) is seen to spread horizontally due to the growth of delaminations. This allows the width of the damage zone to be continuously tracked with the increasing number of fatigue cycles. Chen *et al.* report that this technique allowed the first quantitative, real-time measurement of damage growth during fatigue loading. Acoustography cannot detect all types of defects caused by fatigue loading; the method is similar to conventional ultrasonics in that it can determine the presence of delaminations and other planar defects that are aligned perpendicular to the transmission path of the acoustic waves. However, the technique has difficulty detecting transverse matrix cracks and broken fibres in fatigued composites.

8.3   Acoustic emission

Acoustic emission is an effective NDE technique for continuously monitoring the development of fatigue damage in composites. The acoustic emission technique is described by Burke *et al.*[6] and Miller,[57] and basically involves the detection of low intensity stress waves generated by failure events as they occur, such as delamination and fibre fracture. The stress waves are formed from the strain energy released during a failure event, and propagate to the surfaces where they are detected by acoustic sensors. An attraction of the acoustic emission technique is the ability to monitor damage initiation and accumulation in real-time, which is not possible with most other NDE techniques. Other advantages of acoustic emission are the

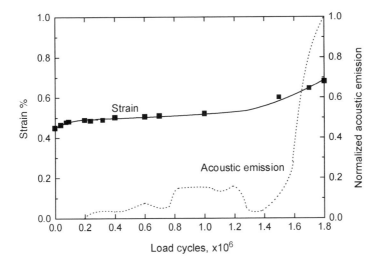

Fig. 8.12   Effect of number of tension–tension load cycles on the strain increase and acoustic emission rate for a boron/epoxy composite tested in load control. (The acoustic emission data has been smoothed). (Data from Williams and Reifsnider.[59])

ability to distinguish between some types of damage and, when a number of sensors are used, to determine the location of failure events.

Acoustic emission is often used to monitor the formation and growth of fatigue damage in composites.[58–66] It is generally found that the inspection of composites using acoustic emission can provide valuable insights about the failure mechanisms that occur at different stages over the fatigue life that ultimately lead to failure. This is because the different fatigue failure mechanisms generate different acoustic emission signals. For example, Chang et al.[58] found that transverse matrix cracks caused by the fatigue loading of carbon/epoxy composites can be identified by the detection of high amplitude acoustic emissions that have a characteristic frequency. Delaminations and fibre–matrix splitting, on the other hand, can be distinguished from matrix cracks by having a much higher acoustic emission rate. In some cases it is possible to distinguish between matrix cracking, delaminations and local fibre failures.[59,65] However, identifying the different fatigue damage mechanisms can be difficult because the characteristic acoustic emission signals are often masked by the much higher intensity signals generated by the friction and rubbing of crack faces with each load cycle. By careful analysis of the acoustic emission spectrum and good noise filtering techniques, it is possible to differentiate between certain types of fatigue damage.

The reliability of the acoustic emission technique to accurately monitor the progression of fatigue damage has been proven in numerous studies.[58,59,62,64–66] For example, Fig. 8.12 shows the relationship between the acoustic emission rate and strain increase for a boron/epoxy composite during a load-controlled fatigue test. It is seen that the strain increases gradually up to about 1.5 million cycles, and then increases more rapidly with further loading as the composite approaches final failure. This trend is mirrored with the acoustic emission results, which initially are low but then increase rapidly towards failure due to the increasing incidence of delamination cracking and fibre fracture. Another example is given in Fig. 8.13, which shows the number of acoustic emission events recorded during the cyclic loading of a carbon/epoxy composite. Also shown in Fig. 8.13 is the change in length of a delamination crack in the laminate that was measured directly by optical microscopy. It is

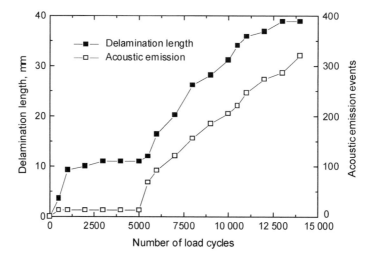

Fig. 8.13 Comparison of delamination length measured by optical microscopy and the number of acoustic emission events during fatigue loading of a carbon/epoxy composite. (Reproduced from Cohen and Awerbuch.[66])

seen that there is a direct correlation between the acoustic emission results and direct optical observation of the growth of delamination damage under fatigue loading. Each change in the rate of damage progression is accompanied by a corresponding change in the accumulation rate of the acoustic emission events.

Fatigue damage to composites can also be detected using the thermo-acoustic emission technique.[67,68] This technique is a modification of conventional acoustic emission, and involves heating the pre-fatigued composite in an oven or using a hand-held heater to a moderate temperature (100–150 °C), followed by cooling to room temperature. During a thermal cycle of heating and cooling, the opposing faces of fatigue cracks rub together due to thermal expansion and the redistribution of residual strains in the composite. The friction caused by rubbing of the crack faces generates an acoustic emission that is detected by sensors. This technique has the potential to detect low levels of fatigue damage that cannot be easily identified using conventional acoustic emission. Sato *et al.*[67,68] detected microcracks in composites caused by fatigue loading using the thermo-acoustic technique. However, the technique is rarely used to detect fatigue damage because it is often not practical to heat and cool the composite.

8.4　Radiography

Radiography is another NDE technique that is often used to monitor the development of fatigue damage in composites. The radiography technique is described in detail by Bryant,[69] and involves irradiating the surface of a material with a burst of neutrons, X-rays or some other form of radiation. In most cases X-rays are used because of the potential danger and expensive equipment needed to irradiate with neutrons. As the radiation passes through the material some of its energy is absorbed before emerging from the opposite side of the sample where the amount of unabsorbed radiation is recorded on a fluorescent screen or X-ray sensitive film. During passage of the radiation through a material the rate of energy

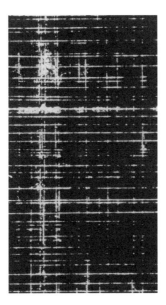

Fig. 8.14 X-ray radiograph showing matrix cracks in the 0° and 90° plies together with internal delaminations initiated at the intersection points of the matrix cracks. (Reprinted from *Composites Science and Technology*, Vol. 25, W.W. Stinchcomb, 'Nondestructive evaluation of damage accumulation processes in composite laminates', pp. 103–118, 1986, with permission from Elsevier Science.)

absorption can be changed by defects that have a different absorption coefficient to the parent material. As a result, the amount of unabsorbed energy for a region containing a defect is different to a damage-free region, and this appears as a bright or dark spot on the screen or film. Modern X-ray radiography systems are able to take real-time film-less images of damaged composites.

Certain types of defects in composites, including those caused by fatigue, are not easily detected using standard X-ray radiography because of poor contrast on the radiograph. In order to enhance the contrast between defects and the parent material, a radio-opaque liquid is applied to the sample before radiography testing which penetrates into surface-breaking flaws. A variety of X-ray sensitive penetrants are available, with the most popular being 1,4 diiodobutane and zinc iodide. Care must be exercised when using a liquid penetrant to ensure it completely fills the cracks and delaminations, and that the liquid does not have a plasticizing effect on the polymer matrix.

Penetrant-enhanced X-ray radiography is often used as a research tool to study the fatigue damage mechanisms in composites.[25,27,32,58,70,71,74] Radiography is a powerful technique for detecting longitudinal, transverse and off-axis matrix cracks, fibre splitting, delamination initiation sites, and delamination cracks caused by fatigue. Radiography can also detect fibre fractures in boron fibre composites caused by excessive fatigue loading by identifying failure of the tungsten core to the boron fibre.[75] However, the technique is not able to detect failure of other engineering fibres such as carbon, glass and aramid.

Radiographic inspections can be performed at regular intervals during fatigue testing to monitor the development of damage over the life of a composite. An example of an X-ray radiograph showing matrix cracks and delaminations in the 0° and 90° plies of a cross-ply carbon/epoxy composite following fatigue loading is shown in Fig. 8.14. As another

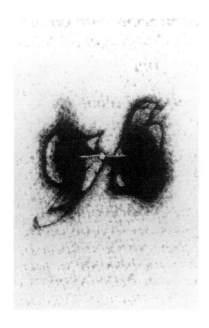

Fig. 8.15   X-ray radiograph showing the distribution of fatigue damage at the edges of a sharp notch in a carbon/epoxy composite following tension–compression fatigue loading. (Reprinted from *International Journal of Fatigue*, Vol. 13, S. Kellas, J. Morton and P.T. Curtis, 'A characteristic fatigue parameter for notched composites', pp. 35–43, 1991, with permission from Elsevier Science.)

example, Fig. 8.15 shows a radiograph of fatigue damage at the ends of a sharp notch in a carbon/epoxy composite. Radiographs provide detailed visual information on the types and distribution of fatigue damage, and quite often show damage that cannot be detected using conventional ultrasonic techniques. Furthermore, the location and orientation of cracks are clearly mapped, and by using high voltage X-rays together with fine grained X-ray film or a high resolution X-ray sensitive detector, it is possible to detect damage less than 1 mm in size. The degree of resolution with X-ray radiography is generally better than with C-scan ultrasonics and many other NDE techniques. A further advantage of radiography is that the technique can be used to observe visually the stress redistributions in composites, particularly those with a notch or hole, as damage develops over the fatigue life.[58,71]

While radiography has the capability to provide detailed information on fatigue damage, it has a number of limitations. One drawback is that radiography cannot easily detect cracks and delaminations that are not filled with a radio-opaque liquid. This is a problem for detecting internal damage sites that are not connected to an external surface. Furthermore, multiple through-thickness damage cannot be detected using incident radiography because, like ultrasonics, the uppermost damage shadows underlying damage. This problem can be avoided by taking radiographs of the fatigued composite from different directions, although this is not always practical. A further drawback is that radiographs show only the fatigue damage in a two-dimension, plan view of a three-dimensional damage field. Although it is possible to produce 3D images of fatigue damage by making stereo-pairs of radiographic images, which is known as stereoradiography.[25,71,73] This method has been used successfully to identify the damage in each ply and interface within a fatigued laminate.

8.5   Thermographic NDE methods

8.5.1   Thermography

Thermography is a popular technique for determining the presence of fabrication defects (e.g. large voids, foreign objects) or impact damage inside composites, although it is not often used to determine the presence of fatigue damage. Active thermography, which is a method that relies on the generation of internal heat to identify the presence of damage, has been used in a few studies to monitor fatigue damage in composites in real-time.[59,75–78] A promising thermography technique for the real-time monitoring of damage in composites is vibrothermography.

8.5.2   Vibrothermography (SPATE)

Vibrothermography or SPATE (Stress patterns analysis by the measurement of thermal emissions) is an active thermography-based technique that is becoming recognized as a powerful NDE tool for obtaining full-field images of damage in materials. The application of the technique for detecting fatigue damage in composites is outlined by Reifsnider et al.,[79] Jones et al.[80] and Heller et al.[81] The technique involves mapping the temperature distribution over a composite surface while under an externally applied load, which can include fatigue loads. Damage in the material changes the internal stress distribution that thereby induces localized heating, which is detected as a hot region by a thermal imaging sensor. This technique has been used to monitor the onset and growth of fatigue damage in composites in real-time, and has the potential to determine changes to the compliance of laminates under increasing number of load cycles.[79,80] While vibrothermography is sensitive to many forms of fatigue damage, including matrix cracks and delamination, it does not readily distinguish between them.

8.6   Eddy currents

The eddy current technique is a NDE tool commonly used for detecting damage in metals and metal-matrix composites,[82] although its usefulness for FRP laminates is limited. The technique is based on the induction of an electric field in a material that is created by a current-carrying coil positioned just above the surface of the component. Damage within the material can induce perturbations in the electromagentic field that results in a change to the impedance of the electrical signal.

The eddy current method is rarely used to inspect for fatigue damage because it is only reliable for detecting fibre breaks in carbon and boron fibre composites. The method cannot identify other forms of damage such as matrix cracks and delamination. Furthermore, the method cannot detect fibre damage in composites reinforced with electrically insulating fibres such as glass and aramid.

8.7   Moiré interferometry

Moiré interferometry has been used for many years to monitor fatigue damage in composites under cyclic loading.[83–85] Shadow Moiré interferometry is a NDE technique that involves covering the surface of a material with a fine grid of closely spaced lines. The material is then loaded and the surface viewed at normal incidence through an optical grid with the same line

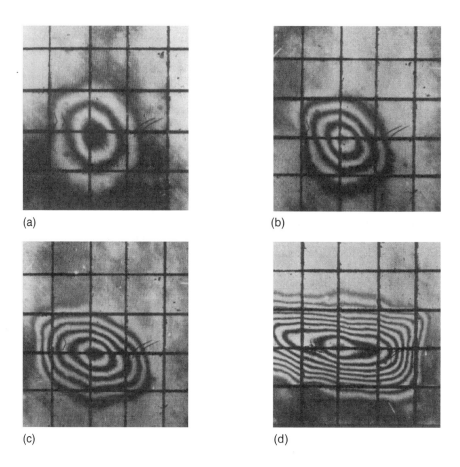

(a)   (b)

(c)   (d)

Fig. 8.16   Shadow Moiré interference fringes showing the growth of fatigue damage in an impact damaged carbon/epoxy composite. The images show the fringe patterns after (a) 0, (b) 36, (c) 72 and (d) 108 series of fatigue loadings. (Reprinted from *Composites*, D.S. Saunders and T.J. Van Blarcium, Vol 19, 'Effect of load duration in the fatigue behaviour of graphite/epoxy laminates containing delaminations', pp. 217–228, 1998, with permission from Elsevier Science.)

spacing. Any out-of-plane deflection of the surface caused by sub-surface damage becomes visible as a series of interference fringes. An example of the application of Moiré interferometry for monitoring the progression of fatigue damage at different stages during the life of a carbon/epoxy composite is shown by the series of interference fringe patterns in Fig. 8.16. This composite was initially damaged by a low energy impact, and then subjected to variable amplitude cyclic loads representative of the fatigue loading of aircraft structures during flight. It is seen that the fringe patterns change shape and expand around the impact site with an increasing number of fatigue load events, and this is due to the spread of delamination damage.

Using Moiré interferometry it is possible to determine approximately the size of fatigue damage by measuring the size of the fringe patterns; although, Saunders and Van Blaricum[85] found that the size of fatigue damage measured using Moiré interferometry is marginally smaller than the true size determined by ultrasonic C-scanning. Further limitations of the technique are that it cannot reliably distinguish between a single delamination and multiple

Table 8.1   Summary of capabilities of NDE techniques for detecting fatigue damage in laminates and sandwich composites

NDE technique	Damage to laminates			Damage to sandwich composites	
	Transverse matrix cracks	Delamination	Fibre fracture	Skin-core debonding	Core damage
Ultrasonics	Difficult	Yes	No	No	No
Acousto-ultrasonics	Yes	Yes	No	No	No
Lamb waves	Yes	Yes	No	No	No
Acoustography	Difficult	Yes	No	No	No
Acoustic emission	Difficult	Yes	Yes	Difficult	Difficult
Thermo-acoustic emission	Difficult	Yes	Yes	–	–
X-ray radiography	Yes	Yes	Boron fibres only	No	No
Thermography	Difficult	Yes	No	–	–
Vibrothermography	Yes	Yes	No	–	–
Eddy currents	No	No	Boron/carbon fibres only	–	–
Moiré interferometry	No	Yes	No	–	No

delaminations in a composite, nor detect fatigue damage that does not cause out-of-plane deflections, such as matrix cracks, fibre–matrix debonding or broken fibres.

8.8   Summary and concluding remarks

There is a diverse range of NDE techniques for detecting fatigue damage in fibre reinforced polymer composites, and the capabilities and limitations of the main methods have been outlined in this chapter. Each technique has the ability to detect certain types of damage; for example ultrasonics can detect delaminations whereas acoustic emission can identify delaminations and fibre failures, but no single method is capable of detecting all the different fatigue damage modes. Table 8.1 lists the types of fatigue damage that can be detected in laminates and sandwich composites using the NDE techniques described in this chapter. Using some of these techniques it is possible to relate the information on fatigue damage to a mechanical property of the laminate. For instance, using Lamb wave ultrasonics it is possible to use the wave speed to relate the density of matrix cracks with the in-plane Young's modulus and, as another example, using acousto-ultrasonics, the stress wave factor with the elastic modulus of a fatigued laminate. However, no single NDE technique has the capability to quantitatively relate the fatigue damage states in a laminate or sandwich composite to the modulus, strength and remaining fatigue life. It is essential that more than one NDE method be used to gain as much information as possible about the different fatigue damage states and residual mechanical properties of a composite. For example, it may be necessary to combine information gained from ultrasonics, acousto-ultrasonics and X-ray radiography to achieve a three-dimensional map of the complex array of fatigue damage in a composite.

This chapter concentrated on those NDE techniques that are commonly used to detect stress-induced fatigue damage in laminates. Much less is known about the capabilities of these techniques for detecting thermal fatigue damage, which can be more difficult to detect than stress-induced damage. It is known that conventional ultrasonics is able to qualitatively detect the presence of thermal fatigue damage, although the capabilities of the many other NDE techniques for identifying thermal damage have not been thoroughly evaluated. Another field of NDE requiring greater investigation is the detection of fatigue damage in sandwich composite materials. While some of the techniques described in this chapter have the capability of detecting fatigue damage in the skins of sandwich composites, none of the methods are reliable for identifying skin-from-core debonding or core damage caused by fatigue loading. This is an area of NDE technology requiring much greater research and development, and there are emerging methods with potential, such as X-ray computer tomography and Compton backscattered X-ray radiography.

8.9   Acknowledgements

This chapter was written with the support of the CRC for Advanced Composite Structures Ltd., Task 1.5.4 'Cost-effective NDI for aerospace'. The author thanks the Australian Research Council (Grant No. DP0211709).

8.10   Information sources

- **The American Society for Nondestructive Testing, Inc. (ASNT)**
  ASNT is the world's largest technical society organized exclusively for the purpose of advancing nondestructive testing (NDT). ASNT is the fusion of NDT-related scientific, engineering and technical knowledge. The Society promotes NDT education, research and the exchange of technical information to its members and other professionals using NDT.
- **NDT Laboratory Links**
  The web-site *www.fsb.hr* contains many useful links to professional societies, journals, laboratories, equipment etc. on NDE.
- **Useful Reference Books**
  - *ASM Handbook: Nondestructive Evaluation and Quality Control*, American Society of Metals, OH, ISBN: 0871700239, 1989.
  - C.J. Hellier, *Handbook of Nondestructive Evaluation*, McGraw-Hill Professional; ISBN: 0070281211, 2001.
  - P.J. Shull, *Nondestructive Evaluation Theory, Techniques, and Applications*, Marcel Dekker, ISBN 0-8247-8872-9, 2002.

8.11   References

1. TALREJA R (2000), 'Fatigue of polymer matrix composites', in *Comprehensive Composite Materials, Vol. 2*, ed. R. Talreja and J-A. E. Månson, Elsevier, Oxford.
2. HERAKOVICH C T and HYER M W (1986), 'Damage-induced property changes in composites subjected to cyclic thermal fatigue', *Engineering Fracture Mechanics*, **25**, 779–791.
3. KASAP S O, YANNACOPOULOS S, MIRCHANDANI V and HILDEBRANDT J R (1992), 'Ultrasonic evaluation of thermal fatigue of composites', *Trans ASME*, **114**, 132–136.
4. FORSYTH D S, KASAP S O, WACKER I and YANNACOPOULOS S (1994), 'Thermal fatigue of composites: ultrasonic and SEM evaluations', *Journal of Engineering Materials and Technology, Trans ASME*, **116**, 113–120.
5. CANTWELL W J and MORTON J (1992), 'The significance of damage and defects and their detection in composite materials: a review', *Journal of Strain Analysis*, **27**, 29–42.
6. BURKE S K, McCOUSLAND S and SCALA C M (1994), 'Nondestructive characterization of advanced composite materials'' *Materials Forum*, **18**, 85–109.

7. BAR-COHEN Y (2000), 'Emerging NDT technologies and challenges at the beginning of the third millennium – Part 1', *Materials Evaluation*, 17–30.
8. BAR-COHEN Y (2000), 'Emerging NDT technologies and challenges at the beginning of the third millennium – Part 2', *Materials Evaluation*, 141–150.
9. HENNEKE E G (1990), 'Ultrasonic nondestructive evaluation of advanced composites', in *Non-Destructive Testing of Fibre-Reinforced Plastics Composites*, Vol. 2, ed. J. Summerscales, Elsevier Applied Science, London, pp. 55–159.
10. BIRKS A S and GREEN R E (1991), *Nondestructive Testing Handbook* (2nd Ed.), Vol 7: Ultrasonic Testing, American Society for Nondestructive Testing, OH.
11. DE ALMEIDA S F M and NETO Z S N (1994), 'Effect of void content on the strength of composite laminates', *Composite Structures*, **28**, 139–148.
12. MOURITZ A P (2000), 'Ultrasonic and interlaminar properties of highly porous composites', *Journal of Composite Materials*, **34**, 218–239.
13. STONE D E W and CLARKE B (1975), 'Ultrasonic attenuation as a measure of void content in carbon-fibre reinforced plastics', *Non-Destructive Testing*, **8**, 137–145.
14. JEONG H (1997), 'Effects of voids on the mechanical strength and ultrasonic attenuation of laminated composites', *Journal of Composite Materials*, **31**, 276–292.
15. HAYFORD D T and HENNEKE E G (1979), 'A model for correlating damage and ultrasonic attenuation in composites', in *Composite Materials: Testing and Design (Fifth Conference)*, ASTM STP 674, ed. S.W. Tsai, American Society for Testing and Materials, pp. 184–200.
16. WILLIAMS J H and DOLL B (1980), 'Ultrasonic attenuation as an indicator of fatigue life of graphite fiber epoxy composite', *Materials Evaluation*, May, 33–37.
17. RICHARDS R J, MORRIS W L and BUCK O (1982), 'Fatigue lifetime predictions from ultrasonically detected laminar defects in a graphite-epoxy composite', in *Review of Progress in Quantitative Nondestructive Evaluation*, Vol. 1, eds. D.O. Thompson and D.E. Chimenti, Plenum, NY, pp. 295–300.
18. SRIVASTAVA V K and PRAKASH R (1987), 'Study of fatigue life of glass fibre/zirconia hybrid composites using an ultrasonic technique', *International Journal of Fatigue*, **9**, 109–113.
19. SRIVASTAVA V K and PRAKASH R (1987), 'Fatigue life prediction of glass fibre-reinforced plastics using the acousto-ultrasonic technique', *International Journal of Fatigue*, July, pp. 175–178.
20. TSUSHIMA S and ONO M (1998), 'Nondestructive evaluation of fatigue damages in FRP using ultrasonic waves', *Proc. of the US–Pacific Rim Workshop on Composite Materials for Ship and Offshore Structures*, 7–9 April, Honolulu, Hawaii.
21. MOURITZ A P, TOWNSEND C and SHAH KHAN M Z (2000), 'Non-destructive detection of fatigue damage in thick composites by pulse-echo ultrasonics', *Composite Science and Technology*, **60**, 23–32.
22. BEGHINI M, BERTINI L and VITALE E (1991), 'Analysis of fatigue delamination growth in carboresin specimens with central hole', *Composite Structures*, **17**, 257–274.
23. SHOUP T A, MILLER J G, HEYMAN J S and ILLG W (1982), 'Ultrasonic chacterization of fatigue and impact damage in graphite epoxy composite laminates', *Proceedings of the 1982 Ultrasonics Symposium*, pp. 960–964.
24. WILLIAMS J H, YUCE H and LEE S S (1988), 'Ultrasonic and mechanical characterizations of fatigue states of graphite epoxy composite laminates', *Materials Evaluation*, **40**, 560–565.
25. BADER M G and BONIFACE L (1983), 'The assessment of fatigue damage in CFRP laminates', *Proc. Of the International Conference on Testing, Evaluation and Quality Control of Composites* (TEQC 83), 13–14 Sept, Guildford, Surrey, pp. 66–75.
26. HAGEMAIER D J and FASSBENDER R H (1985), 'Ultrasonic inspection of carbon-epoxy composites', *Materials Evaluation*, **43**, 556–560.
27. KELLAS S, MORTON J and BISHOP S M (1985), 'Damage development in notched carbon fibre composites subjected to fatigue loading', in *Composite Structures 3*, ed. I.H. Marshall, Paisley, UK, pp. 56–68.
28. NAYEB-HASHEMI H, COHEN M D, ZOTOS J and POORMAND R (1986), 'Ultrasonic characteristics of graphite/epoxy composite material subjected to fatigue and impacts', *Journal of Nondestructive Evaluation*, **5**, 119–131.
29. SCARPONI C and BRIOTTI C (1997), 'Ultrasonic detection of delaminations on composite materials', *Journal of Reinforced Plastics and Composites*, **16**, 768–790.
30. CLARK G and SAUNDERS D S (1991), 'Morphology of impact damage growth by fatigue in carbon fibre composite laminates', *Materials Forum*, **15**, 333–342.

31. SCHUSTER J and FRIEDRICH K (1994), 'Fatigue testing of thermoformed bidirectional LDF™-composites', *Applied Composite Materials*, **1**, 55–68.
32. DANIEL I M, WOOH S-C and LEE J W (1990), 'Non-destructive evaluation of damage development in composite materials', in *Elastic Waves and Ultrasonic Nondestructive Evaluation*, ed. S.K. Datta, J.D. Achebach and Y.S. Rajapakse, Elsevier Science Publishers, B.V., Amsterdam, pp. 183–189.
33. CANTRELL J H, WINFREE W P and HEYMAN J S (1985), 'Profiles of fatigue damage in graphite/epoxy composites from ultrasonic transmission power spectra', in *Recent Advances in Composites in the United States and Japan*, ASTM STP 864, ed. J.R. Vinson and M. Taya, American Society for Testing and Materials, Philadelphia, pp. 197–206.
34. VARY (1982), 'Acousto-ultrasonic characterization of fiber reinforced composites', *Materials Evaluation*, **40**, 650–654, 662.
35. VARY and BOWLES K J (1978), 'Use of an ultrasonic-acoustic technique for non-destructive evaluation of fiber composite strength', *NASA Technical Memorandum, NASA TM-73813*, February.
36. TALREJA R (1988), 'Application of acousto-ultrasonics to quality control and damage assessment of composites', in *Acousto-Ultrasonics: Theory and Applications*, ed. J.C. Duke, Plenum Press, NY, pp. 177–190.
37. HEMANN J H, CAVANO P, KRAUTZ H and BOWLES K (1988), 'Trans-ply crack density detection by acousto-ultrasonics', in *Acousto-Ultrasonics: Theory and Applications*, ed. J.C. Duke, Plenum Press, NY, pp. 319–325.
38. LORENZO L and HAHN H T (1988), 'Damage assessment by acousto-ultrasonic technique in composites', in *Composite Materials: Testing and Design (Eighth Conference)*, ASTM STP 972, ed. J.D. Whitcomb, American Society for Testing and Materials, Philadelphia, pp. 380–397.
39. PRAKASH R (1977), 'Fatigue behaviour of carbon fibre reinforced plastics', *Proceedings of the 6th Canadian Congress on Applied Mechanics*, Vancouver, p. 241.
40. DUKE J C, HENNEKE E G, STINCHCOMB W W and REIFSNIDER K L (1984), 'Characterization of composite materials by means of the ultrasonic stress wave factor', in *Composite Structures 2*, ed. I.H. Marshall, Applied Science Publishers, London, pp. 53–60.
41. TALREJA R, COVADA A and HENNEKE E G (1984), 'Quantitative assessment of damage growth in graphite epoxy laminates by acousto-ultrasonic measurements', in *Review of Progress in Quantitative Nondestructive Evaluation*, ed. D.O. Thompson & D.E. Chimenti, Plenum Press, New York, pp. 1099–1106.
42. GOVADA A, HENNEKE E G and TALREJA R (1985), 'Acousto-ultrasonic measurements to monitor damage during fatigue of composites', in *1984 Advances in Aerospace Sciences and Engineering*, American Society of Mechanical Engineers, NY, pp. 55–60.
43. GUO N and CAWLEY P (1992), 'Lamb waves for the NDE of composite laminates', *Review in Progress in Nondestructive Evaluation*, Vol. 11, ed. D.O. Thompson and D.E. Chimenti, Plenum Press, NY, pp. 1443–1450.
44. CAWLEY P (1994), 'The rapid non-destructive inspection of large composite structures', *Composites*, **25**, 531–357.
45. DAYAL V, IYER V and KINRA V K (1989), 'Ultrasonic evaluation of microcracks in composites', in *Advances in Fracture Research: Proceedings of the Seventh International Conference on Fracture (ICF7)*, 20–24 March, Pergamon Press, pp. 3291–3330.
46. TANG B and HENNEKE E G (1989), 'Lamb-wave monitoring of axial stiffness reduction of laminated composite plates', *Materials Evaluation*, **47**, 928–934.
47. SUN K J (1992), 'Application of guided acoustic waves to delamination detection', *Review in Progress in Nondestructive Evaluation*, Vol. 11, ed. D.O. Thompson and D.E. Chimenti, Plenum Press, NY, pp. 1213–1219.
48. GUO N and CAWLEY P (1993), 'The interaction of Lamb waves with delamination in composite laminates', *Journal of the Acoustic Society of America*, **94**, 2240–2246.
49. SEALE M D, SMITH B T and PROSSER W H (1998), 'Lamb waves assessment of fatigue and thermal damage in composites', *Journal of the Acoustic Society of America*, **103**, 2416–2424.
50. SANDHU J S, WANG H and POPEK W J (1996), 'Acoustography for rapid ultrasonic inspection of composites', *Proceedings of SPIE*, **2944**, 117–120.
51. SANDHU J S, WANG H, POPEK W J and SINCEBAUGH P (1999), 'Acoustography: A side-by-side comparison with conventional ultrasonic scanning', *SPIE Conference on Nondestructive Evaluation of Aging Materials and Composites III*, Newport Beach, CA, March, pp. 163–172.

52. SANDHU J S (1983), 'Liquid crystal technique for examining internal structures', US Patent 4 379 408.
53. SANDHU J S (1987), 'Non-destructive testing system employing a liquid crystal detector cell', US Patent 4 406 550.
54. CHEN A S, ALMOND D P and HARRIS B (2000), 'Acoustography applied to the monitoring of impact damage growth in composites under fatigue conditions', in *Acoustical Imaging*: Vol. 25, ed. M. Halliwell and P.N.T. Wells, Kluwer Academic/Plenum Publishers, pp. 209–216.
55. CHEN A S, ALMOND D P and HARRIS B (2001), 'In situ monitoring in real time of fatigue-induced damage growth in composite materials by acoustography', *Composites Science and Technology*, **61**, 2437–2443.
56. CHEN A S, ALMOND D P and HARRIS B (2001), 'Acoustography as a means of monitoring damage in composites during static or fatigue loading', *Measurement Science and Technology*, **12**, 151–156.
57. MILLER R K (1987), *Nondestructive Testing Handbook, 2nd Ed., Vol. 5: Acoustic Emission Testing*, American Society for Nondestructive Testing, OH.
58. CHANG F H, GORDON D E and GARDNER A E (1977), 'A study of fatigue damage in composites by nondestructive testing techniques', in *Fatigue of Filamentary Composite Materials*, ASTM STP 636, ed. K.L. Reifsnider & K.N. Lauraitis, American Society for Testing and Materials, OH, pp. 57–72.
59. WILLIAMS R S and REIFSNIDER K L (1974), 'Investigation of acoustic emission during fatigue loading of composite specimens, *Journal of Composite Materials*, **8**, 340–355.
60. AWERBUCH J and GHAFFARI S (1986), 'Monitoring progression of matrix splitting during fatigue loading through acoustic emission in notched graphite/epoxy composite', *Proceedings of the Second International Symposium on Acoustic Emission from Reinforced Composites*, The Society of Plastics Industry, Inc, Montreal, Canada, pp. 51–58.
61. ECKLES W F and AWERBUCH J (1986), 'Monitoring acoustic emission in cross-ply graphite/epoxy laminates during fatigue loading', *Proceedings of the Second International Symposium on Acoustic Emission from Reinforced Composites*, The Society of Plastics Industry, Inc, Montreal, Canada, pp. 78–84.
62. MAIER G, OTT H, PROTZNER A and PROTZ B (1986), 'Damage development in carbon fibre-reinforced polyimides in fatigue loading as a function of stress ratio', *Composites*, **17**, 111–120.
63. COHEN J and AWERBUCH J (1988), 'Monitoring delamination progression in composites through acoustic emission during fatigue loading', *Proceedings of the 4th Japan/United States Conference On Composite Materials*, Technomic Publishing Co., pp. 1035–1046.
64. LORENZO L and HAHN H T (1988), 'Damage assessment by acousto-ultrasonic technique in composites', *Composite Materials: Testing and Design (8th Conference)*, ASTM STP 972, ed. J.D. Whitcomb, ASTM, Philadelphia, pp. 380–397.
65. SPARKS C, ODRU P, METIVAUD C and LE FLOC'H C (1992), 'Defect tolerance assessment and non-destructive testing of composite riser tubes', in *1992 OMAE* – Vol. III-A, Materials Engineering, ASME 1992, pp. 209–214.
66. COHEN J and AWERBUCH J (1988), 'Monitoring delamination progression in composites through acoustic emission during fatigue loading', *Proceedings of the Fourth Japan/United States Conference on Composite Materials*, Technomic Publishing Co., pp. 1035–1046.
67. SATO N, KURAUCHI T and KAMIGAITO O (1986), 'Thermo-acoustic emission from damaged composites', *Proceedings of the 31st Int. SAMPE Symposium*, pp. 342–351.
68. SATO N, KURAUCHI T and KAMIGAITO O (1988), 'Detection of damage in composite materials by thermo-acoustic emission measurement', *Journal of Composite Materials*, **22**, 447–458.
69. BRYANT L B (1985), *Nondestructive Testing Handbook*, 2nd Ed., Vol. 3: *Radiography and Radiation Testing*, American Society for Nondestructive Testing, OH.
70. O'BRIEN T K (1982), 'Characterization of delamination onset and growth in a composite laminate', in *Damage in Composite Materials*, ASTM STP 775, ed. K.L. Reifsnider, American Society for Testing and Materials, OH, pp. 140–167.
71. REIFSNIDER K L and JAMISON R (1982), 'Fracture of fatigue-loaded composite laminates', *International Journal of Fatigue*, 187–197.
72. NESTLEROTH J B, ROSE J L, BASLYAM M and SUBRAMANIAN K (1985), 'Physically based ultrasonic feature mapping for anomaly classification in composite materials', *Materials Evaluation*, **43**, 541–546.
73. STINCHCOMB W W (1986), 'Nondestructive evaluation of damage accumulation processes in composite laminates', *Composite Science and Technology*, **25**, 103–118.

74. KELLAS S, MORTON J and CURTIS P T (1991), 'A characteristic fatigue parameter for notched composites', *International Journal of Fatigue*, **13**, 35–43.
75. RODERICK G L and WHITCOMB J D (1975), 'X-ray method shows fibers fail boron-epoxy laminates', *Journal of Composite Materials*, **9**, 391–393.
76. GIBBINS M N (1979), 'Investigation of the fatigue response of composite laminates with internal flaws', MS thesis, Virginia Polytechnic Institute and State University, Blacksburg, VA.
77. WHITCOMB J D (1979), 'Thermographic measurement of fatigue damage', in *Composite Materials: Testing and Design (Fifth Conference)*, ASTM STP 674, ed. S.W. Tsai, American Society for Testing and Materials, OH, pp. 502–516.
78. YEUNG P C (1979), 'Investigation of constraint effects on flaw growth in composite laminates', PhD thesis, Virginia Polytechnic Institute and State University, Blacksburg, VA.
79. REIFSNIDER K L, HENNEKE E G and STINCHCOMB W W (1984), 'The mechanics of vibrothermography', *Mechanics of Nondestructive Testing*, ed. W.W. Stinchcomb, Plenum Press, NY, pp. 249–276.
80. JONES R, HELLER M, LOMBARDO D, DUNN S, PAUL J and SAUNDERS D (1989), 'Thermoelastic assessment of damage growth in composites', *Composite Structures*, **12**, 291–314.
81. HELLER M, WILLIAMS J F, DUNN S and JONES R (1989), 'Thermomechanical analysis of composite specimens', *Composite Structures*, **11**, 309–324.
82. MESTER M L (1986), *Nondestructive Testing Handbook*, 2nd Ed., Vol 4: *Electromagnetic Testing*, American Society for Nondestructive Testing, OH.
83. BAR-COHEN Y (1986), 'NDE of fiber-reinforced composite materials – a review', *Materials Evaluation*, **44**, 446–454.
84. CLARK G and VAN BLARICUM T J (1987), 'Load spectrum modification effects on fatigue of impact-damaged carbon fibre composite coupons', *Composites*, **18**, 243–251.
85. SAUNDERS D S and VAN BLARICUM T J (1988), 'Effect of load duration in the fatigue behaviour of graphite/epoxy laminates containing delaminations', *Composites*, **19**, 217–228.

Part III

Fatigue in different types of composites

9

Short-fibre thermoset composites

G. Caprino, University of Naples "Federico II", Italy

9.1   Introduction

Short-fibre thermoset composites (SFTCs) are suitable for hand lay-up and resin transfer moulding technologies, being ideal materials for cost-sensitive applications requiring moderate to high mass production rates. Unfortunately, the technological flexibility of this class of composites only applies to reinforcements in the form of chopped strand mat (CSM) and is lost when components incorporating highly oriented short fibres are requested. Consequently, CSM is the only reinforcement architecture extensively adopted in the fabrication of industrial SFTC parts. Since the success on the market of the applications concerned is strongly cost-dependent, E-glass fibres embedded in polyester resin (the cheapest combination of fibre and matrix) are almost universally employed,[1,2] although the use of vinyl ester resins[3,4] has increased in recent years.

Starting from the 1970s, a new class of SFTCs, namely sheet moulding compounds (SMCs), appeared on the market.[5,6] Its development was strongly supported by the automotive industry, interested in the availability of low-cost materials having moderate mechanical properties, very high production rates, the ability to reproduce complicated shapes, and good aesthetics. The suitability of SMC not only for closed die moulding,[7,8] but also for injection moulding[9,10] has favoured its adoption in the extensive production of automotive parts. The annual rate of consumption of SMC in North America was higher than 100 000 tonnes in the 1990s.[11] In the same period, more than 3000 SMC parts were produced per day by the automotive industry in Europe.[10] It is expected that the rate of increase will be only moderate in the future, mainly on account of increasingly stringent national regulations requiring recyclability of materials for car components. Probably, this will accelerate the development of formulations and industrial production methods based on low-cost thermoplastic matrices, which should progressively replace thermoset-based SMC in the next few decades.

The study of the monotonic and fatigue behaviour of SFTCs has closely reflected industrial needs. Until the 1970s, most attention was devoted to identifying the failure modes and macroscopic response of CSM.[12–16] Subsequently, much experimental work was carried out on SMC,[17–37] whereas relatively little effort was expended on CSM.[38–43]

9.2   Structure and composition of short-fibre thermoset composites

In both CSM and SMC, the fibre reinforcement is in the form of chopped E-glass strands, made of bundles of fibres randomly oriented in a plane. Each strand is typically 25 to 50 mm long in a CSM and 15 to 25 mm in an SMC, and contains several hundred single fibres about 10 mm in diameter. Owing to the process peculiarities, the individuality of the strands and their original orientations are substantially reproduced in the final part: each strand after polymerization is ellipsoidal in shape, with the major axis perpendicular to the thickness direction, and the local fibre content within it approaches the values typical of a unidirectional lamina. By contrast, the material volume between the strands is filled with resin with only loose fibres present. The fibre content as usually defined then only represents a mean value, which can be misleading when the failure processes likely to occur in the composite are considered. Furthermore, the planar distribution of the reinforcement violates the conditions for transverse isotropy, anticipating a dependence of the elastic properties on the direction in the planes containing the thickness direction.[23]

Typical fibre contents by weight in a CSM range in the field $W_f = 0.20$ to 0.35 (about 0.10 to 0.20 by volume V_f). Reinforcement contents above $W_f = 0.40$ $(V_f \approx 0.25)$ are achievable only with difficulty because of the need to guarantee satisfactory wetting-out of the fibres. Establishing the fibre content by volume of an SMC is not straightforward. The material is usually designated by the label 'Rxx', with R implying 'random' and 'xx' indicating W_f expressed as a percentage. The factor complicating the conversion from W_f to V_f is the presence in the resin of a filler, very often consisting of calcium carbonate, whose main rôles are to lower the cost and to facilitate thickening.

Table 9.1 shows the compositions of typical SMCs. The resin content by weight is approximately constant. Hence, an increase in the fibre content is compensated by a decrease in filler content. When $W_f = 0.65$, no filler at all is usually used, and the material becomes similar to a more conventional CSM. The numbers in parentheses represent the fibre content by volume, and were calculated assuming a density $\rho = 1.25 \times 10^3$ kg m^{-3} for the matrix (a typical polyester resin), $\rho = 2.55 \times 10^3$ kg m^{-3} for the fibre (E-glass), and $\rho = 2.68 \times 10^3$ kg m^{-3} for the filler (calcium carbonate). The V_f values in Table 9.1 are only approximate, as they are dependent on the specific nature of the actual components. They can nevertheless be useful in roughly evaluating the mechanical properties of the SMCs, which indeed, as for all composites, are correlated with V_f, rather than with W_f.

In Table 9.2, the fibre contents by volume corresponding to given W_f values are compared for CSMs and SMCs. The relative difference in fibre content between the two systems becomes significant for low W_f values.

9.3   Static behaviour

9.3.1   Stress/strain response
In Fig. 9.1, typical stress/strain curves for CSM and SMC composites having approximately the same fibre content by volume $(V_f \approx 0.17)$ are shown. As for most engineering materials, the behaviour of an SFTC is linear at sufficiently low levels of stress. However, the elastic modulus is higher for SMC, reflecting the stiffening action of the filler, whose modulus is an order of magnitude greater than the resin modulus. With increasing strain, the curve deviates from proportionality. Generally, this deviation is clearly apparent in the case of SMC, whose curve exhibits an evident knee,[21,24,26,33] whereas it is more gradual for CSM. At final failure, both the stress and strain levels are markedly higher for CSM than for SMC.

Table 9.1 Compositions of typical SMCs

Component	$W_f (V_f)$				
Fibre	0.20 (0.16)	0.30 (0.23)	0.40 (0.31)	0.50 (0.38)	0.65 (0.48)
Resin	0.30 (0.47)	0.30 (0.47)	0.30 (0.47)	0.30 (0.47)	0.35 (0.52)
Filler	0.50 (0.37)	0.40 (0.30)	0.30 (0.22)	0.20 (0.15)	0 (0)

Table 9.2 Correspondence between the fibre content by weight W_f and the fibre content by volume V_f for a CSM and an SMC

W_f	0.20	0.30	0.40	0.50	0.65
V_f for CSM (%)	0.11	0.17	0.25	0.33	0.48
V_f for SMC (%)*	0.16	0.23	0.31	0.38	0.48

* approximate

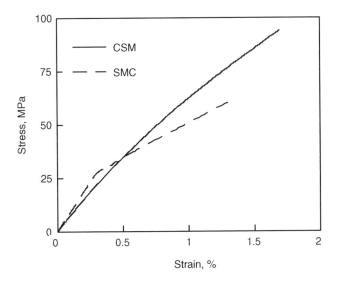

Fig. 9.1 Stress–strain behaviour of CSM and SMC with approximately the same fibre content by volume ($V_f \approx 0.17$).

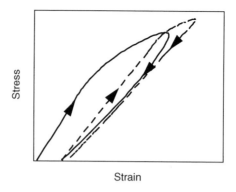

Fig. 9.2   Behaviour of a short-fibre composite under loading–unloading cycles.

The nature of the phenomenon causing the deviation from linearity is revealed when loading–unloading cycles are carried out in which the maximum stress is increased progressively.[33,44] Beyond the proportional limit the unloading curve (Fig. 9.2) is concave, a small permanent deformation is retained at its completion, and an hysteresis loop appears. On reloading, the curve preserves its linearity approximately up to the maximum stress reached in the previous cycle, after which the non-linear behaviour is exhibited again, and the residual deformation slowly increases after unloading. Notably, the elastic modulus in the second cycle is lower (Fig. 9.2) than the initial modulus, indicating that some failure events have occurred in the material structure.[13,14,16, 24,30,31,33,34,44] The characteristics and sequence of the microscopic damage developing under monotonic loading will be illustrated in the next section.

9.3.2   Microscopic failure modes

The results presented here are mainly drawn from the observations reported in [12–16,35,37,40,45] and in [18,20,24,30,31,33–35], concerning CSM and SMC, respectively, from which a marked similarity in the failure development is inferred for the two classes of material.

The first damage in an SFTC, occurring at 30–50% of the tensile strength (0.3–0.6% elongation) and approximately coinciding with the departure from linearity of the stress/strain curve, is debonding at the fibre/matrix interface of fibre bundles oriented perpendicular to the loading direction (grey areas in Fig. 9.3(a)).[16,24,34]

After onset, the failures propagate along the original strands with increasing applied stress, until other strands, oriented at smaller angles to the load direction, are reached and debonding is initiated at their periphery (Fig. 9.3(b)). Besides driving the propagation of the early cracks, the stress increase also causes further debonding within the whole material volume.

The correlation between the progression of debonding and the applied stress is represented by the black circles in Fig. 9.4,[16] where the debond ratio (i.e. the ratio of the total length of debonds observed at the generic applied stress to the total length of debonds at final failure) is plotted against the stress, normalized with respect to the tensile strength. Most of the debonding develops between 30% and 70% of the failure stress, after which the damage tends to level off, reaching a saturation condition. It is only at this point that cracks oriented mainly transverse to the tensile axis and originating from debonds close to each other grow in the resin-rich areas. When these cracks cross a fibre bundle oriented at low angles to the

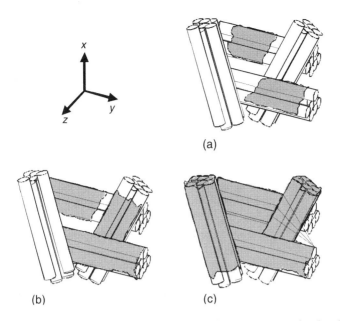

Fig. 9.3   Progression of the failure modes in a short-fibre thermoset composite. Load direction: *x*.
Grey areas: fracture surfaces.

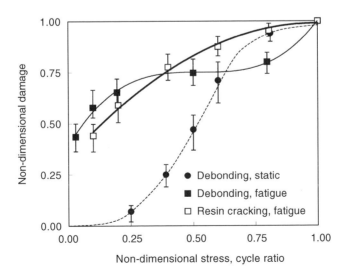

Fig. 9.4   Development of the non-dimensional damage in a CSM under monotonic load and in
fatigue.[16]

loading direction, pull-out of the bundle as a whole occurs, without fibre failures (Fig. 9.3(c)). This observation indicates that all of the fibres in a bundle behave as a single fibre. Consequently, in analysing the failure modes of an SFTC, the usual concept of 'fibre aspect ratio' (the ratio of the fibre length to diameter l/d), which is generally in the range 1000 to 3000, should be substituted by the 'bundle aspect ratio' (the ratio of the fibre length to bundle diameter, L/D), for which values are 20 to 30 for a typical SFTC.

In general, the presence of a filler in SMCs does not alter the failure sequence previously described. It is only for some cases[24,31] of composites with low fibre contents (15–20% by volume), that matrix cracking in filler-rich zones has been documented as the first damage mode. This finding is not unexpected, considering that a low fibre content implies a high filler fraction (Table 9.1). The strain to failure of a particulate composite decreases with increasing filler content;[26,46,47] when the strain to failure of the resin-filler compound becomes lower than the critical strain for debonding, the former mode of failure will precede the latter.

The macroscopic trends in Fig. 9.1 closely resemble the response of multi-axial laminates containing layers oriented perpendicular to the load direction, exhibiting a clear knee point at strain levels typically ranging between 0.3% and 0.6%,[48,49] owing to the formation of cracks running parallel to the fibres in the 90° layers and involving fibre/matrix debonding and resin fracture.[50,51] These cracks are arrested at the interfaces with the neighbouring plies, and grow in number with increasing load, possibly resulting in a saturation level, the so-called 'characteristic damage state'.[52,53] From the transverse cracks, delamination begins to take place before final failure: this phenomenon is comparable to damage propagation along the periphery of fibre bundles oriented parallel to the applied load (Fig. 9.3(c)). Thus, the study of continuous fibre laminates can give valuable information on the behaviour of SFTCs.

Of course, some differences between a laminate and an SFTC have also been observed. Each matrix crack developing in a transverse layer of a laminate grows rapidly until the whole specimen width and the entire layer thickness are covered. The same crack is much shorter and shallower in an SFTC, because its growth is hindered by the fibre bundles oriented parallel to the loading axis encountered during propagation. In addition, final failure involves extensive fibre fracture in a fibre-dominated laminate, whereas failed fibres are seldom observed in an SFTC.

9.3.3   Effect of composition

Many parameters, among which the fibre and matrix type and content, filler content, reinforcement aspect ratio and orientation, and fibre/matrix interface can be varied in fabricating an SFTC. The effect of the material composition on the quasi-static behaviour of the material will be examined in this section.

9.3.3.1   Fibre volume fraction

From micromechanics, both the elastic modulus and the ultimate strength of a composite should increase linearly with increasing V_f. Verifying this statement experimentally for CSMs and SMCs is not as easy as it would appear because of the extreme scatter in the available data,[54,55] reflecting different processing conditions, variability in basic component properties, as well as inaccuracies in the characterization procedures and in the measurement of the fibre content. However, where the uncertainties correlated with these parameters have been kept to a minimum, the expected linearity has been demonstrated for CSM reinforced with glass[39] and carbon fibres,[27] and also for SMC.[26]

Figure 9.5 shows the experimental tensile strengths of CSMs and SMCs reinforced with

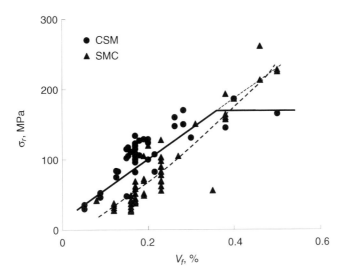

Fig. 9.5   Tensile strength of a random short-fibre reinforced composite σ_r, as a function of the fibre volume fraction V_f.

E-glass fibres as functions of V_f. Some of the data plotted are original, whereas others were drawn from commercial data sheets[56–59] and selected papers available in the literature.[21,31,34,37,39,40,60–64] Where the V_f value for a given SMC was unknown, it was calculated according to the procedure outlined previously for the data in Table 9.1.

A straight line largely represents the dependence of strength on the fibre content for CSM composites, provided V_f is sufficiently low. The experimental points suggest (continuous lines) a levelling off of the property with increasing V_f. Conceivably, this behaviour is a consequence of poor fibre wetting and defects arising in the material structure when unusually high V_f values are obtained by hand lay-up.

Compared to CSM, a low V_f SMC has a lower strength for a given fibre content. With increasing fibre volume fraction, the difference disappears, and the tensile strength of SMC becomes as would be expected from CSM (dashed straight line in the figure). Therefore, at high fibre content the superiority of the controlled fabrication processes adopted for SMC emerges, allowing a more efficient reinforcement distribution and a low void content.

In the ideal case, it is expected that all composites containing continuous fibres aligned with the loading direction, irrespective of V_f, fail when the fibre strain to failure ε_{rf} is achieved. This statement is not verified in practice: while E-glass fibres exhibit a failure strain $\varepsilon_{rf} \approx 3\%$, typical values of the elongation to break ε_r are in the range 2 to 2.5% for fibre-dominated, continuous fibre laminates with layers variously oriented, owing to the statistical distribution of the reinforcement strength.[65,66]

The failure strain of a random SFTC[21,30,31,34,37,39,40,57,60,62,64] tends to increase with increasing V_f (Fig. 9.6), approaching a limit value of 1.8–2% at best. The increase is more evident in the case of an SMC, whose ε_r remains anyhow lower than that of a CSM for a given fibre content. Clearly, the efficiency of an SFTC in exploiting the fibre potentialities is dramatically dependent on V_f, and its mechanical behaviour is increasingly affected by parameters such as matrix, fibre/matrix and filler/matrix interfaces, and fibre ends, as V_f is reduced. The difference in failure strains between CSM and SMC at high V_f, estimated from the results in Fig. 9.6, is presumably attributable to the residual thermal stresses[36] or higher degree of cure associated with the high-temperature cycle of an SMC.[38]

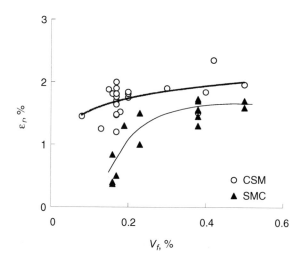

Fig. 9.6   Failure strain of a random-short-glass-fibre reinforced composite ε_r, as a function of the fibre volume fraction V_f.

9.3.3.2   Filler content

Large quantities of filler (i.e. low V_f, see Table 9.1) are deleterious to both strength and failure strain (Figs. 9.5 and 9.6). SMCs not containing fillers (high V_f) behave more or less as CSMs: the knee point in the stress/strain curve, although occurring at about 0.3–0.5% strain, becomes less evident, and the loss in modulus above the knee is less pronounced.[36]

9.3.3.3   Matrix and fibre/matrix interface

Many attempts have been made to delay first failure by improving the interface properties and by using resins characterized by a higher elongation to break. In fact, suitably modifying the fibre surface can considerably raise the transverse failure strain of unidirectional fibre-reinforced plastics[67–69] as well as the first failure strain of SFTCs.[40] Similar results are obtained by increasing the resin flexibility in continuous fibre laminates[70,71] and in CSMs.[15,40] However, even a large increase in matrix elongation to break seldom results in a first failure strain higher than 1–1.2%.[72] This effect is explained by the stress concentration arising along the transverse fibres, highlighted by both continuum mechanics[73,74] and numerical approaches.[72,75,76]

The suppression of some failure modes by the use of more flexible resins does not guarantee a higher tensile strength. From the experiments in reference 15, although the strain to failure of a CSM monotonically increased with increasing strain-to-failure of the matrix, the material strength achieved a maximum with 15 to 20% flexibilizer, but decreased thereafter.

9.3.3.4   Reinforcement aspect ratio

It is expected from micromechanics[77] that the strength along the fibre direction in a short-fibre composite can be improved by increasing the fibre (or bundle) aspect ratio or the fibre volume fraction. This occurrence has been experimentally verified in [78,79], where model composites containing 0.50 V_f of oriented short glass fibres of different lengths ($\ell = 3.2$–25.4 mm) were characterized in tension along the fibre direction. It was found that both the ultimate tensile stress and the elastic modulus increase with increasing aspect ratio. However, the modulus was only mildly affected by the aspect ratio, rapidly approaching the value for a continuous fibre lamina. By contrast, the strength was very sensitive to the aspect ratio, increasing from about 225 MPa for $\ell = 3.2$ mm to 530 MPa for $\ell = 25.4$ mm, which was the maximum length utilized. The longitudinal tensile strength of a comparable unidirectional continuous fibre lamina was about 900 MPa.[78] From the data generated, the authors concluded that the presence of fibre ends weakens the material, which approaches roughly 60% of the strength and strain to failure of the continuous fibre reference.

Interestingly, the ultimate strain along the fibre direction of the unidirectional continuous fibre composite tested in [78] was 2–2.4%. The same strain was steadily reduced with decreasing aspect ratio, until a value of 0.74% was measured for the minimum fibre length utilized. This trend qualitatively agrees with the behaviour depicted in Fig. 9.6, suggesting that the final failure of a random SFTC is strongly conditioned by the fibre strands parallel to the loading direction.

9.3.3.5 Fibre type

Unfortunately, few experimental data are available for SFTCs reinforced with fibres other than glass. The results published concern polyester[27] and epoxy[80] resins reinforced with randomly oriented carbon fibres of different lengths, and epoxy resin reinforced with unidirectional carbon fibres 3 mm in length.[81] Some valuable information can be also obtained from the work of Friedrich et al.,[82] who mechanically characterized classical laminates of various stacking sequences and high fibre content ($V_f = 0.50$–0.55) by using two thermoplastic matrices (polyimide, PI, and polyethersulphone, PES).

In reference 27, a fibre length of 25.4 mm was sufficient to achieve the maximum flexural strength. A slightly lower strength was measured when ℓ was shortened to 12.7 mm. This finding is seemingly in contrast with the results obtained in [80], where the tensile strength was practically unaffected by the fibre length in the range $\ell = 5$–15 mm, whereas a decrease in strength was noted for $\ell = 1$ mm. Possibly, the type of load configuration (flexure,[27] or tension[80]) or the matrix (polyester against epoxy) can play some role in explaining the difference. An even more important factor may be the bundle size, which determines the actual aspect ratio: Tsuchiyama[27] measured strength and modulus reductions as high as 40% and 30%, respectively, when rovings of 30 000 filaments per strand rather than 1000 filaments per strand were utilized in fabricating the material.

Two other tendencies concerning the strain to failure and the stress/strain curve seem to emerge from the results in references 80–82. The strain-to-failure of the fibre-dominated laminates in reference 82 varied in the range 1 to 1.2%, irrespective of the matrix materials, which exhibited markedly different ε_r values (0.76% for PI and 3.7% for PES). This observation supported the conclusion that the mechanical behaviour is mainly governed by the reinforcement, despite the quite short length (3 mm) of the Grafil AS4 fibres used. A comparable elongation at break was found by Hitchen et al.,[80] working on SFTCs reinforced with a relatively low volume fraction ($V_f = 0.14$–0.22) of T300 carbon fibres having different lengths. Finally, the short-fibre unidirectional composite in reference 81 yielded $\varepsilon_r = 0.80\%$ along the fibre direction. The adoption of carbon fibres instead of glass therefore results in a lower material failure strain.

The deviation from linearity with increased load, characteristic of a random SFTC reinforced with glass fibres (Fig. 9.1), is often not easily observed with carbon fibres. The stress/strain curves reported[80] were linear up to failure, and a small non-linearity was found only when the fibre length was shortened to 1 mm. No stress/strain curves were shown in reference 82, but from the strength, strain to failure, and elastic modulus data reported, linear behaviour is easily inferred for the fibre-dominated composites. An interpretation of this occurrence will be given in discussing the fatigue behaviour of SFTCs.

9.4   Fatigue behaviour

9.4.1   Microscopic failure modes

As anticipated, damage development in fatigue follows substantially the same paths as those described in treating the monotonic loading case (Fig. 9.3). The sequence of debonding, matrix cracking, and bundle/matrix pull-out observed in a monotonic test when the stress level is increased is naturally also found with increasing numbers of cycles in fatigue tests carried out at a fixed maximum stress. Nevertheless, some peculiarities in fatigue have also been noted, as highlighted in this section.

In addition to examining the progress of debonding in a CSM under monotonic tensile loading (black circles in Fig. 9.4), Owen and Howe[16] studied the same phenomenon in fatigue. The debonding damage (black squares in Fig. 9.4) rapidly increased at an early stage of fatigue life (measured by the cycle ratio N/N_f, where N is the current number of cycles and N_f is the number of cycles resulting in fatigue failure). A characteristic damage state was then reached, after which the rate of debond growth increased again near the end of the test. The authors also tried to quantify matrix crack development. However, it was possible to accomplish this task only in the case of fatigue, because the tendency to generate matrix cracks under monotonic loading was too limited to allow any reliable measurement. In fatigue, the matrix cracks (open squares in Fig. 9.4) grew with cycle ratio following a quadratic law up to the final failure. The latter occurred without evidence of significant fibre fracture.

An accurate study of the failure modes of SMC was carried out by Wang and co-workers.[28,30] The authors analysed the damage development in an SMC-R50 subjected to cyclic tensile stress with a stress ratio (i.e. the ratio of the minimum to the maximum applied stress) $R = 0.05$, assuming three parameters, $viz.$ the crack length L_c the orientation θ_c and the density D_c to characterize it quantitatively. The crack density was defined as the number of cracks per unit length crossing a straight line parallel to the loading direction. Both the average crack length and crack density at fracture were strongly dependent on the maximum stress, σ_{max}: when σ_{max} increased, the crack density increased accordingly, while the average crack length decreased. This phenomenon was attributed to the fact that a higher stress level favours the initiation of a larger number of microcracks; on the other hand, there is less time for the microcracks to grow, since the fatigue life is shorter. For a given cyclic stress, the microcrack density increased very rapidly during the first cycles and then tended to level off, approaching an asymptotic state. The microcrack size also increased in the very early stages of fatigue, after which it remained approximately unchanged, being 1–2 mm in length.

Microstructural analysis[28,30] revealed the presence of cracking strongly directional with respect to the loading direction. From observations of specimens after fatigue failure, the microcrack orientation was found to be markedly affected by the local fibre content: in fibre-rich regions with fibres parallel to the loading direction, small cracks normal to the loading axis, whose growth was arrested by the fibres, developed in the resin; in matrix-rich areas, longer cracks perpendicular to the load were discovered; in fibre strands with a relatively large angle to the loading direction, cracks were generated at the fibre/matrix interface. Some of the data in reference 30 are rearranged in Fig. 9.7, showing the cumulative distribution of microcrack density (normalized with respect to the total microcrack density D_c) versus microcrack orientation θ_c at selected fatigue loading cycles for $\sigma_{max} = 0.6\ \sigma_r$.

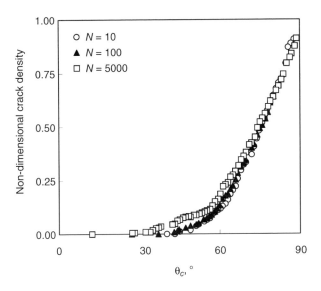

Fig. 9.7   Cumulative distribution of the non-dimensional crack density versus microcrack orientation θ_c, for different fatigue loading cycles. Maximum stress $\sigma_{max} = 0.6\sigma_r$, $R = 0.05$, $f = 2$Hz. Data from Wang et al.[30]

Although the results in Fig. 9. 7 may appear different from the original ones, this depends on the convention adopted for the crack orientation, whose zero coincides with the load direction in the figure, and with the normal to it.[30] From Fig. 9.7, most of the microcracks are oriented in the range 60° to 90° to the load direction. Moreover, the shape of the cumulative distribution is practically independent of the number of fatigue cycles: the orientations of the cracks remain therefore almost unchanged when the damage grows.

Wang and co-workers described analytically the cumulative distribution of microcrack lengths by the use of a Weibull function. The cumulative distribution of the microcrack orientation was accurately modelled by a previous expression,[25,29] deriving from the application of statistical brittle failure mechanics to microcrack initiation and growth in a random SFTC.

The previous description of the failure modes developing in an SFTC under fatigue loading is substantially consistent with the studies by Mandell and Lee[24] and Hour and Seitoglu[34] who examined the behaviour of SMC-R25 and R30, respectively. A common qualitative observation in these pieces of work is the fact that the crack density is higher on the surface than in the interior of the specimen. The results obtained[24] indicate that the crack density after final failure in fatigue is not significantly different from that observed in quasi-static tension, being quite unaffected by the fatigue stress level.

The parallel between SFTCs and classical laminates that we made in treating the monotonic behaviour also holds where fatigue is concerned, suggesting that the fibre ends do not substantially alter the sequence of damage events. An impressive piece of evidence for this behaviour is given by the analysis of the failure mechanisms in $[0/90]_{2s}$ and $[0/\pm45/0]_s$ laminates made of short carbon fibres embedded in PI and PES, carried out in reference 82. As in the case of continuous fibre laminates, cracks originating from the specimen edges and oriented parallel to fibres less favourably oriented with respect to the loading direction were detected early during fatigue. The cracks grew in length and density during cycling, until a saturation condition was reached. Finally, longitudinal splitting in 0° laminae and delamination took place near the end of the fatigue life.

9.4.2 Residual properties

From Fig. 9.2, it is anticipated that the stiffness along the direction of load application falls when an SFTC is subjected to repeated loading. As occurs for continuous fibre laminates,[83,84] the law governing the modulus decrease with number of cycles endured shows three distinct phases. In the first few loading cycles, a sudden decrease in stiffness is observed owing to the growth of microcracks from critical crack nucleation sites evenly distributed within the material volume. This step can occur in the first cycle, provided the applied stress is beyond the linear elastic limit. The rate of growth of the existing cracks and formation of new distributed cracks decreases in the second phase, and the reduction in modulus is accordingly small, following an approximately linear trend on a semi-log scale. The rate of modulus change increases again in the third phase, reflecting the growth of inhomogeneous damage leading to the final failure.

The previous steps are illustrated in Fig. 9.8, where the ratio of the modulus at N cycles E_N to the initial modulus E_0 is plotted against the number of cycles endured for a CSM with $W_f = 0.30$ ($V_f = 0.17$) and an SMC-R50 subjected to tensile fatigue. The data shown were obtained by suitably rearranging the original results in references 40 and 30.

It is not easy to compare residual-modulus data deriving from different sources because, apart from the effect of the material, the stress level adopted also has a strong influence on the trend: the higher the ratio of the maximum applied stress σ_{max} to the composite strength, the larger is the modulus reduction for a given number of cycles, and the lower the fatigue life. Another source of confusion is in the method adopted to evaluate the modulus in fatigue: since the composite accumulates a residual strain at each cycle (Fig. 9.2), assuming the zero strain of the virgin material as the origin for the strains yields a lower value than referring to the current zero of the fatigued material. Sufficient information is not always given in the technical literature to allow unambiguous interpretation of the term 'residual modulus'.

Owing to the modulus decay along the load direction, the strain level increases progressively in a stress-controlled fatigue test. Conversely, when the strain limits are fixed, the actual stress decreases continuously: in reference 44, where a continuous-strand-mat/polyester composite was subjected to strain-controlled cycling, a significant drop in stress, as high as 20%, was noted almost immediately in some tests.

Strain-controlled fatigue tests were also carried out on SMC-R30,[34] cycling the strain between 0 and 0.6%. A phenomenon evident from the stress/strain curves recorded during the progress of fatigue is the fact that the maximum stress falls with increasing number of cycles, while the minimum stress shifts through higher and higher compression values. This agrees with the progressive accumulation of a residual strain in the material during the extension phase, according to the scheme depicted in Fig. 9.2. The modulus in compression is practically unaffected by fatigue: the diffuse microcracking which is responsible for the modulus decrease in tension is not effective in compression. Consequently, the damaged composite becomes a bimodular material, characterized by different elastic behaviour in tension and in compression.[44,85] These considerations highlight the difficulty of interpreting the fatigue data when flexure, rather than tension, is selected as the test method.

Carbon fibres are far more efficient than glass in contrasting the modulus decrease during fatigue. The [0/±45/0]$_s$ short-fibre laminates tested in reference 82 did exhibit a reduction in the secant modulus according to the trend in Fig. 9.8. However, the Young's modulus just

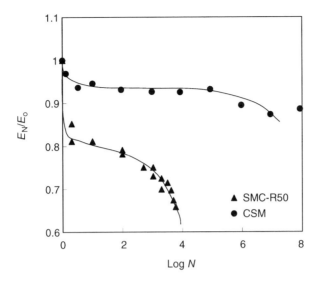

Fig. 9.8 Modulus degradation during fatigue for an SMC-R50 and a CSM. Fibre type: E-glass. Data from references 40 and 30, respectively.

before final failure was only 4–5% lower than the initial value. Within the experimental scatter, no effect at all of the number of cycles on the longitudinal modulus was detected,[80] even when the fibre content was low ($V_f = 0.14$) and the reinforcement length very short (1 mm). This behaviour does not indicate an absence of diffuse damage in the material: microstructural analysis[82] revealed intense microcrack formation, and it is hard to suppose that no damage is present in an SFTC loaded up to about 1% strain, as happened in this work. The explanation is most likely found in the more and more limited contribution of the matrix to the material modulus when the fibre modulus increases. Nevertheless, it should be important to clarify why some short-carbon-fibre-reinforced plastics (CFRPs) suffer less reduction in rigidity than their continuous-fibre counterparts.

Owing to the preferential orientation of the microscopic damage (Fig. 9.7), even a random SFTC becomes anisotropic, so that four elastic constants are necessary to describe its in-plane behaviour. The dependence of these constants on the number of cycles has been assessed by a self-consistent mechanics analysis[30] where their decrease was reliably predicted from the distribution of crack density, length and orientation. Unfortunately, the characterization work required to apply the scheme proposed in this work precludes its use under practical conditions. However, examining the predicted degradation of the stiffness tensor, the authors found that the rate of change of all the constants could be modelled by the power-law:

$$\frac{dD_{ij}}{dn} = A_{ij}(D_{ij})n^{-B} \qquad [9.1]$$

where A_{ij} and B are constant, and D_{ij} is a damage parameter defined as

$$D_{ij} = 1 - \frac{C_{ij}}{C_{ij}^*} \qquad [9.2]$$

C_{ij} in equation [9.2] is the generic element of the stiffness matrix after N cycles, and C_{ij}^* its value in correspondence of a reference number of cycles. It was noted in reference 30 that the constant A_{ij} is a function of C_{ij}, which in turn depends on the cyclic stress variables. By contrast, B is common to all the elastic constants for given fatigue conditions. Equation [9.1] provides a relatively simple tool for predicting the fatigue life in a stiffness-based design.

While Wang and co-workers[30] quantified the damage through the in-plane behaviour of the material, Hour et al.[34] assumed for this purpose an irreversible change in volume. They therefore also measured the strain change along the composite thickness, using an SMC-R30 composite. As inferred from the material structure, the elastic properties along the thickness direction followed a damage law completely different from the in-plane properties. In particular, the Poisson's ratio became negative as cycling progressed, yielding the most impressive indication of structural degradation induced by fatigue.

The development of damage is also reflected by a decrease in residual strength, the extent of which, as for the elastic constants, is strongly dependent on the stress level. Some experimental results, concerning the residual tensile strength of SMC-R50, are collected in Fig. 9.9,[32] where the horizontal dashed lines denote the scatter recorded in the quasi-static characterization of the virgin material. The symbols affected by the continuous horizontal scatter lines represent fatigue failures.

In commenting on the data in Fig. 9.9, the authors noted that a progressive degradation in the tensile strength occurs. A similar trend was found by Owen and Howe,[16] who studied the behaviour of a CSM: their results supported the conclusion that the strength loss is strictly correlated with resin cracking (Fig. 9.4), following the same parabolic law as a function of the cycle ratio N/N_f. By contrast, the decrease in strength was negligible, even after 10^7 cycles at $\sigma_{max}/\sigma_r \approx 0.4$, in the SMC-R50 examined by Denton,[21] and the same phenomenon was observed by Hitchen and co-workers[80] when the residual strength of a random SFTC reinforced with carbon fibres 5 mm in length was measured after 200 000 cycles at a peak strain of 0.7%. Indeed, in the author's opinion, the only feature common to all the data available is the abrupt drop in strength immediately before final collapse, suggesting a sudden death mode of failure. This behaviour renders particularly difficult the task of analytically describing the dependence of the residual strength on the number of cycles, on which many fatigue models rely.[42,43,86,87]

9.4.3   Stress/life (S–N) curves

The laws governing the nucleation and growth of the dominant crack driving the fatigue failure of an SFTC are not well understood at this time, owing to the lack of systematic data allowing the assessment of the different variables involved in the phenomenon. In fact, most of the results available concern random GRPs loaded in tension–tension fatigue with $R = 0$–0.1, whereas there are only a few examples of SFTCs tested under different loading conditions or with more sophisticated reinforcement types.

Apart from the previous problems, another drawback derives from the ambiguity intrinsic in the term 'fatigue sensitivity', which should help compare different materials on a common basis. Qualitatively speaking, the fatigue sensitivity can be defined as the reduction of a given property as a consequence of cycling. When an attempt is made to translate this concept into a quantitative parameter, many uncertainties arise, because the fatigue sensitivity can strongly depend on the particular property considered (e.g. the residual modulus or fatigue life at final failure), the methods used to evaluate it, and the specific loading conditions adopted. Nevertheless, some trends can be established, from which general interpretations of the fatigue behaviour have been attempted, or specific models have been proposed. Highlighting these trends is the main scope of the present section.

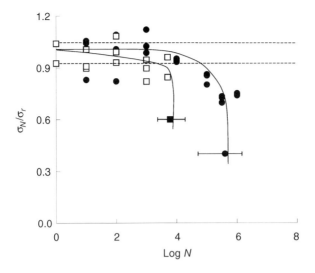

Fig. 9.9   Semi-log plot of the non-dimensional residual strength σ_N/σ_r, against number of cycles N. Material: SMC-R50. $R = 0$. Data from reference 32.

9.4.3.1   Effect of frequency

Different researchers have used frequencies in the range 1 to 20 Hz and higher to generate the experimental data available in the literature. In order to compare the results consistently, a preliminary task is to assess the influence of this parameter on the material response. This would also help investigate the composite behaviour at very high cycles, where increasing the frequency f is unavoidable if acceptably short testing times are to be obtained.

There are two main reasons to fear a frequency sensitivity of a composite:

*   the energy dissipated by hysteresis (Fig. 9.2) heats the specimen, whose temperature increases the more, the higher the frequency;[88,89]
*   for a given stress amplitude, increasing the frequency results in an increase in strain rate.

Irrespective of the reinforcement type, both of these circumstances could markedly affect the behaviour of the matrix, viscoelastic in nature, possibly altering its failure modes. However, the mechanical properties of glass fibres are also rate dependent,[90-92] so that the corresponding properties of their composites are potentially more sensitive to frequency than those reinforced with carbon. The sensitivity of glass fibres to water attack, rendering them time-dependent in the presence of humidity,[93,94] further complicates the picture.

Despite the previous observations, the fatigue behaviour of short-glass-fibre-reinforced thermosets is practically independent of the frequency within the range of f values usually employed. This is shown in Fig. 9.10, where the results concerning SMC-R50 from three different sources,[21,22,28] covering the range $f = 2$ to 20 Hz, are collected to build a typical S/N curve. The black symbols in the figure denote run-outs.

The insensitivity of SFTCs to frequency is also confirmed by the studies of Heimbuck and Sanders,[19] who found no significant effect of frequency on the fatigue behaviour of SMC-R25 and SMC-R65 materials.

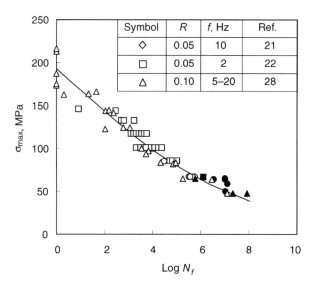

Symbol	R	f, Hz	Ref.
◇	0.05	10	21
□	0.05	2	22
△	0.10	5–20	28

Fig. 9.10   Effect of frequency on the fatigue curve of SMC-R50. Data from references 21, 22, 28.

9.4.3.2   Effect of composition

Since the fibre content is one of the main parameters affecting the monotonic properties of a composite, its effect on the S/N curves of SFTCs is of particular interest. Figure 9.11 collects data for random SMCs with rigid polyester matrices. The figure incorporates the results already presented in Fig. 9.10, which are designated by a common symbol, owing to their substantial consistency.

From an engineering point of view, the best material for a fatigue-sensitive application is the one allowing the highest stress to be applied for a given critical number of cycles. In this sense, the obvious conclusion from Fig. 9.11 is that, within the range of fatigue lives considered, increasing the fibre content is beneficial to the fatigue behaviour. However, when the maximum applied stress decreases, the fatigue curves tend to converge, and the advantage deriving from the high reinforcement content is progressively lowered. Indeed, there can be some fear that, at sufficiently large numbers of cycles, the fatigue curves may even cross each other, rendering the fibres detrimental to the fatigue life.

Of course, the benefit of a high fibre content at low fatigue cycles is mainly correlated with the increase in the monotonic strength of the material. A common method of eliminating the influence of this factor in comparing the response of different composites, also employed for metallic alloys, is to construct the S/N curve by using the ratio σ_{max}/σ_r, rather than σ_{max}. Furthermore, since the fatigue curve approximately follows a linear law in the range 10^2 to 10^6 cycles, covered by most of the experimental results, the slope b of the straight line having the equation:

$$\frac{\sigma_{max}}{\sigma_r} = 1 - b \log N \qquad [9.3]$$

best fitting the data points has often been assumed as a suitable parameter for evaluating the fatigue sensitivity.[22,24,61,81,95–97]

The monotonic strength of glass-fibre-reinforced plastics (GRP) increases with increasing strain rate.[90–92,96] Therefore, in order consistently to normalize σ_{max}, σ_r should be measured

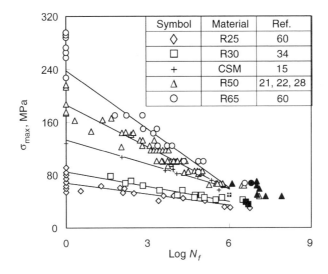

Symbol	Material	Ref.
◇	R25	60
□	R30	34
+	CSM	15
△	R50	21, 22, 28
○	R65	60

Fig. 9.11   Effect of the fibre content on the S–N curve. R = 0–0.1.

at the same (or comparable) strain rate as that used for the fatigue tests. Strength data fulfilling this condition have been plotted on the ordinate axis in Fig. 9.11, whereas σ_r is not shown for the SMC-R30,[34] for which only a monotonic strength value obtained at low strain rate was available.

Table 9.3 shows the b values calculated from the experimental results in Fig. 9.11. In order to evaluate the fatigue sensitivity, all the points in the range 10^2 to 10^6 cycles for each data set were fitted to best-fit straight lines (continuous lines in the figure), of which the slopes were divided by the values of the y intercepts.

From Table 9.3, the fatigue sensitivity steadily increases with increasing fibre content. This phenomenon may be attributed to the adverse effect of fibre ends, which increase in number with the fibre volume fraction for a fixed fibre length. However, this does not seem to be the correct interpretation: a similar trend was observed by Harris and co-workers[81] who found a lower fatigue sensitivity in a low-V_f, short-fibre composite compared with a high-V_f, continuous-fibre laminate. Partridge et al.[98] obtained a remarkable improvement in the fatigue response of GRP laminates by interleaving the individual plies with resin, therefore reducing the overall fibre content. More recently, Mandell and Samborski[99] observed an increase in fatigue sensitivity with increasing the fibre volume fraction, working on continuous-glass-fibre laminates reinforced with different reinforcement architectures. Indeed, in [99] it was also noted that b becomes independent of V_f beyond a limiting value, affected by the reinforcement architecture, which was found to be in the range 0.4 to 0.5 for the GRPs examined.

Figure 9.11 also shows the fatigue behaviour of a CSM with a rigid polyester matrix.[15] Interestingly, this material has a particularly low fibre content ($V_f = 0.13$). In spite of this, its fatigue behaviour at large numbers of cycles is very close to that of the SMC-R50 composite, thanks to its lower fatigue sensitivity.

In ranking different materials on the basis of the parameter b, it must be borne in mind that this parameter has real usefulness only if a linear correlation between σ_{max} and $\log N$ is verified. The run-outs in Fig. 9.11 (black symbols) suggest that this is not the case beyond 10^6 cycles, where the S/N curves tend to flatten out, although the data available are not sufficient to confirm that a fatigue limit, as conventionally defined, exists for composites.

Table 9.3 Fatigue sensitivity b of different random short-fibre thermoset composites

Material	Ref.	b
SMC-R25	60	0.082
SMC-R30	34	0.088
SMC-R50	21, 22, 28	0.115
SMC-R65	60	0.124
CSM	15	0.092

Only tests involving long times could ascertain whether the advantage of a high fibre content is completely lost at very long lives.

Heuristic considerations would suggest that the diffuse damage occurring in a composite is deleterious to its fatigue response. Therefore, one can speculate that the delaying of debonding and matrix cracking by the use of more flexible resins or the modification of the fibre/matrix interface are viable tools for lowering the fatigue sensitivity. This route was attempted by Owen and Rose:[15] besides characterizing in fatigue the CSM already discussed in Fig. 9.11, they also tested an analogous material made by using a flexible polyester resin, and observed the critical number of cycles for debonding, resin cracking, and complete failure. Considering the monotonic behaviour of the two CSMs (log $N_f = 0$ in Fig. 9.12), the flexiblized matrix (black symbols) slightly delays debonding and increases strength, suppressing resin cracking. Nevertheless, in fatigue resin cracking also appears before final failure in the composite with the flexible resin, whose superiority rapidly vanishes at high cycles (low stress levels), as shown by the convergence of the open and black squares.

The S/N curves at final failure of the two composites in Fig. 9.12 are almost the same, whatever the maximum applied stress, suggesting a fatigue life negligibly influenced by the strain to failure of the matrix. Notably, the similarity is also preserved at low cycles, where a clear difference in the resin cracking behaviour is observed. For instance, when $\sigma_{max} \approx$ 80 MPa, the resin cracking begins during the first few loading cycles in the case of the rigid polyester, whereas it takes 10^2–10^3 cycles to occur for the flexible resin; despite this difference, the fatigue lives are practically identical. Thus, it seems that a higher tendency to matrix crack formation does not necessarily result in poorer fatigue behaviour. This conclusion somehow contrasts with the thesis of Owen and Howe,[16] which suggests a correlation between matrix cracking and residual strength.

The absence of a strict correlation between matrix cracking and final failure in fatigue also emerges from Table 9.3: the SMC-R25 composite is notably less sensitive to fatigue than the SMC-R50, although the latter exhibits a lower crack density at failure than the former, under both monotonic and fatigue conditions.[24] This also implies that a high filler content cannot be associated with high fatigue sensitivity.

Conclusions consistent with the results in Fig. 9.12 can be drawn from the data in references 17, 24, concerning SMC-R25. In both cases, an increase in monotonic tensile strength was noted when a flexibilizer was added to the matrix. However, the advantage of the more ductile resin diminished or even disappeared at long lives. A similar tendency has been observed in continuous-fibre composites[81,100] for CFRP laminates. Curtis and Dorey[100] hypothesized that this could reflect a poorer response to fatigue of the flexiblized resins. In fact, Mandell[60] found a correlation between the fatigue behaviour and the brittleness of different resins, with the more brittle matrices performing better in fatigue.

From the data in Fig. 9.12, it is also evident that generating micro-failures in a composite structure subjected to fatigue is practically unavoidable because of the particularly low

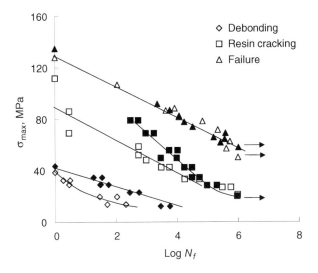

Fig. 9.12   Effect of the matrix on the *S–N* curve of a CSM. Open symbols: rigid polyester; black
symbols: flexiblized polyester. *R* = 0. Data from reference 15.

stress levels which cause debonding. The stress under which this mode of failure is
generated, essentially coinciding with the knee of the monotonic stress/strain curve when
$\log N_f = 0$, is successively reduced during fatigue with increasing number of cycles. This
consideration is of particular concern in the design of tanks for liquid storage, where matrix
failures can give rise to leakage.

In evaluating fatigue sensitivity by the method adopted to obtain the data in Table 9.3, a
particular phenomenon has sometimes been observed:[42,60] the intercept of the straight line
that best fits the fatigue points overestimates the actual monotonic strength of the material.
This suggests that the fatigue curve flattens at very small numbers of cycles (high stress),
being shaped as indicated by the continuous lines in Fig. 9.13, where some of the results
obtained in reference 43 are plotted. This trend seems to be independent of the matrix nature,
fibre length and loading modalities: in reference 43 this was shown by fatiguing in four-
point flexure both thermoplastic and thermosetting matrices reinforced with continuous and
randomly oriented short fibres; other authors have shown the same behaviour for SFTCs in
repeated tension fatigue[18] and in continuous-fibre laminates under reverse loading.[85]

The information in the literature is insufficient to permit the drawing of any useful
conclusion as to the effect of the fibre (or bundle) aspect ratio on the fatigue sensitivity of
SFTCs. This is disappointing because, as previously demonstrated, the present formulations
rarely result in fibre failure, so that the reinforcement potentialities are not fully exploited.
Some indication is given by the *S/N* curves published in reference 80 for random T300-
carbon-fibre/epoxy composites, whose monotonic behaviour has been illustrated previously.
Figure 9.14 plots the results obtained for $\ell = 1$ mm ($V_f = 0.14$) and $\ell = 15$ mm ($V_f = 0.20$). The
straight lines in the figure are the best fits to all of the fatigue data for each single set, from
which *b* values of 0.065 and 0.054, respectively, were calculated for the shorter and the
longer fibres. The fatigue sensitivity therefore seems to increase with decreasing fibre aspect
ratio. If the interpretation of the effect of V_f on *b* is correct, an even larger difference in the
b values would have been measured at equal fibre volume fractions.

A comparison of the fatigue sensitivity data for glass- and carbon-fibre-reinforced

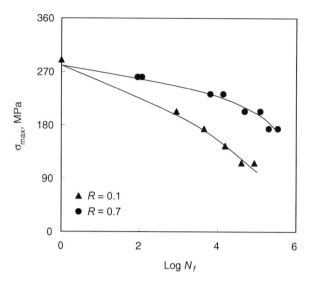

Fig. 9.13   *S–N* curves for a polyester/polyurethane resin reinforced with random continuous glass
fibres loaded in four-point bending. Data from reference 43.

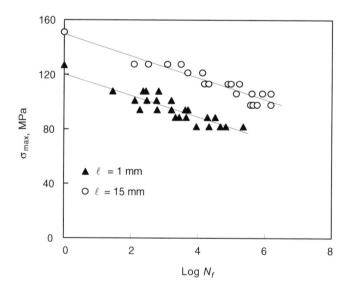

Fig. 9.14   Effect of the fibre length ℓ on the *S–N* curve of random short-fibre carbon/epoxy
composites. $R = 0.1$. Data from reference 80.

SFTCs presented previously reveals that the presence of carbon fibres results in considerably better fatigue performances. This is also confirmed by the behaviour of the
short-fibre-carbon/thermoplastic composites tested in reference 82: irrespective of the
matrix, the fatigue curve was quite flat for the unidirectional material tested along the fibre
direction; a more evident initial slope was exhibited by the *S/N* curves of laminates which

also contained ±45° and 90° fibres, although, remarkably, these were less fatigue sensitive than a typical SFTC reinforced with glass fibres. These findings indicate that the reinforcement type is of primary importance in determining the response of an SFTC not only to monotonic, but also to cyclic loading, and that the use of carbon fibres is a viable means of obtaining composites engineered for fatigue-sensitive applications.

9.4.3.3   Effect of loading conditions

Apart from the frequency, the effect of which has been discussed previously, other extrinsic variables, such as the loading scheme and the stress ratio, can influence the fatigue response of an SFTC.

Some authors have characterized the fatigue behaviour of random-glass-fibre-reinforced composites in simple bending by loading in four-point bending.[17,41] In spite of the potential difficulties arising in interpreting the data obtained by these loading schemes, the S/N curves were consistent with those generated under uniaxial loading. In particular, it was shown[41] that the tensile fatigue curve can be predicted from the flexural data, provided the failure modes in flexure are on the tensile side of the sample.

Increasing the stress ratio in repeated-tension fatigue shifts the S/N curves through higher fatigue lives, as shown in Fig. 9.13. A similar effect, although less evident than in this figure, was found for continuous fibre laminates.[96]

Under fully reversed stress conditions ($R = -1$), a classical laminate is known to have a poorer fatigue response than in pure tension[81,101,102] for a given maximum applied stress, because the microscopic damage modes developing in it are more effective in precipitating failure in compression than in tension. The results available for SFTCs are somehow contradictory: the CSM tested in reference 14 exhibited a fatigue sensitivity $b = 0.176$, far higher than expected from a similar material in pure tension (Table 9.3). However, the SMC-R25 in reference 19 behaved in approximately the same way at $R = 0-0.1$ and $R = -1$. A factor to be considered in evaluating the response of SFTCs in reverse loading is their compression strength, which is generally much higher than the corresponding tensile strength.

9.4.3.4   Additional considerations

From Figs. 9.10 to 9.14, it can be seen that the S/N curves for an SFTC are variously shaped: in some cases, they are reasonably linear up to about 10^6 cycles, and tend to exhibit a lower slope beyond this limit (Figs. 9.10, 9.11); in other cases (Fig. 9.13) a downward curvature is observed at moderately long lives; finally, in some fatigue curves (Fig. 9.14) there is no evidence at all of a variation in slope.

A unifying interpretation encompassing all the previous cases has been proposed by Talreja.[103] According to his theory, the true factor governing failure in fatigue is not the stress, but the strain level. In the strain/loglife domain, three regions can be characterized in the general shape of the fatigue curve. In the first region (high strain, low fatigue life), the failure is determined by fibre breakage, and the fatigue points fall within the experimental scatterband for the monotonic failure strain of the composite. When the strain level is lower (intermediate fatigue life), matrix cracking and fibre/matrix interfacial failure phenomena become predominant, precipitating final collapse in fatigue: the slope of the ε/loglife curve begins to fall, and the transition to the second region takes place. Finally, when very low alternating strains are applied, even the failure mechanisms in the matrix and at the interface become ineffective, and the endurance limit manifests itself by a flattening of the fatigue curve, originating the third region.

There are many indications that, where fatigue is concerned, strain is more significant than stress. When Hitchen and co-workers[80] plotted the data in Fig. 9.14 in an ε/logN diagram, they noted a substantial superposition, and concluded that the fatigue life is determined by the strain, rather than the stress. A similar conclusion was drawn in reference 85, where a combination of chopped strand mat and woven roving was tested under fully reversed stress conditions, with two different matrix materials.

Further evidence of the importance of strain is given by the behaviour of unidirectional continuous-fibre composites. These materials show a linear S–log N curve when loaded parallel with the fibres.[60] The slopes of the straight lines, correlated with the fatigue sensitivity, are strictly dependent on the fibre modulus, increasing with decreasing modulus. Typical b values are in the range 0.08–0.10 for GRP and 0.04–0.05 for CFRP, which compare quite well with the corresponding values of their SFTCs counterparts, emphasizing the importance of the reinforcement in the fatigue response. The correlation between the fatigue sensitivity and fibre modulus is usually explained by noting that, for a given engineering stress, the strain is lower for the more rigid fibres, limiting the microscopic stress in the matrix.[104] Implicit in the previous interpretation is the assumption that, even in a fibre-dominated composite, the matrix is the weak element precipitating final failure.

Harris and co-workers[81] noted that, when a ductile matrix is used in a unidirectional CFRP, some downturn appears in the S–log N curve at 10^5–10^6 cycles. To explain the phenomenon, the authors replotted data from different sources, including carbon-, aramid- and glass-fibre-reinforced plastics, in the perspective of Talreja's model. From the ε–log N diagram, the three régimes hypothesized by Talreja were clearly apparent. Each material exhibited a distinct behaviour in the first region, supporting the statement that the fatigue response in this phase is governed by the reinforcement. Nevertheless, all the curves, irrespective of the fibre type, sensibly converged in the second and third region, where the matrix should predominate in determining fatigue life.

The light continuous lines in Fig. 9.15 enclose the domain of matrix-dominated fatigue for continuous fibre composites, as illustrated in reference 81. The distance between the lines suggests a quite large scatter in the experimental data. There are many valid reasons to anticipate this occurrence.

- The resins considered by Harris et al.[81] were different in nature, ranging from rigid to flexible epoxies.
- The fatigue data employed were generated in load control, so that as the actual engineering strain during each single test increased, the greater was the loss of rigidity; this phenomenon is typically not accounted for in constructing the ε–log N curve, where the maximum strain applied during the first cycle is plotted on the ordinate axis.
- The resin failure in fatigue is governed by the local strain, whose enhancement compared to the engineering strain depends on many factors, such as the fibre modulus and volume fraction, bundle size, etc.

The thick continuous lines in Fig. 9.15 encompass all the fatigue data published in references 80, 82, for random carbon SFTCs, which are not shown to avoid confusion. Owing to the linearity of the stress/strain curve up to failure, the maximum applied stress was simply divided by the material modulus to evaluate the maximum strain during the first cycle.

The dashed lines in Fig. 9.15 represent the fatigue behaviour of SMC-R50, as evaluated from the experimental points in Fig. 9.10. To account for the non-linearity in the stress/strain curve of this material, the initial strain for each stress level was calculated on the basis of the monotonic curve given in reference 21.

Consistent with the findings in reference 81, the SFTCs also seem to converge to a common limit strain at large numbers of cycles, suggesting an endurance limit. The lower

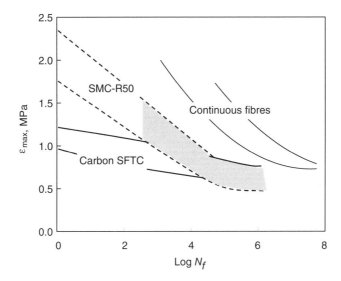

Fig. 9.15 Initial strain vs. fatigue life for different composites.

value for the glass compared to carbon SFTC is somehow anticipated: the initial strain level is preserved throughout the fatigue life when carbon fibres, whose modulus reduction is negligible,[80,82] are employed. By contrast, the actual strain level increases during cycling in the case of the GRP which suffers a larger decrease in rigidity.[21]

From the trend of the carbon SFTCs in Fig. 9.15, the presence of the three regions postulated by Talreja is not evident. This apparently depends on the monotonic failure strain, which is near to the endurance limit strain: the possible transition from one phase to the subsequent may be masked by the flatness of the curve. In fact, from Fig. 9.15 it is also hard to characterize the shift from fibre-dominated to matrix-dominated behaviour for SMC-R50. In facing the same problem, Harris *et al.*[81] plotted the experimental data on a log–log diagram, from which the discontinuity was easily found. Applying this procedure to the SMC-R50 results in Fig. 9.15, the transition point is appreciated at $\log N \approx 10^3$. This information allows us to define roughly the zone of matrix-dominated fatigue (light grey area in the figure). The comparison of the latter with the corresponding zone for continuous-fibre composites suggests that the adoption of short fibres adversely affects the fatigue response, lowering not only the fatigue life for a fixed applied strain, but also the endurance limit strain. This conclusion is reasonable in view of the strain-enhancing effect of the fibre ends, which also lowers the monotonic strain to failure (Fig. 9.6).

Although Talreja's model provides an interesting framework for interpreting fatigue in composites, some experimental observations seem to be in contrast with its basic assumptions. In fact, as discussed previously, the microscopic analysis of the fracture surfaces does not reveal any significant difference between the monotonic and fatigue cases: this would be expected, should a transition from fibre-dominated to matrix-dominated failure modes take place. Moreover, some authors [42,43,86,87] have shown that the general shape of the *S/N* curve can be derived from the hypothesis of a single damage process, continuously reducing the material residual strength with increasing numbers of cycles. Assuming that a monotonically stronger specimen is also stronger in fatigue, the same authors were able to approach the monotonic strength distribution from fatigue data. Of course, this result indicates a strict correlation between the monotonic and fatigue responses, weakening the hypothesis of a change in failure modes as a function of the applied stress level.

9.5 Conclusions

Short-fibre thermoset composites in fatigue exhibit microscopic damage similar to that which is observed under monotonic loading conditions, so that a distinction between a fatigue and a monotonic failure can be made only with difficulty from a fractographic analysis. Common fundamental damage mechanisms also exist in the damage development within these composites and continuous-fibre laminates. However, the latter materials fail by fibre breakage, whereas fractured fibres are seldom found in SFTCs, in which bundle pull-out is the main event driving final collapse.

Unfortunately, a comprehensive analysis concerning the influence of bundle aspect ratio on the monotonic and fatigue response of SFTCs is lacking at this time. This needs to be done, since many attempts based on more flexible resins and modified fibre/matrix interfaces have been unsuccessful in improving their fatigue sensitivity.

From the data available, the main factor influencing the fatigue performances of an SFTC is the fibre type: as with their continuous-fibre counterparts, these materials show better fatigue resistance when higher modulus fibres are employed. In fact, the use of carbon instead of E-glass not only lowers the fatigue sensitivity, but also results in a higher residual modulus, helping in stiffness-critical applications.

As with classical laminates, the S/N curve of an SFTC displays some variations in slope, and seems to approach an asymptotic value at large numbers of cycles. Whether this is an indication of an endurance limit as conventionally defined is not known. According to some authors, strain, rather than stress, is the actual parameter governing the material response under a cyclically varying load; the variations in slope are a consequence of changes in failure modes; the endurance limit actually exists, and is mainly dependent on the matrix. However, the typical trends of the S/N curves have also been modelled effectively from the hypothesis of a single failure mechanism developing throughout the loading history, which seems to be confirmed by the strict correlation between the statistical distribution of the monotonic and fatigue data.

Clearly, the parameters presently adopted to determine the fatigue sensitivity of a composite only hold in the range of moderately high fatigue lives. These parameters become questionable at very large numbers of cycles, where the material response should be assessed for fatigue-critical applications. Establishing whether an endurance limit actually exists, and the factors affecting it, will require a costly and time-consuming testing stage and a thorough identification of the failure modes involved in the progressive material degradation.

9.6 References

1. GHOTRA J S and PIKE S (1993), *Polym. & Polym. Compos.*, **1**(3), 161.
2. IBRAHIM S, POLYZOIS D and HASSAN S (2000), *Canad. J. Civil Eng.*, **27**(5), 850.
3. SRIVASTAVA V K (1999), *Mater. Sci. Eng.*, **263**(1), 56.
4. SRIVASTAVA V K and HOGG P J (1998), *J. Mater. Sci.*, **33**(5), 1129.
5. GALBRAITH C (1999), *Mater. Technol.*, **14**(4), 230.
6. KROLEWSKI S and BUSCH J (1990), *Proc. of Nat. SAMPE Symp. Exhib., Part 2*, Anaheim, Apr 2–5.

7. KAU H-T (1989), *Polym. Eng. Sci.*, **29**(18), 1286.
8. HIRAI T and YAMABE M (1990), *Compos. Struct.*, **14**(1), 3.
9. ATKINS K E, SEATS R L, REX G C, REID C G and GANDY R C (1992), *SAE Technical Paper Series, Int Congr Exp*, Detroit, Feb 24–28.
10. GUILLON D (1993), in *Sheet Moulding Compounds. Science and Technology*, Kia HG Ed, Hanser, Munich.
11. KIA H G (1993), in *Sheet Moulding Compounds. Science and Technology*, Kia HG Ed, Hanser, Munich.
12. OWEN M J and DUKES R (1967), *J. Strain Anal.*, **2**, 272.
13. SMITH T R and OWEN M J (1969), *Mod. Plast.*, **46**(5), 128.
14. OWEN M J, SMITH T R and DUKES R (1969), *Plast. and Polym.*, **37**, 227.
15. OWEN M J and ROSE R G (1970), *Mod. Plast.*, **47**, 130.
16. OWEN M J and HOWE R J (1972), *J. Phys. D: Appl. Phys.*, **5**(9), 1637.
17. REID R J, JONES A H, HEIMBUCK R A and DEVRIES K L (1976), *Rep. TR76-12*, Terra Tek.
18. ROSE R G and HUSTON R J (1978), *Composites*, **9**, 199.
19. HEIMBUCH R A and SANDERS B A (1978), in *Composite Materials in the Automotive Industry*, SV Kulkarni, CH Zweben and RB Pipes Eds, ASME, New York.
20. MCGARRY F J, MANDELL J F and WANG S S (1979), *Research Report R79-2*, MIT.
21. DENTON D L (1979), *The Mechanical Properties of an SMC-R50 Composite*, Owens-Corning Fiberglas, Granville.
22. MANDELL J F, HUANG D D and MCGARRY F K (1981), *Compos. Tech. Rev.*, **3**, 93.
23. MCCULLOUGH R L, JARZEBSKI G J and MCGEE S H (1981), in *The Role of the Polymeric Matrix in the Processing and Structural Properties of Composite Materials*, J C Seferis and L Nicolais Eds, Plenum, New York.
24. MANDELL J F and LEE B L (1982), in *Composite Materials: Testing and Design*, ASTM STP 787, I M Daniel Ed, American Society for Testing and Materials, Philadelphia.
25. WANG S S and YU T P (1982), in *Short-Fibre Reinforced Composite Materials*, ASTM STP 722, B A Sanders Ed, American Society for Testing and Materials, Philadelphia.
26. WATANABE T and YASUDA M (1982), *Composites*, **13**, 58.
27. TSUCHIYAMA N (1982), in Proc. ICCM-IV *Progress in Science and Engineering of Composites*, Japan Society for Composite Materials, Tokyo.
28. WANG S S and CHIM E S M (1983), *J. Compos. Mater.*, **17**, 114.
29. WANG S S, CHIM E S M and SUEMASU H (1986), *ASME J. Appl. Mech.*, **53**(2), 339.
30. WANG S S, SUEMASU H and CHIM E S M (1987), *J. Compos. Mater.*, **21**, 1084.
31. FAUDREE M, BAER E, HILTNER A and COLLISTER J (1988), *J. Compos. Mater.*, **22**, 1170.
32. CHIM E S M and WANG S S (1990), *J. Compos. Technol. Res.*, **12**(4), 223.
33. PERREUX D and SIQUEIRA C (1993), in Proc. ICCM/9 *Composites Behaviour*, Vol. V, Woodhead, Cambridge.
34. HOUR K-Y and SEHITOGLU H (1993), *J. Compos. Mater.*, **27**(8), 782.
35. MERAGHNI F and BENZEGGAGH M L (1993), in Proc. ICCM/9 *Composites Behaviour*, Vol. V, Woodhead, Cambridge.
36. HOFFMAN L, KABELKA J and EHRENSTEIN G W (1995), in Proc. *Int Conf Compos Mater-10*, Vol. I, Woodhead, Cambridge.
37. MARGUERES P, MERAGHNI F and BENZEGGAGH M L (2000), *Composites Part A*, **31**, 151.
38. NORWOOD L S and MILLMAN A F (1980), in Proc. ICCM 3 *Advances in Composite Materials*, Pergamon, Oxford.
39. BARTON D C and SODEN P D (1982), *Composites*, **13**, 66.
40. BOURBAN P-E, CANTWELL W J, KAUSCH H H and YOUD S J (1993), in Proc. ICCM/9 *Composites Behaviour*, Vol. V, Woodhead, Cambridge.
41. D'AMORE A, CAPRINO G and FACCIOLO F (1996), *Adv. Compos. Lett.*, **5**(2), 53.
42. CAPRINO G and D'AMORE A (1998), *Compos. Sci. Technol.*, **58**(6), 957.
43. CAPRINO G, D'AMORE A and FACCIOLO F (1998), *J. Compos. Mater.*, **32**(12), 1203.
44. KALLMEYER A R and STEPHENS R I (1995), *J. Compos. Mater.*, **29**(12), 1621.
45. OWEN M J (1974), in *Composite Materials*, Vol. 5 – *Fracture and Fatigue*, LJ Broutman Ed, Academic Press, New York.
46. AHMED S and JONES F R (1988), *Composites*, **19**, 277.
47. FU S-Y and LAUKE B (1998), *Composites Part A*, **29A**, 575.
48. TSAI S W and AZZI V D (1966), *AIAA J*, **4**(2), 296.

49. OHIRA H and UDA N (1982), in Proc. ICCM-IV *Progress in Science and Engineering of Composites*, Japan Society for Composite Materials, Tokyo.
50. MASTERS J E and REIFSNIDER K L (1982), in *Damage in Composite Materials*, ASTM STP 775, K L Reifsnider Ed, American Society for Testing and Materials, Philadelphia.
51. MCCARTNEY L N, SCHOEPPNER G A and BECKER W (2000), *Compos. Sci. Technol.*, **60**, 2347.
52. BROUTMAN L J and SAHU S (1969), in Proc. of the 24th *Annual Tech. Conf.*, SPI, II-D.
53. STINCHCOMB W W and REIFSNIDER K L (1979), in *Fatigue Mechanisms*, ASTM STP 675, J T Fong Ed, American Society for Testing and Materials, Philadelphia.
54. ZWEBEN C (1989), in *Delaware Composites Design Encyclopaedia*, Vol. 1, L A Carlsson and J W Gillespie Eds, Technomic, Lancaster.
55. CAPRINO G and TETI R (1989), *Sandwich Structures Handbook*, Il Prato, Padua.
56. HAYSITE technical data sheet.
57. OWENS-CORNING technical data sheet.
58. QUANTUM COMPOSITES technical data sheet.
59. PREMIX technical data sheet.
60. MANDELL J F (1990), in *Fatigue of Composite Materials: Composite Materials Series*, Vol. 4, K L Reifsnider Ed, Elsevier, Amsterdam.
61. LUBIN G (1969), *Handbook of Fibreglass and Advanced Plastics Composites*, Van Nostrand Reinhold, New York.
62. CHATURVEDI S K and SIERAKOWSKI R L (1983), *Compos. Struct.*, **1**, 137.
63. BERTHELOT J M (1983), *Fibre Sci . and Technol.*, **18**, 1.
64. JOHNSON A F (1986), *Composites*, **17**, 233.
65. GLUSHKO V I, KOVALENKO V P, MILEIKO S T and TVARDOVSKY V V (1993), *J. Mater. Sci.*, **28**(23), 6307.
66. DIEFENDORF R J and TOKARSKI E (1975), *Polym. Eng. Sci.*, **15**(3), 150.
67. PETERS P W M (1994), *J. Compos. Mater.*, **28**, 507.
68. BENZARTI K, CANGEMI L and DAL MASO F (2001), *Composites Part A*, **32**, 197.
69. HOECKER F, FRIEDRICH K, BLUMBERG H and KARGER-KOCSIS J (1995), *Compos. Sci. Technol.*, **54**, 317.
70. GARRETT K W and BAILEY J E (1977), *J. Mater. Sci.*, **12**, 2189.
71. LEGG M J and HULL D (1982), *Composites*, **13**, 369.
72. DE KOK J M M, MEIJER H E H and PEIJS A A J M (1993), in *Composites Behaviour*, Vol. V, Woodhead, Cambridge.
73. KIES J A (1962), *US Naval Lab. Res. Rep. NRL 5752*.
74. CHAMIS C C (1967), *DMSMD Rep. No. 9*, Case Western Reserve University, Cleveland.
75. ADAMS D F and DONER D R (1967), *J. Compos. Mater.*, **1**, 152.
76. ASP L E, BERGLUND L A and GUDMUNDSON P (1995), *Compos. Sci. Technol.*, **53**, 27.
77. KELLY A and TYSON W R (1965), *J. Mech. Physics Solids*, **13**, 329.
78. KACIR L, NARKIS M and ISHAI O (1977), *Polym. Eng. Sci.*, **17**, 234.
79. KARDOS J L, MASOUMI E and KACIR L (1981), in *The Role of the Polymeric Matrix in the Processing and Structural Properties of Composite Materials*, J C Seferis and L Nicolais Eds, Plenum, New York.
80. HITCHEN S A, OGIN S L and SMITH P A (1995), *Composites*, **26**, 303.
81. HARRIS B, REITER H, ADAM T, DICKSON R F and FERNANDO G (1990), *Composites*, **21**(3), 232.
82. FRIEDRICH K, SCHULTE K, HORSTENKAMP G and CHOU T W (1985), *J. Mater. Sci.*, **20**, 3353.
83. PHILIPPIDIS T P and VASSILOPOULOS A P (2000), *Compos. Sci. Technol.*, **60**, 2819.
84. VAN PAEPEGEM W and DEGRIECK J (2002), *Compos. Sci. Technol.*, **62**, 687.
85. ECHTERMEYER A T, ENGH B and BUENE L (1995), *Composites*, **26**, 10.
86. YANG J N and LIU M D (1977), *J. Compos. Mater.*, **11**, 176.
87. YANG J N (1978), *J. Compos. Mater.*, **12**, 19.
88. HOA S U and NGUYEN Q B (1983), *Polym. Compos.*, **4**, 85.
89. LANG R W and MANSON J A (1987), *J. Mater. Sci.*, **22**, 3576.
90. LIFSHITZ J M (1976), *J. Compos. Mater.*, **10**, 92.
91. CAPRINO G, CRIVELLI VISCONTI I and DI ILIO A (1984), *Compos. Struct.*, **2**, 261.
92. SOUTH J T, REIFSNIDER K L and CASE S W (2001), *J. Compos. Technol. Res.*, **23**(3), 189.
93. AVESTON J, KELLY A and SILWOOD J M (1980), Proc. ICCM 3 *Advances in Composite Materials*, Pergamon, Oxford.
94. SCHUTTE C L, MCDONOUGH W, SHIOYA M and HUNSTON D L (1993), *Proc Materials Research Society Spring Meeting*, Apr 14–16, San Francisco.

95. SIMS G D and GLADMAN D G (1982), *NPL Report DMA (A) 59*.
96. MAYER R M, PEARCE A and WORTHINGTON P J (1984), *Compos. Struct.*, **2**, 305.
97. JONES C J, DICKSON R F, ADAM T, REITER H and HARRIS B (1984), *Proc Roy Soc Lond*, **A396**, 315.
98. PARTRIDGE I, VIRLOUVET P, CHUBB J and CURTIS P (1989), in *Developments in Science and Technology of Composites*, A R Bunsell, P Lamicq and A Massiah Eds, Elsevier, London.
99. MANDELL J F and SAMBORSKI D D (1997), *Rep No SAND97-3002*, Sandia National Laboratory, Albuquerque.
100. CURTIS P T and DOREY G (1986), *Proc Int Conf Fatigue '86*, Sheffield, Sept.
101. SCHUTZ D and GERHARZ I J (1977), *Composites*, **8**, 245.
102. HAN H T, BARTLEY-CHO J and LIM S G (1997), *Rep No DOT/FAA/AR-96/76*.
103. TALREJA R (1981), *Proc. Roy. Soc. Lond.*, **A378**, 461.
104. DHARAN C H (1975), *J. Mater. Sci.*, **10**, 1665.

10

Woven-fibre thermoset composites

N. K. Naik, Indian Institute of Technology, Bombay, India

10.1 Introduction

Traditionally, laminated composites made of unidirectional layers are used for high-performance structural applications. Such composites are characterized by high in-plane specific stiffness and high in-plane specific strength. These composites have clear advantages when the loading is predominantly in-plane. But designers committed to advanced composite structures are looking for different composite configurations which can be tailored to suit different loading conditions. Other mechanical properties required in relation to different loading conditions are: through-thickness stiffness and strength properties, enhanced impact resistance, fatigue resistance, dimensional stability, fracture toughness, damage tolerance, and subtle conformability. Ease of manufacturing is an additional important consideration.

Polymer–matrix composites have two main structural components: reinforcement and polymer matrix. Reinforcement architecture plays an important role in tailoring the mechanical performance of advanced composites. Textile techniques such as three-dimensional (3D) weaving, advanced braiding and knitting and through-thickness stitching of the fabrics have assisted in enhancing the performance of the textile composite structures. Such composites are normally made by using the textile preforms and resin-transfer moulding (RTM). This is a simpler and convenient technique compared to the autoclave moulding technique used for making laminated composite structures from unidirectional prepregs.

Three-dimensional textile composites are strong contenders for the structural applications in the presence of multidirectional mechanical and thermal stresses. Because of the fibre architecture in 3D composites, reinforcement is also present along the thickness direction leading to an increase in the through-thickness stiffness and strength properties. Other advantages are the enhanced delamination resistance, impact/fracture resistance, damage tolerance and dimensional stability. They possess high strain to failure in both tension and compression. The 3D composites are also characterized by ease of fabrication, through the use of resin-transfer moulding of 3D preforms.

Laminated composites made of unidirectional (UD) layers are used in high-technology applications because of their high specific strength and high specific stiffness. These potential properties are realized only if the composite structure is loaded primarily in the plane of the reinforcement. If a composite structure is subjected to loading along other directions, the location of structural failure would be at the fibre/resin interface. This has necessitated the development of fibre-reinforced textile composite structures which possess significant fibrous interconnectivity between adjacent planes of fibres to supplement the relatively weak fibre/resin interface. This interconnectivity would enhance the damage tolerance of composite structures. These requirements have led to the advent of 3D composites.

Weaving, braiding, knitting and through-thickness stitching are the main processes used for making textile preforms. The textile preforms are planar or three-dimensional. The interconnectivity is mainly in the plane of the preform of planar textile preforms. Such materials are known as two-dimensional (2D) textile preforms. The 3D textile preforms for the structural composites are fully integrated continuous-fibre assemblies having multiaxial in-plane and out-of-plane fibre orientations. Normally, using 3D textile preforms and resin transfer moulding, 3D composites are made.

One of the great promises of the 3D textile preforms is the formation of integral structures to near net shape. This has led to their usage in structural applications in aerospace, aircraft and automotive industries. The 3D textile preforms can be manufactured with numerous complex architecture variations to meet the needs of specific applications. The 3D orthogonal interlock woven composites are a class of materials finding increasing use in structural applications.

Orthogonal interlock woven 3D preforms have reinforcement yarns arranged in an orthogonal geometry, with all yarns intersecting at 90° angles. The yarns can be introduced uniformly in each of the three directions to provide quasi-isotropic properties, or in unbalanced amounts when design considerations require anisotropic properties. The orthogonally woven 3D preforms generally have a finer geometrical repeating unit cell.

The 3D textile composites have relatively lower in-plane stiffness and strength properties. For high in-plane specific stiffness and high in-plane specific strength applications, 2D textile composites, especially 2D woven-fabric composites can be competitors to laminated composites made of UD layers. These composites also have relatively higher impact resistance, fatigue resistance, dimensional stability, fracture toughness and damage tolerance characteristics. Further, they have subtle conformability.

The 2D woven fabric is produced by a process of weaving in which the fabric is formed by interlacing the warp and fill (weft) yarns. The fundamental 2D weaves are: plain, twill and satin. The warp and fill yarns are interlaced in a regular sequence of under and over. The integrated nature of these fabrics lends them to easier handling in the subsequent composite fabrication processes, and the nature of the fabric structure enables them to conform to complex curvatures. For the effective use of such composites, their behaviour under different loading conditions should be understood.

Fatigue of materials refers to the changes in properties resulting from the application of cyclic or repeated loads. The mechanical damage caused by cyclic loads during fatigue results in a material failure at lower stress levels than would be required under monotonic loading. Fatigue damage occurs in a material from the initiation and growth of a single crack, or multiple cracks. The damage that progresses during fatigue loading results in a reduction of composite stiffness and load-carrying capability of the structure.

The fatigue behaviour of a material depends upon a large number of parameters such as: maximum applied stress (or strain), fluctuation in the applied stress (or strain), number of stress (or strain) cycles, stress concentrations and stress fluctuation frequency.[1] Material composition, loading history, residual stresses, environmental condition and temperature can also influence the fatigue behaviour.

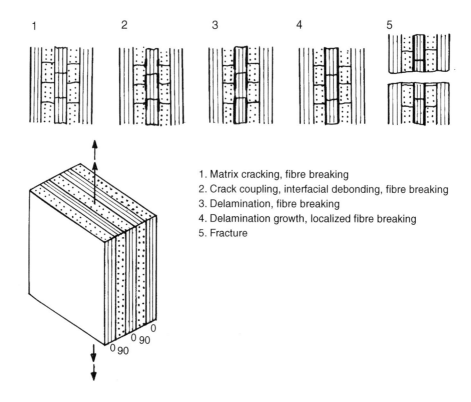

1. Matrix cracking, fibre breaking
2. Crack coupling, interfacial debonding, fibre breaking
3. Delamination, fibre breaking
4. Delamination growth, localized fibre breaking
5. Fracture

Fig. 10.1   Schematic representation of damage development in laminated composites made of UD
layers during fatigue life.

This chapter deals with the fatigue behaviour of 2D woven composites. For comparison, typical results for laminated composites made of UD layers are also presented.

10.2   Fatigue performance of laminated composites

Damage initiation and growth in laminated composites made of UD layers under fatigue loading has been studied for the last three decades and is well documented.[2-5] A schematic representation of damage initiation and growth process is shown in Fig. 10.1. The damage development is multi-staged. The main damage mechanisms observed during fatigue loading are: matrix cracking, crack coupling, fibre/matrix interfacial debonding, delamination, fibre breaking and finally fracture. Figure 10.2 shows damage accumulation as a function of percentage of life behaviour for a typical laminated composite made of UD layers.

Matrix micro-cracks are initiated early in the fatigue process. Matrix cracks are formed first along fibres in the layers inclined to the principal tensile loading direction. A number of parallel cracks appear in a layer during fatigue loading. As the laminate is further stressed, cracking occurs in the other layers also. The crack density increases as the loading continues. This process depends upon the layer stresses and adjacent layers.

As the crack density increases, cracks grow into each other, leading to crack coupling. The cracking process continues until cracks in each layer have attained an equilibrium or saturation spacing and size. At this stage, stress redistribution would limit the initiation of

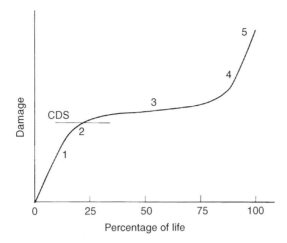

Fig. 10.2   Damage accumulation in laminated composites made of UD layers during fatigue life.

new cracks. But the matrix cracks would be a macroscopic form of damage. This can lead to initiation and development of other damage modes. The saturation or equilibrium spacing of the matrix cracks is a property of the laminate and is independent of loading history. The state of damage given by the saturated and stable matrix cracking pattern in a laminate has been termed the characteristic damage state (CDS).[3]

Fibre/matrix debonding during fatigue loading depends upon the strength of the interfacial bond between the fibre and matrix. Interfacial debonding can combine with other damage mechanisms.

The next damage mechanism would be the initiation and propagation of delamination. The delamination could initiate near the free edges of the laminates because of high induced edge interlaminar stresses. The delamination can occur in the interior of the laminates because of high interlaminar stresses caused by the matrix cracks and fibre breaks. On further loading, the delamination would grow.

During fatigue loading, fibre breakage occurs because of over-straining or over-stressing. Breakage of fibres could take place early because of the lower strain-to-failure values of the weaker fibres relative to that of the polymer–matrix in a laminated composite. Stress concentrations from matrix cracks and interfacial debonding can also lead to early fibre breakage.

During the later stage of damage growth, all the damage modes would be developing rapidly in a fast-decreasing volume of the laminate. As the stress state reaches a critical value, fracture of the laminate would be initiated.

It may be noted that the individual damage mechanisms occur more or less simultaneously. However, matrix cracking may be the dominant damage mechanism in the early stage of the total life of the component. Delamination may dominate during the intermediate state. Accumulation of different damage modes leading to a critical local stress state, and subsequently to fracture of the component, would take place during the later stage.

10.3   Woven-fabric laminated composites

Woven-fabric (WF) composites are characterized by better impact resistance, damage tolerance, high toughness, dimensional stability over a large range of temperature, subtle

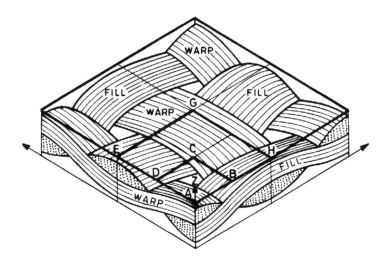

Fig. 10.3   Idealized representative plain-weave fabric lamina.

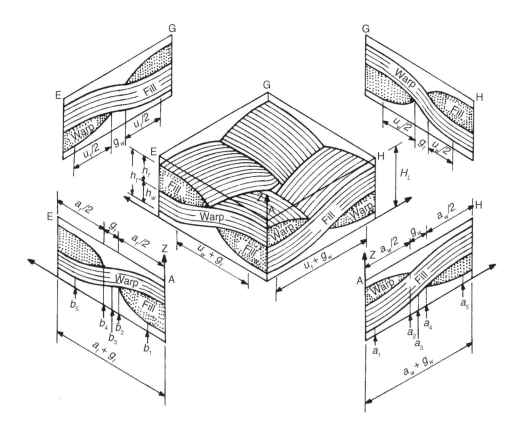

Fig. 10.4   A general plain-weave fabric lamina geometrical representative unit cell.

conformability and ease of manufacturing. But, the in-plane properties are compromised by the use of the reinforcement in fabric form. The mechanical behaviour of WF composites depends upon the type of weave, fabric geometry, fibre volume fraction, laminate configuration and the material system used.[6–12] Plain weave is one of the important fundamental weaves. A biaxial plain-weave fabric is formed by interlacing warp and fill (weft) strands in a regular sequence of one under and one over. An idealized 2D orthogonal plain-weave fabric is shown in Fig. 10.3. A general plain-weave fabric lamina geometrically representative unit cell is shown in Fig. 10.4. The fabric geometry should be chosen to give the best possible properties for the application under consideration. The important fabric parameters are: strand cross-sectional geometry, strand fineness, number of counts, and the weaving conditions (e.g. balanced or unbalanced). Even though the exact cross-sectional area of the strand cannot be controlled during weaving, strand width (a) and strand thickness (h) can be controlled.

The fabric count is the number of strands per unit length along the warp or fill direction. Based on the fabric count and width of the strand, the gap between adjacent strands g can be found. The length of the gap between adjacent strands is referred to as 'the gap' for further discussion. A fabric is tightly woven if there is no gap between adjacent strands. In the case of an open weave, there is some gap between the adjacent strands. Linear density is the weight of strand per unit length, which is a measure of the fineness of the strand and is given by the tex number, g/km. The strand crimp C is a measure of the degree of undulation. The strand crimp is defined as the difference between the straightened strand length and fabric sample length as a percentage of fabric sample length. The strand crimp depends upon a, h and g. The length of the strand as a part of a fabric sample length or unit cell can consist of a straight length and an undulating length within the interlacing region. The undulating length within the interlacing region is referred to as the undulating length u. Depending upon the strand cross-sectional geometry, the undulating length can vary.

A plain-weave fabric can be balanced or unbalanced depending upon the number of counts and the strand properties. If strand properties such as cross-sectional geometry, tex, crimp and the material properties and the number of counts are the same along both the warp and fill directions, the fabric is called a balanced fabric. Otherwise, the fabric is unbalanced. The strand and weave parameters such as strand tex, width and thickness of strand and the number of counts can be controlled during weaving. In turn, balanced or unbalanced, tightly woven or open weaves can be obtained. But, the actual cross-sectional area and the undulating length can be obtained by either photomicrographs or mathematical shape functions.

The term strand is used here to indicate untwisted fibre bundles, twisted fibre bundles or rovings. The property translation efficiency factor will have to be used to derive the properties of the strand from the properties of the filament.

A WF lamina consists of resin-impregnated strands and pure matrix regions. Because of the presence of the pure matrix regions, the fibre volume fraction within the resin impregnated strand and the overall fibre volume fraction within the unit cell are different. The overall fibre volume fraction V_f^o can be determined experimentally. It is defined as the ratio of fibre volume within the unit cell to the volume of the unit cell. Using V_f^o and the strand geometry, the fibre volume fraction within the resin impregnated strand (V_f^s) can be determined. It is defined as the ratio of the volume of the fibre within the unit cell to the total volume of the resin impregnated strands within the unit cell.

A WF laminate is formed by stacking WF layers one over the other, possibly with different orientations as in the case of UD laminates. In UD laminates, a variety of laminate configurations can be obtained by varying the orientation angle of individual layers,

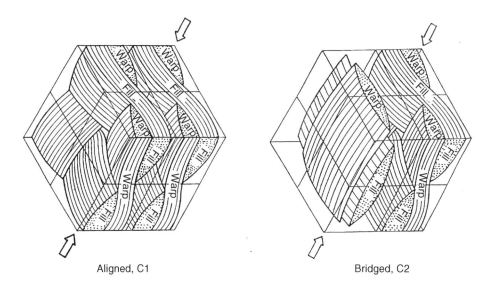

Aligned, C1   Bridged, C2

Fig. 10.5   Stacking of layers in different idealized laminate configurations.

whereas in the case of WF laminates, different stacking patterns can be achieved even without considering the orientations of the layers as a variable.[6-9] This is achieved by shifting the layers of the laminate such that the strands of one layer are not in exact alignment with the strands of the adjacent layers. This shift can be in warp, fill and/or thickness directions.

Figure 10.5 represents the stacking of layers in different idealized laminate configurations. In configuration C1, there is no relative shift between the adjacent layers, i.e. each layer is exactly stacked over the adjacent layer. Such a laminate configuration is referred to as aligned or stacked. In configuration C2, the adjacent layers are shifted with respect to each other by a distance $(a+g)/2$ in both the fill and warp directions. Such a laminate configuration is referred to as bridged or nested. In this case the gap region of one layer is bridged by the interlacing region of the adjacent layer.

It may be noted that WF composites consist of three structural elements, namely, longitudinal strand (warp), transverse strand (fill) and pure matrix regions. For both the configurations, i.e. C1 and C2, in any cross-section perpendicular to the warp direction, the structural-element warp would be present. But the structural-element fill would be present only in the interlacing region to a varying degree. The gap region would consist of only the warp and pure matrix. Hence, the geometry and composition of different structural elements would be different in different cross-sections perpendicular to the warp, i.e. the loading direction.

In an actual laminate, there would be scattered zones of different combinations of shifts of layers with respect to each other. The relative placement of different layers in a laminate is affected by friction between fabric layers, local departure in strand perpendicularity, possible variation of number of counts from place to place in the fabric and the constraints on the relative lateral movement of layers during lamination. A photomicrograph of a typical plain-weave fabric laminate cross-section is shown in Fig. 10.6. Scattered zones of different combinations of shifts can be seen.

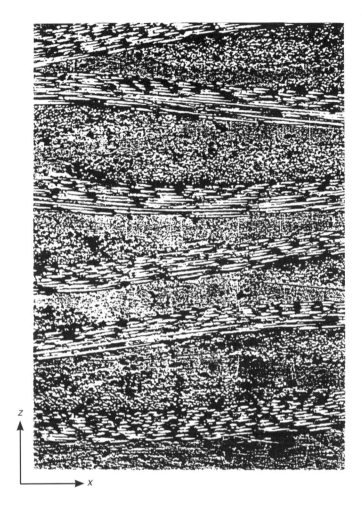

Fig. 10.6 Photomicrograph of a typical plain-weave fabric laminate cross-section.

10.4   Fatigue testing

During the service life, the components undergo different loading cycles. The frequently applied stress states are: tension–tension, tension–compression, compression–compression, flexure, torsion, or combinations of these stress states. The loading can be uniaxial or multi-axial. Furthermore, the stress state can be repeated, reversed or irregular. The fatigue behaviour of the material depends upon a large number of parameters such as: maximum applied stress (or strain), fluctuation in the applied stress (or strain), number of stress (or strain) cycles and stress fluctuation frequency. Stress (or strain) concentration is also an important parameter in the case of WF composites because of the nature of fabric geometry.

Typical parameters used to indicate fatigue loading are:

• Stress range: the difference between the maximum and minimum applied stress levels.
• Mean stress: the algebraic average stress applied.

- Stress ratio (Rvalue): the ratio of minimum stress to maximum stress.
- A value: the ratio of alternating stress to the mean stress.

10.5   Fatigue damage in woven-fabric composites

For the study of the fatigue behaviour of composites, a clear understanding of the damage mechanisms is necessary. Many researchers have investigated microscopic and macroscopic fatigue damage mechanisms for laminated composites made of UD layers. For such materials, qualitative and, in some cases, quantitative results are available and well documented.[2–5] Woven-fabric composites are finding increasing use in different structural applications. Mechanical behaviour of such materials under static loading has been investigated during the last decade. Many investigations are also available of the behaviour of WF composites under fatigue loading.[13–28]

In this section, a discussion of damage mechanisms and damage initiation and growth in WF composites under quasi-static tensile loading is first presented. Details are then given for WF composites under fatigue loading.

10.5.1 Damage development in WF composites under quasi-static tensile loading

Figure 10.7 is a schematic representation of damage growth in WF composites under on-axis uniaxial quasi-static tensile loading; the loading is along the warp direction. The failure can take place in any one of the structural elements: warp, fill and pure matrix region.

In the interlacing region, failure of the longitudinal strand (i.e. the warp-strand failure) could occur in longitudinal tension or shear and of the fill strand in transverse tension. Failure of the transverse strand (i.e. the fill-strand failure) would initiate at the tip as shown in Fig. 10.7(b). As the loading is increased, the fill failure would be progressing towards the mid-section of the interlacing region. In the interlacing region, the pure matrix role is not significant. The failure of the warp strand in longitudinal tension indicates the ultimate failure of the unit cell and therefore of the WF composite. Shear failure in the warp strand and transverse failure in the fill strand are the secondary failure modes. This would lead to a reduction in the stiffness of the WF composites.

In the gap region, the transverse strand (i.e. the fill-strand) is not present. As in the case of the interlacing region, the warp-strand failure could occur in longitudinal tension or shear. The pure matrix in the gap region plays a crucial role in suppressing bending/extension effects. Failure can also initiate in the pure matrix region (Fig. 10.7(c)). If macroscopic damage occurs in the pure-matrix region, the monolithic characteristic of the WF composite would be lost. After a failure in the pure-matrix region, the structural elements, warp and fill, can be treated independently. In this case also, the failure of the warp strand in longitudinal tension represents the ultimate failure of the unit cell and of the WF composite.

During loading, the geometry of the WF composite would change. Whether the failure would initiate in the interlacing region or gap region depends upon the geometry and material properties of the WF laminate.

Figure 10.8 shows secondary failures in WF composites during on-axis uniaxial quasi-static tensile loading. The extent of secondary failures for two cases of h/a ratios are indicated for $g/a = 0.1$. Figure 10.8(a) shows the extent of fill transverse failure and warp shear failure when the ultimate failure takes place for the case $h/a = 0.05$. Fill transverse failure takes place throughout the fill cross-section whereas the warp shear failure takes

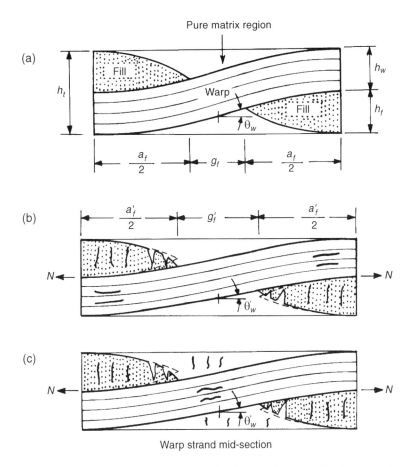

Fig. 10.7   Schematic representation of damage development in woven fabric composites under quasi-static tensile loading. (a) Before loading. (b) and (c) During loading.

place in the gap region. Ultimate tensile failure takes place in the gap region at a resultant stress equal to 530 MPa for a typical plain-weave fabric carbon/epoxy composite. Failure of the pure-matrix region takes place at a resultant stress equal to 495 MPa.

For the case $h/a = 0.2$, failure takes place in the pure-matrix region at a resultant stress equal to 160 MPa. At this stage, transverse failure of the fill takes place only near the tip (Fig. 10.8(b)). Warp shear failure takes place in the gap region. For this configuration, ultimate tensile failure takes place in the interlacing region at a resultant stress equal to 370 MPa.

Different secondary failure modes are: transverse failure of the fill, shear failure of the warp, cracking in the pure-matrix region and possible delamination. Micro-structural damage such as matrix micro-cracking and debonding take place much earlier. The failure of the warp strand in longitudinal tension signifies the ultimate failure.

10.5.2   Damage development in WF composites under fatigue loading

Woven-fabric composites consist of three structural elements, namely, longitudinal strand (warp), transverse strand (fill) and pure matrix regions. The structural elements' warp and fill can be considered as equivalent UD composites. The main damage mechanisms observed

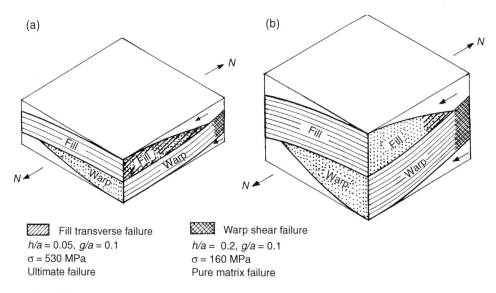

Fill transverse failure   Warp shear failure

h/a = 0.05, g/a = 0.1   h/a = 0.2, g/a = 0.1

σ = 530 MPa   σ = 160 MPa

Ultimate failure   Pure matrix failure

Fig. 10.8   Secondary failures in woven-fabric composites during quasi-static tensile loading.

during fatigue loading can be classified into micro-structural damage within the impregnated strand and the macroscopic damage within the WF composite. The micro structural damage mechanisms are: matrix micro-cracking, fibre/matrix interfacial debonding, fibre breakage and crack coupling. These are similar to the damage mechanisms observed in laminated composites made of UD layers. Matrix micro-cracking can also be initiated in the pure matrix regions.

The macroscopic damage mechanisms are (Figs. 10.9 and 10.10): transverse crack in fill, shear failure in warp, cracks in pure-matrix regions, delamination between fill and warp, delamination between adjacent layers, warp tensile failure and finally fracture. Tensile fracture can take place in the interlacing region or the gap region based on the geometry and the properties of the WF composite.

Figure 10.11 shows the Young's modulus decay and damage accumulation in WF composites during fatigue life. The modulus decay ratio is the ratio of Young's modulus after n cycles to the static Young's modulus. There is rapid decay of the modulus in the early part of the fatigue life. Micro-structural damages and transverse cracks in the fill are formed during this stage. This process continues until the cracks have attained an equilibrium or saturation spacing size. This state of damage has been termed the characteristic damage state. This process is similar to that of laminated composites made of UD layers.

The next damage mechanisms would be shear failure in the warp, cracks in pure-matrix regions, and the initiation and propagation of delamination between fill and warp as well as between adjacent layers. This is the middle stage of damage accumulation.

On further loading, all the damage modes would be rapidly growing. Fracture of the strands occurs at the location of stress concentrations because of over-straining or over-stressing. This would lead to the fracture of the WF laminate. After the initial rapid decay of the modulus, the decay would be gradual during the middle stage.

Damage accumulation is rapid in the early part of the fatigue life because of the strain (or stress) concentrations present in the geometrically repeating unit cell. Because of the interlacing nature of WF composites, damage growth would be slower. Hence, damage accumulation would be gradual in the middle stage of the fatigue life.

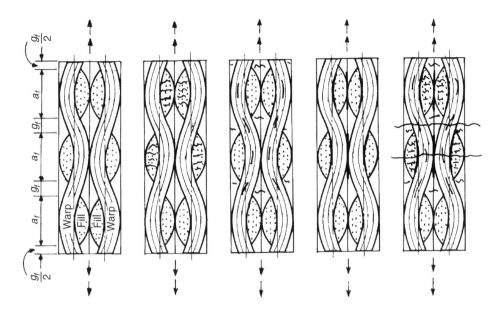

Fig. 10.9   Schematic representation of damage growth in woven-fabric composites during fatigue life: aligned configuration.

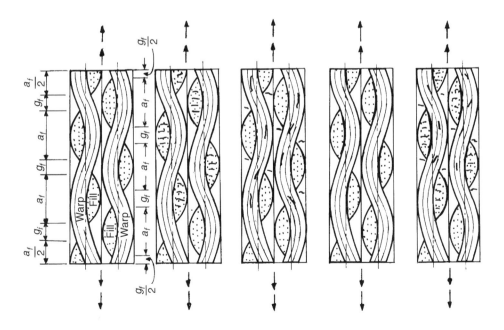

Fig. 10.10   Schematic representation of damage growth in woven-fabric composites during fatigue life: bridged configuration.

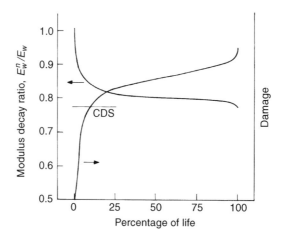

Fig. 10.11   Modulus decay and damage accumulation in woven-fabric composites during fatigue life.

Figures 10.9 and 10.10 present aligned and bridged configurations of WF laminates. Macro-structural damage mechanisms, i.e. transverse cracking in fill, shear failure in warp, cracks in pure-matrix regions, delamination between fill and warp, and delamination between adjacent layers occur more or less simultaneously. During the later stage of damage growth, all the damage modes would be growing rapidly. As the stress state reaches to a critical value, strands would fracture leading to the ultimate failure of the laminate.

10.6   Fatigue loading: stiffness, strength and life

A stress/life (S–N) diagram for a typical plain-weave fabric glass/polyester composite under tensile fatigue loading is presented in Fig. 10.12.[16] Here, the peak stress ratio is the ratio of maximum cyclic stress to monotonic strength and the cycle ratio is the ratio of present number of cycles to number of cycles to failure. Modulus decay is shown in Fig. 10.11. It can be seen that there is rapid decay in modulus as well as strength in the initial part of the fatigue life.

Curtis and Moore carried out fatigue studies on satin-weave fabric carbon/epoxy composites and equivalent laminated composites made of UD layers under tension–compression loading.[13] Laminated composites made of UD layers are designated as 'non-wovens'. Stress/life (S–N) diagrams were presented for three lay-ups: lay-up A $[0/90_2/0]_s$, lay-up B $[\pm45/0/90]_s$ and lay-up C $[0/90/\pm45]_s$ (Fig. 10.13). Here, lay-up A is square-symmetric whereas lay-ups B and C are quasi-isotropic. For both wovens and non-wovens, the monotonic compressive strength was lower than static tensile strength for lay-ups A and C, whereas the tensile strength was lower than the compressive strength for lay-up B for both wovens and non-wovens. Hence, normalization has been made with respect to X_c for lay-ups A and C whereas it has been made with respect to X_t for lay-up B. Strength decay is faster for wovens than for non-wovens of square symmetric lay-up (Fig. 10.13]. On the other hand, strength decay behaviour is nearly identical for both wovens and non-wovens with quasi-isotropic lay-ups.

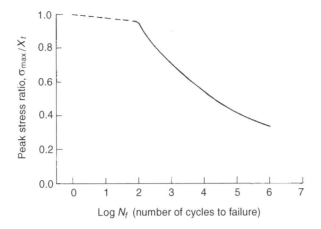

Fig. 10.12   Stress/life (*S–N*) diagram for a typical plain-weave-fabric glass/polyester composite under tensile fatigue loading. (Source: ref 16.)

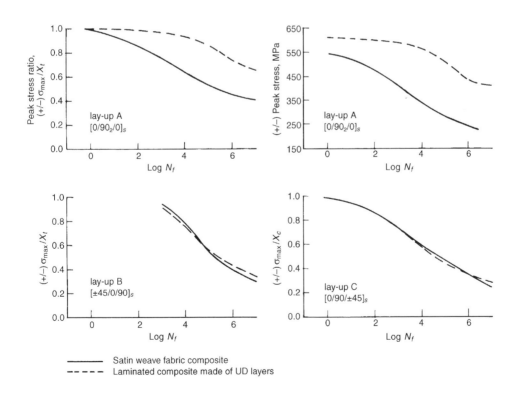

Fig. 10.13   Stress/life (*S–N*) diagram for carbon/epoxy composite under tension–compression fatigue loading. (Source: ref 13.)

10.7   Recent studies of the fatigue behaviour of WF composites

Woven-fabric composites have been finding increasing use in advanced structural applications in recent years. This is because of their enhanced through-thickness stiffness and strength properties, impact resistance, dimensional stability, fracture toughness, damage tolerance and subtle conformability. But although there have been some studies of the fatigue behaviour,[13–31] it is not clearly understood.

Curtis and Moore[13] compared the fatigue behaviour of satin-weave fabric composites and laminated composites made of UD layers. The studies were carried out on carbon/epoxy composites with tension–compression fatigue loading. It was observed that the damage accumulation was faster for WF composites than laminated composites made of UD layers with square symmetric lay-up. With quasi-isotropic lay-ups, the damage accumulation was nearly of the same magnitude for both types of laminates.

Fujii et al.,[16] Takemura and Fujii[18] and Hansen[27] carried out damage development studies under tension–tension fatigue loading. Matrix cracking, cracks in the fill and warp, and delaminations were all observed before the final fracture. Huang[28] presented a fatigue life prediction model for woven-fabric composites subjected to biaxial cyclic loads. This model is based on the unit-cell analysis. The unit cell was subdivided into slices, and each slice was considered as a UD composite.

Amijima et al.,[14] Fujii and Lin[20] and Kawakami and Fujii[23] studied fatigue degradation of glass-fabric polymer composites under tension/torsion biaxial loading. A fatigue-damage-accumulation model based on the theory of continuum damage mechanics has been presented. Flexural fatigue[17] and combined bending and torsion fatigue[25] studies have also been published.

The effect of fatigue damage in WF composites on thermomechanical properties and residual compressive strength has been demonstrated by Mitrovic and Carman.[21] They studied the inter-relationship between thermomechanical properties. Their conclusion was that thermal expansion coefficient measurements may be used as a damage evaluation technique. The fatigue behaviour of carbon/carbon composites has been presented by Ozturk and Moore,[15] Williams et al.[22] and Khan et al.[26] Xiao and Bathias[19] and Kawai et al.[24] compared the fatigue behaviour of unnotched and notched composites.

10.8   Future trends

Woven-fabric composites are finding increasing use in advanced structural applications because of their inherent advantages. There have been many studies of WF composites, and their thermomechanical behaviour under monotonic/quasi-static loading is well understood. But although there have been some studies of fatigue loading, the behaviour is still not well understood.

Figures 10.9 and 10.10 present WF composite configurations stacked in an orderly way. But, in actual practice, WF composite configurations could be as shown in Fig. 10.6. This shows the random distribution of layers with respect to each other. Actual laminate configuration could influence the damage-development mechanism. Further studies are necessary for clear understanding of damage growth during fatigue loading as a function of woven fabric geometry and layer distribution. Further studies are also necessary with different weave structures and material systems for different fatigue loading conditions.

10.9   Nomenclature

a	strand width
C	strand crimp
C1, C2	laminate configurations
E	static modulus of elasticity
g	gap between the adjacent strands
h	maximum strand thickness
h_t	fabric thickness
H_L	total thickness of WF lamina
n	present number of cycles
N	applied force resultant
N_f	number of cycles to failure
u	undulated length in interlacing region
V_f	fibre volume fraction
X_c	monotonic compressive strength along warp
X_t	monotonic tensile strength along warp
σ	applied stress resultant
σ_{max}	applied peak stress during fatigue loading
θ	maximum off-axis angle of the undulated strand

10.9.1   Subscripts
f	quantities in fill direction
w	quantities in warp direction

10.9.2   Superscripts
o	overall properties
n	at number of cycles n
s	quantities of strand
'	quantities at intermediate load

10.9.3   Abbreviations
CDS	characteristic damage state
RTM	resin transfer moulding
S–N	stress/life (diagram)
UD	unidirectional (composite)
WF	woven fabric (composite)
2D, 3D	two-, three-dimensional

10.10   References

1. SURESH S (1998), *Fatigue of Materials*, Cambridge, Cambridge University Press
2. TALREJA R (1987), *Fatigue of Composite Materials*, Lancaster, Technomic Publishing Co., Inc.
3. REIFSNIDER K L (ed) (1991), *Fatigue of Composite Materials*, Amsterdam, Elsevier.
4. JANG B Z (1994), *Advanced Polymer Composites*, ASM International, Materials Park, Ohio, pp. 199–211.

5. PANTELAKIS SP and LABEAS G (2000), 'Constant and variable amplitude fatigue damage of laminated fibrous composites' in *Failure Analysis of Industrial Composite Materials*, eds, Gdoutos E E, Pilakoutas K and Rodopoulos C A, New York, McGraw Hill, pp. 247–298.
6. SHEMBEKAR P S and NAIK N K (1992), 'Elastic behavior of woven fabric composites: II – laminate analysis', *Journal of Composite Materials*, **26**(15), 2226–2246.
7. GANESH V K and NAIK N K (1994), 'Thermal expansion coefficients of plain weave fabric laminates', *Composites Science and Technology*, **51**, 387–408.
8. NAIK N K (1994), *Woven Fabric Composites*, Technomic Publishing Co., Inc., Lancaster, Pennsylvania.
9. GANESH V K and NAIK N K (1996), 'Failure behavior of plain weave fabric laminates under on-axis uniaxial tensile loading: I – laminate geometry', *Journal of Composite Materials*, **30**(16), 1748–1778.
10. NAIK N K and GANESH V K (1996), 'Failure behavior of plain weave fabric laminates under on-axis uniaxial tensile loading: II – analytical predictions', *Journal of Composite Materials*, **30**(16), 1779–1822.
11. GANESH V K and NAIK N K (1996), 'Failure behavior of plain weave fabric laminates under on-axis uniaxial tensile loading: III – effect of fabric geometry', *Journal of Composite Materials*, **30**(16), 1823–1856.
12. NAIK N K, CHANDRASEKHER Y and MEDURI S (2000), 'Polymer matrix woven fabric composites subjected to low velocity impact: part I – damage initiation studies', *Journal of Reinforced Plastics and Composites*, **19**, 912–954.
13. CURTIS P T and MOORE B B (1987), 'A comparison of the fatigue performance of woven and non-woven CFRP laminates in reversed axial loading', *International Journal of Fatigue*, **9**(2), 67–78.
14. AMIJIMA S, FUJII T and HAMAGUCHI M (1991), 'Static and fatigue tests of a woven glass fabric composite under biaxial tension–torsion loading', *Composites*, **22**(4), 281–289.
15. OZTURK A and MOORE R E (1992), 'Tensile fatigue behaviour of tightly woven carbon/carbon composites', *Composites*, **23**(1), 39–46.
16. FUJII T, AMIJIMA S and OKUBO K (1993), 'Microscopic fatigue processes in a plain-weave glass-fibre composite', *Composites Science and Technology*, **49**, 327–333.
17. MIYANO Y, MCMURRAY M K, ENYAMA J and NAKADA M (1994), 'Loading rate and temperature dependence on flexural fatigue behavior of a satin woven CFRP laminate', *Journal of Composite Materials*, **28**(13), 1250–1260.
18. TAKEMURA K and FUJII T (1994), 'Fatigue damage and fracture of carbon fabric/epoxy composites under tension-tension loading', *JSME International Journal, Series A*, **37**(4), 472–480.
19. XIAO J and BATHIAS C (1994), 'Fatigue behaviour of unnotched and notched woven glass/epoxy laminates', *Composites Science and Technology*, **50**, 141–148.
20. FUJII T and LIN F (1995), 'Fatigue behavior of a plain-woven glass fabric laminate under tension/torsion biaxial loading', *Journal of Composite Materials*, **29**(5), 573–590.
21. MITROVIC M and CARMAN G P (1996), 'Effect of fatigue damage in woven composites on thermo-mechanical properties and residual compressive strength', *Journal of Composite Materials*, **30**(2), 164–189.
22. WILLIAMS J C, YURGARTIS S W and MOOSBRUGGER J C (1996), 'Interlaminar shear fatigue damage evolution of 2-D carbon-carbon composites', *Journal of Composite Materials*, **30**(7), 785–799.
23. KAWAKAMI H and FUJII T J (1996), 'Fatigue degradation and life prediction of glass fabric polymer composite under tension/torsion biaxial loadings', *Journal of Reinforced Plastics and Composites*, **15**, 183–196.
24. KAWAI M, MORISHITA M, FUZI K, SAKURAI T and KEMMOCHI K (1996), 'Effects of matrix ductility and progressive damage on fatigue strengths of unnotched and notched carbon fibre plain woven roving fabric laminates', *Composites – Part A: Applied Science and Manufacturing*, **27A**, 493–502.
25. ABOUL WAFA M N, HAMDY A H and EL-MIDANY A A (1997), 'Combined bending and torsional fatigue of woven roving GRP', *Journal of Engineering Materials and Technology*, **119**, 180–185.
26. KHAN Z, AL-SULAIMAN F S and FAROOQI J K (1998), 'Fatigue damage characterization in plain-weave carbon–carbon fabric reinforced plastic composites', *Journal of Reinforced Plastics and Composites*, **17**(15), 1320–1337.
27. HANSEN U (1999), 'Damage development in woven fabric composites during tension-tension fatigue', *Journal of Composite Materials*, **33**(7), 614–639.
28. HUANG Z M (2002), 'Fatigue life prediction of a woven fabric composite subjected to biaxial cyclic loads', *Composites – Part A: Applied Science and Manufacturing*, **33A**, 253–266.

29. XIAO J and BATHIAS C (1994), 'Fatigue damage and fracture mechanism of notched woven laminates', *Journal of Composite Materials*, **28**(12), 1127–1139.
30. FUJII T, SHIINA T and OKUBO K (1994), 'Fatigue notch sensitivity of glass woven fabric composites having a circular hole under tension/torsion biaxial loading', *Journal of Composite Materials*, **28**(3), 234–251.
31. LIN H J and TANG C S (1994), 'Fatigue strength of woven fabric composites with drilled and moulded-in holes', *Composites Science and Technology*, **52**, 571–576.

11

Fatigue of thermoplastic composites

E. K. Gamstedt and L. A. Berglund, KTH, Sweden

11.1   Introduction

11.1.1   Mechanism-based approach

The first question to be asked is whether thermoplastic composites show different fatigue behaviour from other polymer matrix composites, i.e. cross-linked polymer composites, so that they should be treated differently in this context. Although thermoplastics have a fundamentally different molecular structure compared with thermosets, their mechanical behaviour as a composite matrix is not necessarily different. From a purely solid mechanics point of view on fatigue, the thermoplastic composites are not unique since their matrix material is merely described by a different constitutive behaviour. Toughened thermosets can have similar yield strength and toughness as thermoplastics. In generic terms of fatigue mechanisms and failure, thermoplastic and thermoset composites can, in many cases, be addressed jointly as one group of material. Empirical models for fatigue life prediction for engineering design can indiscriminately be used for thermoset and thermoplastic composites alike (e.g. Ma *et al.*[1]). However, there are fundamental differences between thermoplastic matrices and cross-linked thermoset matrices that need to be taken into consideration in the context of fatigue, e.g. the effects of processing, crystallinity, ductility, that may be more pronounced in the case of thermoplastic fatigue. This chapter will treat some of these aspects, in particular those that relate to the underlying fatigue damage mechanisms in thermoplastic composites and the relation to fatigue performance.

Fatigue is the main reason for failure of structural materials in service.[2] If the mechanisms responsible for fatigue degradation were better understood, the weak links in the material could be identified. Measures could then be taken to suppress these deleterious mechanisms by materials design, and thereby reduce the number of service failures of composite structures subject to cyclic loading. The increased use of the composite materials in rotating structures underscores the importance of fatigue in composites.[3] Many of these rotating composite structures, e.g. rotor blades, fly wheels, are made of thermoplastic composites. A better understanding of the operative fatigue mechanisms is also a necessity in the development of physical models to relate the microstructure to the macroscopic fatigue behaviour. The final goal is to be able to tailor the microstructure using quantitative mechanism-based models for optimal structural performance. Cost and manufacturing constraints should, of course, be taken into account. Another advantage with studying the damage mechanisms under fatigue is that this can be done intermittently as damage grows under relatively well-controlled conditions. In static loading, damage development and failure are usually abrupt and sudden processes. Many of the mechanisms observed in fatigue are also present during static loading, although the growth rates are different. Careful inspection of fatigue mechanisms can thus provide useful input in the understanding of static damage processes. Since new thermoplastics are continuously being developed with the intended use as matrix material, the study of damage mechanisms of new thermoplastic composites is of particular interest.

11.1.2   Fatigue-life diagrams

A useful tool to compare fatigue life performance of different materials is the 'fatigue-life diagram'.[4] Fatigue-life data for different materials can be compiled and interpreted with respect to their damage mechanisms at different strain levels. The peak initial strain is plotted with respect to the number of cycles to failure. In Wöhler or S–N curves, the stress level is plotted against the number of cycles to failure. In fatigue-life diagrams, the data points are divided into three different regimes, each pertinent to different damage mechanisms, which is illustrated in Fig. 11.1. This Figure illustrates the case of tensile fatigue of a longitudinal composite with continuous fibres, but fatigue life diagrams can be drawn to represent data for other composites and loading modes, although the mechanisms in the three regions would be different. Region I is the static scatter band, and the damage mechanism is the same as in static failure, i.e. stochastic fibre breakage and link-up of these breaks.[5] Region II is the cycle-dependent fatigue regime, i.e. the progressive region which has a downward slope in a stress-life or strain-life curve. Progressive damage mechanisms must be present in this region to result in this dependence of lifetime on loading. The mechanisms for thermoplastic composites are discussed later on in this chapter. One plausible mechanism is longitudinal debonding which gives rise to further fibre breakage until final failure. The third regime is Region III which concerns the fatigue limit. Below this level, damage will not form, or if damage forms and progresses, it will effectively be stopped by some arrest mechanism.

It should be noted that peak initial strain is used in the ordinate in the fatigue-life diagram. For in-plane loading of multidirectional laminates, all plies are subjected to the same global strain. For axial loading of a longitudinal composite, as depicted in Fig. 11.1, both the fibres and the matrix are exposed to the same global strain. However, most fatigue tests are carried out with constant applied load, i.e. the overall strain is expected to increase during the course of the fatigue test as damage develops and accumulates in the material. For this reason, the maximum strain in the first application of load is used along the ordinate. This strain value can be used as a measure of how much damage has been formed during the first load cycle, i.e. the initial damage state. Any subsequent damage development and the ultimate lifetime would depend on the initial state of damage, which can be reflected by the peak initial strain. Fatigue life diagrams can be useful in interpreting the fatigue behaviour of different materials, in particular for new thermoplastic composites where the damage mechanisms are not known.

11.1.3   Materials and outline

Thermoplastic composites are being used in a large variety of structures that are subjected

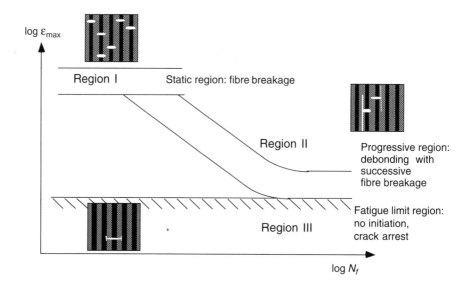

Fig. 11.1   Fatigue life diagram for a unidirectional longitudinal composite in tensile loading, where Region I refers to static failure processes dominated by fibre rupture, region II is the progressive region of joint longitudinal crack growth, e.g. debonding, and fibre breakage, and region III is at the fatigue limit under which damage cannot initiate or is effectively arrested.

to cyclic loading. In aeronautical applications, engineers are naturally concerned with design against fatigue. Candidate thermoplastic composite materials are then e.g. laminates of polyimide or poly(ether ether ketone), reinforced with long carbon fibres. For short fibre applications in larger volume, typical thermoplastic composites materials have e.g. polypropylene or polyamide matrices. These and other thermoplastic composites are examined in this chapter in terms of their fatigue properties and fatigue mechanisms.

The outline of the chapter is based on different classes of thermoplastics and their composites. In general, comparisons with thermoset composites are made if applicable in the following sections. The next section is devoted to fatigue of thermoplastics without any reinforcement. Subsequently, there is a section on fatigue of thermoplastic composites with continuous fibres. Both unidirectional composites and multidirectional laminates are treated. The following section deals with fatigue of short fibre composites, which predominantly pertains to glass-mat thermoplastics and injection-moulded composites. In the final section, a brief outlook to the future of thermoplastic composites is presented.

11.2   Thermoplastics

11.2.1   Advantages and drawbacks

There are several advantages with thermoplastics compared with thermosets, both in composite applications and in their neat form. For instance, the shelf life of thermoplastics is very long, whereas thermoset prepregs should be stored at low temperatures to avoid cross-linking. It is also possible to commingle thermoplastic fibres with the load-carrying fibres as a precursor material which has advantages in handling and manufacturing. Under heat and pressure, the thermoplastic fibres will melt, and a solid composite component will form from the commingled preform. Furthermore, health hazards can be limited by using thermoplastics instead of thermosets. Problems with volatile reactive monomers in thermoset processing are altogether avoided if thermoplastics are used. An environmental benefit is that thermoplastic materials have a higher potential for recycling, since most thermoplastics can be melted and reshaped after use. There are, of course, also a number of disadvantages compared with thermoplastics. They may have relatively high melting points, and residual stresses could become quite high when the structure is cooled to ambient temperatures. This could adversely affect the mechanical properties of the structure. Because of the ductility and high fracture toughness of many thermoplastics, a considerable amount of heat is formed and dissipated after inelastic deformation. This could make thermoplastics materials sensitive to cyclic loading, if the heat cannot be dissipated away from the thermoplastic component.

11.2.2 Mechanical and physical properties

In Table 11.1, a list of different thermoplastics frequently used as composite matrices is found. The glass-transition temperatures are listed, as well as the melting temperatures for the semicrystalline thermoplastics. The values of the mechanical and physical properties are determined at room temperature. The listed mechanical properties are Young's modulus, tensile strength and strain to failure. The thermal expansion coefficients and heat conductivity of the thermoplastic matrix materials are also specified. The typical service temperature would preferably be in the glassy state, i.e. below the glass-transition temperature. All polymers, and especially amorphous thermoplastics, lose most of their stiffness when heated above the glass transition temperature. Thermoplastics used for high-temperature composites should therefore generally have high glass-transition temperatures, e.g. carbon-fibre reinforced polyimide. These are often also more costly. Other disadvantages are brittleness and increased levels of residual thermal strains. For comparison, properties of a standard epoxy used as matrix in composites are included in the table. The fatigue properties are not listed because of lack of systematic data. Furthermore, fatigue properties cannot be directly transferred from the bulk polymer to the composite. As will be discussed in the subsequent section, semicrystalline thermoplastics may have a significantly different morphology in the presence of reinforcing fibres than in their neat form. This morphological difference affects the fatigue properties.

The mean stress field is known to influence crack growth in cyclic loading in polymers to a larger extent than for metallic and ceramic materials. This has been shown for a number of thermoplastic materials by in-situ microscopy.[6] A microscopy investigation by Saib et al.[7] shows that static damage processes set in at higher load levels in fatigue crack growth of poly(ether ether ketone) (PEEK), whereas cyclic modes are more common for lower load levels and slower crack propagation rates. In fatigue of unnotched PEEK specimens, Jones et al.[8] noticed increased ductility up to gross yielding at failure, which is indicative of creep behaviour from the average stress level. Fatigue and creep effects may not readily be separated in cyclic loading of thermoplastics. Fatigue crack propagation in thermoplastics may therefore not be amenable to conventional descriptions such as da/dN–ΔG plots, i.e. crack propagation rate vs. energy release rate range.[9] The ductility and autogenous heating by limited dissipation in some thermoplastics can make linear elastic fracture mechanics inapplicable. Crack growth curves and fatigue life data at alleged isothermal conditions should therefore be interpreted with care for certain thermoplastics and their composites.

The average molecular weight of the thermoplastics polymers is known to affect the fatigue crack propagation rate. Saib et al.[7] measured lower growth rates for high molecular

Table 11.1 Properties at room temperature of different types of thermoplastics used as composite matrices. The properties of a standard epoxy matrix system are included for comparison. The values are averages taken from a large number of sources. Since the reported strains to failure show a very large variability, the range in values is given.

Polymer, abbreviation	Glass transition temperature T_g (°C)	Melting temperature if semicrystalline T_m (°C)	Young's modulus E (GPa)	Strength σ_f (MPa)	Strain to failure ε_f (%)	Thermal expansion coefficient α (10^{-6} K^{-1})	Heat conductivity k (W m^{-1} K^{-1})
Polyethylene, PE	−60	100	1.0	20	10–1500	150	0.40
Polypropylene, PP	−10	170	2.0	35	3–900	120	0.12
Polyamide 6.6, PA 6.6	50	255	2.1	73	5–300	100	0.26
Poly(butylene terephthalate), PBT	66	227	2.3	52	5–300	100	0.22
Poly(ethylene terephthalate), PET	70	−/265[a]	2.7	55	50–350	80	0.20
Poly(ether ether ketone), PEEK	143	334	4.0	95	13–50	45	0.25
Polycarbonate, PC	150	–	2.3	64	8–135	70	0.20
Polyimide, PI (thermoplastic)	250	380	3.0	90	10–100	55	NA[b]
Polyetherimide, PEI	215	–	3.7	100	1–100	40	0.52
Standard epoxy, EP	120–180	–	3.5	50	1–5	60	0.10

[a]There are both amorphous and semi-crystalline qualities of poly(ethylene terephthalate).
[b]Not available.

weight PEEK. Lower molecular weight thermoplastics are also known to show lower resistance to static crack propagation. It was also found that the degree of crystallinity influences crack growth rates, with slightly slower propagation for higher degrees of crystallinity.

11.2.3   Transcrystallinity

When a melt of a semicrystalline polymer is cooled, spherulites form from foreign residues. If fibres are present, the crystallization may nucleate from the fibre surface, and independent spherulite-like entities can then grow from various points along the fibre surface. For a sufficiently high density of nucleating sites, the spherulitic units will impinge on one another so that growth is constrained to the radial direction normal to the fibre surface. The development of this type of crystalline sheath is termed transcrystallization, and the circumferential layer is called the transcrystalline phase. Transcrystallization generally improves the adhesion between the fibre and matrix. Chen and Hsiao[10] measured an increase of more than 40% in interfacial strength from various single fibre systems with a transcrystalline interphase versus those without. A low cooling rate over the melting point facilitates crystallization, and therefore also promotes the formation of transcrystalline interphases in composites. From interfacial shear strengths measured from single carbon fibre/PEEK composites, Nardin *et al.*[11] concluded that cooling rate and degree crystallization strongly affect the interfacial strength. Other factors that promote transcrystallization are high local temperature gradients, high premelting temperature, coating the fibres with a substance that better accommodates the lattice of the crystallizing polymer and presence of low-molecular length fractions of the polymer (see Ishida and Bussi[12]). Micrographs of transcrystalline and amorphous interphases in a semicrystalline thermoplastic are shown in Fig. 11.2. In this case, the formation of transcrystallinity at the interface was controlled by the cooling rate. The development of residual stresses in the fibres and the surrounding matrix will also depend strongly on the crystallization process, and the stress build-up will therefore differ significantly for semicrystalline and amorphous polymer systems as shown by Nielsen and Pyrz.[13] Apart from the crystalline structure itself, an influence of the secondary bonding itself is likely. At slow solidification, a larger degree of secondary bond interaction is expected to develop. It should also be noted that often extremely slow crystallization rates are required for significant formation of transcrystalline zones, which can be achieved for small samples under well-controlled laboratory conditions, but may prove to be difficult to realize in production of composite components where short cycle times are desirable.

11.2.4   Physical ageing and recrystallization

Physical ageing is generally more prevalent in thermoplastics than in thermosets. This type of ageing should be distinguished from degradation and oxidation, since the polymer configuration remains unchanged and only conformation changes take place. It is a phenomenon that manifests itself as changes in physical and mechanical properties over time. Above its glass transition temperature, the polymer can generally reach its thermodynamic equilibrium instantaneously. Below the glass transition temperature, the polymer requires a finite time to attain this equilibrium. During the time of evolution, residual internal stresses will relax, free volume decrease, and stiffness and strength typically improve, whereas fracture toughness could decrease.[14] The rate of change becomes very slow as the thermoplastic approaches its equilibrium in the glassy state for amorphous thermoplastics.

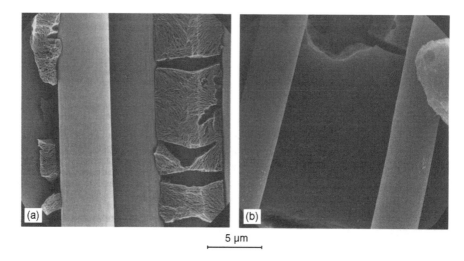

5 µm

Fig. 11.2   Scanning electron micrographs of carbon fibre/PEEK with different cooling procedures: (a) Slowly cooled and isothermally crystallized with transcrystalline zones emanating from
the fibre surface, and (b) quenched and subsequently annealed with no transcrystallinity (from
Tregub *et al.*[42] with permission).

There are indications that physical ageing close to the glass transition temperature improves
the fatigue lives of thermoplastic composites.[15] Since physical ageing makes the creep rates
decrease, which may be a positive factor in the context of fatigue performance. For static
mechanical properties, the decreased matrix toughness is a negative factor. In semicrystalline
thermoplastics, physical ageing may also take place in the rubbery state above the glass
transition temperature, since the amorphous regions are locally constrained by the presence
of crystalline regions.[16] To this end, recrystallization may also take place in the rubbery state.
Davies[17] observed a two-fold increase in Young's modulus for a polyamide thermoplastic
after annealing in the rubbery state for one week.

11.2.5   Development of matrix materials

In the 1980s when thermoplastics appeared as matrix materials in composites, they showed
significant improvements in terms of fracture toughness and damage tolerance to composites based on conventional thermosets such as epoxies, unsaturated polyesters and vinyl
esters. These promising results for the new composites with more ductile and tougher matrix
materials were then expected to apply also for fatigue conditions with a corresponding
resistance to damage formation and failure. Numerous studies have shown since then that
this is rarely the case. In most cases, it turned out that the use of a more ductile and tougher
matrix led to a worse fatigue performance. For instance, in a normalized plot of fatigue-life
data, Harris *et al.*[18] showed a steeper Region II (progressive fatigue region, cf. Fig. 11.1) for
composites with statically more ductile matrices. A more pronounced fatigue sensitivity for
thermoplastic composites compared with a corresponding thermoset composite has also
been found by Curtis[19] and by Gamstedt and Talreja.[20] The reasons for these unwanted
shortcomings in fatigue of thermoplastic composites are discussed in the following two
sections.

11.3   Continuous-fibre composites

11.3.1   Laminates and loading modes

Composite laminates are usually composed of plies with different directions, where each ply is made up of unidirectional continuous fibres held together by a polymer matrix. The lay-up of the plies depends on the anticipated loading of the structure where the laminate will be used. The fatigue behaviour of laminates is highly dependent on the lay-up of the constituent plies. An understanding of fatigue processes in the unidirectional plies is therefore necessary before generalizing to the more complex scenario of a multidirectional laminate, where damage development interacts in the different plies with various orientations. In fatigue of composite laminates, the longitudinal plies are the most important ones, since they essentially control the fatigue life in uniaxial loading of multidirectional laminates with respect to peak values of the applied strain.[21]

The predominant type of loading is constant-amplitude fatigue in tension. Fewer studies have dealt with compressive and biaxial fatigue of composite laminates, maybe because of the technical difficulty in carrying out the tests under well-controlled conditions. Results on compressive and biaxial fatigue behaviour are, however, of particular interest, because of the relatively high propensity of failure in these loading modes in applications. Nevertheless, the simpler case of uniaxial tensile fatigue will be discussed first.

11.3.2   Performance of unidirectional composites

Most investigations presented in the open literature on fatigue of thermoplastic composites with continuous fibres have been concerned with carbon fibre/PEEK. Curtis[19] has investigated the fatigue properties of carbon-fibre reinforced PEEK, and compared the findings with those of a composite material with an epoxy matrix. Unidirectional longitudinal laminates were studied under cyclic tensile loading, and the thermoplastic composite showed inferior fatigue performance with substantially shorter lifetimes for the same strain amplitude in comparison with the thermoset composite. It was observed by drilling a small hole through the laminate, that longitudinal splits grew at a higher rate in the thermoplastic composite. On the fibre microscale of unidirectional and longitudinal composites, Gamstedt and Talreja[20] noticed a higher debond growth rate from fibre breaks in the case of carbon fibre/PEEK compared with carbon fibre/epoxy. The concomitant macroscopic behaviour was shorter fatigue lives and a steeper progressive Region II in the fatigue life diagram for carbon fibre/PEEK as shown in Fig. 11.3. Corroborating results with shorter fatigue lives for carbon fibre/PEEK than for carbon fibre/epoxy in tensile loading of cross-ply laminates were found by Henaff-Gardin and Lafarie-Frenot.[22] Pannkoke and Wagner[23] tested unidirectional carbon fibre composites with epoxy, PEEK, poly(aryl ether ketone) (PAEK) and polycarbonate matrices in tensile fatigue at low temperatures, and found that the three thermoplastic composites had a lower fatigue limit than the epoxy-based composite. It is desirable to have a high fatigue limit since failure is not anticipated within any foreseeable number of load cycles below the fatigue limit. The fatigue limit is frequently used as in design against fatigue for composite structures. Furthermore, Pannkoke and Wagner[23] found that the appearance of the fracture surfaces of different material specimens failed in fatigue showed notable differences. The carbon fibre/PAEK composite showed a brush-like fracture with straggling fibre bundles, whereas the carbon fibre/epoxy composite exhibited a rather planar and brittle crack surface. This difference is a sign of a weaker interface in the thermoplastic composite, and a higher tendency of debond growth during fatigue. Schematic illustrations of brittle planar failure and debond-prone failure with protruding fibres are

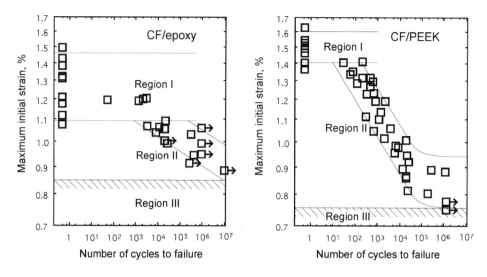

Fig. 11.3   Fatigue life diagrams for tensile loading of unidirectional longitudinal carbon fibre/epoxy and carbon fibre/PEEK (from Gamstedt and Talreja[20] with permission).

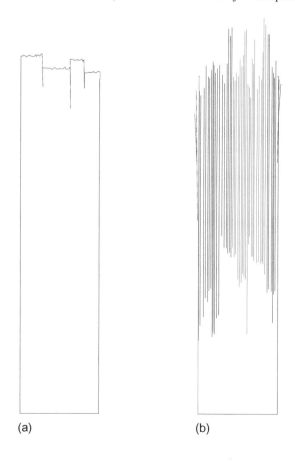

(a)   (b)

Fig. 11.4   Appearance of failed coupons; (a) brittle failure mode common for static loading and strong interfaces, and (b) 'brush' type rupture indicative of fatigue failure and weak interfaces.

shown in Fig. 11.4. During manufacture, thermosets are cured in the presence of fibres, and the reactive groups may bond directly to the fibre or its coating, leading to a strong interface. The thermoplastic, on the other hand, is already polymerized, and rarely forms spontaneous chemical bonds to the fibre. Even if the transcrystalline zone can improve the interfacial adhesion, and thereby suppress debond growth in fatigue, the interfacial strength is higher for carbon fibre/epoxy than for carbon fibre/PEEK and, as observed by Vautey and Favre[24] from fragmentation in single-fibre composite tests. It should be kept in mind that the effective interfacial strength is more complex than fibre-matrix debonding, since matrix toughness and yielding in the vicinity of the interface also enter into the picture.

11.3.3 Progressive mechanisms

Although most comparative studies show inferior fatigue performance for a composite with a more ductile and tough thermoplastic matrix than for a composite with a more brittle thermoset matrix, it should be noted that a few investigations have shown the reverse effect.[25–27] The mechanistic reason for this behaviour is not fully understood. However, since most experimental studies indicate that a tougher thermoplastic matrix mars the fatigue performance of the composite, the underlying mechanisms for this type of behaviour are analysed in the following.

The fatigue mechanisms in longitudinal composites can be described by the schematic illustration in Fig. 11.5. The brittle fibres have almost always a lower strain to failure than the thermoplastic matrix. Since the fibres have a distribution in strain to failure with a non-negligible lower tail, some of the fibres will fail at the first application of load. These fibre breaks will serve as initiation points for further damage development. Longitudinal damage grows by debonding, matrix cracking or yielding. These processes are controlled by the matrix or the fibre-matrix interface. As the longitudinal cracks grow, the local stress profiles in the adjacent fibres will continually change. An overload in a weak part of a nearby fibre may thus result in a new fibre break. Longitudinal cracking can then continue at a higher rate, and result in further fibre breakage and crack growth in a self-escalating manner until the point of final failure. The matrix and its interface to the fibres will undeniably influence the fatigue life of the composite, since they control the progressive mechanism. Experimental support of these mechanisms has been documented by Gamstedt[28] for PEEK and polypropylene based composites. A schematic illustration of the difference in fatigue damage states before failure of carbon fibre/epoxy and carbon fibre/PEEK is shown in Fig. 11.6. The material with the stronger interface and higher resistance to debonding shows few fibre breaks from which matrix cracks have grown out in the transverse direction. In the material with the weaker interface and higher susceptibility to debond propagation, the number of fibre breaks becomes higher from which profuse debonding or longitudinal splitting can continue to emanate. However, at higher load levels and shorter lifetimes, there will not be much as much debonding or longitudinal splitting, and the damage scenario of carbon fibre/PEEK will be more similar to the one of carbon fibre/epoxy in Fig. 11.6. The fatigue behaviour of thermoplastic composite with longitudinal continuous fibres is more matrix or interface dependent at lower load levels, and more fibre dependent at higher load levels, similar to the behaviour of carbon fibre/epoxy. Schadler et al.[29] tested single carbon fibre/polycarbonate microcomposites in cyclic loading under well-controlled conditions, and noticed by microscopy that early damage was dominated by the strength of the fibre, but after fibre failure, the subsequent damage growth was matrix dominated.

Tai et al.[30] detected larger scatter in lifetime for higher amplitudes in tensile fatigue of quasi-isotropic carbon fibre/PEEK laminates, i.e. closer to the static strain to failure in

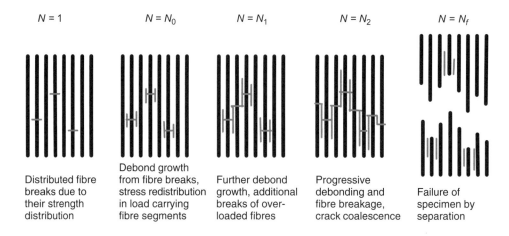

$N = 1$ $N = N_0$ $N = N_1$ $N = N_2$ $N = N_f$

Distributed fibre
breaks due to
their strength
distribution

Debond growth
from fibre breaks,
stress redistribution
in load carrying
fibre segments

Further debond
growth, additional
breaks of over-
loaded fibres

Progressive
debonding and
fibre breakage,
crack coalescence

Failure of
specimen by
separation

Fig. 11.5   Schematic illustration of fatigue damage development until final failure in longitudinal composites, where damage initiates from individual fibre breaks from which longitudinal cracks or debonds propagate.

CF/epoxy   CF/PEEK

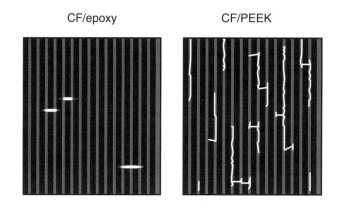

Fig. 11.6   Schematic illustration of fatigue damage states of unidirectional longitudinal carbon fibre reinforced plastics. Carbon fibre/epoxy shows few fibre breaks from which matrix cracks have propagated in the transverse direction, whereas CF/PEEK demonstrates more fibre breaks and abundant longitudinal cracking.

Region I, and proposed a difference in fracture mechanisms depending on the stress level. In view of the fatigue life diagram in Fig. 11.1, the scatter in number of cycles to failure is expected to increase as one approaches the horizontal scatter band in Region I from below. The fatigue damage development, which is controlled by the debond rates at lower amplitudes in Region II, is then becoming more dependent on the stochastic breakage of fibres at higher amplitudes, which is pertinent to Region I.

The interface plays an important role in fatigue of thermoplastic composites. Many thermoplastics are non-polar and have relatively poor adhesion to the fibres by weak van der

Waals' interactions. Inexpensive commodity plastics such as polypropylene and polyethylene are frequently used as matrix material in glass-fibre composites for large-volume applications. The poor fibre-matrix adhesion means that interfacial debonding can set it at an early stage during fatigue and propagate at a higher rate compared with composites where the interface has been modified for improved adhesion and stress transfer. One example is glass fibre reinforced polypropylene. Both static strength[31] and fatigue life[32] can be improved by a very moderate addition of maleic anhydride grafted to the polypropylene chains. It was later shown that the improvement resulted from a more efficient interface that suppressed debond growth.[33] A similar set of typical damage scenarios as those depicted in Fig. 11.6 for carbon fibre/epoxy and carbon fibre/PEEK was noticed for glass fibre composites with a maleic-anhydride modified polypropylene matrix and a pure polypropylene matrix, respectively. Any debond growth means that the local stress would be redistributed and new fibre breaks would arise in debond-prone materials. Further fibre breakage means, in turn, increased debond growth, etc., as shown in Fig. 11.5. With interfacial modifications to achieve better bonding between relatively inert thermoplastics and fibres, the unidirectional tensile fatigue properties could be improved substantially.

Huang *et al.*[34] report that matrix cracking in the transverse plies in cyclic tensile loading of cross-ply laminates is more distinct and regular for carbon fibre/thermoset bismaleimide than for the thermoplastic carbon fibre/polyimide. Even if ply cracking is more irregular and diffuse for composite laminates with a more ductile thermoplastic matrix than for generally more brittle thermosets, damage evolution by ply cracking could still be quantitatively described for various lay-ups and load amplitudes for the thermoplastic polyimide-based composite.[34] Development of fatigue damage in off-axis plies influences stiffness degradation but has limited impact on fatigue life of the laminate, which is controlled by the fatigue-life behaviour of the constitutive longitudinal plies.

11.3.4   Compressive loading

Most studies of fatigue of thermoplastic composites are concerned with tensile loading. In practice though, failure of structures often takes place in the compressively loaded regions. Compressive strength, both in fatigue and static loading, is affected by the type of specimen and the fibre alignment. Precise compressive testing is difficult since global buckling and failure close to the grip zones usually precedes compressive material failure.[35] Alignment of the fibres in the composite has a large influence on the compressive strength. Thermoplastic composites generally have more undulating fibres, since the matrix cannot be transferred as a low-viscous liquid into the fibre arrangement. This is especially the case for commingled fibre and thermoplastic fibre systems.[36] Onset of fibre buckling in compression would therefore occur more readily for the less straight fibres in thermoplastic systems. Higher amplitude of fibre waviness, lower matrix shear modulus and larger fibre–matrix debonds lead to premature buckling. Fleck[37] has compiled a review on the mechanics of compressive failure of composites. Once fibres have buckled, neighbouring fibres will buckle in a successive manner to form kink bands. Buckled fibres can serve as initiation sites for fatigue damage growth, and kink bands can grow during cyclic loading.[38] A micrograph of a fatigue crack in a carbon fibre reinforced plastic is shown in Fig. 11.7. The matrix was a thermosetting epoxy, but a similar type of cracking mechanism is expected for thermoplastic composites. Tai *et al.*[30] found a wrinkled pattern on broken buckled fibres in compressive fatigue of carbon fibre/PEEK. The fracture surfaces of the broken fibres led to distinct regions: a tensile side and a compression side, which indicates buckle failure in local bending of the fibres. Compressive fatigue strength in longitudinal composite laminates is

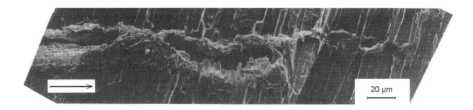

Fig. 11.7   Micrograph of a fatigue crack in a unidirectional 0° carbon-fibre reinforced plastic after 6000 cycles in compression (from Pruitt and Suresh[38] with permission).

controlled by the stiffness and yield properties of the matrix that surround and support the fibres from micro-buckling.[39] In addition to more pronounced fibre waviness in thermoplastic composites, matrix properties can also contribute to the inferior compressive fatigue properties of many thermoplastic composites. In view of the lower stiffness and yield stresses of many thermoplastics compared to densely cross-linked thermosets, the strength in compression is generally lower for thermoplastic composites than for thermoset composites. This is in concert with the results of Moore,[26] who found a significantly inferior compressive fatigue-life behaviour for a unidirectional longitudinal carbon fibre reinforced PEEK tested at an elevated temperature at 120 °C compared with the same material tested at room temperature. At 120 °C the PEEK matrix is relatively close to its glass transition temperature and is more compliant than at room temperature, which can evoke an earlier inception of fibre buckling. Fractographic analyses by Dillon and Buggy[40] also indicate that compressive fatigue is more deleterious for thermoplastic composites. In flexural fatigue with initially equal compressive and tensile loading on each side of the neutral layer, failure in carbon fibre/PEEK was associated with gradual growth of compression cracks, whereas the progressive mechanisms in carbon fibre/epoxy were predominantly on the tensile side of the specimens.

11.3.5   Effects of crystallinity

As mentioned above, the cooling rate influences the formation of transcrystalline zones close to the fibres as well as the overall degree of crystallinity of the composite. This impinges on the static strength and stiffness properties in e.g. carbon fibre/PEEK.[41] Also the fatigue performance of carbon fibre/PEEK depends on the degree and type of crystallinity.[42] In three-point bending fatigue of carbon fibre/PEEK cross-ply laminates, Tregub *et al.*[43] found that, for equal degrees of crystallinity, the fatigue life performance was influenced by matrix morphology, i.e. the type of crystallinity in the matrix. Even if the fatigue properties are dominated by the fibres in the longitudinal layer, there was an effect of matrix morphology. A flatter fatigue-life curve was observed for slowly cooled specimens that were allowed to crystallize isothermally than for specimens that had been quenched and then annealed in the rubbery state to the same degree of crystallinity. It was also confirmed that transcrystalline zones were more widespread in the slowly cooled and isothermally crystallized materials. Slow solidification and the associated transcrystallinity are apparently beneficial, possibly through improved interfacial adhesion.

Folkes *et al.*[44] measured hysteresis loss during cyclic loading with a dynamic mechanical thermal analyser, and found that the loss angle was higher for carbon fibre/PEEK specimens that had been quenched than those that were cooled slowly. The larger hysteresis loss for the rapidly cooled composite with lower crystallinity content would mean that this material is more likely to experience adiabatic heating if the mechanical dissipation cannot be led away. Heating and damage accumulation are known to be mutually accelerating phenomena in cyclic loading until final failure. Folkes et al.[44] also observed a weaker interface with clean protruding fibres from pull-out on the tensile fracture surface for rapidly cooled composite, whereas the slowly cooled composite had a more even and planar fracture surface with fibres covered with more polymer residue, which is characteristic of a more efficient interfacial bond.

Curtis et al.[45] noticed shorter fatigue lives in compressive loading for rapidly cooled unidirectional longitudinal carbon fibre/PEEK laminates than for those that had been cooled slowly from the processing temperature. The lower cooling rate would provide longer time for transcrystalline zones to form around the fibres. These zones have higher shear yield strength and are stiffer than amorphous PEEK formed at faster cooling rates, and could therefore restrain the fibre-buckling discussed above. In tensile fatigue loading of carbon fibre/PEEK angle-ply laminates, there was no noticeable improvement in fatigue performance with slow cooling from the processing temperature.

Bureau et al.[46] point out that the existence of a transcrystalline zone around the fibres is necessary to promote resistance to fatigue crack propagation. If the transition from the transcrystalline phases to an amorphous phase or other crystalline phases is distinct, fatigue cracks are likely to propagate along those interfaces. They found higher propagation rates in mode II cracking in end-notch flexure testing of unidirectional glass-fibre reinforced polypropylene for samples with a well-defined transition between morphological phases in comparison with composites with a smoother transition between transcrystalline and amorphous phases. This behaviour is shown in the micrographs in Fig. 11.8.

11.3.6   Effects of matrix ductility

Hojo et al.[47] have investigated the transferability of matrix toughness and fatigue resistance to delamination toughness and fatigue growth in composites. A thermoplastic composite based on carbon-fibre reinforced PEEK was compared with thermoset composites based on carbon-fibre reinforced epoxies. Under static conditions, the critical energy release rate from mode I double-cantilever beam testing was significantly higher for the thermoplastic composite. The crack propagation rate was quantified for various applied stress intensity factor ranges. The order of crack growth resistance was roughly maintained in fatigue conditions, but the improvements in fatigue thresholds in terms of the stress intensity factor range for the onset of crack propagation ΔK_{th} was far from the measured improvements in fracture toughness under static conditions. In Fig. 11.9, the static fracture toughness is plotted together with an equivalent threshold of the stress intensity factor range for a number of carbon fibre/epoxy composites and carbon fibre/PEEK. This highlights that crack resistances obtained under static conditions for thermoplastic composites cannot directly be transferred to fatigue conditions and low load amplitudes. Furthermore, an increase in static fracture toughness in the neat matrix material results in a considerably diminished increase in delamination fracture toughness in a composite since the presence of constraining fibres inhibits the formation of plastic zones, which are confined to the interfibrillar bays.[48] As pointed out by Asp et al.,[49] composite matrices operate under severe three-dimensionally constrained conditions, where ductility observed in uniaxial loading is often of little relevance.

A fractographic study of the fatigue failures by interlaminar cracking in carbon fibre/ PEEK and carbon fibre/epoxy has been presented by Hiley.[50] It was found that matrix rollers formed in mode II in the wake of the fatigue crack in carbon fibre/PEEK, as shown in

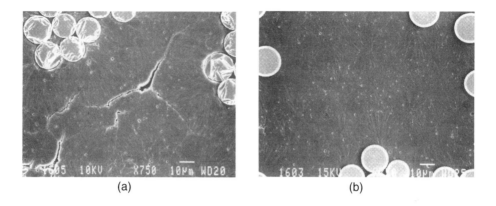

(a)   (b)

Fig. 11.8   Micrographs of glass-fibre reinforced polypropylene: (a) Distinct interfaces between transcrystalline and amorphous zones resulted in rapid fatigue crack propagation, whereas (b) composites with a smoother phase transition gave rise to a higher resistance to fatigue crack propagation (from Bureau et al.[46] with permission).

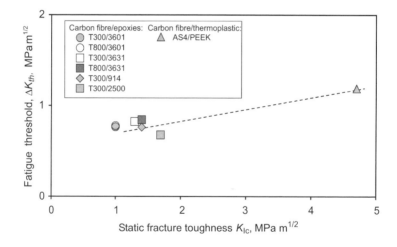

Fig. 11.9   Relation between effective thresholds for crack propagation ΔK_{th} and static fracture toughness of carbon-fibre reinforced plastic laminates. Data from Hojo et al.[47]

Fig. 11.10. The matrix rollers were not unique to the thermoplastic composite, but were also found in a number of epoxy-based composites. They have also been found between delaminated layers by attrition of crack surface asperities during in-plane axial cyclic loading.[51] Even though matrix rollers were found to form in both thermoplastic and thermoset composites, Hiley[50] found that they were considerably longer and formed by smearing and progressive drawing in the PEEK composite. In a number of epoxy composites, the matrix rollers were formed by wear of uneven matrix cracks, typically coalesced shear cusps. Apparently ductile fractographic features were more widespread in the PEEK

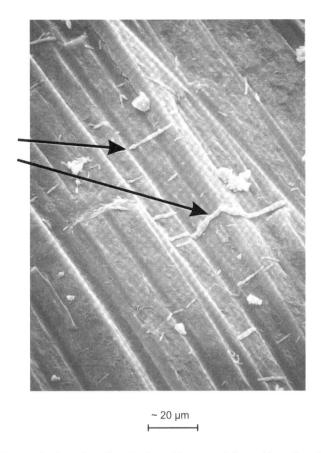

~ 20 µm

Fig. 11.10   Micrograph of matrix rollers (indicated by arrows) formed in carbon fibre/PEEK by wear delaminated fracture surfaces in mode II fatigue (from Hiley[50] with permission).

composite than in the epoxy composites. However, they were more prevalent in static loading than in fatigue, which is another indication of incomplete transfer of ductile toughening mechanisms from static to fatigue conditions. These findings highlight the usefulness of fractographic investigations in mapping the fatigue damage mechanisms, but care should be taken in the analysis of fractographic features, since some of them can stem from the final instable rupture when a considerable amount of elastic energy is released instantaneously. In this case fractography can be complemented by in-situ damage characterization during fatigue, although such methods are usually confined to the surface of the specimen.

In static loading, dissipative inelastic deformation of the polymer matrix contributes to the fracture toughness.[48] The energy is partly dissipated in the formation of damage, but a sizeable part is dissipated as heat, either through conduction, convection or radiation. In fatigue loading of polymer–composite test coupons at intermediate stress levels, it has been estimated that the different means of dissipation are in the same order of magnitude,[52] and neither one of them can generally be neglected in relation to another. For larger specimens or components and higher load frequencies, the load dissipated by heat cannot be led away at the same rate as it is being produced, and as a consequence, heat generation and damage accumulation will increase in an accelerating manner until failure. This effect has been observed in a composite with a thermoplastic poly(butylene terephthalate) matrix.[53] Heat generation and the ensuing temperature rise soften the matrix, which leads to higher local deformation and damage formation. Matrix materials that are ductile and tough under static conditions are therefore likely to show a higher fatigue sensitivity because of heating and increased crack growth or damage formation. High fracture toughness of thermoplastic composites cannot be expected automatically to lead to high fracture resistance under cyclic loading and improved fatigue life. Heat generation and damage formation can be regarded as coupled phenomena, which in severe cases can make fatigue characterization dependent on the specimen geometry and surrounding cooling conditions.

11.3.7   Frequency effects

Another aspect that is closely related to dissipation and heat generation in cyclic loading of thermoplastic composites is the dependency on strain rates or load frequencies. This is of interest in the development of accelerated test methods for characterization of long-term fatigue behaviour. Moore[26] measured a noticeable difference in fatigue lives for a quasi-isotropic carbon fibre/PEEK laminate loaded in cyclic tension at frequencies of 0.5 and 5 Hz. As expected, the composite subjected to the higher load frequency showed shorter lifetimes for equal applied stresses. At higher frequencies, the test coupon heats up and the matrix eventually becomes more compliant and yields at lower stresses. Locally in regions of high stress concentration, the temperature might even exceed the glass transition temperature. For high frequencies it might be necessary to choose a polymer with a higher glass transition temperature for this reason. Fortunately, carbon fibres have a relatively high heat conductivity (up to 100 $Wm^{-1} K^{-1}$ for high modulus fibres in the axial direction), and heat can therefore be dissipated at a sufficiently high rate in the fibre direction. For glass fibres, which have a lower heat conductivity ($\sim$ 10 $Wm^{-1} K^{-1}$), autogeneous heating can be a serious problem at higher frequencies. This is particularly the case when the matrix carries a relatively large share of the applied load. Moore[26] found that the fatigue life reduction for increased load frequencies was more pronounced for $[\pm 45]_{4S}$ angle-ply laminates than for the quasi-isotropic $[-45/0/+45/90]_{2S}$ lay-up. If longitudinal $0°$ plies are present in multidirectional laminates, these plies tend to control the fatigue life of the entire laminate.[21] Lay-up configurations that cause high shear stresses of the constituent plies are generally more frequency sensitive in cyclic loading. This is the situation for $[\pm 45]$ angle-ply laminates where heating arises from large cyclic shear stresses in the matrix material.

The mechanical dissipation can be characterized by the specific damping capacity Ψ along the longitudinal, transverse and shear directions and modelled by generalizing elastic laminate theory to a linear viscoelasticity in cyclic loading.[54] The specific damping capacity is defined as the ratio of the stress–strain hysteresis loss to the stored elastic energy density, and can serve as a measure of the relative hysteresis loss in cyclic loading. Lee *et al.*[55] measured the axial tensile value of Ψ for unidirectional $[0]_{8T}$, cross-ply $[0_2/90_2]_S$, quasi-isotropic $[0/\pm 45/90]_S$ and angle-ply $[45_2/-45_2]_S$ laminates of carbon fibre/PEEK, and the highest relative hysteresis loss came from the angle-ply laminate where the matrix undergoes notable shear loading. For unidirectional laminates, the specific damping coefficient was largest for shear loading Ψ_{LT}, closely followed by transverse loading Ψ_T, whereas the damping in the longitudinal fibre direction Ψ_L was considerably smaller. For thermoplastic composite laminates which show large hysteresis losses and subsequent heating, it might thus be helpful to add longitudinal $0°$ plies to the laminate to mitigate unwanted heating effects.

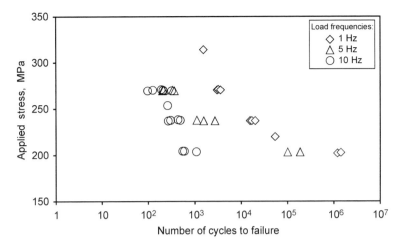

Fig. 11.11   Stress-life data for $[\pm45]_{4S}$ carbon fibre reinforced PEEK in tensile fatigue at various frequencies. (Data from Xiao and Al-Hmouz[56].)

The influence of loading frequency in tensile fatigue of angle-ply carbon fibre/PEEK laminates on hysteretic loss, temperature rise and fatigue life has been investigated by Xiao and Al-Hmouz.[56] The $[\pm45]_{4S}$ specimens were loaded at 1, 5 and 10 Hz at various stress levels. There was a considerable reduction in number of cycles to failure for higher frequencies (see Fig. 11.11), although there was no particular correlation between the frequency and the mechanical loss, defined as the hysteresis of the stress–strain loop for each cycle. However, the heat from the hysteresis loss did not have sufficient time to dissipate at higher frequencies, which resulted in a more rapid increase in temperature. Enhanced autogeneous heating in fatigue at higher frequencies led to softening of the material and premature failure. Heating and damage development are mutually influencing phenomena, and predictive fatigue models for property degradation and lifetime need to address this coupling. This is of particular importance for composites with ductile thermoplastic matrices where temperature rise is prevalent on cyclic loading. Dickson et al.[57] found that the slope of the S–N curve is steeper angle-ply laminates in tensile loading of carbon fibre/PEEK than for carbon fibre/epoxy, which could be explained by more pronounced heating for the PEEK-based composite.

In this section, various aspects specifically for fatigue loading of thermoplastic composites with continuous fibres have been discussed. They include the effects of crystalline morphology, heating, loading frequency and tendency of splitting or debonding. These features also play an important role in fatigue loading of short-fibre thermoplastic composites, although the damage mechanisms are different because of differences in the fibrous microstructure.

11.4   Short-fibre composites

11.4.1   Materials and manufacturing principles

For large volume applications, where material cost and manufacturing cycle time are of more importance than superior mechanical properties, short-fibre thermoplastic composites can provide a useful solution in materials selection. A widely used short-fibre reinforced thermoplastic material is glass-mat thermoplastics (GMT), which typically consists of discontinuous glass fibres with an almost random uniform orientation distribution in a thermoplastic matrix, typically polypropylene. Swirled mats with longer fibres or fibre bundles may also be used as reinforcement in GMT materials. The fibre content is normally between 10 and 40% by volume, which means that the thermoplastic matrix carries a considerable part of the load. GMT materials generally come as preconsolidated sheets, that are fibre mats lightly bonded with thermoplastic granulate. These sheets are heated to a temperature where the thermoplastic softens and are then pressed in a cold mould, whereby the composite consolidates. Complicated geometries may be shaped in a single stroke since the fibre mat deforms and the heated viscous thermoplastic matrix fills the mould during the pressing step. Process cycle times down to below one minute are possible, which makes GMT suitable for large volume applications. The concession for ease of manufacture is inferior mechanical properties compared with continuous-fibre composites.

Injection moulded polyamide-based composites are another example of thermoplastic short-fibre composites. A suspension of short fibres and viscous thermoplastic polymer is injected into a mould. Fibres usually break due to the high stresses as the melt is injected through the orifice at the mould inlet. This shortening of fibres can impair the load-carrying capability of the component.[58] As the fibres flow together with the thermoplastic melt, the fibres will orient themselves along the flow front during filling. A large variability in fibre orientation results, especially close to surfaces, holes, stringers and other protruding structural features of the component. The dimensional stability and structural response to loading are therefore difficult to predict. This is obviously also the case for the fatigue behaviour, since crack propagation will be very dependent on the local fibre orientation at the crack front.

Use of short-fibre composites can be found in automotive applications, such as seat frames, battery trays, rear doors, bumpers, interior panels and various other body components. These components have relatively limited load-carrying functions. Investigations on these materials are therefore more focused on processing aspects than the mechanical properties, in particular the fatigue properties. However, some studies on fatigue behaviour of short-fibre thermoplastic composites can be found in the literature even though they are scarcer than those on fatigue of long-fibre thermoplastic composites. Since short-fibre composite components often have a complex shape with, e.g., holes, rivets and inserts, fatigue cracks generally start from stress concentrations. Fatigue-life data of uniform test coupons are therefore of limited use, and most studies are therefore concerned with fatigue crack propagation, typically measured on compact-tension specimens.

The aspects discussed in the previous section on continuous-fibre thermoplastic composites, such as transcrystallinity, autogenous heating and frequency effects, also apply for short-fibre thermoplastic composites, although effects of the heterogeneous fibrous microstructure can overshadow these aspects in short-fibre composites. The polymer matrix is generally subject to relatively higher stress in short-fibre composites than in composite laminates with continuous fibres. Creep damage and deformation are therefore likely in cyclic loading in addition to damage accumulation due to fatigue loading. Furthermore, the variability in fibre orientation and fibre lengths also affects the fatigue behaviour. These aspects are discussed in the following.

11.4.2   Creep-fatigue interaction

Creep and fatigue effects cannot easily be separated for short-fibre composites. The volume fraction of fibres is considerably smaller for short-fibre composites than for laminated composites with long fibres, and oriented short-fibre composites are difficult to manufacture. This means that the matrix in the short-fibre composites experiences higher stresses than it would in a corresponding laminated composite with long fibres, where a number of plies are usually oriented in the principal stress direction. In cyclic loading with a non-zero average applied stress, creep normally takes place since the matrix undergoes time-dependent deformation in addition to cycle-dependent irreversible deformation. Jones et al.[8] compared the time to failure in creep and fatigue loading, and found that the stress-life curves were similar although the time to failure was considerably longer for creep than for cyclic loading for injection-moulded short carbon-fibre reinforced PEEK. The time-dependent behaviour with polymer creep seems more extensive at higher load levels, whereas cycle-dependent crack growth prevails at lower load amplitudes. Zhou et al.[59] investigated fatigue damage mechanisms in a poly(phenylene ether ketone)-poly(phenylene sulphide) blend reinforced by short glass fibres and found marked matrix yielding at higher stress amplitudes and crack growth at lower stress amplitudes. Corroborating results were obtained by Pegoretti and Ricco[60] in tensile fatigue loading of single-edge notch tension specimens of short glass-fibre reinforced polypropylene, which showed that crack propagation in cyclic loading could be attributed to creep at higher load levels, and to cycle-dependent fatigue propagation at lower load levels. The low-cycle fatigue properties of the polymer matrix are therefore of importance for composite structures subjected to high cyclic stresses.

11.4.3   Effects of fibrous microstructure

As mentioned previously, the fibre orientation distribution will vary in different parts of injection-moulded short-fibre composite components since the fibres orient themselves according to the flow during mould injection. The crack propagation rate strongly depends on the local fibre orientation. Friedrich et al.[61] observed significantly lower propagation rates of fatigue cracks in a short carbon fibre/PEEK composite with fibres predominantly oriented in the load direction perpendicular to the crack plane. The same phenomenon has been observed by Voss and Karger-Kocsis[58] for short glass fibre/poly(butylene terephthalate) composites, and by Pegoretti and Ricco[60] for short glass fibre/polypropylene composites. Crack deflection and even crack arrest was noticed for composites with a high degree of longitudinal fibre orientation. Energy absorption from the fibre pull-out mechanism and the work of fracture of a fibrous composite are expected to be maximized with fibres oriented parallel to the load.[62] With the fibres principally oriented in a transverse direction perpendicular to the load direction, the crack propagation rates were much higher overall.

Another complicating aspect in the analysis of fatigue in short-fibre composites is crack growth irregularity due to the heterogeneous microstructure. If the microstructural features, such as fibre bundles, are in the same scale as the crack growth increments, the propagation typically proceeds in a seemingly erratic accelerating–decelerating manner that refuses to be described by a power-law relationship, such as the Paris law. Hoffman and Wang[63] observed stochastic crack growth and retardation due to the heterogeneous microstructure through mechanisms such as crack bowing and deflection at fibre bundles, debonding, and arrest in chopped glass-mat in a hybrid polyester matrix of thermoplastic poly(ethylene terephthalate) with thermosetting unsaturated polyester and polyurethane. The same non-progressive phenomenon was observed by Gadkaree and Salee[64] in a thermoplastic bisphenol A terephthalate/isophthalate copolyester with high content of spherical fillers. For lower particle contents, it was possible to describe the crack growth rate with the stress intensity factor range, which indicates that if there is a size scale of fibre bundles or particle agglomerations beyond which the crack growth refuses to be described by a specific growth law. Since growth-rate measurements would differ from one test specimen to another because of the variability of the microstructure, such data do not lend themselves to property characterization. A study of damage micromechanisms and micromechanical modelling would instead be the natural way to address this phenomenon.[21]

Karger-Kocsis and Friedrich[65] investigated the influence of fibre length in short-fibre reinforced polyamide 6.6, and found the following rank of decreasing growth rates (da/dN) for a given stress-intensity factor range ΔK: fast growth rate for the matrix material, moderate growth rate for composites reinforced with short chopped glass fibres, and slow growth rate for composites with longer glass fibres. It was found that the composite with longer fibres showed a larger damage zone in front of the crack tip in the compact-tension specimen and the deformation of the matrix was more constrained compared with the shorter-fibre composites and the unreinforced matrix material. The restricted deformation of the matrix suppressed hysteretic heating found in the neat matrix material and materials with composites with shorter fibres and lower fibre contents. Harmia[66] detected a modest increase in temperature by thermography in the close vicinity of the crack tip during fatigue loading of thermoplastic blends with and without reinforcement by discontinuous glass fibres.

Evans et al.[67] studied the fatigue crack growth in short carbon fibre reinforced PEEK, and found a decrease in crack propagation rates for increasing fibre contents. The improved crack growth resistance at higher fibre contents can be attributed not only to primary toughening mechanisms such as fibre bridging and pull-out, but also to crack front bowing and deflection in the presence of fibres.

Friedrich and Karsch[68] investigated fatigue crack growth in glass sphere-filled polyamide 6, and observed that the cracks preferably grew along the interface between the reinforcement and the matrix. An improvement of the interfacial efficiency in particulate composites showing adhesive failure would therefore reduce the crack propagation rate. In fibrous composites, fibre pull-out is a key mechanism in crack propagation. There is an optimum in pull-out energy depending on the fibre length and interfacial adhesion.[62] Nevertheless, interfacial adhesion has an influence on fatigue crack growth resistance in short-fibre composites. Harmia[66] noticed an improvement in resistance to fatigue crack propagation in a short-fibre composite by maleic-anhydride modification of the polypropylene matrix for improved interfacial adhesion. The load frequency effect and accompanying heating is significant for short-fibre thermoplastic composites, since the matrix carries a large part of the applied stress.

11.5   Future of thermoplastic composites

11.5.1   Advanced load-carrying materials

New structural design of load-carrying components requires composite materials that show a higher strain to failure while retaining high strength. This driving force started in the 1980s and is still ongoing. The use of fibres with higher strain to failure also requires a polymer matrix that can sustain higher strains.[25] In that case, brittle thermosets are not adequate, and more ductile thermoplastic matrices are of interest. This has favoured thermoplastics but also toughening of thermoset composites by addition of thermoplastics or rubbers. Addition of thermoplastic interlaminar layers onto thermoset prepregs is another toughening approach, which is known to affect onset of fatigue damage accumulation.[69] Further development of new hybrid thermoset–thermoplastic composites will probably continue.

The processing advantages when using thermoplastic matrices are still not utilized to their full potential. Reduced health hazards, increased shelf life as well as shorter manufacture cycle times are some of these benefits. Preforms of commingled thermoplastic fibres and load-carrying fibres can rapidly be consolidated in to many kinds of composite components. The challenges lie first in the optimization of material structure and processing techniques. Structures manufactured from commingled fibre/thermoplastics can be used in both large volume applications and high-end applications for primary load bearing, where the fatigue performance is of special concern in the latter case.

Supersonic aeroplanes require load-carrying materials with high specific strength and stiffness at higher temperatures than materials in structures used in present-day aeroplanes. High-temperature thermoplastics are being considered for this purpose, but since relatively little is known about long-term durability of these materials, there is a need for development of accelerated testing methodologies to acquire a materials database, primarily focused on fatigue behaviour.[70] Ongoing and future (possibly re-enacted) large-scale projects on research and development for high-speed civil transport will provide a driving force to fulfil this need.

11.5.2 Recyclable materials

Environmental concerns have given rise to awareness of recyclability of composite materials. Since thermoplastics can be remelted, they provide a better alternative than thermosets as a matrix material in terms of recycling. For instance, glass fibre reinforcement may still cause environmental problems in mechanical recycling (difficulties to separate fibres from matrix, and to process regranulates) and thermal recycling (high ash content after incineration). A more attractive alternative would be a thermoplastic composite where the fibres and matrix are made of the same polymer. After service life the composite could be reused in its entirety. Melt-spun isotactic polypropylene fibres in a polypropylene matrix of the same grade is an example of such a material.[71] Interfacial adhesion can be improved if the fibres and matrix are made from chemically similar materials. Efforts to develop such materials combinations will be a growing activity in the future.

Thermoplastic composite materials based on biodegradable and renewable resources will most probably see a growing market. One example is biodegradable polylactides reinforced with natural cellulosic fibres for high-volume applications such as food packaging.[72] Fatigue performance is of little importance in this case, although it should not be altogether ignored. Apart from manufacturing costs, barrier properties and dimensional hygrostability are the most important issues. These properties will, however, be affected by damage induced by cyclic loading, which could be thermal, hygroscopic or mechanical.

On the whole, the future of thermoplastic composites seems bright. There are high potentials in these materials that are yet to be fulfilled. One of the main advantages of polymer composite laminates to light-weight metals and alloys, e.g. aluminium-based materials, is the fatigue resistance of the composite. For load-carrying applications, fatigue is and will be of great importance.

11.6   References

1. MA C C M, LIN S H, TAI N H, WU S H and WU J F, 'Fatigue behavior of quasi-isotropic carbon fiber/ PEEK laminates under tension-tension loading', *Polym. Compos.*, **16**(3), 215–223.
2. DAUSKARDT R H, RITCHIE R O and COX B N (1993), 'Fatigue of advanced materials: Part 1', *Adv. Mater. Process.*, **144**(1), 26–31.

3. GAMSTEDT E K and ANDERSEN S I (2001), *Fatigue Degradation and Failure of Rotating Composite Structures – Materials Characterisation and Underlying Mechanisms*, Report Risø-R-1261(EN), Roskilde, Risø National Laboratory.

4. TALREJA R (1981), 'Fatigue of composite materials: damage mechanisms and fatigue life diagrams', *Proc. Roy. Soc. Lond. A Mat.*, **378**(1775), 461–475.

5. PHOENIX S L and BEYERLEIN I J (2000), 'Statistical strength theory for fibrous composite materials' in Kelly A and Zweben C, *Comprehensive Composite Materials*, **1**, Amsterdam, Elsevier, 559–639.

6. PRUITT L and SURESH S (1993), 'Cyclic stress for fatigue cracks in amorphous solids. Experimental measurements and their implications', *Philos. Mag. A*, **67**(5), 1219–1245.

7. SAIB K S, EVANS W J and ISAAC D H (1993), 'The role of microstructure during fatigue crack growth in poly(aryl ether ether ketone)', *Polymer*, **34**(15), 3198–3203.

8. JONES D P, LEACH D C and MOORE D R (1985), 'Mechanical properties of poly(ether ether ketone) for engineering applications', *Polymer*, **26**, 1385–1393.

9. BRILLHART M and BOTSIS J (1993), 'Fatigue fracture behavior of PEEK', *J. Reinf. Plast. Compos.*, **12**(9), 943–950.

10. CHEN E J H and HSIAO B S (1992), 'The effects of transcrystalline interphase in advanced polymer composites', *Polym. Eng. Sci.*, **32**(4), 280–286.

11. NARDIN M, ASLOUN E M and SCHULTZ J (1991), 'Study of the carbon fiber poly(ether ether ketone) (PEEK) relationship between interfacial strength and adhesion', *Polym. Advan. Technol.*, **2**(3), 115–122.

12. ISHIDA H and BUSSI P (1993), 'Morphology control in polymer composites' in Chou T W *Structure and Properties of Composites*, **13**, Weinheim, VCH, 339–379.

13. NIELSEN A S and PYRZ R (1997), 'In-situ observation of thermal residual strains in carbon/thermoplastic microcomposites using Raman spectroscopy', *Polym. Polym. Compos.*, **5**(4), 245–257.

14. STRUIK L C E (1978), *Physical Aging in Amorphous Polymers and Other Materials*, Amsterdam, Elsevier.

15. D'AMORE A, CAPRINO G, NICOLAIS L and MARINO G (1999), 'Long-term behaviour of PEI and PEI-based composites subjected to physical aging', *Compos. Sci. Technol.*, **59**(13), 1993–2003.

16. STRUIK L C E (1989), 'Mechanical behaviour and physical aging of semi-crystalline polymers 4', *Polymer*, **30**(5), 815–830.

17. DAVIES C R (1996), 'Crystallization behavior and mechanical properties of a nylon-6, -6/6 and – 12 terpolyamide', *J. Appl. Polym. Sci.*, **62**(13), 2237–2245.

18. HARRIS B, REITER H, ADAM T, DICKSON R F and FERNANDO G (1990), 'Fatigue behaviour of carbon fibre reinforced plastics', *Composites*, **21**(3), 232–242.

19. CURTIS P T (1991), 'Tensile fatigue mechanisms in unidirectional polymer matrix composite materials', *Int. J. Fatigue*, **13**(5), 377–382.

20. GAMSTEDT E K and TALREJA R (1999), 'Fatigue damage mechanisms in unidirectional carbon-fibre-reinforced plastics', *J. Mater. Sci.*, **34**(11), 2535–2549.

21. TALREJA R (1993), 'Fatigue of fiber composites' in Chou T W, *Structure and Properties of Composites*, **13**, Weinheim, VCH, 583–607.

22. HENAFF-GARDIN C and LAFARIE-FRENOT M C (1992), 'Fatigue behaviour of thermoset and thermoplastic cross-ply laminates', *Composites*, **23**(2), 109–116.

23. PANNKOKE K and WAGNER H-J (1991), 'Fatigue properties of unidirectional carbon fibre composites at cryogenic temperatures', *Cryogenics*, **31**(4), 248–251.

24. VAUTEY P and FAVRE J-P (1990), 'Fibre/matrix load transfer in thermoset and thermoplastic composites – Single fibre models and hole sensitivity of laminates', *Compos. Sci. Technol.*, **28**(3), 271–288.

25. BARON C, SCHULTE K and HARIG H (1987), 'Influence of fibre and matrix failure strain on static and fatigue properties of carbon fibre-reinforced plastics', *Compos. Sci. Technol.*, **29**(4), 257–272.

26. MOORE D R (1993), 'Long-term mechanical properties of aromatic thermoplastic continuous fibre composites: Creep and fatigue' in Kausch H-H, *Advanced Thermoplastic Composites: Characterization and Processing*, Munich, Carl Hanser Verlag, 194–225.

27. KAWAI M, MORISHITA M, FUZI K, SAKURAI T and KEMMOCHI K (1996), 'Effects of matrix ductility and progressive damage on fatigue strengths of unnotched and notched carbon fibre plain woven roving fabric laminates', *Compos. Part A*, **27**(6), 493–502.

28. GAMSTEDT E K (2000), 'Fatigue in composite laminates – A qualitative link from micromechanisms to fatigue life performance' in Cardon A H, Fukuda H, Reifsnider K L and Verchery G, *Recent Developments in Durability Analysis of Composite Systems*, Rotterdam, A A Balkema, 87–100.

29. SCHADLER L S, LAIRD C and FIGUEROA J C (1992), 'Interphase behaviour in graphite-thermoplastic monofilament composites Part II Cyclic behaviour', *J. Mater. Sci.*, **27**(15), 4035–4044.
30. TAI N H, MA C C M and WU S H (1995), 'Fatigue behaviour of carbon fibre/PEEK laminate composites', *Composites*, **26**(8), 551–559.
31. RIJSDIJK H A, CONTANT M and PEIJS A A J M (1993), 'Continuous-glass-fibre-reinforced polypropylene composites: I. Influence of maleic-anhydride-modified polypropylene on mechanical properties', *Compos. Sci. Technol.*, **48**(1–4), 161–172.
32. VAN DEN OEVER M and PEIJS T (1998), 'Continuous-glass-fibre-reinforced polypropylene composites: II. Influence of maleic-anhydride modified polypropylene on fatigue behaviour', *Compos. Part A*, **29**(3), 227–239.
33. GAMSTEDT E K, BERGLUND L A and PEIJS T (1999), 'Fatigue mechanisms in unidirectional glass-fibre-reinforced polypropylene', *Compos. Sci. Technol.*, **59**(5), 759–768.
34. HUANG X, GILLESPIE JR J W, EDULJEE R F and SHEN Z (2000), 'Matrix cracking behavior of K3B/IM7 composite laminates subject to static and fatigue loading', *Compos. Struct.*, **49**(4), 435–441.
35. HSIAO H M, DANIEL I M and WOOH S C (1995), 'A new compression test method for thick composites', *J. Compos. Mater.*, **29**(13), 1789–1806.
36. DIAO X, YE L and MAI Y-W (1997), 'Fatigue behaviour of CF/PEEK composite laminates made from commingled prepreg. Part 1: Experimental studies', *Compos. Part A*, **28**(8), 739–747.
37. FLECK N A (1997). 'Compressive failure of composites', *Adv. Appl. Mech.*, **33**, 43–117.
38. PRUITT L and SURESH S (1992), 'Fatigue crack-growth in unidirectional graphite epoxy composites under cyclic compression', *J. Mater. Sci. Lett.*, **11**(20), 1356–1360.
39. SLAUGHTER W S and FLECK N A (1993), 'Compressive fatigue of fiber composites', *J. Mech. Phys. Solids*, **41**(8), 1265–1284.
40. DILLON G and BUGGY M (1995), 'Damage development during flexural fatigue of carbon fibre-reinforced PEEK', *Composites*, **26**(5), 355–370.
41. TALBOTT M F, SPRINGER G S and BERGLUND L A (1987), 'The effects of crystallinity on the mechanical properties on PEEK polymer and graphite fiber reinforced PEEK', *J. Compos. Mater.*, **21**(11), 1056–1081.
42. TREGUB A, HAREL H and MAROM G (1994), 'Thermal treatment effects on the crystallinity and the mechanical behaviour of carbon fibre-poly(ether ether ketone) composites', *J. Mater. Sci. Lett.*, **13**(5), 329–331.
43. TREGUB A, HAREL H, MIGLIARESI C and MAROM G (1993), 'The influence of thermal treatment on the fatigue behaviour of APC-2', Miravete A, *Proceedings of the 9th International Conference on Composite Materials*, **5**, Abington, Woodhouse, 677–683.
44. FOLKES M J, KALAY G and ANKARA A (1993), 'The effect of heat treatment on the properties of PEEK and APC2', *Compos. Sci. Technol.*, **46**(1), 77–83.
45. CURTIS D C, DAVIES M, MOORE D R and SLATER B (1991), 'Fatigue behavior of continuous carbon fiber-reinforced PEEK', in O'Brien T K, *Composite Materials: Fatigue and Fracture* (Third Volume), ASTM STP 1110, Philadelphia, American Society for Testing and Materials, 581–595.
46. BUREAU M N, PERRIN F, DENAULT J and DICKSON J I (2002), 'Interlaminar fatigue crack propagation in continuous glass fiber/polypropylene composites', *Int. J. Fatigue*, **24**(2–4), 99–108.
47. HOJO M, OCHIAI S, GUSTAFSON C-G and TANAKA K (1994), 'Effect of matrix resin on delamination fatigue crack growth in CFRP laminates', *Eng. Fract. Mech.*, **49**(1), 35–47.
48. YEE A F (1987), 'Modifying matrix materials for tougher composites', in Johnston N J, *Toughened Composites*, ASTM STP 937, Philadelphia, American Society for Testing and Materials, 383–396.
49. ASP L E, BERGLUND L A and GUDMUNDSON P (1995), 'Effects of a composite-like stress state on the fracture of epoxies', *Compos. Sci. Technol.*, **53**(1), 27–28.
50. HILEY M J (1999), 'Fractographic study of static and fatigue failures in polymer composites', *Plast. Rubber Compos.*, **28**(5), 210–227.
51. GAMSTEDT E K and SJÖGREN B A (2002), 'An experimental investigation of the sequence effect in block amplitude loading of cross-ply composite laminates', *Int. J. Fatigue*, **24**(2–4), 437–446.
52. GAMSTEDT E K, REDON O and BRØNDSTED P (2001), 'Fatigue dissipation and failure in unidirectional and angle-ply glass fibre/carbon fibre hybrid laminates', *Key Eng. Mater.*, **221–222**, 35–48.
53. TAKAHARA A, MAGOME T and KAJIYAMA T (1994), 'Effects of glass fiber-matrix polymer interaction on fatigue characteristics of short glass-fiber-reinforced poly(butylene terephthalate) based on dynamic viscoelastic measurement during the fatigue process', *J. Polym. Sci. Pol. Phys.*, **32**(5), 839–849.
54. ADAMS R D and BACON D G C (1973), 'Effect of fibre orientation and laminate geometry on the dynamic properties of CFRP', *J. Compos. Mater.*, **7**, 402–428.

55. LEE I, KIM B N and KOO K N (1994), 'Dynamic characteristics of thermoplastic composite laminates', *Composites*, **25**(4), 281–286.

56. XIAO X R and AL-HMOUZ I (1998), 'Fatigue behavior of angle-ply AS4/PEEK composite' in Reifsnider K L, Dillard D A and Cardon A H, *Progress in Durability Analysis of Composite Systems*, Rotterdam, A A Balkema, 331–338.

57. DICKSON R F, JONES C J, HARRIS B, LEACH D C and MOORE D R (1985), 'The environmental fatigue behaviour of carbon fibre reinforced polyether ether ketone', *J. Mater. Sci.*, **20**(1), 60–70.

58. VOSS H and KARGER-KOCSIS J (1988), 'Fatigue crack propagation in glass-fibre and glass-sphere filled PBT composites', *Int. J. Fatigue*, **10**(1), 3–11.

59. ZHOU J, D'AMORE A, YANG Y, HE T, LI B and NICOLAIS L (1994), 'Flexural fatigue of short glass fibre reinforced a blend of polyphenylene ether ketone and polyphenylene sulfide', *Appl. Compos. Mater.*, **1**(3), 183–199.

60. PEGORETTI A and RICCO T (2000), 'Fatigue fracture of neat and short glass fiber reinforced polypropylene: Effect of frequency and material orientation', *J. Compos. Mater.*, **34**(12), 1009–1027.

61. FRIEDRICH K, WALTER R, VOSS H and KARGER-KOCSIS J (1986), 'Effect of short fibre reinforcement on the fatigue crack propagation and fracture of PEEK-matrix composites', *Composites*, **17**(3), 205–216.

62. KELLY A (1970), 'Interface effects and the work of fracture of a fibrous composite', *P. Roy. Soc. Lond. A Mat.*, **319**(1536), 95–116.

63. HOFFMAN L and WANG S S (1995), 'Cyclic fatigue crack growth and fracture in knitted randomly oriented short-fiber composite', *Eng. Fract. Mech.*, **52**(6), 1151–1163.

64. GADKAREE K P and SALEE G (1983), 'Fatigue crack-propagation in composites with spherical fillers 1.', *Polym. Compos.*, **4**(1), 19–25.

65. KARGER-KOCSIS J and FRIEDRICH K (1988), 'Fatigue crack growth in short and long fibre-reinforced injection-moulded PA 6.6. composites', *Composites*, **19**(2), 105–114.

66. HARMIA T (1996), 'Fatigue behaviour of neat and long glass fiber (LGF) reinforced blends of nylon 66 and isotactic PP', *Polym. Compos.*, **17**(6), 926–936.

67. EVANS W J, ISAAC D H and SAIB K S (1996), 'The effect of short fibre reinforcement on fatigue crack growth in PEEK', *Compos. Part A*, **27**(7), 547–554.

68. FRIEDRICH K and KARSCH U A (1982), 'Fatigue crack growth and fracture in glass sphere-filled nylon 6', *Polym. Compos.*, **3**(2), 65–74.

69. TAKEDA N, KOBAYASHI S, OGIHARA S and KOBAYASHI A (1999), 'Effects of toughened interlaminar layers on fatigue damage progress in quasi-isotropic CFRP laminates', *Int. J. Fatigue*, **21**(3), 235–242.

70. HIRANO K (2001), 'Current status and future prospects of R&D on construction of design database for advanced composites and structures in Japan' in Ishikawa Y and Sugimoto S, *Proceedings of the 7th Japan International SAMPE Symposium*, Tokyo, SAMPE Japan, 241–244.

71. LOOS J, SCHIMANSKI T, HOFMAN J, PEIJS T and LEMSTRA P J (2001), 'Morphological investigations of polypropylene single-fibre reinforced polypropylene model composites', *Polymer*, **42**(8), 3827–3834.

72. MOHANTY A K, MISRA M and DRZAL L T (2002), 'Sustainable bio-composites from renewable resources: Opportunities and challengers in the green materials world', *J. Polym. Environ.*, **10**(1–2), 19–26.

12

Fatigue of wood and wood panel products

M. P. Ansell, University of Bath, UK

12.1   Introduction

Every engineering material experiences fatigue damage when subjected to cyclic stress or cyclic strain and wood and wood panel products are no exception. The aim of this chapter is to review the response of these materials to fatigue.

   The chapter begins by introducing the structure and properties of wood, a natural composite, and considers conditions under which wood experiences fatigue. Systematic investigations of the fatigue performance of wood were initiated by the need to evaluate the performance of cyclically loaded timber bridges and more recently by the application of laminated wood in wind turbine blades. Research on the fatigue of wood-based panel products began in the 1980s, as an extension of studies on the creep performance of panels in industrial floors. In common with conventional composites, wood and wood-based panel products experience property changes during fatigue, including changes in dynamic modulus and hysteresis loop area, and these changes are reviewed. Infra-red thermography and environmental scanning electron microscopy provide further information on mechanisms of damage development in wood and panel products. The chapter concludes by examining fatigue of timber joints based on bonded-in rods and future research on the fatigue of natural fibre composites.

12.2   The structure and properties of wood and timber

12.2.1   Composite structure of wood

Wood may be defined as the cellular, ligno-cellulosic material produced by growing trees and biologically it is referred to as secondary xylem. Timber is defined as sawn wood, which has been dried to a moisture content in equilibrium with the conditions of intended use. Good introductory texts on wood and timber include Dinwoodie (2000) and Bodig and Jayne (1993).

   Wood is a composite material at many levels and the most obvious feature of this composite structure in temperate woods is the concentric arrangement of annual rings, each

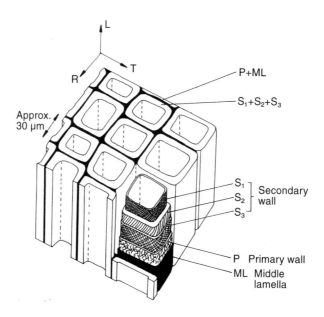

Fig. 12.1   Composite structure of wood cell wall.

ring comprising paler, less dense earlywood (EW) and darker, denser latewood (LW). EW is laid down early in the growth season and contains hollow cells, which permit the passage of moisture. The LW is much denser with thicker cell walls and it has a more structural role in supporting the tree. The LW–EW and EW–LW boundaries are important crack stopping interfaces in wood subjected to static and fatigue loads. Many tropical woods experience climatic conditions of growth that vary little throughout the year and the annual rings are difficult to observe or may be absent. In structural terms, the 'Achilles heels' of wood are the starchy radial cells (medullary rays) that radiate from the pith to the bark. Wood is easily cleaved in these radial–longitudinal planes and the path of fracture in fatigue often deviates onto these planes. The second level of composite structure exists in the wood cell wall (Fig. 12.1).

The longitudinal EW cells or tracheids depicted are discrete units of no more than a few mm in length and of the order of 30 microns in width. In the living tree water passes from the roots to the leaves through the cell voids or lumens. Pit openings in the cell wall allow water to pass from cell to cell. Each cellular unit is a complex composite structure comprising primary and secondary cell walls in concentric layers and each cell is joined to its neighbour by the lignin-rich middle lamella. Black lines in the cell wall (Fig. 12.1), represent the orientation of bundles of cellulose molecules, known as microfibrils with a thickness of approximately 15 nm. The highly crystalline microfibrils are positioned in a matrix of amorphous lignin and predominantly amorphous hemicellulose and the microfibrils may be envisaged as the fibrous phase in a natural polymeric matrix. The S_2 layer is seen to be the thickest, comprising ~85% of the thickness of the cell wall (Dinwoodie, 2000), and the microfibrils adopt a right hand spiral at a small angle (10–30°) to the cell axis. The microfibrils in the S_1 and S_3 layers are cross-laminated in the style of a filament-wound tube.

The wood cell is thus an intricately reinforced, filament-wound, cylindrical, composite structure on an extraordinarily fine scale. Wood is a classic, natural, hierarchical composite demonstrating a composite structure at several levels of subtlety.

12.2.2   Classification of wood and panel products

The picture of wood structure painted above is relatively simple. In practice trees may be divided into the cone-bearing (coniferous) softwoods and the more advanced (in evolutionary terms) hardwoods, which shed their leaves (deciduous) annually. In addition to longitudinal cells and rays, hardwoods contain vessels, which are longitudinal cellular elements with thin cell walls of the order of 1 mm in diameter. Vessels are arranged in diffuse porous or ring porous forms and may be visible to the eye in species such as oak.

Wood may be considered to be elastically orthotropic and properties along the grain are superior to those in the radial (R) or tangential (T) directions (Fig. 12.1). For this reason wood is often peeled or sliced into veneer and cross-laminated as plywood. The mechanical properties are then more balanced in the plane of the sheet. However, peeled veneer is also laminated unidirectionally in order to spread out defects such as knots and splits and to form large beam elements for construction known as laminated veneer lumber (LVL). Much of the work reported in Section 12.3, concerns the fatigue performance of LVL.

A further option is to convert wood strands, chips or fibres into panel products, thereby converting small diameter forest thinnings or wood waste into large area panels suitable for flooring, cladding and engineered timber products such as I-beams. The major products include oriented strand board (OSB), made by pressing strands with some degree of orientation, chipboard, manufactured from randomly oriented, smaller chips and medium density fibre board (MDF) and hardboard, produced by pressing together wood fibres. In all cases, except hardboard, minimum quantities of thermosetting resins are employed to bond the wood particles together, whilst hardboard is consolidated in a wet process. The fatigue properties of chipboard, MDF and OSB are considered in Section 12.3.

12.2.3   Mechanical properties of wood

The response of wood to static and fatigue loads depends fundamentally on the microstructure of the cell wall, the mode of loading and the moisture content. Seasoned timber contains water bound in the cell wall and as the moisture content is reduced by further drying the stiffness and strength of the timber increases and so the fatigue life might be expected to increase. Timber has a lightweight, cellular structure and specific mechanical properties along the grain are comparable to steel, aluminium and GRP (Table 12.1).

Table 12.1   Mechanical properties of engineering materials

Material	Specific gravity	Tensile strength (GPa)	Strength/s.g. (MPa)	Tensile stiffness (GPa)	Stiffness/s.g. (GPa)	Approximate work of fracture (J m^{-2})
High tensile steel	7.8	1.55	199	210	26.9	10^4
High strength Al alloy	2.8	0.4	143	70	25.0	10^4
Sitka spruce ‖ to grain	0.38	0.067	176	8.1	21.3	10^4
Epoxy matrix	1.19	0.029	24	3.38	2.8	10^2
E-glass fibre	2.5	3.4	1360	72	29	10^1
Carbon fibre	1.38	1.7	1230	190	140	10^1
GRP ($V_f = 0.6$)	2.0	0.55	275	40	20	10^5
CFRP ($V_f = 0.6$)	1.5	1.40	666	130	87	10^4

Loaded in tension stress versus strain curves for wood are linear with a limit of proportionality at about 60% of the ultimate stress. Loaded in compression wood has a limit of proportionality at approximately 30 to 50% of the ultimate stress. Furthermore, the compressive strength is of the order of half of the tensile strength. It is worth considering the response of wood to tensile and compressive loads at cellular level. Loaded in compression, the cell wall buckles at a critical stress, accounting for the lower ultimate compressive stress. In tension the helically wound cell wall layers may unfurl as the S_2 layer experiences internal shear interactions between adjoining layers of microfibrils. In compression–compression fatigue, sub-critical cell wall micro-buckles will accumulate, whilst in tension–tension fatigue sub-critical shear damage will build up. In reversed loading, the opening up of damage, previously inflicted in the compressive part of the cycle, may occur during the tensile part of the cycle. Reversed loading with a zero mean load ($R = -1$) is therefore likely to be particularly damaging to timber subjected to fatigue and the static compressive strength of the timber places a ceiling on the amplitude of safe fatigue loads.

12.2.4   Wood and fatigue

The classic quotation concerning wood and fatigue was made by the aircraft designer Dr Fokker in the first half of the twentieth century when he stated (Lewis, 1962) that 'fatigue in properly seasoned wood is unknown'. Although this statement was clearly wrong, the decline in the use of wood in military and civil aircraft, despite the success of the Mosquito and WW2 gliders, ensured that in the aircraft industry exhaustive studies of the fatigue properties of wood became unnecessary. However, from the 1940s work in the USA and, more recently Japan, was published in a steady trickle, stimulated by the need to design timber bridges with more confidence and by a fundamental interest in wood microstructure.

For example, Kommers (1943) tested Douglas fir, Sitka spruce and plywood in repeated and reversed bending, Lewis (1962) fatigued quarter-scale bridge stringers in flexure and shear and Dietz and Grinsfelder (1943) tested plywood under repeated load. Ota and Tsubota (1966, 1967) performed a series of studies on two-ply laminated wood and Imamaya and Matsumoto (1970) tested Sugi in three-point bending. A detailed review of the fatigue of various wood species and wood laminates may be found in Tsai (1987). Tsai comments that, in general, much information presented on fatigue testing methods in published work is notably vague with respect to whether the mode of loading is load-controlled or displacement-controlled and wood is subjected to many different loading configurations. Laminated wood appears to have a similar fatigue life to solid wood, the choice of resin in laminated wood has a minor effect on fatigue life and high moisture contents reduce fatigue life. A review of fatigue in engineering materials (Ansell, 1987) examines wood in conjunction with metal alloys, polymers and composites and concludes that in several respects wood may be treated in a similar way to long fibre composites. More recently, fatigue design has been introduced into the draft for development of the structural Eurocode for timber bridges (DD ENV 1995–2, 1997). A fatigue coefficient k_{fat} and a material safety factor for fatigue, $\gamma_{M,fat}$, are introduced to allow for fatigue loads imposed by wind loads and vehicle loads.

In the late 1970s and early 1980s (Zuteck, 1981) the technology for fabricating wind turbine blades for industrial power generation from laminated wood was developed, based on boat-building techniques developed by the Gougeon Brothers (1985) using WEST SYSTEM epoxy resins. The technology spread to the UK and was taken up by Gifford and Partners of Southampton who set up a company to design commercial wind turbine blades (Ansell et al., 1991). Sections 12.3 to 12.5 explore the results of a series of research programmes on the fatigue properties of wood laminates and panel products conducted at the University of Bath. The work on laminated wood supported the commercial development of laminated wood composite turbine blades in the UK whilst the work on panel products simulated fatigue loads on factory floors resulting from vehicle movements.

The question of fatigue test frequency and mode of control is determined by several factors. Turbine blades, bridge decks and factory floors respond to loads rather than displacements. It is in the nature of fatigue tests that they are accelerated, so in most cases the highest rates of fatigue were selected that did not cause temperature rise from internal friction. Hence constant rates of stress application in load control were selected for fatigue tests allowing low amplitude tests to be conducted at higher frequencies and vice versa.

12.3   Fatigue life of wood and panel products

12.3.1   S–N curves – flexural fatigue of wood laminates

Khaya (*Khaya ivorensis*) laminates comprising 4 mm veneers, bonded with epoxy resin in a vacuum bagging process, were subjected to fatigue tests in four-point bending under load control (Ansell and Tsai, 1984; Tsai and Ansell, 1985, 1990). The effect of moisture content on fatigue life is illustrated in Fig. 12.2 where the R ratio is

$$R = \text{minimum stress/maximum stress,}$$

and the minimum stress is always taken to be the most negative stress in each cycle. Not only does fatigue life decline as moisture content increases but the gradient of the $S/\log N$ curves increases. The authors also evaluated fatigue life as a function of R ratio at a fixed moisture content (Fig. 12.3) and, as the R ratio becomes more negative, the fatigue life falls. R ratios of -0.5 and -1 include load reversals which are particularly damaging. In the case of flexural tests, opposite faces of the beam specimen, between the central rollers, experience equal and opposite stresses. Compressive damage caused by cellular buckling is exacerbated by the tensile portion of each stress cycle.

12.3.2   S–N curves – fatigue of wood laminates in tension, compression and mixed modes

Wind turbine blades fabricated from laminated wood are hollow aerofoil, D-spar structures and as they rotate static and dynamic loads are principally tensile or compressive within the D-spar. Hence axial tests were performed on dumbbell-shaped specimens, designed to carry tensile, compressive and reversed loads (Bonfield and Ansell, 1988, 1991a; Ansell *et al.*, 1989; Bonfield, 1991).

A family of S–N curves for Khaya including static strength data is presented in Fig. 12.4 at R ratios of 0.1 (tension–tension), -1 (reversed loading), -2 and -10 (compression–tension) and 10 (compression–compression). Stress values in fatigue tests with a compressive component to each cycle are represented as negative values to allow all data to be represented on one graph. Whilst the magnitude of the tensile static strength is higher than the compressive strength, the negative slope of the $R = 0.1$ curve is greater than the positive slopes of the curves with compressive components to each cycle. Indeed at $R = 10$ the slope is very shallow and hence fatigue damage only appears to initiate at stresses very close to the static compressive strength. Beyond approximately 10^6 cycles the laminated wood is more fatigue-resistant in compression–compression than in tension–tension in terms of the magnitude of the applied stress.

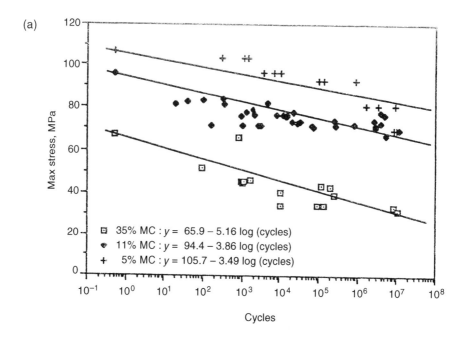

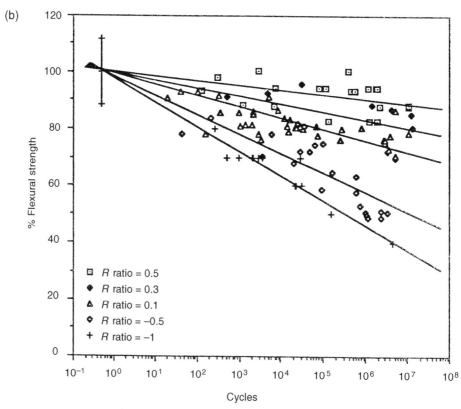

Fig. 12.2   (a) The effect of moisture content on the fatigue life of Khaya laminates fatigued at $R = 0.1$ in flexure, (b) S/log N characteristics for Khaya laminates conditioned at 65% RH and fatigued in four-point flexure as a function of R ratio (Tsai, 1987).

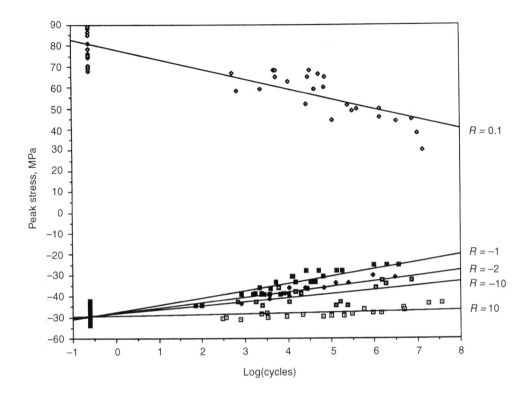

Fig. 12.3   *S*/log*N* data for constant amplitude fatigue of Khaya at five *R* ratios (Bonfield, 1991).

Bonfield and Ansell (1989) also evaluated the performance of Khaya laminates in shear fatigue. The static shear strength of Khaya falls in the range 6 to 13 MPa in two shear modes but the shear fatigue life of tangential–longitudinal (TL) surfaces is superior to radial–longitudinal (RL) surfaces. RL planes are more easily cleaved, explaining this trend.

The moisture content of wood has a strong influence on the fatigue life of wood laminates. Bond and Ansell (1993) reviewed the effect of marine environments on the fatigue performance of wind turbine materials including wood. The aim was to anticipate the wider use of wind turbines offshore and in the last few years a significant number of windfarms have been constructed off the coast of Denmark, The Netherlands, Sweden and the UK.

The literature reported above on the fatigue of wood laminates relates to veneer laminated with epoxy resin. Hacker *et al.* (1993) evaluated the shear strength of laminated wood bonded with epoxy resin, phenol resorcinol formaldehyde (PRF), melamine urea formaldehyde (MUF), urea formaldehyde (UF), polyvinyl acetate (PVA) and phenol formaldeyde (PF). UF and PF were rejected on the basis of incompatibility with the manufacturing process for turbine blades and the epoxy resin, MUF, PRF and PVA were evaluated in fatigue. For these bonded systems the fatigue life ranked in the order epoxy (best), MUF, PRF and PVA, in the same order as the static shear strengths. However, *S*/log *N* curves converged at a life ~10^7 cycles so cost savings are possible as epoxy resin is the most expensive laminating adhesive in this group.

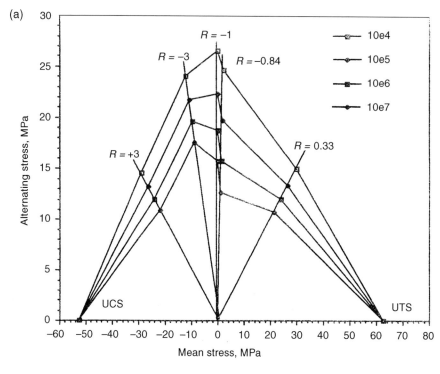

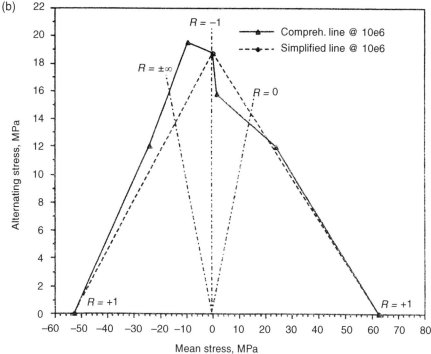

Fig. 12.4   (a) Comprehensive constant life diagram for scarf-jointed poplar laminate derived from 50% median regression curves, (b) comprehensive and simplified constant life lines for lifetime of 10^6 cycles (Bond, 1994).

12.3.3   S–N curves – fatigue of panel products

A long-term evaluation of creep in chipboard at BRE, Princes Risborough, was extended to a parallel study of the fatigue and creep life of chipboard in four-point bending (Thompson *et al.*, 1994a, 1994b, 1996; Bonfield *et al.*, 1994b; Thompson, 1996). Side-matched pairs of specimens were tested in fatigue and creep and the peak fatigue stress was selected to be equal to the static creep stress. *R* ratios of 0.1 and 0.25 were selected. In terms of design loads it was demonstrated that life prediction for chipboard based on creep data is likely to overestimate fatigue life. As the frequency of testing decreases the number of fatigue cycles to failure diminishes.

12.3.4   Constant life diagrams for wood and panel products

Constant life lines allow the fatigue life of materials to be characterized as a function of *R* ratio by plotting mean stress versus alternating stress (Ansell *et al.*, 1993). For composite materials and wood, constant life lines reflect failure in compression-dominated fatigue tests as well as tension-dominated tests, unlike metal alloys where failure in compression-dominated fatigue is not expected. Hence these diagrams are double-sided for wood and wood-based panel products.

Constant life lines are presented by Tsai and Ansell (1990), for flexural fatigue of Khaya, Bonfield and Ansell (1991b), for axially loaded Khaya and by Bonfield *et al.* (1992) and Bond and Ansell (1998a), for alternative wood species and joints. Pritchard (1999) developed constant life lines for medium density fibreboard (MDF), oriented strand board (OSB) and chipboard. For example, in Fig. 12.4(a) constant life lines are presented for scarf-jointed poplar laminate derived from *S–N* curves. By joining the points on the diagram representing the static tensile and compressive strengths to the *R* = –1 point, a simplified, triangulated version of the constant life line (Goodman lines) may be constructed (Fig. 12.4(b)) close in form to the experimental life lines. The simplified version facilitates the process of life prediction referred to in Section 12.3.5 below.

Bond *et al.* (1993) consider the statistical treatment of constant life data for purposes of design optimization and they conclude that the application of 95% tolerance limits to log *N/S* curves and simplified constant life lines provides a reliable estimate of minimum fatigue performance.

12.3.5   Predicting fatigue life of wood laminates from compressive strength

There are probably over 50 000 species of tree, so predicting the fatigue life of an individual species might appear to be problematic. However, it is well known that static properties of wood, such as compressive strength, are closely related to density at a given moisture content (Dinwoodie, 2000). Hence the fatigue life of wood species might also be a function of density and hence static strength. Bond (1994) compared three wood species, namely Khaya, poplar and beech, which were fatigue tested at *R* = –1 (axial reversed loading) at a rate of 400 MPa/s and at 65% RH. Figure 12.5(a) presents log *S*/log *N* curves for the three species and the results are normalized with respect to compressive strength in Fig. 12.5(b).

The normalized curves lie very close to each other and a master curve was generated of the form,

$$S = S_c[0.97 - 0.103 \log N],$$

where N = cycles to failure,

$\quad\quad S_c$ = ultimate compressive strength (UCS)

and $\quad S$ = allowable minimum stress.

(a)

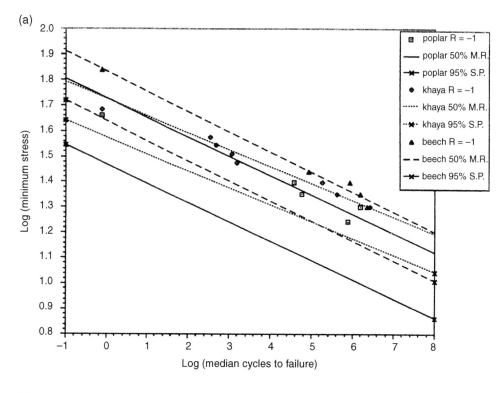

(b)

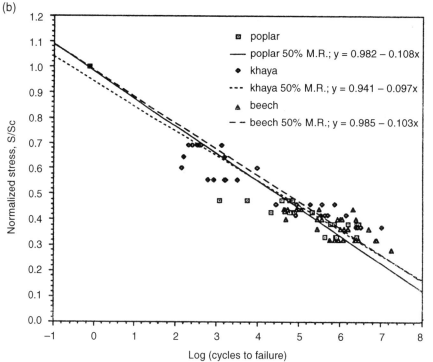

Fig. 12.5   (a) log S/log N curves for Khaya, poplar and beech tested at $R = -1$, based on median data and including 95% survival probability curves, (b) normalized S–N curves at $R = -1$, including all experimental data and 50% median regression curves.

Hence the knowledge of the compressive strength of a wood species is sufficient to generate S/log N curves in axial reversed loading. Simplified constant life diagrams may be constructed from static tensile and compressive strengths and $R = -1$ fatigue data (reversed loading). Hence it is possible by interpolation to predict fatigue life at any R ratio, Section 12.3.2.

12.3.6   Life prediction and complex loading of wood laminates

Rotating components such as wind turbine blades experience a spectrum of loads under conditions of constant wind speed but large load excursions occur during start up and shut down operations. The load spectrum may be visualized as a family of nested stress versus strain hysteresis loops and each hysteresis loop is identified by peak stress and R ratio. The fatigue profile of each loop relates to the S-log N curve for each of an infinity of R ratios and each of these R ratios contributes to the form of the constant life lines for wood laminates (Ansell, 1995). Hence a link may be made between the spectrum of loads experienced by wood components and the fatigue life of the components by analysing the load spectrum and relating the spectrum to fatigue life, embodied in constant life lines, via a Palmgren–Miner rule summation.

Bonfield and Ansell (1990) used a fundamental approach to allow the calculation of the intercept and gradient of S-log N curves at any R ratio from data measured experimentally for Khaya (Fig. 12.3) at five R ratios. The technique involved interpolation of S–N data and R' and R'' ratios were defined to avoid problems associated with R ratios of $\pm\infty$. Bonfield and Ansell (1991b) and Bonfield et al. (1994a) used the life prediction formulae embedded in customized software to predict the life of wood laminates subjected to complex loads. The spectrum WISPERX (Fig. 12.6) was employed to simulate loads experienced by wind turbine blades. WISPERX is a simplified version of the WISPER spectrum, an amalgamation of spectra derived from nine European wind turbines, which does not represent spectrum loading of an individual turbine.

WISPERX was imposed on wood laminates and scaled to several amplitudes. Life predictions were made, based on the number of passes of the WISPERX spectrum. The spectrum was analysed using a rainflow counting algorithm and fatigue life expended was calculated using the life prediction software. The lives predicted were close to experimentally measured values but were conservative, introducing a factor of safety. Bond (1994) developed 'a methodology describing the fabrication of laminated wood composites and their assessment under static and fatigue loading', enshrining this life prediction technique. Bond and Ansell (1994, 1998b) also presented the results of the life prediction analysis for scarf-jointed, laminated poplar and concluded that Palmgren–Miner damage summation values, $D \neq 1$, improve the predictive accuracy of the technique.

12.4   Dynamic property changes in fatigue of wood and panel products

Wood and panel products will progressively experience micro-cellular damage during fatigue, assuming that cyclic stress or strain exceeds the fatigue limit for the material. Following property changes in fatigue allows damage initiation and the rate of damage development to be monitored. The capture of hysteresis loops and integration of the loop area allows the dynamic modulus and energy dissipated per cycle to be measured. In addition, under load control, dynamic creep may occur. Alternatively, under displacement control, dynamic stress relaxation may occur.

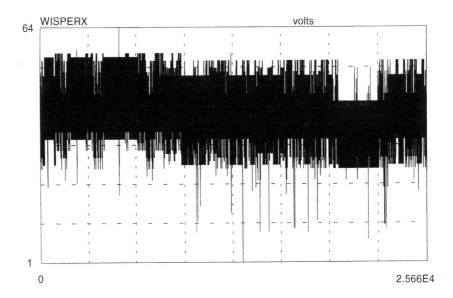

Fig. 12.6   The WISPERX spectrum (Ten Have, 1987).

12.4.1   Dynamic property changes in wood laminates

Bonfield and Ansell (1990), Bonfield *et al.* (1993) and Hacker and Ansell (1994b, 2001) captured hysteresis loops during fatigue programmes on wood laminates under load control. In compression–compression fatigue at $R = 10$ it was only possible to observe significant changes in loop area at peak compressive fatigue stresses close to the static compressive strength of the Khaya laminate (Fig. 12.7(a)). The first loop captured after 10 cycles is slender whilst the final loop captured after 3500 cycles has a lower gradient (dynamic modulus) and increased loop area. Compressive creep occurs in conjunction with fatigue damage development and the hysteresis loop moves along the compressive strain axis. This is to be expected, as the mean stress in a fatigue cycle is effectively a creep stress with an alternating load superimposed upon it. (Likewise a creep test may be thought of as a fatigue test with a cyclic stress of zero amplitude.)

In tension–tension fatigue there is a general trend for loop area to increase and for cyclic creep to occur along the tensile strain axis. In reversed loading (Fig. 12.7(b)) the development of damage is frequently observed to differ in the compressive and tensile portions of the fatigue cycle. The slope of the tensile portion of the loops decreases more rapidly than in the compressive portion of the loop implying that tension–tension loading is ultimately more destructive (see Section 12.3.1).

Property changes are presented graphically by Hacker and Ansell (1994b, 2001) and examples of change in hysteresis loop area at $R = 10$ and $R = -1$ are presented in Fig. 12.8. In compression–compression (Fig. 12.8(a)), the loop area varies from specimen to specimen but there is a general upward trend in loop area close to failure. In reverse loading (Fig. 12.8(b)), the trend is repeated but the increase in loop area just before failure is more marked.

The fatigue modulus approach to following changes in fatigue properties was developed by Hwang and Han (1985) in an investigation of CFRP. As hysteresis loops move along the strain axis, for example, Fig. 12.7, the fatigue modulus decreases. It is defined as the slope of the line linking the origin of the stress versus strain characteristic, at the beginning of the

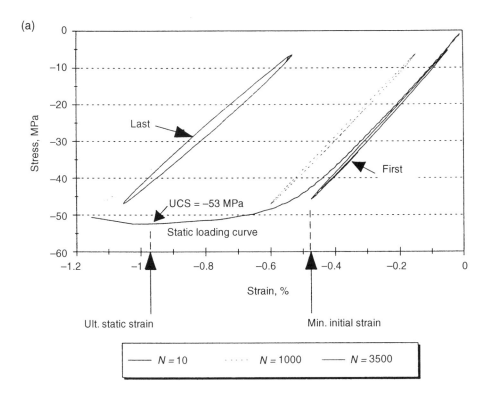

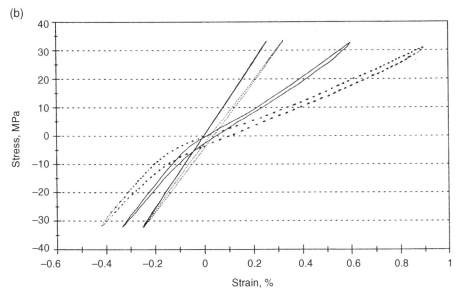

Fig. 12.7   (a) Stress versus strain hysteresis loops for Khaya laminate captured at $R = 10$ with a peak compressive stress of –47.5 MPa after 10, 1000 and 3500 cycles with a static loading curve included for comparison. (b) Hysteresis loops captured at $R = -1$ in reversed loading with a peak stress of 35 MPa after 10, 100 000, 193 453 and 193 655 cycles (Hacker, 1995).

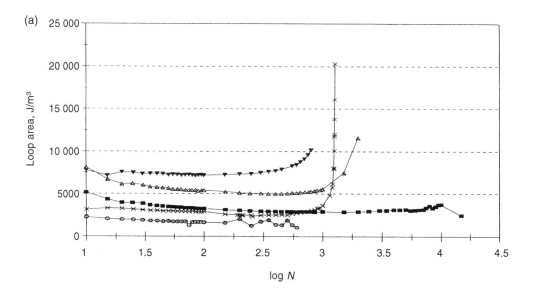

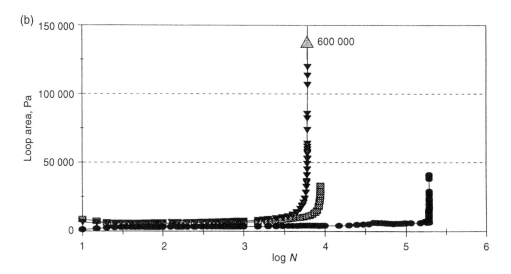

Fig. 12.8   Hysteresis loop area versus log cycles for Khaya laminate fatigued at (a) $R = 10$ (compression–compression) with a peak compressive stress of –52.5 MPa and (b) $R = -1$ (reversed loading) with maximum stress of 35 MPa (Hacker, 1995).

fatigue test, and the maximum of each hysteresis loop. When the fatigue modulus falls to a critical value, then failure may be expected to be imminent and so the fatigue modulus approach may be a convenient life prediction tool. Hacker and Ansell (1994a) applied the fatigue modulus approach to Khaya laminates at $R = 10$ and $R = 0.1$. In compression fatigue the initial gradient of the fatigue modulus versus log cycles characteristic correlated well with fatigue life. Steeper gradients resulted in shorter lives indicating that the approach is a useful life prediction tool. In tensile fatigue the fatigue modulus decreased to a much smaller extent and life prediction was not possible.

Table 12.2   Density values for MDF, OSB and chipboard from X-ray densitometry (From Bucur *et al.*, 1998)

	MDF		OSB		Chipboard	
	Skin	Core	Skin	Core	Skin	Core
Average density (Mg/m³)	1.004	0.618	1.050	0.609	0.923	0.538
Coefficient of variation	5	3	25	14	7	11
Ratio skin/core		1.6		1.7		1.7

Table 12.3   Summary of mean modulus of rupture and median initial modulus of elasticity for MDF, OSB and chipboard at 65%RH and 85%RH

	Mean MOR (MPa)		Median Initial MOE at 60% MOR, (GPa)	
Material	65%RH	85%RH	65%RH	85%RH
MDF	47.9	34.59	4.044	2.415
OSB	27.9	21.7	6.835	1.875
Chipboard	21.0	10.61	4.180	0.704

12.4.2   Dynamic property changes in panel products

The time-dependent properties of wood-based panel products depend on the structural elements from which the panel is pressed. MDF is pressed from a mattress of wood fibre, chipboard is comprised of chips with a maximum length of a few centimetres whilst OSB is made from strands of up to about 10 cm in length. In practice MDF and OSB incorporate a broad distribution of element sizes (Nishimura and Ansell, 2002) and a density profile through the panel thickness (Pritchard *et al.*, 1997; Bucur *et al.*, 1998) is observed. In practice, the profile (Table 12.2) is achieved by control of particle delivery on the production conveyer line and selection of pressing parameters. In general panel cores are less dense than skins, appropriate for carrying bending and shear loads experienced in buildings. The short-term, statically derived mechanical properties of MDF, OSB and chipboard differ significantly. Table 12.3 compares the modulus of rupture, MOR, and modulus of elasticity, MOE, for the three panel products, measured in four-point bending, at 65%RH and 85%RH. MDF has the highest MOR at both RH values but at 65%RH the OSB has the highest MOE. The MOE of all panel materials is markedly reduced at high RH.

Pritchard *et al.* (1996, 2001a,b) compared the fatigue and creep performance of commercial grade chipboard, MDF and OSB. The comparison was based on the application of (i) the same cyclic fatigue stress at 65%RH and (ii) an equivalent applied fatigue stress, namely 60% of the modulus of rupture, MOR, for each panel product at 85%RH. In comparison (i), hysteresis loops were captured after 152 cycles (Fig. 12.9(a)) and compared with the last loop captured before failure (Fig. 12.9(b)). MDF has the highest static strength and, not surprisingly, the longest fatigue life and was fatigue tested at a peak stress of about 50% of its static strength. Just before failure the areas of the hysteresis loops increase for all three panel materials and the dynamic modulus falls. The MDF experiences creep along the strain axis, a function of its fibrous microstructure.

In comparison (ii), the same broad trends are observed at 60% MOR and 85% RH. Figure 12.10(a) presents the first captured hysteresis loops and the dynamic modulus of the MDF

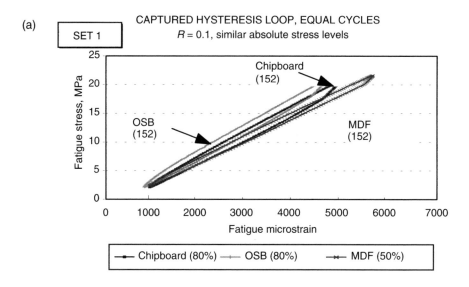

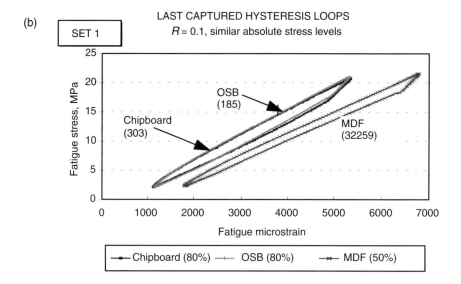

Fig. 12.9   (a) Captured hysteresis loops for OSB, chipboard and MDF at $R = 0.1$ with a peak stress of ~21 MPa after 152 cycles, (b) last captured loops in same tests (Pritchard, 1999).

is greatest at 85%RH, as expected from Table 12.3. The last captured hysteresis loops (Fig. 12.10(b)), reveal high creep rates in chipboard, modest rates in MDF and creep stability in OSB. Cyclic loading has a strong influence on creep rates, especially at high humidities, in these wood-based panel materials (see also papers by Thompson *et al*, 2002a,b). There is strong evidence, from trends in dynamic properties, that a fatigue limit exists at peak cyclic stress levels of less than 20% of the static strength.

(a)

FIRST CAPTURED HYSTERESIS LOOPS

$R = 0.1$, 60% Stress level

85%RH

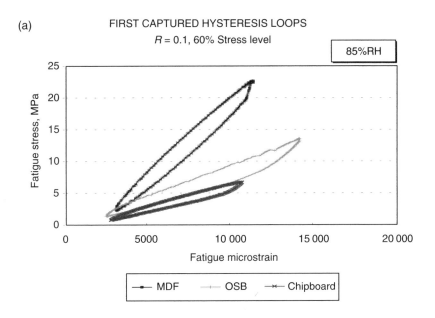

Fatigue stress, MPa

Fatigue microstrain

MDF   OSB   Chipboard

(b)

LAST CAPTURED HYSTERESIS LOOPS

$R = 0.1$, 60% Stress level

85%RH

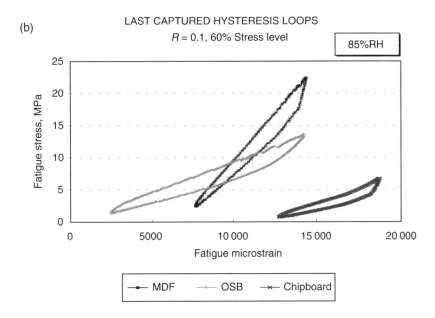

Fatigue stress, MPa

Fatigue microstrain

MDF   OSB   Chipboard

Fig. 12.10   (a) First captured hysteresis loops for OSB, chipboard and MDF at $R = 0.1$, at 60% of MOR, (b) last captured loops in same tests (Pritchard, 1999).

12.5   Fatigue damage development in wood and panel products

12.5.1   Microstructural damage in wood laminates

Tsai and Ansell (1990) examined fatigue damage development on the compressive face of Sitka spruce cycled at 75% of the mean flexural strength at $R = -0.1$ in four-point bending. Dr J.M. Dinwoodie, BRE, provided facilities for optical microscopy of damage development in compressive fatigue. Radial-longitudinal sections were prepared with a wood microtome at a very low blade sectioning angle of approximately 10° to prevent cell wall damage from the sectioning process itself. Sections were observed using polarized light microscopy after 100, 500, 1000, 10 000 and 100 000 cycles. Damage was observed in the cell wall following only 500 cycles of fatigue, manifested as 'X'-shaped kinks in the double cell wall between tracheids. These kinks formed trails running from one cell wall to the next. After 1000 cycles damage trails were quite extensive and after 10 000 cycles, the trails of kinks developed into buckled creases, ultimately visible to the naked eye after 100 000 cycles. In flexural fatigue of beams the compressive face will become damaged first, shifting the neutral axis towards the tensile face. Ultimately, gross failure is manifested by jagged tensile rupture but initial damage is compressive.

A detailed study of static and fatigue damage in axially loaded Khaya-epoxy laminates was performed by Hacker (1995) using an environmental scanning electron microscope (ESEM) at Risø Laboratories in Denmark. Specimens were loaded in tension along the grain in an *in situ*, screw-driven loading jig, incorporating a load cell. The jig was developed by Alan Hever at the Engineering Department of the University of Cambridge. Dog-bone specimens for observation were prepared from unfatigued material and material prefatigued at $R = 0.1$ (tension–tension), $R = 10$ (compression–compression) and $R = -1$ (reversed loading). Specimens were 60 mm long by 8 mm wide with a 15 mm necked zone containing a small transverse notch.

A tangential–longitudinal (TL) plane was observed for unfatigued Khaya. Cracks propagated from the notch moving between ray cell bundles, which emerge on the TL surface, causing shear failure in the longitudinal cell walls and fracture in vessel walls. Microfibrils were observed bridging the cracks between ray cell bundles and microfibrils peeled away from failed cell walls. Khaya, prefatigued at $R = 0.1$, contained longitudinal splits in ray cell bundles and helical cracks in longitudinal cells, corresponding with the helical angle of S_2 microfibrils. On application of a tensile load in the ESEM a clear pattern emerged of crack propagation in the TL plane by a series of steps running through ray cell bundles and jumping from ray to ray by transverse cracking. Incipient transverse cracks were spread uniformly through the microstructure.

Notched specimens, prefatigued at $R = 10$ contained small compression creases and cell wall kinks lying in a range of angles between 45 and 60° to the cell axis. Finer scale cell wall damage was manifested as fine creases on the longitudinal cell walls at angles between 9 and 30°. Macroscopic compression creases appear as areas of gross buckling. Tensile loading allowed the buckled zones to be pulled straight with cracks running directly, transverse to the fibre axis, across the TL plane. Specimens which had been subjected to reversed loading ($R = -1$) contained damage representative of both tensile and compressive fatigue. Tensile damage was more evident in the form of ray cell bundle splitting and S_2 layer cell wall splitting. On loading in the tensile stage, diagonal cracks formed through vessel walls and by transverse cracking through longitudinal cells and ray cell bundles even though the ray cells were split. Transverse cracks initiated from compressive damage. Only $R = -1$ samples exhibited intracellular failure between S_1 and S_2 layers, a manifestation of reversed loading.

12.5.2   Infra-red thermography of wood laminates

Infra-red imaging of laminated wood in fatigue is a valuable technique for following damage development, particularly around joints. Bond *et al.* (1992) evaluated laminated Khaya reverse loaded in axial tension–compression. Laminates were prepared with five layers of veneer and scarf and butt joints were incorporated in the four outer veneers, staggered at equal intervals. The scarf joints were either perfectly laminated or imperfectly laminated by overscarfing or underscarfing to represent manufacturing defects. Samples were tested at three frequencies and the thermographic technique was able to detect the development of hot spots at joints. Not only did the hottest spot move from one joint site to another during test, but temperatures also rose in some cases to over 50 °C in the area of the weakest joint in the few cycles before failure. Infra-red thermography is a suitable technique for monitoring damage development in jointed laminates because of the low thermal conductivity of wood and the presence of stress raisers. The importance of ensuring accurate alignment of joints during manufacture for optimum performance in fatigue is emphasized by Ansell *et al.* (1996).

12.5.3   Microstructural damage in panel products

Crack propagation in chipboard, MDF and OSB was observed in a low voltage electron microscope using the tensile stage described in Section 12.5.1 (Pritchard *et al.*, 1997; Pritchard, 1999). Small specimens were loaded in tension at 90° to the panel skins and cracks propagated from a starter crack in the centre of the core, so that the crack surface was parallel to the plane of the panel skins. The aim was to assess potential mechanisms for fatigue crack growth. MDF is a softwood fibre-based panel and the crack follows a narrow damage zone pulling out complete bridging fibres from either side of the crack as it opens. In OSB softwood strands are pressed together in the manufacturing process, so contact surfaces between strands contain crushed cells, necessary to pack the strands closely together. The cells in the strand centres remain uncrushed. As the crack passes through the OSB core it tends to follow a dominant path around the edges of flakes in the gluelines or passes through easily cleaved RL planes within the strands in an unzipping process. Some fibre bridging across these RL planes is observed. Crack propagation in chipboard is highly diffuse moving on multiple fronts via porous zones between chips and to some extent along RL planes.

The poorly consolidated microstructure of chipboard explains the high degree of underlying creep observed in fatigue tests, especially at high humidities (Section 12.4.2). The fibrous nature of MDF is more akin to the structure of paper but whilst static strengths are high due to good surface perfection, fatigue stability is compromised by slippage between fibres. The high level of surface flaws, caused by strand edges, reduces the strength of OSB. However, the microstructure of OSB is closest to that of solid wood so stability in fatigue, even at high humidities, compares well with MDF and chipboard.

12.6   Fatigue in timber joints

The construction of timber frame buildings and timber bridges is big business worldwide. Much effort has been expended in evaluating the ductility of structural timber joints, particularly in parts of the world such as Japan and the USA where earthquakes are a threat to buildings. Bonded-in steel or reinforced plastic pultruded rods may be bonded directly into timber to form moment-resisting joints. Bainbridge *et al.* (1999) review research on the fatigue performance of bonded-in rods as a function of adhesive type and conclude that epoxy resins are the most effective. The modes of failure of fatigued GRP rods bonded into laminated veneer lumber (LVL) are examined by Madhoushi and Ansell (2001) and factors such as glue line thickness and rate of loading determine whether failure is in the LVL or at the resin to rod interface. The fatigue performance of glulam connections, based on bonded-in steel rods, is assessed by Bainbridge *et al.* (2001) for applications in bridges. The technology is straightforward and effective and may also be used for the repair of structures that experience fatigue.

12.7   Fatigue of natural fibre composites

Like wood, natural organic fibre monofilaments (such as cotton or kapok) or fibre bundles (such as jute, hemp and sisal) may also be treated as natural composites. The lignocellulosic microstructure of natural fibres is based on filament wound cellulose in a lignin/hemicellulose matrix. Natural fibres experience fatigue during spinning into textile fibres and when woven, knitted or braided into flexible fibre assemblies. For example, the tensile fatigue of cotton is described by Hearle *et al.* (1998). There is currently considerable interest in natural-fibre polymer–matrix composites and industrial applications include car components and boat hulls. Natural fibres are used as a substitute for glass fibres in conventional thermoplastic and thermosetting matrices. Much effort is also being expended in developing natural polymeric matrices in order to develop truly sustainable composites. The study of fatigue of natural fibre composites is in its infancy but the literature will surely expand in the near future once manufacturing processes become commercially attractive.

12.8   Conclusions

The large body of evidence presented on the fatigue properties of wood and wood-based panel products demonstrates that the trends in fatigue life, the nature of property changes and treatment of data are closely similar to those for fibre-reinforced composite materials. The development of S–N curves, constant life lines and life prediction models is similar for both classes of material. The difference between wood and fibre composites lies in the cellular nature of wood and the response of the fibrous structure to compressive, tensile and reversed fatigue loads. Whilst, like wood, fibre composites exhibit failure mechanisms such as compressive splitting and kinking, the picture within wood cell walls and throughout the array of longitudinal cells and vessels and the radial cells is far more complex. However, despite the very large number of commercial wood species and wood composite products available for engineering applications, the overall trends in fatigue performance are seen to depend on moisture content and density. In conclusion wood is very capable of carrying dynamic loads and growing trees, timber bridges, aircraft structures and wind turbine blades bear witness to the fatigue integrity of a wide spectrum of wood-based materials.

12.9   Acknowledgements

Research at the University of Bath was funded by SRC, SERC, EPSRC, Department of Energy, DTI and the Building Research Establishment. The author gratefully acknowledges this support.

12.10   References

ANSELL M P (1987), 'Layman's guide to fatigue', in *Wind Energy Conversion 1987*, ed. Galt J M, Mechanical Engineering Publications Ltd., 39–54.

ANSELL M P (1995), 'Fatigue design for timber and wood-based materials', STEP lecture E22, in *Timber Engineering STEP 2, Design – details and structural systems*, Centrum Hout, The Netherlands.

ANSELL M P AND TSAI K T (1984), 'Fatigue testing of wood composites for aerogenerator rotor blades', in *Wind Energy Conversion, 1984*, ed. P. Musgrove, Cambridge University Press, 239–255.

ANSELL M P, BONFIELD P W and TSAI K T (1989), 'Fatigue testing of laminated wood for generator blades', in *Windpower '88*, AWEA 18, Honolulu, Hawaii, American Wind Energy Assn, 113–126.

ANSELL M P, HANCOCK M and BONFIELD P W (1991), 'Wood composites – the optimum fatigue resistant materials for commercial wind turbine blades', *Proc of the Int Timber Eng Conf, London*, 4.194–4.202.

ANSELL M P, BOND I P and BONFIELD P W (1993), 'Constant life diagrams for wood composites and polymer matrix composites', *Proc of the Ninth Int Conf on Composite Materials (ICCM-9)*, Madrid, Spain, ed. Miravete, Antonio, Pub. University of Zaragoza, Woodhead Publishing Ltd., V, 692–699.

ANSELL M P, BOND I P, BONFIELD P W and HACKER C L (1996), 'Fatigue properties of wood composites', Chapter 7, 107–122, in *Design of Composite Structures against Fatigue*, Mechanical Engineering Publications Ltd.

BAINBRIDGE R, METTEM C J and ANSELL M P (1999), 'An overview of research to assess fatigue performance of bonded-in rods for structural timber connections using three adhesive types', *Proc of Workshop 'Damage in wood' COST Action E8*, Bordeaux.

BAINBRIDGE R, HARVEY K, METTEM C J and ANSELL M P (2001), 'Fatigue performance of structural timber connections', *Proc of IABSE Conf 'Innovative wooden structures and bridges*, Lahti, Finland.

BODIG J and JAYNE B A (1993), *Mechanics of Wood and Wood Composites*, Krieger Publishing Company, Melbourne, Florida, USA.

BOND I P (1994), 'The fatigue design of commercial wood composite wind turbine blades', PhD thesis, University of Bath.

BOND I P and ANSELL M P (1993), 'Effect of the marine environment on the fatigue life of wind turbine materials', *Wind Engineering*, **17**(2), 100–107.

BOND I P and ANSELL M P (1994), 'Fatigue testing of wood composites for aerogenerator blades, Part X. Life prediction and variable amplitude testing using extreme 'in-service' load conditions', in *Wind Energy Conversion 1994*, Mechanical Engineering Publications Ltd., 199–204.

BOND I P and ANSELL M P (1998a), 'Fatigue properties of jointed wood composites. Part 1: Statistical analysis, fatigue master curves and constant life diagrams', *J. Mat. Sci.*, **33**, 2751–2762.

BOND I P and ANSELL M P (1998b), 'Fatigue properties of jointed wood composites. Part 2: Life prediction analysis for variable amplitude loading', *J. Mat. Sci.*, **33**, 4121–4129.

BOND I P, HACKER C L, ANSELL M P and DUTTON A G (1992), 'Infra red condition monitoring of different joint geometry samples subjected to reversed ($R=-1$) loading', *Report on the 23rd Meeting of Experts – Fatigue of Wind Turbines*, Golden, Colorado, pub. Research Centre Jülich for the Int Energy Agency, 117–120.

BOND I P, ANSELL M P and HACKER C L (1993), 'Fatigue testing of wood composites for aerogenerator rotor blades. Part VIII. Statistical treatment of constant life data for design optimization', *Procs 1993 Europ Comm Wind Energy Conf*, Lübeck-Travemünde, Germany, H.S. Stephens and Associates, 137–140.

BONFIELD P W (1991), 'Fatigue evaluation of wood laminates for the design of wind turbine blades', PhD thesis, University of Bath.

BONFIELD P W and ANSELL M P (1988), 'Fatigue testing of wood composites for aerogenerator blades, Part III. Axial tension/compression fatigue', in *Wind Energy Conversion 1988*, ed. Milborrow D J, Mechanical Engineering Publications Ltd, 377–383.

BONFIELD P W and ANSELL M P (1989), 'Fatigue testing of wood composites for aerogenerator rotor blades. Part IV – Shear, size effect, modulus changes and block loading', in *EWEC '89 – Proc. Europ Wind Energy Conference*, Peter Peregrinus Ltd, 406–410.

BONFIELD P W and ANSELL M P (1990), 'Fatigue testing of wood composites for aerogenerator rotor blades. Part V. Life prediction analysis and hysteresis', in *Wind Energy Conversion 1990*, eds. Davies T D, Halliday J A and Palutikof J P, Mechanical Engineering Publications Ltd, 19–24.

BONFIELD P W and ANSELL M P (1991a), 'The fatigue properties of wood in tension, compression and shear', *J. Mat. Sci.*, **26**, 4765–4773.

BONFIELD P W and ANSELL M P (1991b), 'Fatigue testing of wood composites for aerogenerator rotor blades. Part VI. Spectrum fatigue loading, life prediction and damage rates', in *Wind Energy Conversion 1991*, eds. Quarton D and Fenton V, Mechanical Engineering Publications Ltd, 311–316.

BONFIELD P W, BOND I P, HACKER C L and ANSELL M P (1992), 'Fatigue testing of wood composites for aerogenerator rotor blades. Part VII. Alternative wood species and joints', in *Wind Energy Conversion 1992*, ed. Clayton B R Pub. Mechanical Engineering Publications Ltd, 243–250.

BONFIELD P W, DINWOODIE J M, ANSELL M P and HACKER C L (1993), 'Damage quantification of wood and wood-based products via stress-strain hysteresis loop capture', *Proc of COST 508 Wood Mechanics Workshop on 'Wood: Plasticity and Damage'*, eds. Birkinshaw C, Morlier P and Seoane I, Limerick, Ireland, 185–203.

BONFIELD P W, ANSELL M P and DINWOODIE J M (1994a), 'Fatigue testing of wood: a detailed guide for the development of life-prediction formulae from fatigue data', *Proc IUFRO S5.02, Int. Timber Engineering Conf*, 163–174, Sydney, Australia.

BONFIELD P W, HACKER C L, ANSELL M P and DINWOODIE J M (1994b), 'Fatigue and creep of chipboard. Part 1, $R = 0.01$', *Wood Sci. and Tech.*, **28**, 423–435.

BUCUR V, ANSELL M P, BARLOW C Y, PRITCHARD J, GARROS S and DEGLISE X (1998), 'Physical methods for characterizing wood composite panel products', *Holzforschung*, **52**, 553–561.

DIETZ A G H and GRINSFELDER H (1943), 'Behaviour of plywood under repeated stresses', *Trans. ASME*, 187–191.

DINWOODIE J M (2000), *Timber: Its Nature and Behaviour*, E & F N Spon, New York.

DD ENV 1995–2 (1997), *Eurocode 5, Design of Timber Structures – Part 2: Bridges*.

GOUGEON BROTHERS (1985), *The Gougeon Brothers on Boat Construction – Wood and WEST SYSTEM Materials,* 4th edn., Gougeon Bros. Inc.

HACKER C L, BOND I P and ANSELL M P (1993), 'Fatigue testing of wood composites for aerogenerator blades. Part IX. Alternative adhesives', in *Wind energy conversion 1993*, ed Pitcher K F, Mechanical Engineering Publications Ltd., 269–274.

HACKER C L and ANSELL M P (1994a), 'Fatigue testing of wood composites for aerogenerator blades, Part XI. Assessment of fatigue damage accumulation using a fatigue modulus approach', in *Wind Energy Conversion 1994*, Mechanical Engineering Publications Ltd., 205–210.

HACKER C L and ANSELL, M P (1994b), 'Stress-strain hysteresis loop capture in the assessment of fatigue damage accumulation in wood composites', *Proc of 5th Europ Wind Energy Assn Conf*, Vol 1, Thessaloniki, Greece, 402–407.

HACKER C L (1995), 'Fatigue damage in wood composites', PhD thesis, University of Bath.

HACKER C L and ANSELL M P (2001), 'Fatigue damage and hysteresis in wood-epoxy laminates', *J. Mat. Sci.*, **36**(9), 609–621.

HEARLE J W S, LOMAS B and COOKE W D (1998), *Atlas of Fibre Fracture and Damage to Textiles*, 2nd edn, Woodhead Publishing Ltd, Cambridge.

HWANG W and HAN K S (1985), 'Fatigue of composites – fatigue modulus concept and life prediction', *J. Composite Materials*, **20**, 154–165.

IMAMAYA N and MATSUMOTO T (1970), 'Studies on the fatigue of wood I', *J. Jap. Wood Res. Soc.*, **20**(2), 53–62.

KOMMERS, W J (1943), 'The fatigue behaviour of wood and plywood subjected to repeated and reversed bending stresses', US Forest Prod. Lab. Rep. No. 1327.

LEWIS G M (1962), 'Fatigue resistance of quarter-scale bridge stringers in flexure and shear', US For Prods Lab Rep No 2236.

MADHOUSHI M and ANSELL M P (2001), 'Fatigue performance of timber connections based on GFRP bonded-in rods', *Proc of First Int Conf of Europ Soc for Wood Mechanics*, Lausanne, Switzerland.

NISHIMURA T and ANSELL M P (2002), 'Monitoring fibre orientation in OSB during production using filtered image analysis', *Wood Sci. and Tech.*, **36**(3), 229–239.

OTA M and TSUBOTA Y (1966), 'Studies on the fatigue of 2-ply laminated wood, Parts I to III', *J. Japan Wood Res. Soc.*, **12**(1), 26–29, **12**(2), 90–95, **12**(5), 210–214.

OTA, M and TSUBOTA Y (1967), 'Studies on the fatigue of 2-ply laminated wood, Parts IV', *J. Japan. Wood Res. Soc.*, **13**(4), 131–137.

PRITCHARD J, THOMPSON R J H, BONFIELD P W and ANSELL M P (1996), 'A comparison of the fatigue and creep performance of commercial grade chipboard, OSB and MDF based on equivalent applied stress levels', *Proc of Int COST 508 Wood Mechanics Conf*, Stuttgart, 409–423.

PRITCHARD J, ANSELL M P, BONFIELD P W, BARLOW C Y and BUCUR V (1997), 'Understanding the fatigue and creep properties of MDF, OSB and chipboard using environmental scanning electron microscopy and x-ray densitometry', Proc of IUFRO S 5.02 Timber Engineering, Copenhagen, Denmark.

PRITCHARD J (1999), 'Fatigue and creep performance of MDF, OSB and chipboard in standard and high humidity environments', PhD thesis, University of Bath.

PRITCHARD J, ANSELL M P, THOMPSON R J H and BONFIELD P W (2001a), 'Effect of two relative humidity environments on the performance properties of MDF, OSB and chipboard. Part 1. MOR, MOE and fatigue life performance', *Wood Sci. and Tech.*, **35**(5), 395–403.

PRITCHARD J, ANSELL M P, THOMPSON R J H and BONFIELD P W (2001b), 'Effect of two relative humidity environments on the performance properties of MDF, OSB and chipboard. Part 2. Fatigue and creep performance', *Wood Sci. and Tech.*, **35**(5), 405–423.

TEN HAVE A A (1987), 'European approaches in standard spectrum development', Report No. NLR MP 87007U, National Aerospace Laboratory, The Netherlands.

THOMPSON R J H, BONFIELD P W, HACKER C L, DINWOODIE J M and ANSELL M P (1994a), 'Creep and fatigue of structural grade chipboard – non-reversed loading in 4-point bending', *Proc Int Conf on Timber*, High Wycombe.

THOMPSON R J H, BONFIELD P W, HACKER C L, DINWOODIE J M and ANSELL M P (1994b), 'Creep and fatigue of chipboard in flexure', *Proc of the Timber Engineering Conf*, Gold Coast, Australia.

THOMPSON R J H (1996), 'Fatigue and creep in wood based panel products', PhD thesis, University of Bath.

THOMPSON R J H, BONFIELD P W, DINWOODIE J M and ANSELL M P (1996), 'Fatigue and creep of chipboard, Part 3. The effect of frequency', *Wood Sci. and Tech.*, **30**, 293–305.

THOMPSON R J H, ANSELL M P, BONFIELD P W and DINWOODIE J M (2002a), 'Fatigue in wood-based panels. Part 1: The strength variability and fatigue performance of OSB, chipboard and MDF', *Wood Sci. and Tech.*, **36**(3), 255–269.

THOMPSON R J H, ANSELL M P, BONFIELD P W and DINWOODIE J M (2002b), 'Fatigue in wood-based panels. Part 2: The strength variability and fatigue performance of OSB, chipboard and MDF', accepted for publication in *Wood Sci. and Tech.*

TSAI K T and ANSELL M P (1985), 'Fatigue testing of wood composites for aerogenerator rotor blades, Part II, Effect of moisture and *R*-ratio', in *Wind Energy Conversion 1985*, ed. Garrad A, Mechanical Engineering Publications Ltd., 285–292.

TSAI K T (1987), 'An investigation into the fatigue behaviour of wood laminates for wind energy converter blade design', PhD thesis, University of Bath.

TSAI K T and ANSELL M P (1990), 'The fatigue properties of wood in flexure', *J. Mat. Sci.*, **22**, 865–878.

ZUTECK M D (1981), 'The development and manufacture of wood composite wind turbine rotors', DOE/NASA Horizontal Axis Wind Turbine Workshop.

Part IV

Life-prediction methods for constant stress and variable stress

13

Physical modelling of damage development in structural composite materials under stress

P. W. R. Beaumont, Cambridge University, UK

13.1   Introduction

This chapter describes a physical approach to modelling crack growth processes and the development of damage in structural composite materials under stress. Modelling techniques are reviewed, with particular emphasis on: the micro-mechanics of cracking; the physical mechanisms and accumulation of damage; the prediction of damage-state; and the influence of damage on the mechanical properties of the composite material with changes in stress. The chapter is illustrated by a number of examples of physical models of the cracking and fatigue behaviour of a variety of polymeric-based material systems containing long strong fibres of carbon, glass or aramid.

13.2   A framework for understanding damage development

Since about the 1960s, the fracture and fatigue behaviour of composite materials based on reinforcing polymers with long strong fibres has been the subject of extensive experimentation and analytical investigation. Yet, despite this acquisition of vast collections of mechanical property data, our ability to predict the structural integrity of a damaged composite subjected to mechanical and thermal stresses and hostile environment remains restricted. This is because our understanding of problems of composite failure is based almost entirely on this store of information being empirical in nature with limited knowledge of the structural changes taking place in the material over time.

Beyond dispute, however, is the fact that by far the largest number of in-service failure problems associated with the development of composite hardware are related to critical stresses that are in-plane interlaminar shear or out-of-plane tensile, or a combination of both (Kedward and Beaumont, 1992). This is of major concern. More often than not, as with all materials, failure of the structural composite begins with localized cracking at points of load concentration. Examples of sites of load intensification in the laminate include: a ply drop, a hole or notch or other discontinuity like a cut-out, a bolted or adhesively-bonded joint, a manufacturing defect, a free-edge, and so forth.

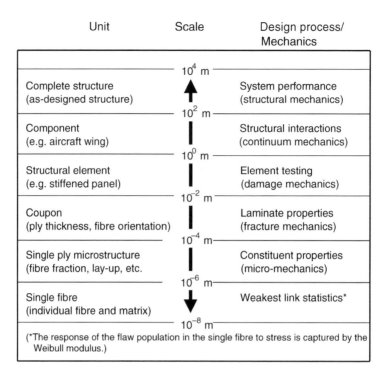

Fig. 13.1   Hierarchy of structural scales ranging from the micrometre to the metre (and greater) level of size, from the single ply to the final structure, and discrete methods of analysis ranging from micro-mechanics to the continuum levels of modelling.

Oversights in composite design, which have led to matrix-dominated load paths, have resulted in the growth of damage in the laminate under stress, in the form of matrix cracks, of splits, of delaminations, and of fibre breaks. These oversights in material and engineering design are the result of a gap that has opened up in our knowledge of the differences in failure behaviour between the composite material and the large-scale composite structure. The origin of this gap can be found in the changing nature of failure as size (length) increases from that of the single ply to the laminate; from the test coupon to the component; and from the sub-assembly to the fully completed structure (Kedward and Beaumont, 1992; Spearing and Beaumont, 1998; Spearing et al., 1998). This lengthscale which spans several orders of magnitude provides a framework for understanding the failure characteristics of the material, on the one hand, and large-scale structure, on the other (Fig. 13.1).

One approach to bridging this gap is to assess in a progression of experiments the effects of fatigue stress on the strength, the stiffness (or modulus), and the life-time by testing in sequence first the test coupon, then the sub-structural element followed by the component, and finally the large-scale structure. This progression of development testing has been termed the 'building block' approach (see, for example, Kedward and Beaumont, 1992). In parallel with experimentation is the design and analysis phase wherein critical areas of the structure are identified and selected for test verification. Any critical strength features are subsequently isolated in the form of small test articles of progressively increasing complexity and size; for example, from a spar shear web to a skin panel rib attachment of an aircraft wing. This building block design methodology is based on transferring empirical information and relating experimental data from one point on that lengthscale to another. Almost always, behaviour at one level can be passed to the next level upwards as one or more parameters or as a simple function.

Empirical methods of design, however, do have serious limitations and shortcomings. While a simple empirical law like Hooke's law may describe an elastic material's response to a tensile stress under ambient conditions, it provides no insight whatsoever in predicting the material's behaviour in multi-axial stressing at elevated temperature. This is because an empirical law is not based on a prior knowledge of the mechanisms of microstructural change. More often than not, they simply will not be known. Obviously, the entire design process by this route is extremely costly and very time-consuming. Furthermore, a serious design issue encountered 'down the road' could result in the complete programme having to begin all over again. Worse still, it could bring the company to the brink of disaster.

There is an alternative route. It is based on sound fundamental understanding of the mechanisms by which damage accumulates with time in the material and structure across those several orders of magnitude of size: from fibre breakage and matrix cracking that lead progressively to ply fracture; from delamination and splitting of the laminate that lead to complete component failure. Application of this approach which can lead to a predictive design methodology requires the identification and understanding of fracture mechanisms in the material at the micrometre level of size and a practical failure analysis of the component on the size scale orders of magnitude greater.

Thus, as the shift of information both ways along this lengthscale proceeds, the design process at each level of size has to include the identification of the crack growth processes and recognition of their significance. Making links or connections between our understanding of material characteristics and component behaviour relies critically on this knowledge of the microscopic and macroscopic structural changes with time over the entire span of size. If we consider understanding all sorts of material behavioural characteristics at the micro level of size, to do with the fibre, matrix and their interaction, we might say that we characterize the properties of the material at that particular scale by reference to the fibre direction. There is no real consideration of the effects of geometry or architecture of the laminate. Any initial material tests are ordinarily carried out on specimens containing fibres aligned unidirectionally. A notch or cut-out in the coupon is considered to be a geometrical aberration. Conversely, at the size of a structural element, we tend to look at the overall geometry of the component and to think of the material properties as being set (in a geometric sense) at a global level. Coming to terms with these differences appears to be a key source of design difficulty because on this lengthscale it is precisely where the material problem becomes a structural one.

13.3   A question of design route

Conventional mechanical design, then, is empirical: it is by trial and error. It works, otherwise you try again and you learn by experience. Conventional design relies upon this enormous store of empirical knowledge built up by experimentation. In addition to drawing upon this vast supply of information, the modern designer in mechanical engineering relies upon two boxes of tools. The first box is called *mathematics and continuum modelling* (sometimes called continuum mechanics); the second is called *micro-mechanical modelling* (sometimes called mechanism modelling or simply micro-mechanics). Materials obey observed rules of behaviour: the laws of mechanics, of thermodynamics, of rate theory, and so on. From these have evolved the continuum theories of elasticity, plasticity, diffusion, reaction rates, etc. Consequently, a store of data collected by experimentation can be manipulated by mathematical methods in a straightforward way. What continuum mechanics is good at is calculating, (without relying on an elaborate test programme), the best length and thickness of a component or article, and the best choice of material to do the job successfully.

13.3.1   Continuum modelling

Close examination of what has happened is that continuum theory has grouped the many variables involved in the design process: working load, displacement, minimum weight, size, etc. If you end up with a single, dimensionless, group, the design is completely constrained. Even if not, and the design has some aspects that you cannot model accurately (like fatigue life of the component), the number of tests to be performed can still be considerably reduced. So, it goes without saying that empiricism is always going to have a role to play in the design process. The important point, however, is that continuum modelling reduces the number of experiments you have to do, and guides you more efficiently to the optimum design.

The problem that still exists, of course, is that the constitutive equations of continuum design are still based on experiment. (A constitutive model is a set of mathematical equations that describe the behaviour of a material element when subjected to an external influence: stress, temperature, etc.) Constitutive models have two aspects: *response* equations and *structural change* equations. Difficulty arises when conditions become stringent, so that more properties are involved in the design process. For example, application of the composite to high temperature under cyclic load may cause the material to crack. The surrounding environment may be chemically active, so the material cracks at an even faster rate. We need constitutive equations for design that include all of these variables including the material properties that in turn depend upon the geometry of the laminate and microstructure of the individual ply. Consequently, the experimental programme from which these constitutive laws are to be devised becomes formidable.

Whilst continuum design is a powerful tool, it has its limitations. Although it provides a description of a material's response to certain stimuli, a uniaxial stress at room temperature, for instance, it gives no help whatsoever in predicting the response of the same material to a new stimulus, a cyclic stress at elevated temperature in a hostile environment. Once again, this is because it contains no information about the principal mechanisms of failure and their dependence on these working conditions. Worse still, when mechanisms of cracking interact, superposition becomes important. And if the interactions are non-linear, the simple constitutive laws break down. A description of the material's response to a new set of circumstances requires a completely new set of experiments from which new continuum rules must be distilled.

13.3.2   Micro-mechanical (physical) modelling

This is where the second box of tools called micro-mechanical modelling can help and is the *raison d'etre* for this chapter. For example, having identified the dominant microscopic processes responsible for fracture, fatigue cracking, thermal stress cracking, or stress corrosion cracking, we can model them using the tools of micro-mechanics and our earlier understanding of the theory of defects, of reaction rates (and so forth). Now we have a different problem; it is that the models, although physically sound, are rarely precise enough to be of much use to an engineer. If your predicted fatigue life is within a factor of ten of the observed life (in this sort of modelling), you are doing very well indeed. Unfortunately, this method based on pure micro-mechanical modelling breaks down in the lack of a precise knowledge of certain microscopic variables, like defect type and size, and flaw or crack distribution, and they simply cannot be measured or determined easily.

But the micro-mechanical models do give something else. Because they have certain broad features, when properly interpreted, they point to rules that the constitutive equations must obey: rules which govern rules, so to speak. These metarules, (as they are called), help us to group the variables in new ways and by so doing reduce the number of independent variables of which there are examples later. The point is this: although micro-mechanical models cannot, by themselves, lead to precise constitutive laws, they do suggest the form that these laws should take, and they put limits (sometimes close limits but not always), on the values of the physical constants that enter them.

The way to exploit this is as follows: the models suggest forms for the constitutive equations, and for the significant groupings of the variables that enter them; empirical methods can then be used to establish the precise functional relations between these groups. The end result is a constitutive equation that contains the predictive power of micro-mechanical modelling with the precision of ordinary curve-fitting of experimental data. In parallel, the broad rules governing material properties can be exploited by creating and checking the data base of material properties that enter the equations. This is to follow the path of *physical model-informed empiricism.* Examples of physical models that follow may help to illustrate what this means.

13.4   A question of physical modelling

What is a physical model? To begin with, a physical or mechanism-based model is a representation of the actual thing (like a two-dimensional ordinance survey map or a three-dimensional physical relief model of a county or state). Although it is an idealisation or massive simplification, it's one that captures the essential characteristics and features of the real thing. In an engineering context, for instance, the model can describe concisely a body of fatigue or fracture stress data. A better model, however, would be one that captures the essential physics of the engineering problem of failure whether it is induced by simple monotonic tensile loading or by repeated (meaning cyclic) loading at elevated temperature. It will illuminate the basic principles that underline the key elements of the fracture or fatigue process. In the situation of a composite material aircraft wing under cyclic stress, it will be the concurrence of matrix cracking and fibre fracture with time that weakens it. And if it is a good fatigue model, meaning it works successfully, then it will predict behaviour of the composite aircraft wing under those stress or environmental conditions that have yet to be studied.

Many problems in the design of the composite material and the composite structure against fatigue are complex and a completely physical treatment isn't always possible. The alternative is to attempt to establish a physical framework on which are built empirical descriptions of the material behaviour. In other words, some of the fatigue variables like maximum stress, stress range or stress amplitude, frequency, numbers of load cycles, temperature, damage-state, are all embedded in the physical model. There are accepted precedents for this. For example, the modelling of thermally activated chemical kinetics, using the law of Arrhenius, has its basis in statistical mechanics. Whilst the activation energy which enters the equation can sometimes be predicted reasonably from molecular models, the value of the pre-exponential factor must be inserted empirically. An example of such a model is the stretching of kinks of molecular dimensions in Kevlar (an aramid) fibre under cyclic loading, (more of which is described later).

13.4.1   Types of physical model

Models are of many types. The empirical model is based on an approximate mathematical equation that describes a set of experimental measurements. This model has no power of prediction and it is dangerous to attempt to use it in this way: it simply must not be applied outside the conditions of the experiment. The problem is that it is unlikely to fit a future set of experimental fatigue data where the test conditions have been changed. A physical model, on the other hand, relies on the established laws of physics and chemistry. This is the ideal model because it derives predictive power from such principles.

At this time, it is helpful to distinguish the static from the dynamic model. A static model is one having properties that do not vary with time. Models of the various failure processes that influence the toughness of a composite is an example provided none of the intrinsic material properties are affected by strain-rate or degrade over time (Wells and Beaumont, 1985a,b, 1987). A dynamic model on the other hand has time-dependent (or rate) effects. An example of a material system that exhibits time or rate effects is Kevlar/epoxy composite. As already mentioned, here the time dependence of stress relaxation comes from the kinetic process of molecular unkinking along the length of the aramid fibre under load. Other dynamic processes can be dependent on viscosity, or diffusion (the diffusion of moisture during the hygrothermal ageing of polymer composites) (Anstice and Beaumont, 1983), or the rate of a chemical reaction in the stress corrosion cracking of glass fibre (Sekine and Beaumont, 1998a,b).

An important question to ask is *'what is the model for?'* Those examples I draw on later illustrate the following: to gain understanding and insight into the physical origin of cracking and the propagation of damage; to capture an aspect of the material's response in an equation or code (a finite element code, for instance); as a guide to the optimization of microstructure (or laminate architecture), to maximize the resistance to cracking and the fatigue endurance of the composite. Another important objective is to predict the material's response under conditions not easily reproduced in the laboratory or when experiments are extremely time consuming and costly to carry out. The complete evaluation of the fatigue behaviour of a component or structure by experiment can take many years.

13.4.2   Identifying the material or engineering problem

Identifying the material or engineering problem may sound straightforward but sometimes the problem contains several sub-problems. For example, in the accumulation of fatigue damage around holes or notches in a composite material, at least three matrix-dominated cracking mechanisms are involved and they do interact (Fig. 13.2). The propagation of a transverse ply matrix crack will interact with an adjacent fibre-matrix interfacial crack. Delamination between layers or plies is affected by splitting in neighbouring layers. In addition, the ends of broken fibres act as stress concentrators and affect the nucleation sites and multiplication of further matrix cracks that also act as stress concentrators. Understanding the interactive effects of these failure mechanisms on fatigue performance is complex to say the least.

Rather than beginning the modelling process with such complexity, it is simpler to model each sub-problem separately and combine the results later, if possible. If the problem is longstanding, like fatigue cracking in composite laminates, there will be a phenomenology-experience, collections of delamination crack growth-rate data, etc., and plots of their dependencies on stress, temperature or time, and the added (or synergistic meaning multiplicative) effects of the environment or interacting mechanisms. Such data and information will allow interrogation of the model in its development. If not, i.e. there is

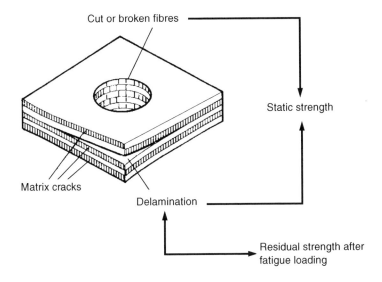

Cut or broken fibres

Static strength

Matrix cracks

Delamination

Residual strength after
fatigue loading

Fig. 13.2   Composites characterized by three material failure modes.

no such phenomenology, then it will be necessary to generate one by conducting experiments.

13.4.3   Development of a physical model

To be useful in structural design, in material system optimization and selection, or in performance prediction, the model should utilize material property data and information that would be routinely available as part of the overall design process. The model should be as simple as possible without losing any of its essential ingredients.

First, identify the desired inputs and outputs of such a model (Spearing and Beaumont, 1998). What do you want to get out of the model? What information do you wish to feed in? What are the microscopic and macroscopic structural variables: fibre length and diameter, fibre volume fraction (fibre to fibre spacing), laminate lay-up geometry or fibre orientation, ply thickness and number of plies; and the boundary conditions, temperature, time, state of stress, number of repeated load cycles, frequency, load spectra and environment? And what are the material properties: fibre strength and modulus, matrix yield stress and ductility, fibre–matrix interfacial (shear) bond strength and interfacial fracture resistance (toughness), the laminate/ply elastic moduli, etc.?

When models couple, the outputs of one may become the inputs to the next. For example, using a physical model, the prediction of a composite's toughness based on its microstructural characteristics and modes of failure can be built into an empirical fatigue damage law (a Paris or power law), (Poursartip *et al.*, 1982a,b,c, 1984, 1986; Ogin *et al.*, 1985; Spearing *et al.*, 1991, 1992a,b,c). This follows the path of *physical model-informed empiricism*. More will be said about this approach later.

13.4.4   Observing and identifying mechanisms

Physical models, those having a physical component based on physical mechanisms, are best established by experimental observation: by the direct observation using optical microscopy of matrix cracks and delamination cracks; by using dye penetrants and X-rays to observe them (Poursartip *et al.*, 1982a,b,c, 1984, 1986; Brown, *et al.*, 1985; Ogin *et al.*, 1985; Ganczakowski *et al.*, 1989, 1990; Kortschot and Beaumont, 1990a,b, 1993; Kortschot *et al.*, 1991; Spearing and Beaumont, 1992a,b; Cowley and Beaumont, 1997; Otunga, 1995; Dimant, 1994; Dimant *et al.*, 1997, 2002). Alternatively, but less satisfactorily, the mechanisms may possibly be inferred by indirect means. The mechanism controlling decohesion of a fibre–matrix bond or matrix cracking under cyclic stress, for instance, can be inferred indirectly by monitoring changes in modulus or damping capacity (mechanical hysteresis) or Poisson's ratio. Failure mechanisms can also be inferred by carrying out post-mortem examination of fractured materials using scanning electron microscopy (SEM) (Wells and Beaumont, 1985, 1987; Vekinis *et al.*, 1993; Shercliff *et al.*, 1994a,b; Otunga, 1995). *In situ* dynamic SEM provides a powerful means of observing mechanisms in action (Gilbert *et al.*, 1983; Mao *et al.*, 1983; Kortschot and Beaumont, 1993; Vekinis *et al.*, 1993). But most importantly, it is dangerous to assume a mechanism without real evidence of its actual operation. Furthermore, it is unwise to assume that an identified mechanism is the dominant one and, therefore, the most important (meaning that it has more influence than any other single mechanism on the material's or component's performance).

13.4.5   Precision of the model

It is sensible to begin by setting relatively modest goals for the precision. A model that begins with an order of magnitude approximation can still help identify the important variables and justify vital physical assumptions. This low level of precision model would be useful in guiding the design of experimental programmes for material screening, to differentiate between competing materials systems or laminate geometry. Knowledge of the precision factor helps in the important process of simplifying the model. At this level, most three dimensional problems can be approximated by one- or two-dimensional equivalents, with a finite element model of a notch tip damage zone, for example. Material properties like fibre strength can be assumed constant even though we know it depends on fibre length and diameter, and on flaw distribution. At each level of refinement of the model in order to improve its precision, it is necessary to ask whether aspects of the problem, neglected at the previous stage, should now be included.

Remember that modelling is an iterative routine. For example, at what stage should the statistical nature of fibre fracture be included in a physical model of the fracture stress (or fatigue life) of the composite? Furthermore, can the fibre fracture model be coupled with models of splitting and delamination processes? Transverse ply (matrix) cracking and delamination cracking can be treated separately or coupled. But it is good policy to continue to exclude aspects that influence the results by less than the current precision target.

Why complicate things if a factor of two can be quite acceptable. By fine tuning a physical model, it is usually possible to provide a close fit to experimental data, while maintaining the inherent predictive capability of the model (Spearing and Beaumont, 1998).

13.5   A question of fatigue

The traditional empirical approach to fatigue is the development of interpolative empirical models from databases, which allow material design allowables to be passed on to the next level of design. But each model requires re-calibrating whenever a new composite material system or laminate stacking sequence is employed, or if the loading or structural configuration changes. In order to obtain a predictive capability of fatigue damage and the resulting fatigue strength, we require a physically-sound model of the fatigue failure processes.

The physical model transforms the inputs into the outputs. It can take the form of algebraic, differential, or integral equations. These may be embedded in a discretized computation where discrete units or cells respond to temperature, body forces, and stress via constitutive equations. The constraints on the models include equilibrium, compatibility, and continuity at their boundaries (continuum modelling or finite element modelling).

13.5.1   Constructing a physical model of damage accumulation

To construct the physical model, once more draw upon the modelling tools of engineering and materials science: the equations and principles of mechanics, kinetics, and exploit existing validated models or previously modelled problems, including fracture mechanics and thermal stress. Some parts of the damage growth process cannot be modelled; they are simply too complex. In such a case, introduce an empirical fit to a set of experimental fatigue data (the phenomenology) – a fatigue power law, for instance.

Composite materials behaviour frequently involves four further levels of complexity: *structural change, multiple mechanisms, linked processes, and spatial variation* (when stress, temperature or other field variables are non-uniform). Structural (or damage) change is exactly that: the structure or damage within it, and thus the behaviour or performance, of the material changes or grows with time (or numbers of cycles in repeated loading). When the composite is loaded to a critical stress, internal cracks form and accumulate within it (matrix or fibre dominated cracking processes, or both of equal importance). This damage weakens the material generally and reduces its stiffness, which in turn increases the rate at which further damage accumulates: there is positive feedback. Constitutive models describing this sort of behaviour are best derived using the internal state variable method. Briefly, the key ideas are that constitutive models have two aspects: response equations and structural change equations.

Consider the design against fatigue cracking of a carbon/epoxy aircraft wing. Crack growth is slow to begin with but it accumulates with time by the simultaneous development of matrix-dominated processes and fibre fracture. The result is a loss of stiffness of the structure. Computing the extent of this sort of fatigue behaviour is difficult because it depends in a sensitive way on both stress and temperature. These, it should be remembered, are not constant; in any real engineering sense they vary with time. The goal of fatigue design in this instance is to predict the state of damage brought about by this complexity of different cracking processes and any consequences of it, like residual (damage) stiffness (or modulus) and residual (damage) strength of the composite, or remaining life-time of the wing.

Fatigue damage in a laminate includes (at least) four modes of failure: transverse ply (matrix) cracking, delamination (cracking between layers), splitting (cracking within $0°$ plies parallel to the fibres), and fibre fracture within the principal load bearing layers. The response equation describes the relationship of (say) current modulus E (a measure of the effect of damage on stiffness of the laminate) to the stress range $\Delta\sigma$ and the current values of the internal state variable, D (Fig. 13.3). We call these internal variables *damage* because they describe a change in the state of a material, brought about by fatigue in this instance. The state variable D evolves with the progressive nature of fatigue damage and describes the current state of the structure (Fig. 13.3). The various modes of failure spread throughout the composite until either the net section stress (there is a loss of section caused by the damage) exceeds the tensile strength, or a single critical crack has evolved, by the concentration of

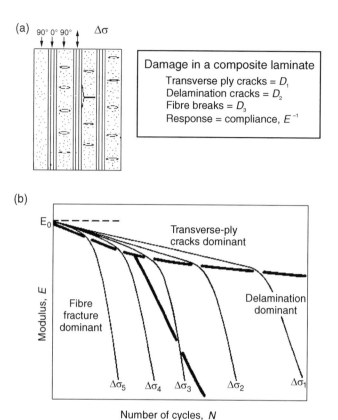

Fig. 13.3   (a) A model of the composite laminate subjected to repeated load cycling $\Delta\sigma_1$, $\Delta\sigma_2$, $\Delta\sigma_3$, etc. with transverse ply cracks, delaminations, and fibre fractures–state variables D_1, D_2, D_3 measure the extent of these damaging mechanisms. (b) The response E, with the dominant failure mechanisms identified. (Based on the work of Poursartip *et al.*, 1982.)

localized fibre breaks in the 0° ply, for instance. Having attained a critical size, this crack then propagates catastrophically across the section.

Consider the fatigue of a cross-ply carbon/epoxy composite; with increasing numbers of load cycles (at low cyclic stress), the modulus falls gently with the onset of transverse ply cracking (Fig. 13.3), (Poursartip *et al.*, 1982a,b,c, 1984, 1986). (This is called high cycle fatigue.) As the stress amplitude increases, an abrupt change in slope designates the onset and domination of delamination cracking. And if the stress amplitude increases even further (now called low cycle fatigue), the important mechanism becomes fibre fracture. The onset of these changes in dominant mode of failure depends on the independent variable stress amplitude $\Delta\sigma$ (temperature constant). With only one such variable, a fairly complete characterization is practicable. But this does not cater for time-varying stress $\Delta\sigma(t)$ and temperature $\Delta T(t)$, or for the effect of changes in stress-state on the fatigue cracking processes. If we try to include them, we find we are dealing with eight or more independent variables: temperature T, stress σ, the frequency (ν_σ, ν_T) and amplitude $(\Delta T, \Delta\sigma)$, the ratios λ of stress invariants and so on:

$$E = f(\sigma,\ \lambda,\ T,\ t,\ \Delta\sigma,\ \Delta T,\ \nu_\sigma,\ \nu_T,\ \text{material properties}) \qquad [13.1]$$

It is possible to set up an experimental programme to characterize the influence of each of these variables on fatigue; that is the direction in which research has moved. But the scope of the test programme would be immense. It can be further complicated, more often than not, because several mechanisms of fatigue cracking are involved. Likewise, the characterization of one range of temperature (for instance) cannot safely be extrapolated into another; a new characterization is needed. The method of extended empiricism just breaks down under the unmanageable load of variables.

Physical (or micro-mechanical) modelling follows a different path. It seeks to identify the underlying microscopic processes responsible for the individual fracture mechanisms and to model each stage of fatigue from first principles. It has had some success: the mechanisms leading to cracking and fatigue failure in composites are now tolerably well understood although not, in engineering terms, well characterized. The problem (as already stated) arises because the micro-mechanical model contains numerous microscopic parameters that define the structure and which can only be determined by microscopic means or observation, and this, in an engineering context, is not practical.

However, the model points to something else, and it is of the greatest value; it suggests the proper form that the constitutive equation should take. Models for composite fatigue have one thing in common; they lead to equations for a *damaged* modulus or strength with time (or load cycles), and they contain the *internal state variable D,* the parameter that characterizes the current mechanical state of the material. (This is often the area fraction of cracks that accumulate during fatigue.) The model suggests a constitutive equation with a completely different form than before. Instead of trying to characterize, for example, modulus E as a function of the independent variables, we now seek to fit data to a coupled set of differential equations, one for the modulus E' and two (or more) depending on the number of damaging mechanisms for damage propagation D_1' and D_2'.

For modulus E and damage D we have:

$$E' = f(\sigma, \lambda, T, D_1, D_2, \text{material properties})$$
[13.2a]

$$D_1' = g_1(\sigma, \lambda, T, D_1, D_2, \text{material properties})$$
[13.2b]

$$D_2' = g_2(\sigma, \lambda, T, D_1, D_2, \text{material properties})$$
[13.2c]

where D_1 describes the damage due to one mechanism and D_2 describes a different damaging mechanism that together lead to composite failure, and E', D_1' and D_2' are their *rates of change* with time (or numbers of cycles); f, g_1, g_2 are simple functions.

There are now three independent variables $(\sigma, T,$ and stress-state, $\lambda)$ whereas before there were eight. These equations can be integrated to track out the change of modulus with the accumulation of damage, and ultimately to predict fracture in a component or the design life. The modulus–time (cycles) response is found by integrating the equations as a coupled set, starting with $E = E_0$ (the undamaged modulus) and $D = 0$ (no damage). Step through the time (cycles), calculating the increments, and thus the current values, of E and D, using these to calculate their change in the next step. Equation [13.2a,b,c] can now be adopted as the constitutive equation for fatigue, and empirical methods can be used to determine the functions f, g_1, g_2. This model-informed empiricism has led to the development of a new branch of mechanics called *damage mechanics*.

13.6   Physical modelling of fatigue damage development

During the fatigue of most (perhaps all), fibrous composites, damage accumulates within them (for example, see Poursartip et al., 1982a,b,c, 1984, 1986). Such damage may have several components: fibre breakage, matrix cracking, delamination, axial splitting, and so forth. Throughout the composite's life, this growth of damage can be monitored non-destructively by measuring one of the properties of the material: the moduli, for instance, or the electrical conductivity, or light scattering, or the X-ray absorption, or ultrasonic attenuation, or the damping coefficient, or by acoustic emission detection.

In the physical model developed by Poursartip et al., (1982a,b,c), fatigue damage is quantified by the variable data D. At the start of life D is zero unless damage D_i has been introduced during fabrication, or by earlier history. Cyclic loading causes the damage to increase from D_i to D_f at which point catastrophic failure of the composite laminate occurs.

Assuming that the damage accumulation rate depends on the cyclic stress range $\Delta\sigma$, the load ratio R and on the current level of D, then:

$$\frac{dD}{dN} = f(\Delta\sigma, R, D) \qquad [13.3]$$

provided temperature, frequency, etc., are constant or have negligible effects.

The life-time (meaning the number of cycles to increase D from D_i to D_f) is found by integrating this equation to give N_f:

$$N_f = \int_{D_i}^{D_f} \frac{dD}{f(\Delta\sigma, R, D)} \qquad [13.4]$$

The difficulty, of course, is that we do not know the function f. But we can monitor with time (or number of load cycles) the tensile Young's modulus E of the composite laminate and the accumulated damage D.

If a relation exists between E and D, we can write:

$$E = E_0 g(D) \qquad [13.5]$$

where E_0 is the initial or undamaged modulus.

Therefore:

$$\frac{1}{E_0}\frac{dE}{dD} = g'(D) \qquad [13.6]$$

g' means the derivative of g with respect to D.

Differentiating equation [13.6] and substituting into equation [13.1], we get:

$$\frac{1}{E_0}\frac{dE}{dN} = g'\left(g^{-1}\left(\frac{E}{E_0}\right)\right) f\left(\Delta\sigma, R, g^{-1}\left(\frac{E}{E_0}\right)\right) \qquad [13.7]$$

where g^{-1} is the inverse of g:

$$D = g^{-1}\left(\frac{E}{E_0}\right) \qquad [13.8]$$

First, we have to establish the function $g(D)$, by experimental means or theoretically, before the damage accumulation function $f(\Delta\sigma, R, D)$ can be determined. The function $g(D)$ depends on the properties and lay-up of the composite laminate, not of how the damage D was introduced. There are now two approaches that can be taken: either a damage accumulation function is proposed and inserted into equation [13.7], and the result compared with experimental data, or data can be collected of E/E_0 as a function of N, the number of load cycles. Then, knowing $g(D)$, the function $f(\Delta\sigma, R, D)$ is determined experimentally using equation [13.9]:

$$f(\Delta\sigma, R, D) = g'\left(g^{-1}\left(\frac{E}{E_0}\right)\right)\frac{1}{E_0}\left(\frac{dE}{dN}\right)$$

[13.9]

This is a relatively straightforward exercise. First, the right-hand side of the equation is evaluated for different values of $\Delta\sigma$ at constant E/E_0 and constant R; secondly, for different values of R at constant $\Delta\sigma$ and constant E/E_0; and thirdly, for different values of E/E_0 at constant $\Delta\sigma$ and constant R. The function $f(\Delta\sigma, R, D)$ can then be determined from a plot of these results.

13.6.1 Example 1: a model of delamination cracking

A quasi-isotropic carbon/epoxy (CFRP) in tensile cyclic loading fails initially by matrix cracking of the 90° ply followed by matrix cracking of the 45° ply; by delamination cracking at the 45° and 90° ply interface; and, finally, by fibre fracture. In high-cycle fatigue (low stress, long fatigue lives), the dominant mode of failure is by delamination (Fig. 13.4). This can be quantified using C-scan to reveal the extent of fatigue delamination growth. Ignoring other forms of damage, we can define the damage parameter D as the normalized delamination area A/A_0, where A is the actual (measured) delamination area and A_0 is the total area available for delamination.

A simple model for the loss of modulus with delaminations growth is:

$$E = E_0 + (E^* - E_0)\frac{A}{A_0}$$

[13.10]

where E^* is the modulus corresponding to a completely delaminated composite (totally separate sub-laminates), i.e. when $A/A_0 = 1$, and then $E/E_0 = 0.65$.

Thus, the function $g(D)$ in equation [13.5] can be expressed as:

$$g(D) = 1 - 0.35D$$

[13.11]

It follows that:

$$D = 2.857\left(1 - \frac{E}{E_0}\right)$$

[13.12]

Thus, from equation [13.9]:

$$f(\Delta\sigma, R, D) = \frac{dD}{dN} = -2.857\left(\frac{1}{E_0}\frac{dE}{dN}\right)$$

[13.13]

The right-hand side of equation [13.13] can easily be evaluated experimentally. Figure 13.5 shows the damage rate dD/dN as a function of $\Delta\sigma$ (for $R = 0.1$). Clearly, there are three regimes of fatigue behaviour:

- a power-law relation between dD/dN and $\Delta\sigma$ over most of the stress range;
- damage rate is much higher than expected from a power law at stresses approaching the ultimate strength; essentially we have a static tensile failure;
- an apparent threshold stress of 250 MPa below which no damage occurs.

This threshold stress corresponds to the stress to initiate the first crack (the 'design ultimate') observed in a simple tensile test.

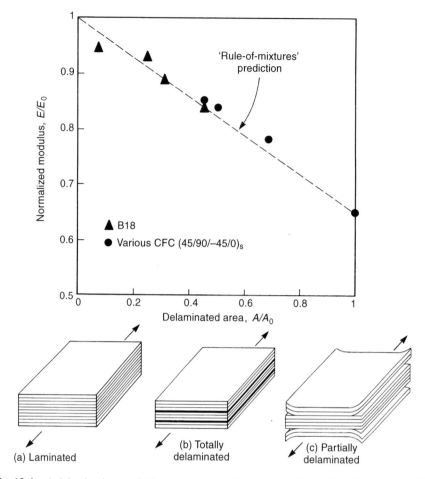

Fig. 13.4   A delamination model based on a rule of mixtures analysis of tensile modulus. The symbols indicate measurements of modulus and delamination area. The laminate is made from a (45/90/-45/0)$_s$ carbon/epoxy. (After Poursartip *et al.*, 1986.)

13.6.1.1   Fatigue life: the terminal damage state

To predict fatigue life, we need to know the critical or terminal damage state D_f at failure. The level of reduced (damaged) modulus at failure depends upon the maximum applied stress σ_{max}. Figure 13.6 shows that the reduced modulus at failure is a linear function of σ_{max}. The reduced modulus (on the horizontal axis) is divided into two parts: for $(1 - E/E_0) \geq 0.35$, the damage due to delamination is D_1; for greater than 0.35, additional damage D_2 is due to fibre breakage and splitting within the 0° plies.

In load-controlled fatigue experiments, the instantaneous strain ε of the composite increases as the damaged modulus E decreases with load cycling (the material 'softens'). After some fatigue cycling at σ_{max}, the increased strain is:

$$\varepsilon = \frac{\sigma_{max}}{E} \qquad\qquad\qquad [13.14]$$

The fatigue life is when the failure strain ε_c of the composite is reached, i.e. when $\varepsilon = \varepsilon_c$. In monotonic tensile loading, and assuming no modulus reduction, then:

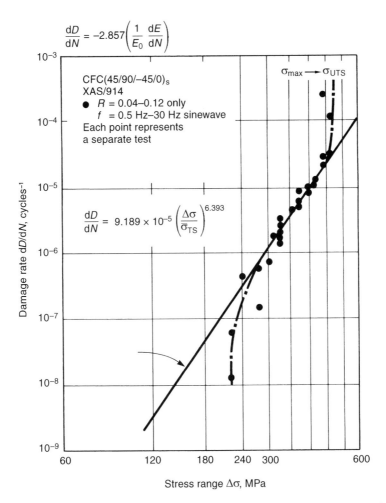

Fig. 13.5   Comparison between observed damage growth-rate and stress range of a quasi-isotropic carbon/epoxy laminate and the power law model prediction. (After Poursartip *et al.*, 1986.)

$$\varepsilon_c = \frac{\sigma_{TS}}{E_0} \qquad\qquad [13.15]$$

Since fast fracture occurs when the strain ε during a fatigue cycle equals ε_c, then by equating equations [13.14, 13.15] and substituting for D_f from equation [13.12], we have at the fatigue life:

$$D_f = D = 2.857\left(1 - \frac{E_f}{E_0}\right) = 2.857\left(1 - \frac{\sigma_{max}}{\sigma_{TS}}\right) \qquad\qquad [13.16]$$

The three broken lines in Fig. 13.6 correspond to equation [13.16] where σ_{TS} takes on values of 550, 600, or 650 MPa, respectively. The constant strain to failure criterion accounts for the data reasonably well.

For power-law damage growth (from Fig. 13.5):

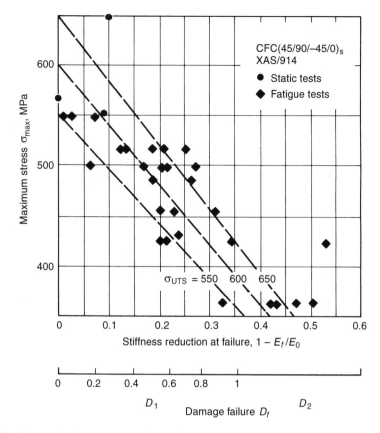

Fig. 13.6   Comparison between experimental data and model prediction of damage at failure and modulus reduction as a function of the maximum cyclic tensile stress. The laminate is made from $(45/90/-45/0)_s$ carbon/epoxy. (After Poursartip *et al.*, 1986.)

$$\frac{dD}{dN} = 9.2 \times 10^{-5} \left(\frac{\Delta\sigma}{\sigma_{TS}} \right)^{6.4} \quad \text{(for } R = 0.1) \tag{13.17}$$

The effect of mean stress is such that:

$$\left(\frac{dD}{dN} \right)_{R \geq 0} = \left(\frac{dD}{dN} \right)_{R=0.1} \times \left(\frac{\sigma_m \, (R \geq 0.1)}{\sigma_m \, (R = 0.1)} \right)^{p} \tag{13.18}$$

where p ≈ 2, depending on the value of Δσ. Substituting for $f(\Delta\sigma, R, D)$ from equations [13.17] and [13.18], we have:

$$N_f = \int_{D_i}^{D_f} 1.1 \times 10^{4} \left(\frac{\Delta\sigma}{\sigma_{TS}} \right)^{-6.4} \frac{\sigma_m \, (R = 0.1)^{p}}{\sigma_m \, (R \geq 0.1)} \, dD \tag{13.19}$$

where D_f is determined by equation [13.16]. We can substitute for σ_{max} and σ_m in terms of Δσ and R:

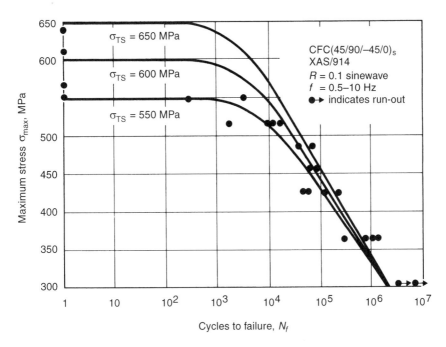

Fig. 13.7   Prediction of an *S–N* curve based on the damage model together with experimental data of load cycles to failure (*R* = 0.1). The solid curves are theroretical curves of life-time for three possible values of tensile strength of a laminate made from (45/90/–45/0)$_s$ carbon/epoxy. (After Poursartip *et al.*, 1986.)

$$\sigma_{max} = \frac{\Delta\sigma}{1-R} \qquad [13.20]$$

By integrating equation [13.19] we obtain:

$$N_f = 3.1 \times 10^{-4} \left(\frac{\Delta\sigma}{\sigma_{TS}}\right)^{-6.4} \left(1.22\frac{1-R}{1+R}\right)^p \left(1 - \frac{\Delta\sigma}{(1-R)\sigma_{TS}}\right) \qquad [13.21]$$

At the start of the fatigue test, $D_i = 0$, whilst D_j is determined using equation [13.16]. Using equation [13.21] we can construct the *S–N* curve (for *R* = 0.1) (Fig. 13.7).

The life prediction is shown by the solid curves choosing three possible tensile strengths of the laminate. There is consistency with this treatment and the observations shown by the experimental data points. At low stress, high-cycle fatigue, any variations in tensile strength have little effect on lifetime, whereas in low-cycle fatigue, small changes can be significant.

13.6.1.2   Variable amplitude loading effects

To predict fatigue lives under variable-amplitude loading we must be able to predict the average damage growth-rate $(dD/dN)_{av}$, and the critical damage level to cause failure D_f. In a variable-amplitude loading sequence, we would expect the critical damage to be determined by the cycle with the highest maximum stress. Let us consider an experiment in which the following two-block loading sequence was run (Poursartip *et al.*, 1986):

$$\Delta\sigma_1 = 328 \text{ MPa} \qquad\qquad \Delta\sigma_2 = 395 \text{ MPa}$$
$$\sigma_{max1} = 365 \text{ MPa} \qquad\qquad \sigma_{max2} = 500 \text{ MPa}$$
$$N_1 = 1000\text{--}2000 \text{ cycles} \qquad\qquad N_1 = 1\text{--}100 \text{ cycles}$$

Since the low stress was maintained for the greater number of cycles, it is not surprising that the observed damage rates were found to lie close to that expected of type 1 cycling on its own. The average measured value of D_f was 0.64. Using equation [13.12] and assuming σ_{TS} lies between 600 and 650 MPa, if the damage at failure is to be determined by the highest maximum stress seen, then:

$$0.48 < D_f < 0.66$$

Likewise if the damage at failure is to be determined by the most frequent maximum stress seen, then:

$$1.12 < D_f < 1.25$$

The observed D_f agrees best with the highest maximum stress criterion.

Let us now consider the simple case of two blocks of duration N_1 and N_2, with corresponding damage rates $(dD/dN)_1$, and $(dD/dN)_2$. Provided there are no load interaction effects, (and this may not be true under all loading conditions), then we may assume a linear sum of the rates to represent the average damage rate:

$$\left(\frac{dD}{dN}\right)_{av} = \frac{N_1}{N_1 + N_2}\left(\frac{dD}{dN}\right)_1 + \frac{N_2}{N_1 + N_2}\left(\frac{dD}{dN}\right)_2 \qquad [13.22]$$

We can check this as follows: in a simple test where $N_1 = 1000$, $\Delta\sigma_1 = 395$ MPa, $R = 0.2$, followed by $N_2 = 2000$, $\Delta\sigma_2 = 328$ MPa, $R = 0.1$, repeated for about 40 000 cycles, we found that $(dD/dN)_{av} = 3.6 \times 10^{-6}$

Using damage rates determined by equation [13.17] for the two separate loading sequences, inserted into equation [13.22], we obtain

$$\frac{dD}{dN} = \frac{1}{3}\left(7.4 \times 10^{-6}\right) + \frac{2}{3}\left(2.25 \times 10^{-6}\right) = 4 \times 10^{-6}$$

which compares well with the observed rate.

13.6.2   Example 2: a model of transverse ply matrix cracking

A dominant mode of fatigue failure of a cross-ply glass/epoxy (GRP) is by matrix cracking within the 90° plies. Figure 13.8 is a schematic which shows a parallel array of idealized matrix cracks of average spacing 2s, or of crack density $(2s)^{-1}$. The damage parameter D is defined by the density of matrix cracks. It uniquely defines the current level of damage (for a given set of test variables, load ratio, frequency, temperature, and so forth).

One effect of this damage is to reduce the stiffness of the composite in the following way (Ogin et al., 1985):

$$E = E_0(1 - cD) \qquad [13.23]$$

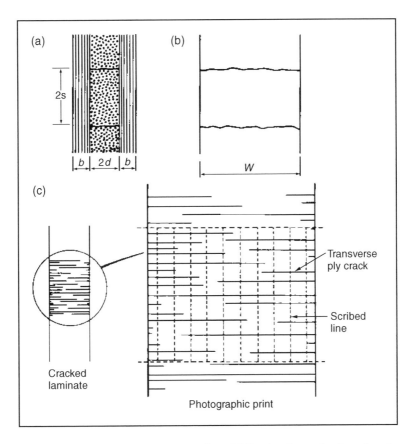

Fig. 13.8   A schematic of transverse ply cracks in a $(0/90)_s$ glass/epoxy laminate based on optical microscopy: (a) shows the edge view of the tensile specimen; (b) shows the front view; (c) shows the method of crack density determination. The crack spacing $2s$ is calculated by counting the average number of cracks cutting the dashed lines and dividing by the total line length. (After Ogin *et al.*, 1985).

where the constant $c = \left(E_0\!\!\big/\!E\right)\left[\left(b + d\big/\!b\right) - \left(E_1\!\!\big/\!E_0\right)\right]\left(2\big/\!\lambda\right)$ is equal to 0.054 (having the dimensions of mm) for this particular $(0°/90°)_s$ laminate. The general form of λ is:

$$\lambda = \left[\frac{\alpha G(b + d)E_0}{d^2 b E_2 E_1}\right]$$

α has the value of 1 or 3 depending on whether in this shear lag model, a linear or a parabolic variation of longitudinal displacement in the transverse ply is assumed, E_1 and E_2 are the Young's moduli of the $0°$ and $90°$ plies of thickness b and d, respectively, and G is the shear modulus of the $90°$ ply in the longitudinal direction.

Differentiating equation [13.23] with respect to the number of load cycles N and combining with equation [13.3] gives:

$$-\frac{1}{cE_0}\frac{dE}{dN} = f\left[\sigma_{max}, \frac{1}{c}\left(1 - \frac{E}{E_0}\right)\right] \qquad\qquad [13.24]$$

As in the case of CFRP, the difficulty is in finding the appropriate form of the damage function. One way, is to consider the stored elastic strain energy between two adjacent matrix cracks. This is treated in the next section.

13.6.2.1   Stress in a cracked transverse ply

The average stored elastic strain energy U between two idealized neighbouring matrix cracks can be expressed as:

$$U = \frac{1}{V} \int_{-s}^{s} \left[\frac{\sigma_2^2 \, W 2d}{2 \, E_2} \right] \tag{13.25}$$

V is the volume of material between these two matrix cracks spaced $2s$ apart (Fig. 13.8). The longitudinal stress in the 90° ply is given by:

$$\sigma_2 = \sigma_\infty \left[\frac{E_2}{E_0} \right] \left[1 - \frac{\cosh(\lambda x)}{\cosh(\lambda s)} \right] \tag{13.26}$$

σ_∞ is the remote applied stress on the laminate. Integrating equation [13.25] we obtain the approximate expression for U:

$$U = \left[\frac{\sigma_\infty}{E_0} \right]^2 E_2 \frac{s}{k} , \tag{13.27}$$

This is for crack spacings between d and $3d$, for which E/E_0 lies between 0.8 and 0.95 (k is a constant for a given value of λ and is equal to 1.3 mm for this particular cross-ply laminate.)

The average stress in the transverse ply σ_{av} depends on the square root of the average crack spacing $2s$ and is obtained by re-writing the stored elastic strain energy U equation as follows:

$$\sigma_{av} = \frac{E_2}{E_0} \left(\frac{1}{k} \right)^{1/2} \sigma \sqrt{2s} \tag{13.28}$$

There is a localized stress disturbance in the vicinity of the matrix crack tip roughly equal in distance to one-half of the ply thickness. The crack tip stress intensity factor K is given by:

$$K = \sigma_{av} \sqrt{2d} \tag{13.29}$$

This comes from the recognition that the build-up of stress at the crack tip does not depend on crack length. By combining equations [13.28] and [13.29]:

$$K = \frac{E_2}{E_0} \left(\frac{2s}{k} \right)^{1/2} \sigma \sqrt{2d} \tag{13.30}$$

13.6.2.2   The crack growth rate of a matrix crack

The growth rate of a single crack can be described by a fatigue (power) law:

$$\frac{dz}{dN} = BK_{max}^m \tag{13.31}$$

For a constant number p of growing matrix cracks (verified by experiment):

$$\frac{da}{dN} = p\left[BK_{max}^{m} \right]$$ [13.32]

B and m are constants dependent on load ratio, stress range, frequency, temperature, etc. (This power law of fatigue damage is similar to the one used for CFRP.)
Now the total matrix crack length a is given by:

$$a = \frac{WL}{2s}$$ [13.33]

In the idealized model, W and L are the width and length of the composite. For damage D we can write $D = (2s)^{-1}$; then equation [13.33] becomes:

$$E = E_0 \left(1 - \frac{c}{2s} \right)$$ [13.34]

Combining equations [13.33] and [13.34] and differentiating with respect to N:

$$\frac{da}{dN} = \frac{WL}{c} \left[-\frac{1}{E_0} \left(\frac{dE}{dN} \right) \right]$$ [13.35]

$\left[-\frac{1}{E_0} \left(\frac{dE}{dN} \right) \right]$ is the tangent of the modulus reduction versus number of load cycles curve at any given value of E/E_0.

We know (from equation [13.29]), that $K_{max} \propto \sigma_{max} \sqrt{2s}$. Thus, by combining equations [13.30], [13.32] and [13.35], and substituting for the average crack spacing, $2s$ (equation [13.34]), we get:

$$-\frac{1}{E_0} \left(\frac{dE}{dN} \right) = A \left[\frac{\sigma_{max}^2}{E_0^2 \left(1 - \frac{E}{E_0} \right)} \right]^{m/2}$$ [13.36]

The introduction of the term E_0^2 makes the right-hand side of the equation dimensionless. A and m are constants. We now have a possible form of the function given by equation [13.3]. The modulus reduction rate

$$\left[-\frac{1}{E_0} \left(\frac{dE}{dN} \right) \right]$$

is simply the tangent to the experimental curve of E/E_0 versus N at any value of E/E_0. (Fig. 13.9). The data fits a power law relation given by equation [13.36].

Finally, it follows that the relationship between the current (damaged) modulus E, the number of load cycles N and the maximum applied stress σ_{max}, is given by:

$$\frac{E}{E_0} = 1 - \left[25.3 \left(\frac{\sigma_{max}}{E_0} \right)^{1.48} N^{0.26} \right]$$ [13.37]

Equation [13.37] is plotted for three values of maximum stress in Fig. 13.10. This is the kind of fatigue design diagram that was advocated three decades ago by Salkind (1971).

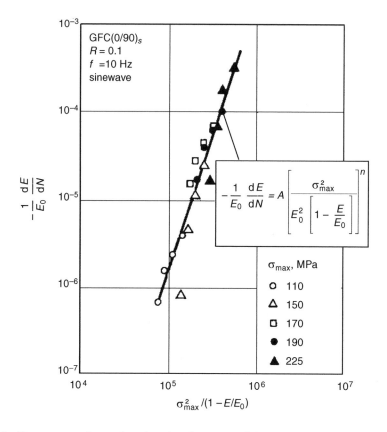

Fig. 13.9 Damage growth rate plotted against the square of the maximum cyclic tensile stress on a log–log scale. The straight line depicts the power law prediction of modulus change with load cycles with $A = 5.65 \times 10^4$ and $m = 5.6$. (After Ogin *et al.*, 1985).

13.6.3   Example 3: a model linking matrix cracking and delamination

Figure 13.11 shows a schematic of the physical model of coupled mechanisms, a much simplified representation of the transverse ply (matrix) crack intersecting a delamination crack or interlaminar crack (Dimant, 1994). The dimensions are indicated and t is the transverse ply thickness. Under monotonic or cyclic loading, the delamination crack extends over part of the interface between two neighbouring transverse ply cracks. If we assume there is no bonding or frictional (sliding) forces acting at the debond, then the transverse ply partially unloads when it cracks. (This may be unrealistic; there might well be a frictional shear force between sliding interfacial crack surfaces because of a compressive force exerted at the interface.)

Under increasing load P, the strain energy release rate G associated with the growth of the mode II delamination crack only is given by:

$$G = \left[\frac{P^2}{2t} \right] \left[\frac{dC}{d\ell_d} \right]$$

[13.38]

The compliance C of the laminate increases by an amount dC as the delamination crack grows by $d\ell_d$ and energy is dissipated in the process.

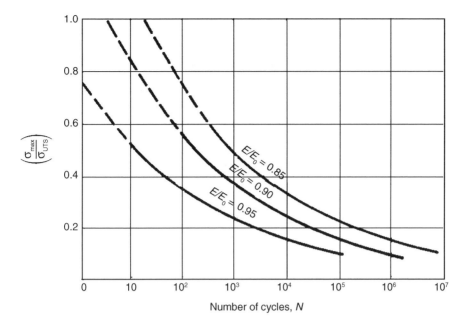

Fig. 13.10   The predicted loss of modulus with load cycles diagram for a (0/90)$_s$ glass/epoxy laminate. (After Ogin *et al.*, 1985)

First, consider the compliance change dC of the interfacial cracked portion a of the laminate and, secondly, the compliance change dC of that remaining portion b of intact interface between the two neighbouring transverse ply cracks (Fig. 13.11). The compliance C and longitudinal modulus E of the laminate are related by:

$$C = L/EA \qquad [13.39]$$

L is the length and A is the cross-sectional area of the laminate. It must follow, therefore, that the compliance C can be determined by evaluating the moduli of the cracked portion a and the uncracked portion b of the laminate. The modulus E_0 of an undamaged, (meaning uncracked), laminate can be estimated using a rule of mixtures for the laminate:

$$E_0 = \left[\frac{b\,E_1 + d\,E_2}{b+d} \right] \qquad [13.40]$$

E_1 and E_2 are the longitudinal and transverse ply moduli, respectively.

Likewise, the reduced or damaged modulus E_c of the delamination cracked portion a depends essentially on the modulus of the longitudinal ply and the cross-sectional area of the laminate:

$$\left[\frac{E_c}{E_0} \right]_a = \left[\frac{b\,E_1}{b\,E_1 + d\,E_2} \right] \qquad [13.41]$$

In terms of the transverse ply crack spacing $2s$ the model can be approximated to:

$$\left[\frac{E_c}{E_0} \right] = \frac{1}{\left[1 + \left(\dfrac{d\,E_2}{b\,E_0} \right) \dfrac{\tanh s}{s} \right]} \qquad [13.42]$$

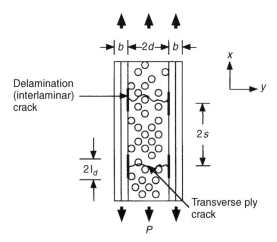

Fig. 13.11   Geometry of two neighbouring transverse ply cracks interacting with local delamination (interlaminar) cracks (edge view). (After Dimant, 1994.)

(This is a similar model to the shear lag model applied to cracking in GRP described in the previous section.)

Extending this model to include local delamination cracking at the tip of the matrix crack, we can estimate the modulus of portion b by considering an 'effective' transverse ply crack spacing $(s - \ell_d)$. Thus, when we substitute $(s - \ell_d)$ into equation [13.42] we obtain:

$$\left[\frac{E_c}{E_0}\right]_b = \frac{1}{1 + \left(\dfrac{d\,E_2}{d\,E_0}\right)\dfrac{\tanh(s - \ell_d)}{s - \ell_d}} \tag{13.43}$$

Hence, the longitudinal modulus of the laminate is calculated simply by using a rule of mixtures for $(E_c/E_0)_a$ and $(E_c/E_0)_b$ which is dependent on the portions of cracked and un-cracked interface:

$$\left[\frac{E_c}{E_0}\right]_{lam} = \frac{\left[\dfrac{E_c}{E_0}\right]_a \left[\dfrac{E_c}{E_0}\right]_b (s)}{\left[\left[\dfrac{E_c}{E_0}\right]_a (s - \ell_d) + \left[\dfrac{E_c}{E_0}\right]_a (\ell_d)\right]} \tag{13.44}$$

Now, by multiplying equation [13.40] by equation [13.41] and substituting into equation [13.39], we obtain the compliance of the cracked portion a:

$$C_a = \frac{\ell_d}{bt\,E_1} \tag{13.45}$$

Similarly, the compliance of un-cracked portion b is obtained by multiplying equation [13.40] by equation [13.43] and substituting into equation [13.39]:

$$C_b = \frac{(s - \ell_d)}{(b\,E_1 + d\,E_2)t}\left[1 + \left(\frac{d\,E_2}{d\,E_1}\right)\frac{\tanh(s - \ell_d)}{s - \ell_d}\right] \tag{13.46}$$

Finally, we have for the compliance of the complete portion of material between the two transverse ply cracks:

$$C_{\text{laminate}} = C_a + C_b \qquad [13.47]$$

Thus:

$$C_{\text{laminate}} = \frac{\ell_d}{(bt\,E_1)} + \frac{(s-\ell_d)}{(b\,E_1 + d\,E_2)t}\left[1+\left(\frac{d\,E_2}{d\,E_1}\right)\frac{\tanh\,(s-\ell_d)}{s-\ell_d}\right] \qquad [13.48]$$

The development of the model so far is as follows: the compliance of any cracked cross-ply laminate is defined in terms of s, ℓ_d, b and d and can be estimated using equation [13.48]. The strain energy release rate G associated with the growth of a crack at the 0/90 interface can be obtained using equation [13.38]. Furthermore, G can be evaluated for the propagation of a local delamination crack at the tip of the ply crack by determining the change of compliance dC, as the delamination crack extends $dC/d\ell_d$. This can be done experimentally by determining a series of values of C and ℓ_d.

For discrete values of s, the incremental change in compliance ∂C is calculated for an incremental change in delamination length $\partial \ell_d$; $\partial C/\partial \ell_d$ is approximately equal to $dC/d\ell_d$. One way of determining the maximum value of $dC/d\ell_d$ is by determining the change of compliance when two delamination cracks first initiate at the tips of two widely spaced ply cracks. Then, under increasing load, as the matrix crack density increases (i.e. the spacing between two neighbouring cracks shortens), and/or the delamination crack extends completely between them, the transverse ply becomes totally load-free.

Thus, the modulus of the laminate approaches a value given by:

$$\left[\frac{E_c}{E_0}\right]_a = \left[\frac{b\,E_1}{b\,E_1 + d\,E_2}\right] \qquad [13.49]$$

The adaptation of the transverse ply cracking model to include the interfacial delamination crack is shown in Fig. 13.12. Curves of longitudinal modulus are drawn for selected crack spacings, 1, 2, 4, 8 times the transverse ply thickness t. In the absence of any delamination, the modulus is indicated on the left axis of the diagram which falls with the growth of a delamination crack. The modulus of a laminate in which the delamination crack has extended completely between two neighbouring matrix cracks is equivalent to having a multiplicity of matrix cracks in the laminate. This is given by equation [13.49]. The damaged modulus is non-linear with delamination crack growth.

The maximum value of $dC/d\ell_d$ can be determined by evaluating equation [13.49] for a large crack spacing s and $\ell_d = 0$, allowing for only a small extension of ℓ_d. The value of $dC/d\ell_d$ is simply the difference between the two compliances divided by the increment in delamination length $4\ell_d$.

Setting arbitrary values of s and ℓ_d, e.g. $s = nd$ (where $n > 2$) and $\ell_d = d$, and for large values of n the maximum value of $dC/d\ell_d$ conveniently simplifies to:

$$\left[\frac{dC}{d\ell_d}\right]_{\text{max}} = \left[\frac{d\,E_2}{4bt\,E_1}\right]\left[\frac{1}{b\,E_1 + d\,E_2}\right] \qquad [13.50]$$

By substituting equation [13.50] and equation [13.38] we obtain for the strain energy release rate:

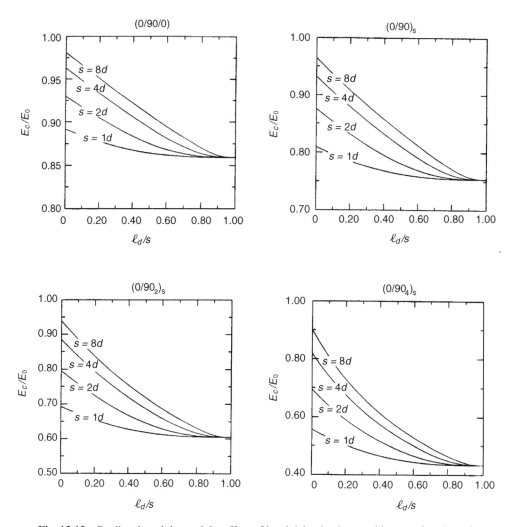

Fig. 13.12   Predicted modulus and the effect of local delamination cracking as a function of transverse ply spacing for a family of glass/epoxy cross-ply laminates. (After Dimant, 1994.)

$$G = \left[\frac{P^2 d\, E_2}{8b t^2\, E_1}\right]\left[\frac{1}{b\, E_1 + d\, E_2}\right]$$ [13.51]

Finally, the minimum required thickness of the transverse ply for the slightest chance of delamination cracking can be predicted by making the load P equal to the final load (equivalent to the laminate strength) measured in an experiment; then increase d until G is equal to G_{IIc}. Experimentally, we can determine G_{IIc} in a fracture mechanics test which turns out to be between 700 and 800 J/m². Alternatively, we can directly observe the onset (or otherwise) of delamination in a family of cross-ply laminates. This, too, would give an indication of the 'crack driving force' G and the minimum required transverse ply thickness for delamination to be possible.

Typically, the fracture strength of a $(0/90_2)_s$ glass fibre-epoxy cross-ply laminate is 1 GPa (corresponding to a failure load of 600 N) for our tensile specimens (Dimant *et al.*, 2002). Substitution of this and other appropriate material parameters into equation [13.50] yields a value for the critical strain energy release rate G_{IIc} for a *mode II* crack in excess of 700 J/m^2. In other words, there will be insufficient energy G to drive a delamination crack in a cross-ply glass/epoxy of any construction unless there are at least four 90° plies present.

Likewise, a typical fracture strength of a $(0/90_6)_s$, carbon/epoxy laminate is 2 GPa, or slightly greater (corresponding to a load of 1150 N on our tensile specimens). Assuming G_{IIc} is more or less independent of fibre type, and substituting these and other appropriate material properties into equation [13.50] would yield a value for the minimum ply thickness t of about 1.6 mm for delamination to be possible. In this case, the answer is equivalent to 6 carbon layers of 90° plies. Jen and Sun (1992) observed the formation of a delamination at a matrix crack in such a laminate. Furthermore, we never observed local delamination at a matrix crack in less than six layers of 90° plies which gives confidence in the predictive powers of this model. Furthermore, it turns out that the strain energy available for delamination at a given load P is greater for the laminate having thicker plies. The available strain energy release rate for driving a delamination crack is greater for glass/epoxy than a laminate containing carbon fibres.

13.6.4 Example 4: a kinetic model of fibre stiffening

A Kevlar® (aramid) fibre contains regularly spaced defect planes having a higher density of chain ends. Segments of the molecular chains in these regions are less well aligned and they can be thought of as kinked segments. Under tension these kinks can straighten, involving some longitudinal extension mechanism. The result is that the axial modulus of the fibre increases with strain. Subsequently, the operation of this mechanism in a KFRP composite under tensile load would result in its modulus increasing. In contrast, the formation of an array of parallel matrix cracks in the transverse plies of the laminate would result in the modulus falling.

To develop a physical model, which describes such modulus variation of the laminate under cyclic tensile stress, requires a consideration of these two separate effects:

* stiffening of the longitudinal plies due to fibre stiffening (the molecular chain unkinking mechanism), and
* transverse ply matrix cracking resulting in a modulus reduction.

First, consider development of the fibre unkinking model (Ganczakovski et al., 1989). Consider the fibre embedded in an epoxy matrix under load. Initially there are n_k^i kinks per unit length of fibre. After a time t a number of the kinks n_u have become unkinked, leaving $(n_k^i - n_u)$ per unit length of fibre in the kinked state. A kinetic equation for the rate of unkinking can now be formulated. The number of kinks that unkink per second depends on the number $(n_k^i - n_u)$ available to do so, on a frequency factor v (a kink vibration frequency), and on an activation energy Q. This activation energy is reduced when a tensile stress σ_c is applied to the composite because work is done when a kink straightens. Let this work be $\sigma_f V^*$ where V^* is the activation volume in kinetic theory and σ_f is the stress on that single fibre.

Using the standard kinetic methods (Ganczakovski et al., 1989), we have:

$$\frac{d\,n_u}{dt} = \left(n_k^i - n_u\right) v \exp{-\left[\frac{Q - \sigma_f V^*}{RT}\right]} \qquad [13.52]$$

Equation [13.52] is tractable if it is supposed that the fraction of kinks that straighten out is small,

$$\left(n_k^i - n_u\right) \approx \left(n_k^i\right) \qquad [13.53]$$

Using the boundary condition $n_u = 0$ when $t = 0$, integrating equation [13.52] and taking logs, we get:

$$n_u = n_{ref} \frac{RT}{Q} \ln\left(1 + \frac{t}{\tau}\right) \qquad [13.54]$$

The time constant τ is given by:

$$\tau = \frac{n_{ref}}{n_k^i} \frac{RT}{vQ} \exp\left\{\frac{Q}{RT}\left[1 - \frac{\left(\sigma_c + \omega\sigma_f^T\right)}{\sigma_{ref}}\right]\right\} \qquad [13.55]$$

Included in the above equation is any initial thermal stress:

$$\sigma_f^T \cdot \omega = V_f + \frac{E_m(1 - V_f)}{E_f}, \text{ and } \sigma_{ref} = \frac{Q\omega}{V} \text{ and } n_{ref} = \frac{Q\omega}{\left[E_m b_b(1 - V_f)V^*\right]}$$

b_k is the average net extension produced when a single kink unkinks.

We have reached the stage in the modelling process where the expression for the number of unkinked fibres needs to be related to the change in modulus. Obviously, the fibre becomes stiffer in proportion to the number of straightened kinks. If E_f^o is the modulus of the fibre in its relaxed state, then we suppose that the modulus E_f after n_u kinks have unkinked, satisfies the relation:

$$\frac{E_f}{E_f^o} = 1 + \beta\left(\frac{n_u}{n_{ref}}\right) \qquad [13.56]$$

where β is a constant. From Ganczakowski et al. (1989):

$$E_f = E_f^o \left[1 + B\ln(1 + t/\tau)\right] \qquad [13.57]$$

with $B = \beta RT/Q$.

Now, with time under load, the number of unkinked segments n_u increases, and the ratio (n_u/n_{ref}) increases starting from a value of zero at the beginning of the test. The quantity (RT/Q) is always much less than unity (typically it is 1/40). Assuming that (n_u/n_{ref}) is greater than 0.05 approximately, at all but very short times, the term $\ln(1 + t/\tau)$ must be much greater than unity. It follows, therefore, that for most of the time during which the stiffness of the fibre is rising

$$\ln\left(1 + \frac{t}{\tau}\right) \approx \ln\frac{t}{\tau} \qquad [13.58]$$

so that E_f may be written approximately as

$$E_f = E_f^o\left[1 + B\ln\frac{t}{\tau}\right] \qquad [13.59]$$

We can now use this model to write an expression for the stiffness of an aligned ($0°$) KFRP under tensile load as a function of time:

$$E_1^s = E_f^o V_f \left[1 + B \ln\left(\frac{t}{\tau}\right) \right] + E_m \left(1 - V_f\right)$$

[13.60]

which may be abbreviated as

$$E_1^s = E_1[Y + Z\ln(t)]$$

[13.61]

where E_1 is the initial modulus of the unidirectional composite

$$\left[= V_f\, E_f^o + \left(1 - V_f\right)E_m \right],$$ and Y and Z are given by

$$Y = -\frac{B V_f\, E_f^o}{E_1}\ln\tau \qquad\qquad Z = \frac{B V_f\, E_f^o}{E_1}$$

[13.62]

Data for the modulus change in unidirectional laminates under fatigue loading are plotted against $\ln t$ in Fig. 13.13 for three different levels of stress σ_{max}. Presenting the data in this way produces straight lines of equal gradient, displaced from one another on the modulus axis, so that at any given time the greatest modulus increase occurs at the highest applied stress. This is expected from the kinetic model, equation [13.61], if we equate σ_c in the model with σ_{max} and note that the parameter Y increases with increasing σ_c.

The modulus change of unidirectional KFRP under static load also gives a straight line when plotted against $\ln t$ (Fig. 13.13). The lack of a modulus increase at short times is perhaps a result of relaxation of the laminate when the static load is removed with insufficient time to read the modulus.

To quantify the stiffening effect, first the parameters Y and Z in equation [13.62] must be found. This is done empirically, using the data in Fig. 13.13: taking $Z = 0.095$ (independent of stress) and $Y = 1.003$, 1.018 and 1.043 for stress levels of 340, 450 and 670 MPa, respectively. Note that from equation [13.61], Y is proportional to $\ln\tau$, and combining this with equation [13.55] for τ means that Y would be expected to vary linearly with stress. Since the above values are reasonably consistent with this idea, a simple linear interpolation can be used to calculate the appropriate value of Y for a given longitudinal ply stress level in the cross-ply laminate.

We now set up the equation to enable us to subtract the stiffening effect of the fibres from the overall change in modulus of the laminate to give us the effect of the transverse ply (matrix) cracking mechanism. The experimental measurement of laminate modulus that has its origins in the fibre stiffening mechanism, when combined with the matrix cracking mechanism, can now be written as:

$$E^* = \left(E_1^s V_{f1} + E_1 V_{f2}\right)(1 - cD)$$

[13.63]

where E_1^s is given by equation [13.60].

Combining equations [13.61] and [13.63], and recalling that $E_0 = E_1 V_{f2} + E_2 V_{f2}$, then

$$E^* = E_0(1 - cD) + E_1 V_{f1}\,(1 - cD)(Y + Z\ln t - 1)$$

[13.64]

Hence:

$$(1 - cD) = \frac{E}{E_0} = \frac{E^s}{E_0 + E_1 V_f\,(Y + Z\ln t - 1)}$$

[13.65]

where E denotes the reduced (damaged) modulus of the laminate as a result of transverse ply cracking only.

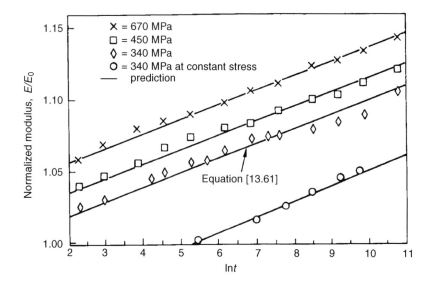

Fig. 13.13   Comparison between measurement of tensile modulus versus time in the cyclic loading of $(0)_2$ Kevlar/epoxy at maximum stresses of: 670 MPa, 450 MPa, 340 MPa. Also shown are data obtained at constant stress of 340 MPa. (After Ganczakowski *et al.*, 1986).

Equation [13.65] can be manipulated to deduce a modulus reduction with load cycles curve (due to matrix cracking only), from the experimentally determined modulus versus load cycles curve for (0/90) and $(0/90_2)_s$ laminates. These are shown in Fig. 13.14(a) and (b) and are similar in shape to those obtained for GRP shown above.

At this point, recall the model for GRP based on fracture mechanics ideas. In that model, a stress intensity factor is estimated for a transverse ply crack and the growth of cracks under fatigue loading is assumed to follow the power law relation. Recall that the expression for the stiffness reduction rate with cycling is given by equation [13.36]:

$$-\frac{1}{E_0}\left(\frac{dN}{dE}\right) = A\left[\frac{\sigma^2_{max}}{E_0^2\left(1-\dfrac{E}{E_0}\right)}\right]^{m/2}$$

where σ_{max} is the maximum stress in the fatigue cycle, m is the exponent in the power relation and A is a constant for a given laminate. Integrating to give an expression for the modulus reduction as a function of cycle number:

$$\frac{E}{E_0} = 1 - \left[A\left(\frac{m}{2}+1\right)\right]^{1/(m/2+1)}\left(\frac{\sigma_{max}}{E_0}\right)^{m/(m/2+1)} N^{1/(m/2+1)} \qquad [13.66]$$

Since Ogin *et al.* (1985) found that by comparing experimental data with equation [13.66] for GRP, m turns out to be equal to 5.7, and for CFRP it was found to be as high as 30, in the absence of other information, we select $m = 10$ for KFRP. Taking a value for $A = 5 \times 10^7$ for

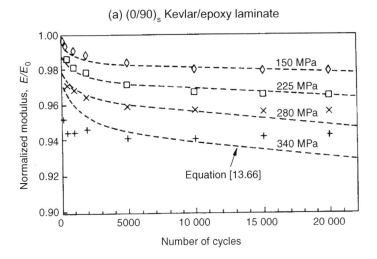

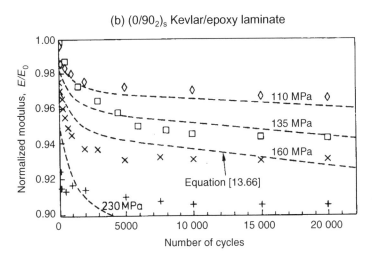

Fig. 13.14 Experimental data of modulus with load cycles at the maximum tensile stresses indicated. Equation [13.66] is superimposed for each stress level for (a) $m = 10$ and $A = 5 \times 10^7$; (b) $m = 10$ and $A = 5 \times 10^9$. (After Ganczakowski *et al.*, 1986)

the $(0/90)_s$ laminate and 5×10^9 for $(0/90_2)_s$ material, equation [13.66] predicts the trend of the modulus reduction with load cycle data reasonably well (with the effect of the fibre stiffening mechanism subtracted out), (Fig. 13.14).

Figure 13.15 shows the modulus reduction with crack density, using data from fatigue tests (again with fibre stiffening subtracted out) at a variety of stress levels together with the same shear-lag models used for GRP. The data appear to lie between the two shear lag models suggesting that the assumptions made in our analyses are reasonable.

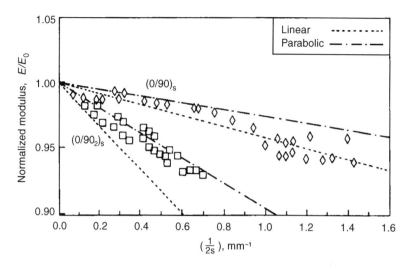

Fig. 13.15   Comparison between experiment and theory where modulus is plotted against density of transverse ply cracks for two lay ups of Kevlar/epoxy laminate. The dashed lines represent the shear lag analysis assuming linear (small dashes) and parabolic (long dashes) variations of the longitudinal displacement in the transverse ply. (The stiffening effect of the Kevlar fibre has been subtracted out). (After Ganczakowski *et al.*, 1986.)

13.7   Physical modelling of fatigue damage development at stress concentrators

13.7.1   Mechanisms of damage at holes and notches

Under mechanical loading in tension, a variety of polymeric-based composite systems containing a notch or hole, sustain damage in the vicinity of the stress concentrator (see, for example, Kortschot *et al.*, 1990a,b, 1991; Kortschot and Beaumont, 1993; Spearing *et al.*, 1991, 1992a,b,c; Otunga, 1995; Dimant, 1994; Dimant *et al.*, 1997, 2002). Examination of these damage zones shows that cracking in a variety of composites involves similar components of failure from one material system to the next (Fig. 13.16).

These cracking processes include:

- Splitting in the 0° plies.
- Transverse ply cracking in the 90° plies.
- Delamination cracking at the 0°/90° interfaces.
- Fibre fracture in the 0° plies.

These are *coupled* mechanisms. With increasing stress or number of load cycles, the notch tip damage or process zone in cross-ply CFRP (approximating a triangle in shape), simply grows in size (Fig. 13.16). Essentially, the delamination angle (indicated in Fig. 13.17 as α), remains constant (α is the angle made between the split and the delamination). This is called self-similar cracking and, therefore, it follows that the extent of damage growth can be explicitly quantified by the measurement of two failure parameters only; of split length l and of delamination angle α. Since α appears to be constant (for a given material system, stress range, temperature, and environment), any monitoring of fatigue damage-growth requires only the single measurement of l as a function of load cycles N to quantify the degree of

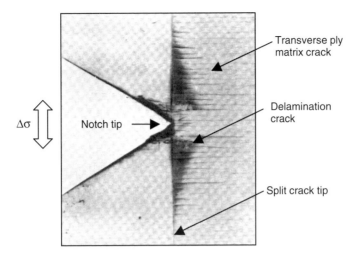

Fig. 13.16   An X-ray picture of sub-critical damage at a notch tip in a (90/0)s carbon/epoxy laminate in monotonic tensile loading. The triangular shape of the damage zone does not vary with load cycling; it simply grows in size. (After Kortschot *et al.*, 1990a,b, 1991.)

damage. Under increasing stress or load cycling, damage propagates until a terminal damage state is attained. Catastrophic (unstable) fracture of the composite is triggered by the simultaneous fracture of neighbouring fibres in the 0° plies, localized to the notch tip front (Kortschot et al., 1990a,b, 1991; Kortschot and Beaumont, 1993).

In the Kortschot, Ashby, Beaumont model, two phenomena govern the total failure process and they act in synergy. Firstly, localized interlaminar (delamination) and intralaminar (splitting and transverse ply) cracks grow either by a quasi-static fracture mechanism or by a fatigue (or time-dependent) mechanism. Secondly, these cracks modify the stress field in front of the notch tip that leads to notch *blunting*. Under monotonic (or cyclic) loading, catastrophic failure of the composite occurs when the reduced (localized) strength of the 0° ply (by the accumulation of fibre breaks close to the notch tip) is exceeded by the local intensification of tensile stress. Competition exists, therefore, between the blunting effects of the propagating delamination crack and split, and a *weakening* of the 0° ply by localized fibre fracture. Furthermore, each transverse ply crack acts as a stress concentrator and they can initiate the breaking of neighbouring fibres in the adjacent 0° plies. These transverse ply cracks, however, need not be explicitly modelled in the first instance since the applied load is carried essentially by the 0° plies. The role of the 90° ply is simply to act as a shear spring transferring stress across the split. This is unaffected by the multiplicity of transverse ply cracks (Kortschot *et al.*, 1991a,b).

There are complications in the modelling process. Composite strength is a stochastic quantity that depends on the volume of material under stress. Secondly, composite strength is not constant in fatigue where time-dependent and environment-sensitive processes act at the fibre level. This is particularly so for glass fibre (Sekine and Beaumont, 1998a,b). In addition, the delamination angle α may be sensitive to a number of material factors, (lay-up, matrix toughness, bond strength) and extrinsic conditions (temperature, ageing), (Cowley and Beaumont, 1997a,b,c,d). Whilst α can be measured for a given material system and set of test conditions, it is not straightforward to model.

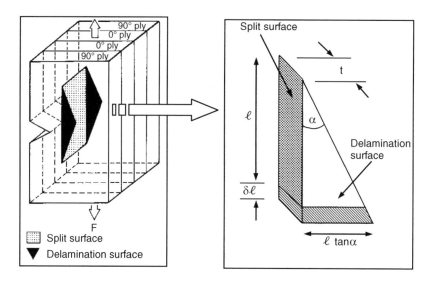

Fig. 13.17   A simplified damage zone model of a split and two delaminations at a notch tip in a (90/0)$_s$ carbon/epoxy laminate. l is split length, α is the delamination angle, and t is ply thickness. δl represents an increment of split growth under increasing tensile load or number of load cycles. The segment of the damage zone shown is one-quarter of the total damage zone size. (After Kortschot *et al.*, 1990, 1991.)

13.7.2   Example 5: A model of damage and fracture stress

The model is set up in two parts:

* assessment of sub-critical damage D and damage growth-rate, dD/dN;
* determination of the localized (notch tip) stress field and the 0° ply fracture stress with increasing D.

The damage growth-rate is a function of the applied stress to the power of 2, (see below), and it can be assessed by the measurement of l from which dl/dN (= dD/dN) is determined. The local notch tip stress field is determined by finite element analysis whilst the in situ tensile strength of the 0° ply is measured by experiment (Kortschot *et al.*, 1990a,b, 1991).

A physical model of damage at a hole or notch in a cross-ply carbon/epoxy composite consists of this combination of a split in each 0° ply and a triangular-shaped delamination crack at each 0/90 interface, (a schematic of these coupled mechanisms is shown in Fig.13.17). This idealization of a damage zone, which extends in a self-similar manner, allows a global analysis based on a global strain energy release-rate G that can be calculated solely on the applied tensile loading. Such calculations utilize a crude finite element representation of this idealized triangular-shaped damage zone (Fig. 13.18).

In a single load cycle, for the damage zone to grow by an increment of split length δl the energy absorbed in forming these new crack surfaces is given by:

$$\delta E_{ab} = G_s t\delta l + G_d \left(l \tan\alpha \right)\delta l \qquad\qquad [13.67]$$

where the fracture energies of splitting and delamination are designated G_s and G_d, respectively, and t is the thickness of a single ply. Energy is dissipated when the split and (coupled) delamination extend with corresponding increase in specimen compliance δC;

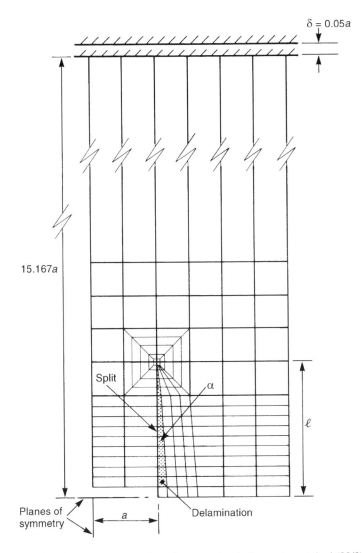

Fig. 13.18   Finite element representation of one quadrant of a centre notched (90/0)s carbon/ epoxy laminate. The mesh consists of two superimposed layers of elements in the same configuration, representing the 90° and 0° plies. (After Spearing *et al.*, 1992a,b,c.)

$$\delta E_r = \frac{1}{2} P^2 \delta C \qquad\qquad [13.68]$$

P is the applied load on one quadrant of the specimen (i.e. $P = \sigma A/4$).

   For the damage zone to grow, $\delta E_r \geq \delta E_{ab}$, i.e. the energy *released* must be greater than the energy *absorbed*:

$$\frac{1}{2} P^2 \delta C \geq G_s \, t \delta \ell + G_d \, \ell \delta \ell \, \tan \alpha \qquad\qquad [13.69]$$

In the limiting case, $E_r = E_{ab}$:

$$\frac{1}{2}\frac{P^2}{t}\frac{\partial C}{\partial \ell} = G_s + G_d \frac{\ell \tan \alpha}{t} \qquad \text{(i.e. } G = G_c). \qquad [13.70]$$

Thus, G is equated, via a Griffith-type energy balance, to the appropriate fracture energies of splitting G_s and delamination G_d where the total toughness G_c (or work of fracture in J/m^2), is the sum of these two mechanisms. The expression above can be evaluated by determining $\delta C/\delta \ell$ numerically using the finite element model. G_s can be obtained experimentally from the stress to initiate splitting, whilst G_d is determined from the rate of split growth with increasing stress. In practice, they become empirical parameters used to fine-tune the model. (In the case of cyclic loading (see below), the accumulation of fatigue damage, characterized by the experimental measurement of split growth-rate, $d\ell/dN$, and the calculated cyclic global strain energy release-rate ΔG obeys an empirical cyclic damage growth-rate (power) law. The exponent for the power law is determined by experiment).

It follows, then, for split (damage) growth under monotonic loading:

$$\ell = \frac{P^2(\partial C/\partial \ell)}{2\,G_d \tan \alpha} - \frac{G_s}{G_d}\left(\frac{t}{\tan \alpha}\right) \qquad [13.71]$$

A non-dimensional ratio of ℓ/a (where a denotes notch length), is dependent on the square of the applied load P (or remote applied stress σ_∞); the other terms can be considered as constants used to fine tune the model (Fig. 13.19).

Essentially, equation [13.71] predicts the damage zone size as a function of the applied stress to the power of 2:

$$\frac{\ell}{a} = C_1 \sigma_\infty^2 \qquad [13.72]$$

The second part of the model is to relate the fracture stress of the damaged laminate to the actual damage-state at the notch tip. From the finite element model of Kortschot et al. (1990a,b,1991), we know that the stress concentration factor at the notch tip decreases with increasing split length due to blunting effects. We also know that the localized stress gradient in the vicinity of the notch tip becomes less severe with increasing split growth. The consequences of these blunting mechanisms are a corresponding increase in localized volume of 0° ply material at the notch tip loaded to a particular peak stress and a corresponding decrease in its fracture stress. Given, therefore, that the tensile strength of the 0° ply is dependent on the size of the damage zone and on the equivalent volume of ply* under peak stress at the notch tip, then, the localized strength of the 0° ply σ_f^0 can be characterized using a Weibull weakest link statistics model.

The two parts of the model act in synergy. The net effect of this competition between mechanisms that can simultaneously blunt notches and reduce the 0° ply strength is to increase, for the major part of fatigue lifetime, the residual fracture stress of the damaged laminate (until, that is, extensive fibre fracture kicks in). The model must include the current state of damage, the local notch tip stress concentration factor, and the current volume of 0° ply under peak stress at the tip. Such coupling between damage growth and the volumetric (size) dependence of the 0° ply strength is the origin of the so-called *hole size effect* frequently observed in composite materials (see equation [13.78] below).

---

*The equivalent volume is the volume of material which would have the same probability of failure as the material in the (non-uniform) stress distribution of interest if it were loaded uniformly to the peak stress (or other characteristic stress) in the stress distribution.

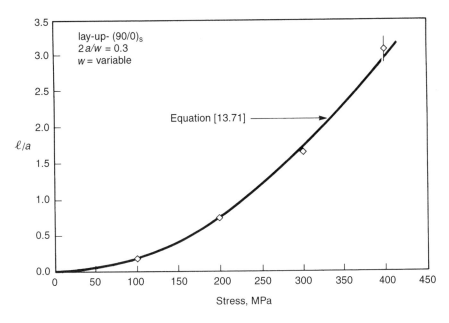

Fig. 13.19 Prediction of split (damage) growth and measurement of split length (normalized by notch length) for a (90/0)$_s$, carbon/epoxy laminate in monotonic loading. The dependence of the extent of damage on the square of applied stress can be seen.
(After Kortschot *et al.*, 1990a,b, 1991.)

A straightforward tensile stress failure criterion (which, as we will see, can be applied to fatigue strength) is simply:

$$\sigma_f^\infty = \frac{\sigma_f^0}{K_t} \qquad [13.73]$$

where σ_f^∞ is the remote failure stress of the notched composite; σ_f^0 is the localized tensile strength of the $0°$ ply in the damage zone close to the notch tip; and K_t is the terminal notch tip stress concentration factor and can be obtained from finite element modelling. σ_f^0 is a material property which can be determined independently. Furthermore, the local strength of the $0°$ ply within the damage zone depends on the size of that zone (just like the strength of a brittle solid depends on its volume):

$$\sigma_f^0 = \sigma_0 \left[\frac{V_0}{KV} \right]^{1/\beta} \qquad [13.74]$$

σ_0 and V_0 are the mean failure stress and reference volume of the test piece. KV is the equivalent volume of the $0°$ ply at the peak stress in the damage zone; its value depends on zone size (characterized by ℓ), $0°$ ply thickness t and notch length a. β is the Weibull modulus. Re-writing equation [13.73]:

$$\sigma_f^0 = \sigma_0 \left[\frac{V_o}{C_2 \left(\dfrac{\ell}{a} \right) (a^2 t)} \right]^{1/\beta}$$

[13.75]

$$= C_3 \left\{ C_2 \left(\frac{\ell}{a} \right) a^2 \right\}^{-1/\beta}$$

For a centre-notched $(90/0)_s$ laminate (Kortschot et al., 1990a,b):

$$K_t = C_4 \left[\frac{\ell}{a} \right]^{-0.28}$$

[13.76]

In effect, the damaged strength of a $(90/0)_s$ laminate in terms of notch size can be quantified by combining equations [13.72], [13.74] and [13.75].

After considerable manipulation we get a prediction of strength in terms of the damage zone size:

$$\sigma_f^\infty = C_5 \left[\left[\left(\frac{\ell}{a} \right) a^2 \right]^{\frac{1}{m}} \frac{\ell^{0.28}}{a} \frac{}{C_4} \right]$$

[13.77]

This equation can be manipulated once more to show the strength dependence on notch size (the notch size effect):

$$\frac{C_1 \sigma_f^{\infty[1-2(0.28)]}}{C_1 C_3 \left[C_2 \left(C_1 \sigma_f^{\infty 2} \right)^{(1/\beta)} \right]} = a^{2/\beta}$$

[13.78]

Setting $\beta = 20$ and combining the constants into a single constant:

$$\sigma_f^\infty = C_6 a^{-0.2}$$

[13.79]

Although there is no straightforward analytical solution, it is relatively easy to solve the equation by iterative computational methods. There is only one independent variable σ^∞ in these equations. Figure 13.20 shows the comparison between prediction and theory. Any inaccuracy is of the same order as experimental scatter. The model has been applied without prior knowledge of the actual terminal damage state in the material. Furthermore, the overall form of the model is apparently correct. Also, there have been no curve-fitting parameters to improve the fit of the data!

13.7.3   Example 6: A model of damage and fatigue strength

A physical model for the tensile strength of a fatigue damaged composite is based on the observation that no further damage, beyond that observed by load cycling, occurs in the material that may subsequently be loaded monotonically to catastrophic fracture (Spearing et al., 1991, 1992a,b,c).

A model of post-fatigue strength requires only two (uncoupled) steps:

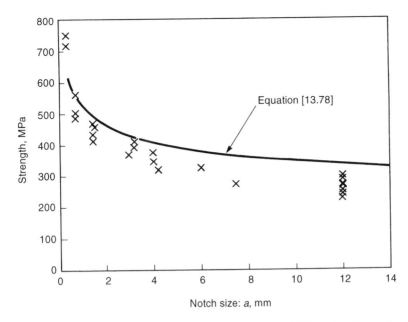

Fig. 13.20   The quasi-static notch strength of a centre-notched $(90/0)_s$ carbon/epoxy laminate. The damage-based model overestimates the experimental data because it does not include the effect of the transverse ply cracks within the 90° plies. (After Kortschot *et al.*, 1990a,b, 1991.)

- a model of damage growth-rate using a fatigue (power) damage law;
- a model of 0° ply (localized) strength in the fatigue damage zone.

The starting point is the fatigue damage growth (power) law:

$$\frac{d\ell}{dN} = \lambda_1 \left(\Delta G \right)^{\frac{m}{2}}$$
[13.80]

As the split length grows with load cycling, so does the delamination area increase with a dependence on ℓ, implying that ΔG has to be normalized by the current toughness G_c given by equation [13.70]:

$$\frac{d\ell}{dN} = \lambda_2 \left[\frac{\frac{1}{2}\Delta P^2 \left(\frac{\partial C}{\partial \ell} \right)}{G_s t + G_d \ell \tan \alpha} \right]^{\frac{m}{2}}$$
[13.81]

This removes the need for a pre-multiplying constant having awkward units. The model identifies that the extent of damage for a given stress range $\Delta\sigma$ (corresponding to ΔP), scales with specimen size (since damage grows in a self-similar manner). This implies that ℓ/a is the appropriate normalization for the extent of notch-tip damage (see, for example, Fig. 13.19). So, for an initial split length ℓ_o, predicted using equation [13.71], the split length after N load cycles is given by the integral form of equation [13.80]:

$$\ell = \frac{1}{G_d \tan \alpha} \left[\lambda_2 \Delta G^{\frac{m}{2}} \left(\frac{m+2}{2} \right) \left(G_d \tan \alpha \right) N + \left. G_s t + G_d \ell_o \tan \alpha \right.^{\frac{(m+2)}{2}} \right]^{\frac{2}{(m+2)}}$$
[13.82]

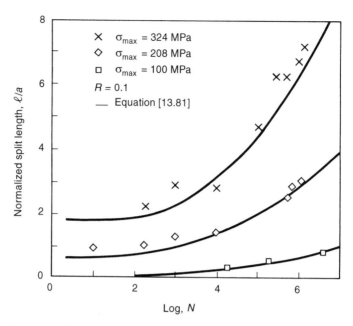

Fig. 13.21 Comparison between the fatigue damage model and experimental data of normalized split length as a function of load cycles. Increasing the maximum cyclic stress increases the extent of damage for a given number of cycles as predicted by the model. The material is a $(90/0)_s$ carbon/epoxy laminate. (After Spearing *et al.*, 1992a,b,c.)

It only remains to identify values for λ_2, m, and $(\partial C/\partial \ell)$ to obtain Fig. 13.21.

13.7.3.1   Predicting fatigue damage in $(90_i/0_j)_{ns}$ laminates

The nature of mechanically induced damage is essentially the same for all laminates containing 0° and 90° plies of varying thickness t (α varies only slightly with thickness). Quite simply, the area of delamination scales with the number of 0/90 interfaces (Fig. 13.22). The net result is that laminates having thick ply groups, e.g. $(90_4/0_4)_s$, sustain the greater extent of damage at a given stress or particular number of load cycles compared to laminates with ungrouped plies (e.g. $(90/0)_{4s}$) (Fig. 13.23). Conveniently, this generic similarity allows the same finite element model as used by Kortschot *et al.* (1990a,b); the meshes for the $(90/0)s$ calibration specimens are adjusted by modifying the relative ply thickness. Also, the strain energy release-rate simply scales with laminate thickness.

$(90_i/0_j)_s$ laminates

For this family, ΔG increases linearly with ply thickness, it. In this family, there are two interfacial delaminations only that can grow. Since delamination growth is the dominant energy absorbing process (predominantly *mode* II fracture), and delaminations have a greater surface area than splits), then the ratio $\Delta G/G_c$ increases as i increases. The fatigue damage law has to be revised accordingly (and in terms of applied stress σ):

$$\frac{d\ell}{dN} = \lambda_2 \left[\frac{\frac{1}{2}\left(\Delta\sigma_\infty^2\right)\left(it\right)\frac{\partial C}{\partial \ell}}{G_s it + G_d \ell \tan \alpha} \right]^{\frac{m}{2}}$$

[13.83]

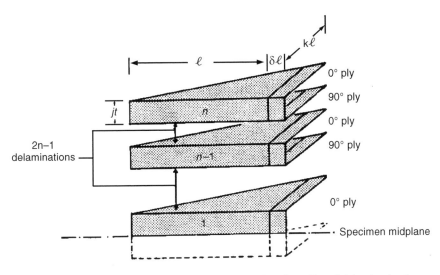

Fig. 13.22 Geometry of a notch tip damage zone showing the split and delamination in one-eighth of a double-edge notched tensile specimen. The laminate is $(90/0)_{ns}$ carbon/epoxy. (After Kortschot *et al.*, 1990, 1991.)

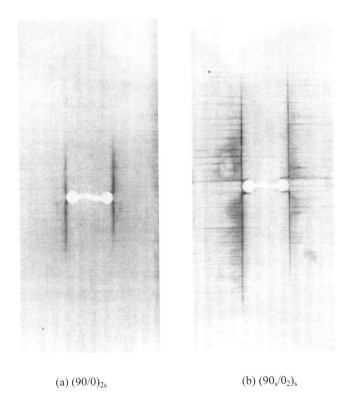

(a) $(90/0)_{2s}$ (b) $(90_s/0_2)_s$

Fig. 13.23 X-ray photographs of fatigue damaged specimens to the same cyclic stress and number of load cycles ($\Delta\sigma = 208$ MPa; $R = 0.1$; $N = 10^6$ cycles). The thicker ply laminate of carbon/epoxy shows the larger degree of damage. Similar observations are seen when these materials are loaded in monotonic tension. (After Spearing *et al.*, 1992a,b,c.)

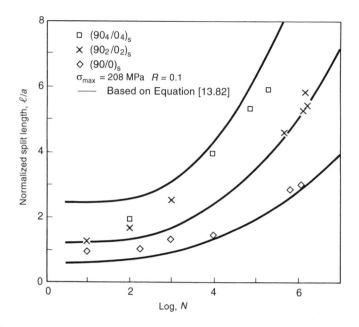

Fig. 13.24 This set of data fatigue damage to the same cyclic stress and number of load cycles ($\Delta\sigma$ = 208 MPa; R = 0.1; N = 10^6 cycles), taken from similar X-ray photographs to those shown in the previous figure, indicates that thicker ply laminates of carbon/epoxy exhibit the larger degree of damage. (After Spearing *et al.*, 1992a,b,c.)

Figure 13.24 illustrates the increasing rate of fatigue damage with increasing ply thickness.

(90/0)_s laminates
Laminates with 90° and 0° plies of unequal thickness can be modelled in a similar way. The relative ply thickness of these layers in the finite element meshes are simply adjusted. Because $\partial C/\partial l$ increases with increasing thickness of the 0° plies, laminates having j greater than i will exhibit more rapid damage propagation than a $(90/0)_s$ laminate.

In this case, the revised fatigue damage law has the form:

$$\frac{d\ell}{dN} = \lambda_2 \left[\frac{\frac{1}{2}\left(\Delta\sigma_\infty^2\right)\left(i+j\right)t\left(\frac{\partial C}{\partial \ell}\right)}{G_s it + G_d \ell \tan\alpha} \right]^{\frac{m}{2}}$$

[13.84]

(90/0)_ns laminates
In this series, ply thickness is constant and equal for the 90° and 0° laminate; only the number of 90/0 interfaces varies. Through half the laminate thickness, there are a maximum number of $2n-1$ interfaces possible at which delaminations can propagate. Since the surface area of the split is $nt\ell$, and $\partial C/\partial l$ scales with the number of plies, then the equation for split growth (from equation [13.70] becomes:

$$\frac{1}{2}\frac{P^2}{nt}\frac{\partial C}{\partial \ell} = G_s + G_d\frac{(2n-1)\tan\alpha}{nt}$$

[13.85]

(i.e. $G = G_c$).

It follows that the fatigue damage law has to be modified to:

$$\frac{d\ell}{dN} = \lambda_2 \left[\frac{\frac{1}{2}\left(\Delta\sigma_\infty^2\right)\left(nt\right)\left(\frac{\partial C}{\partial \ell}\right)}{G_s nt + G_d\left(2n - 1\right)\ell \tan\alpha} \right]^{\frac{m}{2}}$$

[13.86]

As the number of plies increases, so the model predicts that the rate of damage propagation decreases slightly.

13.7.3.2   Predicting fatigue strength

The prediction of fracture stress of the laminate in terms of the damage zone size is given by equation [13.76]. Examination of fatigue damaged specimens and the measurement of the terminal split length (equivalent to the damage zone size) enables, therefore, a prediction of residual or post-fatigue strength. It requires calculation of the notch tip stress concentration factor and the 0° ply strength (which are both functions of split length). Comparison between prediction and experimental measurement is shown in Fig. 13.25. If higher values of split length are obtained with prolonged cycling, higher residual strengths result reflecting notch tip blunting effects. Once fibre fracture at the notch tip in the 0° ply starts to dominate, the residual strength will begin to fall.

Now the quasi-static fracture stress of a $(90°/0°)_s$ carbon/epoxy is about 360 MPa which truncates the fatigue strength curve shown above. The increase in residual fatigue strength with load cycles reflects the greater size of the damage zone and its notch tip blunting effects.

Fatigue strength versus cycles diagram
In many ways, a prediction of post-fatigue notch strength is simpler than the prediction of notch strength in monotonic loading. We know that after fatigue loading there is no further damage growth during the residual strength test. A successful strength prediction, therefore, depends on two distinct steps:

• modelling damage growth; and
• equating strength to damage size at the end of the fatigue test.

The split length for the (90/0) laminate after N cycles is given by (after equation [13.81]):

$$\frac{\ell}{a} = C_1\left[\Delta\sigma^m N + C_7\right]^{\frac{2}{(m+2)}}$$

[13.87]

Substituting into equation [13.76]:

$$\sigma_f^\infty = C_8\left\{1 + C_9\left[\left(\Delta\sigma^m + C_7\right)^{\frac{2}{(m+2)}}\right]_a 2\right\}^{1/\beta} \frac{\left[\left(\Delta\sigma^m N + C_7\right)^{\frac{2}{(m+2)}}\right]^{0.28}}{C_4}$$

[13.88]

C_8, C_9 etc. are combinations of material constants which can be derived from earlier expressions.

Equation [13.87] allows residual strength to be predicted as a function of the specimen geometry, notch size, fatigue loading (Fig. 13.26). The level of effectiveness of the model is limited by the accuracy of both the damage growth prediction and the damage-based strength model. The overall accuracy of the model is comparable to the scatter of the experimental data due to inherent material variability.

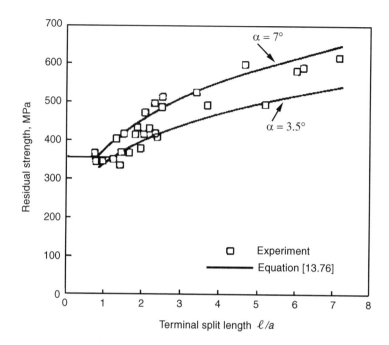

Fig. 13.25   The fatigue damage model combined with the simple failure criterion predicts experimental data of residual (fatigue) strength reasonably accurately. The laminate is (90/0), carbon/epoxy. The sensitivity to delamination angle is shown. The higher the delamination angle, the greater the residual strength. (After Spearing *et al.*, 1992a,b,c.)

13.8   Computer implementation

Physical models often rely on numerical methods for their implementation. For example, notch-tip stress distributions and global strain energy release-rates are most easily obtained by relatively crude finite element representations of the damaged zone (Fig. 13.18). In the case of cross ply laminates, the 0° and 90° plies are modelled as discrete elastic orthotropic layers in plane stress. Usually it is not necessary to simulate the fully three-dimensional nature of the problem. Furthermore, it makes it possible to perform parametric studies: of the effects of varying damage zone shape and size; varying material properties that are effected by temperature or environment; and in processing, changing ply thickness and lay-up geometry, and residual stress-state on the strain energy release-rates and stress distributions (Spearing and Beaumont, 1998).

Delaminations are simulated by decoupling nodes between adjacent layers over the delaminated area, and splits are represented by decoupling nodes within the 0° ply. For cyclic loading, the calibration procedure requires an intermediate step in which damage is monitored up to 10^6 cycles. Such observations and measurements are necessary in order to determine the empirical parameters of the fatigue damage power law. The fatigue model is capable of predicting fatigue damage growth and post-fatigue residual strength, for a range of hole sizes, ply thicknesses, stacking sequences, and fatigue history (Spearing and Beaumont, 1998).

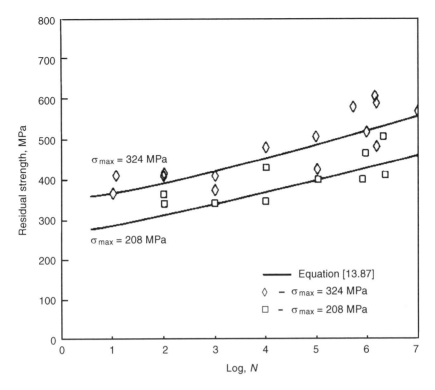

Fig. 13.26   The combined fatigue damage model and simple tensile failure criterion predicts the residual strength increasing with load cycles. For a given number of cycles, the extent of damage is greater for the higher fatigue stress. Laminate is $(90/0)_s$ carbon/epoxy. (After Spearing *et al.*, 1992a,b,c.)

13.9   Summary and final remarks

Physical modelling provides the means to assess the relative severity of different fatigue loading regimes, constant amplitude vs. variable amplitude spectra, frequency effects and R-ratio effects as well as load/environment interactions. Furthermore, the economic advantage of reducing the high cost of vast experimental programmes in assorted environments and stress-states having duration of many thousands of hours is potentially huge. The capability of physical modelling is important in the design of experimental test programs that ensure critical loading regimes are examined. Such models are valuable inasmuch as they draw attention to the precise features of the failure process that have wider significance and implications.

Added benefits include more options being made available to the designer, a reduced need for extensive and costly testing and more efficient and shorter design iteration cycles. This last point requires elaboration. Modelling a particular problem is only a sub-element of the overall design process. The philosophy behind the physical modelling approach has general applicability. In particular, the foundation of physical modelling could be applied to solving a range of problems in composites. Existing design methodologies at the higher structural size scales can be supported and justified by fundamental understanding at lower size scales.

In critical fatigue situations, where the objective is to design for longevity, durability, and structural integrity, then the balance is shifted in favour of physical modelling and away from the empirical approach. It is in this area that the application of the physical model is most powerful.

Successful modelling of physical processes can be achieved by following a set of steps: identify the physical mechanisms (preferably by direct observation); construct the model (using previously modelled problems or applying existing modelling tools); test the model (by comparing with data) and tune the model (lumping together empirical parameters). In other words, determine the dominant mechanism(s); simplify it (them); and exploit the modelling successes of others in materials science and engineering.

Even now the job is still incomplete; the last word is *iterate*.

13.10   Acknowledgements

Much of the groundwork on which this chapter is based has its origins in the research carried out with my research students at Cambridge and colleagues in the Engineering Department. It is a special pleasure to acknowledge the work of Prof Anoush P Poursartip, Prof Mark T Kortschot, Dr Helena L Ganczakovski, Prof S Mark Spearing, Dr Steve Ogin, Dr Ron Dimant, Dr Kevin Cowley, Dr Hugh R Shercliff, and Prof Paul A Smith. This work has benefited considerably from the input of Prof Michael F Ashby.

13.11   References

ANSTICE P D and BEAUMONT P W R (1983), 'Hygrothermal ageing and fracture of glass fibre-epoxy composites', *Journal of Material Science*, **18**, 3404–3408.

BEAUMONT P W R and SEKINE H (2002), 'Physical modelling of the engineering problems of composites and structures', *Key Engineering Materials*, **221–222**, pp. 255–266. Trans. Tech. Publications, Switzerland.

BEAUMONT P W R and SPEARING S M (1990), 'Development of fatigue damage mechanics for application to the design of structural composite components', EUROMECH 269: *Mechanical Identification of Composites*, Published by Elsevier Applied Science, Edited by Vantrin and Sol pp. 311–326. St-Etienne, France, 3rd–6th December.

BROWN D J, GILBERT D G, BEAUMONT P W R, NIXON W C and WINDLE A H (1985), 'Microcracking and fracture in bulk polymers and composite films', *6th International Conference: Deformation, yield and fracture of polymers'* 1st–4th April, Cambridge, England, pp. 74.1–74.4. The Plastics and Rubber Institute, London.

COWLEY K D and BEAUMONT P W R (1997a), 'Part 1 – Damage accumulation at notches and the fracture stress of carbon fibre–polymer composites: combined effects of stress and temperature', *Composites Science and Technology*, **52**, 295.

COWLEY K D and BEAUMONT P W R (1997b), 'Part 2 – Modelling problems of damage at notches and the fracture stress of carbon fibre–polymer composites: matrix, temperature and residual stress effects', *Composites Science and Technology*, **52**, 310.

COWLEY K D and BEAUMONT P W R (1997c), 'Part 3 – The interlaminar and intralaminar fracture toughness of carbon fibre–polymer composites: the effect of temperature', *Composites Science and Technology*, **52**, 325.

COWLEY K D and BEAUMONT P W R (1997), 'Part 4 – The measurement and prediction of residual stresses in carbon fibre–polymer composites', *Composites Science and Technology*, **52**, 334.

DIMANT R A (1994), 'Damage mechanics of composite laminates'. Cambridge University Engineering Department PhD Thesis.

DIMANT R, BEAUMONT P W R and SHERCLIFF H (1997), 'Damage and fracture of glass fibre-epoxy laminates; modelling the failure processes', *International Conference on Composite Materials* (ICCM-11), Brisbane, Australia, (July). Published by Woodhead Publishing Limited, Cambridge, UK.

DIMANT R, SHERCLIFF H and BEAUMONT P W R (2002), 'Evaluation of a damage-mechanics approach to the modelling of notched strength in KFRP and GRP', *Composites Science and Technology*, **62**, 255–263.

GANCZAKOWSKI H L, BEAUMONT P W R and SMITH P A (1989), 'On the modulus of KFRP laminates in static and fatigue loading', *ICCM-6 and ECCM -2 International Conference: Composite Materials*, September, London, Volume 3 pp. 3.166–3.175. Published by Elsevier Applied Science, Editors: Matthews, Buskell, Hodgkinson, Morton.

GANCZAKOWSKI H L and BEAUMONT P W R (1989), 'Behaviour of Kevlar fibre-epoxy laminates under static and fatigue loadings – Part 1', *Composites Science and Technology*, **36**, 299–319.

GANCZAKOWSKI H L, ASHBY M F, BEAUMONT P W R and SMITH P A (1990), 'Behaviour of Kevlar fibre-epoxy laminates under static and fatigue loading – Part 2', *Composites Science and Technology*, **37**, 371–392.

GILBERT D G, BEAUMONT P W R and NIXON W C (1983), 'Direct observations of the micromechanisms of fracture in polymeric solids using the SEM', *ICCM – IV International Conference: Mechanical Behaviour of Materials*, Stockholm, Sweden (15th–19th August). Vol. 2 pp. 705–710. Pergamon Press, Editors: Carisson and Ohison.

GILBERT D G, BEAUMONT P W R and NIXON W C (1984), 'Direct observations of dynamic fracture mechanisms in polymeric materials', *Journal of Materials Science Letters*, **3**, 961–964.

JEN K C and SUN C T (1992), 'Matrix cracking and delamination prediction in graphite-epoxy laminates'. *Journal of Reinforced Plastics and Composites*, **11**, 1163–1175.

KEDWARD K T and BEAUMONT P W R (1992), 'The treatment of fatigue and damage accumulation in composite design', *International Journal of Fatigue* **14**(5), 283–294.

KORTSCHOT M T and BEAUMONT P W R (1990a), 'Damage mechanics of composite materials I: Measurement of damage and strength', *Composites Science and Technology*, **39**, 289–302.

KORTSCHOT M T and BEAUMONT P W R (1990b), 'Damage mechanics of composite materials II: A damage-based notched strength model', *Composites Science and Technology*, **39**, 303–326.

KORTSCHOT M T, BEAUMONT P W R and ASHBY M F (1991), 'Damage mechanics of composite materials III: Prediction of damage growth and notched strength', *Composites Science and Technology*, **40**, 147–166.

KORTSCHOT M T and BEAUMONT P W R (1991), 'Damage mechanics of composite materials IV: Effect of lay-up on damage growth and notched strength', *Composites Science and Technology*, **40**, 167–180.

KORTSCHOT M T and BEAUMONT P W R (1993), 'Damage-based notched strength modeling: a summary', in *Composite Materials: Fatigue and Fracture*, Edited by T. K. O'Brien, *ASTM STP 1110*, 55–71.

MAO T H, BEAUMONT P W R and NIXON W C (1983), 'Direct observation of crack propagation in brittle materials', *Journal of Materials Science Letters*, **2**, 613– 616.

OGIN S L, SMITH P A and BEAUMONT P W R (1985), 'Matrix cracking and stiffness reduction during the fatigue of a (0/90) CFRP laminate', *Composites Science and Technology*, **22**, 23–31.

OGIN S L, SMITH P A and BEAUMONT P W R (1985),'A stress intensity factor approach to fatigue growth of tranverse ply cracks', *Composites Science and Technology*, **24**, 47–59.

OTUNGA M G (1995) 'Fatigue damage accumulation in carbon fibre laminates', PhD thesis, University of Cambridge.

POURSARTIP A and BEAUMONT P W R (1982), 'A damage approach to the fatigue of composites', *IUTAM Symposium: Mechanics of Composite Materials*, Virginia Polytechnic Institute, Blackburg, Virginia, USA (16th–19th August) pp. 449–456.

POURSARTIP A and BEAUMONT P W R (1986), 'Fatigue damage mechanics of a carbon fibre composite laminate: Part 2', *Composites Science and Technology*, **25**, 283–299.

POURSARTIP A, ASHBY M F and BEAUMONT P W R (1982a), 'Damage accumulation during fatigue of composites', *Scripta Metallurgica*, **16**, 601–606.

POURSARTIP A, ASHBY M F and BEAUMONT P W R (1982b), 'Damage accumulation during fatigue of composites', *4th International Conference (ICCM-IV). Progress in Science and Engineering of Composites*, Tokyo, Japan (25th–28th October). Japan Society for Composite Materials, Vol I pp. 693–700.

POURSARTIP A, ASHBY M F and BEAUMONT P W R (1982c), 'Damage accumulation in composites during fatigue', *Proceedings of the 3rd RISØ International Symposium: Fatigue and Creep of Composite Materials*, 6–10 September, Roskilde, Denmark, pp. 279–284.

POURSARTIP A, ASHBY M F and BEAUMONT P W R (1984), 'The fatigue damage mechanics of fibrous composites', *Polymer NDE*, Terma do Vimeiro, Portugal (4th–5th September) pp. 250–260. Published by Technomic Publishers, Basel, Switzerland. Editor: KHG Ashbee.

POURSARTIP A, ASHBY M F and BEAUMONT P W R (1986), 'Fatigue damage mechanics of a carbon fibre composite laminate: Part 1', *Composites Science and Technology*, **25**, 193–218.

SALKIND M J (1971), *Composite Materials: Testing and Design, ASTM STP 497*, 20–22 April, Anaheim, California, USA.

SEKINE H and BEAUMONT P W R (1998a), 'A physically based micromechanical theory of macroscopic stress-corrosion cracking in aligned continuous glass fibre-reinforced polymer laminates', *Composites Science and Technology*, **58**(10), 1659–1665.

SEKINE H and BEAUMONT P W R (1998b), 'A physically-based micromechanical theory and diagrams of macroscopic stress corrosion cracking of glass-epoxy composites', *8th US–Japan Conference on Composite Materials*, Baltimore, 24th–25th September.

SHERCLIFF H R, VEKINIS G and BEAUMONT P W R (1994a), 'Direct observation of the fracture of CAS-Glass/SiC Composites – Part 1 delamination', *Journal of Materials Science*, **29**, 3643–3652.

SHERCLIFF H R, BEAUMONT P W R and VEKINIS G (1994b), 'Direct observation of the fracture of CAS-Glass/SiC Composites – Part 2 notched strength, *Journal of Materials Science*, **29**, 4184–4190.

SPEARING S M and BEAUMONT P W R (1992a), 'Fatigue damage mechanics of composite materials I: Experimental measurement of damage and post-fatigue properties', *Composites Science and Technology*, **44**, 159–168.

SPEARING S M and BEAUMONT P W R (1992b), 'Fatigue damage mechanics of composite materials III: Prediction of post-fatigue strength', *Composites Science and Technology*, **44**, 299–307.

SPEARING S M and BEAUMONT P W R (1998), 'Towards a predictive design methodology of fibre composite materials'. *Applied Composite Materials*, **5**(2), 69–94.

SPEARING S M, BEAUMONT P W R and ASHBY M F (1991), 'Fatigue damage mechanics of notched graphite-epoxy laminates', in *Composite Materials: Fatigue and Fracture*, Edited by T. K. O'Brien, *ASTM STP 1110*, 596–616.

SPEARING S M, BEAUMONT P W R and ASHBY M F (1992a), 'Fatigue damage mechanics of composite materials II: A damage growth model', *Composites Science and Technology*, **44**, 169–177.

SPEARING S M, BEAUMONT P W R and KORTSCHOT M T (1992b), 'The fatigue damage mechanics of notched carbon fibre/PEEK laminates', *Composites*, **23**, 305–311.

SPEARING S M, BEAUMONT P W R and SMITH P A (1992c), 'Fatigue damage mechanics of composite materials IV: Prediction of residual stiffness', *Composites Science and Technology*, **44**, 309–317.

SPEARING S M, LAGACE P A and MCMANUS H L N (1998), 'On the role of lengthscale in the prediction of failure of composite structures: assessment and needs', *Applied Composite Materials*, **5**(3), 139–149.

VEKINIS G, ASHBY M F and BEAUMONT P W R (1993), 'The micromechanies of fracture of alumina and a ceramic-based fibre composite: modelling the failure processes', *Composites Science and Technology*, **48**, 325.

WELLS J K and BEAUMONT P W R (1985a), 'Debonding and pull-out processes in fibrous composites', *Journal of Materials Science*, **20**, 1275–1284.

WELLS J K and BEAUMONT P W R (1985b), 'Crack tip energy absorption processes in fibre composites', *Journal of Materials Science*, **20**, 2735–2749.

WELLS J K and BEAUMONT P W R (1987), 'Prediction of *R*-curves and notched tensile strength for composite laminates', *Journal of Materials Sciemce*, **22**, 1457–1468.

14

Micromechanical models

K. Reifsnider and S. Case, Virginia Tech, USA

14.1   Introduction

Fatigue is a phenomenon; it is an engineering definition based on the observation that the repeated application of environments that do not cause initial failure may cause subsequent failure after many cycles of application. The environments may be mechanical loading alone, or combinations of environments such as temperature, corrosive conditions, and dynamic or cyclic mechanical conditions. 'Failure' may have the classical definition of mechanical rupture, or more contemporary definitions based on failure to meet more general performance criteria. The focus of the present discussion is mechanical performance under combined applied conditions, especially combinations of mechanical, thermal and chemical environments.

If fatigue is defined in terms of mechanical behaviour, then a preponderance of data for a remarkable range of materials show that fatigue life scales to strength more often than any other engineering parameter. Hence, the physical processes that control life generally alter strength. Therefore, strength is a fundamentally sound metric for fatigue life. But it can also be used as a damage metric, for the purpose of assessing specific histories of variable applied conditions. This idea is illustrated in Fig. 14.1.

We consider that the level of applied stress is represented by failure functions Fa and that the remaining strength after some period of application is represented by Fr. If Fa^1 is applied for n_1 cycles, we say that the remaining strength is reduced to point (1) in Fig. 14.1. We regard all other applied conditions as producing the same 'damage' if the reduction in remaining strength is the same. In particular, the equivalent number of cycles at load level Fa^2, for example, is n_{12} in the diagram. Therefore, if we now change our load level from Fa^1 to Fa^2, then the remaining life will be given by n_2 in the diagram. It is clear that these predicted results can be easily verified, at any time during the test, i.e. we can measure remaining strength by stopping the test, and we can compare predicted life with measurements for any sequence (or continuous variation) of loading. So it is possible to predict and measure intermediate information. Moreover, since it is clear from the diagram that the sequence of application of cycles gives a different predicted result (strength vs. time and total life), that prediction can be checked as well. Finally, since the model of these strength changes is actually a simulation of the mechanistic fatigue processes, the sensitivity to

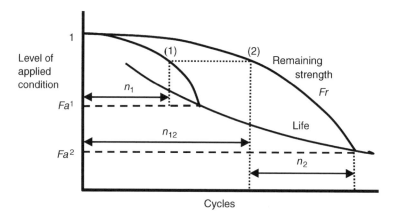

Fig. 14.1   Strength as a damage metric for the representation of damage accumulation and sequence effects.

intermediate data means that physical measurements can be used to stimulate the simulation, and thereby to greatly improve the accuracy of the predictions of remaining strength and life. Verification of all of these benefits and advantages has appeared in the literature cited in the discussion below.

The observations that define the phenomenon of fatigue in composite materials are the subject of the present series in which this chapter appears. The details of the material behaviour at the local level that drive these phenomena are the object of continuing research. However, the present approach is motivated by exactly those details, i.e. the philosophy discussed below is driven by the need to be able to understand, describe and predict the manner in which composite materials come apart in terms of how they are put together.

With this in mind, we begin by defining the classes of composite materials to be addressed in this discussion and the general features of fatigue in those materials that are particularly germane to our development.

14.2   Damage accumulation in composite materials

Self-similar single defect propagation is not a generally useful fundamental physical mechanism to represent the fatigue phenomenon in composite materials. Composite materials are exceptionally resistant to fatigue failure for precisely that reason. They are designed to be damage tolerant. The heterogeneous constituents of composite materials may sustain multiple, distributed localized fractures with little influence on the global properties that control the life of the material or component.

Perhaps the most important example of this fact is the multiple fractures observed in the ceramic fibres in a ceramic matrix composite, such as the SiC/SiC system shown in Fig. 14.2.

Even in this very brittle system, the surrounding matrix material (and the interface between the fibres and the matrix) applies sufficient 'gripping' to transfer stress back into the ends of a fibre near a break, and at the same time, to stop the crack in the fibre from propagating across the specimen cross-section to cause global failure. This is how composites work; this is what they do best. They are remarkably tolerant of damage, and they can be

Fig. 14.2   Micrographs of SiC fibres with multiple breaks in a SiC/SiC system in which the matrix has been etched away after quasi-static loading.

used (and are often designed to be used) to perform engineering functions in the presence of 'damage'. Although composites are designed to be damage tolerant at the global level, their properties (such as stiffness and strength) may change greatly during the life of a component, prior to the final failure event. Stiffness changes of 30–40% are possible, for example, in ceramic composites. In some cases, these property changes are due to micro-damage in the constituents, such as matrix cracking, fibre fracture, debonding of interfaces, and delamination. In other cases, the changes are due to changes in material state in the constituents, caused by applied environments, i.e. by mechanical, chemical, thermal and other environments. The use of strength as a metric to predict remaining life is motivated by the fact that classical representations and models of fatigue and fracture typically deal with changes in stress state, but not with material state changes. The concept of strength as a damage metric overcomes this fundamental barrier since strength depends on both the stress state and the material state, and relates those two field variables in a single metric.

Since the interaction of these changes in stress state and material state and the manner in which they control the fatigue behaviour of composites are the focus of this chapter, we will begin by defining some of the salient details that we want to include in our discussion.

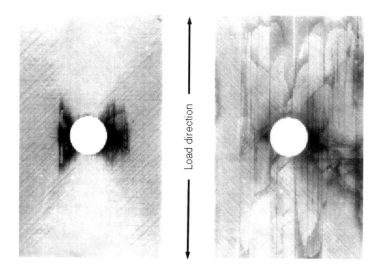

Fig. 14.3   Damage patterns in quasi-isotropic graphite/epoxy centre notched coupons at 90% of life for high load level (left, 1.9 K cycles) and low load level (right, 2380 K cycles).

14.3   Changes in stiffness

An example of damage development during the fatigue of notched composite laminates is shown in Fig. 14.3.

As the figure shows, low-load long-life specimens or components undergo greater damage than high-load short-life specimens for the same fraction of life. The low-load condition is more common for applications; the high-load condition is more common for laboratory characterization. Viable models and philosophy must correctly account for these differences. Changes in stiffness of these specimens caused by the extensive matrix cracking (and some delamination around the hole) can be substantial, tens of per cent depending on the details of the specimen and the hole size. However, the specimen on the right is stronger than the one on the left, i.e. the monotonic decrease in stiffness during the life of these specimens is not accompanied by a monotonic decrease in strength. In the first half of life (and often a larger fraction) the strength of such a specimen may increase, with measured increases being more than 30% in tension in some cases.[1,2] Compressive strength may also increase in the early part of life.

At the local level, point-wise stiffness may be a function of time or cycles of applied loading (or both), i.e. stiffness changes due to processes like microcracking and creep are likely to influence $\sigma_{if}(t)$, the load-direction normal stress in the zero degree plies which control the remaining strength of the notched laminate. For a cross-ply laminate, for example, matrix cracking in the 90° plies will 'shed' normal stress onto the 0° plies, but matrix cracking and delamination near a notch can relax the local stress concentration. Hence, reduction of the stiffness of the 90° plies as a function of cycles of loading is an experimental characterization that must be entered into an iterative analysis of the stresses in the 0° plies, as a function of cycles of loading. Stiffness changes during cyclic loading typically have the form shown in Fig. 14.4.

In addition to the stiffness changes due to matrix cracking, viscoelastic creep may also reduce the stiffness of the plies, especially in matrix-dominated directions (depending on the

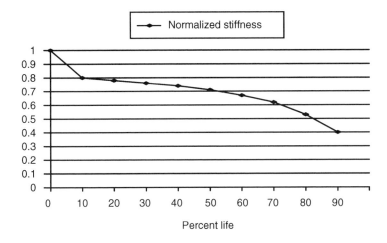

Fig. 14.4   Typical stiffness change of 90° plies in a laminate under cyclic loading.

type of material system involved). It is typical to represent those changes by a reduction in the stiffness transverse to the fibre reinforcement direction, generally written as E_2, as a function of time and temperature, using a standard 'shift factor.' The relationships for this case are shown in Fig. 14.5. The change in transverse stiffness with time is shown in the plot on the left of Fig. 14.5, while the point of entry for zero time is shown by the shift factor (as a function of temperature) on the right-hand diagram in Fig. 14.5. Hence, the transverse stiffness is reduced to the fraction of 0.532 of its initial value over 27 orders of magnitude of time (in units of log(minutes)), using the left-hand diagram, and there is an initial reduction by a fraction of 0.867 for a temperature of 500 °C, according to the diagram on the right. These changes can be entered into classical laminate analysis to calculate the stress in the 0° plies as a function of time. The stiffness changes due to creep are superposed on those caused by matrix cracking for each increment of time, i.e. the fractional reductions can be multiplied over small increments of time to achieve a piecewise linear superposition approximation of the combined changes.

Other characterizations are needed if there are other processes that contribute to a change of stress state or material state, as represented above. However, it is important to note that changes in stiffness are a necessary part of modelling life, they are not sufficient to predict life. We mentioned above that the strength of a laminate with a non-uniform stress state may increase while the stiffness decreases, and the stiffness changes are complex functions of the stress state, and the specimen shape as well as the material type. So stiffness is not a sufficient metric for the estimation of remaining life, i.e. it is not a suitable damage metric for general situations. But stiffness as a function of position does determine local stress (and strain) distributions for a given loading, so tracking and modelling the large stiffness changes that can occur in composite materials for acceptable service conditions is a critical part of a viable life estimation model.

14.4   Changes in local material strength

The values of principal material strengths $X_{ij}(t)$ are also measurable quantities. Initial experiments in tension, compression, and shear in three orthogonal planes will yield the full complement of tensor values of X_{ij} for any anisotropic material, uniquely. But those values

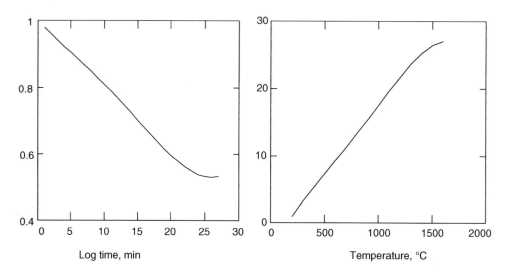

Fig. 14.5   Normalized matrix stiffness as a function of time (left) and shift factor as a function of temperature (right) for a Ni/CAS system.

are also functions of time, i.e. most materials under some range of applied conditions exhibit time-dependent fracture, or stress rupture, as it is often called. Actually, stress rupture is nearly always associated with elevated temperatures, and is known to be greatly influenced by temperature. Hence, the quantity that must be obtained from characterizations is really $X_{ij}(t,T)$. Typically, such tests are difficult to run, and expensive to conduct, so models are needed to 'fill in the gaps' between available data. A typical form, written for the Ni/CAS material being used here for illustration:

$$X(t, T) = 1 - 0.208 \log(t) \left[3.478 \left(\frac{T - 298}{2590 - T} \right) \right]$$

This behaviour is shown in Fig. 14.6.

It should be noted that the experimental characterization shown in Fig. 14.6 is for lamina-level (or ply level) behaviour. We have shown that it is also possible to express the principal material strengths in terms of micromechanical representations, that allow one to represent the global stress rupture behaviour in terms of that of the constituents and their interfacial behaviour.[2] In that instance, characterization of the time-dependent failure of the individual constituents and interfaces is the basis for this representation, but the general philosophy is unchanged.

Strength changes may be caused by a variety of physical phenomena. For polymers, for example, physical ageing (changes in free volume) and chemical ageing may alter the matrix strength in a composite. Any physical effect that alters the strength of the fibres may greatly affect composite strength. But surprisingly, variations in the stiffness or strength of the interface between the fibre and matrix can also greatly alter composite strength.[15-19] For ceramic matrix composites, for example, if the bonding between the fibres and matrix increases as a function of time at temperature, the strength of the composite may decrease substantially.

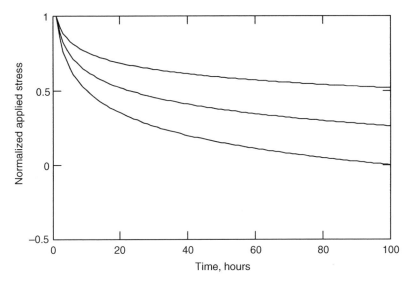

Fig. 14.6   Stress rupture behaviour of a Ni/CAS composite at 600 °C (top), 800 °C (middle) and 962 °C (bottom).

14.5   Strength: an internal state variable and damage metric

The present chapter investigates the concept of evolution of strength in fibrous composite systems as a method of predicting life. In particular, the conceptual foundations of the 'critical element method', developed by the authors, are defined and systematically combined to construct a philosophy for the prediction of remaining strength and life of composite materials in the presence of combined mechanical, thermal and environmental applied conditions that may produce concomitant fatigue, creep and stress rupture. A more complete development of this philosophy can be found in the book titled *Damage Tolerance and Durability of Composite Material Systems*, published by Wiley Interscience (2002).

14.6   Strength of a composite material: 'Critical element' concepts

Defining strength in fibrous composite materials cannot generally be done by simply identifying a single 'stress level' that causes failure. Such composites are generally anisotropic and inhomogeneous, so that the stress state in the material is nearly always complex, even when only one stress is applied at the global level. In addition, the material strength at the local level is also anisotropic and spatially non-uniform. One must select, then, specific stress values and compare them to the correct corresponding strength values to construct a proper 'strength' concept at the global level. The most common engineering method for doing this is to define a 'failure function'. A failure function is a scalar generally written as

$$Fa = Fa\left(\frac{\sigma_{ij}}{X_{ij}}\right),$$

where Fa lies between 0 and 1, $Fa = 1$ defining failure of the material. A number of different expressions based on this form have been proposed over the years. The more 'natural' choice is to compare the stresses in the composite directions (1: fibre direction, 2: perpendicular or matrix direction) to their respective strengths (X: tensile strength, Y: transverse strength, S: shear strength). For a lamina subjected to in-plane loading, the so-called maximum stress criterion can be written as:

$$Fa = \max\left[\frac{\sigma_1}{X}, \frac{\sigma_2}{Y}, \frac{\tau_{12}}{S}\right]$$

depending on which ratio is maximum. In this failure function, no interaction between the failure strengths X, Y and S is considered. In other words, axial, transverse and shear failures are presumed to occur independently. But as has been said before, a stress applied in only one direction at the global level results in a complex stress state at the local level. For brittle polymer and ceramic composites, the failure strain of the matrix may be smaller than the failure strain of the fibre. For a uniaxial lamina loaded at an off-axis angle (angle between the loading direction and the fibre direction), matrix cracking in planes parallel to the fibre direction is observed because of high σ_2. Typically between 0° and 12° or so, τ_{12} at the fibre/matrix interface becomes important leading to interfacial sliding. Between 12° and 90°, τ_{12} decreases, σ_2 increases and the growth of interfacial cracks in an opening mode takes place. But for any angle, final failure is directly dependent on the combination of σ_1, σ_2 and τ_{12}. Failure functions like the Tsai–Hill function, for example, are able to take into account a complex combination of stresses. The Tsai–Hill expression can be seen as an extension of Von Mises' isotropic yield criterion. For a unidirectional composite lamina with in-plane loading, it is written as:

$$Fa = \frac{\sigma_1^2}{X^2} - \frac{\sigma_1 \cdot \sigma_2}{X^2} + \frac{\sigma_2^2}{Y^2} + \frac{\tau_{12}^2}{S^2}$$

This expression is widely used, and typically shows reasonable agreement with experiment.

Many continuous fibre composites are made up of plies or laminae that are bonded together to form a laminate. The discussion of strength for each of those laminae is essentially the same as the details mentioned in the previous section, with the addition of the effect on ply stresses of the accommodation each ply must make to deform with the same strain as its neighbours. (There are also edge effects, discussed below.) For the laminate, each ply may fail, in various ways, and the failure of the laminate can be said to be defined by 'last ply failure', in some sense.

The most typical approach to the definition of the strength of laminates is to address the failure of each ply with increasing load level or time. In that sense, one can define a 'first ply failure', and subsequent ply failures as the internal stress state changes due to internal relaxation. There is an accepted practice in the composite engineering field for calculating the progressive internal stress state, by reducing (or 'discounting') the stiffness in damage-affected directions in those plies that fail. This 'ply discount' method assumes that stress in the matrix of those plies is redistributed, with the effect of increasing various stress components in the other plies. If one calculates the strength of the last ply to fail as a function of this redistribution process, then it is clear that this 'failure function' will be increasing, even for a constant applied global loading.

If failure is defined by fracture, then the last ply to fail can be called a 'critical element,' in the sense that global failure is defined by the local failure of that ply. Then one might consider the failure function in that critical element as a canonical parameter for the definition of strength, or remaining strength in the process of progressive failure of the plies in the laminate.

This is, in fact, the fundamental foundation of the 'critical element theory', that we have developed.[1-12] The concept of a local failure function in the critical element changing with loading history, or more precisely, with changes in internal stress state (the numerator of the failure function) or material state (the denominator of the failure function) is the foundation of the remaining strength philosophy that we have constructed over a period of about 15 years. Before explaining how these concepts are used for fatigue (and for combined fatigue, creep, and stress rupture), we introduce one more fundamental feature of the philosophy that is critical to the more general case of non-uniform stress states.

14.7   Non-uniform stress states: characteristic material dimensions

So far we have examined the concept of strength in laminae, and strength in laminates, subjected to remote loading at the global level. However, for those discussions, it was assumed that the local stresses are uniform. Most applied conditions involve non-uniform stress states and non-uniform strength as a point function. In order to extend our development of the critical element concept to those situations, we will discuss an illustrative example, the familiar problem of a coupon laminate plate with a centre hole (e.g. Fig. 14.3). A uniaxial loading is applied to the coupon. We consider stresses at the ply level, exactly as we did for the uniform stress case, and form a failure function at that level in the critical element. However, as Wu[13], Waddoups and Eisemann,[14] and subsequently Whitney and Nuismer[15] have shown, the strength of notched laminates is controlled by a characteristic volume of material. It is necessary for us to write our failure function in this critical element or characteristic volume of material near the notch.

A convenient method of doing that has been suggested by Whitney and Nuismer, although their suggestion has been modified in the present approach. Whitney and Nuismer suggested that failure occurs when the average stress $\bar{\sigma}_x(y)$ over some characteristic material distance A along the radial direction transverse to the loading axis is equal to X_0, the strength of the unnotched material. This characteristic distance is a material property independent of laminate geometry and stress distribution. The failure criterion is written by Whitney and Nuismer as:

$$\frac{\sigma_{ap}}{X_0} = \frac{2 \cdot (1 - \xi)}{(2 - \xi^2 - \xi^4)}$$

where σ_{ap} = loading applied on the laminate in the x direction, $\xi = r/(r+A)$, and r = hole radius. This form also shows that the notched laminate strength depends on the hole radius r. The larger the hole, the larger the volume of material subjected to high stress. The probability of having a large flaw in this volume is greater and as a consequence the strength is lower.

14.8   Strength evolution

The preceding concepts and methods can be extended to the most general case of the calculation of remaining strength and life of composite materials and structures under mechanical, thermal, and environmental applied conditions that produce combinations of fatigue, creep, and stress rupture (time-dependent failure). The first step in the philosophy is to carefully identify the failure mode that is induced by the applied conditions, using experimental methods. Then, using the precepts described above, a failure function form is selected to describe the final failure event (e.g. fibre failure in a critical element, etc.). Then all of the processes that cause changes in the stress state or material state in that critical element are characterized by rates as a function of the applied conditions and (generalized) time.

Failure modes are primarily (but not exclusively) a function of the stress state in the critical element, under the thermal conditions expected in service. If the fibres in the zero-degree plies near a notch over some characteristic distance control the quasi-static failure in a notched coupon, they will probably be the critical element under long-term conditions. There are important exceptions to this generality, that we will discuss below. A major reason for the validity of the generality is the fact that most engineering composites are designed to be fibre controlled, i.e. the stiffness and strength of a 'well-designed' composite are usually dominated by the fibre reinforcement. This, in turn, is driven by the fact that the fibre reinforcement is often comparatively insensitive to temperature, time, fatigue and other long-term environments. However, laboratory observations provide the surprising fact that the tensile strength in the fibre direction of a polymer composite coupon, for example, can change by 15–34% when the matrix properties or the fibre-matrix couplings change due to temperature or local constituent variations, even though the fibres are unaffected by those changes.[16–20] Hence, we must add that failure modes can change due to applied environments such as temperature, chemical agents, and time or cycles. For the present philosophy, the failure mode must be determined for the conditions to be modelled, preferably by experimental characterization. If that is not possible, experience available in the literature can often be used to anticipate that failure mode.

However, the damage development shown for 190 000 cycles of loading, (a), and for about 2 380 000 cycles of loading, (b) in Figure 14.3, illustrates another essential feature of this philosophy. The initial stress state and material state of the material are greatly altered by the history of loading. In fact, for the low stress levels applied for practical engineering applications, the amount of damage that occurs before failure is very great, much larger than the damage that occurs in laboratory tests for shorter times at larger stress levels.

The central theme of the present approach, then, is to track the changes in the stress state and material state in the critical element as functions of the duration and history of the applied conditions, as well as the constituent properties and the rates of the degradation processes that act to change properties. Our problem is to combine those elements in a self-consistent way, such that the interactions and collective effects of, say, fatigue, creep, stress rupture, and other phenomena are retained, in the spirit of the critical element philosophy.

Elements of this approach have been described in earlier publications.[1–12] Neither thermodynamics or statistical mechanics are applicable to systems that are not in equilibrium. Many non-equilibrium processes are, however, of great importance to engineering problems. Classical examples include chemical reactions and solidification of super-cooled liquids. In the present context, these processes include micro- (or sub-micro-) defect formation and accumulation, which is generally dissipative and spontaneous.

Kinetic theory is uniquely suited to the description and interpretation of the speeds or rates associated with non-equilibrium processes. Typically, kinetic theory is used to derive relationships such as the equation of state of a material. The most common example is the equation of state for an ideal gas, which is easily derived from a simple consideration of the kinetic energy of the molecules in a control volume. However, we will be concerned with the kinetic theory of solids, and we will take a broad interpretation of the purview of kinetic theory. In particular, we will address the general question of the rate of damage initiation and

Table 14.1   Chart showing occupation of damage states as a function of the energy/rate needed to create that damage state

						Number of duplicates	Probability of state
Energy →	0	e	2e	3e	4e		
division ↓							
1	3			1		4	4/20
2	2	1	1			12	12/20
3	1	3				4	4/20
Probability of event	40/20	24/20	12/20	4/20	0/20	20 (total)	

accumulation, and try to examine the question of how to construct appropriate equations of state for material volumes in which such damage processes are active to define the 'state of the material'. The most familiar discussion of this aspect of kinetic theory is generally concerned with deformation and recovery processes in homogeneous materials, especially metals. Although we will use those foundations in the general sense, our focus will be on the description of processes that may, alternatively, be defined by sequences of discrete events such as micro-crack formation, debonding, constituent–boundary separation, and constituent fracture in inhomogeneous systems. In contrast to the robust literature on the micromechanics of kinetic theory in metals, the subject of kinetic theory is in the very early formative stages for composite systems.

We consider the general accumulation of discrete local damage events (defined as 'observables' such as single or multiple fibre fractures, or micro-crack formation) and assume that the energy involved in their formation is also discrete. We assume that the damage events are being formed by a process (such as fatigue loading or sustained loading with time) that supplies input energy at a steady rate, i.e. that the available energy per unit time is fixed. We also assume that the damage events can 'exchange' energy by means of the elastic response of the continuum in which they exist. Then we address the question of how these discrete events are populated by a given energy input. To illustrate the fundamental nature of our argument, we will first postulate a simple example, and then generalize our argument in the limit. For that purpose, we consider four damage events that have discrete energy values of 0, e, $2e$, $3e$, or $4e$, with a total system energy (per unit time) of $3e$. Ultimately, we will let the value of e go to 0 in the limit, as the number of damage events goes to infinity to create continuous variables for the rate process of damage accumulation. At present, we ask, what are all the possible divisions of the available energy among the states? Table 14.1 shows a chart of those possibilities.

We assume that all divisions of the total energy occur with the same probability. Table 14.1 shows that there are three possible arrangements (or 'divisions') of the available energy among the damage events. Then the probability that a given division will occur is the total number of duplicate divisions divided by the total number of divisions, including all duplicates. Finally, the probability of populating a given damage event with a given energy is the sum of the number of events having that energy in each division multiplied by the probability of that division, which are the (un-normalized) fractions on the bottom line of Table 14.1. If one plots those numbers as a function of energy e, one obtains a perfect fit to an exponential having the form

$$P(e) = A \times \exp[\frac{e}{e_{av}}] \qquad\qquad [14.1]$$

which has the form of a Boltzman distribution. Although space does not allow us to present the details, the rigorous derivation of this form from the conditional probability that n articles can occupy q cells, given by:

$$P_i = \frac{q_i!}{n_i!\,(q_i - n_i)!}$$

[14.2]

is well known. In equation [14.1], e_{av} is the average energy of all damage events. Equation [14.1] assumes that we have taken our discrete energy levels to the infinitesimal limit of a continuous variable.

We now introduce the familiar damage mechanics 'continuity', Ψ, defined in the usual way with a value of 1 when the state of the material is 'undamaged', and 0 when the material is 'completely damaged'.[21] As an essential feature of the present model, we interpret this continuity parameter as the normalized *probability* of survival of our material, and with that definition, refer to it as the 'state of the material'. Then we argue that this variable is, in fact, the left-hand side of equation [14.1], i.e. we can write:

$$\Psi = A \times \exp[-\frac{e}{e_{av}}]$$

[14.3]

which now represents the probability of survival of the material as a function of the occupied energy level of the damage states e. Finally, we make a postulate that the occupied energy is proportional to the total time over which energy is supplied to the system (at our steady rate), and specify that

$$\Psi = A \times \exp[-\eta\tau^j] \qquad \text{where} \qquad \tau = \frac{t}{\hat{\tau}}$$

[14.4]

in which t is a time variable (such as sidereal time), j is a material parameter, and $\hat{t}$ is a characteristic (or average) time associated with the process. Characteristic times of damage processes have been discussed by Christensen[22] and Miyano *et al.*[23] They could be a stress rupture life, a fatigue life, a stress corrosion life, etc., in the context of the present discussion. Taking the natural logarithm and the variation of equation [14.4], one obtains the rate equation for the change in material state due to damage accumulation as a function of generalized time, shown below.

$$\frac{\delta\Psi}{\delta\tau} = \eta\Psi j\tau^{j-1}$$

[14.5]

Then we introduce a second postulate, that the continuity of the material can be set equal to the quantity $(1-Fa)$, where Fa is the 'failure function' that applies to a specific controlling failure mode. In general, Fa has the general form suggested by Hill[24] and others, i.e. it is a function of (local) stress components divided by the corresponding material strength components. We could then write

$$\Psi = 1 - Fa\left(\frac{\sigma_{ij}}{X_{ij}}\right)$$

[14.6]

Although the continuity is almost certainly a more complex function of Fa, this simple first approximation is correct in the limit; when the applied load is null, the probability of survival is unity, and when the appropriate failure function reaches unity, the probability of survival is null, i.e. fracture is 'predicted'. Finally, since we are presently considering a damage process with progressive time, we postulate that the remaining strength Fr is given by

$$Fr = 1 - \Delta Fa\left(\frac{\sigma_{ij}(\tau)}{X_{ij}(\tau)}\right) \qquad [14.7]$$

where it is understood that the changes in the failure function are being induced by the damage process. Then combining equations [14.5]–[14.7], and taking $\eta = 1$ we obtain

$$Fr = 1 - \int_{0}^{\tau_1} (1 - Fa\left(\frac{\sigma_{ij}(\tau)}{X_{ij}(\tau)}\right)j\tau^{j-1}d\tau \qquad [14.8]$$

This basic form of the strength evolution equation has been used by us for a dozen years, with many industrial partners, to solve various applied problems in which time, temperature, and cyclic loading are explicit influences.[1–12] Before looking at an example application of this equation, we note some recent refinements of the form of equation [14.8] that have proven to be very useful. Suppose that fatigue is the dominant process for the determination of remaining strength, and assume that the characteristic 'time' to failure can be represented by N, the fatigue life. Then we argue that we can express that life in terms of the stress in the direction of the fibres of the most heavily loaded plies, and write a one-dimensional equation of the form:

$$\frac{\sigma_f(\tau)}{X_t(\tau)} = A + B(\log(N(\tau)))^p \qquad [14.9]$$

where σ_f is the fibre direction stress (which may be changing with time due to stress redistribution caused by matrix cracking in other plies, for example), X_t is the unidirectional tensile strength in the direction of the fibres (which may be decreasing due to oxidation of the fibres, etc.), and A, B, and p are material constants. If we introduce the frequency of cyclic loading f, so that the number of cycles of loading n is given by $n = f \times t$, then equation [14.8] can be stated in the form:

$$Fr(t_1) = 1 - \int_{0}^{t_1} (1 - Fa(\frac{\sigma_{ij}(t)}{X_{ij}(t)})) j \left(\frac{ft}{N(t)}\right)^{j-1} d(\frac{ft}{N(t)}) \qquad [14.10]$$

where all of the variables are evaluated at the local level, in the 'critical element', as we have discussed it.

The nature of the inputs to equation [14.10], illustrated in Fig. 14.7, is determined by two requirements. First, it must be possible to measure all necessary inputs to any practical model using straight forward engineering tests, like fatigue, creep, and stress rupture characterizations. Second, the measurements must produce independent input data, not coupled to other behaviour. Hence, fatigue data for input is usually developed at temperatures and under conditions that eliminate any time-dependent behaviour. Creep is carefully measured in such a way to avoid cracking and fatigue. The effects of matrix cracking (on stiffness) are measured under conditions that avoid creep or stiffness changes induced by other phenomena, and so on.

These independent characterizations are recombined in equation [14.10] by their collective

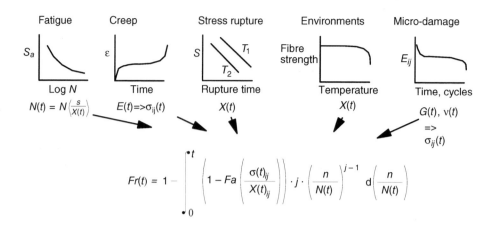

Fig. 14.7   Nature of the inputs to the residual strength evolution equation.

effect on the arguments in

$$Fa\left(\frac{\sigma_{ij}}{X_{ij}}\right)$$

If creep changes stiffness, for example, and matrix cracking also changes stiffness (in the same increment of time), the changes are added together to alter the state of stress in the numerator of Fa. If corrosion changes material strengths and thermodynamical microstructural changes also alter material strengths, then their respective incremental changes are added to alter the denominator of Fa in that time increment. So the method of combining effects is piecewise linear. It should also be noted that the coupling of effects is accounted for in this process. If creep reduces the local stress that is driving crack initiation, for example, the reduced stress level is used in the calculation of the next incremental matrix cracking rate. The incremental evaluations of the integral in equation [14.10] bring all coupled effects together by updating the independent variables that enter the rate equations for all degradation processes with each incremental evaluation of the integral.

14.9   Applications

Figure 14.8 shows the engineering methodology associated with the method, and embodied in the MRLife code published by the Materials Response Group at Virginia Tech. Quasi-static characterization is needed for initial properties (at the lamina level or at the fibre/matrix/ interphase level), and the damage and failure modes. This defines the initial stress state and material state. Characterization of cyclic degradation (fatigue, at room temperature), stiffness change with time (creep), time-dependent material degradation (stress rupture), or other degradation processes with generalized time and history provide rates that modify the kernel of the integral. The resulting remaining strength Fr and life are highly non-linear, sequence-dependent functions of all applied conditions. Numerous predictions of remaining strength and life for numerous combinations of fatigue, creep, and stress rupture effects have been made and checked against experimental data for applications from jet engine parts to off-shore flexible pipe.

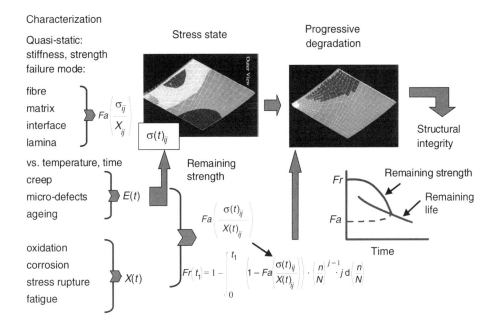

Fig. 14.8   Schematic diagram of the critical element application methodology.

Figure 14.9 shows data and predictions for an early version of SiC/SiC composite. The predictions combine the effects of matrix cracking (which causes large stiffness changes in this case), creep rupture (largely due to oxidation), and cyclic fatigue loading. A more thorough description of the data and methodology can be found in references 2 and 10. The test coupons were plain weave, 25 mm wide by 150 mm long, 1.25 mm thick. Some of the experimental data were developed in our laboratory, and other data were taken from the literature. Remaining strength measurements were made at temperature.

In Fig. 14.9(a), predicted life values are compared to observed data for a variety of high-temperature ceramic composite tests, including mission loading, hold times, different shaped loading ramp combinations, and spike and hold sequences. These and many other comparisons were done in connection with a variety of industrial partners including the General Electric Engine Division, Pratt & Whitney, United Technologies, Westinghouse, Allied Signal Composites, Martin Marietta, Babcock and Wilcox (now McDermott Technologies, Inc.), DuPont, and Solar Turbines. The physical data and general guidance provided by those partners were critical to the construction of a robust approach to the present problem.

In Fig. 14.9(b), predicted remaining strength is compared to observed values for a DuPont Lanxide enhanced material (an early developmental version of that material) at 982 °C. Literally hundreds of these comparisons have been made with comparable results. These predictions are somewhat unique; very few remaining strength predictions have appeared in the literature. However, they are essential for man-rated structures since damage tolerance is the certification procedure required by the FAA, for example.

Figure 14.10 shows a prediction developed in association with the Wellstream Corporation, for high-pressure, off-shore flexible pipe. At the test temperatures for that figure, these unidirectional, fibre-dominated specimens showed time-dependent failure, i.e. stress rupture

(a)

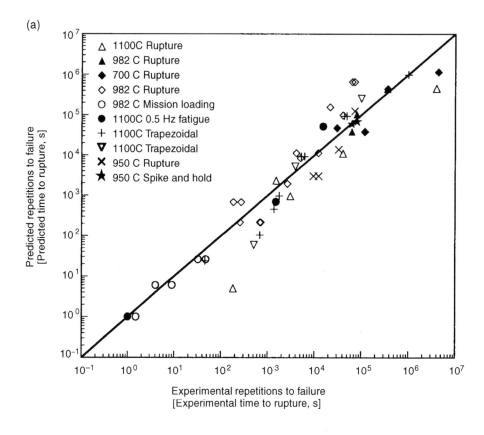

Experimental repetitions to failure
[Experimental time to rupture, s]

(b)

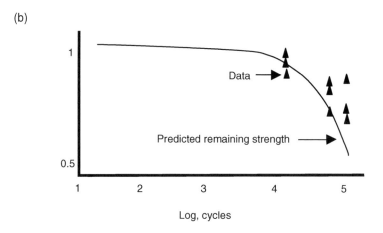

Log, cycles

Fig. 14.9 (a) Predicted vs. observed life for various combinations of fatigue, creep and stress rupture, and (b) predicted vs. observed remaining strength for one loading condition.

behaviour. Fatigue degradation (due to wave motion, primarily) was also a factor. The combined effect is predicted, and observed, to be a nonlinear combination of these two dominant physical degradation phenomena. Predictions of this type were made for tensile loading and bend-loading.

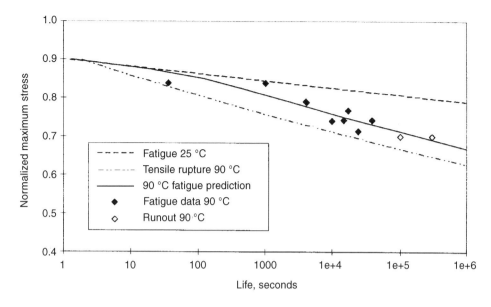

Fig. 14.10   Predicted and observed life for combined fatigue and stress rupture for a carbon fibre, polymer composite at a temperature of about 90% of the matrix Tg.

The top curve in Fig. 14.10 is the room-temperature fatigue data for the unidirectionally reinforced carbon/PPS composite, under uniaxial tensile loading. The bottom curve is the creep rupture data under that type of loading, recorded at 90 °C. (The T_g of the matrix material is about 130 °C.) The predictions and data are for the combined situation of fatigue at 90 °C. It is seen that the combined behaviour is a very nonlinear combination of the two degradation processes. The predictions of equation [14.10] involve the changes in Fa caused by both effects together, as a function of time (and cycles). These effects are time dependent, sequence dependent, and cyclic rate dependent, all of which have an effect on the stress state σ_{ij} or the material state X_{ij} in the failure function $Fa(\sigma_{ij}/X_{ij})$.

14.10   Conclusions

We have presented an outline of an approach to the prediction of remaining strength and life of brittle material systems in which damage accumulation is responsible for the degradation of properties and performance. The approach, based on the critical element method developed earlier, and founded on the concept of a generalized failure function, follows accepted engineering practice for the interpretation of strength in composite materials and structures. The practicality, utility, and validity of the approach has been established by applications in association with more than two dozen industrial organizations and groups over 15 years.

Frontiers and opportunities associated with this approach are abundant. Although we have not had space for the development here, the entire philosophy can be cast in terms of micromechanics, of stiffness and strength. (Recent releases of MRLife include such modules.) But micromechanical strength models are still incompletely developed for many damage and failure modes. Viscoelastic representations currently used are essentially linear; nonlinear models are only now being introduced to the code. Stiffness change due to damage development is the subject of countless papers and a large body of literature. But even crack density as a function of time or cycles is still difficult to estimate from first principles. Kinetics is a well-developed analytical concept, but there are only a few first-principle simulations of the kinetics of stress rupture, and those are for failure models that are incompletely verified.

And the application of such models to structures has another set of challenges. As Fig. 14.8 implies, this approach can be (and is being) applied on an element-by-element basis for FEM analysis of high-temperature structures, such as combustor liners. However, these are highly non-linear problems, so that the sequence of internal stepping and adjustments of stiffness and material strength variables is significant – but largely unexplored.

Despite these and many other needs, the present approach offers the field a general method that is soundly based on mechanics and materials fundamentals, sensitive to mechanistic degradation mechanisms, and easily supported by well-established engineering characterization methods that provide independent data. The method can support advances by other investigators in nearly all areas of mechanics and materials, and, therefore, offers a method of bringing other fundamental work to the applications community. Finally, the approach can be used as a guide to the development of systematic experimental data for the development of material and structural systems, and for the life cycle cost estimation of engineering systems.

14.11   Acknowledgements

The authors gratefully acknowledge the support of the Air Force Office of Scientific Research under grant F49620-95-1-0217 and NASA Langley under contract NAS1-19610 for the work on high temperature polymer composites, the support of the National Science Foundation under grant no. DMR9120004 for the micromechanical modelling. Thanks also go to McDermott Technologies Inc. under contract 90189/CER1286 and the Virginia Center for Innovative Technologies under grant MAT-94-015 for support of the ceramic composite research.

14.12   References

1. REIFSNIDER K L, Ed. (1991), *Fatigue of Composite Materials*, London: Elsevier Science Publishers.
2. REIFSNIDER K L and CASE S W (2002), *Damage Tolerance and Durability of Composite Material Systems*, John Wiley Sons, Inc., New York.
3. REIFSNIDER K L and STINCHCOMB W W (1986), 'A critical element model of the residual strength and life of fatigue-loaded composite coupons,' *Composite Materials: Fatigue and Fracture, ASTM STP 907*, H.T. Hahn, Ed., Philadelphia, PA: American Soc. for Testing and Materials, 298–313.
4. REIFSNIDER K L (1992), 'Use of mechanistic life prediction methods for the design of damage tolerant composite material systems,' *ASTM STP 1157*, M.R. Mitchell and O. Buck Eds., Philadelphia, PA: American Society for Testing and Materials, 205–223.
5. GAO Z and REIFSNIDER K L (1993), 'Micromechanics of tensile strength in composite systems,' *Proc. Fourth Symp. on Composite Materials: Fatigue and Fracture*, Indianapolis, in: ASTM 1156, W.W. Stinchcomb and N.E. Ashbaugh, Eds., Philadelphia, PA: ASTM, 453–470.
6. REIFSNIDER K L and GAO Z (1991), 'Micromechanical concepts for the estimation of property evolution and remaining life,' *Proc. Intl. Conf. on Spacecraft Structures and Mechanical Testing*, Noordwijk, The Netherlands, 24–26 April: (ESA SP-321, Oct. 1991), 653–657.
7. XU Y L and REIFSNIDER K L (1993), 'Micromechanical modeling of composite compression strength,' *Journal of Composite Materials*, 27(6), 572–588.
8. SUBRAMANIAN S, REIFSNIDER K L and STINCHCOMB W W (1995), 'Tensile strength of unidirectional

composites: the role of efficiency and strength of fiber–matrix interface,' *Journal of Composites Technology and Research, JCTRER*, 17(4) (October 1995), 289–300.

9. REIFSNIDER K L (1995), 'Evolution concepts for microstructure–property interactions in composite systems,' *Proc. IUTAM Symp. On Microstructure-Property Interactions in Composite Materials*, Aalborg, Denmark, R. Pyrz, Ed., New York, NY: Kluwer, 327–348.

10. REIFSNIDER K L, CASE S W and IYENGAR N (1996), 'Recent advances in composite damage mechanics,' *Proc. Conf. On Materials and Mechanical Testing*, European Space Agency, Noordwijk, Netherlands, 27–29 March 1996, SP-386, European Space Agency, 483–490.

11. REIFSNIDER K L (1996), 'A micro-kinetic approach to durability analysis: the critical element method,' *Progress in Durability of Composite Systems*, A.H. Cardon, K.L. Reifsnider and H. Fukuda, Eds., Balkema, Rotterdam, 3–11.

12. STINCHCOMB W W and BAKIS C E (1990), 'Fatigue behavior of composite laminates,' *Fatigue of Composite Materials*, K.L. Reifsnider, Ed. New York, NY: Elsevier Science Publishers, 105–180.

13. WU E M (1968), 'Fracture mechanics of anisotropic plates,' in *Composite Materials Workshop*, S.W. Tsai, J.C. Halpin and N.J. Pagano, Eds., Technomic Pub. Co., Inc., Stamford, Conn., pp. 20–43.

14. WADDOUPS M E, EISEMANN J R and KAMINSKI B E (1971), 'Macroscopic fracture mechanics of advanced composite materials,' *Journal of Composite Materials*, **5**, 446.

15. WHITNEY J M and NUISMER R J (1974), 'Stress fracture criteria for laminated composites containing stress concentrations,' *Journal of Composite Materials*, **8**, 253.

16. SUBRAMANIAN S (1994), 'Effect of fiber/matrix Interface on the long term behavior of cross-ply laminates,' Dissertation, Department of Engineering Science and Mechanics, Virginia Polytechnic Institute & State University, January.

17. LESKO J J, SWAIN R E, CARTWRIGHT J M, CHIN J W, REIFSNIDER K L, DILLARD D A and WIGHTMAN J P (1994), 'Interface developed from sizings and their chemical–structural relationship to composite performance,' *Journal of Adhesion*, **45**, 43–57.

18. LESKO J J, ELMORE J S, CASE S W, SWAIN R E, REIFSNIDER K L and DILLARD D A (1994), 'A global and local investigation of compressive strength to determine the influence of the fiber/matrix interface,' Compression Response of Composite Structures, *ASTM STP 1185, American Society for Testing and Materials*, Philadelphia, pp. 228–240.

19. LESKO J J, SUBRAMANIAN S, DILLARD D A and REIFSNIDER K L (1994), The influence of fiber size developed interfaces on interlaminar fracture toughness,' *SAMPE, Proceedings of the 39th International Symposium*, Anaheim, CA, April.

20. LESKO J J (1994), 'Interphase properties and their effects on the compression mechanics of polymeric composites,' Dissertation, Department of Engineering Science and Mechanics, Virginia Polytechnic Institute & State University, August.

21. KACHANOV L M (1986), *Introduction to Continuum Damage*, T. Hahn, Ed., Philadelphia: Am. Soc. for Testing & Materials, pp. 298–313. Mechanics, Martinus Nijhoff Pub., Boston.

22. CHRISTENSEN R M (1981), 'Lifetime predictions for polymers and composites under constant load,' *Journal of of Rheology*, **25**(5), 517–528.

23. MIYANO Y, MCMURRAY M K, ENYAMA J and NAKADA M (1994), 'Loading rate and temperature dependence on flexural fatigue behavior of a satin woven CFRP laminate,' *Journal of Composite Materials*, **28**(13), 1250–1260.

24. HILL R (1948), 'A theory of yielding and plastic flow of anisotropic metals,' *Proc. Roy. Soc., Series A*, Vol. 193.

15

A computational mesodamage model for life prediction for laminates

P. Ladevèze and G. Lubineau, LMT Cachan, France

15.1 Introduction

A major challenge in composite design consists of predicting the life of a composite structure subjected to complex loading. The damage state has to be calculated at any point and at any time up to final fracture. Damage refers to the more or less gradual development of microcracks, leading to macrocracks and, finally, to rupture. Macrocracks are simulated as completely damaged zones.

One approach for laminated composites is based on what we call a damage mesomodel, which will be described here with particular emphasis on fatigue loading. Damage is considered to be uniform throughout the thickness of each single layer (Ladevèze, 1986; Ladevèze and Le Dantec, 1992; Allix and Ladevèze, 1992). In addition, continuum damage models with delay effects are introduced (Ladevèze, 1989; Ladevèze *et al.*, 2000). A sound physical basis was recently given to the mesomodel (Ladevèze and Lubineau, 2001, 2002a): it was proved that this mesomodel can be interpreted as the result of the homogenization of microscale models, for which a large body of theoretical and experimental work exists (see Nairn and Hu, 1994; Nairn, 2000; Henaff-Gardin *et al.*, 1992; Berthelot, 2002). We shall also focus on these micro–meso relationships, which are very useful for building fatigue models. It appears that the induced fatigue phenomenon is fibre/matrix debonding within the plies. We show that this is compatible with classical fatigue models.

The mesomodel has been used for various continuous fibre laminates, primarily for aeronautical and spatial applications.

15.2 The damage scenarios on the micro structural scale (Fig. 15.1)

Scenario 1, related to transverse microcracking, is characterized by the microcrack density (1/ρ). Scenario 2 introduces delamination at the tips of the microcracks. Scenario 3, which is not usually introduced on the 'micro' scale, is naturally homogenized on the mesoscale; it can be interpreted as fibre/matrix debonding within the plies; it is the main phenomenon

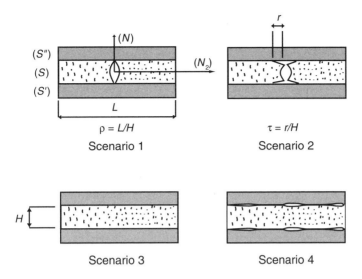

Fig. 15.1   The damage scenarios on the 'micro' scale.

for $[45/{-}45]_{2n}$ laminates for quasi-static loadings (Lagattu and Lafarie-Frénot, 2000). Scenario 4 defines diffuse damage of the interface, which can be considered as homogenized on the mesoscale.

For quasi-static increasing loading, we start with Scenarios 3 and 4. Following percolation, we obtain transverse microcracks, followed by Scenario 1. Scenario 2 occurs later and its evolution is generally catastrophic (Ladevèze and Lubineau 2001, 2002a). For fatigue loading, we consider that the induced fatigue phenomenon is the scenario 3 (or 4), which introduces a certain amount of damage within the plies and a drop in the critical values of the different energy release rates.

15.3   The 3D damage model for laminates according to scenarios 3 and 4

Scenarios 3 and 4 alone are introduced. We use the classical continuum mechanics framework in which a structure is described as a set of substructures (the plies) connected through their interfaces.

Let $\underline{N}_1$ be the direction of the fibres of the ply being considered, $\underline{N}_2$ the transverse direction and $\underline{N}$ the direction orthogonal to the plane $(\underline{N}_1, \underline{N}_2)$. The energy density for layer i ($i \in [1,2,\ldots,n]$) is:

$$e_{\text{layer }(i)}\left(\pi\varepsilon\pi, \sigma\underline{N}\right) = \frac{1}{2}\left[\frac{\sigma_{11}^2}{E_1^0} + \left(\frac{\langle\sigma_{22}\rangle_+^2}{E_2^0} + \frac{\langle\sigma_{33}\rangle_+^2}{E_3^0}\right)\frac{1}{1-\tilde{d}'}\right.$$

$$+ \left(\frac{\langle\sigma_{22}\rangle_-^2}{E_2^0} + \frac{\langle\sigma_{33}\rangle_-^2}{E_3^0}\right) - \sigma_{11}\sigma_{22}\left(\frac{\nu_{12}^0}{E_1^0} + \frac{\nu_{21}^0}{E_2^0}\right) - \sigma_{11}\sigma_{33}\left(\frac{\nu_{13}^0}{E_1^0} + \frac{\nu_{31}^0}{E_3^0}\right)$$

$$\left. - \sigma_{22}\sigma_{33}\left(\frac{\nu_{23}^0}{E_2^0} + \frac{\nu_{32}^0}{E_3^0}\right) + \left(\frac{\sigma_{12}^2}{G_{12}^0} + \frac{\sigma_{13}^2}{G_{13}^0}\right)\frac{1}{1-\tilde{d}} + \frac{\sigma_{23}^2}{G_{23}^0}\frac{1}{1-\tilde{d}_{23}}\right]$$

[15.1]

with

$$\pi\varepsilon\pi = \begin{bmatrix} \varepsilon_{11} & \varepsilon_{12} \\ \varepsilon_{12} & \varepsilon_{22} \end{bmatrix}$$

[15.2]

and

$$\begin{bmatrix} \varepsilon_{11} \\ \varepsilon_{22} \\ \varepsilon_{12} \end{bmatrix} = \begin{bmatrix} \dfrac{1}{E_1^0} & -\dfrac{v_{12}^0}{E_1^0} & 0 \\ -\dfrac{v_{21}^0}{E_2^0} & \dfrac{1}{E_2^0(1-\tilde{d}')} & 0 \\ 0 & 0 & \dfrac{1}{2G_{12}^0(1-\tilde{d})} \end{bmatrix} \begin{bmatrix} \sigma_{11} \\ \sigma_{22} \\ \sigma_{12} \end{bmatrix} + \begin{bmatrix} -\dfrac{v_{13}^0}{E_1^0} \\ -\dfrac{v_{23}^0}{E_2^0} \\ 0 \end{bmatrix} [\sigma_{33}]$$

where π is the projector onto the plane $(\underline{N}_1, \underline{N}_2)$; we assume an isotropic transverse behaviour of the $\underline{N}_1$ axis, the damage indicators being $\tilde{d}$ and $\tilde{d}'$.

For interface j ($j \in [1, 2, \ldots, n+1]$), we take into consideration the following strain energy density:

$$e_{\text{interface } (j)}(\sigma\underline{N}) = \frac{1}{2}\left[\frac{\sigma_{33}^2}{k_1^0(1-\tilde{d}_1)} + \frac{\sigma_{13}^2}{k_{II}^0(1-\tilde{d}_{II})} + \frac{\sigma_{23}^2}{k_{III}^0(1-\tilde{d}_{III})}\right]$$

[15.3]

Generally, $k_{II}^0 = k_{III}^0$ and $\tilde{d}_{II} = \tilde{d}_{III}$.

Inelastic strains can be introduced (Ladevèze, 1986, 1994). We feel that Scenario 3 is quite important for fatigue loading; it can be considered as the major one. One writes ($\tilde{d}_{23}$ being defined in terms of $\tilde{d}'$ and $\tilde{d}$):

$$\tilde{d} = \tilde{d}_s + \tilde{d}_F \quad ; \quad \tilde{d}' = \tilde{d}'_s + \tilde{d}'_F$$

[15.4]

where $\tilde{d}_s$ and $\tilde{d}'_s$ denote the quasi-static part (Ladevèze and Le Dantec, 1992). $\tilde{d}_F$ and $\tilde{d}'_s$ follow classical fatigue laws, with the damage forces being:

$$\tilde{Y}_{d'} = \frac{1}{2}\left(\frac{\langle\sigma_{22}\rangle_+^2}{E_2^0} + \frac{\langle\sigma_{33}\rangle_+^2}{E_3^0}\right)\frac{1}{(1-\tilde{d}')^2}$$

[15.5]

$$\tilde{Y}_d = \frac{1}{2}\left(\frac{\sigma_{12}^2}{G_{12}^0} + \frac{\sigma_{13}^2}{G_{13}^0}\right)\frac{1}{(1-\tilde{d})^2}$$

Such classical fatigue laws can be found in (Lemaitre, 1992).

Remark 1: ε is the total strain; it contains the dilatation part.

15.4   The 'micro' modelling of laminate composite for scenarios 1 and 2

Scenarios 1 and 2 are introduced. The impact of Scenario 3 is twofold. First, the (S) material is damaged. In addition, the scenario modifies the critical values of the different energy release rates for each layer.

$$G_{T,C} = G_{T,C}^0\left(1 - \beta_T\langle\tilde{d}\rangle\right)$$

$$G_{D,C} = G_{D,C}^0\left(1 - \beta_C\langle\tilde{d}\rangle\right)$$

[15.6]

In practice, we take $\beta_T \approx 1.5$ (Ladevèze and Lubineau, 2002b). $<\tilde{d}>$ is the mean value throughout the thickness. In fact, we assume that the micromodel of the laminated composite for Scenarios 1 and 2 is the same as that which can be found in (Ladevèze and Lubineau, 2001, 2002a) for quasi-static loadings. The thickness of the laminated composite is now completely defined by two critical energy release rate values G_T and G_D (Nairn and Hu, 1992).

Then, taking as an example pure mode I, we write:

$$G_T = \frac{H}{2}\tilde{\sigma}_{22}{}^2 G_T^u \leq G_{T,C}$$

$$G_D = \frac{H}{2}\tilde{\sigma}_{22}{}^2 G_D^u \leq G_{D,C}$$

[15.7]

where G_T^u and G_D^u are called 'unit energy release rates' and H is the ply thickness. The energy release rates can be calculated by using the basic layer problem defined in Fig. 15.2.

The cracked layer S is made with an homogenized damaged material (Scenario 3). The upper and lower parts are assumed to be homogenized. As a consequence of the existence of microcracks, the stress $\tilde{\sigma}$ solution of the 3D problem defined in Section 3 is no longer a solution here. There are residuals along the cracks. Introducing periodic conditions, we obtain a classical 2D problem, which can be solved, for various values of the parameters (stacking sequences, thicknesses, . . .), by using the finite-element method with a relatively refined mesh (Ladevèze and Lubineau, 2001, 2002a). It has been proved that the classical energy release rates associated with the microdamage indicators ρ, τ^+, τ^- are approximately 'ply-material' quantities: they depend only slightly on the different parameters, which are the thicknesses, the stacking sequence, etc. Figure 15.3 shows this property for various stacking sequences.

It follows that the quasi-intrinsic curves

$$G_T \leftrightarrow \left(\frac{1}{\rho}; \tau^+; \tau^-\right) \text{ and } G_D \leftrightarrow \left(\frac{1}{\rho}; \tau^+; \tau^-\right)$$

can be calculated for different values of (ρ, τ^+, τ^-), but for a specific laminate. Finite elements can be used in the calculation.

At the tips of the microcracks, transverse microcracking and delamination are competing mechanisms. Transverse microcracking occurs first. It has been proved that, for an increasing loading, once the delamination mechanism has been excited, the behaviour is catastrophic; the so-called 'saturation phenomenon' is observed (Ladevèze and Lubineau, 2002a). This result can be shown experimentally (Ogihara and Takeda, 1995). On the microscale, Scenarios 1 and 2 then follow in a very simple manner.

We note that it is possible to differentiate between modes I and II by modifying equation [15.7].

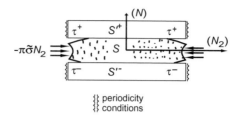

Fig. 15.2   The basic layer problem.

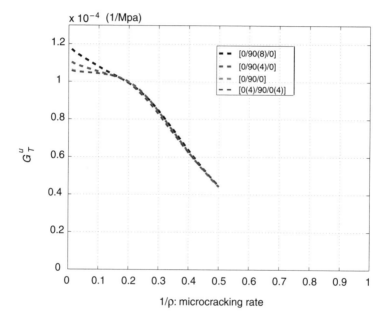

Fig. 15.3 $G_T^u \leftrightarrow (1/\rho)$ for various stacking sequences.

15.5   Mesomodel of the laminated composite (Fig. 15.4)

To proceed further, it is interesting to homogenize the micromodel of Scenarios 1 and 2 in order to obtain a computational model suitable for the analysis of laminated structures.

15.5.1   The fundamental link between the micro-mesomodels

It was proved in (Ladevèze and Lubineau, 2001, 2002a) that the mesomodel can be interpreted as the result of a homogenization process. In the general case, the fundamental link between the micro- and the mesomodel is (Ladevèze and Lubineau, 2002c):

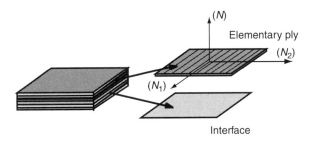

Fig. 15.4   The mesomodel of the laminated composite.

$$\left. \pi\varepsilon^{\mathrm{meso}}\underline{\pi}\right|_{\Gamma_{\mathrm{meso}}} = \left\langle \pi\varepsilon^{\mathrm{micro}}\underline{\pi}\right\rangle\Big|_{\Gamma_{\mathrm{micro}}}$$

$$\left. \sigma^{\mathrm{meso}}\underline{N}\right|_{\Gamma_{\mathrm{meso}}} = \left\langle \sigma^{\mathrm{micro}}\underline{N}\right\rangle\Big|_{\Gamma_{\mathrm{micro}}}$$

[15.8]

Figure 15.5 illustrates the different averages.

15.5.2   Micro–meso relations

Here, we consider relatively plane macrostresses. It was proved that the relationships between (ρ, τ^+, τ^-) and the meso-damage indicators associated with stiffness variations are approximately 'ply–material' relationships; for most engineering composites, they do not depend on the stacking sequence or the thicknesses. This property is also true for the forces, which are the conjugate quantities on the mesolevel of the kinematics variables of damage.

We then calculate the functions $\bar{a}, \bar{a}', \bar{b}, \bar{b}'$, such that:

$$\bar{d} = \bar{a}(\rho, \tau^+, \tau^-)$$

$$\bar{d}' = \bar{a}'(\rho, \tau^+, \tau^-)^{\cdot}$$

[15.9]

$$G_T = \bar{b}\left(Y_{\bar{d}}, Y_{\bar{d}'}\right)$$

$$G_D = \bar{b}'\left(Y_{\bar{d}}, Y_{\bar{d}'}\right)$$

[15.10]

We recall that the calculation is carried out on the basic layer problem for one particular laminate. $\bar{d}$ appears as a parameter which is prescribed as uniform within the cracked layer. Equations [15.7], [15.9] and [15.10] define the mesodamage evolution law for Scenarios 1 and 2.

15.6   Comparison with experiments for $[0_n/90_m]_s$

In our interpretation, only Scenario 3 is affected by fatigue. The growing rate of diffuse damage should be an intrinsic function of associated forces and of the current level of diffuse damage, so that:

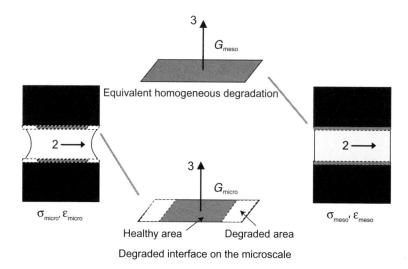

Fig. 15.5   The fundamental link between the micro- and mesoscale.

$$\frac{\partial \tilde{d}_F}{\partial N} = A\left[\tilde{Y}_{\tilde{d}}, \tilde{Y}_{\tilde{d}}, \tilde{d}, \tilde{d}'\right]$$ [15.11]

Then, propagation of diffuse damage by fatigue will be responsible for the decrease of the critical energy release rate $G_{T,C}$. As far as microcracking is concerned, it is nothing more than a direct consequence of this phenomenon.

To justify equation [15.11], it is enough to prove that, the loading being fixed, an intrinsic relationship exists between $\partial \tilde{d}_F/\partial N$ and $\tilde{d}$.

15.6.1   Classical model for fatigue

We now discuss our intrepretation in the light of several micromechanics considerations. A classical fatigue development law in micromechanics is (Liu and Nairn, 1990):

$$\frac{\partial D}{\partial N} = AG_T^m$$ [15.12]

where D is the crack density within the ply, and G_T is the energy release rate associated to propagation of microcracking. A and m are experimentally identified intrinsic quantities. In pure mode I for instance, G_T can be classically written as:

$$G_T = \frac{H}{2}\tilde{\sigma}_{22}^{max^2} \cdot \frac{1}{\tilde{E}_2} \cdot f\!\left(\frac{1}{\rho}\right)$$ [15.13]

where H is the thickness of the ply, $\tilde{\sigma}_{22}^{max}$ the maximum effective stress during the cycle, $\tilde{E}_2$ the transverse modulus of the material of the ply and f is an intrinsic function of ρ (f does not depend on the thickness of the ply or on the stacking sequence).

In that sense, by considering that $D = 1/H\rho$, equation [15.12] can be rewritten:

$$\left[\frac{\partial \frac{1}{\rho}}{\partial N} \cdot \frac{1}{f(\rho)^m} \right] = H \cdot \left(\frac{H}{2} \right)^m \cdot \left[A \cdot \left(\frac{\tilde{\sigma}_{22}^{max^2}}{\tilde{E}_2} \right)^m \right]$$

[15.14]

Equation [15.14] gives a link between two dimensionless quantities.

We note that is not clear how the identification of the model takes into account the fact that all the cracks do not cross completely the width of the sequence.

We also note that, to us, the model does not seem coherent with the quasi-static description of damage involving a critical value for the energy release rate.

15.6.2   Equivalent $\tilde{d}'$ fatigue damage law

We recall that, for a given material with diffuse damage, we have the following expression of the critical energy release rate:

$$G_{T,C} = G_{T,C}^0 \left(1 - \beta_T \tilde{d} \right) \le G_{T,C}^0$$

[15.15]

During the whole microcracking process, the maximum energy release rate during a cycle remains equal to the critical value if new transverse microcracks appear; so, by using relationships [15.13] and [15.15]:

$$G_{T,C}^0 \left(1 - \beta_T \tilde{d} \right) = \frac{H}{2} \tilde{\sigma}_{22}^{max^2} \cdot \frac{1}{\tilde{E}_2} \cdot f \left(\frac{1}{\rho} \right)$$

[15.16]

Equation [15.16] can be rewritten:

$$\frac{1}{f \left(\frac{1}{\rho} \right)} = H \cdot h(\tilde{d})$$

[15.17]

where h is an intrinsic function of $\tilde{d}$ for a given loading. Equation [15.14] can now be rewritten in terms of $\tilde{d}'$.

$$\frac{\partial \tilde{d}_F}{\partial N} = -\frac{1}{H \cdot h'} \frac{f'}{f^2} \cdot \frac{\partial \frac{1}{\rho}}{\partial N} = -\frac{f'}{f^2} \cdot \frac{1}{h'(2h)^m} \cdot \left[A \cdot \left(\frac{\tilde{\sigma}_{22}^{max^2}}{\tilde{E}_2} \right)^m \right]$$

[15.18]

In our description, relationship [15.18] is equivalent to [15.12]. This is in quite good accordance with our interpretation since it is a link of the form:

$$\frac{\partial \tilde{d}_F}{\partial N} = A \left[\tilde{Y}_{\tilde{d}'}, \tilde{Y}_{\tilde{d}}, \tilde{d}, \tilde{d}' \right]$$

[15.19]

Moreover, that link depends weakly on the ply-thickness (let us notice that, for a given value of $\tilde{d}$, the thickness influences relationship [15.18] through ρ, which must verify equation [15.17].

This relationship has been plotted in Fig. 15.6 for different plies with different thicknesses (the effective loading being kept constant).

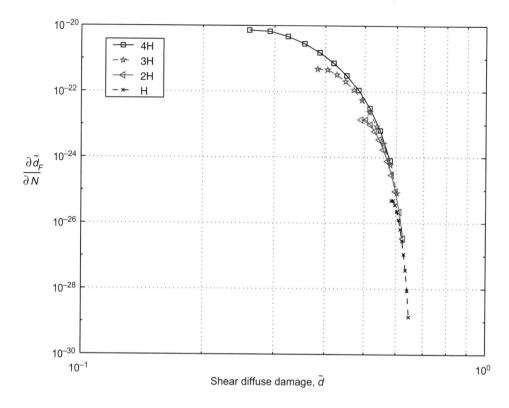

Fig. 15.6 $\partial \tilde{d}_F/\partial N \leftrightarrow \tilde{d}$ for a classical carbon epoxy material and for different thicknesses of the considered ply (the unit thickness H is equal to 0.125 mm).

We may conclude that classical fatigue laws are compatible with our fatigue modelling which has a sound physical basis.

15.7   Perspectives

Thanks to recent work devoted to the relationship between micromechanics and mesomechanics, a fairly simple model for fatigue loading has been introduced. Fatigue behaviour occurs only for Scenario 3, which is related to fibre/matrix debonding; all other mechanisms, including transverse microcracking, function as in the case of quasi-static loading, but are modified by the additional damage resulting from Scenario 3. The fatigue model can be easily included in a finite-element code, as was done for quasi-static loadings in (Ladevèze et al., 2000). However, macrostresses are assumed to be approximately planar, which is not a valid hypothesis near the edges. An extension taking macro-delamination cracks into account is being developed; this requires the introduction of a second basic problem, called the 'basic interface problem' (Ladevèze and Lubineau, 2002c).

15.8 References

ALLIX O and LADEVÈZE P (1992), Interlaminar interface modelling for the prediction of laminate delamination, *Composite Structures*, **22**, 235–242.

BEHESHTY M, HARRIS B and ADAM T (1999), An empirical fatigue-life model for high-performance fibre composites with and without impact damage. *Composite A*, **30**, 1159–1169.

BERTHELOT J (2002), Transverse cracking and delamination in cross-ply glass-fibre and carbon-fibre reinforced plastics laminates: static and fatigue loading. *Applied Mechanics Review*. To appear.

HARRIS B, ALMOND D, ADAM T, BEHESHTY M and LEE J (1999). Fatigue-life prediction methods for fibre composites in the undamaged and damaged conditions. In *Proceedings of the 7th International Conference, Fatigue 99*, **3**, 1719–1724. (Higher Education Press, Beijing, China, and EMAS, Cradley Heath, UK), Beijing, China, June 1999.

HENAFF-GARDIN C, LAFARIE-FRÉNOT M-C, BRILLAUD J and ELMAHI A (1992), Influence of the stacking sequence on fatigue transverse ply cracking in cross-ply laminates. In Masters, J., ed., *Damage Detection in Composite Materials, ASTM STP 1128*, American Society for Testing and Materials, pp. 236–255. Philadelphia.

LADEVÈZE P (1986), On damage mechanics of composites. In C. Bathias and D. Menkès, editors, *Proceedings of JNC5*, pp. 667–683, Paris. Pluralis Publication. (in French).

LADEVÈZE P (1989), About a damage mechanics approach. In Baptiste, D., editor, *Mechanics and Mechanisms of Damage in Composite and Multimaterials*, pp. 119–142. MEP.

LADEVÈZE P (1994), Inelastic strains and damage. In R Talreja, editor, *Damage Mechanics of Composite Materials*, pp. 117–136. Elsevier.

LADEVÈZE P, ALLIX O, DEU J and LÉVÈQUE D (2000), A mesomodel for localisation and damage computation in laminates. *Computer Methods in Applied Mechanics and Engineering*, **183**, 105–122.

LADEVÈZE P and LE DANTEC E (1992), Damage modelling of the elementary ply for laminated composites. *Composites Science and Technology*, **43**(3), 257–267.

LADEVÈZE P and LUBINEAU G (2001), On a damage mesomodel for laminates: micro-meso relationships, possibilities and limits. *Composites Science and Technology*, **61**(15), 2149–2158.

LADEVÈZE P and LUBINEAU G (2002a). An enhanced mesomodel for laminates based on micromechanics. *Composites Science and Technology*, **62**, 533–541.

LADEVÈZE P and LUBINEAU G (2002b), On a damage mesomodel for laminates: micromechanics basis and improvement. *Mechanics of Materials*, **35**, 763–775.

LADEVÈZE P and LUBINEAU G (2002c), Pont entre les 'micro' et 'méso' mécaniques des composites stratifiés. *Comptes-Rendus à l'Académie des Sciences*. Accepted, to appear.

LAGATTU F and LAFARIE-FRÉNOT M (2000), Variation pf PEEK matrix crystallinity in APC-2 composite subjected to large shearing deformation. *Composites Science and Technology*, **60**, 605–612.

LEMAITRE J (1992), *A Course on Damage Mechanics*. Springer-Verlag.

LIU S and NAIRN J (1990), A fracture mechanics analysis of composite microcracking fatigue experiments. *In Proc. of the 5th Meeting of the American Society of Composites*, pp. 287–295.

NAIRN J (2000), Matrix microcracking in Composites. In R Talreja and J A E Manson, ed., *Polymer Matrix Composites*, pp. 403–432. Elsevier Science.

NAIRN J and HU S (1992), The initiation and growth of delaminations induced by matrix microcracks in laminated composites. *International Journal of Fracture*, **57**, 1–24.

NAIRN J and HU S (1994), Matrix microcracking. In R Talreja, editor, *Damage Mechanics of Composite Materials*, pp. 187–243. Elsevier Science.

OGIHARA S and TAKEDA N (1995), Interaction between transverse cracks and delamination during damage process in CFRP cross-ply laminates. *Composites Science and Technology*, **54**(4), 395–404.

16

A statistical study of the fatigue performance of fibre-reinforced composite laminates

X. Diao, PreciCad Inc., Canada, L. Ye and Y-W. Mai, University of Sydney, Australia

16.1 Introduction

The cyclic fatigue response of continuous-fibre-reinforced composite laminates has been the subject of active research effort over several decades. Much experimental work has been done to provide a fairly comprehensive understanding of damage mechanisms developed under tensile and/or compressive fatigue loading of high-performance fibrous composite materials. To predict the strength degradation of a composite laminate under fatigue loading, a number of residual strength models have been proposed. The first, referred to as the 'wear out model', proposed by Halpin, Jerina and Johnson (1973), was based on the classic crack growth process in metallic materials. Realising that fatigue failure of composites is not dictated by the initiation and growth of a dominant crack as in metallic materials, Hahn and Kim (1975) assumed that the rate of residual strength reduction was inversely proportional to the residual strength. From this deterministic residual strength equation and the monotonic strength distribution they obtained the fatigue life distribution. Following the same approach, Yang and co-workers (Yang and Liu, 1977; Yang, 1978; Yang and Jones, 1978) independently proposed a three-parameter model for strength degradation.

Basically, these models were all phenomenological in approach. Fundamental damage mechanisms that occurred in the composites during cyclic fatigue, such as matrix cracking, fibre/matrix interface debonding, delamination and fibre breakage etc. were not explicitly included. It is also not clear what kinds of dominant damage mechanisms were responsible for the reduction of residual strength; nor how these damage mechanisms cause the final failure of the composite laminates. Reifsnider and Stinchcomb (1986) proposed an essential model for predicting the residual strength and fatigue life of composite laminates. In their model the concepts of the critical element and the subcritical element were introduced, and the model predicts the residual strength of the whole composite laminate on the basis of a deterministic degradation law of a critical element. Because the damage growth is usually non-uniform in a critical element, the degradation behaviour of the critical element is statistical in nature and not deterministic. The deterministic critical element approach is not

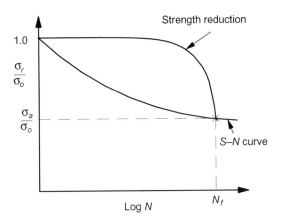

Fig. 16.1 Schematic diagram of strength reduction of composite materials under fatigue loading.

therefore sufficient to predict the residual strength of composite laminates, and a statistical approach should be developed.

The main aim of this study was to develop a statistical cumulative damage model that has the capacity of describing and predicting the residual strength and fatigue life of composite laminates subjected to cyclic loading.

16.2 Fatigue and methodology

Figure 16.1 is a schematic illustration of the residual strength reduction caused by a fatigue damage process and the *S–N* curve of a composite laminate subjected to cyclic loading. Failure is defined at the intersection of the two curves. Before a model is developed, it is necessary to discuss the physical mechanisms of fatigue damage that cause the degradation of strength. It was observed from past experiments by Reifsnider, Kenneth and Stinchcomb (1977), Charewicz and Daniel (1986), Jamison *et al.* (1984), Reifsnider and Jamison (1982) that fatigue damage in a composite laminate involves many damage modes/events, as shown in Fig.16.2. These damage modes emerge and dominate the process of damage accumulation at different stages, and contribute to the final failure of the composite laminate. However, the interactions between them make the study of fatigue damage very complicated. Hence, the phenomenological approach was frequently used in previous studies in order to simplify the problem. In this chapter, a statistical model was developed to reduce the phenomenological characteristics of the fatigue damage behaviour of composite laminates.

During fatigue loading many damage events occur in some specific elements (or plies) in a composite laminate while other elements remain virtually uninvolved throughout most of the fatigue life (Reifsnider and Stinchcomb, 1986). These elements that remain uninvolved usually carry a major part of the load, and failure of these elements after sustaining a significant amount of damage at the final stage will result in fracture of the composite laminate and define the lifetime. In this sense, these elements are 'critical'. The elements that are actively involved in the fatigue damage development are considered 'subcritical elements', because the failure of these elements only results in internal stress/load redistribution, but does not directly cause the fracture of the composite laminate. Since the critical elements define the failure of the laminate, their strength degradation behaviour determines

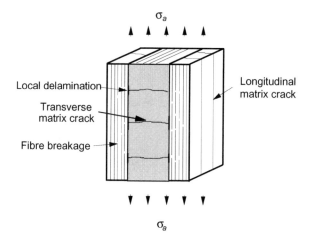

Fig. 16.2   Schematic representation of damage modes in a composite laminate. (After Reifsnider and Stinchcomb, 1986.)

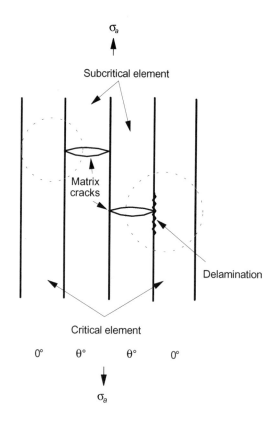

Fig. 16.3   A model of representative volume with critical and subcritical elements involving regions of stress redistribution due to matrix cracking and local delamination. (After Reifsnider and Stinchcomb, 1986.)

the laminate property profile. For a fibre-reinforced composite laminate containing zero-degree plies, the first and most common damage mode that occurs is matrix cracking in the fibre direction in the off-axis plies, such as 90° and 45° plies, which is normally through the ply thickness and across the width of the specimen. The density of matrix cracks increases with increasing applied load and fatigue cycles until the matrix cracks are saturated, which was referred to as the characteristic damage state (CDS). After this stage, fibre breakage begins to intensify in the adjacent plies in the regions of high stresses associated with the matrix cracks, near the ply interface as sketched in Fig. 16.2. As load cycling continues, secondary cracks begin to form in the regions near the tips of the matrix cracks at the ply interfaces and, at the same time, local delamination initiates and propagates as shown in Fig. 16.3. In the process of damage development, due to their preferential failure, the off-axis plies will continuously shed load to the zero-degree plies. In this case, the load acting on the 0° plies increases with time until their fatigue strength is reached, which results in the fracture of the composite laminate. Therefore, 0° plies can be considered as the 'critical elements', while the off-axis plies the 'subcritical elements'.

It was proposed by Highsmith and Reifsnider (1982) and Reifsnider (1990) that a direct relationship exists between the change in stiffness and the local axial stress in the 0° plies of a composite laminate. Thus, a practical way to evaluate the cyclic load imposed on the critical elements can be developed using non-destructive techniques that measure the changes in the stiffness of a laminate during cyclic fatigue.

16.2.1   Physical model

From the above discussion, the fatigue damage process in composite laminates can be summarized as follows.

*   The damage in a composite laminate under cyclic loading is a cycle-dependent dynamic process caused by the microscopic structural damage of different modes. The behaviour of fatigue damage is random, rather than deterministic, hence the residual properties of the composite laminate are also statistical in nature.
*   The fatigue behaviour and life of a composite laminate are controlled by the fatigue response of the critical (load-carrying) element in the laminate. The fatigue behaviour of the critical element can be described by using a fatigue theory based on residual strength degradation, which can be formulated in terms of experimental measurements on the axial performance of the material associated with the critical element.
*   The damage in a composite laminate commences preferentially in the subcritical element and meanwhile results in internal load redistribution, thereby increasing the cyclic load on the critical element and accelerating its degradation. Damage development is reflected in the stiffness reduction, so that the global laminate stiffness change can be used to evaluate the stress redistribution process.
*   The residual strength of a composite laminate is determined by the evolution of the critical element in a statistical manner. Failure occurs when the residual strength of the critical element reduces to the maximum cyclic load on it, after it sustains significant damage. The average cycle number corresponding to fatigue failure is the life of the laminate for the fatigue load applied.

16.2.2   Methodology of model development

On the basis of the fatigue damage process, a statistical model for the residual strength of a composite laminate can be constructed in the way described in Fig. 16.4. To evaluate

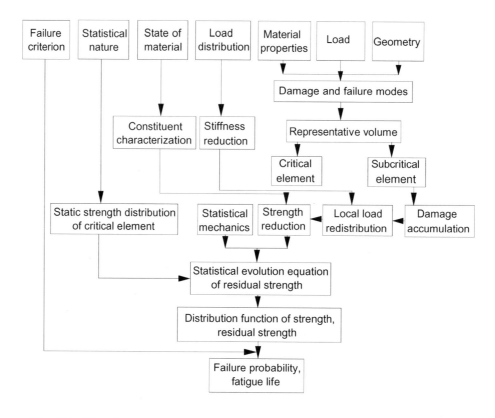

Fig. 16.4   Flowchart of statistical model for evaluation of residual strength and fatigue life.

damage development and failure of a composite laminate, a representative volume element, shown in Fig. 16.3, was considered. The fatigue response of the composite laminate was determined by the degradation behaviour of the critical element, which is represented by some constituent characterization. Because only the performance of the critical element in a specific direction (e.g. loading direction) is needed, such a constituent characterization can be used for different laminates regardless of their configurations (stacking sequence, etc.). The degradation rate of the critical element is accelerated by the stress redistribution due to the damage development in the subcritical element. If these changes are properly analysed as well defined boundary-value problems, the local stress redistribution can be calculated as a function of the damage accumulation. In this model, the stiffness reduction of the laminate will be used as an indicator of the local stress redistribution. The statistical nature of fatigue damage enters the model through the monotonic strength distribution of the material associated with the critical element. The randomness and fluctuation in degradation behaviour of the critical element were not considered in this present approach. On the basis of statistical mechanics and a constituent degradation law of residual strength, the statistical evolution equation of residual strength was then established. With the monotonic strength distribution of the critical element as the initial condition, the density distribution function of residual strength and, consequently, the residual strength of the composite laminate at a given cycle can be determined. When the mechanical properties of the composite laminate degrade to such an extent that the failure criterion is satisfied, fracture may occur. Consequently, the failure probability, reliability and fatigue life can be determined from the density distribution function for residual strength, as shown schematically in Fig.16.5.

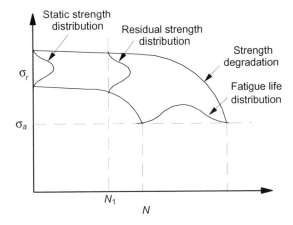

Fig. 16.5   Schematic diagram of statistical distribution of static strength, residual strength and fatigue life.

16.3   Statistical model

16.3.1   Strength degradation model

It was assumed that the degradation rate of residual strength of the critical element under cyclic loading of constant amplitude can be described by the wear-out model proposed by Halpin *et al.* (1973), thus:

$$\frac{\mathrm{d}\sigma_{cr}}{\mathrm{d}N} = -\frac{A\sigma_{ca}^{\gamma}}{\gamma\sigma_{cr}^{\gamma-1}} \qquad [16.1]$$

where σ_{cr} is the residual strength of a critical element at N cycles, σ_{ca} the applied cyclic stress acting on the critical element, and A and γ two dimensionless constants determined from experiments. The maximum cyclic stress acting on the critical element can be expressed by:

$$\sigma_{ca} = h(N)\sigma_{a} \qquad [16.2]$$

where $h(N)$ is a stress redistribution function and σ_a the maximum applied cyclic stress on the laminate. With progressive damage development due to cyclic fatigue, the stress acting on the critical element will increase gradually because of the internal load redistribution resulting from the preferential failure of the subcritical element, as schematically shown in Fig. 16.5.

Here a density distribution function $f(\sigma_{cr},N)\mathrm{d}\sigma_{cr}$ of residual strength was introduced for the critical element, defined as the probability that the strength of a critical element changes from an initial value σ_0 to a residual strength, between σ_{cr} and $\sigma_{cr}+ \mathrm{d}\sigma_{cr}$, at N cycles. From the continuous equation of probability, the evolution equation of the density distribution function of residual strength is (Diao *et al.*, 1995):

$$\frac{\partial f(\sigma_{cr},N)}{\partial N} + \frac{\partial}{\partial\sigma_{cr}}\left\{\frac{\mathrm{d}\sigma_{cr}}{\mathrm{d}N} f(\sigma_{cr},N)\right\} = 0 \qquad [16.3]$$

The initial static strength density distribution of the critical element was assumed to obey a two-parameter Weibull (1951) function:

$$f(\sigma_{cr}, N=1) = \alpha \frac{\sigma_{cr}^{\alpha-1}}{\beta^\alpha} \exp\{-(\frac{\sigma_{cr}}{\beta})^\alpha\} \qquad [16.4]$$

where α and β are the shape and scale parameters, respectively, determined from the experimental data for the monotonic strength of the critical element.

With equations [16.3] and [16.4] and the assumption that the relation between the residual strength of the critical element σ_{cr} and the composite laminate σ_r is the same as that between the applied cyclic stresses on the critical element and the laminate, as expressed by equation [16.2], the density distribution function of the residual strength of the composite laminate $f_l(\sigma_r, N)$ can be derived (Diao et al., 1995). The accumulative distribution function of the laminate $F(\sigma_r, N)$ can then be obtained, defined as the probability that the strength of the laminate is greater than σ_r, after being loaded by the cyclic stress with the maximum σ_a for N cycles,

$$F(\sigma_r, N) = 1 - \exp\{-(\frac{\sigma_r}{\beta})^\alpha [h^\gamma(N) + A(\frac{\sigma_a}{\sigma_r})^\gamma \int_1^N h^\gamma(n)dn]^{\frac{\alpha}{\gamma}}\} \qquad [16.5]$$

16.3.2   Failure probability and reliability

When the residual strength reduces to the maximum of applied cyclic stress, i.e. $\sigma_r = \sigma_a$, equation [16.5] reduces to the failure probability of the laminate $P(\sigma_a, N)$ defined as the probability that the laminate does not survive the maximum cyclic stress σ_a for N cycles,

$$P(\sigma_a, N) = 1 - \exp\{-(\frac{\sigma_a}{\beta})^\alpha [h^\gamma(N) + A\int_1^N h^\gamma(n)dn]^{\frac{\alpha}{\gamma}}\} \qquad [16.6]$$

Actually, $P(\sigma_a, N)$ is the cumulative distribution function of fatigue life for the laminate. The reliability function of the laminate $R(\sigma_a, N)$ can be obtained from $P(\sigma_a, N)$:

$$R(\sigma_a, N) = 1 - P(\sigma_a, N) = \exp\{-(\frac{\sigma_a}{\beta})^\alpha [h^\gamma(N) + A\int_1^N h^\gamma(n)dn]^{\frac{\alpha}{\gamma}}\} \qquad [16.7]$$

From these two functions it can be found that $R(\sigma_a = 0, N) = 1$ or $P(\sigma_a = 0, N) = 0$ and $R(\sigma_a \to \infty, N) = 0$ or $P(\sigma_a \to \infty, N) = 1$. Physically, these mean that a composite laminate subjected to a larger maximum cyclic stress is easier to fail. Conversely, the smaller the applied maximum cyclic stress, the more reliable the laminate is. Similarly, it can be shown that $R(\sigma_a, N \to \infty) = 0$ or $P(\sigma_a, N \to \infty) = 1$, which means that, when the fatigue cycles tend to infinity, the laminate will definitely fail. All these limit solutions agree with experimental observations.

16.3.3   Residual strength and fatigue life

Given the density distribution function for residual strength, the expected residual strength of the composite laminate and its square deviation can be directly calculated by averaging, i.e.

$$\overline{\sigma_r} = \int_{\sigma_a}^\infty \sigma_r \frac{\partial F(\sigma_r, N)}{\partial N} d\sigma_r \qquad [16.8]$$

$$\overline{\Delta\sigma_r^2} = \int_{\sigma_a}^\infty (\sigma_r - \overline{\sigma_r})^2 \frac{\partial F(\sigma_r, N)}{\partial N} d\sigma_r \qquad [16.9]$$

With the failure probability defined in equation [16.6], the average fatigue life of the composite laminate and its square deviation can also be calculated.

$$N_f = \int_1^\infty N \frac{\partial P(\sigma_a, N)}{\partial N} dN \qquad [16.10]$$

$$\overline{\Delta N_f^2} = \int_1^\infty (N - N_f)^2 \frac{\partial P(\sigma_a, N)}{\partial N} dN \qquad [16.11]$$

For large N, the fatigue life is derived from equation [16.10] as,

$$N_f = \int_1^N \exp\{-(\frac{\sigma_a}{\beta})^\alpha [h^\gamma(N) + A \int_1^N h^\gamma(n) dn]^{\frac{\alpha}{\gamma}}\} dN \qquad [16.12]$$

From the above evaluations, it can be seen that the distribution function for residual strength, failure probability, reliability, and the distribution function for fatigue life, as well as the fatigue life itself, are determined from the present statistical model on the basis of the following factors:

* degradation behaviour of residual strength for the material associated with the critical element;
* monotonic strength distribution of the critical element; and
* a function describing stress redistribution.

All these factors can be determined from either experimental measurements or theoretical evaluations. For example, the first two factors can be achieved by determining the material parameters in the wear-out model (equation [16.1]), A and γ, as well as two Weibull parameters α and β in equation [16.4] in terms of static strength data and S–N curve of the material associated with the critical element. The third factor is determined from the mechanisms of fatigue damage in the subcritical element and the stress redistribution process in composite laminates during fatigue loading.

16.4   Stress redistribution function

The stress redistribution function is one of the most important aspects of this statistical approach, and it describes the internal load redistribution process and the change of the stress acting on the critical element caused by various damage mechanisms, shown in Fig. 16.6. As discussed in Section 16.2, for a first-order approximation, the change of the stress acting on the critical element can be evaluated by the stiffness reduction of the laminate from the classical laminate theory, then the stress redistribution function can be defined by,

$$h(N) = \frac{\sigma_{ca}}{\sigma_a} = \frac{E_c(N)}{E_X(N)} \qquad [16.13]$$

where E_c and E_X are, respectively, the stiffness of the critical element and the composite laminate in the loading direction. When the volume fraction k of the critical element in the laminate and the stiffness of the subcritical element $E_s(N)$ are known, $E_X(N)$ can be determined by the rule of mixtures.

$$E_X(N) = kE_c(N) + (1 - k) E_s(N) \qquad [16.14]$$

In this way, the various damage mechanisms will be phenomenologically included in the predictions of the residual strength and fatigue life through evaluation of the stiffness reduction of the composite laminate.

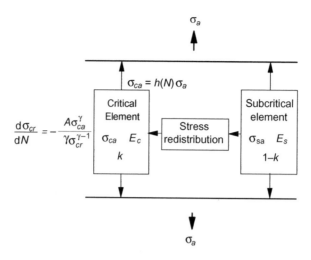

Fig. 16.6   Schematic diagram of load distribution in a representative volume.

16.4.1   Damage mechanisms

During fatigue loading, the local stress state in each lamina in a composite laminate changes continuously due to damage accumulation, which reduces the lamina stiffness, and consequently the stiffness of the entire laminate.

As discussed in Section 16.2, for a cross-ply composite laminate subjected to uniaxial tensile fatigue loading, the predominant mechanisms are the formation and multiplication of intralaminar matrix cracks in the 90° plies up to CDS, observed during the first 80% of the logarithmic lifetime by Daniel, Lee and Yaniv (1987). These mechanisms are responsible for significant stress redistribution, which must be addressed in predicting the fatigue life of a composite laminate in accordance with the damage development process.

16.4.2   Shear-lag model for cross-ply laminates

Shear-lag analyses have been used extensively by many researchers, such as Highsmith and Reifsnider (1982), Laws and Dvorak (1988), Tan and Nuismer (1988), Lee and Daniel (1990), to model the stiffness loss of composite laminates as a function of the matrix crack density for the cases of static loading. In this study, the shear-lag analysis by Lee and Daniel (1990) was extended to describe the fatigue cycle-dependent progressive matrix cracking, stiffness reduction and to define the stress redistribution function for fatigue life predictions of cross-ply laminates.

The simple shear-lag model was developed on the basis of the following assumptions.

- The transverse matrix cracks initiate when the stress in the 90° plies reaches the transverse tensile strength.
- The transverse matrix cracks are uniformly distributed in the 90° plies.
- The stress fields in both 0° and 90° plies are uniform in the transverse direction and the deformation in the direction of matrix cracks is small and can be neglected so that the problem is one-dimensional, i.e. plane strain.

It must be mentioned here that the discussion is confined to laminates with much smaller

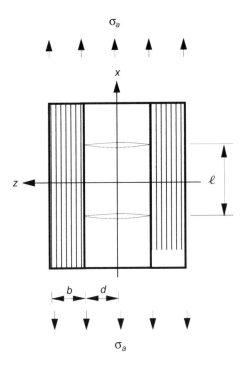

σ_a

x

z

ℓ

b d

σ_a

Fig. 16.7   Geometry and loading condition of a cross-ply laminate.

thickness in comparison to their width and length. Therefore, the thickness effect is not considered in this approach.

Consider a cross-ply laminate of $[0_m/90_n]_s$ lay-up subjected to a uniaxial tensile fatigue stress, σ_a, with a stress ratio $R=0$, as illustrated in Fig. 16.7, b and d denote the half-thickness of the $0°$ and $90°$ plies, designated by subscripts 1 and 2, respectively, and l is the matrix crack spacing. The first cracking in the $90°$ plies occurs when the axial stress in those plies σ_{x2} is equal to the transverse tensile strength of the lamina F_{2T} followed by redistribution of the stress state within the laminate and simultaneous stiffness reduction of those plies as well as the entire laminate. From the one-dimensional shear-lag analysis by Lee and Daniel (1990), the axial stress distributions in layers $0°$ and $90°$ plies are expressed as:

$$\sigma_{x1} = \frac{E_1}{E_0}\left\{1 + \frac{E_2 d}{E_1 b}\frac{\cosh(\xi x)}{\cosh(\frac{\xi l}{2})}\right\}\sigma_a + \left\{1 - \frac{\cosh(\xi x)}{\cosh(\frac{\xi l}{2})}\right\}\sigma_{t1} \qquad [16.15]$$

$$\sigma_{x2} = \frac{E_2}{E_0}\left\{1 - \frac{\cosh(\xi x)}{\cosh(\frac{\xi l}{2})}\right\}(\sigma_a + \frac{E_0}{E_2}\sigma_{t2}) \qquad [16.16]$$

where E_1 and E_2 are the longitudinal and transverse Young's moduli of the unidirectional lamina, E_0 is the stiffness of the undamaged laminate expressed by the rule of mixtures equation [16.14]:

$$E_0 = \frac{b}{b+d}E_1 + \frac{d}{b+d}E_2 \tag{16.17}$$

and σ_{t1} and σ_{t2} are the residual thermal stresses from curing in the $0°$ and $90°$ plies, respectively, balanced to each other, i.e. $b\sigma_{t1} + d\sigma_{t2} = 0$. The shear-lag parameter ξ is determined by Lee and Daniel (1990):

$$\xi^2 = \frac{3(d+b)E_0\,G_{12}G_{23}}{bdE_1 E_2 (dG_{12} + bG_{23})} \tag{16.18}$$

where G_{12} and G_{23} are the shear moduli in the x–y and y–z planes of the lamina, respectively. The reduced axial stiffness of the laminate E_X for a crack spacing l is:

$$E_X = \frac{E_0}{1 + \dfrac{2}{\xi l}\dfrac{E_2 d}{E_1 b}\tanh(\dfrac{\xi l}{2}) + \dfrac{E_0\,\sigma_{t1}}{E_1\sigma_a}\left[1 - \dfrac{2}{\xi l}\tanh\left(\dfrac{\xi l}{2}\right)\right]} \tag{16.19}$$

From equation [16.16] it can be seen that the transverse stress in the $90°$ plies reaches its maximum at the middle points of each pair of existing cracks. Thus, these are the most probable sites of new cracks, if the applied stress or fatigue cycle increases. According to the assumptions mentioned previously, new matrix cracks form in the $90°$ plies where the maximum transverse stress between any two cracks reaches the transverse tensile strength of the lamina. Then, the crack spacing l can be obtained from equation [16.16], i.e. $\sigma_{x2} = F_{2T}$ at $x = 0$.

$$l = \frac{2}{\xi}\cosh^{-1}(\frac{1}{\zeta}) \tag{16.20}$$

where

$$\zeta = 1 - \frac{F_{2T}}{\dfrac{E_2}{E_0}\sigma_a + \sigma_{t2}} \tag{16.21}$$

The above discussion can be extended to describe the stiffness reduction and stress redistribution process of composite laminates subjected to fatigue loading with the introduction of a fatigue failure function. It should be noted that the formation of transverse matrix cracks is not instantaneous for the case of fatigue loading, but continuous with the fatigue cycling due to the inhomogeneous microstructures (Jamison et al., 1984). Consequently, the matrix crack density should be dependent on fatigue cycle. The failure criterion proposed by Hashin and Rotem (1973) was adopted as an extension of the maximum strength criterion for fatigue loading, which states that the failure in the $90°$ plies occurs when the maximum stress equals the fatigue failure strength $F_2(N)$ at a specified fatigue cycle, i.e.

$$\{\sigma_{x2}\}_{max} = F_2(N) \tag{16.22}$$

The fatigue failure function $F_2(N)$ was determined from the S–N curve of $90°$ plies in material characterization (Hashin and Rotem, 1973). Thus, ζ_f for the case of fatigue loading is obtained from equation [16.21],

$$\zeta_f = 1 - \frac{F_2(N)}{\dfrac{E_2}{E_0}\sigma_a + \sigma_{t2}} \tag{16.23}$$

Substituting equations [16.20] and [16.23] into equation [16.19] yields the stiffness of the laminate as a function of the applied cyclic stress and fatigue cycle,

$$E_X(N) = \frac{E_0}{1 + \dfrac{E_2\sigma_{t1}}{E_1\sigma_a} + \dfrac{E_2}{E_1}\left[\dfrac{d}{b} - \dfrac{E_0\,\sigma_{t1}}{E_2\sigma_a}\right]\sqrt{1 - \zeta_f^{\,2}}\Big/\cosh^{-1}(\dfrac{1}{\zeta_f})} \tag{16.24}$$

Then the stress redistribution function can be expressed as,

$$h(N) = \frac{E_1}{E_0}\left\{1 + \dfrac{E_2\sigma_{t1}}{E_1\sigma_a} + \dfrac{E_2}{E_1}\left[\dfrac{d}{b} - \dfrac{E_0\,\sigma_{t1}}{E_2\sigma_a}\right]\sqrt{1 - \zeta_f^{\,2}}\Big/\cosh^{-1}(\dfrac{1}{\zeta_f})\right\} \tag{16.25}$$

The residual thermal stresses in both 0° and 90° layers are determined as:

$$\sigma_{t1} = \frac{dE_1 E_2}{(b+d)E_0}(\alpha_{t2} - \alpha_{t1})\Delta T \tag{16.26}$$

$$\sigma_{t2} = -\frac{bE_1 E_2}{(b+d)E_0}(\alpha_{t2} - \alpha_{t1})\Delta T \tag{16.27}$$

where α_{t1} and α_{t2} are the longitudinal and transverse thermal expansion coefficients of unidirectional composite laminates, respectively, and ΔT is the temperature change.

When $N = 1$, equations [16.23] and [16.24] revert to the case for static loading, i.e. [16.19] and [16.21]. When N tends to infinity, the value of $(1 - \zeta_f^2)^{1/2}/\cosh^{-1}(1/\zeta_f)$ approaches unity, thus $E_x = bE1/(b + d)$ and $h(N) = (b + d)/b$. This means that, when the applied stress or the number of fatigue cycle is very large, the stiffness of the laminate is reduced to that of 0° plies and the applied load is solely carried by these plies. After the stress redistribution function is obtained from equation [16.25] on the basis of the transverse fatigue failure function of the unidirectional laminate, the residual strength and fatigue life of cross-ply laminates of a specified lay-up can be evaluated from the statistical model. A similar treatment to the stress redistribution process was also used by Fukunaga et al. (1984) to study the static strength of cross-ply laminates. It must be noted that the above discussion on the stress analysis and stiffness reduction is normally limited to the $[0_m/90_n]_S$ laminates with $n < 4$. When n is large, other forms of damage such as delamination and their interactions with transverse matrix cracks might be involved.

16.5   Evaluation of fatigue performance of composite laminates

16.5.1   AS4/3501-6 composite laminates

The statistical model and method for determining the stress distribution function were applied to describe the fatigue behaviour of the AS4/3501-6 cross-ply laminates (Lee, Daniel

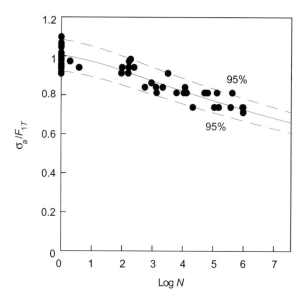

Fig. 16.8   *S–N* curve of AS4/3501-6 carbon/epoxy 0° laminate in comparison with experimental data from Lee, Daniel and Yaniv (1989). ----- 95% confidence level.

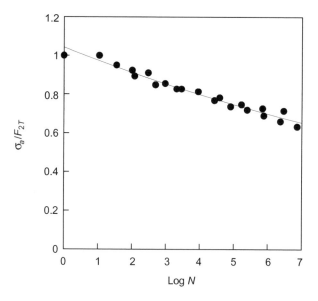

Fig. 16.9   *S–N* curve of AS4/3501-6 carbon/epoxy 90° laminate in comparison with experimental data (•) from Lee, Daniel and Yaniv (1989).

and Yaniv, 1989) of different lay-ups under tension–tension fatigue loading with a stress ratio of 0.1 and frequency of 10 Hz. For evaluation of the residual strength and fatigue life of these composite laminates, the degradation behaviour of residual strength and the static strength distribution of the 0° plies must be determined. This can be done by using the data regression method based on experimental data for the monotonic strength and *S–N* curves for the unidirectional laminates.

Table 16.1   Parameters for statistical strength distribution of AS4/3501-6 carbon/epoxy unidirectional composite by fitting to experimental data

Stacking	γ	A	α	β[MPa]
[0]$_8$	37.45	0.0896	29.5	2394.4

From Lee, Daniel and Yaniv (1989).

Table 16.2   Mechanical properties of AS4/3501-6 carbon/epoxy unidirectional composite

Property	Value
Longitudinal modulus E_1 (GPa)	142.0
Transverse modulus E_2 (GPa)	10.3
In-plane shear modulus G_{12} (GPa)	7.6
Out-of-plane shear modulus G_{23} (GPa)	3.8
Longitudinal tensile strength F_{1T} (MPa)	2372.0
Transverse tensile strength F_{2T} (MPa)	57.2
Longitudinal thermal expansion coefficient α_{t1} ($\mu\varepsilon/°C$)	−1.8
Transverse thermal expansion coefficient α_{t2} ($\mu\varepsilon/°C$)	27.0
Ply thickness (cm)	0.0127

From Lee, Daniel and Yaniv (1989).

16.5.1.1   Unidirectional laminate

The experimental data for the monotonic strength and the fatigue life for AS4/3501-6 carbon/epoxy 0° unidirectional laminates are shown in Fig.16.8. From these data, the best fitted parameters for degradation of residual strength and static strength distribution of 0° plies can be obtained, listed in Table 16.1.

With these parameters, the S–N curve of the 0° unidirectional laminate was estimated in Fig. 16.8. The dashed lines correspond to a confidence level of 95%. It can be seen that the estimations correlate with the experimental data very well.

16.5.1.2   Cross-ply laminates

The experimental data of fatigue life for AS4/3501-6 carbon/epoxy 90° unidirectional laminates obtained by Lee, Daniel and Yaniv (1989) and the best fit curve are shown in Fig. 16.9. From the mechanical properties of the composite listed in Table 16.2 and the shear-lag model, the axial modulus of AS4/3501-6 carbon/epoxy cross-ply laminate [0,90$_2$]$_S$ was calculated as a function of matrix crack density from equation [16.24] and compared with the experimental data as well as the results without the effects of residual thermal stresses in Fig. 16.10. The residual thermal stresses σ_{r1} and σ_{r2}, calculated from equations [16.26] and [16.27] using the materials properties in Table 16.2 and $\Delta T = 100\ °C$, have only marginal effects on the mechanical response of the laminate, and therefore they were neglected in the following discussions for the sake of simplicity. When the transverse fatigue failure function of the 90° plies (Fig. 16.9) is considered, the variation of the transverse crack density in the same laminate with number of cycles for different levels of the applied stress was calculated from equations [16.20] and [16.23]. The predictions of the matrix crack density at different cycle numbers and the experimental results obtained by Lee, Daniel and Yaniv (1989) are plotted in Fig. 16.11, where good agreement can be found, especially at the low stress levels.

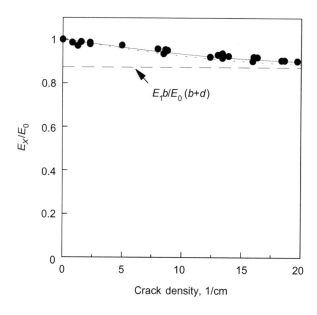

Fig. 16.10   Normalized axial stiffness of $[0,90_2]_s$ AS4/3501-6 carbon/epoxy laminate as a function of transverse crack density, with ----- and without —— residual stress: • experimental results from Lee and Daniel (1990).

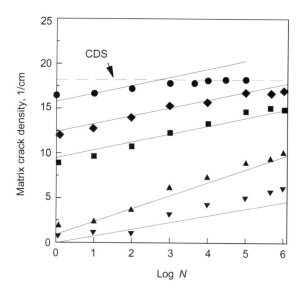

Fig. 16.11   Transverse crack density in $[0,90_2]_s$ AS4/3501-6 carbon/epoxy laminate as a function of cycle number for different stress levels (experimental results from Lee, Daniel and Yaniv (1989). ▼ $s_a = 28\% F_{XT}$, ▲ $s_a = 35\% F_{XT}$, ■ $s_a = 53\% F_{XT}$, ◆ $s_a = 66\% F_{XT}$, • $s_a = 85\% F_{XT}$.

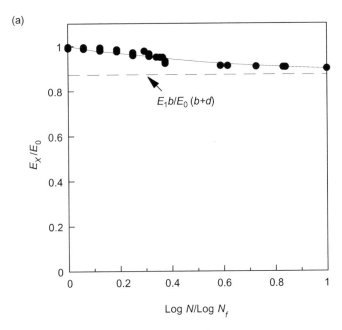

Fig. 16.12(a)   Stiffness of $[0,90_2]_s$ AS4/3501-6 carbon/epoxy laminate versus logarithmic normalized cycle number for cyclic stress levels of $\sigma_a = 28\% F_{XT}$ (•: experimental data from Daniel, Lee and Yaniv (1987).)

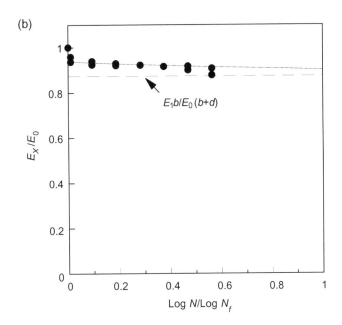

Fig. 16.12(b)   Stiffness of $[0,90_2]_s$ AS4/3501-6 carbon/epoxy laminate versus logarithmic normalized cycle number for cyclic stress levels of $\sigma_a = 53\% F_{XT}$ (•: experimental data from Daniel, Lee and Yaniv (1987).)

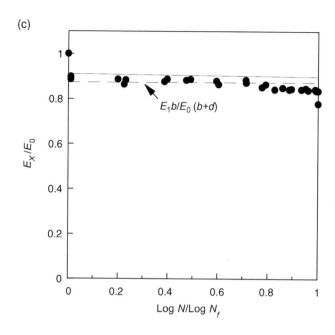

Fig. 16.12(c)   Stiffness of $[0,90_2]_s$ AS4/3501-6 carbon/epoxy laminate versus logarithmic normalized cycle number for cyclic stress levels of $\sigma_a = 85\% F_{XT}$ (•: experimental data from Daniel, Lee and Yaniv (1987).)

When the applied stress level is as high as 85% of the static strength of the laminate, the shear-lag model seems to overestimate the crack density at high cycle numbers where a saturated crack density for CDS exists. However, it does describe the trend of change of the axial modulus from the initial value E_0 to the final value $E_1 b/(b+d)$. Variations of the axial stiffness with cycle number for the laminate subjected to cyclic stress levels of 28%, 53% and 85% of the static strength were calculated, shown in Figs. 16.12(a), 16.12(b) and 16.12(c), respectively. For the stress levels of 28% and 53% of the static strength, the predicted stiffness reduction of the laminate (Fig. 16.12(a) and 16.12(b) agrees very well with experimental data by Daniel, Lee and Yaniv (1987). The prediction seems to under-estimate the stiffness reduction when the cycle number or the fatigue stress is large, as shown in Fig. 16.12(c) for a fatigue stress level of 85% of the static strength with the predicted curve being almost always above the experimental data. The difference becomes more significant when the normalized logarithmic cycle number is over 0.8. This is because the shear-lag model used in this discussion only deals with transverse matrix cracking that was assumed to be responsible for the major part of stiffness reduction during the first 80% of the entire logarithmic fatigue life of a cross-ply composite laminate, while the effects of other damage mechanisms such as longitudinal matrix crack splitting, local delamination and fibre breakage on stiffness reduction were not included. The variations of the stress redistribution function with cycle number are also predicted in Fig. 16.13. It can be seen that the stress redistribution function is clearly dependent on the fatigue stress levels, especially at the beginning of fatigue loading, and the difference tends to diminish when the cycle number is large. This means the stress transfer to the 0° plies is faster when the laminate is subjected to a high stress due to the more severe damage (higher transverse matrix crack density) in the transverse plies (Fig. 16.10). When the normalized cycle number approaches unity, the

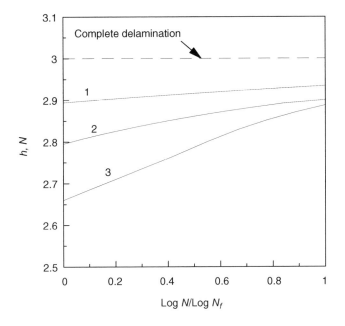

Fig. 16.13   Stress distribution functions of $[0,90_2]_s$ AS4/3501-6 carbon/epoxy laminate under cyclic stress levels of $\sigma_a = 28\%F_{XT}$, $\sigma_a = 53\%F_{XT}$ and $\sigma_a = 85\%F_{XT}$.

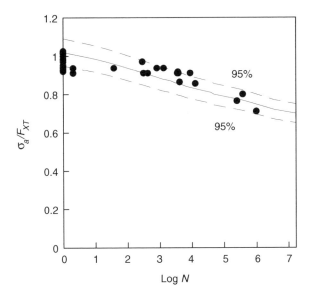

Fig. 16.14   *S–N* curve for $[0,90_2]_s$ AS4/3501-6 carbon/epoxy laminate in comparison with experimental data (•) from Lee, Daniel and Yaniv (1989), – – – –: 95% confidence level.

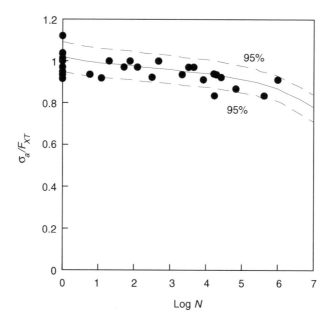

Fig. 16.15   S–N curve for $[0_2,90_2]_s$ AS4/3501-6 carbon/epoxy laminate in comparison with experimental data (•) from Lee, Daniel and Yaniv (1989), – – – –: 95% confidence level.

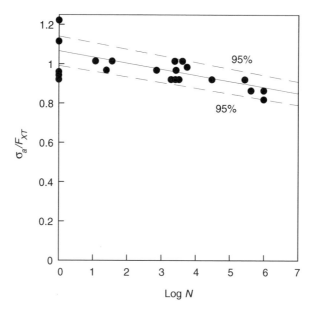

Fig. 16.16   S–N curve for $[0,90_4]_s$ AS4/3501-6 carbon/epoxy laminate in comparison with experimental data (•) from Lee, Daniel and Yaniv (1989), – – – –: 95% confidence level.

Table 16.3   Properties of AS4/3501-6 carbon/epoxy cross-ply composite laminates

Property	$[0,90_2]_s$	$[0_2,90_2]_s$	$[0,90_4]_s$
Longitudinal modulus E_0 (GPa)	54.2	77.2	36.6
Static tensile strength F_{XT} (MPa)	779	1186	456

From Charewicz and Daniel (1986).

transverse matrix crack density tends to be high and almost all the applied load is carried by the longitudinal (0°) plies, so that the stress distribution function is almost the same for different stress levels.

With the properties listed in Tables 16.1–16.3, the fatigue life of AS4/3501-6 carbon/ epoxy cross-ply laminates of various $[0_m/90_n]_s$ lay-ups can be predicted from equations [16.12], [16.23] and [16.24]. The S–N curves for $[0,90_2]_s$, $[0_2,90_2]_s$ and $[0,90_4]_s$ laminates were predicted from the statistical model and are compared with the experimental results obtained by Lee *et al.* (1989) in Figs. 16.14–16.16. The dashed lines denote a confidence level of 95%. Good agreement can be seen between the predictions and the experimental data for all three laminates. It should be noted that the model seems to somewhat overesti- mate the fatigue strength corresponding to small fatigue life due to the same reason discussed previously. For more accurate predictions of the fatigue residual strength of composite laminates, the effects of other damage mechanisms, such as longitudinal matrix crack splitting, local delamination and fibre breakage, on the stress redistribution process should be included in the model.

16.5.2   Carbon-fibre/PEEK composite laminates

Using a similar approach, the statistical model was also applied to describe fatigue performance of AS4-CF/PEEK commingled unidirectional $[0]_{16}$, $[90]_{16}$ and cross-ply $[0_2,90_2]_{2s}$ laminates under tension–tension fatigue loading with a stress ratio of 0.1 and a frequency of 8 Hz (Diao, Ye and Mai, 1997).

16.5.2.1   Unidirectional laminates

The fatigue performance of the CF/PEEK unidirectional laminates was analysed on the basis of the S–N curves of the laminates, shown in Figs. 16.17 and 16.18, respectively, under longitudinal and transverse fatigue loading. The cumulative distribution function of fatigue life was calculated from equation [16.6] for fatigue stresses of 50%, 60% and 70% of the static strength, and the best fitted parameters for degradation of residual strength and static strength distribution of 0° and 90° plies were obtained, listed in Table 16.4 with mechanical properties of the CF/PEEK composite summarized in Table 16.5. With these parameters, the S–N curves of the 0° and 90° unidirectional laminates were estimated in Figs. 16.17 and 16.18, respectively. The dashed lines correspond to a confidence level of 95%, and the correlation between the calculated curves and the corresponding experimental data is excellent.

16.5.2.2   Cross-ply $[0_2/90_2]_{2s}$ laminates

With the fatigue properties of the CF/PEEK unidirectional laminates, the fatigue behaviour of the CF/PEEK $[0_2,90_2]_{2s}$ cross-ply laminate can be simulated by using the statistical model and the shear-lag analysis. The normalized stiffness of the CF/PEEK $[0_2,90_2]_{2s}$ cross-ply

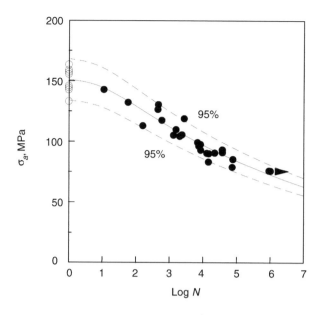

Fig. 16.17   *S–N* curve of [0]$_{16}$ CF/PEEK laminate (o: static data, ●: fatigue data).

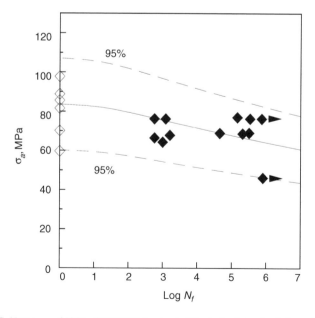

Fig. 16.18   *S–N* curves of [90]$_{16}$ CF/PEEK laminate (◇: static data, ◆: fatigue data) and pure PEEK.

Table 16.4 Parameters for statistical strength distribution of CF/PEEK commingled uni-fabric unidirectional composite by fitting to experimental data

Stacking	γ	A	α	β(MPa)
$[0]_{16}$	15.87	0.1117	21.80	1549.25
$[90]_{16}$	42.19	0.0629	9.78	88.19

From Diao, Ye and Mai (1997).

Table 16.5 Mechanical properties of commingled CF/PEEK unidirectional composite

Property	Value
Longitudinal modulus E_1 (GPa)	124.6
Transverse modulus E_2 (GPa)	9.03
In-plane shear modulus G_{12} (GPa)	6.0
Out-of-plane shear modulus G_{23} (GPa)*	6.0
Longitudinal tensile strength F_{1T} (MPa)	1507.1
Transverse tensile strength F_{2T} (MPa)	88.6
Longitudinal thermal expansion coefficient α_{t1} ($\mu\varepsilon$/°C)	0.28
Transverse thermal expansion coefficient α_{t2} ($\mu\varepsilon$/°C)	30.0
Glass transition temperature of PEEK matrix T_g (°C)	143
Ply thickness (cm)	0.0138

From Diao, Ye and Mai (1997).
*assumed value.

laminate subjected to fatigue stresses of 60% or 70% of the static strength was calculated as a function of the normalized fatigue cycle with the stress redistribution function defined in terms of the shear-lag analysis, compared with the corresponding experimental data in Fig. 16.19. It can be seen that the prediction underestimates the stiffness reduction at high fatigue cycles. The reason is attributed to the fact that the prediction was based on progressive transverse matrix cracking in the 90° plies only, and other damage mechanisms such as delamination and fibre breakage, which developed at the late stage of fatigue damage (Diao, Ye and Mai, 1997), were not included. The strength degradation of the CF/PEEK $[0_2,90_2]_{2S}$ cross-ply laminate subjected to fatigue stress levels of 50%, 60%, 65% and 70% of the static strength, was calculated from equation [16.8], compared with the corresponding experimental data in Fig. 16.20. The predicated degradation of residual strength shows good agreement with experimental data. The cumulative distribution of fatigue life was calculated for fatigue stress levels of 60%, 65% and 70% of the static strength in terms of equation [16.6], shown in Fig. 16.21. Excellent agreement between predictions and experimental data can be seen. Finally, the S–N curve of the CF/PEEK $[0_2,90_2]_{2S}$ cross-ply laminate predicted from [16.12] is shown in Fig. 16.23. The prediction agrees well with the experimental data.

16.6   Concluding remarks

A statistical model has been developed for evaluation of the residual strength and fatigue life of fibre-reinforced polymer-matrix composite laminates, on the basis of the statistical nature of fatigue damage and the concept of a representative volume of the critical and subcritical elements.

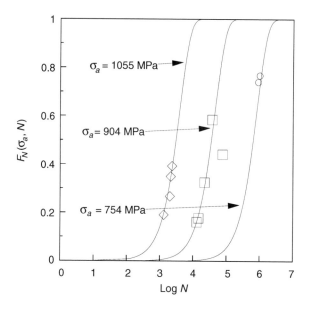

Fig. 16.19   Cumulative fatigue life distribution of unidirectional CF/PEEK $[0]_{16}$ laminate, (o: $\sigma_a =$ 50%F_{1T}, □: $\sigma_a = 60\%F_{1T}$, ◊: $\sigma_a = 70\%F_{1T}$), ————: simulation.

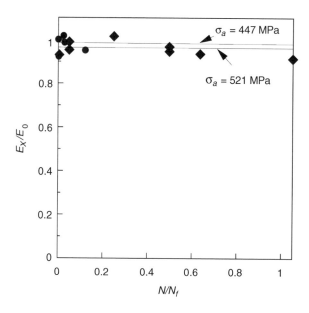

Fig. 16.20   Normalized axial stiffness of CF/PEEK $[0_2,90_2]_{2S}$ laminate as a function of normalized fatigue cycle (●: $\sigma_a = 60\%F_{XT}$, ◆: $\sigma_a = 70\%F_{XT}$).

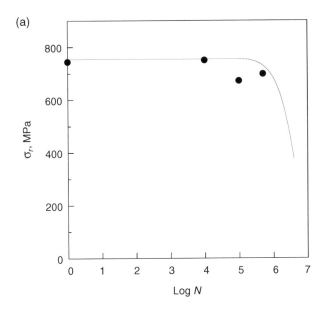

Fig. 16.21(a)   Residual strength of CF/PEEK $[0_2,90_2]_{2S}$ cross-ply laminate under fatigue stress of 50% ultimate strength, (●: experimental data), ———— simulation.

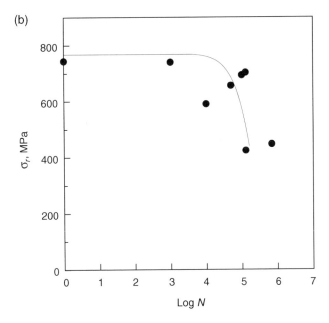

Fig. 16.21(b)   Residual strength of CF/PEEK $[0_2,90_2]_{2S}$ cross-ply laminate under fatigue stress of 60% ultimate strength, (●: experimental data), ———— simulation.

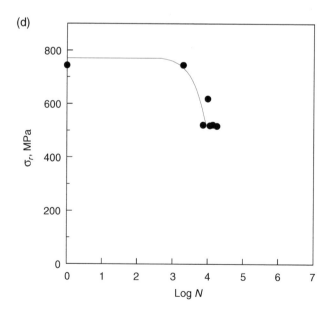

Fig. 16.21(c)   Residual strength of CF/PEEK $[0_2,90_2]_{2S}$ cross-ply laminate under fatigue stress of 65% ultimate strength, ($\bullet$: experimental data), ———— simulation.

Fig. 16.21(d)   Residual strength of CF/PEEK $[0_2,90_2]_{2S}$ cross-ply laminate under fatigue stress of 70% ultimate strength, ($\bullet$: experimental data), ———— simulation.

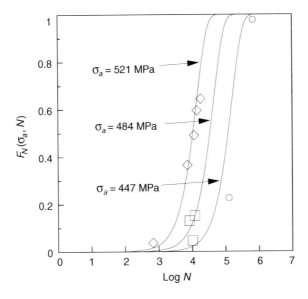

Fig. 16.22   Cumulative fatigue life distribution of CF/PEEK $[0_2,90_2]_{2S}$ cross-ply laminate in comparison with experimental data (o: $\sigma_a = 60\%F_{1T}$, □: $\sigma_a = 65\%F_{1T}$, ◇: $\sigma_a = 70\%F_{1T}$), ———— simulation.

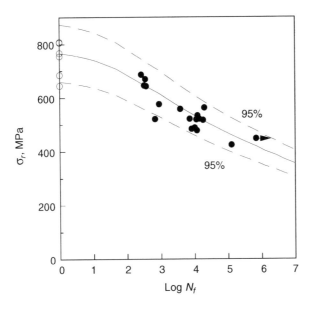

Fig. 16.23   *S–N* curve of CF/PEEK $[0_2,90_2]_{2S}$ cross-ply laminates, (o: static data, •: fatigue data), ———— simulation, — — — — 95% confidence level.

The statistical model can be further modified to include the stochastic nature of the strength degradation with the assumption that the parameters defining the residual strength degradation rate, i.e. γ and A, are random variables, which formulates a stochastic fatigue theory as has been done for metals.

Although the shear-lag analysis was applied to characterize the stress redistribution process due to matrix cracking for cross-ply laminates, much work is required to improve the simulation of the stress redistribution process in accordance with different damage modes during fatigue and to determine the stress redistribution function for general laminate configurations. This would involve the comprehensive modelling of stiffness reduction in the damage accumulation process. By combining the framework of the statistical model and features of the actual damage mechanisms as well as the representative element concept, it should be possible to formulate a statistical theory that simulates the damage accumulation process and predict the fatigue performance of composite materials more accurately. In addition, the statistical model should also be extended to study the cumulative damage of composite laminates subjected to multi-stage fatigue loading.

16.7   Acknowledgements

We would like to thank the University of Sydney and the Australian Research Council (ARC) for the support of this work. L Ye acknowledges the support of a Visiting Professorship at the City University of Hong Kong; and Y-W Mai also thanks the ARC for a Federation Fellowship award.

16.8   References

CHAREWICZ A and DANIEL I M (1986), Damage mechanisms and accumulation in carbon/epoxy laminates, in *Composite Materials: Fatigue and Fracture*, ASTM STP-907, ed. Hahn H.T., Philadelphia, pp.274–297.

DANIEL M I, LEE J W and YANIV G (1987), Damage mechanisms and stiffness degradation in graphite/epoxy composite, in *Proceedings of ICCM-6 and ECCM-2*, ed. Matthews F. L., Buskell N. C. R., Hodgkinson J. M., and Morton J., Elsevier Applied Science, London, pp.4.129–4.138.

DIAO X, YE L and MAI Y-W (1995), A statistical model for residual strength and fatigue life of composite laminates, *Comp Sci & Tech*, **54**, 329–336.

DIAO X, YE L and MAI Y-W (1997), Fatigue behaviour of CF/PEEK composite laminates made from commingled prepreg – Part I and Part II, *Composites*, **28A**, 739–755.

FUKUNAGA H, CHOU T W, PETERS P W M and SCHULTE K (1984), Probabilistic failure strength analysis of graphite/epoxy cross-ply laminates, *J Comp Mater*, **18**, 339–356.

HAHN H T and KIM R Y (1975), Proof testing of composite material, *J Comp Mater*, **9**, 297–311.

HALPIN J C, JERINA K L and JOHNSON T S (1973), Characterisation of composites for the purpose of reliability evaluation, in *Analysis of the Test Methods for High Modulus Fibres and Composite*, ASTM STP-521, ed. Whitney J.M., Philadelphia, pp.5–64.

HASHIN Z and ROTEM A (1973), A fatigue failure criterion for fibre reinforced materials, *J Comp Mater*, **7**, 448–464.

HIGHSMITH A L and REIFSNIDER K L (1982), Stiffness-reduction mechanisms in composite laminates, in *Damage in Composite Materials*, ASTM STP-775, ed. Reifsnider K.L., Philadelphia, pp.103–117.

JAMISON R D, SCHULTE K, REIFSNIDER K L and STINCHCOMB W W (1984), Characterisation and analysis of damage mechanisms in tension-tension fatigue of graphite/epoxy laminates, in *Effects of Defects in Composite Materials*, ASTM STP-836, ed. D.J.Wilkins, American Society for Testing and Materials, Philadelphia, pp.21–55.

LAWS N and DVORAK G J (1988), Progressive transverse cracking in composite laminates, *J Comp Mater*, **22**, 900–916.

LEE J W and DANIEL I M (1990), Progressive transverse cracking of crossply composite laminates, *J Comp Mater*, **24**, 1225–1243.

LEE J W, DANIEL I M and YANIV G (1989), Fatigue life prediction of cross-ply composite laminates, in *Composite Materials: Fatigue and Fracture*, Vol. 2, ASTM STP 1012, ed. Lagace P. A., Philadelphia, pp.19–28.

REIFSNIDER K L, HENNEKE E G and STINCHCOMB W W (1977), Defect-property relationships in composite materials, in *Proceedings of the 14th Annual Society of Engineering Science Meeting*, Lehigh University, Bethlehem, PA, pp.14–16.

REIFSNIDER K L and JAMISON R D (1982), Fracture of fatigue-loaded composite materials, *Int J Fatigue*, **4**, 187–197.

REIFSNIDER K L and STINCHCOMB W W (1986), A critical-element model of the residual strength and life of fatigue-loaded composite coupons, in *Composite Materials: Fatigue and Fracture*, ASTM STP-907, ed. Hahn H. L., Philadelphia, pp.298–313.

REIFSNIDER K L (1990), Damage and damage mechanics, in *Fatigue of Composite Materials*, ed. Reifsnider K.L., Series ed. Pipes R.B., Elsevier and Science Publishers, pp.11–77.

TAN S C and NUISMER R K (1988), A theory for progressive matrix cracking in composite laminates, *J Comp Mater*, **23**, 1029–1041.

WEIBULL W (1951), A statistical distribution function of wide applicability, *J Appl Mech*, **18**, 293–297.

YANG J N and LIU M D (1977), Residual strength degradation model and theory of periodic proof tests for graphite/epoxy laminates, *J. Comp Mater*, **11**, 176–203.

YANG J N (1978), Fatigue and residual strength degradation for graphite/epoxy composites under tension-compression cyclic loadings, *J Comp Mater*, **12**, 19–39.

YANG J N and JONES D L (1978), Statistical fatigue of graphite/epoxy angle-ply laminates in shear, *J Comp Mater*, **12**, 371–389.

17

Analysis of matrix crack-induced delamination in composite laminates under static and fatigue loading

M. Kashtalyan, University of Aberdeen, UK and C. Soutis, University of Sheffield, UK

17.1 Introduction

The failure process of fibre-reinforced composite laminates subjected to static or fatigue tensile or thermal loading involves sequential accumulation of intra- and interlaminar damage in the form of matrix cracking and delamination. Intralaminar matrix cracks running parallel to the fibres in off-axis plies of the laminate are the dominant damage mechanism during the initial stages of the failure process. These cracks are either arrested at the interface or cause interfacial failure leading to delamination and/or cracking in the adjacent plies due to high interlaminar stresses at the ply interface. Under quasi-static loading, the strain corresponding to the nucleation of matrix cracking decreases with increasing 90° ply thickness (Parvizi et al., 1978). Under fatigue loading, transverse ply cracking may occur very early in the fatigue life of the specimen, with the cycle number at formation increasing with the decreasing loading amplitude (Daniel and Charewicz, 1986).

Studies of delaminations induced by matrix cracking have been focusing predominantly on delaminations caused by transverse cracks, i.e. matrix cracks in the 90° plies of a laminate. Crossman and Wang (1982) made comprehensive observations of transverse cracking and delamination in balanced symmetric $[\pm 25/90_n]_s$, $n = 0.5; 1; 2; 3; 4; 6; 8$ graphite/epoxy laminates. A significant reduction in the delamination onset strain was noted for the laminates with $n \geq 4$. A transition from edge delamination to local delaminations growing from the tips of matrix cracks in the 90° ply occurred between $n = 3$ and $n = 4$.

The onset and growth of edge delamination in $[(\pm 30)_2/90/\overline{90}]_s$ graphite/epoxy laminates under static tension and tension–tension fatigue loading was studied by O'Brien (1982). Stiffness loss was monitored simultaneously with delamination growth and found to decrease linearly with delamination size.

Charewicz and Daniel (1986) observed damage accumulation in AS-4/3501-6 carbon/ epoxy cross-ply laminates under tension–tension fatigue. They observed five different damage mechanisms, namely transverse cracking in the 90° plies; randomly distributed longitudinal cracking in the 0° plies; profound localized longitudinal cracking; delamination at the 0/90 interface along transverse cracks, particularly in $[0/90_4]_s$ and $[90_4/0]_s$ laminates; small local delamination at the intersection of longitudinal and transverse cracks.

Initiation and growth of local delaminations from the tips of transverse cracks in cross-ply $[0/90_n]_s$, $n = 2$; 4; 6, carbon/epoxy laminates under static tension and tension–tension fatigue was examined respectively by Takeda and Ogihara (1994) and Takeda *et al.* (1995). Delamination was noted to grow more rapidly and extensively in the laminates with thicker 90° plies.

When a cross-ply laminate is subjected to biaxial tensile or thermal loading, matrix cracking can occur both in the 90° and 0° plies and local delaminations can then initiate and grow from the tips of these cracks. Henaff-Gardin *et al.* (1996a,b) observed damage development in carbon/epoxy cross-ply $[0_4/90_4]_s$ laminates under thermal cycling in the temperature range from –200 °C to +130 °C. The first damage mode observed consisted of matrix cracks in 0° and 90° plies. These cracks grew in number more or less rapidly and reached a saturation stage. The crack multiplication in the 90° plies was faster than in the 0° plies, which agrees with the observations of Charewicz and Daniel (1986) under mechanical fatigue loading. Most of the matrix cracks spanned the entire width or length of the specimen. In two groups of tests, characterized by heating the specimens to a higher temperature (90 °C or 130 °C), a second damage mode was observed. It consisted of delaminations between 0° and 90° plies along the pre-existing cracks. This kind of damage formed when cracks began to saturate in number. First delaminations nucleated along the 0° ply cracks, followed by delaminations along the 90° ply cracks.

Kobayashi *et al.* (2001) observed damage development in carbon/epoxy AS4/PEEK $[0_2/90_2]_s$ cross-ply laminates under thermal cycling in the temperature range from –196 °C to +150 °C or 250 °C. The first damage mode observed consisted of matrix cracks in 0° and 90° plies. Most of the matrix cracks spanned the entire width or length of the specimen. Then delaminations initiated along the matrix cracks in the 0° ply.

Delaminations induced by angle ply matrix cracks in carbon/epoxy $[0_2/\theta_2/-\theta_2]_s$, $\theta = 20°$, 25°, 30° laminates subjected to tension fatigue loading were observed by O'Brien and Hooper (1991) and O'Brien (1991). Matrix cracks formed near the stress free edge and delaminations, bounded by the free edge and the crack, developed in the $\theta/(-\theta)$ interface. They were termed partial local delaminations.

Figure 17.1 summarizes schematically types of crack-induced delaminations in some composite laminates. They include transverse crack tip delaminations in cross-ply and balanced symmetric laminates (Fig. 17.1(a)), transverse and longitudinal crack tip delaminations in cross-ply laminates (Fig. 17.1(b)), uniform (Fig. 17.1(c)) and partial (Fig. 17.1(d)) local delaminations induced by angle ply matrix cracks, crack induced edge delaminations (Fig. 17.1(e)).

17.2   Stiffness properties of cracked laminates with delaminations

Stiffness loss due to delaminations has not been as thoroughly investigated as their initiation and growth. O'Brien (1985) was apparently the first to examine the influence of matrix crack tip delamination on the laminate stiffness and strength. The linear degradation of the laminate modulus with delamination area, observed for graphite/epoxy laminates (O'Brien, 1985), was predicted also for glass/epoxy laminates using a simple rule of mixture analysis (Caslini *et al.*, 1987). A simple 1D shear lag analysis using the concept of interlaminar shear layer (Fukunaga *et al.*, 1984) was extended by Takeda and Ogihara (1994) to the laminates

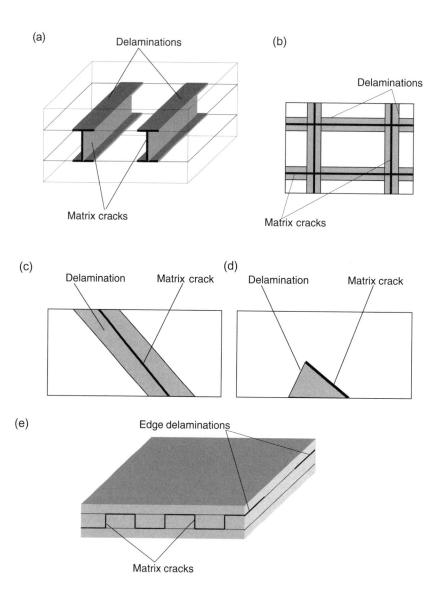

Fig. 17.1   Types of matrix crack induced delaminations in fibre-reinforced composite laminates: (a) transverse crack tip delaminations in cross-ply and balanced symmetric laminates; (b) transverse and longitudinal crack tip delaminations in cross-ply laminates (front view); (c) uniform local delamination induced by angle ply matrix cracks (front view); (d) partial local delamination induced by angle ply matrix cracks uniform across the laminate width (front view); (e) edge delamination.

containing delamination originating from the tips of transverse cracks and used to predict the Young's modulus reduction. Theoretical predictions for the $[0/90_n]_s$ ($n = 2,4,6$) CFRP cross-ply laminates were in good agreement with experimental data. Better agreement of shear lag predictions for the Young's modulus reduction with the experimental data was observed, however, when the interaction between transverse cracks and delaminations was taken into account (Ogihara and Takeda, 1995).

Zhang *et al.* (1994b) extended a modified 2D shear lag approach (Zhang *et al.*, 1992a,b) to analyse balanced $[\pm\theta_m/90_n]_s$ laminates damaged by transverse cracking and local delaminations growing from transverse crack tips. Closed-form expressions were derived for the reduced stiffness properties of the damaged 90° layer, representing them as functions of cracking density and relative delamination area.

Transverse ply cracking and transverse crack tip delaminations in the general symmetric laminates with the central 90° ply have been theoretically investigated by Zhang *et al.* (1999). A sublaminate-wise first-order shear deformation theory was extended to the case of delaminations induced by transverse cracks. The extension stiffness reduction of the constrained 90° ply was calculated as a function of delamination length and transverse cracking spacing. Numerical results have revealed that stiffness reduction of the 90° ply strongly depends upon the orientation of the adjacent ply group, with the remote constraining layer having negligible influence.

In all the above studies of crack induced delaminations it was assumed that delamination surfaces and matrix crack surfaces are stress-free. Besides that, delaminations were assumed to behave in a self-similar manner, i.e. boundary conditions prescribed at the delaminated surfaces were assumed to be the same for small and large delaminations. More recently, Ashkantala and Talreja (1998) and Berthelot and Le Corre (2000) examined transverse crack tips delaminations in cross-ply laminates with shear friction between the delaminated plies. While Berthelot and Le Corre (2000) assumed the magnitude of the interlaminar shear stress at the delaminated interface to be constant, i.e. independent of delamination length, Ashkantala and Talreja (1998) considered both linear and cubic polynomial shear stress distribution at the delamination interface. Selvarathinam and Weitsman (1998, 1999) observed and modelled, by means of finite elements and shear lag methods, delaminations induced by matrix cracking in cross-ply laminates under environmental fatigue, with delamination surfaces loaded with hydrostatic pressure.

To estimate degraded stiffness properties of the laminate damaged by cracks and delaminations, stress analysis needs to be carried out first. Figure 17.2 shows a schematic of a symmetric $[(S)/\phi]_s$ laminate, consisting of the outer sublaminate (S) and the inner ϕ-layer damaged by matrix cracks and local delaminations growing from their tips at the $(S)/\phi$ interface. The outer sublaminate (S), or layer 1, may consist of either a single layer or a group of layers and can also be damaged (in this case it needs to be replaced in the analysis with an equivalent homogeneous layer with reduced stiffness properties). The laminate is referred to the global Cartesian co-ordinate system xyz and local co-ordinate system $x_1x_2x_3$, with the axis x_1 directed along the fibres in the damaged ϕ-layer, or layer 2. The laminate is subjected to in-plane biaxial tension $\bar{\sigma}_x$ and $\bar{\sigma}_y$. Since the laminate is symmetric, no coupling exists between in-plane loading and out-of-plane deformation. Matrix cracks are assumed to be spaced uniformly, with crack spacing $2s$, and span the whole width of the laminate. Local delaminations are assumed to be strip shaped, with strip width $2l$ (Fig. 17.2).

Due to the periodicity of damage, the stress analysis may be carried out over a representative segment containing one matrix crack and two crack tip delaminations. Due to symmetry, it can be further restricted to one-quarter of the representative segment, (Fig. 17.3) referred to the local co-ordinate system $x_1x_2x_3$.

For cross-ply laminates with transverse and longitudinal crack tip delaminations (Fig. 17.1(b)), a representative segment could be defined by intersecting pairs of transverse and longitudinal cracks. However, analysis of such segment is rather cumbersome even in the absence of delaminations (Hashin, 1987; Tsai and Daniel, 1992; Henaff-Gardin *et al.*, 1996a,b). Kashtalyan and Soutis (1999a,b, 2000a,b) suggested analysing cross-ply laminates with damage in both plies using the Equivalent Constraint Model (Fan and Zhang, 1993).

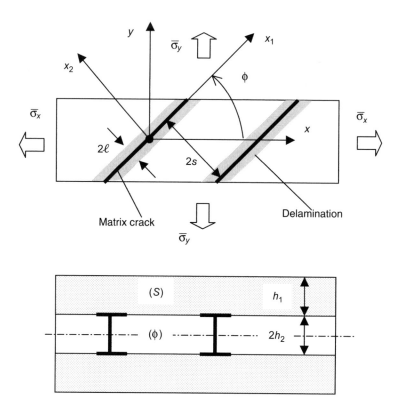

Fig. 17.2 Front and edge views of a $[(S)/\phi]_s$ laminate subjected to biaxial tensile loading and damaged by matrix cracks and uniform local delaminations. Local $(x_1 x_2 x_3)$ and global (xyz) co-ordinate systems for the damaged ϕ-layer (front view in the negative $x_3 \equiv z$ direction).

Instead of the damaged laminate, two ECM laminates are considered and analysed simultaneously. In the first laminate, $0°$ layers contain damage explicitly, while $90°$ plies are replaced with equivalent homogeneous ones with reduced stiffness properties. These reduced stiffness properties are assumed to be known from the analysis of the second laminate, in which the $90°$ layer contains damage explicitly, while the damaged $0°$ plies are replaced with equivalent homogeneous ones with reduced properties, assumed to be known from the analysis of the first laminate. Thus, problems for both laminates are inter-related. Application of the Equivalent Constraint Model to quasi-isotropic laminates with matrix cracking in all but $0°$ layers was presented by Zhang and Herrmann (1999).

17.2.1   Stress analysis

Let $\{\bar{\sigma}^{(1)}\}$ and $\{\bar{\varepsilon}^{(1)}\}$ denote the in-plane microstresses and microstrains in the layer 1, and $\{\bar{\sigma}^{(2)}\}$ and $\{\bar{\varepsilon}^{(2)}\}$ denote the in-plane microstresses and microstrains in the layer 2 (i.e. stresses and strains averaged across the respective layer thickness). Since it is assumed that there is no frictional contact between the layers in the locally delaminated portion of the representative segment $(0 < |x_2| \ell, |x_3| < h_2)$, the in-plane microstresses in the delaminated portion are $\bar{\sigma}_{22}^{(1)} = \bar{\sigma}_{12}^{(2)} = 0$, i.e. this region is stress-free. Assumption of stress-free crack tip delamination surfaces, and the resulting implication that the portion of the damaged ply bounded by

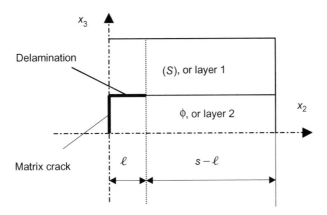

Fig. 17.3   A quarter of the representative segment containing matrix crack and delamination.

matrix crack and delamination surfaces is stress-free, has been widely used in the studies of delaminations. Besides that, delaminations are assumed to behave in a self-similar manner, i.e. the boundary conditions prescribed at the delaminated surfaces are assumed to be the same for small and large delaminations.

In the perfectly bonded region $(\ell < |x_2| < s)$ of the representative segment, stresses are determined from the equilibrium equations

$$\frac{d}{dx_2}\tilde{\sigma}_{j2}^{(2)} - \frac{\tau_j}{h_2} = 0 \quad j = 1,2 \tag{17.1}$$

where τ_j are the interface shear stresses and h_2 is the thickness of the ϕ-layer.

By averaging the out-of-plane constitutive equations for both layers across the layer thickness, the interface shear stresses τ_j can be expressed in terms of the in-plane displacements and shear lag parameters K_{ij} as

$$\tau_j = K_{j1}(\tilde{u}_1^{(1)} - \tilde{u}_1^{(2)}) + K_{j2}(\tilde{u}_2^{(1)} - \tilde{u}_2^{(2)}). \tag{17.2}$$

The shear lag parameters K_{11}, K_{22}, $K_{12} \equiv K_{21}$ are determined assuming that the out-of-plane shear stresses $\tilde{\sigma}_{j3}^{(k)}$ vary linearly with x_3 (Fig. 17.4), see Appendix I. Substitution of equation [17.2] into equation [17.1] and subsequent differentiation yields

$$\frac{d^2}{dx_2}\tilde{\sigma}_{j2}^{(2)} + K_{j1}(\tilde{\gamma}_{12}^{(1)} - \tilde{\gamma}_{12}^{(2)}) + K_{j2}(\tilde{\varepsilon}_{22}^{(1)} - \tilde{\varepsilon}_{22}^{(2)}) = 0 \quad j = 1,2 \tag{17.3}$$

The strain differences $(\tilde{\varepsilon}_{22}^{(1)} - \tilde{\varepsilon}_{22}^{(2)})$ and $(\tilde{\gamma}_{12}^{(1)} - \tilde{\gamma}_{12}^{(2)})$, involved in equation [17.3], can be expressed in terms of stresses $\tilde{\sigma}_{12}^{(2)}$, $\tilde{\sigma}_{22}^{(2)}$ using the constitutive equations for both layers, the laminate equilibrium equations below:

$$\chi\{\tilde{\sigma}^{(1)}\} + \{\tilde{\sigma}^{(2)}\} = (1 + \chi)[T]\{\bar{\sigma}\} \tag{17.4a}$$

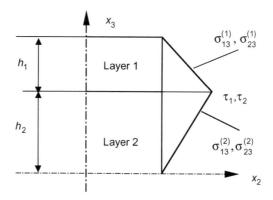

Fig. 17.4   Variation of out-of-plane shear stresses.

$$[T] = \begin{bmatrix} \cos^2\phi & \sin^2\phi & 2\sin\phi\cos\phi \\ \sin^2\phi & \cos^2\phi & -2\sin\phi\cos\phi \\ -\sin\phi\cos\phi & \sin\phi\cos\phi & \cos^2\phi - \sin^2\phi \end{bmatrix}$$

[17.4b]

$$\{\bar{\sigma}\} = \{\sigma_x, \sigma_y, 0\}^T, \quad \chi = h_1/h_2$$

[17.4c]

and the assumption of the generalized plane strain condition

$$\tilde{\varepsilon}_{11}^{(1)} = \tilde{\varepsilon}_{11}^{(2)}$$

[17.5]

In the local co-ordinate system $x_1 x_2 x_3$, layer 2 is orthotropic

$$\begin{Bmatrix} \tilde{\varepsilon}_{11}^{(2)} \\ \tilde{\varepsilon}_{22}^{(2)} \\ \tilde{\gamma}_{12}^{(2)} \end{Bmatrix} = \begin{bmatrix} \hat{S}_{11}^{(2)} & \hat{S}_{12}^{(2)} & 0 \\ \hat{S}_{12}^{(2)} & \hat{S}_{22}^{(2)} & 0 \\ 0 & 0 & \hat{S}_{66}^{(2)} \end{bmatrix} \begin{Bmatrix} \tilde{\sigma}_{11}^{(2)} \\ \tilde{\sigma}_{22}^{(2)} \\ \tilde{\sigma}_{12}^{(2)} \end{Bmatrix}$$

[17.6a]

while layer 1 is anisotropic

$$\begin{Bmatrix} \tilde{\varepsilon}_{11}^{(1)} \\ \tilde{\varepsilon}_{22}^{(1)} \\ \tilde{\gamma}_{12}^{(1)} \end{Bmatrix} = \begin{bmatrix} \hat{S}_{11}^{(1)} & \hat{S}_{12}^{(1)} & \hat{S}_{16}^{(1)} \\ \hat{S}_{12}^{(1)} & \hat{S}_{22}^{(1)} & \hat{S}_{26}^{(1)} \\ \hat{S}_{16}^{(1)} & \hat{S}_{26}^{(1)} & \hat{S}_{66}^{(1)} \end{bmatrix} \begin{Bmatrix} \tilde{\sigma}_{11}^{(1)} \\ \tilde{\sigma}_{22}^{(1)} \\ \tilde{\sigma}_{12}^{(1)} \end{Bmatrix}$$

[17.6b]

where $[\hat{S}^{(k)}]$ is the compliance matrix for the kth layer.

Finally, equation [17.3] can be reduced to a system of two coupled second-order ordinary differential equations (see Appendix II)

$$\frac{d^2\tilde{\sigma}_{12}^{(2)}}{dx_2^2} - N_{11}\tilde{\sigma}_{12}^{(2)} - N_{12}\tilde{\sigma}_{22}^{(2)} - P_{11}\bar{\sigma}_x - P_{12}\bar{\sigma}_y = 0$$

[17.7a]

$$\frac{d^2 \tilde{\sigma}_{22}^{(2)}}{dx_2^2} - N_{21}\tilde{\sigma}_{12}^{(2)} - N_{22}\tilde{\sigma}_{22}^{(2)} - P_{21}\overline{\sigma}_x - P_{22}\overline{\sigma}_y = 0 \qquad \text{[17.7b]}$$

Here N_{ij} and P_{ij} are laminate constants depending on the layer compliances $\hat{S}_{if}^{(k)}$, layer thickness ratio χ, shear lag parameters K_{11}, K_{22}, K_{12} and angle ϕ (Appendix II).

Equations [17.7a] and [17.7b] can be uncoupled at the expense of increasing the order of differentiation, resulting in a fourth-order non-homogeneous ordinary differential equation

$$\frac{d^4 \tilde{\sigma}_{22}^{(2)}}{dx_2^4} - (N_{11} + N_{22})\frac{d^2 \tilde{\sigma}_{22}^{(2)}}{dx_2^2} - (N_{21}N_{12} - N_{11}N_{22})\tilde{\sigma}_{22}^{(2)}$$
$$+ [N_{11}(P_{21} + \alpha P_{22}) - N_{21}(P_{11} + \alpha P_{12})]\overline{\sigma}_x = 0 \qquad \text{[17.8]}$$

Here $\alpha = \overline{\sigma}_y / \overline{\sigma}_x$ is the biaxiality ratio. The boundary conditions for equation [17.8] are prescribed at the stress-free boundary between locally delaminated and perfectly bonded portions of the representative segment

$$\tilde{\sigma}_{22}^{(2)}\big|_{x_2 = \pm \lambda} = 0 \quad \tilde{\sigma}_{12}^{(2)}\big|_{x_2 = \pm \lambda} = 0 \qquad \text{[17.9]}$$

Finally, the in-plane microstresses can be expressed in the following form

$$\tilde{\sigma}_{11}^{(2)} = a_{22}\tilde{\sigma}_{22}^{(2)} + a_{12}\tilde{\sigma}_{12}^{(2)} + b_x\overline{\sigma}_x + b_y\overline{\sigma}_y \qquad \text{[17.10a]}$$

$$\tilde{\sigma}_{j2}^{(2)} = \left[A_j \frac{\cosh \lambda_1 (x_2 - s)}{\cosh \lambda_1 (s - \lambda)} + B_j \frac{\cosh \lambda_2 (x_2 - s)}{\cosh \lambda_2 (s - \lambda)} + C_j \right]\overline{\sigma}_x \quad j = 1,2 \qquad \text{[17.10b]}$$

where coefficients a_{22}, a_{12}, b_x and b_y are given in Appendix II, λ_j are the roots of the characteristic equation and A_j, B_j and C_j are constants depending on N_{ij} and P_{ij}, see Appendix III.

In cross-ply and balanced laminates the outer sublaminate S is orthotropic, with compliances $\hat{S}_{16}^{(1)} = \hat{S}_{26}^{(1)} = 0$ and stiffnesses $\hat{Q}_{45}^{(1)} = 0$. In this case shear lag coefficients $K_{12} \equiv K_{21} = 0$ vanish, and equilibrium equations are reduced to two uncoupled second-order differential equations. Details of this case are given elsewhere (Zhang et al., 1994b; Kashtalyan and Soutis, 1999a; Kashtalyan and Soutis, 2000a).

17.2.2   Stiffness degradation due to delaminations

To determine the reduced stiffness properties of the damaged laminate, an 'equivalent' laminate, in which the damaged layer is replaced with an 'equivalent' homogeneous one with degraded stiffness properties, is considered. In the local co-ordinate system $x_1 x_2 x_3$, the constitutive equations of the 'equivalent' homogeneous layer are

$$\{\overline{\sigma}^{(2)}\} = [Q^{(2)}]\{\overline{\varepsilon}^{(2)}\} \qquad \text{[17.11]}$$

In the local co-ordinates, the modified in-plane stiffness matrix $[Q^{(2)}]$ of the homogeneous layer equivalent to the damaged one is related to the in-plane stiffness matrix $[\hat{Q}^{(2)}]$ of the undamaged layer as

$$[Q^{(2)}] = [\hat{Q}^{(2)}] - \begin{bmatrix} (\hat{Q}_{12}^{(2)})^2 / \hat{Q}_{22}^{(2)} \Lambda_{22} & \hat{Q}_{12}^{(2)} \Lambda_{22} & 0 \\ \hat{Q}_{12}^{(2)} \Lambda_{22} & \hat{Q}_{22}^{(2)} \Lambda_{22} & 0 \\ 0 & 0 & \hat{Q}_{66}^{(2)} \Lambda_{66} \end{bmatrix}$$ [17.12]

Here Λ_{22}, Λ_{66} are the in-situ damage effective functions (IDEFs) (Zhang *et al.*, 1992a). They can be expressed in terms of lamina macrostresses and macrostrains as

$$\Lambda_{22} = 1 - \frac{\overline{\sigma}_{22}^{(2)}}{\hat{Q}_{12}^{(2)} \overline{\varepsilon}_{11}^{(2)} + \hat{Q}_{22}^{(2)} \overline{\varepsilon}_{22}^{(2)}} \qquad \Lambda_{66} = 1 - \frac{\overline{\sigma}_{12}^{(2)}}{\hat{Q}_{66}^{(2)} \overline{\gamma}_{12}^{(2)}}$$ [17.13]

The lamina macrostresses $\{\overline{\sigma}^{(2)}\}$ and macrostrains $\{\overline{\varepsilon}^{(2)}\}$ are obtained by averaging, respectively, microstresses $\{\tilde{\sigma}^{(2)}\}$, equation [17.10], and microstrains $\{\tilde{\varepsilon}^{(2)}\}$, equation [17.6a], across the length of the representative segment. The lamina macrostresses $\overline{\sigma}_{ij}^{(2)}$ are

$$\overline{\sigma}_{11}^{(2)} = a_{22}\overline{\sigma}_{22}^{(2)} + a_{12}\overline{\sigma}_{12}^{(2)} + b_x\overline{\sigma}_x + b_y\overline{\sigma}_y \qquad \lambda_j^* = h_2\lambda_j$$ [17.14a]

$$\overline{\sigma}_{j2}^{(2)} = \left[A_{j2} \frac{D_{mc}}{\lambda_1^*(1-D_{ld})} \tanh \frac{\lambda_1^*(1-D_{ld})}{D_{mc}} + B_{j2} \frac{D_{mc}}{\lambda_2^*(1-D_{ld})} \tanh \frac{\lambda_2^*(1-D_{ld})}{D_{mc}} + C_{j2}(1-D_{ld}) \right] \overline{\sigma}_x$$

for $j = 1,2$

[17.14b]

where $D^{mc} = h_2/s$ denotes relative crack density and $D^{ld} = l/s$ denotes relative delamination area. The macrostrains in the individual homogeneous layers and the laminate are assumed to be equal:

$$\overline{\varepsilon}_{11}^{(1)} = \overline{\varepsilon}_{11}^{(2)} = \overline{\varepsilon}_{11} \qquad \overline{\varepsilon}_{22}^{(1)} = \overline{\varepsilon}_{22}^{(2)} = \overline{\varepsilon}_{22} \qquad \overline{\gamma}_{12}^{(1)} = \overline{\gamma}_{12}^{(2)} = \overline{\gamma}_{12}$$ [17.15]

Using the constitutive equations for layer 1, equation [17.6b], and equations of the global equilibrium of the laminate, equation [17.4], the lamina macrostrains in layer 2 are

$$\{\overline{\varepsilon}^{(2)}\} = [\hat{S}^{(1)}]\chi^{-1}((1+\chi)[T]\{\overline{\sigma}\} - \{\overline{\sigma}^{(2)}\})$$ [17.16]

where the transformation matrix $[T]$ is given by equation [17.4b]. Thus, the lamina macrostresses, equation [17.14], and macrostrains, equation [17.16], are determined as explicit functions of the damage parameters D^{mc}, D^{ld}.

Finally, the modified stiffness matrix $[\overline{Q}]_2$ of the 'equivalent' homogeneous layer in the global co-ordinates xyz can be obtained from the modified stiffness matrix $[Q^{(2)}]$ in the local co-ordinates, equation [17.12], as

$$[\overline{Q}]_2 = [T]^{-1}[Q^{(2)}][T]^{-T}$$ [17.17]

where the transformation matrix $[T]$ is given by equation [17.4b]. The extension stiffness matrix $[\overline{A}]$ of the 'equivalent' laminate in the global co-ordinates xyz can then be determined as

$$[\overline{A}] = \sum_k [\overline{Q}]_k h_k \qquad k = 1,2$$ [17.18]

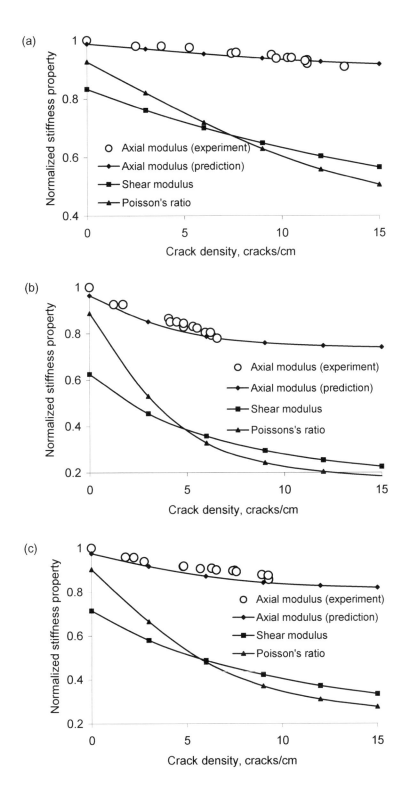

Fig. 17.5   Stiffness reduction due to transverse crack tip delaminations in T800H/3631 cross-ply laminates as a function of crack density: (a) $[0/90_2]_s$; (b) $[0/90_4]_s$; (c) $[0/90_6]_s$.

where $[\bar{Q}]_1$ is the in-plane stiffness matrix of layer 1, or the outer sublaminate, in the global co-ordinates.

17.2.3 Stiffness properties of cracked cross-ply laminates with delaminations

Figure 17.5 shows stiffness reduction in T800H/3631 carbon/epoxy $[0/90_n]_s$, $n = 2,4,6$ cross-ply laminates containing transverse cracks and delaminations. The axial modulus E_x, shear modulus G_{xy} and Poisson's ratio v_{xy}, normalized by their values in the undamaged state, are plotted against the transverse crack density. The relative delamination area is 10%, which corresponds to $l/s = 0.1$. For the axial modulus, predictions are compared to experimental data obtained by Takeda and Ogihara (1994) and appear to be in acceptable agreement. However, the predictions show that reduction in shear modulus and Poisson's ratio due to crack tip delamination is more significant.

Observed damage development (Henaff-Gardin et al., 1996b) and predicted stiffness reduction in a cross-ply $[0_4/90_4]_s$ T300/914 carbon epoxy laminate during thermal cycling is shown in Fig. 17.6(a). The cycle consisted of cooling to $-200\,°C$ and heating to $+90\,°C$ (Henaff-Gardin et al., 1996b). Crack density in the 90° and 0° plies was measured; however, the size of growing delaminations that accompanied longitudinal cracks was not. Predictions of reductions in the axial E_x and shear G_{xy} moduli as well as the Poisson's ratio v_{xy}, normalized by their values in the undamaged state, are shown along with the measured crack densities in the 90° and 0° plies as a function of number of cycles. As cracks develop, the shear modulus and Poisson's ratio undergo significant reduction, while reduction in axial modulus remains less than 5%. This indicates that the shear modulus and the Poisson's ratio could be much better parameters to characterize stiffness degradation of the laminate than the axial modulus.

Since the size of the delamination area was not measured during cycling, reduction of the stiffness properties of the $[0_4/90_4]_s$ T300/914 laminate due to delaminations was predicted using assumed delamination sizes. Strip-width of the transverse delamination was set to zero, while that of the longitudinal delamination allowed to vary from zero to 50%. In other words, longitudinal delaminations were assumed to have propagated from the crack tip to one-quarter of the distance between two cracks. This seems to be a reasonable assumption, consistent with X-ray radiographs obtained by Henaff-Gardin et al. (1996b). In Figs. 17.6(b) and 17.6(c), predicted reductions of the axial E_x, transverse E_y and shear G_{xy} moduli as well as Poisson's ratio v_{xy}, normalized by their values in the undamaged state, are plotted as a function of the relative delamination area. The axial modulus appears to be unaffected by the growth of delamination, while transverse modulus is further reduced, but not significantly (Fig. 17.6(b)). The reduction in the shear modulus is more pronounced than in the Poisson's ratio (Fig. 17.6(c)). Crack densities in 90° and 0° plies were taken as $C_2 = 4.5$ cracks/cm and $C_1 = 3$ cracks/cm respectively, which corresponds to saturation values reached during $-200\,°C/+90\,°C$ cycling. Under uniaxial loading, longitudinal delaminations appear to be more important than the transverse ones, since they result in isolation of the portions of the load-bearing 0° plies, which become prone to fibre breakage. Under biaxial loading, the importance of one set of delaminations over the other depends very much on the biaxiality and ply thickness ratios.

17.2.4 Stiffness properties of cracked angle-ply laminates with delaminations

Matrix cracking in off-axis plies is known to introduce some shear-extension coupling into balanced symmetric angle-ply laminates, however, of much smaller extent than that exhibited

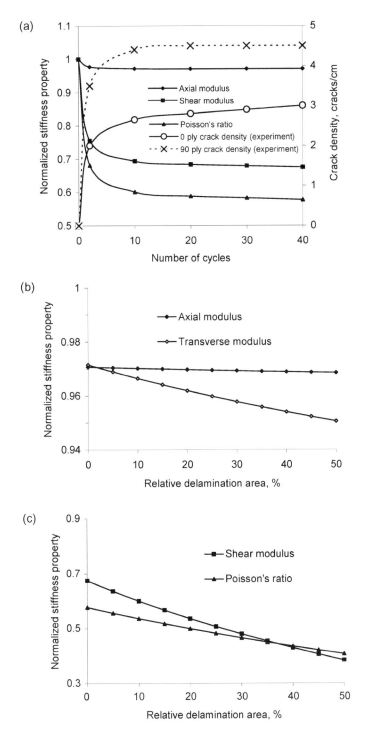

Fig. 17.6   Stiffness reduction in a $[0_4/90_4]_s$ T300/914 laminate subjected to –200 °C/+90 °C thermal cycling: (a) stiffness reduction due to matrix cracking and matrix crack density as a function of number of cycles; (b) axial and transverse moduli reduction due to longitudinal crack tip delamination as a function of delamination area D^{ld}; (c) shear modulus and Poisson's ratio reduction due to longitudinal crack tip delamination as a function of delamination area D^{ld}.

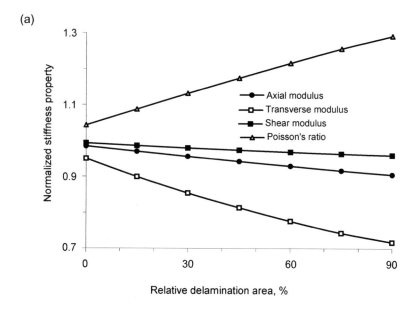

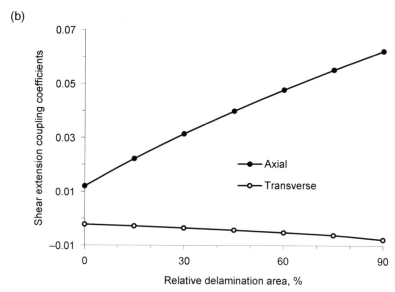

Fig. 17.7 Stiffness reduction due to delaminations in a cracked $[0_2/30_2/-30_2]_s$ AS4/3506-1 laminate as a function of relative delamination area D^{ld}: (a) normalized moduli and Poisson's ratio; (b) shear-extension coupling coefficients. Matrix crack density 2 cracks/cm.

in unbalanced symmetric angle-ply laminates (Kashtalyan and Soutis, 2000c). The lay-ups to represent balanced and unbalanced laminates were chosen respectively as $[0_2/\theta_2/-\theta_2]_s$ and $[0_2/\theta_2]_s$. The orientation of the cracked middle layer is therefore $\phi = -\theta$ for $[0_2/\theta_2/-\theta_2]$, laminate and $\phi = \theta$ for $[0_2/\theta_2]_s$ laminate. The material system is AS4/3506-1 graphite/epoxy that was earlier considered by O'Brien and Hooper (1991) and O'Brien (1991). Its lamina properties are as follows: $E_{11} = 135$ GPa, $E_{22} = 11$ GPa, $G_{12} = 5.8$ GPa, $v_{12} = 0.301$, single ply thickness $t = 0.124$ mm.

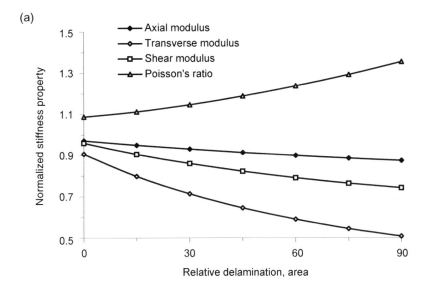

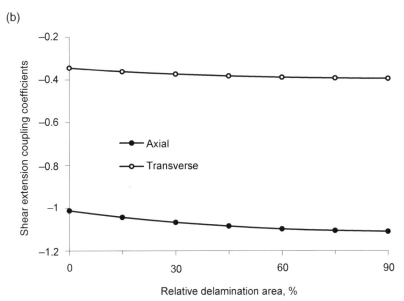

Fig. 17.8   Stiffness reduction due to delaminations in a cracked $[0_2/30_2]_s$ AS4/3506-1 laminate as a function of relative delamination area D^{ld}: (a) normalized moduli and Poisson's ratio; (b) shear-extension coupling coefficients. Matrix crack density 2 cracks/cm.

Figure 17.7 shows the variation of the laminate residual stiffness properties with the relative delamination area $D^{ld} = \ell/s$ in the balanced $[0_2/30_2/-30_2]_s$ laminate. Axial modulus E_x, transverse modulus E_y, shear modulus G_{xy} and major Poisson's ratio v_{xy} normalized by their value for the undamaged laminate are plotted in Fig 17.7(a). The axial/transverse shear-extension coupling coefficients that characterize shearing in the xy plane caused respectively by axial/transverse stress are plotted in Fig. 17.7(b). Matrix crack density in the inner ($-30°$)-ply is assumed equal to $C = 2$ cracks/cm. Values at $D^{ld} = 0$ indicate residual stiffness properties of the laminate at this crack density without delaminations. It can be seen that local delaminations further decrease the laminate moduli and, for the considered lay-up, increase the Poisson's ratio (Fig. 17.7(a)). Matrix cracking in angle-ply laminates is known to introduce the coupling between extension and shear (Soutis and Kashtalyan, 2000). In balanced $[0_2/\theta_2/-\theta_2]_s$ laminates uniform local delaminations result in an increase in the absolute value of the axial shear-extension coupling coefficient for $\theta < 45°$ and of the transverse shear-extension coupling coefficient for $\theta > 45°$. However, all shear-extension coupling coefficients are significantly smaller than those for unbalanced laminates (see later Fig. 17.8(b))

Figure 17.8 shows the variation of the laminate residual stiffness properties with the relative delamination area D^{ld} in the unbalanced $[0_2/30_2]_s$ laminate. Axial modulus E_x, transverse modulus E_y, shear modulus G_{xy} and major Poisson's ratio v_{xy} normalized by their value for the undamaged laminate are plotted in Fig. 17.8(a). The axial/transverse shear-extension coupling coefficients that characterize shearing in the xy plane caused by respectively axial/transverse stress are plotted in Fig. 17.8(b). Matrix crack density in the 30°-ply is assumed equal to $C = 2$ cracks/cm, values at $D^{ld} = 0$ indicate residual stiffness properties of the laminates at this crack density without delaminations. It can be seen that reduction of the laminate moduli and, for the considered lay-up, increase of the Poisson's ratio due to local delaminations are more significant in the unbalanced $[0_2/30_2]_s$ laminate than in the balanced $[0_2/30_2/-30_2]_s$ laminate with the same orientation of the damaged ply. Matrix cracking and crack tip delaminations are expected to amplify the shear–extension coupling exhibited in the undamaged unbalanced $[0_2/\theta_2]_s$ laminates. As in balanced $[0_2/\theta_2/-\theta_2]_s$ laminates, crack tip uniform local delaminations in unbalanced laminates result in an increase in the absolute value of the axial shear-extension coupling coefficient for $\theta < 45°$ and of the transverse shear-extension coupling coefficient for $\theta > 45°$.

17.2.5   Influence of constraining ply orientation

It was shown by Zhang *et al.* (1999) that the reduction of the axial stiffness of the 90° ply in symmetric laminates with the central 90° layer strongly depends upon the orientation of the adjacent ply group, with the remote constraining layers having negligible influence. Kashtalyan and Soutis (2000a) examined the effect of the adjacent ply orientation in balanced $[\pm\theta_m/90_n]_s$ laminates on the reduction of the laminate axial and shear moduli as well as Poisson's ratio due to local delaminations induced by transverse ply cracks. Figures 17.9(a)–(c) illustrate reduction ratios for stiffness properties of CFRP $[\pm\theta_2/90_4]_s$ laminates as functions of the constraining ply orientation angle θ. The material system is T300/934 carbon/epoxy, with the following lamina properties: $E_{11} = 144.8$ GPa, $E_{22} = 11.38$ GPa, $G_{12} = 6.48$ GPa, $v_{12} = 0.3$, single ply thickness $t = 0.132$ mm. To establish the contribution of transverse crack tip delaminations into the stiffness loss, reduction of elastic properties due to transverse cracking only (without delaminations, i.e. when $\ell = 0$) is shown for comparison (hatched lines). Delamination length is taken to be equal to 4 ply thicknesses. Crack half-spacings are $s = 40t$ and $s = 20t$. This is equivalent to crack densities of approximately $C = 1$ cm^{-1} and $C = 2$ cm^{-1}, respectively.

Numerical results reveal different degrading effect of transverse crack tip delaminations on the stiffness properties of a balanced $[\pm\theta_2/90_4]$ laminate. Cross-ply laminates ($\theta = 0$) show the smallest reduction of the axial modulus (Fig. 17.9(a) due to transverse crack tip delaminations. Degradation of axial stiffness due to delaminations monotonously increases with an increase in the constraining ply orientation angle. It is also more significant in the laminate with a higher crack density (smaller crack spacing). For the shear modulus and

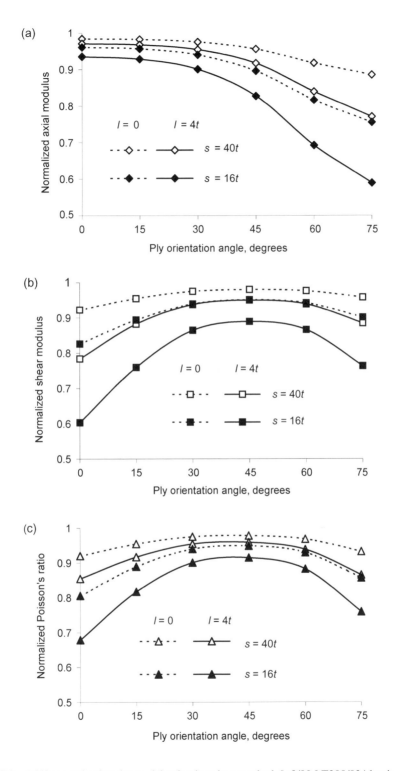

Fig. 17.9   Stiffness reduction due to delaminations in a cracked $[\pm\theta/90_4]_s$ T300/934 laminate as a function of the constraining ply orientation angle θ: (a) axial modulus; (b) shear modulus; (c) Poisson's ratio.

Poisson's ratio (Figs. 17.9(b) and 17.9(c), a different trend is observed. The most severe reduction of these elastic properties due to delaminations occurs in cross-ply laminates, while laminates with constraining ply orientation $\theta = 45°$ are the most resistant to the loss of the shear stiffness due to delaminations. For the axial modulus, the same slope of reduction ratio curves (Fig. 17.9(a) for $s = 40t$, $\ell = 4t$ (smaller crack density and delaminations) and $s = 16t$, $\ell = 0$ (larger crack density, no delaminations) is worth noticing. It suggests that the effect of the transverse tip delaminations on the laminate axial modulus is similar to that achieved by an increase in the crack density, and this 'equivalent' crack density is almost independent of θ.

17.3   Delamination onset and growth prediction

17.3.1   Analytical and finite elements modelling of crack tip delaminations

O'Brien (1985) suggested a simple closed-form expression for the strain-energy release rate for local delaminations growing uniformly from transverse crack tips. The expression is based on simple load shearing rules and the classical laminated plate theory. It gives the strain energy release rate that depends only on the laminate lay-up and thickness, the location of the cracked ply and subsequent delaminations, the applied load and the laminate width, and is independent of delamination size and matrix crack density. In the nomenclature of this paper it is given by

$$\frac{G^{ld}}{\bar{\varepsilon}_{xx}^2} = \frac{N\hat{E}_x^2 h}{2m}\left(\frac{1}{(N-n)\hat{E}_{ld}} - \frac{1}{N\hat{E}_x}\right) \qquad [17.19a]$$

where h is the laminate thickness, N is the number of plies, n is the number of cracked plies, $\hat{E}_x$ and $\hat{E}_{ld}$ are, respectively, the laminate modulus and the modulus of the locally delaminated sublaminate as calculated from the laminated plate theory. Parameter m has a value of 2 if the cracked ply is in the interior of the laminate, corresponding to local delamination on either side of the matrix crack, and that of 1 if the cracked ply is a surface ply.

Later, O'Brien (1991) showed that this simple closed-form expression is valid for the total strain energy release rate associated with uniform local delamination growing from an angle ply matrix crack. For example, the strain energy release rate for local delamination in the $(\theta/-\theta)$ interface of a $[0_2/\theta_2/-\theta_2]_s$ laminate with matrix cracks in the $(-\theta)$-ply is

$$\frac{G^{ld}}{\bar{\varepsilon}_{xx}^2} = \frac{3\hat{E}_x^2 h}{2}\left(\frac{1}{4\hat{E}_{ld}} - \frac{1}{6\hat{E}_x}\right) \qquad [17.19b]$$

Since the locally delaminated $[0_2/\theta_2]_T$ sublaminate is asymmetric, the value of $\hat{E}_{ld}$ in equation [17.19b] will depend on whether the presence of bending–extension and shear–extension coupling is reflected in the modulus calculation. For all ply orientation angles θ (i.e. from 5° to 90°), the influence of shear-extension coupling on the value of $\hat{E}_{ld}$ and therefore the strain energy release rate was found to be significant. The shear constraint resulted in a greater $\hat{E}_{ld}$ and, hence, a correspondingly lower strain energy release rate. However, the effect of bending-extension coupling was proved to be small (O'Brien, 1991). It is worth noticing that the strain energy release rate given by equation [17.19b] is independent from the delamination size. Also, the effect of matrix cracking is not taken into account when calculating the laminate modulus $\hat{E}_x$.

Using a quasi-3D finite elements (FE) analysis, Salpekar and O'Brien (1991) found that the strain energy release rate for uniform local delamination calculated from O'Brien's (1985) expression matched the value obtained by FE analysis in the laminate interior. FE results for uniform local delaminations initiating from a transverse crack in cross-ply $[0_2/90_4]_s$ and balanced $[\pm45/90_4]_s$ glass/epoxy laminates indicated that the strain energy release rate was higher near the free edge. It increased with delamination length and reached a constant value at delamination length of about four-ply thicknesses from the transverse crack in the interior as well as near the edges. However, the peak value of strain energy release rate near the free edge has yet to be verified by convergence studies.

Nairn and Hu (1992) used two-dimensional variational mechanics to analyse crack tip delaminations in $[(S)/90_n]_s$ laminates, where (S) denotes a balanced sublaminate, e.g. $(\pm\theta_m)$. They predicted that matrix cracking should reach some critical density before delamination initiates. The critical crack density for delamination initiation is determined by material properties, laminate structure as well as fracture toughnesses for matrix cracking and delamination. It is nearly independent of the properties of the supporting sublaminate (S). They also showed that O'Brien's expression for strain energy release rate applies only to delaminations induced by isolated matrix cracks, i.e. when crack density is very small and the influence of neighbouring cracks is negligible. For crack densities, at which delaminations are observed to initiate, the strain energy release rate depends both on delamination size and crack density.

Armanios et al. (1991) applied a shear deformation theory and sublaminate approach to analyse local delaminations originating from transverse cracks in CFRP $[\pm25/90_n]_s$ laminates. Predictions of their model, which also takes into account hygrothermal effects, are in reasonable agreement with delamination onset strain data by Crossmann and Wang (1982).

Zhang et al. (1999) studied delaminations induced by transverse cracking at the $(\phi/90)$ interfaces in $[\ldots/\phi_i/\phi_m/90_n]_s$ laminates loaded in tension. In particular, they were interested in the constraining effect of the immediate neighbouring plies and remote plies on stiffness reduction and strain energy release rate for delaminations. A sublaminate-wise first-order shear deformation theory was used to analyse stress and strain fields. It was found that the strain energy release rate for local delamination and stiffness reduction of the constrained transverse plies largely depends on a local lay-up configuration of a damaged laminate. The authors suggested that the strain energy release rate for local delamination at the $(\phi/90)$ interface in a $[\ldots/\phi_i/\phi_m/90_n]_s$ can be analysed using a $[\phi_m/90_n]_s$ laminate, where the 90°-plies and their next neighbouring plies are subjected to the same laminate strain.

The shear lag method was successfully used by several authors to model onset and growth of transverse crack tip delaminations. Dharani and Tang (1990) used the shear lag method to determine the interlaminar shear and normal stresses at the delamination tip. Delamination was assumed to occur when the maximum interlaminar shear stress reached a critical value. Governing equations, formulated in terms of finite differences, were solved numerically using an eigen-value technique.

Zhang et al. (1994a,b) used a 2D improved shear lag analysis to predict the strain energy release rate for edge and local delaminations in balanced symmetric $[\pm\theta_m/90_n]_s$ laminates. For edge delamination, they were able to capture a zigzag delamination pattern, i.e. edge delamination switching from one $(\theta/90)$ interface to another through a matrix crack, and improve O'Brien's formula for strain energy release rate for edge delamination (O'Brien, 1982) incorporating the effect of matrix cracking. For local delaminations, they obtained the strain energy release rate as a function of crack density and delamination area. Their predictions for delamination onset strain agree well with experimental data of Crossman and Wang (1982) and capture the transition from edge to local delamination quite accurately.

Ogihara and Takeda (1995) used a modified shear lag method featuring interlaminar shear layer to predict the strain energy release rate for transverse crack tip delaminations in cross-ply $[0/90_n]_s$ laminates and to model interaction between transverse cracking and delamination. However, the effect of cracking/delamination interaction was found to be negligible in prediction of delamination growth.

More recently, Selvarathinam and Weitsman (1998, 1999) observed and modelled, by means of finite elements and shear lag methods, delaminations induced by matrix cracking in cross-ply laminates under environmental fatigue. By comparing strain energy release rates associated with matrix cracking and delamination, they were able to explain the extensive delaminations and reduced crack densities that arise under immersed fatigue conditions, as compared with fatigue in air.

Using an improved 2D shear lag method (Zhang et al., 1992) and the Equivalent Constraint Model of the damaged ply (Fan and Zhang, 1993), Kashtalyan and Soutis (1999a, 2000a) examined the effect of crack tip delaminations on stiffness reduction. For cross-ply $[0_m/90_n]_s$ laminates, local delaminations along transverse as well as longitudinal cracks were considered (Fig. 17.1(b)). It was established that reduction in the laminate shear modulus and Poisson's ratio is much more significant than in the axial modulus. For balanced symmetric $[\pm\theta_m/90_n]_s$, the effect of constraining ply orientation angle θ on reduction of the laminate in-plane stiffness properties was also examined.

While transverse crack tip delaminations have been the subject of numerous studies in the literature, delaminations growing from the tips of angle ply cracks have received considerably less attention.

O'Brien and Hooper (1991) and O'Brien (1991) observed matrix crack induced delaminations in symmetric angle-ply $[0_2/\theta_2/-\theta_2]$ carbon/epoxy laminates under quasi-static and fatigue tensile loading ($\theta = 15°$; $20°$; $25°$; $30°$). Delaminations occurred in the $(\theta/-\theta)$ interface, bounded by the cracks in the $(-\theta)$-ply and the stress free edge. The laminated plate theory and a quasi-3D finite element analysis were used to examine stresses in the $(-\theta)$-ply. For the considered range of ply orientations, stresses normal to the fibres were found to be compressive and shear stresses along the fibres to be high in the laminate interior, while near the free edge high tensile stresses normal to the fibres were present.

O'Brien and Hooper (1991) and O'Brien (1991) observed matrix crack induced delaminations in symmetric angle-ply $[0_2/\theta_2/-\theta_2]_s$ carbon/epoxy laminates under quasi-static and fatigue tensile loading ($\theta = 15°$; $20°$; $25°$; $30°$). Two closed form expressions for strain energy release rate were derived on the basis of simple load shearing rules: one for a local delamination growing from an angle ply matrix crack with a uniform delamination front across the laminate width (Fig. 17.1(c)), and one for a partial local delamination growing from an angle ply matrix crack and bounded by the free edge (Fig. 17.1(d)). As for the transverse crack tip delamination (O'Brien, 1985), the strain energy release rate for uniform local delamination was independent of delamination size and matrix crack density, while for partial local delamination it depended on delamination length. However, when the matrix crack length and the corresponding delamination length along the free edge is small, the difference between the uniform and partial delamination solutions was found to be insignificant.

Salpekar and O'Brien (1993) used a 3D FE analysis to study matrix crack induced delaminations in $(0/\theta/-\theta)_s$ graphite/epoxy laminates ($\theta = 15°$; $45°$) loaded in tension. For $(0/45-45)$ laminate, the strain energy release rate for local delamination growing uniformly in the $(45/-45)$ interface from the matrix crack in the $(-45°)$-ply was found to be higher near the laminate edge than in the interior of the laminate.

Later, Salpekar et al. (1996) computed strain energy release rates associated with local delamination originating from matrix cracks and bounded by the free edge in $(0/\theta/-\theta)_s$ and $(\theta/-\theta/0)_s$ graphite/epoxy laminates using a 3D FE method. The total strain energy release rate was calculated using three different techniques: the virtual crack closure technique, the equivalent domain integral technique, and a global energy balance technique. For both lay-ups analysed, the fraction of the total strain energy release rate associated with mode I was greatest near the matrix crack and decreased near the free edge. It also decreased with increasing delamination length and was influenced by matrix crack length. However, no comparison with O'Brien's (1991) closed-form expressions for uniform and partial local delaminations was made.

Kashtalyan and Soutis (2002) examined local delaminations growing uniformly from the tips of matrix cracks in the mid-layer of a general symmetric laminate loaded in tension. The approach by Zhang et al. (1994), earlier developed for local delaminations growing from the transverse crack tips in balanced symmetric $[\pm\theta_m/90_n]_s$ laminates, has been extended to local delaminations associated with angle ply matrix cracks (Fig. 17.1(c)) and used to predict strain energy release rate and the laminate residual stiffness as functions of matrix crack density and delamination length. For the strain energy release rate, comparison with the O'Brien's closed-form expression for uniform local delamination (O'Brien, 1991) was made.

17.3.2   Calculation of strain energy release rate using the equivalent laminate concept

The total strain energy release rate G^{ld} associated with local delaminations growing from the tips of matrix cracks is equal to the first partial derivative of the total strain energy U stored in the damaged laminate with respect to the total delamination area A^{ld} provided the applied strains $\{\bar{\varepsilon}\}$ are fixed and the matrix crack density $C = (2s)^{-1}$ remains unchanged

$$G^{ld} = -\frac{\partial U}{\partial A^{ld}}\bigg|_{\{\bar{\varepsilon}\},C} \qquad\qquad [17.20]$$

The strain energy release rate can be effectively calculated using the 'equivalent' laminate introduced in the previous section. In the global co-ordinates, the total strain energy stored in the laminate element with a finite gauge length L and width w is

$$U = \frac{wL}{2}\sum_k (z_k - z_{k-1})(\{\bar{\varepsilon}\} + \{\bar{\varepsilon}_k^{thermal}\} + \{\bar{\varepsilon}_k^{hygro}\})^T [\bar{Q}]_k (\{\bar{\varepsilon}\} + \{\bar{\varepsilon}_k^{thermal}\} + \{\bar{\varepsilon}_k^{hygro}\})$$

$$[17.21]$$

where $\{\bar{\varepsilon}_k^{thermal}\}$ and $\{\bar{\varepsilon}_k^{hygro}\}$ are respectively residual thermal and residual hygroscopic strains in the laminate due to the temperature and moisture difference between the stress-free and actual state, and $[\bar{Q}]_k$ is the in-plane reduced stiffness matrix of layer k in the global co-ordinates.

Noting that the area of a single crack tip delamination is $a^{ld} = 2\,\ell w/|\sin\phi|$, Fig. 17.2, the total delamination area is equal to

$$A^{ld} = 2a^{ld}CL = 2LwD^{ld} /|\sin\phi| \qquad\qquad [17.22]$$

If hygrothermal effects are neglected, the strain energy release rate, calculated from equations [17.20] to [17.22], is

$$G^{ld}(\bar{\varepsilon}, D^{mc}, D^{ld}) = -\frac{h_2}{2}\{\bar{\varepsilon}\}^{\mathrm{T}}\frac{\partial[\bar{Q}]_2}{\partial D^{ld}}\{\bar{\varepsilon}\}|\sin\phi| \qquad\qquad [17.23]$$

Under uniaxial strain, equation [17.23] simplifies to

$$G^{ld}(\bar{\varepsilon}_{xx}, D^{mc}, D^{ld}) = -\frac{h_2}{2}\bar{\varepsilon}_{xx}^2\frac{\partial\bar{Q}_{xx,2}}{\partial D^{ld}}|\sin\phi| \qquad\qquad [17.24]$$

Calculation of the residual in-plane axial stiffness $\bar{Q}_{xx,2}$ using equation [17.12] and the transformation formulae given by equation [17.17], yields the strain energy release rate associated with local delamination in terms of the in-situ damage effective functions (IDEFs) $\Lambda_{22}, \Lambda_{66}$ and stiffness properties of the undamaged material $\hat{Q}_{ij}^{(2)}$ as

$$G^{ld}(\bar{\varepsilon}_{xx}, D^{mc}, D^{ld}) = \frac{h_2}{2}\bar{\varepsilon}_{xx}^2\left[\left(\frac{\hat{Q}_{12}^{(2)2}}{\hat{Q}_{22}^{(2)}}\cos^4\phi + 2\hat{Q}_{12}^{(2)}\sin^2\phi\cos^2\phi\right.\right.$$

$$\left.\left.+\hat{Q}_{22}^{(2)}\sin^4\phi\right)\frac{\partial\Lambda_{22}}{\partial D^{ld}} + 4\hat{Q}_{66}^{(2)}\sin^2\phi\cos^2\phi\frac{\partial\Lambda_{66}}{\partial D^{ld}}\right]|\sin\phi| \qquad [17.25]$$

The first partial derivatives of IDEFs that appear in equation [17.25] are explicit functions of the damage parameters D^{mc}, D^{ld} and can be calculated analytically.

Figure 17.10 shows the normalized strain energy release rate $G^{ld}/\bar{\varepsilon}_{xx}^2$, calculated from equation [17.25] as a function of the delamination length normalized by the single ply thickness ℓ/t in an AS4/3506-1 $[0_2/25_2/-25_2]_s$ laminate. Crack half-spacings are $s = 40t$ and $s = 20t$. This is equivalent to the crack densities of approximately $C = 1$ cm^{-1} and $C = 2$ cm^{-1}, respectively. It can be seen that the present approach gives the strain energy release rate for uniform local delamination that depends both on crack density and delamination length. The result of equation [17.19b] for the same lay-up is found to be equal to 12.7 MJ/m^2 provided shear-extension coupling and bending-extension coupling are taken into account (O'Brien, 1991). Still, it is much higher than our predictions, since equation [17.19b] applies to delamination induced by an isolated matrix crack.

Figure 17.11 shows predictions of the normalized strain energy release rate $G^{ld}/\bar{\varepsilon}_{xx}^2$ associated with uniform local delamination in carbon/epoxy AS4/3506-1 balanced $[0_2/\theta_2/-\theta_2]_s$ laminates calculated from equation [17.25]. Results are plotted as a function of the relative delamination area D^{ld} and are given for the range of ply orientation angle θ from 15° to 75°. Matrix crack density in the inner $(-\theta)$-ply of the laminate is assumed to be equal to $C = 1$ crack/cm. It may be seen that the normalized strain energy release rate depends linearly on the relative delamination area, decreasing as the delamination area increases. This relationship is observed for all ply orientation angles up to $D^{ld} = 80\%$, after which the value of $G^{ld}/\bar{\varepsilon}_{xx}^2$ falls more steeply. For the same delamination area, the normalized strain energy release rate associated with local delamination is higher for greater values of θ.

Figure 17.12 shows predictions of the normalized strain energy release rate $G^{ld}/\bar{\varepsilon}_{xx}^2$ associated with uniform local delamination in unbalanced $[0_2/\theta_2]_s$ laminates calculated from equation [17.25]. Results are plotted as a function of the relative delamination area D^{ld} and are given for the range of ply orientation angles θ from 15° to 90°. Matrix crack density in the inner θ-ply of the laminate is assumed to be equal to 1 crack/cm. As in balanced laminates (Fig. 17.11), the strain energy release rate decreases as the delamination area increases.

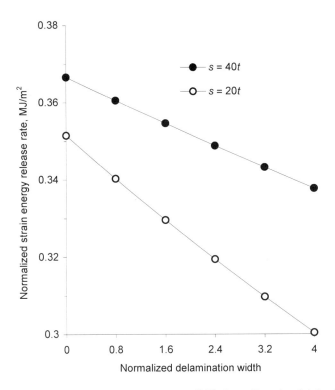

Fig. 17.10   Normalized strain energy release rate $G^{ld}/\bar{\varepsilon}_{xx}^2$ for uniform local delamination in a cracked $[0_2/25_2/-25_2]_s$ AS4/3506-1 laminate as a function of normalized delamination length λ/t.

However, in unbalanced laminates the dependence of the normalized strain energy release rate on the relative delamination area is non-linear for all ply orientation angles. Also, for the same delamination area, the normalized strain energy release rate associated with local delamination is not necessarily higher for greater values of θ. For example, for delaminations with $D^{ld} < 40\%$ the value strain energy release rate for the $[0/60]_s$ laminate is greater than for the cross-ply $[0/90]_s$ laminate, while for $D^{ld} > 40\%$ the opposite is true.

Figure 17.13 shows predictions of the normalized strain energy release rate $G^{ld}/\bar{\varepsilon}_{xx}^2$ at the onset of local delamination ($D^{ld} = 0$) as a function of the crack density in the $(-\theta)$-ply of carbon/epoxy AS4/3506-1 balanced $[0_2/\theta_2/-\theta_2]_s$ laminates. It can be seen that, for the same crack density, the normalized strain energy release rate at the delamination onset is higher for greater values of θ, which will translate into lower onset strain value. For all ply orientation angles θ, strain energy release rate at the delamination onset depends linearly on matrix crack density, slightly decreasing as the crack density increases. For instance, for the $[0_2/45_2/-45_2]_s$ laminate the difference between the values of $G^{ld}/\bar{\varepsilon}_{xx}^2$ at 0.5 cracks/cm and 5 cracks/cm is 8.5%. Reduction in the normalized strain energy release rate value will translate into a decrease in the delamination onset strain in laminates with a higher matrix crack density.

Figure 17.14 shows predictions of the normalized strain energy release rate $G^{ld}/\bar{\varepsilon}_{xx}^2$ at the onset of local delamination ($D^{ld} = 0$) as a function of the crack density in the θ-ply of AS4/3506-1 unbalanced $[0_2/\theta_2]_s$ laminates. For all ply orientation angles θ, strain energy release rate at the delamination onset depends linearly on matrix crack density, slightly decreasing

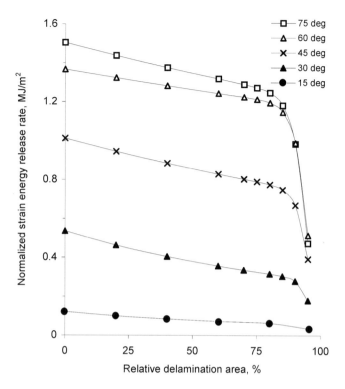

Fig. 17.11   Normalized strain energy release rate $G^{ld}/\bar{\varepsilon}_{xx}^2$ for uniform local delamination in a cracked $[0_2/\theta_2/-\theta_2]_s$ AS4/3506-1 laminate as a function of relative delamination area D^{ld}. Matrix crack density 1 crack/cm.

as the crack density increases. This will translate into an increase in the delamination onset strain in laminates with higher matrix crack density.

The issue of transition from angle-ply matrix cracking to delamination is not addressed here and is a subject of ongoing research. For transverse cracking in the 90°-ply, energy considerations governing transition to local delamination have been examined by Nairn and Hu (1992) and Selvarathinam and Weitsman (1998, 1999).

17.3.3   Mode separation (Modes I and II)

Even under the uniaxial loading damage development in the off-axis plies of general symmetric laminates always occurs under mixed mode conditions due to shear-extension coupling. It is therefore important in the calculation of the total strain energy release rate to be able to separate Mode I and Mode II contributions. For a $[(S)/\phi]_s$ laminate with damaged ϕ-layer modelled by an 'equivalent' laminate, the total strain energy release rates for crack tip uniform local delaminations is equal to the first partial derivative of the portion of the total strain energy stored in the 'equivalent' homogeneous layer with respect to damage are

$$G^{ld} = -\frac{\partial U^{(2)}}{\partial A^{ld}}\bigg|_{\{\bar{\varepsilon}\},C} \tag{17.26}$$

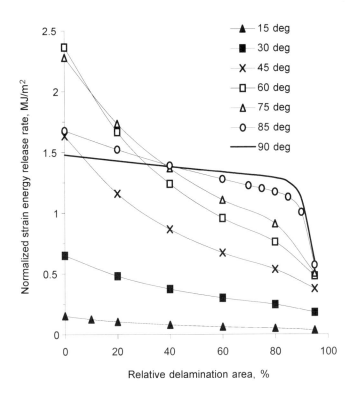

Fig. 17.12   Normalized strain energy release rate $G^{ld}/\bar{\varepsilon}_{xx}^2$ for uniform local delamination in a cracked $[0_2/\theta_2]_s$ AS4/3506-1 laminate as a function of relative delamination area D^{ld}. Crack density 1 crack/cm.

In the local co-ordinates (Fig. 17.2), this portion of the total strain energy can be separated into extensional and shear parts

$$U^{(2)} = U_I^{(2)} + U_{II}^{(2)} = Lwh_2(\bar{\sigma}_{11}^{(2)}\bar{\varepsilon}_{11}^{(2)} + \bar{\sigma}_{22}^{(2)}\bar{\varepsilon}_{22}^{(2)}) + Lwh_2\bar{\sigma}_{12}^{(2)}\bar{\gamma}_{12}^{(2)} \qquad [17.27]$$

Under uniaxial strain $\bar{\varepsilon}_{xx}$, strains and stresses in the 'equivalent' homogeneous layer are

$$\{\bar{\varepsilon}^{(2)}\} = \{\cos^2\phi, \sin^2\phi, 2\cos\phi\sin\phi\}^T\bar{\varepsilon}_{xx},$$

$$\{\bar{\sigma}^{(2)}\} = [Q^{(2)}]\{\cos^2\phi, \sin^2\phi, 2\cos\phi\sin\phi\}^T\bar{\varepsilon}_{xx} \qquad [17.28]$$

where the modified stiffness matrix $[Q^{(2)}]$ of the 'equivalent' homogeneous layer in the local co-ordinates is given by equation [17.12]. Substitution of equations [17.22], [17.27] and [17.28] into equation [17.26] gives Mode I and Mode II contributions into the total strain energy release rate as follows:

$$G_I^{ld} = -\frac{\partial U_I^{(2)}}{\partial A^{ld}} = \bar{\varepsilon}_{xx}^2 f_1(D^{ld}) \qquad [17.29a]$$

$$f_1(D^{ld}) = \frac{h_2}{2}\left(\frac{\hat{Q}_{12}^{(2)2}}{\hat{Q}_{22}^{(2)}}\cos^4\phi + 2\hat{Q}_{12}^{(2)}\sin^2\phi\cos^2\phi + \hat{Q}_{22}^{(2)}\sin^4\phi\right)\frac{\partial\Lambda_{22}^{(2)}}{\partial D^{ld}}|\sin\phi| \qquad [17.29b]$$

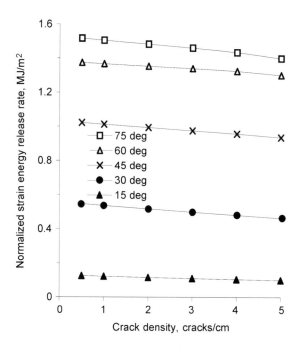

Fig. 17.13   Normalized strain energy release rate $G^{ld}/\bar{\varepsilon}_{xx}^2$ for uniform local delamination in a cracked $[0_2/\theta_2/-\theta_2]_s$ AS4/3506-1 laminate as a function of crack density. Relative delamination area $D^{ld} = 0$ (onset of delamination).

$$G_{II}^{ld} = -\frac{\partial U_{II}^{(2)}}{\partial A^{ld}} = \bar{\varepsilon}_{xx}^2 f_2(D^{ld}) \qquad [17.30a]$$

$$f_2(D^{ld}) = 2h_2 \hat{Q}_{66}^{(2)} \frac{\partial \Lambda_{66}^{(2)}}{\partial D^{ld}} \cos^2 \phi \, |\sin^3 \phi| \qquad [17.30b]$$

These expressions can be used with appropriate fracture criteria to estimate the onset of local delamination in an already cracked laminate. The resulting total strain energy release rate G^{ld} = $G_I^{ld} + G_{II}^{ld}$ coincides with equation [17.25].

Using equations [17.29] and [17.30], the contributions of Mode I and Mode II into the total strain energy release rate $G^{ld}/\bar{\varepsilon}_{xx}^2$ at the onset of local delamination ($D^{ld} = 0$) are estimated for balanced $[0_2/\theta_2/-\theta_2]_s$ laminates and plotted in Fig. 17.15 as a function of the cracked $(-\theta)$-ply orientation angle. It can been seen that $G_I^{ld}/\bar{\varepsilon}_{xx}^2$ increases monotonically with increasing θ, while $G_{II}^{ld}/\bar{\varepsilon}_{xx}^2$ reaches a maximum value at approximately $\theta = 50°$. Also, for $[0_2/30_2/-30_2]_s$ and $[0_2/45_2/-45_2]_s$ laminates $G_{II}^{ld} > G_I^{ld}$. Figure 17.15 suggests that delamination will initiate at relatively low applied strain in a 90° cracked lamina driven mainly by Mode I, while in a 15° cracked lamina it will initiate at considerably higher applied strain.

Contributions of Mode I and Mode II into the total strain energy release rate $G^{ld}/\bar{\varepsilon}_{xx}^2$ at the onset of local delamination ($D^{ld} = 0$) in unbalanced $[0_2/\theta_2]_s$ laminates are plotted in Fig. 17.16 as a function of the cracked θ-ply orientation angle. It can been seen that $G_I^{ld}/\bar{\varepsilon}_{xx}^2$ reaches a maximum value at approximately $\theta = 75°$ while $G_{II}^{ld}/\bar{\varepsilon}_{xx}^2$ reaches a maximum value at approximately $\theta = 55°$.

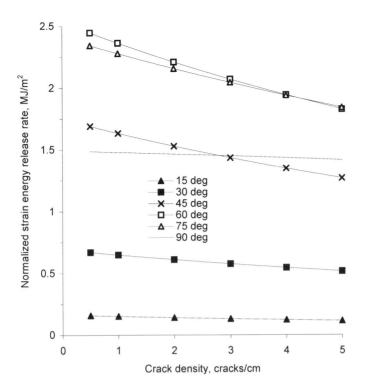

Fig. 17.14   Normalized strain energy release rate $G^{ld}/\bar{\varepsilon}_{xx}^2$ for uniform local delamination in a cracked $[0_2/\theta_2]_s$ AS4/3506-1 laminate as a function of crack density. Relative delamination area D^{ld} = 0 (onset of delamination).

To predict the onset of delamination in an already cracked $[(S)/\phi]_s$ laminate under static loading, a mixed mode fracture criterion can be used

$$\left(\frac{G_I}{G_{IC}}\right)^M + \left(\frac{G_{II}}{G_{IIC}}\right)^N = 1 \qquad [17.31]$$

where G_{IC} and G_{IIC} are, respectively, Mode I and Mode II interlaminar fracture toughnesses, and M and N are exponents dependent on the material system. For example, for a glass/epoxy system, following Rikards *et al.* (1998), the exponents M and N can be taken as $M = 1$, $N = 2$. Then, to predict cracking onset strains, G_I^{ld} and G_{II}^{ld} values are calculated from equations [17.29] and [17.30], and the delamination onset strain $\bar{\varepsilon}_{xx}$ can found as a root of the following equation:

$$\bar{\varepsilon}_{xx}^4 \left(\frac{f_2(D^{ld})}{G_{IIC}}\right)^2 + \bar{\varepsilon}_{xx}^2 \left(\frac{f_1(D^{ld})}{G_{IC}}\right) = 1 \quad \text{when} \quad D^{ld} = 0 \qquad [17.32]$$

Further work is required to validate theoretical predictions. For the lay-ups, damage modes and loading conditions examined in this study the experimental data are currently not available.

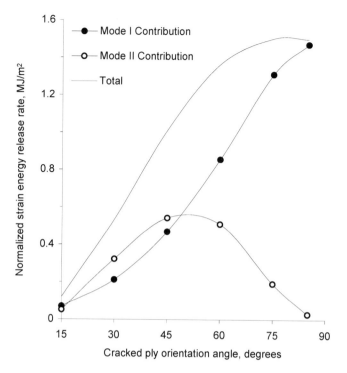

Fig. 17.15   Normalized strain energy release rates $G_I^{ld}/\bar{\varepsilon}_{xx}^2$ (Mode I contribution), $G_{II}^{ld}/\bar{\varepsilon}_{xx}^2$ (Mode II contribution) and $G^{ld}/\bar{\varepsilon}_{xx}^2$ (total) in a cracked $[0_2/\theta_2/-\theta_2]_s$ AS4/3506-1 laminate as a function of cracked $(-\theta)$-ply orientation angle. Matrix crack density 1 crack/cm, relative delamination area D^{ld} = 0 (onset of delamination).

Under fatigue loading, calculated strain energy release rates together with collected experimental data on damage growth, will be used to identify parameters in the modified Paris law that describes delamination growth. Suitability of the modified Paris law to characterize delamination growth in $[0/90_m]_s$, $m = 2,4,6$, cross-ply laminates with transverse matrix cracks has been examined by Takeda *et al.* (1995).

Using damage growth predictions, reduction in stiffness can be estimated as a function of the number of fatigue cycles. If the residual stiffness can then be related to both the residual strength and the fatigue life of the specimen, it may become a powerful tool in assessing the reliability of composite materials.

17.4   Conclusions

Failure process of a composite laminate under quasi-static or fatigue loading involves sequential accumulation of intra- and interlaminar cracking. Matrix cracking parallel to the fibres in the off-axis plies is the first damage mode observed. It triggers development of other harmful resin-dominated modes such as delaminations.

Here, analytical modelling of crack tip delaminations in composite laminates subjected to static and fatigue loading is presented and discussed. A 2D shear-lag analysis is used to determine ply stresses in a representative segment and the equivalent laminate concept is applied to derive expressions for Mode I, Mode II and the total strain energy release rate

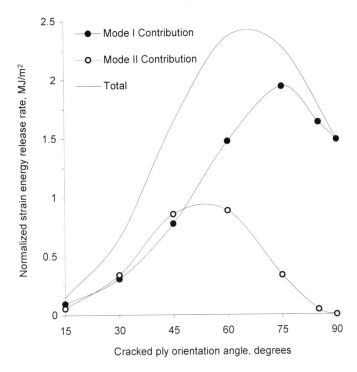

Fig. 17.16   Normalized strain energy release rates $G_I^{ld}/\bar{\varepsilon}_{xx}^2$ (Mode I contribution), $G_{II}^{ld}/\bar{\varepsilon}_{xx}^2$ (Mode II contribution) and $G^{ld}/\bar{\varepsilon}_{xx}^2$ (total) in a cracked $[0_2/\theta_2]_s$ AS4/3506-1 laminate as a function of cracked θ-ply orientation angle. Matrix crack density 1 crack/cm, relative delamination area $D^{ld} = 0$ (onset of delamination).

associated with uniform local delaminations. These expressions could be used with appropriate fracture criteria to estimate the onset of local delamination in an already cracked off-axis laminate.

When a cross-ply laminate is subjected to tension–tension fatigue or thermal cycling, matrix cracking can occur in both plies and local delaminations can initiate and grow along transverse and longitudinal matrix cracks. For this case, an approach based on the Equivalent Constraint Model of the damaged laminate has been developed, which takes into account interaction between all damaged modes (Kashtalyan and Soutis, 1999a, 2000a). Verification of this approach in the absence of delaminations was made in (Kashtalyan and Soutis, 1999b, 2000b).

Stiffness degradation due to delaminations has not been as extensively investigated as their growth. Few theoretical studies were concerned with reduction of the laminate axial stiffness due to local delaminations induced by transverse cracking in cross-ply and general symmetric laminates with central 90° ply.

For cross-ply $[0_m/90_n]_s$ and balanced symmetric $[\pm\theta_m/90_n]_s$ laminates with central 90° ply, it is established that transverse crack tip delaminations cause significant reduction of the laminate shear modulus. Both under uniaxial and biaxial loading, contribution of transverse crack tip delaminations into the total reduction of the shear modulus can exceed that of transverse cracking. Cross-ply laminates with transverse crack tip delaminations show the smallest reduction of the axial modulus and the largest reduction of the shear modulus and Poisson's ratio. Predictions for crack patterns observed experimentally during thermal fatigue reveal that longitudinal matrix cracking and delaminations in cross-ply laminates can cause reduction in the shear modulus and Poisson's ratio (up to 60%, depending on the amount of damage). These stiffness properties therefore appear to be better non-destructive test parameters than the axial modulus and could be used to monitor damage development in fatigue.

For angle-ply laminates, it is established that, for the same ply orientation angle, crack density and delamination area, damage induced changes in stiffness properties are much more significant in unbalanced $[0_2/\theta_2]_s$ laminates than in balanced $[0_2/\theta_2/-\theta_2]_s$ laminates.

Dependence of strain energy release rates and the laminate stiffness properties on delamination area, crack density and ply orientation angle θ is examined for balanced $[0_2/\theta_2/-\theta_2]_s$ and unbalanced $[0_2/\theta_2]_s$ carbon/epoxy laminates. It is found that strain energy release rate depends linearly on crack density both in balanced and unbalanced laminates. The dependence on delamination area is linear in balanced and non-linear in unbalanced laminates. Mode I contribution into the total strain energy release rate increases monotonically with increasing cracked ply orientation angle in balanced $[0_2/\theta_2/-\theta_2]_s$ laminates and reaches a maximum at $\theta = 75°$ in unbalanced $[0_2/\theta_2]_s$ laminates. However, dependence of Mode II contribution on the cracked ply orientation angle in balanced and unbalanced laminates is similar – it reaches a maximum values at θ between 50° and 55°.

Comparison with results obtained by O'Brien (1991) shows that O'Brien's closed-form expression for uniform local delamination significantly overestimates the value of the total strain energy release rate leading to lower theoretical strains for the initiation of local delamination and therefore over-conservative designs. Also, it gives the total strain energy release rate as being independent of delamination area and does not take into account the cumulative effect of damage.

In future work, the analytical predictions will be compared to numerical (finite elements) and experimental data, which for the lay-ups, damage modes and loading conditions examined in this study are currently not available.

Fatigue life prediction for composite materials has generally not been a major issue in the design of composite structures, due to low ultimate design strain levels. However, if composite materials are to be used to their full potential, design strain levels will have to rise and damage growth in fatigue will have to become a serious design consideration. Major deficiencies in existing life prediction methodologies for composite materials often force large safety factors to be adopted. To develop improved life predicting methodologies that would result in more weight- and cost-effective composite structures, the understanding of the fatigue failure process in composites needs to be broadened and links between observ-able damage/failure mechanisms and fatigue life need to be established. Residual stiffness-based fatigue life prediction theories have a significant advantage over the residual strength-based theories, since the residual stiffness is a well-defined engineering property that is easily measured and interpreted, and unlike residual strength and fatigue life does not involve the destruction of the test specimen. Stiffness changes may also be directly related to damage development through various models based on the observable micro-damage.

17.5   Acknowledgements

Financial support of this research by the Engineering and Physical Sciences Research Council (EPSRC/GR/L51348) and the UK Ministry of Defence is gratefully acknowledged.

17.6   References

ARMANIOS E A, SRIRAM P and BADIR A M (1991), 'Fracture analysis of transverse crack-tip and free-edge delamination in laminated composites', in O'Brien T K, *Composite Materials: Fatigue and Fracture*, ASTM STP 1110, Philadelphia PA, ASTM, 269–286.

ASHKANTALA N and TALREJA R (1998), 'A mechanistic model for fatigue damage evolution for composite laminates', *Mechanics of Materials*, **29**(2), 123–140.

BERTHELOT J M and LE CORRE J F (2000), 'A model for transverse cracking and delamination in cross-ply laminates', *Composites Science and Technology*, **60**(7), 1055–1066.

CASLINI M, ZANOTTI C and O'BRIEN T K (1987), 'Study of matrix cracking and delamination in glass/epoxy laminates', *Journal of Composites Technology and Research*, **9**(4), 121–130.

CHAREWICZ A and DANIEL I M (1986), 'Damage mechanisms and accumulation in graphite/epoxy laminates', in Hahn H T, *Composite Materials: Fatigue and Fracture*, ASTM STP 907, Philadelphia PA, ASTM, 274–297.

CROSSMAN F W and WANG A S D (1982), 'The dependence of transverse cracking and delamination on ply thickness in graphite epoxy laminates', in Reifsnider K L, *Damage in Composite Materials*, ASTM STP 775, Philadelphia PA, ASTM, 118–139.

DANIEL I M and CHAREWICZ A (1986), 'Fatigue damage mechanisms and residual properties of graphite/epoxy laminates', *Engineering Fracture Mechanics*, **25**(5–6), 793–808.

DHARANI L R and TANG H (1990), 'Micromechanics characterization of sublaminate damage', *International Journal of Fracture*, **46**(2), 123–140.

FAN J and ZHANG J (1993), 'In-situ damage evolution and micro/macro transition for laminated composites', *Composites Science and Technology*, **47**(2), 107–118.

FUKUNAGA H, CHOU T W, PETERS P W M and SCHULTE K (1984), 'Probabilistic failure strength analysis of graphite/epoxy cross-ply laminates', *Journal of Composite Materials*, **18**(4), 339–356.

HASHIN Z (1987), 'Analysis of orthogonally cracked laminates under tension', *Transactions ASME Journal of Applied Mechanics*, **25**(5–6), 771–778.

HENAFF-GARDIN C, LAFARIE-FRENOT M C and GAMBY D (1996a), 'Doubly periodic matrix cracking in composite laminates Part 1: General in-plane loading', *Composite Structures*, **36** (1–2), 113–130.

HENAFF-GARDIN C, LAFARIE-FRENOT M C and GAMBY D (1996b), 'Doubly periodic matrix cracking in composite laminates Part 2: Thermal biaxial loading', *Composite Structures*, **36** (1–2), 131–140.

KASHTALYAN M and SOUTIS C (1999a), 'A study of matrix crack tip delaminations and their influence on composite laminate stiffness', *Advanced Composites Letters*, **8**(4), 149–156.

KASHTALYAN M and SOUTIS C (1999b), 'Application of the Equivalent Constraint Model to investigate stiffness properties of transversally cracked and split FRP laminates', *Advanced Composite Letters*, **8**(5), 205–211.

KASHTALYAN M and SOUTIS C (2000a), 'The effect of delaminations induced by transverse cracking and splitting on stiffness properties of composite laminates', *Composites Part A: Applied Science and Manufacturing*, **31**(2), 107–119.

KASHTALYAN M and SOUTIS C (2000b), 'Stiffness degradation in cross-ply laminates damaged by transverse cracking and splitting', *Composites Part A: Applied Science and Manufacturing*, **31**(4), 335–351.

KASHTALYAN M and SOUTIS C (2000c), 'Modelling stiffness degradation due to matrix cracking in angle-ply composite laminates', *Plastics, Rubber and Composites*, **29**(9), 482–488.

KASHTALYAN M and SOUTIS C (2002), 'Analysis of local delamination in composite laminates with angle ply matrix cracks', *International Journal of Solids and Structures*, **39**(6), 1515–1537.

KOBAYASHI S, TERADA K, OGIHARA S and TAKEDA N (2001), 'Damage mechanics analysis of matrix cracking in cross-ply CFRP laminates under thermal fatigue', *Composites Science and Technology*, **61**(12), 1735–1742.

NAIRN J A and HU S (1992), 'The initiation and growth of delaminations induced by matrix microcracks in laminated composites', *International Journal of Fracture*, **57**(1), 1–24.

O'BRIEN T K (1982), 'Characterization of delamination onset and growth in a composite laminate', in Reifsnider K L, *Damage in Composite Materials*, ASTM STP 775, Philadelphia PA ASTM, 140–167.

O'BRIEN T K (1985), 'Analysis of local delamination and their influence on composite laminate behavior', in Johnson W S, *Delamination and Debonding of Materials*, ASTM STP 876, Philadephia PA, ASTM, 282–297.

O'BRIEN T K (1991), Local delamination in laminates with angle ply matrix cracks: Part II Delamination fracture analysis and fatigue characterization, NASA Technical Memorandum 104076/AVSCOM Technical Report 91–B–011.

O'BRIEN T K and HOOPER S J (1991), Local delamination in laminates with angle ply matrix cracks: Part I Tension tests and stress analysis, NASA Technical Memorandum 104055/ AVSCOM Technical Report 91–B–010.

OGIHARA S and TAKEDA N (1995), 'Interaction between transverse cracks and delamination during damage progress in CFRP cross-ply laminates', *Composites Science and Technology*, **54**(4), 395–404.

PARVIZI A, GARRETT K W and BAILEY J E (1978), 'Constrained cracking in glass fibre-reinforced epoxy cross-ply laminate', *Journal of Materials Science*, **13**(1), 195–201.

RIKARDS R, BUCHHOLZ F G, WANG H, BLEDZKI A K, KORJAKIN A and RICHARD H A (1998), 'Investigation of mixed mode interlaminar fracture toughness of laminated composites by using a CTS type specimen', *Engineering Fracture Mechanics*, **61**(3–4), 325–342.

SALPEKAR S A and O'BRIEN T K (1991), 'Combined effect of matrix cracking and free edge on delamination', in O'Brien T K, *Composite Materials: Fatigue and Fracture*, ASTM STP 1110, Philadelphia PA, ASTM, 287–311.

SALPEKAR S A and O'BRIEN T K (1993), 'Analysis of matrix cracking and local delamination in (0/ theta /– theta)$_s$ graphite epoxy laminates under tensile load', *ASTM Journal of Composites Technology and Research*, **15**(2), 95–100.

SALPEKAR S A, O'BRIEN T K and SHIVAKUMAR K N (1996), 'Analysis of local delaminations caused by angle-ply matrix cracks', *Journal of Composite Materials*, **30**(4), 418–440.

SELVARATHINAM A S and WEITSMAN Y J (1998), 'Transverse cracking and delamination in cross-ply gr/ep composites under dry, saturated and immersed fatigue', *International Journal of Fracture*, **91**(2), 103–116.

SELVARATHINAM A S and WEITSMAN Y J (1999), 'A shear-lag analysis of transverse cracking and delamination in cross-ply carbon-fibre/epoxy composites under dry, saturated and immersed fatigue conditions', *Composites Science and Technology*, **59**(14), 2115–2123.

SOUTIS C and KASHTALYAN M (2000), 'Delamination growth and residual properties of cracked orthotropic laminates under tensile loading', Journal of Thermoplastic Composite Materials, **15**(1), 13–22.

TAKEDA N and OGIHARA S (1994), 'Initiation and growth of delamination from the tip of transverse cracks in CFRP cross-ply laminates', *Composites Science and Technology*, **52**(3), 309–318.

TAKEDA N, OGIHARA S and KOBAYASHI A (1995), 'Microscopic fatigue damage progress in CFRp cross-ply laminates', *Composites Part A: Applied Science and Manufacturing*, **26**(12), 859–867.

TSAI C L and DANIEL I M (1992), 'Behavior of cracked cross-ply composite laminates under shear loading', *International Journal of Solids and Structures*, **29**(4), 3251–3267.

ZHANG J, FAN J and SOUTIS C (1992a), 'Analysis of multiple matrix cracking in [$\pm\theta_m$/90$_n$]$_s$ composite laminates Part 1: In-plane stiffness properties', *Composites*, **23**(5), 291–298.

ZHANG J, FAN J and SOUTIS C (1992b), 'Analysis of multiple matrix cracking in [$\pm\theta_m$/90$_n$]$_s$ composite laminates Part 2: Development of transverse ply cracks', *Composites*, **23**(5), 299–304.

ZHANG J and HERRMANN K P (1999), 'Stiffness degradation induced by multilayer matrix cracking in composite laminate', *Composites Part A: Applied Science and Manufacturing*, **30**(5), 683–706.

ZHANG J, SOUTIS C and FAN J (1994a), 'Effects of matrix cracking and hygrothermal stresses on the strain energy release rate for edge delamination in composite laminates', *Composites*, **25**(1), 27–35.

ZHANG J, SOUTIS C and FAN J (1994b), 'Strain energy release rate associated with local delamination in cracked composite laminates', *Composites*, **25**(9), 851–862.

ZHANG J, FAN J and HERRMANN K P (1999), 'Delaminations induced by constrained transverse cracking in symmetric composite laminates', *International Journal of Solids and Structures*, **36**(6), 813–846.

17.7   Appendices

17.7.1   Appendix I

Variation of the out-of-plane shear stresses has the form:

$$\sigma_{j3}^{(2)} = \frac{\tau_j}{h_2} x_3, \quad 0 \le |x_3| \le h_2, \quad j = 1,2 \quad \sigma_{j3}^{(1)} = \frac{\tau_j}{h_1}(h - x_3), \quad h_2 \le |x_3| \le h \qquad [17.33]$$

Constitutive equations for the out-of-plane shear stresses

$$
\left\{ \begin{array}{c} \sigma_{13}^{(k)} \\ \sigma_{23}^{(k)} \end{array} \right\} \approx \begin{bmatrix} Q_{55}^{(k)} & Q_{45}^{(k)} \\ Q_{45}^{(k)} & Q_{44}^{(k)} \end{bmatrix} \frac{\partial}{\partial x_3} \left\{ \begin{array}{c} u_1^{(k)} \\ u_2^{(k)} \end{array} \right\}, \quad i = 1,2
$$
[17.34]

After substituting equation [17.34] into equation [17.33], multiplying them by x_3 and by $h - x_3$ respectively and integrating with respect to x_3 we get:

$$
\frac{h_1}{3} \left\{ \begin{array}{c} \tau_1 \\ \tau_2 \end{array} \right\} = \begin{bmatrix} \hat{Q}_{55}^{(1)} & \hat{Q}_{45}^{(1)} \\ \hat{Q}_{45}^{(1)} & \hat{Q}_{44}^{(1)} \end{bmatrix} \left(\left\{ \begin{array}{c} \tilde{u}_1^{(1)} \\ \tilde{u}_2^{(1)} \end{array} \right\} - \left\{ \begin{array}{c} V_1 \\ V_2 \end{array} \right\} \right), \qquad \frac{h_2}{3} \left\{ \begin{array}{c} \tau_1 \\ \tau_2 \end{array} \right\} = \begin{bmatrix} \hat{Q}_{55}^{(2)} & 0 \\ 0 & \hat{Q}_{44}^{(2)} \end{bmatrix} \left(\left\{ \begin{array}{c} V_1 \\ V_2 \end{array} \right\} - \left\{ \begin{array}{c} \tilde{u}_1^{(2)} \\ \tilde{u}_2^{(2)} \end{array} \right\} \right)
$$
[17.35]

Here $\{V\} = \{u^{(1)}\}\big|_{x_3=h_2} = \{u^{(2)}\}\big|_{x_3=h_2}$ are the in-plane displacements at the interface. After rearranging equation [17.35] become:

$$
\left\{ \begin{array}{c} \tilde{u}_1^{(1)} \\ \tilde{u}_2^{(1)} \end{array} \right\} - \left\{ \begin{array}{c} \tilde{u}_1^{(2)} \\ \tilde{u}_2^{(2)} \end{array} \right\} = \left(\frac{h_1}{3} \begin{bmatrix} \hat{Q}_{55}^{(1)} & \hat{Q}_{45}^{(1)} \\ \hat{Q}_{45}^{(1)} & \hat{Q}_{44}^{(1)} \end{bmatrix}^{-1} + \frac{h_2}{3} \begin{bmatrix} \hat{Q}_{55}^{(2)} & 0 \\ 0 & \hat{Q}_{44}^{(2)} \end{bmatrix}^{-1} \right) \left\{ \begin{array}{c} \tau_1 \\ \tau_2 \end{array} \right\}
$$
[17.36]

Inversion of equation [17.36] leads to

$$
\left\{ \begin{array}{c} \tau_1 \\ \tau_2 \end{array} \right\} = \begin{bmatrix} K_{11} & K_{12} \\ K_{21} & K_{22} \end{bmatrix} \left(\left\{ \begin{array}{c} \tilde{u}_1^{(1)} \\ \tilde{u}_2^{(1)} \end{array} \right\} - \left\{ \begin{array}{c} \tilde{u}_1^{(2)} \\ \tilde{u}_2^{(2)} \end{array} \right\} \right)
$$
[17.37]

with

$$
[K] = \left(\frac{h_1}{3} \begin{bmatrix} \hat{Q}_{55}^{(1)} & \hat{Q}_{45}^{(1)} \\ \hat{Q}_{45}^{(1)} & \hat{Q}_{44}^{(1)} \end{bmatrix}^{-1} + \frac{h_2}{3} \begin{bmatrix} \hat{Q}_{55}^{(2)} & 0 \\ 0 & \hat{Q}_{44}^{(2)} \end{bmatrix}^{-1} \right)^{-1}
$$
[17.38]

17.7.2   Appendix II
On referring to the constitutive equations, equation [17.6], the generalized plane strain condition, equation [17.5], becomes

$$
\hat{S}_{11}^{(1)}\tilde{\sigma}_{11}^{(1)} + \hat{S}_{12}^{(1)}\tilde{\sigma}_{22}^{(1)} + \hat{S}_{16}^{(1)}\tilde{\sigma}_{12}^{(1)} = \hat{S}_{11}^{(2)}\tilde{\sigma}_{11}^{(2)} + \hat{S}_{12}^{(2)}\tilde{\sigma}_{22}^{(2)}
$$
[17.39]

Using the laminate equilibrium equations, equation [17.4]), stresses in the constraining layer (layer 1) can be excluded, so that the microstress component $\tilde{\sigma}_{11}^{(2)}$ is given by:

$$\tilde{\sigma}_{11}^{(2)} = a_{22}\tilde{\sigma}_{22}^{(2)} + a_{12}\tilde{\sigma}_{12}^{(2)} + b_x\bar{\sigma}_x + b_y\bar{\sigma}_y$$

$$a_{22} = -\frac{\hat{S}_{12}^{(1)} + \chi\hat{S}_{12}^{(2)}}{\hat{S}_{11}^{(1)} + \chi\hat{S}_{11}^{(2)}}, \qquad a_{12} = -\frac{\hat{S}_{16}^{(1)}}{\hat{S}_{11}^{(1)} + \chi\hat{S}_{11}^{(2)}}$$

$$b_x = \frac{(1+\chi)(\hat{S}_{11}^{(1)}\cos^2\phi + \hat{S}_{12}^{(1)}\sin^2\phi - \hat{S}_{16}^{(1)}\sin\phi\cos\phi)}{\hat{S}_{11}^{(1)} + \chi\hat{S}_{11}^{(2)}}$$

[17.40]

$$b_y = \frac{(1+\chi)(\hat{S}_{11}^{(1)}\sin^2\phi + \hat{S}_{12}^{(1)}\cos^2\phi + \hat{S}_{16}^{(1)}\sin\phi\cos\phi)}{\hat{S}_{11}^{(1)} + \chi\hat{S}_{11}^{(2)}}$$

Strain differences are expressed in terms of stresses as:

$$\begin{Bmatrix} \tilde{\gamma}_{12}^{(1)} - \tilde{\gamma}_{12}^{(2)} \\ \tilde{\varepsilon}_{22}^{(1)} - \tilde{\varepsilon}_{22}^{(2)} \end{Bmatrix} = -\frac{1}{\chi}\begin{bmatrix} L_{11} & L_{12} \\ L_{21} & L_{22} \end{bmatrix}\begin{Bmatrix} \tilde{\sigma}_{12}^{(2)} \\ \tilde{\sigma}_{22}^{(2)} \end{Bmatrix} + \frac{1}{\chi}\begin{bmatrix} M_{11} & M_{12} \\ M_{21} & M_{22} \end{bmatrix}\begin{Bmatrix} \bar{\sigma}_x \\ \bar{\sigma}_y \end{Bmatrix}$$

[17.41]

Here

$$L_{11} = \hat{S}_{66}^{(1)} + a_{12}\hat{S}_{16}^{(1)} + \chi\hat{S}_{66}^{(2)}, \qquad\qquad L_{12} = \hat{S}_{26}^{(1)} + a_{22}\hat{S}_{16}^{(1)}$$

$$L_{21} = \hat{S}_{26}^{(1)} + a_{12}\hat{S}_{12}^{(1)} + \chi a_{12}\hat{S}_{12}^{(2)} \qquad L_{22} = \hat{S}_{22}^{(1)} + a_{22}\hat{S}_{12}^{(1)} + \chi(\hat{S}_{22}^{(2)} + a_{22}\hat{S}_{12}^{(2)})$$

[17.42a]

$$M_{11} = (1+\chi)\left[(\hat{S}_{16}^{(1)} + a_{12}\hat{S}_{11}^{(2)})\cos^2\phi + (\hat{S}_{26}^{(1)} + a_{12}\hat{S}_{12}^{(1)})\sin^2\phi - (\hat{S}_{66}^{(1)} + a_{12}\hat{S}_{16}^{(1)})\sin\phi\cos\phi\right]$$

$$M_{21} = (1+\chi)\left[(\hat{S}_{12}^{(1)} + a_{22}\hat{S}_{11}^{(1)})\cos^2\phi + (\hat{S}_{22}^{(1)} + a_{22}\hat{S}_{12}^{(1)})\sin^2\phi - (\hat{S}_{26}^{(1)} + a_{22}\hat{S}_{16}^{(1)})\sin\phi\cos\phi\right]$$

$$M_{12} = (1+\chi)\left[(\hat{S}_{16}^{(1)} + a_{12}\hat{S}_{11}^{(2)})\sin^2\phi + (\hat{S}_{26}^{(1)} + a_{12}\hat{S}_{12}^{(1)})\cos^2\phi + (\hat{S}_{66}^{(1)} + a_{12}\hat{S}_{16}^{(1)})\sin\phi\cos\phi\right]$$

$$M_{22} = (1+\chi)\left[(\hat{S}_{12}^{(1)} + a_{22}\hat{S}_{11}^{(1)})\sin^2\phi + (\hat{S}_{22}^{(1)} + a_{22}\hat{S}_{12}^{(1)})\cos^2\phi + (\hat{S}_{26}^{(1)} + a_{22}\hat{S}_{16}^{(1)})\sin\phi\cos\phi\right]$$

[17.42b]

Substitution into the equilibrium equations, equation [17.3], yields the following coupled second order differential equations:

$$\frac{d^2}{dx_2}\begin{Bmatrix} \tilde{\sigma}_{12}^{(2)} \\ \tilde{\sigma}_{22}^{(2)} \end{Bmatrix} - \frac{1}{h_1}\begin{bmatrix} K_{11} & K_{12} \\ K_{21} & K_{22} \end{bmatrix}\left(\begin{bmatrix} L_{11} & L_{12} \\ L_{21} & L_{22} \end{bmatrix}\begin{Bmatrix} \tilde{\sigma}_{12}^{(2)} \\ \tilde{\sigma}_{22}^{(2)} \end{Bmatrix} + \begin{bmatrix} M_{11} & M_{12} \\ M_{21} & M_{22} \end{bmatrix}\begin{Bmatrix} \bar{\sigma}_x \\ \bar{\sigma}_y \end{Bmatrix}\right) = 0$$

[17.43]

or

$$\frac{d^2}{dx_2}\begin{Bmatrix}\tilde{\sigma}_{12}^{(2)}\\ \tilde{\sigma}_{22}^{(2)}\end{Bmatrix} - \begin{bmatrix}N_{11} & N_{12}\\ N_{21} & N_{22}\end{bmatrix}\begin{Bmatrix}\tilde{\sigma}_{12}^{(2)}\\ \tilde{\sigma}_{22}^{(2)}\end{Bmatrix} + \begin{bmatrix}P_{11} & P_{12}\\ P_{21} & P_{22}\end{bmatrix}\begin{Bmatrix}\bar{\sigma}_x\\ \bar{\sigma}_y\end{Bmatrix} = 0 \qquad [17.44]$$

where $[N] = h_1^{-1}[K][L]$ and $[P] = h_1^{-1}[K][M]$, with matrices $[K]$, $[L]$ and $[M]$ defined by equations [17.38], [17.42a] and [17.42b], respectively.

17.7.3   Appendix III

$$A_1 = \frac{\lambda_1^2 - N_{22}}{N_{21}}A_2, \quad B_1 = \frac{\lambda_2^2 - N_{22}}{N_{21}}B_2, \quad C_1 = -\frac{C_2 N_{22} + P_{21} + \alpha P_{22}}{N_{21}} \qquad [17.45]$$

$$A_2 = -\frac{(P_{21} + \alpha P_{22})(N_{21}N_{12} - N_{11}N_{22}) + R\lambda_2^2}{(\lambda_2^2 - \lambda_1^2)(N_{21}N_{12} - N_{11}N_{22})} \qquad [17.46]$$

$$B_2 = \frac{(P_{21} + \alpha P_{22})(N_{21}N_{12} - N_{11}N_{22}) + R\lambda_1^2}{(\lambda_2^2 - \lambda_1^2)(N_{21}N_{12} - N_{11}N_{22})} \qquad [17.47]$$

$$C_2 = \frac{R}{N_{21}N_{12} - N_{11}N_{22}}, \quad R = N_{11}(P_{21} + \alpha P_{22}) - N_{21}(P_{11} + \alpha P_{12}) \qquad [17.48]$$

18

Fatigue strength of composites under variable plane stress

T. P. Philippidis and A. P. Vassilopoulos, University of Patras, Greece

18.1   Introduction

Typical modern composite structures such as aeronautical vehicles and wind turbine rotor blades are subjected to severe dynamic loads of both stochastic and deterministic nature. The stress state in their primary structural elements, in the form of thin and moderately thick shells made of laminated fibre-reinforced plastics, can be assumed plane, i.e. composed of two normal components and an in-plane shear component of the stress tensor. A formidable task for designers is life prediction of such components subjected to irregular stress histories caused by multiaxial loads of variable amplitude. There are many critical decisions related to this issue which must be taken concerning both the experimental characterization of relevant mechanical material properties and the establishment of reliable life prediction methods.

In dealing with laminated FRP materials, mechanical properties such as the elasticity, strength and hygro-thermal property tensors can be measured for the entire laminate, as a homogeneous anisotropic medium, an approach called 'direct characterization'. Alternatively, mechanical properties can be measured for each individual layer and theoretical methods can then be used to predict the laminate behaviour. There are pros and cons for both approaches. In the former, results are valid only for the specific lay-up and cannot be used in an optimization design algorithm. In addition, for asymmetric or unbalanced stacking sequences, there are property couplings that cannot be measured appropriately. The latter approach, 'ply to laminate characterization', although successfully implemented for elastic and hygro-thermal properties, is still a more or less unresolved issue concerning strength prediction of laminated composites due to modelling difficulties of damage progression and interaction effects. The situation is even more complicated in the case of fatigue strength and life prediction.

Systematic research efforts on fatigue property characterization of GRP composites, has led to the development of substantial databases in the last decade and the establishment of reliable life-prediction methodologies.[1–10] However, these experimental investigations were mainly focused on axial property characterization of various laminates, i.e. direct characterization in only one direction of an anisotropic medium. Therefore, all this effort and accumulated experimental results, including constant-amplitude (CA) and variable-amplitude (VA) loading are of limited help when life prediction under multidimensional stress histories is required.

Although in the literature one can find a certain number of publications from experimental investigations on multiaxial fatigue of FRP composites,[11–18] most of these studies treat only partially the subject of life prediction under irregular plane states of stress. They concentrate mostly on the introduction and validation of fatigue strength criteria suitable for CA multiaxial proportional loading without addressing the issue of life prediction under variable load spectrum conditions. An exception in the above is presented in a series of publications by Lessard and co-workers,[19–23] where a complete life-prediction methodology, even for a 3D state of stress, is established. Their approach is based on a 'ply to laminate characterization' scheme, dealing with damage accumulation issues under VA loading by adopting appropriate residual-strength engineering models. Another paradigm, consisting of a complete life-prediction methodology under variable plane stress histories and an experimental database for a glass-fibre-reinforced polyester (GRP) $[0/\pm45]_s$ laminate, was presented in a series of publications by the present authors.[24–29] Fatigue strength allowable values in the various material symmetry axes are derived based on the 'direct characterization' approach for a number of different CA loading cases. Experimental verification of the entire methodology is performed by means of VA complex stress tests.[29,30]

The theoretical formulation of life prediction schemes, although dependent on the material experimental characterization, i.e. whether a direct or a ply-to-laminate procedure was implemented, consists mainly of the following tasks; (i) S–N curve formulation, (ii) constant-life diagram definition, e.g. of Goodman-type, (iii) cycle counting methodology, (iv) multiaxial fatigue strength criterion and (v) damage accumulation rule. It is to be expected that different choices in each of the above steps have their merits relative to an eventual successful life prediction. Although this has been investigated in a number of projects[7,31–33] for axial stress states, i.e. tension/compression in only one material direction, there is a gap in the literature concerning multi-dimensional stress states.

A complete life-prediction methodology for FRP laminates under histories of irregular plane stress is detailed herein and alternative implementations for each one of the aforementioned tasks are discussed. Verification of the predictions is provided by comparison with experimental data from GRP laminates. A comprehensive implementation example is also presented for the case of a composite rotor blade root area structure. Although discussion is limited to 2D states of stress, extending the methodology to cover 3D cases could be done in a straightforward manner.

18.2   Life prediction under combined stress: theoretical considerations

18.2.1   Problem statement

Structural components made of composite laminates are by definition lightweight and operate mostly under stochastic, dynamic conditions, e.g. in wind turbine rotor blades and aeronautical applications. The stress state arising in the moderately thick shell structure of such a component is at best of 2D character; in cases where there are cut-outs in the form of circular holes for joining purposes and where thickness variations and increased thickness parts are encountered, a 3D stress analysis should be foreseen. Without loss of generality, we

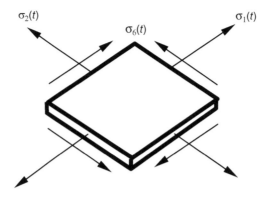

Fig. 18.1   Plane stress state.

shall consider a laminated composite shell under a state of plane stress, i.e. two normal and one shear stress resultants. The laminated FRP composite is further considered as a homogeneous orthotropic medium, i.e. a direct material characterization is sought instead of a ply-to-laminate approach. Therefore, the state of stress at a control element is as shown in Fig. 18.1, where the principal material system is assumed co-axial with the physical coordinate system.

The stress history functions, $\sigma_1(t)$, $\sigma_2(t)$, $\sigma_6(t)$, can be in general of any form, but for many practical applications they can be considered as being proportional, i.e. of the same shape but different magnitude. The life-prediction methodology presented in what follows is valid only for proportional stress histories. Although there are techniques to cope with non-proportional multiaxial fatigue in metallic materials, no such theoretical or experimental studies are available for anisotropic composite materials.

Reliable life prediction for a FRP laminated component operating under the aforementioned conditions, i.e. plane state of proportional stress histories, is discussed in the following sections.

18.2.2   Fatigue strength criterion

Fatigue strength criteria, accounting for multidimensional states of stress in composite materials, date back by not more than about 30 years. Most of the proposed limiting functions[11-18] were based on modifications of static failure criteria to take into account number of cycles, frequency and other factors relevant to cyclic loading. Hashin and Rotem,[11] for example, proposed a fatigue strength criterion for fibre-reinforced materials, which is assumed to take into account the different failure modes exhibited. They considered two failure modes for unidirectional materials; fibre and matrix failure modes. In the case of multidirectional laminates,[34] another failure mode, the interlaminar, is encountered. For the implementation of this criterion three S–N curves need to be defined experimentally and it can be applied only for materials for which failure modes can be clearly discriminated, i.e. it is not easily applicable for woven or stitched fabrics.

The present authors have introduced a modification of the failure tensor polynomial, to account for cyclic loading, henceforth denoted by FTPF, which was shown satisfactorily to predict fatigue strength for the entire range of composite materials investigated under off-axis or multiaxial loading.[25] The failure tensor polynomial,[35] when expressed with respect to the material symmetry axes of an orthotropic medium under plane stress, is given by:

$$F_{11}\sigma_1^2 + F_{22}\sigma_2^2 + 2F_{12}\sigma_1\sigma_2 + F_1\sigma_1 + F_2\sigma_2 + F_{66}\sigma_6^2 - 1 \le 0 \qquad [18.1]$$

where,

$$F_{11} = \frac{1}{XX'}, F_{22} = \frac{1}{YY'}, F_{66} = \frac{1}{S^2} \qquad\qquad [18.2]$$

$$F_1 = \frac{1}{X} - \frac{1}{X'}, F_2 = \frac{1}{Y} - \frac{1}{Y'}$$

X, X' stand for tension and compression strengths along direction 1 of the material principal system, Y, Y' are the corresponding values for the transverse direction, while S is the shear strength. The specific choice of the off-diagonal term, F_{12}, was shown to lead to completely different failure theories.[36] The form of F_{12} used in this study is:[37]

$$F_{12} = -\frac{1}{2}\sqrt{F_{11}F_{22}} \qquad\qquad [18.3]$$

FTPF assumes the same functional form as equation [18.1], however, the components of failure tensors are functions of the number of cycles N the stress ratio R and the frequency f of the loading:

$$F_{ij} = F_{ij}(N,R,f), \ \ F_i = F_i(N,R,f) \qquad\qquad [18.4]$$

Available experimental data for any type of continuous-fibre-reinforced polymer strongly suggest the form of functional dependence of failure tensor components shown in relation [18.4]. This implies an increased complexity of experimental strength characterization compared to static loading, since it is no longer sufficient to discriminate solely between tension or compression, and loading rate, but also between the same type of loading, e.g. tension, at different R values or loading frequency f. In FTPT, in-plane fatigue strength of an orthotropic material is characterized by means of three experimentally derived S–N curves:[25]

$$X(N,R,f) = X_0 N^{-\frac{1}{k_X}}$$

$$Y(N,R,f) = Y_0 N^{-\frac{1}{k_Y}} \qquad\qquad [18.5]$$

$$S(N,R,f) = S_0 N^{-\frac{1}{k_S}}$$

Failure tensor components are defined by:

$$F_{11} = \frac{1}{X^2(N,R,f)}, F_{22} = \frac{1}{Y^2(N,R,f)}, F_{66} = \frac{1}{S^2(N,R,f)}, \qquad [18.6]$$

$$F_{12} = \frac{-1}{2X(N,R,f)Y(N,R,f)}, F_1 = F_2 = F_6 = 0.$$

Finally, fatigue strength or life under plane stress state and specific R and f cycling parameters is predicted using the equation:

$$\frac{\sigma_1^2}{X^2(N)} + \frac{\sigma_2^2}{Y^2(N)} - \frac{\sigma_1\sigma_2}{X(N)Y(N)} + \frac{\sigma_6^2}{S^2(N)} - 1 = 0. \tag{18.7}$$

It must be noted that the three S–N curves $X(N)$, $Y(N)$ and $S(N)$ in the above equations are derived for the same loading conditions R, f as of the actual stress state $\{\sigma_1, \sigma_2, \sigma_6\}$

The experimental determination of $X(N)$, $Y(N)$ is performed by means of axial fatigue tests along the respective principal material direction. Characterizing the fatigue shear strength $S(N)$ is more complicated as expensive and sophisticated testing equipment and specimens are required. A simple experimental technique was adopted in Reference 25, according to which $S(N)$ was considered equal to half the value of the fatigue strength of a flat coupon cut off-axis at 45° and loaded axially. This choice yielded satisfactory results for reversed loading, $R = -1$, but its performance was proved less effective for other loading types such as $R = 10$ and $R = 0.1$. Nevertheless, as is shown in what follows, adopting for $S(N)$ the value of the fatigue strength of a flat coupon cut off-axis at 45° and axially loaded, divided by 2.2 instead of 2, fits satisfactorily most of the experimental data.[28]

18.2.3   Damage accumulation and cycle counting strategy

Consider the case of CA cyclic stresses developed in the control element of Fig. 18.1, possibly of different R ratios but proportional, i.e. in-phase. Life prediction under these conditions is performed in a straightforward manner, by solving for N the non-linear equation [18.7]. $X(N)$, $Y(N)$, and $S(N)$ are replaced in equation [18.7] from relations [18.5] and should correspond to the same R ratios as the acting stress components σ_1, σ_2 and σ_6. Instead of relation [18.7], any other suitable fatigue strength criterion could be used. Comparison with experimental results is easily interpreted as only the assumption for the failure condition enters into examination.

The situation is getting more complicated when induced stresses act as blocks of varying CA, i.e. the kth block consists of the set $\{\sigma_1^k(N_k), \sigma_2^k(N_k), \sigma_6^k(N_k)\}$ and in general $\sigma_i^p(N_p) \neq \sigma_i^q(N_q)$, $p \neq q$. The same conditions, as in the previous case, apply for the various stress components. Although the number of cycles to failure N_{kf} is easily predicted, as previously for each block of constant amplitude, it is not evident how partial damage fractions, defined as the ratio of applied number of cycles to the allowable one, N_k/N_{kf} could be summed to give a total damage coefficient.

Furthermore, when transient dynamic loads induce stochastic spectra for each stress component, another source of uncertainty enters the life prediction procedure; an appropriate method of comparing applied VA stress and experimentally known S–N data is sought. It is necessary to analyse the stress series, to count the number of full cycles, of a specific mean value and R ratio, occurring during fatigue so as to reduce the case to that of block loading.

A number of cycle counting methods have been proposed in the literature, including rainflow, range-pair-range, level crossing, peak counting, simple range counting etc., which are adequately described in ASTM E-1049.[38] Discrepancies between the various methods may yield quite different results, especially concerning a small number of high damaging cycles of large ranges, and may affect drastically the efficiency of life prediction methodology. For the results presented herein, a rainflow algorithm[39] was implemented for cycle counting.

A total damage coefficient is usually introduced to indicate remaining life. Various damage accumulation rules, both linear and non-linear, have been proposed for FRP composites in recent decades, e.g. references 40, 41. Non-linear rules are in essence fitted to experimental data from spectrum testing, to determine the parameters of their damage functions, which then are valid only for this specific stress history. On the other hand, the linear Palmgren–Miner rule, widely accepted for industrial applications despite its possible shortcomings, is simple and necessitates only data from CA S–N curves.

Nevertheless, the rule was proposed and used up-to-now for axial stress states to determine damage induced from normal or shear stress components or, for metals, equivalent stress. For plane stress states occurring in composite laminates, the authors have generalized the use of the linear rule, by defining as partial damage factor of the kth counted block, $\{\sigma_1^k(N_k), \sigma_2^k(N_k), \sigma_6^k(N_k)\}$, of N_k cycles,[25] the value:

$$D_k = \frac{N_k}{N_{k_f}}.$$

[18.8]

In the above relation N_{k_f} is substituted by solving for N the fatigue strength criterion, equation [18.7], for the specific loading block characteristics. Summing-up all partial damage coefficients provides the value of totally induced damage, which should be kept below unity.

When all of the above mentioned issues affecting life-prediction efficiency are taken into account, the procedure for such a task, i.e. predicting the life of components made of composite materials under VA plane stress states, will consist of the following three steps:

- Select a suitable cycle counting method to derive number of operating cycles for each different stress state identified.
- Using an appropriate fatigue strength criterion, define allowable number of cycles for each stress state block.
- Calculate total damage by means of a suitable damage accumulation rule

Such a procedure is implemented in this paper to predict the life of a GRP composite laminate under variable-amplitude plane stresses. Issues related to the experimental characterization of the material, such as S–N curve formulation, constant life diagrams etc., are discussed in the following paragraphs.

18.3   Experimental and property evaluation

As previously stated, the aim is to predict the fatigue strength of a composite laminate under VA plane stress. To this end, material characterization should be carried out first and this can be accomplished by testing either the constituent plies of the laminate or coupons made of the entire stacking sequence, i.e. considering the multi-layer medium as a homogeneous anisotropic material.

In the context of this study, the second method, i.e. 'direct characterization', was preferred. A systematic experimental investigation was performed,[26,27] consisting of monotonic and fatigue tests of straight-edged coupons cut at various directions from a GRP laminate. The stacking sequence of the E-glass/polyester plate consists of four layers: 2 × UD, unidirectional lamina of 100% aligned warp fibres, with a weight of 700 g/m² as outer layers and 2 × stitched, ±45°, of 450 g/m², 225 g/m² in each off-axis angle. Details on material specifications, plate preparation, coupon geometry and manufacturing can be found in[26]. Considering as 0° direction that of the UD layer fibres, the lay-up can be encoded as [0/±45]$_S$. Straight-edged coupons were cut, with a diamond saw wheel at 0°, on-axis, and 15°, 30°, 45°, 60°, 75° and 90° off-axis orientations, to produce a complex plane state of stress when loaded axially.

Monotonic and fatigue tests were performed with 335 coupons in total. 31 coupons were tested statically to provide ultimate stresses, both in tension (UTS) and compression (UCS). 257 coupons were tested under CA axial cyclic load for the determination of 17 S–N curves at various off-axis directions and loading conditions, R = 0.1, 0.5, –1 and 10. 47 coupons, cut on- and off-axis, were subjected to VA loading tests, using two quite different load spectra. The first one was a modified version of the standardized for wind turbine rotor blades WISPERX[42,43], while the second was composed from simulated data, derived through aeroelastic calculations[44] for a certain fatigue loading case of a 14 m GRP rotor blade.[45] All tests were carried out in a closed-loop hydraulic MTS test rig of 250 kN capacity.

18.3.1   S–N curves

The CA cyclic tests, of sinusoidal waveform, were carried out at a load control mode.[27] In total, 17 S–N curves were defined experimentally at various off-axis loading directions, under four different stress ratios, namely, R = 10 (C–C), R = –1 (T–C), R = 0.1 and R = 0.5 (T–T). The frequency was kept constant at 10 Hz for all the tests as no appreciable temperature increase was detected during cycling at various loading conditions.

In most of the cases, tests were continued up to 10^6 cycles or until coupon failure, whichever occurred first. In particular, for the on-axis coupons, 0°, under reversed loading, R = –1, tests were continued for up to 5×10^6 cycles. For all tests including compressive cycles, an anti-buckling jig[24] as described was used. At least three coupons were tested at each one of the four or five stress levels of any S–N curve. All tests were conducted at room temperature, 18–22 °C.

As was mentioned previously, axial tests on coupons cut off-axis, at an angle θ, from principal material directions were performed to induce complex stress states in the principal coordinate system of the GRP laminate. In that case the biaxiality ratios σ_2/σ_1 and σ_6/σ_1 as a function of θ, take values that are equal to $\tan^2\theta$ and $\tan\theta$, respectively.

Typical S–N curves for on-axis, 0°, and coupons cut at 60° off-axis, tested under R = 10 are shown in Fig. 18.2. Regression curves are of the form:

$$\sigma_{max} = \sigma_o N^{\frac{1}{k}}, \tag{18.9}$$

where σ_{max} denotes the applied maximum stress while σ_o and k are material constants. For the fitting, N is considered as the dependent variable and σ_{max} as the independent one. Detailed experimental data on number of cycles to failure for each coupon tested under various stress ratios R and off-axis angle θ are presented elsewhere.[27]

18.3.2   Statistical analysis

To derive useful design allowable properties, i.e. S–N curves at a 95%–99% reliability level, statistical analysis of the experimental data is necessary. Two methods are dominant nowadays in the literature for treatment of fatigue data from composites. One proposed by Whitney[46] is based on two assumptions: a classical power law representation of the S–N curve, e.g. as in equation [18.9], and that the probability of survival at any stress level can be modelled adequately by a two-parameter Weibull distribution. The second method, proposed by Sendeckyj,[47] adopts the 'strength-life equal-rank assumption' according to

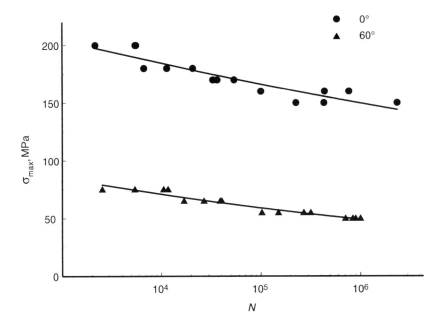

Fig. 18.2   *S–N* curves of GRP [0/±45]$_s$ laminate.

which the strongest specimen has either the longest fatigue life or the highest residual strength at run out.

The basic difference between these two methods, which also determines the occasional superiority of one over the other, is the way they handle fatigue data. For the method proposed by Whitney, a number of data points at predetermined cyclic stress levels is needed for the determination of the parameters of the Weibull distribution. On the other hand, the method proposed by Sendeckyj needs coupon tests at several different stress levels as it transforms fatigue data into equivalent static strength data and then obtains the maximum likelihood estimates for the two-parameter Weibull distribution describing the equivalent static strength response. Nevertheless, for the GRP laminate investigated herein, it was proved that reliability results for the *S–N* curves derived using both methods were almost identical.[48]

For the statistical modelling of the experimental data discussed in this work, the method established by Whitney was implemented. *S–N* curves at any desired reliability level are defined by:

$$\sigma_{max} = \sigma_0 \left\{ [-\text{Ln}P_s(N)]^{\left(\frac{1}{\alpha_f k}\right)} \right\} N^{\left(\frac{1}{k}\right)}$$

[18.10]

Model parameters σ_0, α_f and k are presented in Table 18.1 for each set of on- and off-axis tests, at various *R* ratios. Therefore, using the above equation, design allowable values at a specified reliability level $P_s(N)$ can be easily derived for the GRP laminate under investigation.

18.3.3   Constant-life diagrams

Determining the monotonic strength of an anisotropic material under plane stress conditions is a relatively easy task, as the only assumption affecting the result is the validity of the

Table 18.1 Fatigue strength model parameters

Direction	R = 10			R = −1			R = 0.1			R = 0.5		
	α_f	σ_o	$1/k$	α_f	σ_o	$1/k$	α_f	σ_o	$1/k$	α_f	σ_o	$1/k$
0°	1.750	299.33	0.0502	1.548	166.05	0.0511	2.668	635.84	0.1054	1.379	399.36	0.0500
15°							2.326	194.36	0.0755			
30°	4.797	360.44	0.1150	1.367	129.54	0.0751						
45°	1.776	274.49	0.0838	1.012	129.56	0.0670	1.669	194.31	0.0970	2.296	183.20	0.0722
60°	3.071	163.11	0.0869	1.725	140.05	0.0969						
75°							2.196	83.33	0.0817			
90°	1.734	80.02	0.0517	1.389	125.38	0.1010	3.789	62.29	0.0738			

failure condition. From the experimental point of view, only the strain rate of the test seems to affect drastically the measured strength. On the other hand, trying to determine fatigue strength or predicting the life of a multi-directional FRP laminate under irregular plane stress histories, is far more complicated and uncertain, as many more influencing factors are involved. In similar cases, difficulties are avoided by increasing the test effort for property characterization. However, theoretical assumptions and engineering models are still necessary to implement life prediction algorithms.

Cycle counting results, in the form of number of cycles for specific mean and range values, from realistic load spectra, e.g. WISPER,[42] indicate an extremely large number of R-ratios for which respective S–N curves should be defined experimentally. To reduce the test effort, the dependence of fatigue life on R-ratio is modelled by defining constant-life-diagrams, (CLD). For their determination, S–N curves at some R-ratios, preferably at $R = 10$ (C–C), $R = -1$ (T–C) and $R = 0$ or $R = 0.1$ (T–T), along with static strengths, UTS and UCS, should be determined experimentally. Then, S–N curves under different R-ratios are calculated by interpolation between known static and fatigue strengths. The most common method is to use linear interpolation between the S–N curves at two known R-ratio values but more sophisticated models have also been proposed.[49]

Under plane-stress conditions and with respect to the fatigue strength criterion discussed in a previous section, CLDs should be formulated for all three relevant strength properties, i.e. $X(N)$, $Y(N)$ and $S(N)$. Obviously, the experimental effort must be tripled, at least, since fatigue shear tests might be proved more time consuming. In fact, experimental evidence from the test results of this study, indicates that simplistic approaches such as those suggested in state-of-the-art design codes for composites, e.g. linear Goodman theory necessitating only one experimental S–N curve at $R = -1$, could lead to erroneous predictions.

For example, in Fig. 18.3 constant life curves for $N = 10^4$ and 10^8 are presented, for the $X(N)$ property of the [0/±45]$_S$ GRP laminate, i.e. axial tests with coupons cut along the fibre direction of the 0° layers. Solid lines are linear interpolations between experimental results whereas dashed lines are Goodman predictions, which for low cycle fatigue are quite conservative (a Gerber parabola would be more appropriate). On the other hand, for high cycle fatigue, the linear prediction is more accurate. By considering the respective results for the transverse material direction, property $Y(N)$, shown in Fig. 18.4, it is concluded that Goodman linear approach is highly optimistic for both low- and high-cycle fatigue. Therefore, a higher number of experimental data than usual is needed to cope with multidimensional stress states of anisotropic materials.

The CA data from the experimental program described earlier are sufficient to determine constant life diagrams for the [0/±45]$_S$ GRP laminate. This information will be used in the

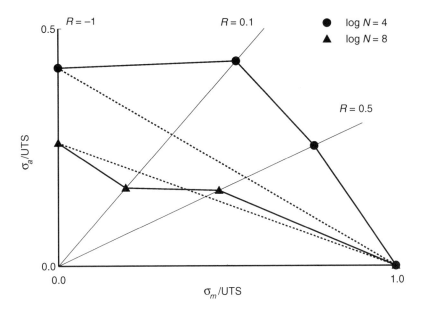

Fig. 18.3   Constant life curves vs. linear Goodman law. [0/±45]$_s$ on-axis.

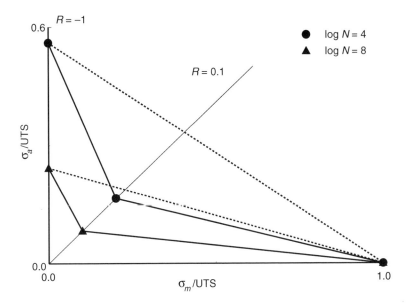

Fig. 18.4   Constant life curves vs. linear Goodman law. [0/±45]$_s$ at 90° off-axis.

sequel to implement the life prediction methodology and calculate $S-N$ curves under any R-ratio extracted from the cycle counting of the applied VA time series.

18.3.4   Variable amplitude

For the application of spectrum loading it was decided to keep the frequency constant instead of the strain rate, in order to obtain data under loading conditions similar to those used for the constant amplitude testing. Constant frequency produces higher loading rates for higher stress levels, however, this was also the case in CA testing with constant frequency, during the determination of an $S-N$ curve. Nevertheless, as is also reported in the literature, there is no significant difference in fatigue life of GRP composites if either constant frequency or loading rate is used.[3]

Two different time series were used as spectrum test loads; the first one was a modified version of WISPERX, which is a short version of WISPER (WInd SPEctrum Reference), a standardized spectrum composed of flap load measurements from nine different rotor blades made of different materials like steel, GRP and wood/epoxy, operating in horizontal axis wind turbines with diameters between 11.7 and 100 m, situated at different locations.[42,43] WISPER consists of 265 423 load reversals or 132 711 load cycles. Application of WISPERX needs about 1/10 of the time needed for WISPER. It consists of 25 663 load reversals or 12 831 load cycles, and this was achieved by omitting cycles with range smaller than 17 levels. Ideally, WISPER and WISPERX should cause the same amount of damage if applied on a test coupon.

WISPER(X) sequence is a row of integers ranging from 1 to 64 indicating load reversal points. Zero level in the original sequence is at level 25. To obtain higher or lower maximum stress (strain), each one of the integers is multiplied by a constant value. In this study, a modified WISPERX spectrum was used. To avoid compressive cycles and the need for anti-buckling devices, WISPERX was used considering 0 as zero level instead of level 25, and thus only tensile stresses were developed in each coupon. Consequently, the modified spectrum henceforth denoted as MWISPERX, is in fact a shifted version of the original, consisting though of the same number of cycles, i.e. 12 831. Time series of MWISPERX spectrum for a maximum applied stress of 100 MPa is presented in Fig. 18.5.

A test series consisting of 30 coupons, cut on-axis, 0°, and also 30° and 60° off-axis from the multidirectional laminate was performed using the MWISPERX load spectrum. The test frequency was kept constant at 10 Hz, resulting in a time interval of 50 msec from peak to trough, irrespective of the load range. The total number of specimens was distributed as follows: 15 coupons at 0° were tested at three different stress levels, 10 coupons, 30° off-axis, were also tested at three different maximum stress levels and finally, 5 coupons cut at 60°, at two different stress levels.

A second test series composed of 17 coupons was also performed: 8 cut on-axis, 0°, and tested at two different stress levels, 6 at 30° off-axis, tested at three different stress levels and 3 coupons cut at 60°, tested at just one stress level. A different spectrum, henceforth denoted EPET573, was used for this test series. It is a simulated load history, derived by means of aeroelastic calculations for a 14 m wind turbine rotor blade and it is representative of flap bending moment fluctuations on a cross-section of the blade located 2.414 m from the root. The load case definition[50] is for normal operating conditions at a wind speed of 21 m/s. Its duration is 10 min and consists of 3893 loading reversals, or 1946 load cycles. When the time series is normalized with respect to its minimum value and rounded to integer numbers, it has a maximum value of 157, a minimum of 1, while the mean value is 71.47.

The time series of EPET573 spectrum for a maximum applied stress of 100 MPa is presented

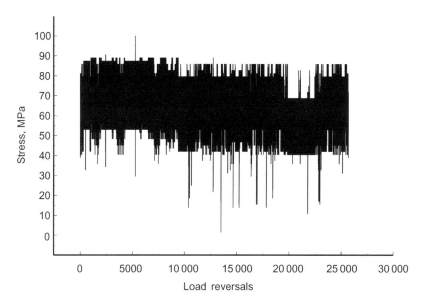

Fig. 18.5   MWISPERX stress time series, σ_{max}=100 MPa.

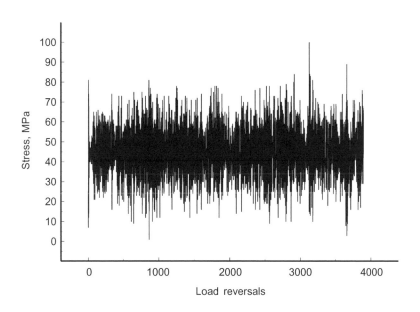

Fig. 18.6   EPET573 stress time series, σ_{max}=100 MPa.

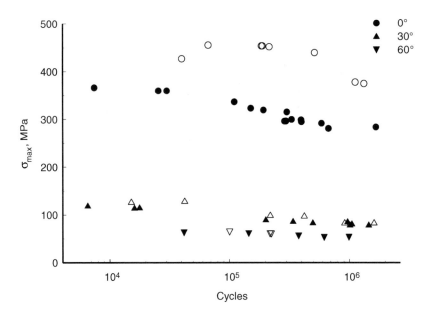

Fig. 18.7   Maximum stress of spectrum sequence vs. number of passes. Closed symbols denote experimental data from MWISPERX, open ones from EPET573.

in Fig. 18.6. Comparison of Figs. 18.5 and 18.6 leads to the conclusion that EPET573 spectrum is much more 'irregular' than MWISPERX, which can be considered as a sequence of blocks of almost constant loading patterns. The latter is known by definition to contain mostly cycles of relatively high stress ranges, which is not the case for the former. Apparently, even if these two load spectra were of the same number of cycles, MWISPERX is expected to be more damaging.

For both test series, experiments were terminated upon coupon ultimate failure. Results are presented as number of cycles at failure or equivalent number of passes of the applied irregular spectrum. Stress level was determined by the maximum value of the spectrum, which was multiplied by a different constant each time to achieve different levels of loading. Test data are summarized in Fig. 18.7, for both MWISPERX and EPET573 spectra. Details on number of cycles to failure for each coupon are given elsewhere.[29,30] The difference of the two fatigue spectra is well reflected on test results since for the same maximum stress, coupons tested under EPET573 spectrum sustain the load for a greater number of cycles.

18.4   Verification of life prediction methodology

Experimental results from VA tests previously presented and shown in Fig. 18.7, are used in this section to validate the life prediction methodology for various stress states of the laminate under investigation. Also, CA test results will be used in the form of CLD prediction curves. For the case of on-axis, 0°, VA loading, single normal stress in one of the principal material axes is developed, whereas respective off-axis coupon tests at 30° and 60° are representative of complex plane stress conditions in the material symmetry system.

Given the irregular load series applied to coupon testing, which in the case of off-axis loading produces proportional stress tensor components in the principal material frame, the procedure can start with cycle counting. A rainflow counting algorithm is implemented providing number of full cycles, at a specific range and mean value, per stress tensor component. Each bin of similar cycles corresponds to a unique stress ratio value R and since stress histories are considered proportional, the same number of cycles per R value correspond to each stress component. There are of course differences in the maximum value of the cycle.

Once the number of operating cycles is counted, the number of allowable ones under the same stress conditions must be derived by using the FTPF criterion, as described in Section 18.2. The calculation of the number of allowable cycles N_{kf} is accomplished by solving for N equation [18.7] in which σ_i, $i = 1,2,6$ are the operating (for N_k cycles of stress) components of the complex fatigue stress state and the material allowable properties $X(N)$, $Y(N)$ and $S(N)$ correspond to the same conditions as σ_i, i.e. determined under the same R ratio, loading frequency, temperature etc. Since after cycle counting, a multitude of bins at different R ratios is derived, constant life diagrams, different for each property, are used to interpolate fatigue strengths under any R ratio. CA data discussed in Section 18.3.1 are used to this end.

The last step in the procedure is the calculation of partial damage factors, defined by equation [18.8] and, based on Miner's linear accumulation rule, they predict total damage coefficient D. It is assumed that failure occurs when $D = 1$.

This process was used to calculate fatigue life for the coupons of the VA test series described in Section 18.3.4. For both spectra, MWISPERX and EPET573, damage coefficients were calculated and theoretical predictions were plotted together with experimental data for comparison. As mentioned in Section 18.3, plane stress states were produced in the principal material system as a consequence of off-axis loading of the coupons. In that case, stress components of the complex stress state can be expressed as functions of the load orientation angle and the axial stress σ_x by means of well-known transformation relations:

$$\sigma_1 = \sigma_x \cos^2 \theta$$
$$\sigma_2 = \sigma_x \sin^2 \theta \qquad\qquad\qquad [18.11]$$
$$\sigma_6 = \sigma_x \sin \theta \cos \theta$$

It is evident, that fatigue stress components σ_1, σ_2 and σ_6, are of the same functional form as that of σ_x differing only in magnitude.

Predicted damage coefficients or number of spectrum passes are compared to experimental data in Figs. 18.8 and 18.9 for both MWISPERX and EPET573 spectra applications. In Fig. 18.8 data from on- and off-axis tests under MWISPERX spectrum are presented. It is clearly shown that the procedure followed can satisfactorily predict the fatigue behaviour of the material under plane stress conditions as in all cases, for on- and off-axis tests, theoretical number of passes seem to be well corroborated by the experimental data. For the implementation of the software by means of which theoretical predictions were derived, CA fatigue data and tabulated static material properties[27,28] were used. In the definition of CLD curves, ultimate strength values derived from static tests at strain rates similar to those realized in the VA series were used wherever available.

For the case of the alternative spectrum, EPET573, theoretical predictions do not compare so favourably with experimental data for all cases considered, see Fig. 18.9. At a first glance, predictions for 30° off-axis tests seem to be in fair agreement with the experimental data, although as a general trend, theoretical damage coefficients are conservative estimates of actual values. Several reasons could cause the discrepancies observed. Let us exclude first some of them; the fatigue strength criterion, FTPF, accounting for the plane stress state effect, implemented in the present computer code, is certainly not the cause since, as can

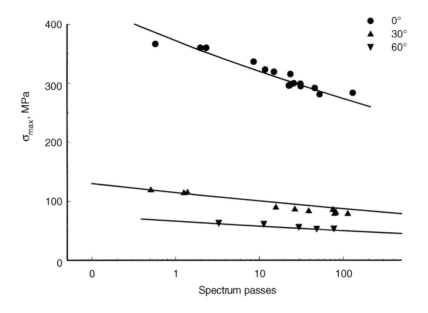

Fig. 18.8   Maximum stress of MWISPERX vs. spectrum passes. Comparison of theoretical predictions (solid line) and test results.

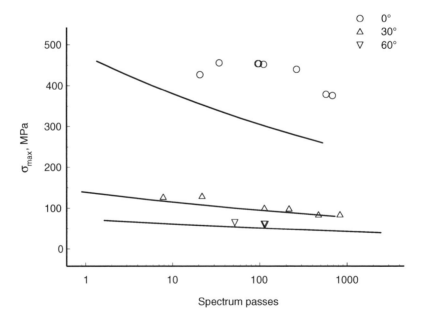

Fig. 18.9   Maximum stress of EPET573 vs. spectrum passes. Comparison of theoretical predictions (solid line) and test results.

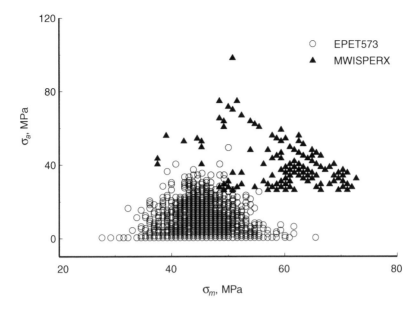

Fig. 18.10   Counted cycles coordinates in the $(\sigma_a - \sigma_m)$ plane. $\sigma_{max} = 100$ MPa for both spectra.

be observed from Fig. 18.9, the larger deviations between theory and experiment occur for the on-axis test series. However, for this case the strength criterion is not applicable at all, since for the single normal stress component, allowable number of cycles is directly derived from the CLD definitions.

The *S–N* formulations, on the other hand, were used with remarkable success for the MWISPERX result evaluation and no doubt logically exist as for their validity. Most probably, the cause of disagreement should be attributed to the form itself of EPET573 spectrum. In contrast to MWISPERX, which could be characterized as a sequence of blocks of constant high-range cycles, resulting from accelerated testing requirements, EPET573 is an entirely irregular spectrum with successive alternations between high and low-range cycles. For the same value of maximum stress in both spectra, MWISPERX is composed mostly of high-range cycles while EPET573, as shown in Fig. 18.10, where the position of counted cycles from both spectra is indicated in the $\sigma_a–\sigma_m$ plane, contains many low-range cycles.

From the above it is concluded that either the CLD resolution, as currently implemented by interpolating between three *R*-ratios, i.e. 10, –1 and 0.1, and/or the linear damage accumulation rule assumption are not proved efficient in producing accurate predictions for this case. Although in the average, for both spectra investigated, theoretical predictions should be considered satisfactory, doubt is cast on the effectiveness of validating prediction formulations against experimental data derived by using standard, compressed spectra instead of realistic stress simulations derived for specific design load cases.

Regardless of the accuracy of the predictions, a strong effect of the plane stress state was observed in comparisons with data from both test series. For the off-axis loading cases, even a few degrees of misalignment yielded substantially different theoretical predictions. This proves the drastic role of transverse-to-the-fibre normal and shear stress components on failure of the laminate investigated, since even slight deviations of the off-axis loading direction from the actual one, towards increasing the values of σ_2 and σ_6 in the principal material system, reduce drastically the expected number of passes of both load spectra.

18.5   Structural application example: Inboard part of a rotor blade

Motivated by the pronounced effect on life prediction results exhibited by the plane stress state, as observed when comparing with experimental data from off-axis tests, an example case study was undertaken to highlight implications for a realistic structural application. A composite wind turbine rotor blade was considered since it is treated by state-of-the-art design codes,[50,51] as typical beam-like structure in which fatigue life calculations are limited in considering only the action of the normal stress component in the beam axis direction. The life-prediction methodology as presented earlier is used in this section to show the effect of transverse normal and shear fatigue stress components in defining operational life of a typical wind turbine rotor blade.

A 30 m GRP wind turbine rotor blade, for which detailed finite-element models, material properties and design load case definitions were available, was analysed for this case study. When loads of variable amplitude act on the rotor blade, a different plane stress state $\{\sigma_1(t), \sigma_2(t), \sigma_6(t)\}$ is established at every nodal point, or discrete element. For this application, stress at a point is, in fact, the value of the respective in-plane stress resultant divided by the actual thickness of the laminate at that point. We will assume that since all three stress components are produced from the same excitation, they all have the same time dependence, which is also the same with the time function of the external load, i.e. σ_1, σ_2 and σ_6 time series are proportional to each other. Thus, if the external load is expressed by e.g. WISPERX time series, then $\sigma_1(t)$, $\sigma_2(t)$, and $\sigma_6(t)$, would be the same as WISPERX, multiplied each time by different factors, defined from the stress analysis and dependent on element location in the blade skins.

Position of elements where typical plane stress states are developed in the load currying skins of the rotor blade under realistic load distributions is shown in Fig. 18.11. In-plane stress tensor components from these elements were used as maximum values, i.e. multiplying factors, of the original WISPERX integer number sequence. Multiaxiality ratios, corresponding to different typical stress states in the blade are given for each element in Table 18.2. For comparison purposes, the absolute value of the axial normal stress component, σ_1, is kept the same in all discrete elements although of different sign as seen in Table 18.2, where by T and C, tensile or compressive stresses were denoted respectively. Two different values of σ_1 were used in the calculations, 360 and 180 MPa, representative of two different fatigue stress level conditions, low and high cycle fatigue. The specific values have no structural importance, but are compatible with the material database discussed herein; it is assumed that the stacking sequence of the blade skin is similar to the lay-up $[0/\pm45]_{nS}$ of the laminate considered in this study. Low-cycle fatigue cases of Table 18.2 correspond to a nominal number of cycles equal to 2.35×10^4 while for high-cycle conditions the respective number is 2.86×10^8 cycles.

Application of the aforementioned procedure for the calculation of fatigue strength or life prediction for each of the discrete elements examined, yields impressive results on the contribution of transverse normal and shear stress components in reducing fatigue life. Two different calculation suites were performed for each case. A 'state-of-the-art' where σ_2 and σ_6 are neglected and the stress state is composed only of the axial stress component σ_1, and a refined one, along the lines of the procedure presented herein, where all the components of the plane stress tensor are taken into account. Results are presented as dimensionless ratios of predicted spectrum passes for the first type of calculation over that of the latter, i.e. they are indicative of how many times life is overestimated when neglecting the effect of the transverse normal and shear stress.

As can be seen in Table 18.2, life prediction for element 1, lying on top of the main glass

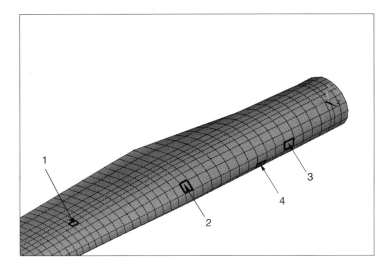

Fig. 18.11   Location of elements representative of typical stress states in a wind turbine rotor blade.

fibre girder, is unaffected by the presence of other than the axial plane stress components, since σ_2 and σ_6 are negligible. In all other elements considered, lying mostly in the leading edge of the blade, allowable number of cycles is drastically reduced when all stress components of the stress tensor are considered and the synergistic effect of transverse normal and shear stress is taken into account in the calculations. Life overestimation is more pronounced for low-cycle fatigue stress level whereas it is highly dependent on the stress state composition; element 4, the only one considered in this example with a tensile axial stress, presenting the greater value of this overestimating life factor.

A more systematic way of presenting the effect of different stress states on life prediction overestimation is shown in Fig. 18.12, where again this dimensionless ratio of calculated fatigue life considering $\sigma_2 = \sigma_6 = 0$ over that taking account of the complex stress state is plotted against the biaxiality ratio σ_2/σ_1 for low and high-cycle stress levels and two different values of the ratio σ_6/σ_1. Obviously, in all examined cases fatigue life is significantly affected by the presence of transverse normal and shear stresses. Interesting to note that for all calculations, results of which are shown in this figure, these two stress components have magnitudes less than 5% of the longitudinal normal stress and life is still overestimated by a factor up to 16. Again, low-cycle fatigue stress levels promote this overestimation trend.

18.6   Concluding remarks

The theoretical background along with a thorough experimental verification of a life prediction methodology for multidirectional composite laminates under irregular load sequences has been presented in this chapter. Although the procedure could be applied to 3D stress states, actual implementation, of both the theoretical formulation and the material database, is limited to plane stress conditions. Furthermore, loading spectra are assumed to produce a plane stress state in which components of the stress tensor are proportional time series. This requirement is imposed by the cycle counting method implemented in the computational procedure.

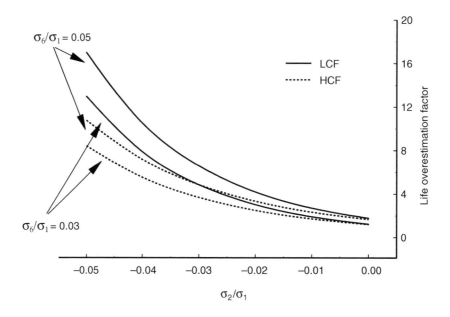

Fig. 18.12   Life overestimation factor for different complex stress states.

Material property evaluation follows a direct characterization approach; the laminated plate is tested in its symmetry directions and respective fatigue strength parameters are derived. The proposed procedure is therefore suitable for life prediction purposes of a structural component designed against ultimate (monotonic) or stability critical loads. If fatigue design optimization is required, a 'ply-to-laminate' prediction methodology and associated ply characterization techniques should be adopted instead.

To demonstrate the procedure, experimental results from an extensive experimental programme consisting of static and fatigue tests on coupons cut on- and off-axis from a multidirectional GRP laminate were used. VA fatigue tests as well as CA cycling, at various R-ratios, were performed at a constant frequency of 10 Hz. Plane stress states were simulated by loading the coupons off-axis. Proportional stress series components, though of different maximum, minimum and mean values, were developed in this way.

S–N curves at various R-ratios were statistically processed and CLD formulations were appropriately defined to implement the prediction algorithm. For the verification cases presented herein, where comparison of theoretical predictions and experimental results is discussed, allowable material properties at a reliability level of 50% were used.

Table 18.2   Life overestimation factors

Element	σ_2/σ_1	σ_6/σ_1	σ_1	High-cycle	Low-cycle
1	−7.0E-05	−5.0E-03	C	1.008	1.009
2	−0.070	0.030	C	19.945	35.570
3	0.008	0.198	C	203.071	358.309
4	−0.030	−0.186	T	266.085	526.680

The prediction methodology is implemented in three main software routines; cycle counting of load spectrum, multiaxial fatigue strength criterion and damage accumulation rule. Although specific choices for each of the above issues were made, in principle the method could be implemented in a different way; success criterion is only the good prediction of the experimental results. Nevertheless, for the cycle counting, a Rainflow counting algorithm[39] was selected whereas, fatigue strength under multidimensional stress states was assessed by using a criterion introduced by the authors, due to its efficiency in predicting satisfactorily the fatigue behaviour of many different composite material systems under various loading conditions.[25] Finally, the Palmgren–Miner linear damage rule was adopted because of its simplicity and because it is the only predictive scheme, i.e. no fitting procedures on test results are required, widely accepted. Moreover, it yields successful results for GRP laminated composites in general. Non-linear regression models could also be evaluated to improve accuracy of theoretical calculations.

Application of the method to predict number of spectrum passes, applied on test coupons loaded on- and off-axis at 30° and 60°, using two different irregular load histories, yielded satisfactory results and has proved the suitability of the procedure for the GRP laminate investigated herein. However, prediction accuracy was found to be dependent on the test load spectrum and this point deserves further examination.

Finally, a life prediction case study was performed, demonstrating the use of the method in structural applications. Analysis results from a finite element model of a 30 m GRP rotor blade has provided plane stress state examples, from various locations in the blade skin, for which fatigue life evaluation was assessed for low- and high-cycle conditions. Stress tensor component histories were assumed proportional to the WISPERX spectrum. Results indicated that even small values of transverse normal, σ_2, and shear, σ_6, stresses, with respect to the axial (along the blade axis) normal stress component, σ_1, have a strong effect and contribute to drastic life reduction. It was calculated that for values of σ_2 and σ_6 not higher than 5% of σ_1 life is reduced by up to 16 times with respect to the situation where only the axial normal stress component was acting.

18.7   References

1. DE SMET B J and BACH P W (1994), Database FACT: *Fatigue of Composites for Wind Turbines*, ECN-C-94-045.
2. MANDELL J F and SAMBORSKY D D (1997), DOE/MSU *Composite Material Fatigue Database: Test Methods, Material and Analysis*, SAND97-3002.
3. ANDERSEN S I, BACH P W, BONEE W J A, KENSCHE C W, LILHOLT H, LYSTRUP A and SYS W, *Fatigue of Materials and Components for Wind Turbine Rotor Blades*, Directorate-General XII, Science, Research and Development, EU-16684 EN.
4. MAYER R M (1996), *Design of Composite Structures Against Fatigue: Applications to Wind Turbine Blades*, Mechanical Engineering Publications Ltd.
5. VAN DELFT D R V, RINK H D, JOOSSE P A and BACH P W (1994), 'Fatigue Behaviour of Fibreglass Wind Turbine Blade Material at the Very High Cycle Range' *Proceedings of the European Wind Energy Conference*, Thessaloniki, Greece, **1**, 379–384.
6. ECHTERMEYER A T (1994), 'Fatigue of glass reinforced composites described by one standard fatigue lifetime curve' *Proceedings of the European Wind Energy Conference*, Thessaloniki, Greece, **1**, 391–396.
7. JOOSSE P A, VAN DELFT D R V and BACH P W (1994), 'Fatigue design curves compared to test data of fibreglass blade material' *Proceedings of the European Wind Energy Conference*, Thessaloniki, Greece, **3**, 720–726.
8. KENSCHE C W (1994), 'Lifetime of Glass/Epoxy Rotor Blade Material under Impact and Moisture' *Proceedings of the 3rd Symposium on Wind Turbine Fatigue*, Petten, Holland: IEA, April 21–22, 137–143.

9. VAN DELFT D R V, DE WINKEL G D and JOOSSE P A (1996), 'Fatigue behaviour of fiberglas wind turbine blade material under variable loading', *Proceedings of the 4th Symposium on Wind Turbine Fatigue*, Stuttgart, Germany: IEA, February 1–2, 75–80.

10. KENSCHE C W (1996), 'Which slope for glass/epoxy fatigue curve?', *Proceedings of the 4th Symposium on Wind Turbine Fatigue*, Stuttgart, Germany: IEA, February 1–2, 81–85.

11. HASHIN Z and ROTEM A (1973), 'A fatigue criterion for fiber reinforced materials', *J Compos Mater*, **7**, 448–464.

12. OWEN M J and GRIFFITHS J R (1978), 'Evaluation of biaxial stress failure surfaces for a glass fabric reinforced polyester resin under static and fatigue loading', *J Mater Sci*, **13**, 1521–1537.

13. FOUND M S (1985), 'A review of the multiaxial fatigue testing of fiber reinforced plastics', in Miller K J and Brown M W, *Multiaxial Fatigue, ASTM STP 853*, American Society for Testing and Materials, Philadelphia, 381–395.

14. FAWAZ Z and ELLYIN F (1994), 'Fatigue failure model for fibre-reinforced materials under general loading conditions', *J Compos Mater*, **28**(15), 1432–1451.

15. TORU FUJII and FAN LIN (1995), 'Fatigue behaviour of a plain-woven glass fabric laminate under tension/torsion biaxial loading', *J Compos Mater*, **29**(5), 573–590.

16. JEN M-H R and LEE C-H (1998), 'Strength and life in thermoplastic composite laminates under static and fatigue loads. Part I: Experimental', *Int J Fatigue*, **20**(9), 605–615.

17. SMITH E W and PASCOE K J (1989), 'Biaxial fatigue of a glass-fiber reinforced composite. Part 1: Fatigue and fracture behaviour', in Brown M W and Miller K J, *Biaxial and Multiaxial Fatigue*, EGF3, Mechanical Engineering Publications, London, 367–396

18. SMITH E W and PASCOE K J (1989), 'Biaxial fatigue of a glass-fiber reinforced composite. Part 2: Failure criteria for fatigue and fracture' in Brown M W and Miller K J, *Biaxial and Multiaxial Fatigue*, EGF3, Mechanical Engineering Publications, London, 397–421.

19. LESSARD L B and SHOKRIEH M M (1995), 'Two-dimensional modeling of composite pinned-joint failure', *J Compos Mater*, **29**(5), 671–697.

20. SHOKRIEH M M, LESSARD L B and POON C (1997), 'Three-dimensional progressive failure analysis of pin/bolt loaded composite laminates', in *Bolted/bonded joints in polymeric composites*, AGARD CP 590, 7.1–7.10.

21. SHOKRIEH M M and LESSARD L B (1997), 'Multiaxial fatigue behaviour of unidirectional plies based on uniaxial fatigue experiments–I. Modelling', *Int J Fatigue*, **19**(3), 201–207.

22. SHOKRIEH M M and LESSARD L B (1997), 'Multiaxial fatigue behaviour of unidirectional plies based on uniaxial fatigue experiments–II. Experimental evaluation', *Int J Fatigue*, **19**(3), 209–217.

23. DIAO X, LESSARD L B and SHOKRIEH M M (1999), 'Statistical model for multiaxial fatigue behavior of unidirectional plies', *Compos Sci and Tech*, **59**, 2025–2035.

24. PHILIPPIDIS T P and VASSILOPOULOS A P (1999), 'Fatigue of composite laminates under off-axis loading', *Int J Fatigue*, **21**, 253–262.

25. PHILIPPIDIS T P and VASSILOPOULOS A P (1999), 'Fatigue strength prediction under multiaxial stress', *J Compos Mater*, **33**(17), 1578–1599.

26. PHILIPPIDIS T P and VASSILOPOULOS A P (2000), 'Fatigue design allowables of GRP laminates based on stiffness degradation measurements', *Compos Sci and Tech*, **60**(15), 2819–2828.

27. PHILIPPIDIS T P and VASSILOPOULOS A P (2002), 'Complex stress state effect on fatigue life of GRP laminates. Part I, experimental', *Int J Fatigue*, **24**, 813–823.

28. PHILIPPIDIS T P and VASSILOPOULOS A P (2002), 'Complex stress state effect on fatigue life of GRP laminates. Part II, theoretical formulation', *Int J Fatigue*, **24**, 825–830.

29. VASSILOPOULOS A P and PHILIPPIDIS T P (2001), Life prediction of GRP laminates under variable amplitude complex stress states', *Proceedings of the 2nd Hellenic Conference on Composite Materials*, Patras, Greece, pp.127–144.

30. PHILIPPIDIS T P and VASSILOPOULOS A P (2002), 'Life prediction methodology for GFRP laminates under spectrum loading', (Submitted for Publication).

31. RONOLD K O and ECHTERMEYER A T (1996), 'Estimation of fatigue curves for design of composite laminates', *Compos Part A*, **27A**, 485–491.

32. SUTHERLAND H J and VEERS P S, 'The development of confidence limits for fatigue strength data', *Wind Energy 2000*, ASME/AIAA.

33. BOND I P (1999), 'Fatigue life prediction for GRP subjected to variable amplitude loading', *Compos Part A*, **30A**, 961–970.

34. ROTEM A (1979), 'Fatigue Failure of Multidirectional Laminate', *AIAA Journal*, **17**(3), 271–277.

35. TSAI S W and WU E M (1971), 'A general theory of strength for anisotropic materials', *J Compos Mater*, **5**, 58–80.

36. THEOCARIS P S and PHILIPPIDIS T P (1991), 'On the validity of the tensor polynomial failure theory with stress interaction terms omitted', *Compos Sci and Tech*, **40**, 181–191.
37. TSAI S W and HAHN H T (1980), *Introduction to Composite Materials*, Technomic 1980.
38. ASTM E 1049-85 (1997), Standard practices for cycle counting in fatigue analysis.
39. DOWNING S D and SOCIE D F (1982), 'Simplified rainflow counting algorithms', *Int J Fatigue*, **4**, 31–40.
40. OWEN M J and HOWE R J (1972), 'The accumulation of damage in a glass-reinforced plastic under tensile and fatigue loading, *J Phys D: Appl. Phys* **5**, 1637–1649.
41. HWANG W and HAN K S (1986), 'Cumulative damage models and multi-stress fatigue prediction', *J Compos Mater*, **20**, 125–153.
42. TEN HAVE A A (1988), 'WISPER: Introducing variable-amplitude loading in wind turbine research', *10th BWEA Conference*, London, UK.
43. TEN HAVE A A (1988), 'WISPER: a standardized fatigue load sequence for HAWT-blades' in proceedings, *EWEC'88*, Henring, Denmark, 448–452.
44. RIZIOTIS V A and VOUTSINAS S G (2000), 'Fatigue loads on wind turbines of different control strategies operating in complex terrain', *J Wind Engng and Industrial Aerodynamics*, **85** 211–240.
45. PHILIPPIDIS T P, LEKOU D J and VASSILOPOULOS A P (1997), 'National project EPET II #573, 1st semester 1997, Technical Report (in Greek), University of Patras.
46. WHITNEY J M (1981), 'Fatigue characterization of composite materials. in Lauraitis K N, *Fatigue of Fibrous Composite Materials, ASTM STP 723*, American Society for Testing and Materials, pp. 133–151.
47. SENDECKYJ G P (1991), 'Life prediction for resin-matrix composite materials', in Reifsnider K L *Fatigue of Composite Materials, Composite Materials Series, 4*, Elsevier.
48. PHILIPPIDIS T P and VASSILOPOULOS A P (1998), 'National project EPET II #573, 'Statistical evaluation of fatigue data', 1st semester 1998 Technical Report (in Greek), University of Patras.
49. GATHERCOLE N, REITER H, ADAM T and HARRIS B (1994), 'Life prediction for fatigue of T800/5245 carbon-fibre composites: I. Constant amplitude loading', *Fatigue* **16**, 523–532.
50. DRAFT IEC 61400-1, Ed.2 (88/98/FDIS): 'Wind turbine generator systems–Part 1: Safety requirements', 1998.
51. GERMANISCHER LLOYD (1993), 'Rules and regulations, IV-Non-marine technology', Part 1-Wind Energy.

19

Life prediction under service loading spectra

L. J. Lee and K. E. Fu, National Cheng Kung University, Taiwan

19.1   Introduction

While composite materials are employed increasingly in the aircraft industry, it requires a methodology to characterize the fatigue damage in service before they can be used confidently. Extensive research efforts were conducted to investigate the degradation of the residual stiffness, because the measurement of stiffness for composite laminates can be used to inspect the fatigue damage in service and provide the reference for the establishment of maintenance schedules. Many residual stiffness degradation models were proposed to relate the stiffness loss to a specific damage mechanism, e.g. delamination of composite laminates.[1-6] However, the stiffness reduction of composite laminates is the result of a combination of all the damage mechanisms such as matrix cracking, fibre breakage, matrix–fibre debonding and delamination. It is very difficult, if not impossible, to model all these damage mechanisms in an easy-to-use stiffness degradation model. For this reason, other researchers established modulus reduction models through the phenomenological point of view.[7-11] Recently, Yang *et al.*[12] proposed a stiffness degradation model, which has been used successfully to predict the residual stiffness for fibre-dominated composite laminates under constant amplitude loading. Later, Yang, Lee, Sheu[13] extended this model to include the effects of the non-linear stress–strain relationship and permanent plastic information which occur in matrix-dominated composite laminates. All the studies mentioned above dealt with the composite laminates under constant amplitude fatigue loading. However, service loadings to aircraft structures are random in nature. To predict the stiffness degradation for composite laminates in service needs further investigation.

To achieve structural integrity and reliability, a methodology for characterizing fatigue damage under service loading and relating it to the material properties, e.g. stiffness, strength, and life, is necessary. Although service loadings to aircraft structures are inherently random, they are usually represented by repetitions of block loadings for convenience. In References 14, 15, a particular service loading spectrum of an aircraft was idealized by 20 statistically equivalent loading blocks. This is achieved as follows. The loading spectrum, corresponding to 500 flight hours or 596 flights, is composed of 19 440 cycles with different stress levels and stress ratios, see Fig. 19.1(a). It consists of 98 different segments of constant amplitude cycles. This loading spectrum is simplified by dividing it into 20 small blocks as

(a)

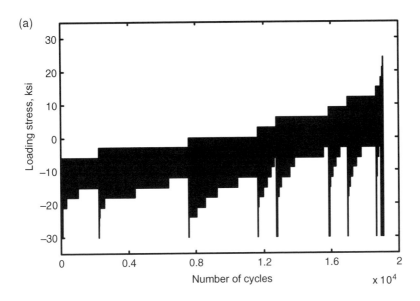

Fig. 19.1(a)   Spectrum loading obtained from the upper surface of the horizontal tail of a fighter plane.

(b)

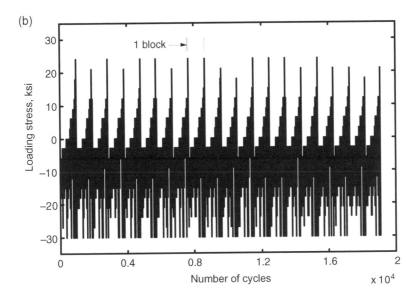

Fig. 19.1(b)   Idealized block-type spectrum loading.

shown in Fig. 19.1(b). Stress cycles in each of the 98 segments are first distributed equally to each of the 20 blocks. If the number of stress cycles in a segment is not a multiple of 20, then each of the remaining stress cycles that are less than 20 is distributed randomly to a block. In this manner, every loading block will have a similar probabilistic characteristic. Then, a stochastic stiffness degradation model for composite laminates subjected to block-type spectrum loadings is presented. The statistical distribution of the residual stiffness at any service time is derived for composite laminates subjected to different levels of block-type loading spectra. Furthermore, the statistical distribution of the fatigue life is also predicted with the aid of a new empirical failure criterion. This approach is very useful at the later stage of the fatigue design, when the service loading spectrum to a particular type of aircraft structure is well defined and the scheduled inspection and maintenance are important concerns.

At the stage of preliminary design, however, service loads may not be precisely identified and only constant amplitude fatigue data are available. Under this circumstance, it is important to establish a methodology from which the fatigue behaviour, such as the stiffness/strength reduction and fatigue life, under service loads can be predicted based on the available constant amplitude fatigue data. In the literature, Yang and Du[16] developed such a methodology for predicting the residual strength and fatigue life under block-type spectrum loadings. Their methodology was verified by experimental data. The methodology proposed by Yang and Du is based on the residual strength degradation model, suggested by Yang, et al.,[17-19] under constant amplitude cyclic loadings.

In this paper, an alternative method for predicting the statistical fatigue behaviour of composite laminates subjected to block-type loading spectra will be developed using the constant amplitude stiffness reduction data. The method is based on the stiffness degradation model under constant amplitude loadings proposed by Yang et al.[12] The difference between the present method and the one proposed by Yang and Du[16] is that the constant amplitude stiffness degradation data is used rather than the constant amplitude fatigue life data. The advantage of using the stiffness reduction as a measure of the fatigue damage versus the use of the residual strength is that the former can be measured non-destructively allowing for a fatigue damage tracking, whereas the latter cannot be measured without destroying a specimen.

After deriving the stiffness reduction under block-type spectrum loadings, the fatigue failure criterion presented in References 14, 15 will be used to derive the statistical distributions of the failure stiffness and fatigue life. The predictive capabilities of the methods developed in this study are then demonstrated by experimental results.

19.2   Stiffness degradation under block-type loading spectrum

The stiffness degradation model for fibre-dominated composite laminates under constant amplitude fatigue loading proposed by Yang et al.[12] is given by:

$$\frac{dE(n)}{dn} = -E(0)Qvn^{v-1} \tag{19.1}$$

in which n is the number of load cycles, $E(0)$ is the initial stiffness and $E(n)$ is the stiffness at the nth load cycles. Integrating equation [19.1] from n_1 to n_2, the residual stiffness at the n_2 cycle becomes

$$E(n_2) = E(n_1) - E(0)Q(n_2^v - n_1^v) \tag{19.2}$$

Experimental results indicate that Q and v have a linear relation and v can be expressed as a linear function of the stress level S, so the residual stiffness $E(n_2)$ can be written as

$$E(n_2) = E(n_1) - E(0)(d + a_2BS)(n_2^{a_3+BS} - n_1^{a_3+BS})$$ [19.3]

in which a_2, a_3 and $d = a_1 + a_2a_3$ are parameters and B is a random variable. Experimental results further indicate the parameters a_2, a_3 and d and the random variable B are dependent upon the stress ratio, $R = S_{min}/S_{max}$.

Consider a block-type loading spectrum consisting of repetitions of identical cycle blocks. In each cycle block, there are k segments. Each segment, say the ith segment, consists of n_i constant amplitude load cycles defined by a maximum stress S_i and a stress ratio R_i. If the stress ratio is greater than −1 or smaller than 1, S_i represents the maximum stress; if the stress ratio is smaller than −1 or greater than 1, S_i represents the minimum stress. Let a specimen be subjected to the first cycle block. According to the residual stiffness degradation model given in equation [19.3], the residual stiffness after each segment of the loading cycles can be expressed as

$$E(n_{11}) = E(0)(d_1 + a_{21}B_1S_1)(n_{11}^{a_{31}+B_1S_1})$$

$$E(n_{12}) = E(n_{11}) - E(0)(d_2 + a_{22}B_2S_2)(n_{12}^{a_{32}+B_2S_2} - n_{11}^{a_{32}+B_2S_2})$$

$$\vdots$$ [19.4]

$$E(n_{1k}) = E(n_{1(k-1)}) - E(0)(d_k + a_{2k}B_kS_k)(n_{1k}^{a_{3k}+B_kS_k} - n_{1(k-1)}^{a_{3k}+B_kS_k})$$

in which n_{1i} represents the total number of stress cycles at the ith segment in the first cycle block, and it is expressed as $n_{1i} = \Sigma_{q=1}^{i} n_q$. In equation [19.4], $E(n_{1k})$ is the stiffness after the first cycle block and it can be rewritten as $E(1)$.

Summation of equation [19.4] yields the residual stiffness after the first cycle block $E(1)$,

$$E(1) = E(0)\sum_{i=1}^{k}(d_i + a_{2i}B_iS_i)(n_{1i}^{a_{3i}+B_iS_i} - n_{1(i-1)}^{a_{3i}+B_iS_i})$$ [19.5]

Note that a_2, a_3, d and B depend on the stress ratio R_i for the ith segment of a loading block. Hence, they have been denoted by a_{2i}, a_{3i}, d_i and B_i. For a specimen subjected to the block-type loading spectrum described above, the residual stiffness after n loading blocks can be obtained by a block-by-block summation process similar to equations [19.4] to [19.5] as

$$E(n) = E(0)\left(1 - \sum_{j=1}^{n}\phi_j\right)$$ [19.6]

where

$$\phi_j = \sum_{i=1}^{k}(d_i + a_{2i}B_iS_i)(n_{ji}^{a_{3i}+B_iS_i} - n_{j(i-1)}^{a_{3i}+B_iS_i})$$

$$n_{ji} = (j-1)\bar{n} + \sum_{q=1}^{i}n_q$$

$$\bar{n} = \sum_{q=1}^{k}n_q$$

In equation [19.6], ϕ_j is the amount of stiffness reduction due to the jth loading block, n_{ji} indicates the total number of applied stress cycles at the ith segment in the jth block, and $\bar{n}$ is the total number of cycles in a loading block. Note that n_q is the total number of stress cycles in the qth segment of a cycle block as described previously.

Equation [19.6] is the stiffness degradation model under block-type loading spectra derived on the basis of the constant amplitude stiffness degradation model. To predict the statistical distribution of the residual stiffness $E(n)$ after the nth loading block using equation [19.6] the parameters $(a_{1i}, a_{2i}$ and $a_{3i})$, the statistical distribution of B_i for each stress ratio R_i and the statistical distribution of $E(0)$ should be determined from constant amplitude fatigue data. Experimental data indicate that the distributions of both $E(0)$ and B_i can be represented by lognormal distributions.[12] The initial stiffness $E(0)$ is statistically independent with respect to the random variables B_i ($i = 1, 2, \dots k$). However, random variables $B_1, B_2, \dots B_k$ are completely correlated indicating that the normalized random variable η is identical, i.e.

$$\eta = \frac{\ln B_1 - \mu_{\ln B_1}}{\sigma_{\ln B_1}} = \frac{\ln B_2 - \mu_{\ln B_2}}{\sigma_{\ln B_2}} = \dots = \frac{\ln B_k - \mu_{\ln B_k}}{\sigma_{\ln B_k}} \qquad [19.7]$$

in which η is the standardized normal random variable with the distribution function $\Phi[]$, i.e.

$$F_\eta(z) = \Phi(z) \qquad [19.8]$$

It follows from equation [19.7] that each random variable B_i can be expressed in terms of η, i.e.

$$B_i = \exp\{\eta \sigma_{\ln B_i} + \mu_{\ln B_i}\}. \qquad \text{for } i = 1, 2, \dots k \qquad [19.9]$$

Consequently, the stiffness degradation model given by equation [19.6] involves only two statistically independent random variables, i.e. $E(0)$ and η. The distribution function of the residual stiffness $E(n)$ after the nth loading block can be obtained from the distributions of $E(0)$ and η through the transformation of equation [19.6]; with the result,

$$F_{E(n)}(x) = \int_0^\infty F_{E(0)}\left[\frac{x}{1 - \sum_{j=1}^n \phi_j(z)}\right] f_\eta(z) dz \qquad [19.10]$$

in which

$$F_{E(0)}(x) = \Phi\left[\frac{\ln x - \mu_0}{\sigma_0}\right]$$

and

$$f_\eta(z) = \frac{1}{\sqrt{2\pi}} \exp\left\{-\frac{z^2}{2}\right\}.$$

In equation [19.10], μ_0 and σ_0 are the mean values and standard deviation of $\ln E(0)$, respectively.

19.3   Statistical distribution of fatigue life

To predict the statistical distribution of fatigue life under block-type spectrum loadings based on the stiffness degradation model, equation [19.6], a fatigue failure criterion should be established. In Reference 15, a failure criterion for composite laminates subjected to compressive-dominated spectrum loadings was proposed, i.e.

$$E(N) = E(0)\frac{S}{S + A_0 R(0)}$$

[19.11]

in which $E(N)$ is the stiffness at failure, $R(0)$ is the ultimate strength of the composite laminate and A_0 is a parameter to be determined. Equation [19.11] also holds for compressive-dominated constant amplitude loadings that constitute each segment of a loading block. Thus, equation [19.11] can be expressed for these constant amplitude loadings as

$$E(N)_i = E(0)\frac{S_i}{S_i + A_{0i} R(0)} \qquad i = 1,2, \ldots k$$

[19.12]

in which $E(N)_i$ is the failure stiffness for the constant amplitude cycles in the ith segment with a maximum stress S_i and stress ratio R_i. Of course, the constant A_{0i} depends on the constant amplitude characteristics of the ith segment.

The assumption that fatigue failure occurs when the residual strength is reduced to the fatigue stress level is quite reasonable and it has been used extensively in the literature.[17-20] For composite specimens subjected to block-type loading spectra, fatigue failure will occur when the residual strength is reduced to the maximum stress level S in the loading spectra. Consequently, the failure stiffness $E(N)$ under block-type loading spectra can be written as

$$E(N) = E(0)\frac{S}{S + A_{0m} R(0)}$$

[19.13]

in which A_{0m} is associated with the segment consisting of maximum constant amplitude cycles in a loading block. The procedures for the determination of A_{0m} from data are described in Reference 15.

Since the distributions of the initial stiffness $E(0)$ and the ultimate strength $R(0)$ can be represented by lognormal and two-parameter Weibull distribution functions, respectively, the distribution function of the failure stiffness $E(N)$ can be obtained through the transformation of equation [19.13] as follows,

$$F_{E(N)}(x) = \int_0^\infty \Phi \left[\frac{\ln\left(x\frac{S + A_{0m} r}{S} \right) - \mu_0}{\sigma_0} \right] f_{R(0)}(r)\,dr \qquad x \geq 0$$

[19.14]

where $f_{R(0)}$ is the probability function of the ultimate strength $R(0)$, i.e.

$$f_{R(0)} = \frac{\alpha}{y}\left(\frac{y}{\beta}\right)^{\alpha} \exp\left\{-\left(\frac{y}{\beta}\right)^{\alpha}\right\} \qquad y \geq 0 \tag{19.15}$$

in which α is the shape parameter and β is the scale parameter.

With the stiffness degradation model, equation [19.6], and the failure stiffness criterion, equation [19.13], the statistical distribution of the fatigue life can be derived in the following. Substituting the failure stiffness, equation [19.13], into the stiffness degradation model, equation [19.6], one can express the fatigue life in terms of the number of cycle blocks N in an implicit form as follows:

$$1 - \sum_{j=1}^{N} \phi_j(\eta) = \frac{S}{S + A_{0m}R(0)} \tag{19.16}$$

in which N is the fatigue life representing the number of cycle blocks to failure and $\phi_j(\eta)$ is defined by equations [19.6] and [19.8]. It is mentioned again that S is the maximum stress level in the block loading spectrum.

Equation [19.16] shows that the fatigue life N depends on the random variables η and $R(0)$. Using the theorem of total probability, the distribution function of the fatigue life can be obtained from that of η and $R(0)$, through the transformation of equation [19.16] as follows:

$$F_N(x) = \int_{-\infty}^{\infty} F_{R(0)}\left[\frac{1}{A_{0m}}\left(\frac{S}{1 - \sum_{j=1}^{x} \phi_j(z)} - S\right)\right] f_\eta(z)\,dz \tag{19.17}$$

in which

$$F_{R(0)}(r) = 1 - \exp\left\{-\left(\frac{r}{\beta}\right)^{\alpha}\right\}, \qquad r \geq 0$$

$$f_\eta(z) = \frac{1}{\sqrt{2\pi}} \exp\left\{-\frac{z^2}{2}\right\} \tag{19.18}$$

19.4   Experimental program

An experimental test program performed on specimens of $[0^0/90^0/\pm45^0]_{2s}$ T300/976 carbon/epoxy laminates was designed to verify the theoretical models. There were three sizes of specimens for three different kinds of tests. The nominal dimensions of the specimens for tensile tests were 229 mm (9 in) long by 38 mm (1.5 in) wide. Compressive tests are performed using IITRI fixtures, and the nominal dimensions of the specimens were 127 mm (5 in) long by 12.7 mm (0.5 in) wide. In order to prevent buckling in the compressive-dominated fatigue tests, side-support guiding fixtures were used and the specimens size was

184 mm (7.25 in) long and 38 mm (1.5 in) wide. End taps were used to prevent specimens from being damaged at the grips of the testing machine. All tests were performed using an MTS 810 universal testing machine which was closed loop series with a load capacity of 100 kN. The testing system was equipped with a 458.91 Microprofier and connected with a microcomputer through a TESTLINK interface, which permits simulations of complex loading conditions.

Before performing fatigue tests, static tests which involve two stages were first conducted. The first stage was to investigate the static behaviour under tension and compression loadings. Eight specimens were tested statically at a loading rate of 2 mm/min to failure under tension and compression, respectively. The ultimate strength for each specimen was obtained. For tensile tests, four specimens were tested and the average tensile strength was 549.3 MPa. For compressive tests, the other four specimens were tested and the average compressive strength was –538.4 MPa. Experimental results show that the ultimate strength is the same (within the experimental variation) for both tension and compression loadings. As a result, the fatigue behaviour under the block-type loading spectrum can be investigated based on the maximum stress level no matter whether the stress is compressive or tensile.

In the second stage, 12 specimens were tested to failure in tension for the purpose of determining the stress level in fatigue tests. The loading rate of the static tests was 2.5 cm/s, close to that of the fatigue. The average tensile strength of these specimens was 579.8 MPa with a standard deviation of 21.29 MPa. The average value of initial stiffness was 42.9 GPa with a standard deviation of 0.469 GPa. The block-type spectrum loading presented[15] was used herein, as shown in Fig. 19.1(b), to verify the theoretical predictions, which consisted of twenty statistically equivalent blocks. There are 98 different segments of constant amplitude cycles and 72 different stress ratios in the entire spectrum. Four different minimum compressive stress levels –376.7, –405.9, –434.9 and –463.8 MPa, corresponded to 65, 70, 75 and 80 per cent of the static ultimate strength, respectively, were chosen to represent the different severity of the loading spectrum.

To predict the fatigue behaviour under block-type loading, constant amplitude fatigue tests must be conducted to determine the model parameters appearing in equaton [19.6]. Experimental results indicate that the model parameters a_2, a_3, d and the random variable B depend on each stress ratio R_i in the loading spectrum. It is impractical to determine all the model parameters through experimental tests. Consequently, six stress ratios in the loading spectrum, –5, –1.66. –1.0, –0.5, –0.1, and 5, and four stress levels for each stress ratio, as shown in Table 19.1, were chosen to generate the fatigue stiffness degradation data. Three specimens were tested for each stress level. Therefore, a total of 72 specimens was tested. All fatigue tests were performed at a loading frequency of 10 Hz.

The stiffness was calculated by a linear regression of the load vs. displacement data. Only thirty data points in the central portion of the load–displacement data were used to perform the regression analysis in order to eliminate any possible non-linear effects introduced by the upper and lower end points of the data sets.

19.5   Experimental verification

The procedures for estimating parameters a_{1i}, a_{2i}, a_{3i} and the distributions of random variables B_i and $E(0)$ under constant amplitude fatigue loadings for six stress ratios, –5, – 1.66, –1.0, –0.5, 0.1, and 5, have been described.[12] The results are shown in Table 19.2. Indeed, the experimental data indicate that parameters a_{1i}, a_{2i}, a_{3i}, $\mu_{\ln B_i}$, and $\sigma_{\ln B_i}$ vary with respect to the stress ratio R_i. Therefore, interpolations or extrapolations are used to estimate

Table 19.1   Constant amplitude fatigue tests conducted for various stress ratios and maximum stress amplitude

Stress ratio	Maximum stress amplitude (MPa)	Maximum stress amplitude ($\%\sigma_u$)
−1	231.92	40
−1	260.91	45
−1	289.90	50
−1	318.89	55
−1.66	260.91	45
−1.66	289.90	50
−1.66	318.89	55
−1.66	347.88	60
−5	289.90	50
−5	318.89	55
−5	347.88	60
−5	376.87	65
−0.5	347.88	60
−0.5	376.87	65
−0.5	405.86	70
−0.5	434.85	75
5	318.89	55
5	347.88	60
5	376.87	65
5	405.86	70
0.1	434.85	75
0.1	449.34	77.5
0.1	463.84	80
0.1	492.83	85

Table 19.2   Summary of parameters for constant amplitude fatigue data sets

Data set	No. 1	No.2	No.3	No.4	No.5	No.6
Stress ratio	−1	−1.66	−5	−0.5	5	0.1
a_1	0.08433	0.07039	0.06278	0.10364	0.05664	0.03899
a_2	−0.49805	−0.29675	−0.19874	−0.56117	−0.24278	−0.12763
ρ	−0.8500	−0.9468	−0.9372	−0.9503	−0.9808	−0.8439
a_3	−0.01213	−0.04634	−0.28744	−0.08600	−0.08079	−0.06932
$\mu_{E(0)}$	42.844	42.566	42.418	42.659	42.772	42.777
$\sigma_{E(0)}$	0.8241	0.4726	0.6495	0.7237	1.0114	0.89284
$\mu_{\ln B}$	−7.9114	−7.5284	−6.4281	−7.5454	−7.1733	−7.3071
$\sigma_{\ln B}$	0.17726	0.29758	0.14993	0.11258	0.25321	0.39541

the model parameters a_{1i}, a_{2i}, a_{3i}, $\mu_{\ln B_i}$, and $\sigma_{\ln B_i}$ for other stress ratios R_i in the loading spectrum. The estimation procedures will be described in the following paragraph. Since the initial stiffness $E(0)$ is independent of the stress ratio, the statistical distribution of $E(0)$ can be estimated from all the experimental data sets without interpolation or extrapolation. For other stress ratios in the loading spectrum, parameters a_{1i}, a_{2i}, a_{3i}, $\mu_{\ln B_i}$, and $\sigma_{\ln B_i}$ can be determined by interpolation or extrapolation based on the aforementioned six data sets and the constant fatigue life diagram. This method has been suggested by Yang and Du[16] to

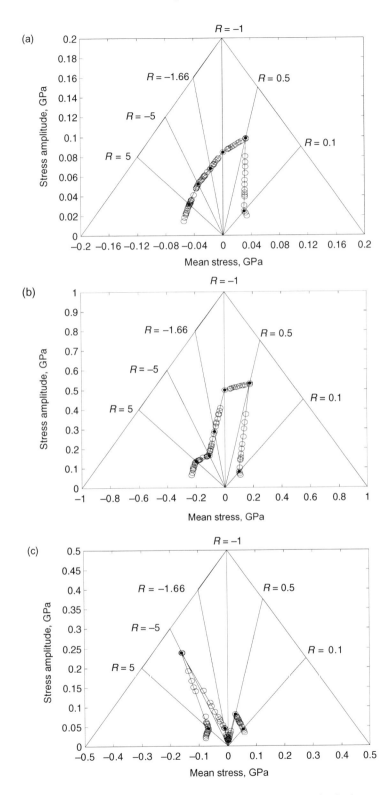

Fig. 19.2 Evaluation of various model parameters for different stress ratios in the spectrum loading: (a) a_1; (b) a_2; (c) a_3; (d) μ_{lnB}; (e) σ_{lnB}.

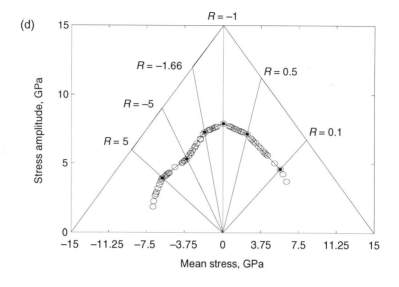

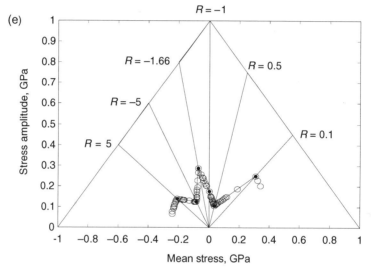

Fig. 19.2 cont.

determine the parameters in the residual strength degradation model. In this method, the magnitude of a model parameter is measured by the radial distance from the origin of coordinates in the constant fatigue life diagram along the constant stress ratio line, see Fig. 19.2(a). For example, six values of a parameter a_{1i} obtained from six available data sets, corresponding to six different stress ratios, are indicated by dots in Fig. 19.2(a). Then, a linear interpolation line between any two of the six dots is made. Values of a_{1i} for other stress ratios in the loading spectrum are obtained by the intersection of the linear interpolation line and the constant stress ratio line, as depicted with open circles in Fig. 19.2. For $1 < R < 5$ and $0.1 < R < 1$, the values of a_{1i} cannot be determined by interpolation and are assumed to be equal to the values of a_{1i} under $R = 5$ and $R = 0.1$, respectively. The same procedures are used to estimate a_{2i}, a_{3i}, $\mu_{\ln B_i}$, and $\sigma_{\ln B_i}$ as shown in Fig. 19.2(b)–(e). These results are given in Table 19.3. Parameters μ_0 and σ_0 are determined from all fatigue data and the results are $\mu_0 = 3.751$ and $\sigma_0 = 0.180$.

Table 19.3   Parameter values for various stress ratios in the spectrum loading

Stress ratio	a_1	a_2	a_3	$\mu_{\ln B}$	$\sigma_{\ln B}$
∞	0.05772	−0.22007	−0.1086	−6.74936	0.19756
10.0167	0.05721	−0.22667	−0.09709	−6.86953	0.21281
9	0.05712	−0.22829	−0.09486	−6.89953	0.21665
8	0.05701	−0.23035	−0.09227	−6.93792	0.2216
7	0.05689	−0.2331	−0.8918	−6.98963	0.22834
6	0.05676	−0.23697	−0.08543	−7.06277	0.23805
5.0083	0.05663	−0.24272	−0.08083	−7.17212	0.25305
5	0.05663	−0.24278	−0.08079	−7.17327	0.25321
4.5	0.05663	−0.24278	−0.8079	−7.17327	0.25321
4	0.05663	−0.24278	−0.08079	−7.17327	0.25321
3.5	0.05663	−0.24278	−0.08079	−7.17327	0.25321
3	0.05663	−0.24278	−0.08079	−7.17327	0.25321
2.6667	0.05663	−0.24278	−0.08079	−7.17327	0.25321
2.5042	0.05663	−0.24278	−0.08079	−7.17327	0.25321
2.5	0.05663	−0.24278	−0.08079	−7.17327	0.25321
2.3333	0.05663	−0.24278	−0.08079	−7.17327	0.25321
2	0.05663	−0.24278	−0.08079	−7.17327	0.25321
1.75	0.05663	−0.24278	−0.08079	−7.17327	0.25321
0.25	0.03899	−0.12763	−0.06932	−7.3071	0.3954
0.1667	0.03899	−0.12763	−0.06932	−7.3071	0.3954
0	0.04296	−0.14505	−0.07018	−7.1783	0.26502
−9	0.06048	−0.20431	−0.18081	−6.49195	0.16266
−8	0.0608	−0.20331	−0.19198	−6.47853	0.16042
−7	0.06123	−0.20209	−0.20852	−6.4632	0.15769
−6	0.06184	−0.2006	−0.23554	−6.44604	0.15428
−5.0083	0.06276	−0.19875	−0.28681	−6.42827	0.14996
−5	0.06277	−0.19874	−0.28744	−6.42813	0.14992
−4	0.06328	−0.20687	−0.16526	−6.51554	0.15995
−3.5	0.06373	−0.21327	−0.12748	−6.58717	0.16804
−3.3389	0.06392	−0.21588	−0.11729	−6.61682	0.1714
−3	0.06444	−0.22263	−0.09833	−6.69427	0.18024
−2.6667	0.06515	−0.23163	−0.0824	−6.79859	0.19243
−2.5042	0.0656	−0.23726	−0.07546	−6.86397	0.20029
−2.5	0.06561	−2.3742	−0.07528	−6.8658	0.20052
−2.3333	0.06618	−0.24441	−0.06867	−6.94676	0.21057
−2.0033	0.06774	−0.26352	−0.0569	−7.16507	0.23975
−2	0.06776	−0.26376	−0.05679	−7.16779	0.24014
−1.75	0.06955	−0.28605	−0.04895	−7.41414	0.27788
−1.6694	0.07029	−0.29553	−0.04661	−7.51564	0.2953
−1.6667	0.07032	−0.29589	−0.04653	−7.51938	0.29596
−1.5	0.07233	−0.31987	−0.03007	−7.56367	0.2625
−1.431	0.07336	−0.33254	−0.02576	−7.58632	0.24864
−1.4	0.07386	−0.3389	−0.02414	−7.59827	0.24267
−1.3333	0.07505	−0.35433	−0.02114	−7.62836	0.23027
−1.25	0.07679	−0.37775	−0.01813	−7.67573	0.21565
−1.2484	0.07682	−0.37824	−0.01808	−7.67673	0.21539
−1.2	0.07798	−0.39465	−0.01663	−7.71033	0.20733
−1.1667	0.07884	−0.4074	−0.01572	−7.73637	0.20197
−1	0.08432	−0.49804	−0.01213	−7.91144	0.17726
−0.9971	0.08437	−0.49818	−0.01217	−7.90782	0.17675
−0.8571	0.08744	−0.50706	−0.01514	−7.7467	0.15429
−0.8333	0.08809	−0.50905	−0.01586	−7.72245	0.15085
−0.8	0.08907	−0.51211	−0.01704	−7.69039	0.1462
−0.75	0.09071	−0.5174	−0.01929	−7.64692	0.13959
−0.7143	0.09204	−0.52173	−0.02141	−7.61968	0.13513

Table 19.3 cont'd

-0.6667	0.09402	-0.52835	-0.02508	-7.58899	0.1295
-0.6232	0.09609	-0.53533	-0.03059	-7.56728	0.12468
-0.6	0.09731	-0.53946	-0.03458	-7.55843	0.12223
-0.5714	0.09892	-0.54498	-0.04143	-7.55036	0.11932
-0.5	0.10364	-0.56117	-0.08599	-7.54543	0.11257
-0.4985	0.10323	-0.55686	-0.08592	-7.54235	0.11271
-0.4286	0.08654	-0.40406	-0.08255	-7.40581	0.12019
-0.4	0.08107	-0.36231	-0.08128	-7.35675	0.1238
-0.3739	0.0766	-0.33069	-0.08018	-7.31555	0.12742
-0.3333	0.0705	-0.29069	-0.07856	-7.25865	0.13379
-0.2857	0.06443	-0.25409	-0.07683	-7.2036	0.14262
-0.25	0.06052	-0.23199	-0.07565	-7.17106	0.15042
-0.2493	0.06044	-0.23158	-0.07563	-7.17047	0.1506
-0.2	0.05578	-0.20672	-0.07417	-7.13875	0.16352
-0.1667	0.05304	-0.19273	-0.07329	-7.12616	0.17401
-0.1429	0.05125	-0.18388	-0.07271	-7.12169	0.18257
-0.1246	0.04997	-0.17766	-0.0723	-7.12088	0.18984

On the basis of constant amplitude fatigue data, we have determined all the parameters and necessary information for the residual stiffness degradation model subjected to block-type spectrum loadings. The residual stiffness degradation model, equation [19.6], can be used to predict the statistical distribution of the residual stiffness subjected to spectrum loadings at any maximum stress level S as shown in equation [19.10].

For example, the distribution of the residual stiffness at the 200th block for $S = 376.7$ MPa is computed from equation [19.10]. The results are displayed in Fig. 19.3 as a solid curve. Also shown in the figure as solid circles for comparison are the experimental data obtained from the spectrum fatigue tests, which were presented in References 14 and 15. In a similar manner, theoretical predictions and experimental results for the distributions of residual stiffness at the 400th loading block are presented in Fig. 19.4. These figures demonstrate that the theoretical predictions correlate well with the experimental results. The predictions of the residual stiffness at different numbers of loading blocks for this stress level as well as for the other stress levels correlate equally well with the experimental results.[21] However, due to space limitation, they will not be presented here.

To predict the distributions of the failure stiffness and fatigue life using equation [19.14] and [19.17], respectively, the lognormal distribution of $E(0)$ and the Weibull distribution of $R(0)$ have been assumed. Second stage static data described in the previous section were used to estimate the respective distribution parameters with the results: $\mu_0 = 3.756$, $\sigma_0 = 0.0149$, $\alpha = 33.17$, and $\beta = 589.4$. In addition, failure stiffness data are available from baseline con-stant amplitude fatigue tests for six stress ratios, i.e. $R = -5, -1.66, -1, -0.5, 1, 5$. These data and equation [19.12] are used to determine the A_{0i} values for each stress ratio

Table 19.4 Values of parameters A_0 determined from constant amplitude fatigue data for six stress ratios

Data set	No. 1	No. 2	No. 3	No. 4	No. 5	No. 6
Stress ratio	-1	-1.66	-5	-0.5	5	0.1
A_0	0.05630	0.07055	0.05965	0.12916	0.05259	0.07008

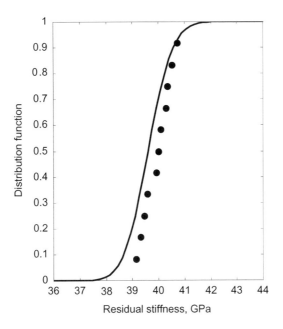

Fig. 19.3   Correlation between predicted distribution of residual stiffness E(200) and experimental results; $S = 376.7$ MPa.

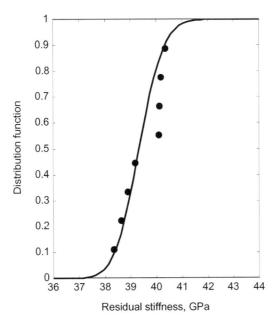

Fig. 19.4   Correlation between predicted distribution of residual stiffness E(400) and experimental results; $S = 376.7$ MPa.

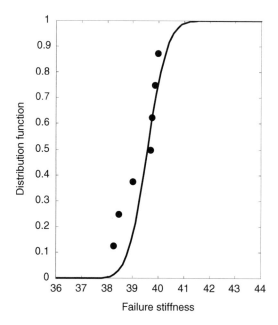

Fig. 19.5   Correlation between predicted distribution of failure stiffness and experiment results; $S = 376.7$ MPa.

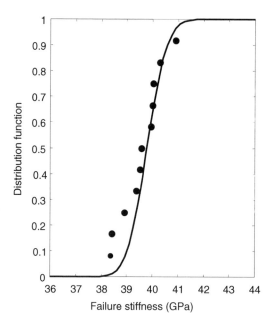

Fig. 19.6   Correlation between predicted distribution of failure stiffness and experimental results; $S = 405.9$ MPa.

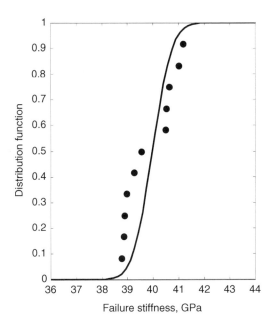

Fig. 19.7   Correlation between predicted distribution of failure stiffness and experimental results; $S = 434.9$ MPa.

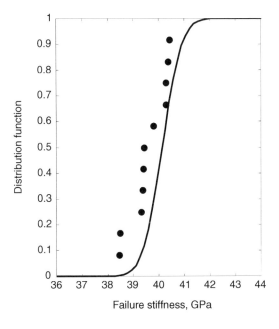

Fig. 19.8   Correlation between predicted distribution of failure stiffness and experimental results; $S = 463.8$ MPa.

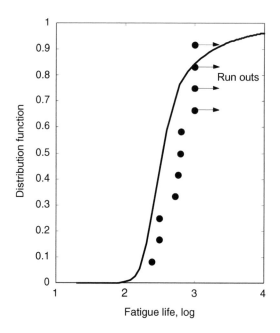

Fig. 19.9   Correlation between predicted fatigue life distribution and experimental results; $S = 376.7$ MPa.

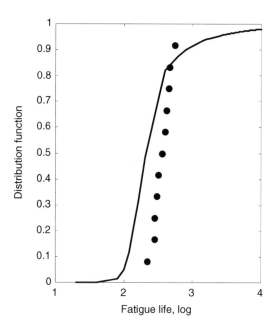

Fig. 19.10   Correlation between predicted fatigue life distribution and experimental results; $S = 405.9$ MPa.

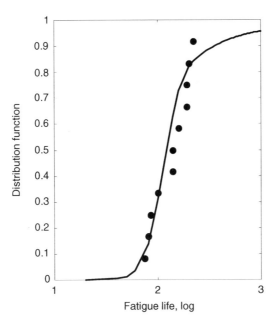

Fig. 19.11   Correlation between predicted fatigue life distribution and experimental results;
$S = 434.9$ MPa.

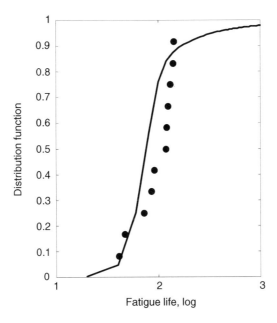

Fig. 19.12   Correlation between predicted fatigue life distribution and experimental results;
$S = 463.8$ MPa.

and the results are shown in Table 19.4. As derived in equation [19.13], the failure stiffness $E(N)$ under block-type spectrum loading corresponds to the segment that results in maximum $E(N)$. Such a segment usually is associated with the maximum stress level S and the minimum A_{0i} value. In the present case, this segment corresponds to the stress ratio $R = 5$ and hence A_{0m} $= 0.0526$ is used (see Table 19.3). Note that failure stiffness data for run out specimens, i.e. N $> 10^6$ cycles, are not available. Therefore, run out specimens are not used in the determination of A_{0i}.

With $A_{0m} = 0.0526$, equation [19.14] is used to compute the distribution of the failure stiffness of composite laminates subjected to block-type loading spectra at various maximum stress levels. The results for $S = 463.8, 434.9, 405.9$ and 376.7 MPa are presented in Figs. 19.5 to 19.8 as solid curves. The corresponding experimental data are shown in these figures as solid circles for comparison. As demonstrated in Figs. 19.5 to 19.8, the correlations between the experimental results and the theoretical predictions are quite satisfactory.

The statistical distributions of the fatigue life for composite specimens subjected to different levels of block-type spectrum loadings were derived in equation [19.17]. With the parameter values determined from the baseline constant amplitude stiffness degradation data, equation [19.17] is used to predict the distribution of the fatigue life under different levels of block-type loading spectra. The results are displayed in Figs. 19.9 to 19.12 as solid curves. The experimental data obtained from the spectrum fatigue tests are also shown in the figure as solid circles. As demonstrated in Figs. 19.9 to 19.12, the correlations between the experimental results and the theoretical predictions for the distribution of the fatigue life at different levels of block-type spectrum loadings are quite reasonable.

19.6   Conclusions

Theoretical and experimental studies have been conducted for the fatigue behaviour of composite laminates subjected to service loads that are idealized by block-by-block loading spectra. The fatigue behaviour is characterized by the degradation of the residual stiffness which can be measured nondestructively in service. The residual stiffness under expected service loading spectra is derived from the residual stiffness degradation model under constant amplitude cyclic loadings. Then, the statistical distributions of the residual stiffness and fatigue life under service loading spectra are derived based on the constant amplitude fatigue results. This approach is very useful at the preliminary design stage in which service loads are not well defined and the baseline data under service loads are not available. An experimental test program has been conducted on $[0°/90°/\pm45°]_{2s}$ carbon/epoxy laminates to generate statistically meaningful data for the verifications of the theoretical predicative abilities. The correlations between the experimental results and the theoretical predications for the statistical distributions of the residual stiffness and fatigue life have been demonstrated to be quite satisfactory.

The capability for predicting the fatigue behaviour of composite laminates under service loading spectra, based on the information of constant amplitude fatigue, is extremely important for the fatigue design of composite structures. The contribution of this approach to the state-of-the-technology in fatigue of composite laminates is very significant.

19.7 References

1. HAHN, H T and KIM R Y (1976), 'Fatigue behavior of composite laminates,' *Journal of Composite Materials*, **10**, 156–180.
2. JOHNSON W S (1982), 'Mechanisms of fatigue damage in boron/aluminum composites,' *Damage in Composite Materials*, ASTM STP 775, K.L. Reifsnider, ed. American Society for Testing and Materials, 83–102.
3. JOHNSON W S (1983), 'Modeling stiffness loss in boron/aluminum laminates below the fatigue limit,' *Damage in Composite Materials*, ASTM STP 813, T.K. O'Brien, ed., American Society for Testing and Materials, 160–176.
4. O'BRIEN T K (1982), 'Characterization of delamination onset and growth in a composite laminate,' *Damage in Composite Materials*, ASTM STP 775, K.L. Reifsnider, ed., American Society for Testing and Materials, June, 140–167.
5. DANIEL I M and CHAREWICZ A (1986), 'Fatigue damage mechanisms and residual properties of graphite/epoxy laminates,' *Engineering Fracture Mechanics*, **25**(5/6), 793–808.
6. OGIN S L, SMITH P A and BEAUMONT P W R (1985), 'Matrix cracking and stiffness reduction during the fatigue of a (0/90)s GFRP laminate,' *Composites Science and Technology*, **22**, 23–31.
7. HWANG W and HAN K S (1986), 'Fatigue of composites-fatigue modulus concept and life prediction,' *Journal of Composite Materials*, **20**, March, 125–153.
8. WHITWORTH H A (1987), 'Modeling stiffness reduction of graphite/epoxy composite laminates,' *Journal of Composite Materials*, **21**, April, 362–372.
9. O'BRIEN T K and REIFSNIDER K L (1977), 'Fatigue damage: stiffness/strength comparisons for composite materials,' *Journal of Testing and Evaluation*, **5**(5), 384–393.
10. CAMPONESCHI E T and STINCHCOMB W W (1982), 'Stiffness reduction as an indicator of damage in graphite/epoxy laminates,' *Composite Materials: Testing and Design (Sixth Conference)*, ASTM STP 787, American Society for Testing and Materials, pp. 225–246.
11. YANIV G, LEE J W and DANIEL I M (1990), 'Damage development and shear modulus degradation in graphite/epoxy laminates,' *Composite Materials: Testing and Design (Ninth Volume)*, ASTM STP 1059, American Society for Testing and Materials, pp. 404–416.
12. YANG J N, YANG S H and JONES D Y (1990), 'A stiffness degradation model for graphite/epoxy laminates,' *Journal of Composite Materials*, **24**, July, pp. 753–769.
13. YANG J N, LEE L J and SHEU D Y (1992), 'Modulus reduction and fatigue damage of matrix dominated composite laminates,' *Composite Structures*, **21**, 91–100.
14. LEE L J, FU K E and YANG J N (1993), 'Fatigue damages of composite laminates under service loading,' *Proceeding of ICCM/9, Composites Behavior*, **5**, Edited by Antonio Miravete, 12–16, July , pp. 723–730.
15. LEE L J, FU K E and YANG J N (1993), 'Prediction of fatigue damage and life for composite laminates under service loading spectrum,' *Composites Science and Technology*, **56**, 635–648.
16. YANG J N and DU SHANYI (1983), 'An exploratory study for fatigue of composites under spectrum loading,' *Journal of Composite Materials*, **17**, November, pp. 511–526.
17. YANG J N and LIU M D (1977), 'Residual strength degradation model and theory of periodic proof tests for graphite/epoxy laminates,' *Journal of Composite Materials*, **11**, April, 176–203.
18. YANG J N (1978), 'Fatigue and residual strength degradation for graphite/epoxy composites under tension–compression cyclic loading,' *Journal of Composite Materials*, **12**, January, 19–29.
19. YANG J N and JONES D L (1981), 'Load sequence effect on fatigue of composite materials,' *Fatigue on Fibrous Composite Materials*, ASTM STP 723, American Society for Testing and Materials, 213–233.
20. YANG J N, YANG S H and JONES D L (1989), 'A stiffness-based statistical model for predicting the fatigue life of graphite/epoxy laminates,' *Journal of Composites Technology and Research*, **11**(4), Winter, 129–134.
21. FU K E (1994), 'Tracking of fatigue damage and life prediction for composite laminates under service loading spectrum,' Ph.D. Dissertation, National Cheng Kung University, Tainan, Taiwan, R.O.C., June 1994.

20

A parametric constant-life model for prediction of the fatigue lives of fibre-reinforced plastics

B. Harris, University of Bath, UK

20.1   Introduction

The ideal procedure for predicting the fatigue life of fibre composites would be based on a detailed understanding of the manner in which microstructural damage accumulates in such a material and of the way in which this damage affects the residual properties of the composite. Such a procedure can only be developed if a large body of information is already available for each material in question. A designer may often need to assess the suitability of a potential material for a particular application well in advance of the availability of such a body of knowledge. Parametric models, such as that described in this paper, offer the possibility of predicting the likely fatigue response of a fibre-reinforced plastic on the basis of a very limited body of fatigue data. At its present stage of development this model also appears capable of allowing for the presence of damage caused to the composite by low-velocity impacts.

20.2   The nature of fatigue processes in composites

Fatigue in metals progresses by the initiation of cracks and the intermittent propagation of one of these cracks until catastrophic failure results. Failure occurs with little warning and with little sign of gross distortion except at the final tensile region of fracture. In ordinary high-cycle (low-stress) fatigue, where stress levels away from the crack tip are low, the properties of the metal remote from the crack are only slightly changed during fatigue. The strengths of metals are not greatly changed by cyclic loading in the high-cycle régime. Although work-hardening or work-softening may occur in metals undergoing low-cycle fatigue, the usual effect of fatigue at low stresses is simply to harden the metal slightly. Generally speaking, a stronger material will have a higher fatigue resistance, the fatigue ratio (fatigue limit divided by tensile strength) being roughly constant. This might be thought of as offering the most basic form of the 'strength-life equal-rank' assumption for life prediction.[1,2]

By contrast with metals, fibre composites are inhomogeneous and anisotropic. They accumulate damage in a general rather than a localized fashion, and failure does not always occur by the propagation of a single macroscopic crack. The micro-structural mechanisms of damage accumulation, including fibre breakage and matrix cracking, debonding, trans-verse-ply cracking, and delamination, occur sometimes independently and sometimes interactively, and the predominance of one or other may be strongly affected by both materials variables and testing conditions.

At low stress levels during monotonic loading or at an early stage of life during cyclic loading most types of composite sustain damage, and this damage is distributed throughout the stressed region. The damage does not always cause an immediate reduction in the strength of the composite although it often reduces the stiffness. Such strength reductions as might occur (in the process described as *wear-out*) are sometimes off-set in the early stages of life by slight increases in strength, known as *wear-in*. These increases may be caused by such mechanisms as the improved fibre alignment which results from small, stress-induced, viscoelastic or creep deformations in the matrix. At a later stage in the life the amount of damage accumulated in some region of the composite may become so great that the residual load-bearing capacity of the composite in that region falls to the level of the maximum stress in the fatigue cycle and failure ensues. This process may occur gradually, when it is simply referred to as degradation, or catastrophically, when it is termed *sudden-death*. Changes of this kind do not necessarily relate to the propagation of a single crack, and this must be recognized when attempting to interpret composites fatigue data obtained by methods developed for metallic materials.

20.3   Cracks in composites

Whether or not a pre-existing crack in a composite will propagate under the action of a cyclic load depends upon the nature of the composite. In highly anisotropic composites of high fibre content, a crack normal to the fibres will often refuse to propagate in mode-I growth, but will be diverted into a splitting mode. In composites like unidirectional carbon-fibre-reinforced plastics (CFRPs) this may result in a brittle, end-to-end splitting failure which simply eliminates the crack. By contrast, in glass-reinforced plastic (GRP) laminates containing woven-roving or chopped-strand mat reinforcement crack-tip damage may remain localized by the complex geometry of the fibre array and the crack may proceed through this damaged zone in a fashion analogous to the propagation of a crack in a plastically deformable metal.[3]

One of the more difficult issues for users of composites is the question of whether or not fracture-mechanics ideas may be used for fatigue design and life-prediction purposes. The crack-stopping ability of composites, which results from their inhomogeneity on a fine scale (the fibre/matrix interface) and on a gross scale (laminated structure) makes it difficult in many cases to apply a fracture mechanics approach to fatigue testing and design. The difficulty is most acute with unidirectional composites or laminates pressed from preimpregnated sheets of continuous and non-woven fibres. Stress concentrating effects of notches and holes may be almost completely eliminated by large-scale splitting in the 0° and 45° plies and by delaminations between the plies, the net result often being disintegration of the composite. By contrast, in laminates containing woven cloth or CSM reinforcement, or in mouldings containing random chopped fibres, the scale of this damage is limited by the structure of the composite and cracks and notches will often propagate in a more normal fashion, especially in wide plates. Owen and Bishop[3] have shown that it is possible to use a fracture-mechanics approach, based on the Paris power law:[4]

$$\frac{da}{dN} = A(\Delta K)^p \qquad\qquad [20.1]$$

relating the crack growth rate da/dN to the range of stress intensity factor ΔK for some GRP laminates. To overcome the problem of accurately defining crack length, a compliance calibration was used to determine an *equivalent* crack length, a procedure somewhat similar to that of using a plastic- or process-zone size correction when applying fracture mechanics to other materials. Underwood and Kendall[5] have also used a fracture-mechanics approach to study the growth of a damage zone during the fatigue of notched GRP laminates and Vancon *et al.*[6] have shown that, for the very much simpler case of propagation of delamination cracks in multi-ply laminates, fracture mechanics methods and the Paris power law are straightforwardly applicable. Unfortunately, however, the number of situations where such an approach can be applied is very limited.

The foregoing is not intended as a definitive treatise on the issue of damage mechanisms. Other chapters in this book will provide the necessary coverage of that field. It is intended merely to draw the reader's attention, at an early stage, to the complexity of the fatigue failure process in order to highlight the unexpected fact that a relatively simple parametric model, such as is proposed in this chapter, can apparently be successfully applied to a wide variety of composite types.

20.4   Life prediction: the alternatives

An ideal procedure for predicting the fatigue life of fibre composites would be based on a detailed understanding of the manner in which microstructural damage accumulates in the composite and of the way in which this damage affects the residual properties of the material. Such a procedure can only be developed if a large body of information, including details of the multiplicity of microstructural damage events and a substantial fatigue data base, is already available for each material in question.

There have been many attempts to develop life-prediction methods for reinforced-plastics, but the large variety of composite structures and the complexity of the response of these materials to stress makes it very difficult to develop universally applicable models. Some of the established methods are based on structural models, while others are less specific.

There is a familiar postulate, known as the strength-life equal-rank assumption, to which we have already referred. This postulate, not originally developed for composite materials, states that there is a correlation between the monotonic tensile strength and the life expectancy of a sample of nominally identical components. As applied to composites, the implication is that, if a series of composites are ranked according to their tensile strengths, then their fatigue responses will be similarly ranked. Although Barnard *et al.*[2] have argued that the model may be applicable to a wide variety of composite types and loadings, the potential danger of the basic assumption can be seen from the group of stress/loglife (σ/log N_f) curves for a range of carbon-fibre composites consisting of various combinations of fibres and resins, but of similar $[(\pm45,0_2)_2]_s$ lay-ups, shown in Fig. 20.1. The σ/log N_f curves are of different shapes; there is no obvious pattern of responses that can be linked to specific fibre types; and the resin matrix exerts stronger effects, in modifying the apparent performance

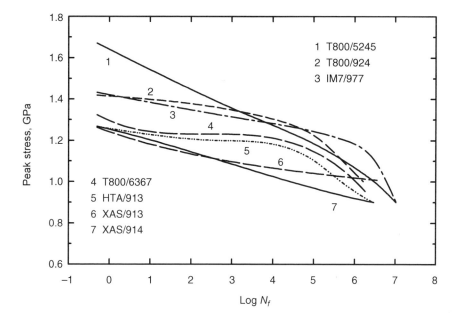

Fig. 20.1   Median stress/log N_f curves for repeated-tension fatigue ($R = 0.1$) for seven varieties of carbon-fibre composite, all with the layup $[(\pm 45,0_2)_2]_s$ (Harris *et al.*,[26] 1997).

of a given variety of fibre, than might have been expected. The individual curves also sometimes cross and recross, which would appear to rule out the possibility of using the strength/life assumption. And, although there is a general trend that higher strength laminates have longer fatigue lives, in detail it would appear to be unsafe to rely on such a crude ranking procedure. Another defect in the ranking model is that it attempts to relate only tensile strength to fatigue life: it gives no clues as to how a given material might behave under compression or combined tension/compression fatigue. It is known that the compression strength of a composite laminate will usually be much lower than its tensile strength, but there seems to be no simple relationship between the two, as illustrated in Table 20.1 for a range of CFRP laminates, including all of those referred to in Fig. 20.1.

Most of the structure-based procedures depend on modelling the degradation of material properties as a consequence of microstructural damage (e.g. Lee *et al.*,[7] 1989; Hwang and Han,[8] 1989) and many are based on the concept of the 'characteristic damage state' (CDS) developed by Reifsnider and co-workers (see, for example, Reifsnider *et al.*,[9] 1979; Reifsnider,[10] 1991, and the article by Reifsnider and Case in this volume[11]). A 'physical' approach was also adopted by McCartney[12-14] and Smith and Ogin.[15]

Many of these methods involve both statistical and laminate-theory analyses and give reasonably good predictions. But most require a good deal of prior data determination and are structure specific. In practice, a designer may often need to assess the suitability of a potential material for a particular application well in advance of the availability of such a body of knowledge, and in such a case a parametric, or 'black-box' model may well fill a much needed gap. Although a high level of understanding of the mechanisms of fatigue damage accumulation and the effects of this damage on the ability of a material or structure to sustain the service loads for which it was originally designed is of importance to materials developers, it must be acknowledged that the designer has little interest in the actual

Table 20.1   Experimental tension and compression strengths for various epoxy-based CFRP laminates referred to in this paper

Material	Lay-up	Fibre volume fraction, V_t	Tensile strength, σ_t (GPa)	Compression strength, σ_c (GPa)	Ratio (σ_c/σ_t)
HTA/913	$[(\pm45,0_2)_2]_s$	0.65	1.27	0.97	0.77
HTA/982	$[(\pm45,0_2)_2]_s$	0.65	1.19	0.91	0.76
IM7/977	$[(\pm45,0_2)_2]_s$	0.65	1.43	0.90	0.63
T800/924	$[(\pm45,0_2)_2]_s$	0.65	1.42	0.90	0.63
T800/5245	$[(\pm45,0_2)_2]_s$	0.65	1.67	0.88	0.53
T800/6376	$[(\pm45,0_2)_2]_s$	0.65	1.30	0.73	0.56
HTA/919	$[(\pm45,90,0)_2]_s$	0.60	0.73	0.59	0.81

physical mechanisms of degradation. What he needs is simply a way of analysing available data to predict the likelihood of failure under a specified set of conditions. In recent years artificial neural networks (ANNs) have emerged as a new branch of computing suitable for applications in a wide range of fields. They offer a means of dealing with multi-variate properties for which there is no exact analytical model and fatigue seems to be the kind of materials property that is suitable for ANN analysis. Neural networks provide a compact way of coping with the large amounts of characterization data generated in the study of a multi-variate dependent property such as fatigue. They also provide a very simple means of assessing the likely outcome of the application of a specified set of conditions, precisely what is required by a designer who needs to make safe use of complex fatigue data for complex materials like composites. The use of ANNs for the prediction of the fatigue lives of composites has been discussed by Lee et al.,[16] by Aymerich and Serra,[17] and is also reviewed by Lee and Almond in this volume.[18] In a very recent paper, Jarrah et al. have also used a 'neuro-fuzzy' approach to life prediction.[19]

20.5   A parametric constant-life model for life prediction

An alternative approach, not altogether un-related to the neural-network method, is that which is embodied in a parametric constant-life model developed over a period of years at the University of Bath.[20-28] Working successively with a variety of composite materials and laminate lay-ups, Harris and his co-workers obtained fatigue data over a wide range of stress ratios R, defined as the ratio of the (algebraically) minimum to maximum stresses in the fatigue cycle, i.e. $\sigma_{min}/\sigma_{max}$, and they observed regular patterns of behaviour which they made the basis of a parametric description of the stress/R-ratio/life 'environment' for composite fatigue, a model which appears to be valid for a wide variety of material types and structures.

The analysis is based on the observation of families of stress/life curves such as those shown in Fig. 20.2, taken from Harris et al.[26] In this case, the data cover five R ratios, from repeated tension ($R = +0.1$), with increasing proportions of compression load, through fully reversed stress ($R = -1$) to repeated compression ($R = +10$). For $R = 0.1$ the stress does not fall completely to zero in each cycle in order to ensure that the test could be run without an anti-buckling guide. For all other R ratios, the tests were carried out with an anti-buckling guide, as described in the original papers. The reversed compression tests were also carried out without completely unloading in order to avoid the discomfort of having an infinite value of the R ratio. The two data points shown on the extreme left at log $N_f = -0.301$ represent the

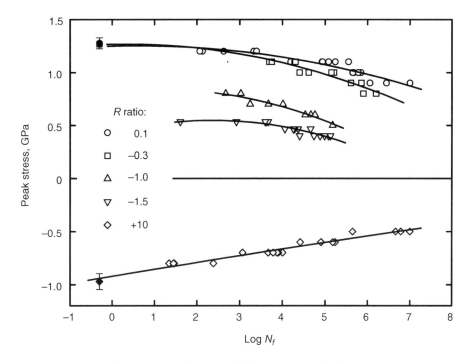

Fig. 20.2   Stress/loglife data for an HTA/913 CFRP laminate of $[(\pm45,0_2)_2]_s$ lay-up. The curves are second-order polynomial fits to the data.

monotonic tension and compression strengths of the laminate, with standard deviations, compression being treated as negative. The curves drawn through the points in this case are best-fit second-order polynomials, but any appropriate curve may be fitted for the purposes of the model as long as it gives a reasonable indication of the general lay of the data points and permits a limited amount of extrapolation where necessary (see, for example, parametric models suggested by Spindel and Haibach,[29] Nishijima,[30] and Barnard et al.[2]).

From the fitted curves, constant-life curves of the Goodman[31] type can then be obtained. The procedures are well known, and many authors have shown such diagrams for a variety of composite materials (see, for example, Owen and Morris,[32] Gerharz[33] and Kim[34]). Generally speaking, little attempt has previously been made to study the forms of these curves in a systematic fashion. In the work at Bath, however, research on a range of carbon-fibre and glass-fibre composites indicated that, major differences in composite characteristics notwithstanding, there appeared to be a consistent bell-shaped form to these constant-life curves, as shown in Fig. 20.3, which could be described by a relationship between the alternating stress and the mean stress:

$$a = f(1 - m)^u(c + m)^v \qquad\qquad [20.2]$$

In this equation, a is the normalized alternating component of stress σ_{alt}/σ_t, m is the normalized mean stress, σ_m/σ_t, and c is the normalized compression strength of the laminate, σ_c/σ_t, the normalizations being all with respect to the *tensile* strength of the material. There are notionally three adjustable parameters u, v and f, all three of which are functions of the fatigue life. The bell-shaped curve given by this relationship is not necessarily symmetric and may not even be centred on the alternating-stress axis ($m = 0$). The establishment of

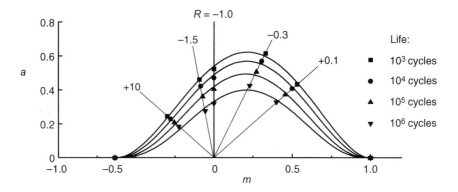

Fig. 20.3   Constant-life plots for a T800/924 $[(\pm 45,0_2)_2]_s$ laminate.

equation [20.2] has involved a number of modifications to the model, including early consideration of a parabolic function[21] (where the parameters u and v were both equal to unity), but the model in the general form shown above is more widely applicable to a variety of materials.

From early work it was apparent that the parameter f mainly controlled the height of the curve, and the most recent work suggests that it is a function of the ratio of the compression strength to the tensile strength, i.e. of the parameter c in equation [20.2],[28] as shown by the data for a life of 10^5 cycles (Fig. 20.4). There are two obvious options for the form of this relationship. In several of our earlier publications we have proposed a relationship of the form:

$$f = Ac^{-p}$$
[20.3]

where A and p are also functions of N_f. At the time of publication of our 1999 paper,[28] work had been completed on five varieties of carbon-fibre-reinforced plastic (HTA/913, HTA/982, T800/924, T800/5245 and IM7/977, and one glass-reinforced plastic, E-glass/913, all with the same $[(\pm 45,0_2)_2]_s$ lay-up. In addition to fatigue work on these laminates in the virgin state, experiments were also carried out on the HTA/913, HTA/982 and E-glass/913 composites after being subjected to damage by low-velocity impacts. Remarkably, equation [20.3] appeared to be valid for all of these materials and conditions, as illustrated by Fig. 20.4. The difference between equation [20.3] and a simple reciprocal relationship is very small and the statistical fit is just as good, but experience has shown that predictions made with f values determined from equation [20.3] are somewhat better than those made from a reciprocal relationship. The empirical variations of A and p with log N_f, deduced from the database covering all of the materials described above, CFRP and GRP, are given by:

$$A = 0.94 + 0.03.\log N_f - 0.016.\log N_f$$
[20.4]
$$p = 0.938 + 8.4.10^{-4}\exp\left(\frac{\log N_f}{1.016}\right)$$

Values of the exponents u and v are determined by the shapes of the two 'wings' of the bell-shaped curve, u relating to the slope of the contour in the 'tensile' mean stress zone and v the slope in the 'compressive' mean stress zone. They are often quite similar in value, unless the constant-life curves are very asymmetric, and for a wide range of CFRP materials their

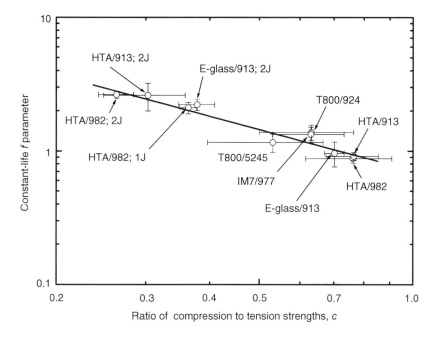

Fig. 20.4   Constant-life f parameter as a function of the strength ratio $c = \sigma_c/\sigma_t$ for a constant life of 10^5 cycles. Data are the results of Beheshty and Harris for CFRP and GRP laminates in the virgin and impact-damaged conditions. The linear best-fit line shown gives the functional relationship: $f = 0.71c^{-1.05}$.

values are close to 2, varying relatively slowly with log N_f. Beheshty et al.[28] showed that the mean values of u and v for all of their CFRP laminates were 2.18 and 2.4, respectively, with coefficients of variation of about 10%. However, for prediction purposes, more accurate initial predictions can be obtained by using the mean variations with log N_f:

$$u = 0.033.\log N_f + 2.032$$

[20.5]

$$v = 0.068.\log N_f + 2.089$$

Beheshty et al.[28] also noted that there was no obvious manner in which the physical nature of the different laminates (fibre type, resin type, level of fibre surface treatment) was reflected in the observed values of u and v, although the variations with log N_f were slightly different from laminate to laminate. As will be seen later, the u,v relationships for GRP laminates are different from those for CFRPs.

It can be seen that the parameters u and v of equation [20.2] and A and p of equations [20.4] effectively define the complete stress/R-ratio/life surface of the CFRP and GRP materials referred to above, or of any similar material for which the values of the tensile and compression strengths are known. Admittedly these are materials all having the same lay-up of $[(\pm45,0_2)_2]_s$, but the results include samples which had sustained low-velocity impact damage prior to being subjected to fatigue cycling. We shall address this apparent limitation later in this chapter, but first we propose a method whereby this parametric knowledge, gleaned from many experiments on different materials, may be used to predict either the fatigue response of any one of the above materials under cycling conditions for which test results had not previously been obtained, or the likely fatigue response of a material of like character (at this stage we limit the discussion thus) for which little or no fatigue data have yet been obtained.

20.5.1   Suggested life-prediction procedures

20.5.1.1   Stage 1. Prediction from strength data only
If no information other than the tensile and compression strengths is available for a given composite, a preliminary attempt can be made to predict stress/life curves on the basis of accumulated data for other related materials. The variation of f as a function of life $f(\log N_f)$ is known from the material strength properties and equations [20.3] and [20.4] and, and the variations of u and v with $\log N_f$ are given by equations [20.5]. The procedure is to solve the two simultaneous equations:

$$a = A(\log N_f)c^{-p(\log N_f)}(1 - m)^{u(\log N_f)}(c + m)^{v(\log N_f)}$$ [20.6]

$$a = m\left(\frac{1 - R}{1 + R}\right)$$ [20.7]

equation [20.7] being derived from the conventional definition of the stress ratio R:

$$R = \frac{\sigma_{mean} - \sigma_{alt}}{\sigma_{mean} + \sigma_{alt}}$$ [20.8]

The solution may be easily obtained by means of software such as MathSoft's *Mathcad*, which can be programmed to give the resulting relationship between a and N_f directly as the stress/loglife curve for any required R ratio. It should be noted, however, that in order to avoid the singularity in solving equations [20.6] and [20.7] for the fully reversed loading condition it is necessary to use an R value of, say, $R = -1.0001$ instead of -1.0. This correction can be built into the Mathcad worksheet, and the slight falsification makes no significant difference to the calculated curve.

As an example of this initial stage, we have used the method to predict the $\sigma/\log N_f$ curves for R ratios of $R = 0.1$ and -0.3 for a T800/6376 composite of lay-up $[(\pm 45,0_2)_2]_s$ for which we published a limited amount of fatigue data many years ago[35] before the constant-life approach was developed as a predictive model.

The predicted curves, together with the relevant experimental data are shown in Fig. 20.5. The original data sets show considerable scatter, but the predicted curves provide reasonably conservative estimates of the fatigue behaviour at the two R ratios in question. The mean percentage deviations (of experimental fatigue *stresses* from the predicted curve) are about 6% for $R = 0.1$ and about 11% for $R = -0.3$. Predictions for other R ratios can also be made, if required.

20.5.1.2   Stage 2. Improving the prediction by the acquisition of fatigue data
If the initial fatigue-life predictions appear encouraging, the next step is to carry out a limited fatigue-test programme in order to provide enough data to generate more appropriate values of u and v, including their dependences on life. If fatigue data are obtained at three or four stresses at, say, three R ratios, the predictions of the model will then become gradually more refined and reliable. The virtue of this method is that it can provide designers with useful design information at very early stages in the development of new materials, before detailed

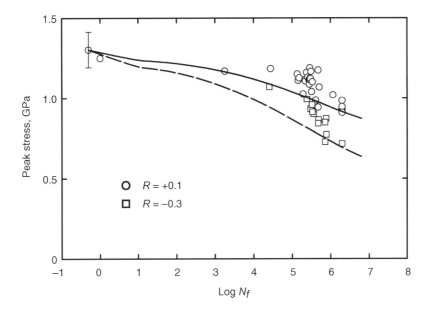

Fig. 20.5   Predicted S/log N_f curves for a T800/6376 $[(\pm 45,0_2)_2]_s$ laminate. The prediction is based only on the tensile and compression strengths, and uses u and v values which are the mean values for other CFRP laminates.

descriptions of the fatigue response have become available. While this may well be all that is necessary for non-critical applications, in the case of critical applications such as aircraft structures it would of course always be necessary to confirm predictions from any model before a design could be validated. The full procedure to be followed in obtaining dependable life predictions is as follows.

- Stress/life data are accumulated, as suggested above, at several stresses at each of perhaps three R ratios. The choice of an appropriate 'life' value requires detailed consideration of statistical models suitable for the purpose of the analysis, or, more specifically, to the design requirements related to safety considerations: this is considered in Section 5.3 of this chapter.
- Suitable mathematical functions are fitted to the stress/life data: second- or third-order polynomials have been used hitherto, but, as mentioned earlier, more appropriate functions may be used if they can be shown to be preferable.
- Interpolations are made at selected lives (e.g. 10^4, 10^5, 10^6, etc. cycles) and data pairs (m,a) are calculated from these interpolations at particular R ratios together with previously measured tension and compression strengths.
- The data are plotted as an (m,a) diagram (such as that shown in Fig. 20.3) and curves of the form of equation [20.2] are fitted through the data points by non-linear curve-fitting routines such as those provided by Mathcad. Values of the parameters u and v are then evaluated, and their variations with log N_f are established. This is facilitated even when relatively few data are available by the fact that f is pre-determined to an adequate degree of accuracy by the known values of the tensile and compression strengths and the existing empirical knowledge embodied in equations [20.4].

It is then possible to predict σ/log N_f curves for any desired R ratio by solving the same two

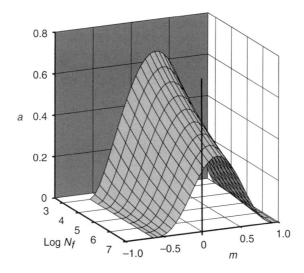

Fig. 20.6   Predicted constant-life curves for a T800/924 CFRP laminate of $[(\pm45,0_2)_2]_s$ construction (Gathercole *et al.*, 1994).

simultaneous equations as before, equations [20.6] and [20.7], now incorporating the new experimental data for the life dependencies of u and v. The prediction process can be further refined if needed by collecting further data. The quality of the life prediction will improve as the experimental program described above progresses and values of the various parameters used in the predictive equations are refined for the specific material in question, although, as we shall see, data sets consisting of only 20 or 30 test results will usually give an excellent approximation to the results of a fully implemented test programme. All of the operations described above can be carried out in Mathcad, templates being constructed so as to obviate the need for repetitive inputting of old data.

The output of this analysis can be in one of two forms, depending on the requirements of the user. The first is a three-dimensional generalization of the constant-life (m,a) plot in the form of a surface plot showing the full variation of $(a,m,\log N_f)$, as shown in Fig. 20.6. Alternatively, a family of stress/life curves of conventional form can be produced for ranges of lives that are consistent with the original experimental data window.

An important question about the extent to which the model is improved as further data are acquired can be shown by reference to a re-analysis of one of the data sets that was obtained some years ago for a T800/924 $[(\pm45,0_2)_2]_s$ CFRP laminate, the same material referred to in Fig. 20.3. A series of selections were made from the data set in order to imitate a test programme, so that the first 17 'tests', then successively 22, 30 40, and finally the full test set of 88 results were 'available' for the analysis, the constant-life model being re-fitted at each stage. The effect of increasing the number of fatigue test results is shown in Fig. 20.7, the points identifying the intermediate fits, while the full curve is the same one that was originally fitted to the full data set of 88 tests. It can be seen that the model is robust, the shape of the constant-life curve changing very little as the 'test programme' advances. Thus, a designer could have a reasonable degree of confidence in predictions of the model at a relatively early stage instead of having to wait in the normal way for a full data set to be obtained.

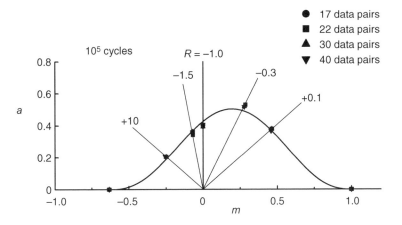

Fig. 20.7   Constant-life plots for a T800/924 $[(\pm45,0_2)_2]_s$ laminate, showing the effect of increasing the number of fatigue test results.

20.5.1.3   Materials differences

The preceding discussion has been largely concerned with CFRPs since this kind of composite has been more intensively researched than any other. And while it appears that the discussion relating to the parameter f is equally valid for both CFRPs and GRPs, as shown by Fig. 20.4, the same is not true of the parameters u and v. The constant-life curve defined by equation [20.2] for a GRP is still bell-shaped, but is considerably further displaced from the ordinate than the curves for similar carbon-fibre-reinforced plastics, and the values of u and v are different, varying more strongly with log N_f. Starting values of the constants in equations [20.5] appropriate for GRPs require further experimental investigation since the values given by Beheshty et al.[28] relate to a series of tests on only one GRP laminate:

$$u = 0.542.\log N_f + 0.283$$

[20.9]

$$v = 0.741.\log N_f + 0.624$$

We also suggest that the constant-life model as developed so far is applicable only to reinforced thermosets. No experiments have been carried out on any thermoplastic–matrix composites, although some very early preliminary work on unidirectional carbon-fibre/ PEEK showed fatigue behaviour that was very similar to that of a comparable carbon/epoxy laminate (similar V_f and fibre type).[36]

It was mentioned in Section 20.5 that the experimental data on which the constant-life model is based included test results for a range of CFRPs and one GRP laminate both in the virgin condition and after being subjected to damage by low-velocity impacts. It appears that the parameter f is uniquely determined by the strength ratio c and that its variation with log N_f is independent of fibre and resin types and of the state of damage. The ratio c is changed by exposure to impacts because of the effect on the laminate strengths, especially the compression strength, as illustrated in Fig. 20.9. The effect of increasing the level of impact damage on the constant-life plot is shown for an HTA/918 CFRP laminate in Fig. 20.10.[28] It appeared from these results that stress/life curves for materials damaged by low-velocity impact could also be predicted from data for the undamaged laminate provided the changes

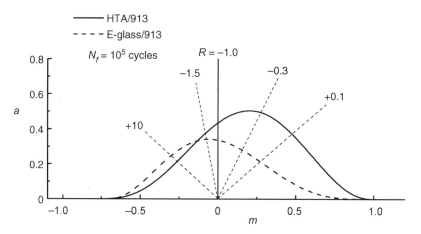

Fig. 20.8   Constant-life plots for HTA/913 CFRP and E-glass/913 GRP laminates of $[(\pm45,0_2)_2]_s$ construction for a life of 10^5 cycles (Beheshty et al.,[28] 1999).

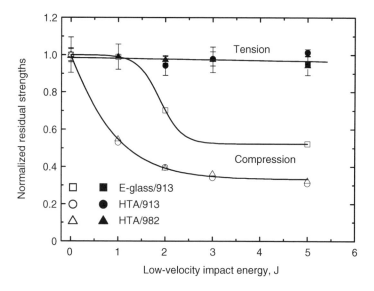

Fig. 20.9   Effect of low-velocity impact on the residual compression and tensile strengths of HTA/913 and HTA/982 CFRP laminates and E-glass/913 (data are normalized with respect to the strength of the undamaged material). All laminates are of lay-up $[(\pm45,0_2)_2]_s$.

in the tensile and compression strengths caused by the impact damage are known. It is clear from Fig. 20.10, however, that whereas the effect of impact damage on the f parameter is incorporated within the overall relationship between f and the strength ratio, c, (for both CFRPs and GRPs), the same is not true for the values of u and v.

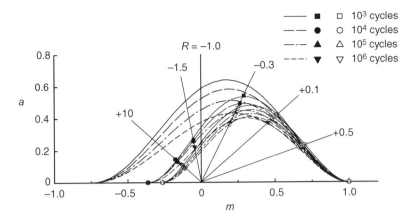

Fig. 20.10   Constant-life plots for virgin and damaged [(±45,0₂)₂]ₛ HTA/982 carbon/epoxy laminate. Closed symbols are for 1 J impact; open symbols for 2 J impact. The data points are shown only for the damaged material in order to avoid confusion.

20.5.2   Recent developments

Although this model works well for a range of composite materials, both CFRP and GRP, with and without impact damage, at this stage its validity as a practical life-prediction model can be considered firm only for laminates with a lay-up of [(±45,0₂)₂]ₛ. Critics have argued that, since the process of damage accumulation in composites is strongly dependent on the lay-up and the reinforcement style (i.e. woven/non-woven; type of weave, etc.), it could not be said to be universally applicable. Although this is valid reasoning, it nevertheless seems likely from what we have already shown that the range of applicability of the constant-life model may be wider than could be expected from mechanistic arguments. At the same time, it is appreciated that there is a need for more extensive validation before the model could be generally accepted. This wider applicability has therefore been tested in three ways:

(a) with reference to earlier work carried out at Bath,
(b) with references to a database of fatigue test results for other materials made available to us by QinetiQ, Farnborough, and
(c) through a small collaborative research programme in which a new CFRP laminate, not hitherto included in the work, has been provided by QinetiQ and fatigue tested at the University of Cambridge.[37]

For the first of these, data of Adam *et al.*[38] for undirectional carbon/Kevlar-49/epoxy hybrid laminates, unidirectional XAS/914 CFRP, and the [(±45,0₂)₂]ₛ T800/6376 CFRP mentioned earlier have been re-analysed. For the second, results for some T300/914 CFRP composites with lay-ups including (±45,0₂)ₛ both woven and non-woven, (0,90,90,0)ₛ woven, and (0,90,±45)ₛ quasi-isotropic woven laminates were provided. The test data for all of these materials, which included tension and compression strengths and fatigue data for two *R* ratios only, were fitted to the constant-life model, as described above, and in each case equation [20.2] gave a reasonable fit to the available data. The values of the parameter *f* were obtained and these are plotted in Fig. 20.11, together with all of the CFRP and GRP data points from Fig. 20.4. The full curve in Fig. 20.11 is the same best-fit curve as that drawn in Fig. 20.4 (i.e. equation [20.3]), and it can be seen that the new data are as close to the line

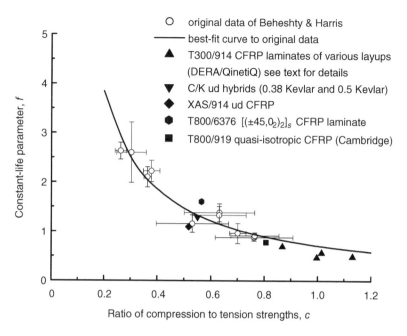

Fig. 20.11   Constant-life f parameter as a function of the strength ratio $c = \sigma_c/\sigma_t$ for a constant life of 10^5 cycles. Open data points are the results of Beheshty and Harris for CFRP and GRP laminates in the virgin and impact-damaged conditions, and the line is the best-fit curve through the points, originally fitted on a log–log plot. The filled points are for other composites, as indicated.

as normal experimental scatter, different testing techniques, etc., could possibly allow. It may be seen that the group of points for the T300/914 laminates show no indication of any differences in behaviour arising from either the variations in lay-up or the fact that one laminate is constructed from woven-cloth reinforcement and the others from prepreg. These results confirm the belief that the model is generally applicable, regardless of material, lay-up, or, by implication, mechanisms of failure.

In the exercise mentioned in (c) above, a new HTA/919 quasi-isotropic CFRP laminate never tested at Bath was supplied to Helen Carroll at the Department of Metallurgy & Materials Science in Cambridge. Carroll provided strength and fatigue-test data as they were obtained so that the constant-life model could be applied in the manner described in Sections 20.5.1.1 and 20.5.1.2. In the first instance, the tensile and compression strengths were given, and life predictions made for four R ratios, 0.1, –0.3, –3.33 and 10 for which fatigue test results were subsequently to be obtained. The next batch of data included 19 tests for R ratios of 0.1 and 10; the predictions were then revised on the basis of the newly established empirical variation of u and v with $\log N_f$. The final complete data set, a total of 71 test results at the R ratios referred to above, was then provided. In order to see whether the second prediction could be improved upon if some data at $R = -0.3$ had been available earlier, a selection of 20 results from $R = 0.1, -0.3$ and 10 were arbitrarily selected and a new prediction made. Finally, the analysis was applied to the complete data set. The four graphs illustrating this sequence of predictions, in each case in juxtaposition with the full data set, is shown in Fig. 20.12. For each prediction, the standard deviation for the fit was obtained from the mean square errors (for the stresses rather than the lives) and a mean percentage error was obtained by taking the modulus of each deviation of the predicted stress from

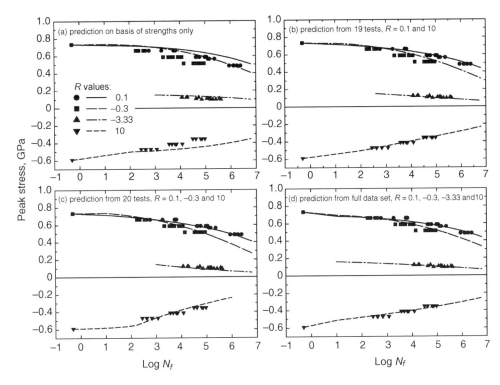

Fig. 20.12 Stress/loglife data for HTA/919 [(±45, 90, 0)$_2$]$_s$ CFRP laminate. The added curves are successive predictions obtained by using information about the variation of u and v with log N_f from gradually acquired experimental fatigue-test data, as indicated a), b), etc.

experimental stress as a percentage of the experimental stress and averaging over the full σ/log N_f curve. The results are given in Table 20.2. Although the standard deviations are more meaningful, the percentages are easier to grasp. The initial deviations are in the range 10 to 20%, but they fall rapidly when even a small test database is available. The percentage errors for the $R = -3.33$ predictions appear rather large because the actual peak stress levels against which the deviations are being normalized are very low: the actual standard deviations are quite small. The final level of agreement (i.e. with predictions made from the full data base) offer only marginal improvements over those obtained from a mere 20 test results.

20.5.3   Statistical aspects of the model

The mechanical properties of practical composites are almost always variable, to a greater or lesser extent, and it is not surprising, therefore, that the variability of the fatigue response of a composite is even greater than that associated with metallic materials. Stress/life data may be obtained by testing single samples at many different stress levels, or by carrying out replicate tests at rather fewer stresses: the latter is usually considered to be the more satisfactory method because it provides statistical information at each stress, and provides probability/stress/life curves in addition to median-life or mean-life curves such as those which we have used in the foregoing discussion.

One of the problems is to know how many replicate tests to carry out at each stress level since, given the cost of fatigue-testing programmes, the smaller the number of tests that can be used to establish a 'safe' σ/log N_f curve, the better. From a statistical point of view it is usually accepted that at least 20 replicate tests may be necessary before the user can have any

Table 20.2   Indicators of goodness of fit of predictions from the constant-life model relative to actual experimental data for a quasi-isotropic HTA/919 T[(±45,90,0)$_2$]$_s$

Prediction for R	From strengths only mean u and v vs. log N_f		From initial 19 test results at $R = 0.1$ and 10		From selected 20 test results at $R = 0.1$, −0.3 and 10		From full data set R = 0.1, −0.3, −3.33 and 10	
	sd of fit	mean % error	sd of fit	mean % error	sd of fit	mean % error	sd of fit	mean % error
0.1	0.055	9	0.016	2	0.018	2	0.020	2
−0.3	0.082	13	0.040	6	0.027	4	0.027	4
−3.33	0.025	22	0.009	6	0.018	15	0.006	4
10	0.073	16	0019	3	0.032	6	0.020	4

The errors are relative to the stress axis.

confidence in a statistical analysis of results.[39] But when stress/life curves are required at, say, five different R ratios, even five tests at each stress level may be all that can be provided in a reasonable amount of time, especially at long lives.

A variety of distributions have been used to characterize fatigue lives, but the three-parameter Weibull function is often considered to be the most appropriate model for this purpose. The form of the cumulative distribution function used for fatigue is:

$$P(N_f; \alpha, \beta, \lambda) = 1 - \exp\left[-\left(\frac{N_f - \alpha}{\beta} \right)^{\lambda} \right] \qquad [20.10]$$

where P is the probability of a life N_f. The location parameter α defines a number of cycles for which there is zero probability of failure, and β, the scale parameter, is a characteristic or normalizing value of life. For metallic materials, the value of the shape parameter λ is often in the range $2 < \lambda < 6$,[40] whereas several recent studies of CFRP fatigue suggest that for these materials $1 < \lambda < 2$.[41,25]

Although we often work in terms of median or mean lives when discussing fatigue data, to a designer the requirements are much more restrictive The desired failure probability for such a structure as an aircraft would probably be at a very low level, say 5%, instead of the 50% level implied by the median life. An even more appropriate 'life' parameter may be the minimum extreme value obtained from an application of the theory of extreme values.[42]

One of the characteristics of the Weibull model is its reproductive property,[43] a consequence of which is that for a population of results that is well modelled by the Weibull distribution certain other features of the population, such as the minimum extreme values, will also be described by a Weibull distribution. The exact distribution of the smallest observations in sets of data that are described by a Weibull model also fits a Weibull model. Thus, if we have replicate data sets of fatigue lives at a given stress and R ratio which is described by the two-parameter version of equation [20.10], with shape parameter λ and scale parameter β (α being equal to 0), the smallest observations of these data sets also exhibit a Weibull distribution similar to that of the parent distribution and with the same value of the shape factor m but rescaled by $n^{1/\lambda}$. The characteristic minimum value for a test sample of n tests will therefore be ($\beta/n^{1/\lambda}$) and the modal value of the distribution (i.e. the most probable value) will be given by:

$$\frac{\beta}{n^{1/\lambda}}\left(1-\frac{1}{\lambda}\right)^{1/\lambda}$$

If, on the other hand, the desired level of failure probability happens to be the 5% level ($q = 0.05$), then the appropriate value of 'life' is given by:

$$\beta\left[\ln\left(\frac{1}{1-q}\right)^{1/\lambda}\right]$$

Thus, from a series of replicate data sets of fatigue lives at various cyclic stress levels, a stress/life/probability (or S/N/P) diagram, such as that shown in Fig. 20.13 can be drawn, provided the distribution parameters, β and λ, can be obtained for each data set. From a design point of view, the lower curve in this diagram, representing some given failure probability, is clearly of more interest to the engineer than any other part of the data, but it can only be obtained by statistical means which requires reliable values of the two distribution parameters, β and λ. This, in turn, calls for replicate data sets of at least 20 test results for each stress level and R ratio, a requirement which carries with it a serious time/cost disincentive.

However, Whitney[41] has shown that, where only small numbers of life values are available at a number of different stress levels, the data may be pooled to give an overall value of the Weibull shape parameter, λ, this value then being used to obtain working stress/loglife curves for any given failure probability. This is done by normalizing each test-stress data set with respect to the mean life, the characteristic life β (the scale factor of the Weibull distribution for the data set), or the median life for the data set, pooling all data sets for all stress levels and all R ratios, and then re-ranking them in order to allot a new failure probability function to each point. The virtue of this procedure is that a much larger population is being used to derive the value of the Weibull shape parameter and calculations of an expected life based on that λ value will be much more reliable than ones obtained from the much smaller data sets for each individual stress level. Examples of pooled data sets are shown in the probability plots in Fig. 20.14 for three of the materials referred to in this chapter [$(\pm 45,0)_2)_2]_s$ IM7/997 carbon/epoxy and E-glass/913 laminates from our earlier work and the quasi-isotropic HTA/919 laminate which is the subject of Fig. 20.12. The curves are non-linear curve fits to the data for the three-parameter Weibull distribution of equation [20.10] and, not unexpectedly for normalized data, the three values of the scale parameter, β, are close to unity. Likewise, the three values of α are close to zero, implying that a two-parameter Weibull model would be equally appropriate for these data sets. The differences between the three values of the shape parameter λ are the only distinguishing features. We have previously commented on the difference between values of λ obtained for CFRP and GRP laminates of identical lay-up,[28] and it is interesting to note the slight difference in Fig. 20.14 between the values for the two CFRP materials of different lay-up. A clearer view of the differences is given in Table 20.3 which includes all of the data,[23] together with that for the HTA/919 laminate. The values are all maximum likelihood estimates based on a two-parameter Weibull model. It can be seen that, for the range of [$(\pm 45,0)_2)_2]_s$ carbon/epoxy composites, the shape factor varies relatively little, having a mean value of 1.31 and standard deviation of 0.25, whereas the value for the quasi-isotropic HTA/919 is somewhat larger, about 2.3. The value for the GRP laminate falls between these two. Thus, although in the early stages of an appraisal of the likely fatigue response of a new laminate, a starting value

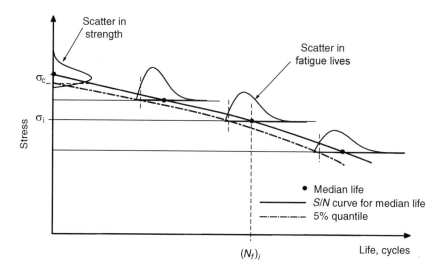

Fig. 20.13   Effects of variability in strength and fatigue life on the definition of the $\sigma/\log N_f$ curve. The scatterband of lives is jointly defined by the upper and lower probability limits of the fatigue data sets and the monotonic strength distribution.

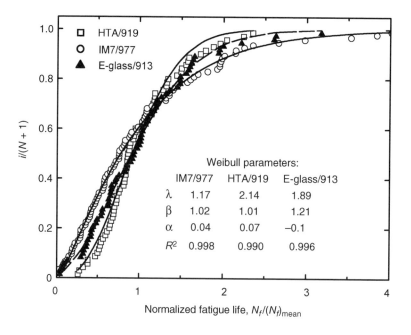

Fig. 20.14   Three-parameter Weibull plots of pooled normalized fatigue lives for $[(\pm45,0_2)_2]_s$ IM7/919 (CFRP) and E-glass/913 (GRP) laminates and a quasi-isotropic $[(\pm45,90,0)_2]_s$ HTA/919 CFRP laminate. The lives for a given stress level are normalized with respect to the mean life (N_f mean).

Table 20.3 Weibull shape parameters for normalized fatigue-life data sets for a range of CFRP and GRP laminates with and without impact damage

Material	Designation	Lay-up	Condition	Number of tests	Shape parameter, m
CFRP	T800/5245	$[(\pm45,0_2)_2]_s$	virgin	164	1.18
CFRP	T800/924	$[(\pm45,0_2)_2]_s$	virgin	88	1.50
CFRP	IM7/977	$[(\pm45,0_2)_2]_s$	virgin	93	1.21
CFRP	HTA/913	$[(\pm45,0_2)_2]_s$	virgin	88	1.63
CFRP	HTA/982	$[(\pm45,0_2)_2]_s$	virgin	122	1.01
CFRP	HTA/919	$[(\pm45,90,0_2)_2]_s$	virgin	69	2.29
CFRP	HTA/913	$[(\pm45,0_2)_2]_s$	2J damage	41	0.85
CFRP	HTA/982	$[(\pm45,0_2)_2]_s$	1J damage	62	0.70
CFRP	HTA/982	$[(\pm45,0_2)_2]_s$	2J damage	43	0.97
GRP	E-glass/913		virgin	47	1.60
GRP	E-glass/913		2J damage	47	1.82

The shape parameters were determined as maximum likelihood estimates for a two-parameter Weibull distribution.

of, say, 1.5 could be taken for λ in order to make predictions of an extreme-value or quantile *S/N* curve along the lines described above, it is clear that the value used should be adjusted appropriately as test data become available.

From the point of view of life prediction, it is interesting to know how soon in a fatigue-testing programme the pooling of test data can be used to give a reasonable indication of the likely value of the Weibull shape parameter which is needed for the application of the extreme-value relationships given above, particularly since we have shown earlier that a mere 20 or so fatigue test data, for judiciously selected R ratios and stress level, may be sufficient for reasonable predictions of stress/life curves. An attempt has been made to obtain this information by effectively 'replaying' fatigue-test programmes for some of our laminates and pooling the data at different stages as results are 'acquired'. An example is shown in Fig. 20.15 where results for the fatigue of a T800/924 $[(\pm45,0_2)_2]_s$ CFRP laminate are compared with the more recent data for the HTA/919 laminate referred to in Section 5.2. For the T800/924 laminate, the results from the data base for this material were selected on an informed basis, in an effort to obtain initially two or three results at given stresses for several R values. Pooling was carried out after 6, 10, 14, 17, 22, 30, and 40 data pairs were selected from the full data set of 88 test results. A maximum likelihood estimate of λ was made by means of Mathcad, which also returns the standard error of the estimate. The four data points for the HTA/919 composite follow the programme sequence described in reference (37) and Section 4.2 of this chapter. The comparison is shown in Fig. 20.15. It can be seen that, provided an informed choice of 'test conditions' is made for the testing programme, a reasonable estimate of the final value of the shape factor is obtained after only about 20 fatigue tests have been run. Failure to exercise such control results in poor early estimates of λ, as shown by the results of a second 'virtual' test sequence for the T800/924 laminates which was carried out by allowing a random-number computer programme to select test results from the whole data set.[44]

20.6   Conclusions

• Life-prediction methods which are based on mechanistic models of materials degradation under load are usually preferred by materials scientists. The logic of this is

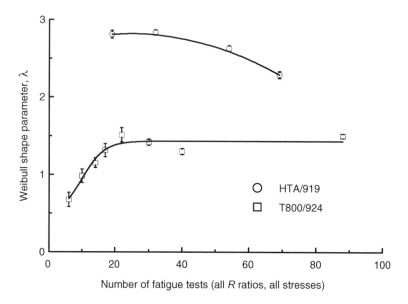

Fig. 20.15   Change in the value of the shape factor λ estimated by the maximum likelihood method for a two-parameter Weibull model, as the number of fatigue test results increases. The error bars are the standard deviation for the fit. Fatigue of T800/924 $[(\pm45,0_2)_2]_s$ and HTA/919 $[(\pm45,90,0)_2]_s$ CFRP laminates.

inescapable, but it could be said that no generally applicable model of this kind is yet available. Parametric models offer a realistic alternative when there is a shortage of experimental data. One such parametric model, which has been developed over a number of years at the University of Bath has been described.

* The model is a constant-life model which is able to describe the stress/life/R-ratio failure surface of a given laminate in terms of the monotonic tensile and compression strengths of the material and three empirical parameters, referred to as f, u and v. For a given class of materials (e.g. CFRP of given lay-up) the values of u and v are close to 2 and do not vary greatly with life or material characteristics, while the parameter f, a function of the ratio of the compression and tensile strengths, varies with life.

* The model is valid for glass-reinforced plastics as well as for the carbon-fibre composites for which it was originally developed, although the extent to which this has been validated is very limited at the present time. The same relationship between f and c fits GRP and CFRP, but the u and v values for GRP are different from those for CFRP.

* The effect of low-velocity impact on the fatigue response of both CFRP and GRP laminates has been studied and it appears that the constant-life model can also be applied to damaged laminates. The changes in fatigue response that occur as a result of impact damage can be incorporated in the model from a knowledge of only the monotonic strengths of the damaged laminate. Thus, the fatigue response of a damaged laminate can be predicted if these properties are known, without the need, at least in the first instance, for experimental fatigue data.

* Although originally developed to describe the fatigue behaviour of a group of CFRP laminates of a single lay-up, i.e. $[(\pm45,0_2)_2]_s$, the model has more recently been shown to be valid for a wide range of other composites, including unidirectional CFRP laminates, unidirectional carbon/Kevlar hybrids, and CFRP laminates of cross-ply and quasi-isotropic lay-up, including both pre-preg and woven-fibre materials.

20.7   Acknowledgements

The research on which this chapter is based has been carried out over a long period of time, mainly with the financial support of the Ministry of Defence through the former DERA (now QinetiQ, Farnborough). The author is grateful to DERA/QinetiQ and to those members of the staff at Farnborough who have supported and encouraged the work, in particular Professor Graham Dorey, Professor Paul Curtis, Mr Matthew Hiley, and, most recently, Dr Andrew Davies. The author is also grateful to Dr Davies for giving him access to a DERA fatigue data base from which the test results identified in this paper as being provided by DERA/QinetiQ were taken. The work at the University of Bath has always been a team effort, and although the contributors are indicated in the list of references, it is a pleasure to acknowledge the work of my collaborators Tom Adam (who originally proposed the ideas behind the constant-life model), Harry Reiter, Richard Dickson, Chris Jones, Gerard Fernando, Nick Gathercole, Hosain Beheshty, and, most recently, Helen Carroll of the Department of Metallurgy and Materials Science in Cambridge who provided the fatigue data for the HTA/919 laminate as part of a collaborative programme also sponsored by QinetiQ, Farnborough.

20.8   References

1. CHOU P C and CROMAN R (1978), Residual strength in fatigue based on the strength-life equal-rank assumption, *J Compos Mater*, **12**, 177–194.
2. BARNARD P M, BUTLER R J and CURTIS P T (1988), The strength-life equal-rank assumption and its application to the fatigue-life prediction of composite materials, *Int J Fatigue*, **10**, 171–177.
3. OWEN M J and BISHOP P T (1974), *J Phys D: Appl Physics*, **7**, 1214–1224.
4. PARIS P C, GOMEZ M P and ANDERSON W E (1961), A rational analytic theory of fatigue, in *The Trend in Engineering*, University of Washington, Washington, USA.
5. UNDERWOOD J H and KENDALL D P (1975), Proc 2nd International Conference on Composite Materials (ICCM2) (editors E Scala, E Anderson, I Toth and BR Noton) volume 2, Metallurgical Society of AIME, New York, 1122–1147.
6. VANCON M, ODORICO J and BATHIAS C (1984), *Comptes Rendus des Quatrièmes Journées Nationales sur les Composites* (JNC4), (Editions Pluralis, Paris), 93–120.
7. LEE J W, DANIEL I M and YANIV G (1989), *Composite Materials: Fatigue and Fracture (2)* STP 1012 (editor PA Lagace), American Society for Testing and Materials Philadelphia USA, 19–28.
8. HWANG W B and HAN K S (1989), *Composite Materials: Fatigue & Fracture (2)* STP 1012 (editor PA Lagace), 87–102.
9. REIFSNIDER K L, HENNEKE E and STINCHCOMB W W (1979), *Defect–property relationships in composite materials: AFML-TR-81 part 4*, US Air Force Wright Laboratories, Dayton, Ohio, USA.
10. REIFSNIDER K L (1991), Damage and damage mechanics, chapter 2 in *Fatigue of Composite Materials*, Composite Materials Series volume 4, edited by KL Reifsnider, Elsevier Amsterdam, 11–77.
11. REIFSNIDER *ET AL.* (2002), Micromechanical models, in *Fatigue in Composites*, editor B Harris, (Woodhead Publishing Ltd, Abington, UK), 413–431.
12. McCARTNEY L N (1996), Framework for the prediction of ply cracking in any symmetric laminate subject to general in-plane loading, NPL Report CMMT(A)51, December 1996.
13. McCARTNEY L N (1997), Predicting non-linear behaviour in multiple-ply cross-ply laminates resulting from micro-cracking, Proc. IUTAM Symposium on *Non-linear Analysis of Fracture*, Cambridge, 3–7 September 1995, Kluwer Academic Publishers, Dordrecht–Boston–London 1997, pp.379–390.
14. McCARTNEY L N (1998), Predicting transverse crack formation in cross-ply laminates resulting from microcracking, *Compos Sci and Technol*, **58**, 1069–1081.
15. SMITH P A and OGIN S L (2000), Characterisation and modelling of matrix cracking in a (0/90)$_{2s}$ GRP laminate loaded in flexure, *Proc. Roy. Soc. Lond.*, **A456**, 2755–2770.
16. LEE J A, ALMOND D P and HARRIS B (1999), The use of neural networks for the prediction of fatigue lives of composite materials, *Composites*, **30A**, 1159–1169.

17. AYMERICH F and SERRA M (1998), Prediction of fatigue strength of composites by means of neural networks, *Key Engg Mater*, **144**, 231–240, Proceedings 3rd Seminar on *Experimental Techniques and Design of Composite Materials* Calgiari, Italy, Oct 1996.

18. LEE J A and ALMOND D P (2002), A neural-network approach to fatigue-life prediction, in *Fatigue in Composites*, editor B Harris, Woodhead Publishing Ltd, Abington, UK, 569–589.

19. JARRAH M A, AL-ASSAF Y and EL KADI H (2002), Neuro-fuzzy modelling of fatigue-life prediction of ud glass-fibre/epoxy composites, *J Compos Mater*, **36**, 685–700.

20. ADAM T, DICKSON R F, JONES C J, REITER H and HARRIS B (1986), A power-law fatigue damage model for fibre-reinforced plastic laminates, *Proc Inst Mech Engrs: Mech Eng Sci*, **200(C3)**, 155–166.

21. ADAM T, FERNANDO G, DICKSON R F, REITER H and HARRIS B (1989), Fatigue life prediction for hybrid composites, *Int J Fatigue*, **11**, 233–237.

22. ADAM T, GATHERCOLE N, REITER H and HARRIS B (1992), Fatigue-life prediction for carbon-fibre composites, *Advanced Compos Letters*, **1**, 23–26.

23. GATHERCOLE N, REITER H, ADAM T and HARRIS B (1994), Life prediction for fatigue of T800/5245 carbon-fibre composites: I Constant-amplitude loading, *Int J Fatigue*, **16**, 523–532.

24. BEHESHTY M H and HARRIS B (1997), Post-impact fatigue behaviour of CFRP and the growth of low-velocity impact damage during fatigue, *Proc International Conference on Fatigue of Composites (ICFC), Paris*, (Société Française de Métallurgie et de Matériaux, Paris), 355–362.

25. HARRIS B, GATHERCOLE N, REITER H and ADAM T (1997), Fatigue of carbon-fibre-reinforced plastics under block-loading conditions, *Composites*, **A28**, 327–337.

26. HARRIS B, GATHERCOLE N, LEE J A, REITER H and ADAM T (1997), Life prediction for constant-stress fatigue in carbon-fibre composites, *Phil Trans Roy Soc (Lond)*, **A355**, 1259–1294.

27. BEHESHTY M H and HARRIS B (1998), A constant-life model of fatigue behaviour for carbon-fibre composites: the effect of impact damage, *Compos Sci and Technol*, **58**, 9–18.

28. BEHESHTY M H, HARRIS B and ADAM T (1999), An empirical fatigue-life model for high-performance fibre composites with and without impact damage, *Composites*, **A30**, 971–987.

29. SPINDEL J E and HAIBACH E (1981), *Statistical Analysis of Fatigue Data STP 744* (editors RE Little and JC Ekvall), American Society for Testing and Materials, Philadelphia, USA, 89–113.

30. NISHIJIMA S (1987), *Statistical Research on Fatigue and Fracture* (Current Japanese Materials Research 2) (editors T Tanaka, S Nishijima & M Ichikawa), Elsevier Applied Science London, 1–19.

31. GOODMAN J (1899), *Mechanics Applied to Engineering*, Longman Green, Harlow, UK.

32. OWEN M J and MORRIS S (1972), *Carbon Fibres: Their Composites and Applications*, Plastics Institute London, 292–302.

33. GERHARZ J J (1982), *Practical Considerations of Design Fabrication and Tests for Composite Materials*, AGARD Lecture Series no 124 (Director B Harris), AGARD/NATO, Neuilly, Paris, paper 8.

34. KIM R Y (1988), *Composites Design 4th Edition* (editor SW Tsai), (Think Composites, Dayton, Ohio, USA), chapter 19.

35. HARRIS B, REITER H, ADAM T, DICKSON R F and FERNANDO G (1990), Fatigue behaviour of carbon fibre reinforced plastics, *Composites*, **21**, 232–242.

36. DICKSON R F, JONES C J, HARRIS B, LEACH D C and MOORE D R (1985), Environmental fatigue behaviour of carbon-fibre-reinforced poly(ether ether ketone), *J Mater Sci*, **20**, 60–70.

37. HARRIS B, CARROLL H and DAVIES A (2002), Validation of a parametric constant-life model for fatigue-life prediction for carbon-fibre composites, submitted to *Advanced Composites Letters*, October 2002.

38. ADAM T, FERNANDO G, DICKSON R F, REITER H and HARRIS B (1989), Fatigue life prediction for hybrid composites, *Int J Fatigue*, **11**, 233–237.

39. LEE J A, HARRIS B, ALMOND D P and HAMMETT F (1997), Fibre composite fatigue-life determination, *Composites*, **28A**, 5–15.

40. FREUDENTHAL A M and GUMBEL E J (1953), On the statistical interpretation of fatigue tests, *Proc Roy Soc (Lond)*, **A216**, 309–332.

41. WHITNEY J M (1981), *Fatigue of Fibrous Composite Materials STP 723*, American Society for Testing and Materials Philadelphia USA, 133–151.

42. CASTILLO E (1988), *Extreme Value Theory in Engineering*, Academic Press, Boston/London.

43. BURY K V (1975), *Statistical Models in Applied Science*, J Wiley & Sons, London.

44. HARRIS B (2001), The fatigue behaviour of fibre-reinforced plastics and life prediction, in *Actas del Cuarto Congreso Nacionale de Materiales Compuestos, MATCOMP '01*, Gijon, Spain, November 2001, (Editors A Fernández Canteli, FT Belzunce and F Paris), Bitácora Publicidad SL, Gijon, Spain, 3–42.

21

A neural-network approach to fatigue-life prediction

J. A. Lee and D. P. Almond, University of Bath, UK

21.1   Introduction

The ideal approach to the characterization of composite fatigue would be to research fully every new composite material so that the fatigue response under every set of conditions was completely understood. However, the fatigue testing of materials is a time-consuming and expensive exercise. The nature of fatigue experiments means testing machines are tied up for long periods of time and there can be a delay before statistically meaningful results are produced. If every fatigue condition is to be investigated, this results in many different experiments involving many variables. The problem is compounded by the proliferation of new materials requiring evaluation and the increasingly demanding applications for these materials. This drives the need for more accurate fatigue-life predictions.

A potential solution to this requirement is offered by artificial neural networks (ANNs). ANNs are an alternative to conventional programmed computing and are based on the operation of the brain. Research into ANNs has been expanding rapidly since the late 1980s and is now at a stage of development for ANNs to be used successfully in many applications. The analysis of fatigue life data is similar to many of these applications in which the pattern recognition and data classification capabilities of ANNs are utilized. ANNs offer a means of handling many multi-variate parameters for which an exact analytical model does not exist or would be difficult to develop. ANNs also provide a compact method of considering large amounts of data and a simple means of assessing the likely outcome of a complex problem with a specified set of conditions. The analysis of fatigue data requires all these capabilities. In particular, engineering designers need to make safe use of complex fatigue life data for complicated materials like composites.

ANNs are a type of computer program that can be 'taught' to emulate relationships in sets of data. Once the ANN has been 'trained', it can be used to predict the outcome of another new set of input data, e.g. another composite system or a different stress environment. This chapter describes the application of ANNs to the prediction of the fatigue lives of composite materials. It is split into the following sections:

(i)   Background – in this section the neural network approach will be presented. This will include a discussion on biological neural networks, multi-variate non-linear mappings, artificial neural network models, generalization and the use of artificial neural networks in practice.
(ii) Application of ANNs to analysis of fatigue life data – this part of the chapter will detail how ANNs can be applied to the analysis of fatigue life data. The following will be considered: the optimum architecture and inputs; use of a trained ANN to predict the fatigue life properties of a new material; block loading data analysis; suggested procedure and, a comparison with other fatigue life models.
(iii) Future trends and further information.

21.2   Background

Since its inception by Babbage, Turing and von Neumann, computing has largely performed tasks through the use of a programmed and linear approach. Artificial neural networks (ANNs) or parallel distributed processors, are an alternative to conventional computing. Based on the operation of the brain, ANNs find the solution to a problem by learning from a set of examples.

21.3   Biological neural networks

Comprising around 10^{11} electrically active cells, or neurons, each connected to 10^4 others, the human brain is the most complex structure known at present.[1] The process of learning was first theorised by Hebb.[2] Each neuron is essentially a stand-alone analogue logical processing machine which receives many inputs which are combined within the neuron in one of several different ways depending on the neuron type. If sufficient active inputs are accepted at once and a threshold level is exceeded, the neuron sends, or 'fires', a signal to other connected neurons in the form of an electrical impulse called the action potential. Neurons are therefore either on or off exhibiting an 'all-or-nothing' characteristic.

   The ability of biological neural networks to learn is achieved by modifications to the network through the couplings between the neurons. It is believed that favourable connections are reinforced by the release of more neuro-transmitters causing more receptors on the dendritic side of the synaptic junction to open, thereby increasing the coupling, or connection weights, between neurons. The processing speeds of the individual neurons are slow compared to current digital computing times, but massive parallelism results in an overall 'brain' or system processing speed, which is far greater than present day supercomputers. Moreover, the parallel nature of the brain gives it 'fault tolerance' or the ability to operate satisfactorily even when some of the neurons are damaged. Similarly, biological neural networks exhibit 'graceful degradation', where their performance reduces slowly with continual damage, instead of a sudden catastrophic failure as in the case of serially connected digital computers.

21.4   Multi-variate non-linear mappings

The most widely used class of ANNs are known as feed-forward networks. These can be considered as non-linear mathematical functions[3] where a set of independent input variables,

$x_1, \ldots, x_d$ is transformed into a set of dependent output parameters, $y_1, \ldots, y_{d'}$. To aid the analysis, the variables are usually grouped into vectors, input vector $x \equiv (x_1, \ldots, x_d)$ and output vector $y \equiv (y_1, \ldots, y_{d'})$. The transformation is described by two characteristics: the network configuration; and the set of weight parameters $(w_1, \ldots, w_j)$ whose values are established through 'learning' from an example data set. Again, the weights can be grouped together into a vector w giving the equation $y = y(x;w)$ where y is a function of x which is parameterized by w. In this manner ANNs can be compared to standard techniques for curve fitting by using polynomial functions, where the coefficients describing the polynomial correspond to the weights of the ANN and the 'training' process corresponds to the calculation of the coefficients. However, ANNs differ from simple polynomials in two important ways. Unlike polynomials, ANNs can have several inputs and outputs. Secondly, ANNs have the ability to represent efficiently several different function types whereas multi-variate polynomials require large numbers of adjustable coefficients. As a result, ANNs have the ability to learn a general solution to a problem described by the training examples alleviating the requirement for the often tedious or mathematically complex task of deriving a first-principles model of the process under study.

Training is achieved by determining values for the weights in the network. The process of learning can be visualized by considering polynomial curve fitting through sets of n points. If the points are indexed from $q = 1$ to $q = n$, and each point has a value x and an associated target value for the output y, denoted by t. Then the process of curve fitting is intended to minimize the error between the desired value at any point t_q, with the corresponding value predicted by the polynomial function $y(x_q;w)$. Standard fitting procedures attempt to minimize the square of the differences, summed over all points. This can be described mathematically as an expression for the error E:

$$E = \frac{1}{2} \sum_{q=1}^{n} \{y(x_q;w) - t_q\}^2 \tag{21.1}$$

From this it can be seen that the error is a function of w. Consequently, the curve can be fitted by choosing a value for w, which minimizes the error.

The above process describes the basics of ANN learning. Unlike polynomials, the relationship between the functions and the weights in ANNs is non-linear resulting in a more complex procedure for minimizing the error. This process is achieved by means of optimization algorithms.

In addition to solving the interpolation problems, ANNs can be applied to classification. This task involves mapping a list of measured features, the input pattern, onto a set of categories which lie on the weight space. The simplest case involves two measurements leading to a two-dimensional weight space. By defining a boundary which separates the categories, classification becomes a process of deciding on which side of the boundary the data points lie. The process of classification can be explained by considering a two-input data set where the task is to separate the outputs into two classes, 0 and 1. A linear separator could be used to divide the weight space into two zones but, this line must be correctly defined to accurately classify the two categories. The straight line can be defined as:

$$y = mx + c \tag{21.2}$$

where y and x are the inputs, m is the gradient of the line; and c is the intercept with the y axis. A linear separator for this example would have a negative slope giving:

$$y = c - mx \qquad \text{(Fig. 21.1)} \tag{21.3}$$

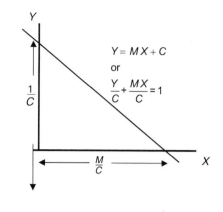

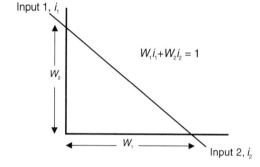

Fig. 21.1   Illustration of how a linear classification training process of an artifical neural network can be compared with the equation of a straight line.

or

$$y + mx = c \qquad [21.4]$$

Dividing through by c gives:

$$\frac{1}{c}y + \frac{m}{c}x = 1 \qquad [21.5]$$

A general form of this equation is:

$$w_1 i_1 + w_2 i_2 = 1 \qquad [21.6]$$

where i_1 and i_2 are the inputs; and w_1 and w_2 are the allocated weights. As a result the weight space is divided into two regions by a line with the above equation with:

$$w_1 i_1 + w_2 i_2 > 1 \text{ above the line, and}$$

$$w_1 i_1 + w_2 i_2 < 1 \text{ below the line.}$$

However, this boundary may not be classifying the sets with sufficient accuracy. Subsequently, the weights, and hence the discriminating function, must be determined by training. In this way the classification problem can be compared to the polynomial case with the assignment of weights relating to learning.

The training procedure for classification begins by randomizing the weights and thereby setting an arbitrary discriminating function. After assigning a threshold value, the inputs and

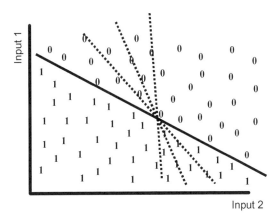

Fig. 21.2 Classification iterations.

the corresponding output values are presented. The weighted sums $(w_1 i_1 + w_2 i_2)$ are calculated and compared with the outputs. If the classification is correct, the weights are retained. If the weighted sums and the outputs differ, the classification is incorrect and the error must be calculated. This error is then used to alter the weights proportionally, as shown in Fig. 21.2. This procedure is repeated until the weight space is correctly defined in accordance with the training data.

As the number of inputs, and hence the number of dimensions, increases, it becomes more difficult to visualize the classification exercise but the process is essentially the same as that for the two-input case. For example, three inputs would require a planar decision boundary but four or more inputs require discriminant functions which are impossible to represent geometrically.

21.5   Artificial neural network models

There are several models for ANNs but two of these, multi-layer perceptron (MLP) and radial basis functions (RBF), dominate the practical applications.

21.5.1   The basic neuron

Figure 21.3 shows the simple mathematical model of a single neuron as proposed by McCulloch and Pitts in 1943.[4] The basic function of the neuron is to transform a set of input variables x_i, $(i = 1, \ldots, d)$ into an output variable z. The first stage of the transformation is to multiply the inputs by a weight parameter w_i, which simulates the synaptic strength in the biological networks. All the weighted inputs are then added together to give a total input:

$$a = \sum_{i=1}^{d} w_i x_i + w_0 \qquad\qquad [21.7]$$

An offset parameter or bias w_0 is added to provide a mechanism for including other influences thereby attempting to model the fact that real neurons are affected by factors other than direct inputs. Typically, w_0 is set permanently to 1 meaning the bias is continually on. This gives:

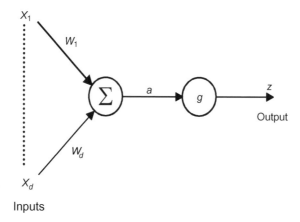

X_1

W_1

Σ a g

z

Output

W_d

X_d

Inputs

Fig. 21.3   McCulloch and Pitts' model of a single neuron.

$$a = \sum_{i=0}^{d} w_i x_i \text{ where } x_0 = 1 \tag{21.8}$$

The weights, including the bias, can be either positive or negative to indicate their excitatory or inhibitory nature, respectively.

To mimic the firing rate of the biological neuron, the parameter a is then operated on with a non-linear activation function $g()$ to give:

$$z = g(a) \tag{21.9}$$

McCulloch and Pitts used a step function in their original model but most networks now use a sigmoidal threshold function. The reasons for this are discussed later. Since the processing is from the inputs through the neuron to produce the output, the system is known as feed-forward. ANNs are constructed by linking many of these simple processing units.

21.5.2   The multi-layer perceptron

The simplest neural network has a single layer of neurons and can be represented pictorially, as in Fig. 21.4, or mathematically by the expression for the outputs z_j:

$$z_j = g\left(\sum_{i=0}^{d} w_{ij} x_i\right) \tag{21.10}$$

where w_{ij} is the weight from inputs i to j (the bias has been set to 1) and $g()$ is an activation function. This was the configuration, in conjunction with step threshold functions, used widely in the early experiments considering ANNs[5]. However, it was discovered that these arrangements had limited computational capabilities and could not handle problems which were linearly inseparable, such as the exclusive-or (XOR) problem.[6]

The failure of the single-layer perceptron to solve relatively simple problems led to ANNs being dismissed and as a result the amount of research carried out declined. This problem was compounded by the fact that a suitable training algorithm could not be found.

Following a paper by Hopfield[7] where he reviewed previous work on ANNs and

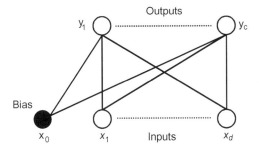

Fig. 21.4   Single layer perceptron.

suggested that the development of the field required a shift in thinking to a more practical viewpoint there was a resurgence in research into ANNs and a solution to the XOR problem was published in 1986 by McCelland and Rummelhart[8] and was called the multi-layer perceptron. This new model consisted of two successive layers and two associated layers of weights. A middle layer comprising hidden units was added, so called because the activation values were not directly accessible. The crucial innovation was the replacement of the step function with a differentiable sigmoidal activation function which is required for the network to train. Now the output from the network was determined by the transformation by the hidden layer of the output from the input layer:

$$y_k = \bar{g} \left(\sum_{j=0}^{m} \bar{w}_{kj} z_j \right)$$

[21.11]

where $\bar{w}_{kj}$ are the weights in the second layer. Again, a bias term is added.

The equations for the outputs from the input and hidden layers can be combined into:

$$y_k = \bar{g} \left[\sum_{j=0}^{m} \bar{w}_{kj} \, g \left(\sum_{i=0}^{d} w_{ij} x_i \right) \right]$$

[21.12]

There are two main choices for the sigmoidal function: the tanh function;

$$g(a) = \tanh a \equiv \frac{e^a - e^{-a}}{e^e + e^{-e}}$$

[21.13]

and the logistic sigmoid;

$$g(a) = \frac{1}{1 + e^{-a}}$$

[21.14]

As stated earlier, the process of training is to determine weights to give the smallest value for the error function. Alternatively, this can be visualized as establishing the minimum in a surface described by the error function, shown in Fig. 21.5. There will be two types of minima: global – the lowest of the whole surface; and local. Algorithms must have the ability of finding the global minimum whilst being able to escape from local minima.

The most common algorithm is back-propagation which uses a technique called gradient

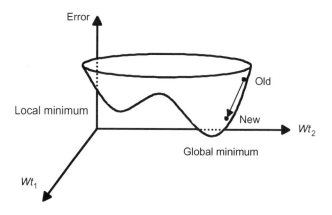

Fig. 21.5   Representation of the ANN error surface.

descent learning to minimize the error.[9] This technique measures the error and the rate of change of that error. This leads to the largest modifications to the weights when the error is largest. As the slope decreases in approaching a minimum, the changes in the weights become smaller. This procedure can be summarized:

$$\Delta w_t = \eta \frac{dE}{dw_t} + h\Delta w_{t-1} \qquad [21.15]$$

where η is the learning rate, dE/dw is the rate of change of the error with respect to weight for a given weight and h is a constant which determines the effect of past weight changes.

The $h\Delta w_{t-1}$ is a momentum term which increases training speeds without causing instability.[10] This is particularly necessary when the errors describing the decision surface are widely different. An extreme case is when the surface resembles a long thin trough. Here the learning rate has to be small in the direction of the walls to prevent thrashing but this also makes learning along the direction of the trough floor very slow. The momentum term allows learning to be larger for shallow slopes than for directions in which the error gradient is higher. The process of training is the same as described earlier with the weight-adjustment step calculation being the back-propagation stage.

21.5.3   Radial basis function networks

Although the multi-layer perceptron is the most widely applied ANN model, it suffers from several drawbacks. Firstly, to optimize the network configuration requires many repetitions of the training process therefore it can be time consuming and/or computationally intensive. Secondly, the training process involves many non-linear transformations, making analysis of the trained network complex, particularly the traceability of the decision making process. Lastly, if the error surface is very rugged, there is the risk of the network converging on one of the local minima and not on the global minimum. A potential solution to the above problems is offered by radial basis function networks (RBFs).[11] Whereas the multi-layer perceptron classifies the weight space by hyper-planes, RBFs use hyper-ellipsoids. The hyper-ellipsoids are defined by basis functions of the form $\phi(x)$. The Gaussian function is typically used to define the basis functions: for the qth data point:

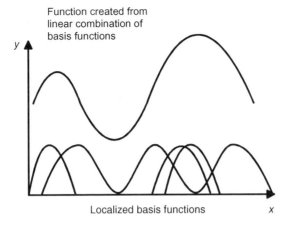

Fig. 21.6   The RBF discriminant function $y(x)$.

$$\phi_q(x) = \exp\left\{ -\frac{|x - x_q|}{2\sigma^2} \right\}$$ [21.16]

where σ defines the width of the function; and x_q represents the centre. If the distribution of the inputs is known, this should be reflected in the basis function.

The RBF is a single discriminant function which is constructed from a linear combination of a set of the above functions as described in Fig. 21.6 and can be represented as:

$$y_k = \sum_{j=1}^{n} \bar{w}_{kq} \phi_q(x)$$ [21.17]

Consequently, once the basis function has been selected, the parameter w_{kq} is all that needs to be determined allowing a solution to the problem to be estimated. Alternatively, the connections between the input and hidden layer nodes are determined by the basis functions, with the weights of the hidden to output nodes the values determined by linear optimization.

If there are equal numbers of basis functions and inputs, this can lead to problems in generalization as noisy data points are also classified and very similar data points may be apportioned into different groups. The purpose of ANNs is to establish and mimic underlying trends in the data as opposed to providing an exact match. Consequently, a good general representation of the data can be achieved by using fewer basis functions than inputs.

21.6   The use of artificial neural networks in practice

When using ANNs in practice, the first step is to construct the model within the work space of the software. The software is typically an analysis tool, which allows the user to create artificial neural networks in a visual and interactive manner. The ANN model can consist of:

- a training data sheet comprised of the following fields – training inputs, training targets, validation inputs, validation targets and query inputs;
- a network including the training algorithm;

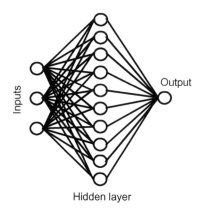

Inputs

Output

Hidden layer

Fig. 21.7   Schematic representation of the typical architecture of an artifical neural network.

- scaling function. This function is necessary to adapt the input data into a form for use in the network. It takes the form of a 'squashing' function, which compresses the input data set into a range from one to zero. The output from the network must be re-scaled before the results can be analysed;
- output data sheet for displaying the results of the ANN interrogation process;
- an error graph for displaying the current status of the training process.

Once the skeleton of the ANN model has been developed, the data is imported into the appropriate fields of the training data sheet. The architecture of the network is then constructed. A typical network is described in Fig. 21.7 and consists of input nodes, one for every data group within the training data, nodes in hidden layer(s), and output node(s). In this project the network consisted of three or seven input nodes, ten nodes in one hidden layer, and one output node.

With the appropriate training algorithm selected, the network is ready to train. The overall training processes are similar whichever algorithm is used. The input part of the training data set is presented to the network and the network response is stored. Each response value is subtracted from the corresponding input target value thereby giving an error for each output. A weight adjustment is calculated for each weight and the weights modified potentially to reduce the overall error of the network. The process is then repeated until the performance value exceeds a pre-determined threshold, e.g. maximum average error. Each cycle of the training process is called an epoch. The average error at any given point during training is displayed on the graph giving the user an indication as to whether the network is converging or not.

After the training process has been completed and the network has 'learned' any patterns from the training data set, the network is now ready to be interrogated with a new query data set. The query data set is presented to the network in the same manner as the training inputs were during the training process and the network estimates the outputs based on the knowledge it has gained from the training process. This is how the ANN can be used as an estimation/predictive/classification tool. The outputs from the network can then be compared with the actual values and the error calculated. In this way the performance of the ANN is determined.

21.7   Application of artificial neural networks to the analysis of fatigue life data

21.7.1   Introduction

As described earlier, the training data set is contained in two groups: inputs and targets. The inputs are selected through a series of trials and can include such fields as measures of the stress environment and associated probabilities of failure for a given number of fatigue cycles to failure. It is good practice to train the ANN with as few input fields as possible as this allows an adequately detailed definition of the stress environment whilst minimizing the amount of information the ANN has to interpret. For the analysis of fatigue life data, the corresponding target set would consist of the Log(number of cycles to failure) for the associated inputs. An example of a training data set would be:

- Training inputs – σ_{max}, σ_{min}, probability of failure;
- Training targets – Log (number of cycles to failure).

Consequently, by using this combination of parameters, the number of cycles to failure for a given probability and stress environment could be predicted by the ANN.

The accuracy of the trained network is confirmed by using a pre-selected query data group. One approach is to take a section of training database and use this to interrogate the ANN. The average root mean square (rms) error is calculated for the outputs from each trained network and this can be used as the measure of the accuracy of the trained ANN. The rms error is calculated from the relationship:

$$\mathrm{rms} = \frac{\sum_n (x_n - t_n)^2}{\sum_n (t_n - \overline{t})^2} \qquad\qquad [21.18]$$

where x_n is the output value from the network from the nth input string, t_n is the target value for the nth input string, and $\overline{t}$ is the average of the target values.

It is generally recognized[12,13] that, although the amount of data required is problem dependent, to obtain a sufficient level of confidence, the input database should contain at least the following number of entries N_e:

$$N_e = 3 \times [(I \times H) + (H \times O) + H + O] \qquad\qquad [21.19]$$

where I is the number of input fields or categories; H is the number of nodes in the hidden layer; and O is the number of output nodes.

The above formula has been derived empirically and the reasons for its suitability are still being researched.[13] It is possible that this size of input training database provides a sufficiently large group to include most of the important features of the training information thereby allowing the ANN to capture the general qualities of the data. If an ANN of three input nodes, ten hidden nodes and one output node was to be used then, according to equation [21.19], the input database should have at least 123 examples if the outputs from the ANN can be used with confidence.

Two factors contribute to the performance of the ANN – the architecture of the network and the quality and format of the input data. Both these influences are evaluated empirically through a series of trials. This typically entails a set of ten replicate experiments for each network arrangement.

21.8   Optimum artificial neural network architecture

The architecture of the ANN, in particular the number of hidden nodes and hidden layers, is established empirically through a series of trials which determine the smallest network which allows convergence in the shortest training time. By choosing the simplest network configuration, it is assumed that the ANN is able to capture the features of the data set and still maintain generalizing qualities, increasing the potential for the ANN to give accurate outputs when queried with new data sets.

21.9   Selection of inputs for training the artificial neural network

As stated earlier, ANNs used in this type of application tend to be trained under fully supervised conditions. Every input training data string has an associated target training data string. Therefore, the supervised ANN training requires two sets of data – inputs and targets. One possible output and therefore the training target is log (number of cycles to failure). There are several potential training inputs including:

- R ratio (ratio of minimum stress to peak stress),
- peak stress (σ_{max}),
- minimum stress (σ_{min}),
- probability of failure,
- stress range ($\sigma_{max} - \sigma_{min}$),
- average stress [($\sigma_{max} + \sigma_{min}$)/2].

The optimum set of inputs are taken to be those training inputs which produce a trained ANN with the lowest average rms error when interrogated.

To increase the accuracy of the ANN the training field can be focused on areas of interest. In this way, any *a priori* knowledge can be built upon. For example, a reduced range of values of probability of failure can be selected as it can be assumed that this is the region of most interest to the design engineering community with engineers wanting to know when the earliest failures would be likely to occur.

21.10   Constant stress amplitude fatigue

Following establishment of the most appropriate network architecture, and training it with suitable data sets, predictions of constant amplitude fatigue life can be obtained. A more comprehensive description of this type of application is described.[14] The predictive ability of the neural network is described through two examples of constant amplitude fatigue life prediction discussed here, namely for 5% and 50% failure of probability. The latter is equivalent to the median life normally used to plot stress/life curves, but the former is more representative of the extreme-value level of prediction used in critical design areas. Figure 21.8 describes predicted and actual 'lives' for the 5% level for a HTA/913 laminate, and in Fig. 21.9 predictions for the 50% level are compared with the median life data for a T800/ 924 carbon-fibre/epoxy laminate with a lay up of $[(\pm45, 0_2)_2]_s$. In both the 5% and 50% cases the modelling is reasonably accurate. The work carried out as part of Reference 14 found that the ANN is generally more accurate at the 50% level. Modelling at the 5% level presents a more challenging task for the network as it is axiomatic and there are fewer data at the extremes of the probability distribution than near the median. With more parameters to

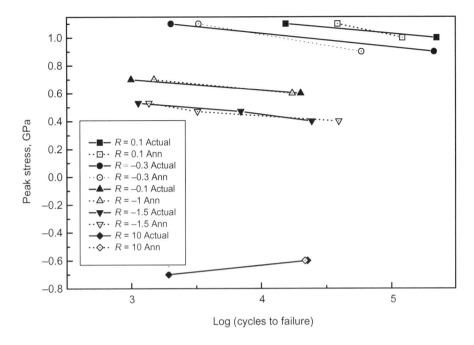

Fig. 21.8   5% *S–N* curves for HTA/913. The solid lines are created from the actual data for the fatigue lives. The dotted lines describe the estimates produced by the ANN.

model, the classification task of the network is made more difficult. For both the 5 and 50% levels, the ANN is more accurate with plots for R ratios of -1.0 and -1.5 than for other values, again because these are near the centre of the R-ratio range, while others (-0.5 or $+10$, for example) are near the extremes.

21.11   New material application

There are two approaches to this application. The first is to use the fatigue-life data for one material over several stress conditions to predict the fatigue response for the same composite system under a new and different stress regime. For example, the ANN could be trained with fatigue life data for one material for three R ratios, each at two or three stress levels $R = 0.1$, $R = -0.3$ and $R = 10$. The query set could then comprise data strings for a single R ratio, $R = -1$.

The second approach is to train the ANN with data for several composite systems and predict the fatigue life properties of a separate composite material. When the fatigue performance of a completely new composite system is being predicted by training the ANN with fatigue life data for other materials, the ANN is trained by using the same approach as for a single composite material investigation. The query data set would then, for example, contain data obtained for all the R ratios and corresponding stress levels available for the new material. Moreover, to differentiate between the various training materials additional training data fields may be required. Monotonic properties can be used for this discriminating purpose: tensile strength, compressive strength, tensile modulus and strain to failure.

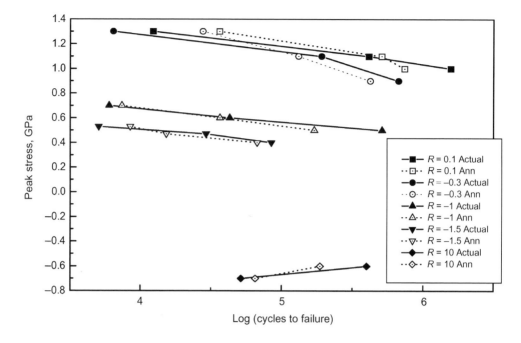

Fig. 21.9 *50% S–N curves for T800/924.* The solid lines are created from the actual data for the fatigue lives. The dotted lines describe the estimates produced by the ANN.

These material characteristics can be collected more rapidly than fatigue life data and as a result are aligned to the overall strategy of examining ways of reducing testing without impairing predictive accuracy. These particular monotonic properties are suggested because these parameters are readily available for most materials.

21.12   Block-loading data analysis

There are many possible ways of applying the ANN to the prediction of the fatigue lives of block-loading experiments, but because of space limitations only three will be discussed. The first method considers using the same pre-processing of the data as used in the constant amplitude experiments. The ANN is trained by using descriptors of the stress environment and an associated probability of failure. The output from the ANN is a prediction of the log(number of cycles to failure). The network is trained and interrogated as in the case of the constant-stress amplitude fatigue-life trials.

The second approach that can be considered for training the ANN to predict the block-loading fatigue lives of fibre-composite materials is to use block descriptions and either the Miner number or block of failure as outputs. The inputs to the ANN are the four peak stress levels for the four units that comprised the blocks. For two-unit block-loading fatigue results, the two units can be repeated to make a block of four. This allows the results of two- and four-unit block-loading tests to be combined. In this way the input database for training the ANN can be made as large as possible. Therefore, the confidence in any predictions made by using the ANN will be maximized. The training targets for each training input string are either the corresponding Miner number or the block of failure, e.g.

Training inputs	Training targets
$\sigma_{max1}, \sigma_{max2}, \sigma_{max3}, \sigma_{max4}$	Miner number
1.3 GPa, 1.1 GPa, −0.636 GPa, 1 GPa	0.4

The final method considered for training the ANN to predict the block-loading fatigue lives of fibre-composite materials is to attempt to describe the damage the material has sustained from previous cycles of fatigue loading and then predict whether the composite can withstand the next unit of loading. If a means of accurately describing the amount of damage contained within the material can be established, the ANN could be used to predict whether or not the material would fail or survive on the next unit of the block. The first training input string would describe the composite in the as-manufactured condition plus the damage that the first unit of the block-loading programme would impart on the material. The expected damage could be described by the Miner number. The block-loading conditions where each unit constituted 0.5% of the median constant-amplitude fatigue life would be expected to impart 0.05 of the damage for each unit. Therefore, the first training input string would contain an initial damage value of zero and a final damage quotient of 0.05. The second training input string would comprise of an initial damage state of 0.05 and a final damage condition of 0.1. The training input strings would continue in this fashion until a Miner number of one was reached. If the material failed with a Miner number corresponding to more than one, this value could be used instead. In this case the input data strings are then extended up to the higher Miner number. The training target would be a one, if the material was expected to survive, and a zero if it was expected to fail. Failure would occur if the damage expected from the next unit of the block-loading programme exceeded the remaining strength of the material.

21.13   Suggested procedure for applying neural networks to fatigue life data

As a means of summarizing this chapter and as an aid to understanding this subject, the following describes one successful approach for applying ANNs to fatigue-life predictions.

- The training base for the ANN should be constructed from monotonic and fatigue life data for relevant composite materials. The monotonic properties could be tensile strength, compressive strength, strain to failure and tensile modulus. If possible, the fatigue-life data should include values for three stress levels at three R ratios, e.g. $R = 0.1$, $R = 10$ and $R = -0.3$. The other training input could be the required level of failure probability. For most design engineering purposes, the range of failure probability should be between 0.025 and 0.5. It is recommended that the probabilities should have a 0.025 increment. This provides an appropriate amount of information for training the ANN. The training inputs to the ANN would consist of the fields shown in Table 21.1. This training database contains seven inputs and one output. There is an input data-string and a corresponding output for each increment of the probability of failure. The database should contain examples of data-strings for every peak-minimum stress combination deemed relevant for training. Table 21.1shows a limited selection of data-strings. In practice, the database for one material would be large and include hundreds of data-strings.
- The monotonic properties of the new material should be collected first. The same four material characteristics as used for the training materials should be used. The monotonic

Table 21.1

	Training inputs						Training targets
	Monotonic properties			Fatigue properties			
Tensile strength (GPa)	Compression strength (GPa)	Strain to failure (%)	Tensile modulus (GPa)	Peak stress (GPa)	Minimum stress (GPa)	Probability of failure	Number of cycles to failure
1.27	0.97	1.73	70	1.1	0.11	0.025	8986
1.27	0.97	1.73	70	1.1	0.11	0.050	15469
1.27	0.97	1.73	70	1.1	0.11	0.075	21346

properties are easier to obtain than the fatigue data. This allows the training database to be constructed as quickly as possible, permitting, in turn, early ANN predictions. The monotonic properties will provide the ANN with sufficient information to provide a rough estimate of the fatigue lives of the new material.

- The query database should be constructed with the same seven parameters as the training input database.
- The suggested optimum ANN architecture is seven input nodes, one hidden layer of twenty-one nodes and one output node. However, a series of trials should be conducted to establish the smallest ANN which provides the lowest error.
- The ANN is then trained and interrogated to give predictions of fatigue life for the required R ratios and peak stresses over the probability range 0.025–0.5. This provides the data required to plot 50% and 5% stress/'life' curves. It is recommended that the training and querying process be repeated ten times. These repetitions ensure that the impact of any variations in network training are minimized.
- Fatigue testing of the new material is carried out as usual in order to obtain an experimental database of fatigue lives. It is suggested that the fatigue testing is carried out for three peak stresses at each of the R ratios 0.1, 10 and –0.3. These data allow the ANN to provide the most accurate predictions with the least amount of information. If time permits, it is recommended that the number of cycles to failure for at least 20 separate failures be recorded for each stress level. This is the minimum number of samples required to provide an adequate level of statistical confidence in the results, if pooling by the Whitney approach[15] is not adopted. From these data, the three-parameter Weibull distribution parameters can be estimated by using the maximum likelihood method and the stress/log(cycles to failure) data determined for 5% and 50% probabilities of failure.
- The experimental data are then compared with the output of the ANN. The accuracy of the output of each ANN is measured by calculating the average rms error for all the query data points. The most accurate ANN is selected and saved.
- If the accuracy of the predictions from this ANN is too low, additional data are required to train the network. One option is to remove the experimental fatigue life data for one R ratio from the query database and insert these into the ANN training database. The training and interrogation process is repeated to determine the most accurate ANN.
- Additional fatigue life data sets for different R ratios can be added to the training inputs, thereby potentially increasing the accuracy of the output from the ANN. The process is repeated until the desired level of accuracy is achieved.
- The differences in the mechanical properties and fatigue responses of glass and carbon reinforced plastics mean that the use of CFRP fatigue life data to predict the fatigue lives

of glass-reinforced materials, or vice versa, is not recommended unless a large database of material properties is available.

- Similarly, the lay-up of the test coupons should be the same for all the materials evaluated by using the ANN. Further work is required to establish the influence of laminate lay-up on the predictive abilities of the ANN.

21.14   Comparison with other methods

An average rms error can give an indication of the performance of a numerical model. This metric has been used earlier. Another approach for evaluating the accuracy of a predictive technique is to compare its output with that of other statistical approaches. Many statistical life-prediction techniques have been developed. Sendeckyj[16] divides these life-prediction models into four groups:

- empirical, e.g. Hahn;[17]
- residual strength, e.g. Yang;[18]
- stiffness degradation, e.g. Highsmith and Reifsnider;[19]
- actual damage mechanisms, e.g. Wang and co-workers.[20]

However, it is not a straightforward task to compare the results of models, especially if the outputs from techniques from different groups (i–iv, above) are compared. The various fatigue theories use different parameters for measuring the fatigue damage. As a result each model gives its prediction of fatigue life in unique terms.

Residual strength and stiffness degradation models are relatively easy to compare. The outputs from the respective groups of models can be equated readily. The actual damage-mechanism fatigue theories do not provide a prediction of fatigue life at all. These theories do not include an ultimate failure criterion. Instead damage-mechanism models, as their group name suggests, use an experimental means of analysing the damage resulting from fatigue, e.g. matrix crack density. Therefore, these three groups of models need the required intermediate data (residual strength, modulus, matrix crack density) to be collected during fatigue testing. This intermediate information either was not available for the composite materials in the existing database or was not collected during this project. The ANN was not trained with residual strength or intermediate modulus data. Moreover, the ANN output described failure due to fatigue damage. Therefore, the results of the fatigue life predictions from the ANN could not be compared readily with any of the above models.

The remaining group of fatigue life prediction hypotheses consists of the empirical models. However, a direct comparison of the outputs from the ANN and the results from any of the empirical theories was still difficult. The majority of the empirical fatigue models derive material constants as part of the analyses. These parameters are material specific. As a result it is difficult to translate the results of one study across to another project.

One model has been developed which allows the ANN fatigue life predictions to be compared with another statistical technique. The constant-life model[21] uses fatigue life parameters similar to those of the ANN analysis. The outputs from the two approaches are also similar. This allows a comparison to be made between the predictions of fatigue life from the constant-life model and the ANN. The comparison can take the form of using prior knowledge of other composite systems plus some limited data on the material under investigation to predict a set of S–N curves for this 'new' material. The following describes a comparative study that was undertaken as part of research activities at the University of Bath.

Prior knowledge was taken for three CFRP composite systems (T800/5245, T800/924 and HTA/913) and took the form of the fatigue life data for five ratios. These data were combined with the tensile and compression strengths for each material. The material under investigation was IM7/977. The limited existing information used in the models was the fatigue life data for $R = 0.1$ and, the tensile and compression strengths for IM7/977.

Before the comparison study is discussed the constant-life model will be described briefly. A more complete description of this model can be found in Chapter 20 of this book. The constant-life model is applied to the fatigue life prediction of composite materials in the following manner. The fatigue life data are plotted for a known and similar composite system to the material under investigation. In this case T800/924 was selected. Third-order polynomial curves are then fitted to the fatigue life data. The full data set, rather than the median-life data, is preferred as it is believed to give more accurate results where the S–N curve is very flat. This is often the case for high-performance carbon-fibre-reinforced plastics at $R = 0.1$.

The three coefficients determined from the curve-fitting exercise are then input into a spreadsheet along with the monotonic tension and compressive strengths σ_t and σ_c, respectively. By using equation [21.20], data pairs (m, a) are calculated.

$$a = f(1 + m)^u(c + m)^v \tag{21.20}$$

where $a = \sigma_{alt}/\sigma_t$, $m = \sigma_m/\sigma_t$, $\sigma_{alt} = \frac{1}{2}(\sigma_{max} - \sigma_{min})$, $\sigma_m = \frac{1}{2}(\sigma_{max} + \sigma_{min})$ and $c = \sigma_c/\sigma_t$.

For the first fit the constants f, u and v are taken to be the same as for a similar and known composite material, again T800/924.

The data pairs (m, a) are then plotted along with the normalized tensile strength σ_t and compression strengths, σ_c. By using the parameters f, u and v for T800/924, a normalized constant-life diagram is created. These plots contains curves for given lives. These lives are selected as providing the window of most use to design engineers: 10^4, 10^5 and 10^6 cycles.

The actual values for IM7/977 for $R = 0.1$ at the given number of cycles are then added to the plot. The values of u and v are altered to ensure that the curves fit the actual data. The middle curve, 10^5 cycles, is created first. This is achieved by setting $u = v$ and fitting the constant-life curve generated by equation [21.20] to the monotonic end-points and the one fatigue point ($R = 0.1$) for IM7/977. By adjusting u, the constant-life curves for 10^4 and 10^6 are created. The dependence of u (and v) on the constant-life curves is thus determined. The appropriate values of u and v for a given log(number of cycles) are then input into equation [21.20] along with a value of f. Other work[22] has shown that $f = 1.3$ is an appropriate value for this task. A second equation:

$$a = m\frac{(1 - R)}{(1 + R)} \tag{21.21}$$

where a and m are the same as in equation [21.20] and R is the ratio of minimum to peak stress, is needed. By simultaneously solving equations [21.20] and [21.21] various peak stresses and corresponding cycles to failure for given R ratios can be calculated. These data pairs can then be plotted as standard S–N curves.

The results of the fatigue-life predictions from the constant-life model and from the ANN are both plotted in Fig. 21.10. The actual median-life S–N curves are also displayed in this figure. The solid lines describe the actual medial lives. The dashed lines with solid markers represent the predicted median-life curves from the constant-life model. The dotted lines with open symbols describe the ANN median-life predictions.

It is still difficult to make a direct comparison as the constant-life model starts with a set

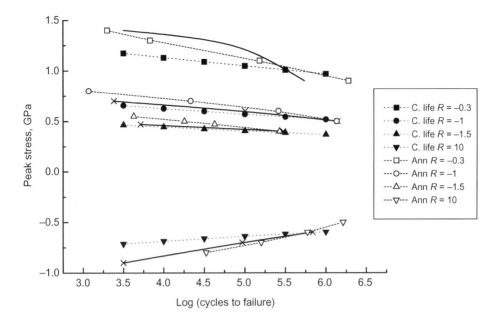

Fig. 21.10 *S–N* curves for the two models and the actual fatigue-life data for IM7/977. The solid lines are created from the actual data for the fatigue lives. The dotted lines with open symbols describe the estimates produced by the ANN. The dashed lines with filled markers represent the curves predicted by the constant-life model.

number of cycles to failure whereas the ANN is trained to predict a given number of cycles to failure. However, it can be seen from Fig. 21.10 that both models give good predictions of the actual fatigue response for IM7/977. The constant-life model predicted *S–N* curves for *R* = –1 and *R* = –1.5 show a high level of agreement with the experimental data. However, the constant-life model predicted curves for the other two *R* ratios, –0.3 and 10, do not follow the experimental data as closely. The constant-life model does not appear to be able to capture the non-linear nature of the *S–N* curves for *R* = –0.3 and *R* = 10. Although the constant-life predicted curves for *R* = –0.3 and R = 10 are less accurate, they give safe predictions. Both these predicted curves are conservative which is more acceptable from a designer's point of view.

The ANN model does not predict the *S–N* curves for *R* = –1 and *R* = –1.5 as closely as the constant-life model. The ANN predicted *S–N* plots are non-conservative. The ANN predicted peak stresses for given cycles to failure are all higher than the actual data for both *S–N* curves. However, the ANN predicted fatigue-lives follow the trend of the actual data. There is a close correlation between the ANN and the actual *S–N* curves. The predicted *S–N* curves for *R* = –0.3 and *R* =10 given by the ANN are closer to the actual data than those given by the constant-life model. Like the constant-life model the ANN does not capture the non-linear nature of the *R* = –0.3 *S–N* curve. Instead the ANN predicts a straight line with a gradient which appears to average out the values of the actual data. Apart from the fatigue response at a large number of cycles, the ANN gives conservative results. The ANN predicted curve for *R* = 10 shows excellent agreement with the actual data. In this case the ANN has accurately predicted a non-linear *S–N* curve. Moreover, the plot coincides almost exactly with the actual data.

The above discussion suggests that the predicted outputs for fatigue-lives from the ANN compare favourably with an existing statistical technique. Therefore, this increases confidence in the use of ANNs for this application.

21.15   Future trends

Advancing technology has placed higher and higher demands on materials performance over the last few decades. Conventional materials have become increasingly unable to meet these new requirements. Consequently, there has been an upsurge in the research and application of different material types such as composite systems. The characterization of these materials will require new tools and techniques to be developed if the necessary test data are to be delivered to the design community in a timely manner and to an acceptable level of quality. ANN software has the potential to be part of this suite of analysis tools.

As computing power increases so the speed of parallel processing will rise. In addition to speeding up the design process, this will allow more model iterations to be evaluated or more complex problems to be tackled. For example, the response of a material to impact, thermal conditioning and mechanical fatigue could be analysed simultaneously.

The power of ANN software is more likely to be realized when the ANN is combined with other laws, rules or knowledge-based systems. This will permit *a priori* knowledge to be captured and presented to the ANN. By allowing the ANN to concentrate on the classification and pattern recognition of a reduced and relevant data set, this will potentially enhance the effectiveness of the system.

Ultimately it is envisaged that ANN software will be integrated with the standard computer-aided design (CAD) or finite-element packages as part of a digital enterprise. In this way the ANN will be transparent to the CAD user but the software will guide the design process acting in a similar fashion to an expert system.

21.16   Acknowledgements

We are grateful to the Engineering and Physical Science Research Council for financial support of this programme of work. We acknowledge the many contributions of Professor B. Harris who was associated with all of this work and who was a co-recipient of the research grant that made it possible. We also acknowledge the importance of the availability of a large experimental database obtained in the course of a series of programmes supported by the Ministry of Defence through the former Royal Aircraft Establishment at Farnborough.

21.17   References

1. BEALE R and JACKSON T (1992), *Neural computing: an introduction*, IOP Publishing Ltd, Bristol, p. 5.
2. HEBB D O (1949), *The organisation of behaviour*, Wiley, New York.
3. BISHOP C M (1995), *Neural networks for pattern recognition*, Clarendon Press, Oxford.
4. MCCULLOCH W S and PITTS W (1943), A logical calculus of the ideas immanent in nervous activity, *Bulletin of Mathematical Biophysics*, **5**, 115–133.
5. ROSENBLATT F (1962), *Principles of neurodynamics: perceptrons and the theory of brain mechanisms*, Spartan Books, New York.
6. MINSKY M and PAPERT S (1969), *Perceptrons: an introduction to computational geometry*, MIT Press, Massachusetts.

7. HOPFIELD J J (1982), Neural networks and physical systems with emergent collective properties, *Proc. Nat. Acad. Sci.*, **79**, 2554–2558.

8. MCCLELLAND J L and RUMELHART D E (1987), *Parallel distributed processing: explorations in the microstructure of cognition*, vol 1: *Foundations*, MIT Press, Massachusetts.

9. ROBBINS H and MONRO S (1951), A stochastic approximation method, *Annals of Math. Stats.*, **22**, 400–407.

10. PLAUT D, NOWLAN S and HINTON G E (1986), Experiments on learning by back propagation, Technical report CMU-CS-86-126, Dept. of computer science, Carnegie Mellon University, Pittsburgh, USA.

11. POWELL M J D (1987), Radial basis functions for multi-variable interpolation: a review. In Mason J C and Cox M G (Eds.), *Algorithms for approximation*, Clarendon Press, Oxford, pp. 143–167.

12. TOUCHE ROSS AND CO. (1993), *Best practice guidelines for developing neural computing applications – overview*, Department of Trade and Industry, May, p. 12.

13. BISHOP C M (1995), Neural networks: a principled perspective, Neural computing research group report, NCRG/95/014, Aston University.

14. LEE J A, ALMOND D P and HARRIS B (1999), The use of neural networks for the prediction of fatigue lives of composite materials, *Composites*, **A3**, 1159–1169.

15. WHITNEY, J M (1981), *Fatigue of fibrous composite materials* STP 723, American Society for Testing and Materials, Philadelphia, USA, pp. 133–151.

16. SENDECKYJ G P (1991), Life prediction for resin–matrix composite materials, in Reifsnider K L (Ed), *Fatigue of composite materials*, Elsevier Science Publishers B.V., Amsterdam, pp. 431–484.

17. HAHN H T (1979), Fatigue behaviour and life prediction of composite laminates, in Tsai S W (Ed.), *Proc. 5th conf. on composite materials: testing and design*, ASTM, STP 674, pp. 383–417.

18. YANG, J N (1977), Reliability prediction for composites under periodic proof tests in service, in *Proc. 4th conf. on Composite Materials: Testing and Design*, ASTM, STP 617, pp. 272–295.

19. HIGHSMITH A L and REIFSNIDER K L (1982), Stiff-reduction mechanisms in composite laminates, in Reifsnider K L (Ed.), *Damage in Composite Materials*, ASTM, STP 775, pp. 103–117.

20. CHOU P C, WANG A S D and MILLER H (1982), Cumulative damage model for advanced composite materials, AFWAL-TR-84-4083, Sept.

21. HARRIS B, GATHERCOLE N, LEE J A, REITER H and ADAM T (1997), Life prediction for constant-stress fatigue in carbon-fibre composites, *Phil. Trans. Roy. Soc., Lond. A*, **355**, 1259–1294.

22. GATHERCOLE N, HARRIS B, REITER H and ADAM T (1994), Fatigue damage growth and life prediction for CFRP composites, 3rd Progress report on Research agreement no. CB/FRN/9/4/2112097, DRA, Farnborough, UK.

Part V

Fatigue in practical situations

22

The fatigue performance of composite structural components

M. D. Gilchrist, University College Dublin, Ireland

22.1   Introduction

Over the past 20 years, or more, extensive research has been conducted into the fatigue behaviour of fibre-reinforced plastics (FRP). Much of this work has concentrated on unidirectional materials in an attempt to understand the underlying failure mechanisms and the role played by the fibre, the matrix, and the fibre/matrix interface. More recently, attention has shifted to multi-directional laminates, and the development of fatigue damage has been characterized.

The general perception is that FRP composites are not susceptible to fatigue. However, this view is only sustainable when considering unidirectional materials, and the fact that it appears relevant to multidirectional materials is only because of the low design strain limits imposed to counter the effects of impact damage.[1] If design limits are raised, to benefit from fibres with higher failure strain, say, then the increased strains on the matrix are certain to mean that fatigue will become a problem.[2]

Perhaps not surprisingly, in view of the number of test specimens needed, and the associated expense, little published information is available on the fatigue of FRP structures (as opposed to FRP materials). It is clear that the crucial issue encountered with most structures, but not often with simple coupons, is the presence of through-thickness stresses. Such stresses are most likely to cause failure.[3] One of the difficulties encountered during design is identifying regions of the structure where these stresses may exist; if the stresses are not recognized, steps cannot be taken to mitigate their effect.

The present chapter reviews recent published work that covers general methodology, damage development and applications. Many of the studies have an aeronautical bias, but the general points should apply in other fields.

22.2   General approach

Several methodologies have been used to validate the fatigue performance of composite structures.[3] Although these approaches have been developed for aerospace in order to get airworthiness certification, they could be used for other types of structure. The procedures are based on a 'pyramidal' scheme involving a large number of coupon tests, through structural details to sub-component testing and, finally, a small number (possibly as small as one) of component tests. Clearly, predictive methods are urgently required to reduce the cost of testing.

22.2.1   Damage-tolerance methodology

The damage-tolerance approach assumes that the largest undetectable defect exists at the most critical location in the structure, and that structural integrity is maintained throughout defect growth, which should be discovered at the next scheduled inspection. The present state of knowledge suggests that designs should be based on zero growth, the final, rapid-growth phase being much shorter than the initiation phase.

   To support this methodology appropriate analytical and experimental studies are required. The stress/structural analysis should identify the critical parts of the structure and be capable of calculating the details of the associated three-dimensional stress distribution. Potential danger sites are free edges, bolt holes, cut-outs, ply terminations, section changes, skin/stringer junctions, etc., as well as areas of impact damage and manufacturing flaws. The experimental programme should simulate, as appropriate, the conditions that exist in the full-scale component.

   A significant drawback of this approach is, currently, the absence of reliable failure criteria, especially for mixed-mode delamination growth. Also, present finite-element technology does not permit detailed study of all, or even a few, of the critical sites in a large structure.

22.2.2   Safe-life/reliability methodology

A statistically-based approach can be used to determine strength, life and reliability of composite structures. The success of this methodology relies on the choice of the population model, the two-parameter Weibull model being frequently employed.

   A further key requirement is the availability of a sufficiently complete test database; clearly an expensive operation. As noted above, a pyramidal building-block approach is needed and the tests should encompass the effects of the operating environment and through-thickness properties (in addition to the commonly determined in-plane character-istics). The database should describe, to the desired level of confidence, the failure mode, the data scatter and the variability of the structural response.

   A particular problem with this, and indeed the previous, methodology is the need to characterize out-of-plane failures. Whilst some delamination modes are well understood, recognized test techniques do not exist for tensile failure and the increased environmental sensitivity can lead to high scatter. Failure to correctly predict the failure mode of the structure or component would indicate the inapplicability of this methodology.

22.2.3   Wear-out methodology

Wear-out methodology has been successfully applied to a number of major components on US military aircraft.[3] The drawback of the method is the (current) need to conduct a proof test on full-scale components. The method relies on adequate definition of the critical load conditions for static tests, and for residual strength and stiffness tests after fatigue cycling. The approach is ideally suited to developmental structures and has the merit that 'gates' can

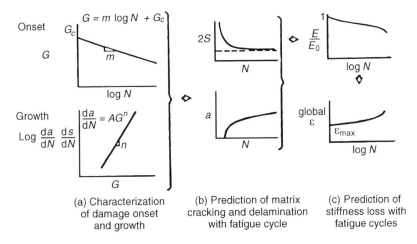

Fig. 22.1   The prediction of stiffness loss and strain increase from energy release rate data.[7]

be imposed on the use of the component as test programmes proceed. On the basis of adequate knowledge of their variability, the method could be applied to production quality components, with a much reduced level of full-scale proof testing.

The reduction in strength is described in terms of a 'wear-out rate' which, in turn, depends on a damage accumulation rate, and ways of measuring the latter. Damage mechanics studies, such as those of Beaumont and co-workers at the University of Cambridge,[4] and Chapter 13 are expected to improve the prediction of damage development and thus enhance the capabilities of the wear-out methodology.

22.3   Damage growth and life prediction

The types of damage seen in composites under fatigue loading have been studied in great detail and widely reported.[5,6] In essence, matrix cracking occurs very early in the life (during the first few loading cycles), followed later by delamination and eventually fibre fracture. Highest rates of damage growth are seen within the first 10% and final 10% of the life.

Much valuable work has also been done, albeit mainly on simple coupons, by researchers at NASA, Langley, particularly by O'Brien on delamination initiation and growth. In a recent paper O'Brien[7] outlines an approach for predicting fatigue life which is based on a damage tolerance philosophy. As O'Brien points out, a principal difficulty is that delamination growth occurs very rapidly over a small range of load, and hence of the strain energy release rate G, which is used to characterize growth. Because of the associated uncertainty an alternative, and conservative, approach would be to set design strain levels below the threshold for delamination growth.

O'Brien's approach is based on relating damage growth to stiffness reduction which, of course, depends on lay-up, fibre and matrix moduli, matrix crack spacing and density, delamination area, etc. Equations are quoted for stiffness loss due to matrix cracking, edge delaminations and delaminations growing from matrix cracks (see Appendix). Data are required from which damage growth can be characterised, as illustrated in Fig. 22.1. The technique is expected to work well when one type of damage predominates. However, its application in general, when several mechanisms interact, is unlikely to be straightforward.

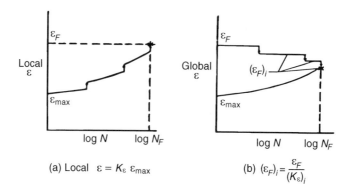

Fig. 22.2   Effective reduction in ε_F due to local delamination accumulation through the laminate's thickness.[7] Suffix F denotes failure.

Although characteristic curves can be obtained, the interaction of mechanisms means that these are no longer generic (i.e. related to a 'material' parameter such as G), but depend on 'structural' variables such as ply thickness and stacking sequence.

Even assuming that a generic description of stiffness loss with cycles could be obtained, this alone is insufficient; final failure (0°-ply fracture) is also governed by local strain concentrations. The suggested mechanism is that matrix cracks, which themselves will not provoke 0° fibre failure, cause local delaminations, and an accumulation of the latter through the thickness at a particular location raises the local fibre strain to the ultimate value, albeit at a global strain below that to cause monotonic failure (see Fig. 22.2(a)).

An alternative view of this failure process is shown in Fig. 22.2(b). The effective global failure strain is assumed to decrease each time a new, local, delamination forms until final failure occurs. Such an approach does not require a prediction of damage growth with cycles provided the laminate stiffness loss, and hence the increase in global strain, can be monitored in real-time. In this case the decrease in effective failure strain is given by an appropriate strain concentration factor (see Appendix). However, for structures, as opposed to coupons, real-time stiffness monitoring is likely to be impractical and a criterion of no damage growth should be adopted.

O'Brien verified the approach just described for quasi-isotropic glass-fibre/epoxy test coupons in zero-tension fatigue. He also suggests that the method can be used for compressive loading although fail-safety of the laminate would then be assessed on the likelihood of local or global laminate buckling, arising from accumulated delaminations rather than on tensile failure of the 0° plies. For application of the technique to structures it is assumed that the relevant characterizations are conducted on materials identical to those used in the structure, under identical environments and loading conditions.

A more appropriate, i.e. structural, prediction is made by Liao and Reifsnider[8] for a CFRP hip implant. Whilst the approach has general applicability it is, effectively, only two-dimensional and hence could not identify the through-thickness stresses that often cause structural failure.[3] The authors use a strength-of-materials approach, essentially a beam idealization, to calculate the stress distribution in the component, on the premise that a finite-element analysis would be too costly. This issue demonstrates the dilemma underlying predictive methods; a detailed (3D) stress analysis is required to identify the critical through-thickness stresses, but hardware and software limitations often make such an FE analysis impractical.

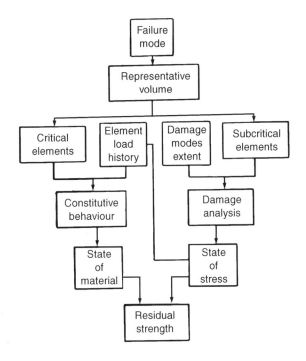

Fig. 22.3   Conceptual diagram of the critical element model.[8]

The life prediction of Liao and Reifsnider[8] is based on a critical-element concept, as shown in Fig. 22.3. Firstly, the failure mode of the component is established (either by monotonic testing, by computation or by experience). According to the associated failure mechanism(s), a representative volume in the component is identified. The process of property degradation as a result of damage accumulation in this representative volume eventually causes failure of the component. The volume is subdivided into critical and subcritical elements. The latter sustain damage (e.g. matrix cracking) during cycling causing a redistribution of stresses which leads, eventually to failure of the critical elements (and, hence, the structure). The response of subcritical elements is determined by mechanics analysis and of critical elements by phenomenological information (e.g. an S–N curve) and constitutive equations. Finally, it is suggested, the residual strength is given by applying a failure criterion (e.g. Tsai-Hill) to the critical element.

The success of the method is clearly dependent on selecting the correct representative volume, i.e. on identifying from the stress analysis the cross-section at which failure is most likely to occur. Whilst this might be carried out with some confidence for beam-like components, it is obviously more problematic for a complex structure.

Another simplified method is given by Chamis and Ginty,[9] again based on laminate analysis and hence omitting through-thickness stresses. A number of assumptions are made: all ply strengths are degraded at the same rate by fatigue; all types of fatigue (mechanical, thermal, moisture) degrade laminate strength linearly on a semilog plot. All types of defect are modelled as an equivalent circular hole and stress concentration factors calculated for positions around the circumference. From these the maximum ply stresses are calculated.

The method, outlined by Shiao and Murthy[10] is used to predict damage initiation only. However, a number of empirical 'constants' are required and this undermines the generic nature of the approach.

22.4   An approach to full-scale testing

Currently no methodology exists for predicting the fatigue life of a structure. Consequently one, or more, tests on the full-scale component are always required. For complex structures two difficulties arise; characterizing the full-scale loads (magnitude, frequency, spectrum) and representing these loads on the test specimen (support positions, actuator locations, load magnitudes, directions and frequencies).

A rigorous approach to this problem is given by Tomashofski *et al.*[11] Although applied to helicopter fuselages, the technique could be used for other applications such as cars, off-shore structures, wind turbines, etc. The method, referred to by Tomashofski *et al.* as generalized force determination (GFD) allows one to calculate the forces that should be applied to the test actuators to simulate the real-life environment, and to modify the test rig if necessary.

A prerequisite for the technique is an accurate assessment of the, in their case flight, loads acting on the structures. Thus, it is implied that appropriate instrumentation has been installed to measure strains and accelerations on a sufficient number of representative full-scale structures for the real-life loading to be characterized. This does not mean, of course, conducting the measurements over the lifetime of the structure; it is merely necessary to identify the pattern of forces/strains/frequencies to which the item is subjected.

The structural response and the test specimen excitations are related by the matrix equation:

$$X = YF \tag{22.1}$$

In equation [22.1], X is a vector of actual structural responses (strains and/or accelerations) measured at selected points on actual structures in normal operation; F is a vector of excitations to be applied to the test specimen; Y a matrix of response derivatives. For example,

$$Y_{ij} = \delta X_{ij}/\delta F_j$$

represents the structural response at location i due to a unit excitation at location j.

In applying equation [22.1] it is assumed that the excitations are of sufficient magnitude to ensure linear structural response (Y_{ij} are functions of frequency only). The objective is to determine F, having first obtained Y by calibration of the test specimen. The calibration is achieved by applying m sets of independent loads (m actuator locations) and measuring responses using the same n parameters as those in the real-life monitoring. Care may need to be taken in selecting the m sets of loads and ensuring that Y is of appropriate form ('informationally conditioned'), as explained by Tomashofski *et al.*[12]

$$Y = X_c F_c^{-1} \tag{22.2}$$

where the subscript c indicates the calibration test.

Next the test excitations F_t required for a specified actual condition (flight, say) X_f are found from

$$F_t = Y^{-1} X_f \tag{22.3}$$

At this stage it is possible to identify inconsistent load distributions or unrealistic actuator load magnitudes, and actuators can be repositioned. Finally the predicted test response X_t is given by:

$$X_t = YF_t \tag{22.4}$$

22.5   Reliability

As a consequence of the non-fail safe nature of metal rotor blades, the helicopter industry has developed techniques for assessing the reliability of fatigue-loaded components. The traditional approach has been to calculate a safe life (number of hours or cycles) after which the item is replaced, whether, or not, it has suffered damage.[13] This extremely conservative approach, implying large factors of safety, uses factored S–N curves (mean minus 3 standard deviations) together with extreme ('top of scatter') values of loads. Essentially, this is a deterministic approach in that it is assumed that the variation of the various parameters with cycles can be represented by equations.

It has been shown, for metal components, that such a deterministic approach gives the safe life with a reliability exceeding 0.999999.[14] The latter analysis is based on representing load and strength variables by appropriate statistical distributions from which probabilities can be calculated. A larger range of variables is addressed, again for metals, by Viswanathan et al.[15]

The general approach is applied to a composite component by Krasnowski and Viswanathan[16] with the objective of determining the reliability of a new structure before it enters service. Clearly this is a more difficult task than with metals in view of the complex damage forms seen in composites. Two issues are considered: 'durability', defined as the probability that the part will not be removed from service as a result of finding visible delamination; and 'reliability', defined as the probability that the part will not fail during service as a consequence of either catastrophic fracture or no longer meeting functional requirements (e.g. a large drop in stiffness).

The durability is clearly influenced by whether or not the structure is inspected, as illustrated in Fig. 22.4. The mathematical analysis allows calculation of either the durability at the end of specified inspection intervals, or the determination of required inspection intervals to obtain a desired durability.

The reliability analysis[16] depends on defining a load spectrum and a strength spectrum, the latter necessarily being based on coupon (rather than full-scale) tests, together with data on energy release rates for delamination growth (the only damage type considered). The coupon tests would be conducted for material, environment and loading conditions identical to those used for the full-scale structure being designed.

The method was illustrated by application to a GRP main rotor yoke. S–N and reliability curves for failure (in this case stiffness loss) were found for yokes that were both inspectable and non-inspectable.

A similar approach to calculating reliability, but based on a general description of damage, is given by Talreja.[17]

22.6   Applications

22.6.1   Metal–matrix composites

Metal matrix composites have potential applications as pistons within diesel engines. Myers and Chi[18] found that both the tensile mechanical and thermal fatigue properties of aluminium alloy reinforced with ceramic fibres were improved over those of unreinforced materials in the range of maximum engine operating temperature. Two different ceramic fibres were considered: Saffil, manufactured by ICI, and Fibrefrax, by Carborundum, having alumina/silica percentage compositions by weight of 96/4 and 48/52, respectively. A squeeze-forming process (squeeze casting) was used to infiltrate preforms at volume fractions of 0.10

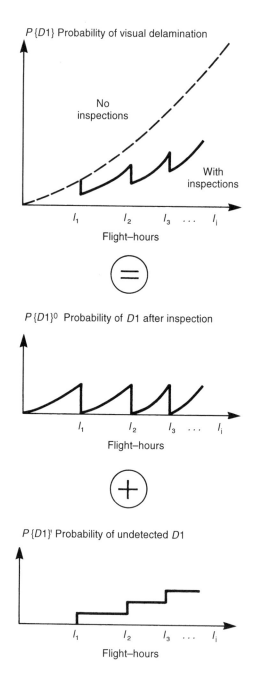

Fig. 22.4   Probability of visual delamination D1 with inspections at intervals I_i.[16]

and 0.15, giving discs of material of 114 mm diameter and 25 mm thickness. Test coupons were machined from these discs such that the longitudinal axis of the specimens lay in the plane of a disc. Tensile specimens had a cylindrical gauge section of length 30.5 mm and uniform diameter 6.35 mm whereas fatigue specimens were of 19 mm gauge length and

5 mm diameter. Fatigue tests were carried out under axial strain control at 200, 350 and 400 °C with a load ratio of $R = -1$ in accordance with ASTM E606-80. A stress/strain parameter P, which accounted for the differences in material modulus due to the reinforcements as well as cyclic stress or strain amplitude, was used to compare the relative fatigue performance of the different materials:

$$P = [(\Delta\varepsilon/2)(\Delta\sigma/2)E]^{1/2}$$

Fatigue performance was presented in terms of stress/strain parameter versus the number of cycles to failure. At the highest temperature, i.e. 400 °C, the fatigue life of unreinforced alloy was approximately an order of magnitude less than that of the variously reinforced alloys, whilst at 200 °C the fatigue lives of unreinforced and reinforced materials were almost identical and were an order of magnitude greater than those at 400 °C.

22.6.2   Fibre-reinforced concrete

Fibre-reinforced concrete was shown to have increased fatigue life and ductility over those of plain concrete under both uniaxial and biaxial compressive load conditions.[19] The addition of fibres to concrete increased fatigue life since fibres were beneficial in resisting mortar cracking. Maximum strength increased by some 50% under biaxial compression fatigue when fibres were added to the cement whilst the increase under uniaxial load was almost negligible. Carbon steel fibres were used to reinforce concrete test specimens made with a Portland cement. The fibres were smooth with a cross-section of 0.01 in × 0.022 in and were 1 in long. The average tensile strength of the steel fibres was 414 MPa (60 ksi) and a 1% by volume of fibres was used. Plate specimens, of dimensions 6 in × 6 in × 1.5 in were cut from 6 in × 6 in × 20 in cast concrete blocks. Two different failure mechanisms were observed in the plain and fibre concrete. Plain concrete subjected to monotonic or fatigue compression failed due to a splitting mechanism: under uniaxial compression, splitting was along the loading direction perpendicular to the plate whilst the splitting was parallel to the plate under biaxial loading. Fibre-reinforced concrete under both monotonic and fatigue compression, however, failed as a result of the formation of fault planes.

22.6.3   Anchoring systems

Fini et al.[20] defined a fatigue test which reproduces the alternate bending stresses induced on an anchor insulator by Aeolian vibrations of a conductor. Such insulators are used for 132–150 kV overhead electricity wires and can consist of a composite core surrounded by an external protective housing, possibly of silicone rubber, and metallic end fittings which are linked to the core to transmit the mechanical load from the conductors to the core and from the core to the tower.[21] The composite core consists of between 0.4 to 0.7 volume fraction of unidirectional glass-fibre/resin. A mechanical fatigue test, at a frequency of 6.5 Hz, has been devised which subjects an insulator to cyclic bending such that the maximum strains reach 0.3%. At intervals during a fatigue test, the insulator is immersed in an acidic solution representing in-service environmental degradation. Ten million cycles have been estimated as the service life of an insulator. However, no insulators had been tested by the authors to this particular standard.

An anchorage system used by Budelmann et al.[22] was based on unidirectional E-glass fibres embedded in a polyester matrix (0.7 fibre volume fraction) which formed a 7.5 mm diameter tendon. The tendon was embedded in a polymer mortar and this was encased within a steel cylinder, as shown in Fig. 22.5. Fatigue failure was due to superficial wear, and

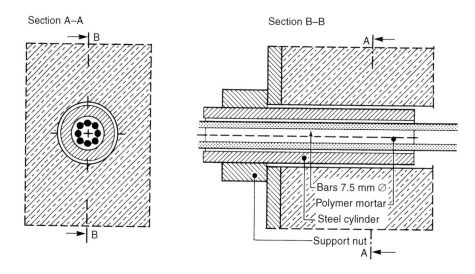

Fig. 22.5   Bond-anchored unidirectional GRP.[22] A steel tube, threaded on both sides, rests against concrete via a nut. The interstices between the GRP bars and the cylindrical tube are filled by a mortar composite of quartz sand and unsaturated polyester resin.

consequent fibre fracture, between the GRP tendons and the polymer mortar. The fatigue strength of these bond-anchored tendons proved to be only one third that of high-strength prestressed steel wire in wedge anchors.

22.6.4 Helicopters

A strategy for establishing fatigue design allowables governing composite helicopter structures was proposed by Rich and Maass[23] based on a constant life diagram (i.e. Goodman diagram). This required a range of R ratio tests, unlike extrapolating from $R = 0.1$ in metals, since the fatigue results exhibited a reduction in strength when tested under tension–compression ($R = -1.0$) from that of tension-tension ($R = 0.1$). However, this proposed strategy does not appear to have been adopted and developed into standardized industrial design procedures. In a similar exercise sponsored by the US Army,[24] manufacturers were invited to calculate the fatigue life, using their own particular calculation strategies,[25–30] of a hypothetical steel pitch link of 12.5 mm diameter with one thread per mm. The purpose of this exercise was to establish a standardized fatigue-analysis method. It is interesting to note that this was being done for metallic rather than composite components only some 20 years ago.

Maloney[31] described the fatigue behaviour of three different helicopter components: composite S-glass/epoxy main rotor blades for the AH-1 Cobra helicopter, a one half scale composite carbon/epoxy rotor hub for the CH-54 helicopter and a circulation control rotor for the H-2/CCR helicopter. Delaminations within the laminate of constant cross-section area were detected using ultrasonic C-scan after manufacture in two development blades for the AH-1. However, after a combined flight loading of 20×10^6 fatigue cycles and 10 000 ground-air-ground cycles, a comparison of initial and final scans for these blades and specimens revealed no significant change of the indicated delamination. The composite rotor hub was designed to sustain a load level above the endurance limit of existing hubs made from titanium forgings for no less than 10^6 cycles.

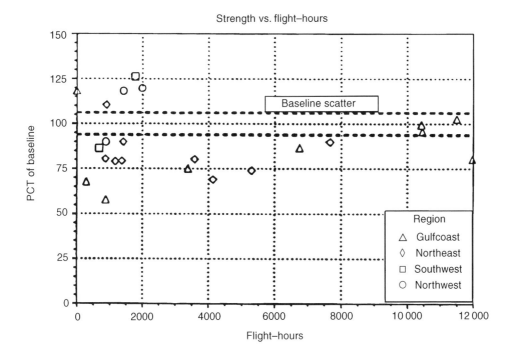

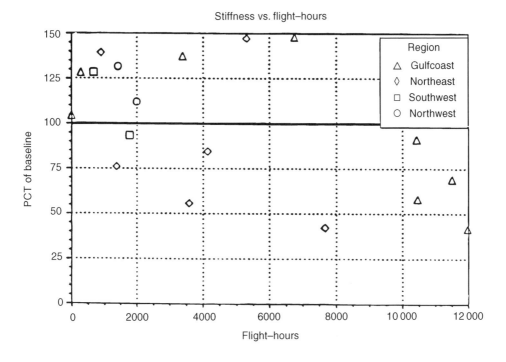

Fig. 22.6   Degradation of the strength and stiffness of forward fairings from Bell 206L LongRanger helicopter.[32]

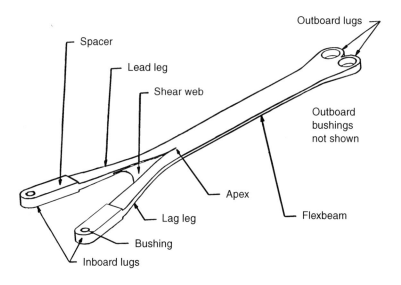

Fig. 22.7   Composite main rotor flexbeam.[33]

In the course of testing, a fatigue crack developed after 602 000 cycles from one of the attachment bolt holes in the central metal element of the pan plate, which was bonded to the carbon/epoxy plate material. After increasing the bolt clamp-up, the test was continued to 10^6 cycles without any development of damage from the metal into the composite. The circulation control rotor for the H-2/CCR helicopter was made from a hybrid of carbon and glass fibres, together with an extruded aluminium spline. During fatigue tests, the metal proved to have poorer fatigue performance than the composite and a number of fatigue fractures occurred in the metal components. These fractures generally involved the complete cross-section of the aluminium extrusion but had very little progression into the composite laminate. In general the crack in the metal spline induced either a short corresponding crack in the composite or a small local delamination of the composite, both of which were limited in extent and non-propagating even after 5×10^6 cycles.

Smith and Wilson[32] investigated the in-service fatigue performance of four different external helicopter components: vertical fin, forward fairing (engine cowl), litter door and baggage door. The vertical fins were sandwich constructions made from T300/788 carbon/epoxy skins over a GRP honeycomb core, whilst Kevlar/epoxy was used in the manufacture of the other components. The various components were used for up to 12 000 flight–hours throughout North America, after which they were removed and tested for stiffness and residual strength in monotonic tests which duplicated their attachment to the actual airframe. The scatter of baseline strength data was established by destructively testing five sample parts for each component. Subsequent tests which fell within this baseline scatter were deemed to have no measurable change in strength. Baseline stiffness measurements were made on all parts except for the vertical fin. These initial stiffness values were the result of only a single sample for each component and consequently there was no scatter upon which to base subsequent test results. No trend was evident to indicate degradation of vertical fin strength and all of the tested fins maintained strength values greater than that required for certification. Figure 22.6 details the scatter recorded from the strength and stiffness tests of the forward fairings. The strengths of the forward fairings fell within 50%–125% of the mean baseline strength, although even when the strength had been degraded by 50% it was

(a)

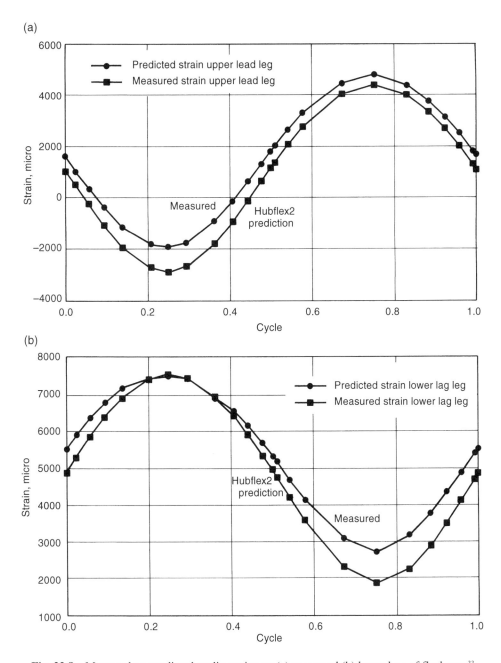

Fig. 22.8   Measured vs. predicted cyclic strains on (a) upper and (b) lower legs of flexbeam.[33]

well above the required level for a fairing. Stiffness measurements on the forward fairings fell within 40%–150% of baseline. This was supposedly due to the use of an insufficiently sensitive dial gauge to monitor displacements. The litter doors had stiffness values well below the baseline stiffness. This was most likely due to delaminations in small areas near the edges and hinges. Strength and stiffness of the baggage doors were up to 50% and 70%, respectively, of the baseline data.

A composite main rotor flexbeam, shown in Fig. 22.7, which has integral lugs to attach it to the central hub and to a rotor blade, has been developed by McDonnell Douglas. The flexbeam is made from glass/epoxy composite with the primary load bearing fibres being unidirectional S2-glass. Reinforcing plies are made from E-glass cloth placed at ±45°. E-glass plies at the flexbeam mid-plane are designated as the shear web whilst the unidirectional loops above and below this web are interspersed with 10% ±45° cloth. The strain levels which existed in the legs of the flexbeam were measured during a single fatigue cycle and compared against those predicted using in-house finite element software, as shown in Fig. 22.8. Fatigue tests on developmental flexbeams[33] indicated that failure initiated from the delamination of a ply although, after significant delamination had occurred, the flexbeam was able to sustain the span-wise centrifugal force for at least 1.3 additional lifetimes.

Mardoian and Ezzo[34] tested the fatigue performance of three horizontal stabilizers and eight tail rotor spars which were taken from Sikorsky S-76 helicopters over a 9-year period and had accumulated up to 6000 flight hours. The horizontal stabilizers, made from ±45° Kevlar/epoxy with carbon/epoxy beam cap reinforcements, had been designed for monotonic loading, whilst the tail rotor spars, of unidirectional carbon/epoxy, were primarily designed to withstand fatigue loads. The monotonic design loads on the left and right sides of a horizontal stabilizer are given in Fig. 22.9, together with the location and magnitudes of the loads used in full-scale fatigue tests. The monotonic design loads are not identical for the left and right sides of the stabilizer since its design condition is asymmetric. Fatigue tests on the tail rotor spars consisted of combined edgewise (in-plane) and flat-wise bending together with a steady centrifugal (axial) load and torsion. The constant centrifugal load corresponded to the centrifugal force on a rotor operating at 110% of the normal speed, whilst the cyclic loads were in phase and their absolute values were varied to cause fatigue failure within 10^5 to 5×10^5 cycles. Comparison of the roll and yaw moment versus cycles to fracture curves for the stabilizers to that of an unused production stabilizer revealed no difference, whilst the cyclic shear stress vs. cycles to crack initiation for the tail rotor spars was within 5% of certification data.

22.6.5 Pipes and cylinders

Lucas and Sainsbury-Carter[35] and Salkind[36] tested the axial fatigue performance of thin-walled tubular specimens with a view to recommending that they be used for characterizing the behaviour of composite materials since, for most laminate design applications, the internal stress state approaches that within a cylindrical specimen. This is because most laminate edges are actually bonded to a finite stiffness supporting structure, for the purpose of load introduction, and consequently the induced interlaminar shear stresses are small and do not contribute to the primary stress state within the component. The tubular specimens were fabricated by winding 75 mm wide tape around a 38 mm diameter mandrel such that fibre orientations were ±45° to the major axis of the specimen.

A total of 78 thin-walled, 25.4 mm diameter tubular carbon/epoxy (T300/1034) tubes, of lay-ups $[0°/90°]_s$ were tested under fatigue conditions by Francis et al.[37] Axial tension, torsion and biaxial cyclic tests were run at 5 Hz whilst internal pressure cycling was done at 0.5 Hz, a limitation imposed by the testing system. A stress ratio of $R = 0.1$ was used in all cases. Each tube contained a 4.8 mm diameter circular hole penetrating one wall midway along the tube length. It transpired that the S–N curve for the $[0°/90°]_s$ notched tubes was very flat under axial fatigue (no 'wear-out'). In other words, if a specimen survived the first loading cycle, stress relaxation appeared to take place in the matrix, resulting in a more homogeneous stress state within the tube. Peak strains were recorded throughout most of the

(a) S-76 horizontal stabilizer static limit design loading

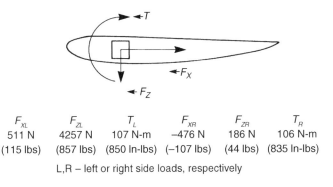

F_{XL}	F_{ZL}	T_L	F_{XR}	F_{ZR}	T_R
511 N	4257 N	107 N-m	−476 N	186 N	106 N-m
(115 lbs)	(857 lbs)	(850 In-lbs)	(−107 lbs)	(44 lbs)	(835 In-lbs)

L,R – left or right side loads, respectively

(b) S-76 horizontal stabilizer location and magnitude of fatigue test loads

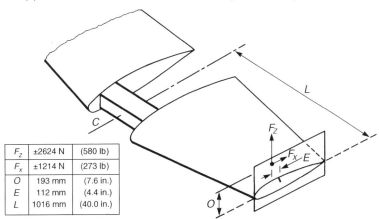

F_Z	±2624 N	(580 lb)
F_X	±1214 N	(273 lb)
O	193 mm	(7.6 in.)
E	112 mm	(4.4 in.)
L	1016 mm	(40.0 in.)

Fig. 22.9   Static design loads and full scale fatigue loads on the horizontal stabilizer of a Sikorsky S76 helicopter.[34]

uniaxial tests although high strains and long test duration caused premature strain gauge failure in many cases. However, some gauges survived entire fatigue tests until ultimate failure of the tube and plots of normalized strain, $\varepsilon/\varepsilon_0$ (ε_0 = strain on first cycle), against fatigue cycles indicated that the onset of failure could be detected for certain matrix dominated loading modes. For instance, in the case of the $[\pm45°]_s$ notched tubes, strain increased quite rapidly just prior to failure for both the axial tension and internal pressure fatigue tests.

The torsional fatigue behaviour of carbon-fibre/epoxy cylinders was compared for cylinders having fibres oriented parallel to the longitudinal cylindrical axis and at angles of ±45° to the axis by Fujczak.[38] The slopes of the two S–N curves were almost parallel to each other (Fig. 22.10). However, a plot of shear strain, obtained by measuring the angle of twist of the cylinder over a known length, against fatigue cycles indicated that shear strain is a more sensitive parameter for describing fatigue life than torsional stress in the cylinders. Furthermore, shear strain of cylinders at any given time during the fatigue life indicated that the remaining life of the component is independent of the fibre orientation (Fig. 22.11).

Owen and Griffiths[39] attempted to evaluate various criteria for predicting the failure of

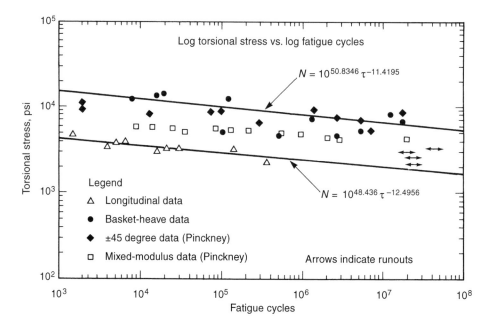

Fig. 22.10   Torsional *S–N* curve of carbon-fibre/epoxy cylinders.[38]

thin-walled tubes of glass-fabric-reinforced polyester resin subjected to both monotonic and fatigue axial loading and internal pressure. Some 370 tubes that were tested had been manufactured by wrapping sections of resin-soaked fabric through some five turns around a mandrel with a 40 mm circumferential overlap. Earlier work[40] confirmed that flat laminates had equal strengths in the warp and weft directions of the fabric. The overlap joint was seen to affect the cylinder response at low cycles but became negligible at 10^6 cycles. The overlap region tended to delaminate at high stresses and thereby precipitated complete failure. This was not observed at lower fatigue stresses.

The fatigue failure of five filament-wound glass/epoxy pipes over different ranges of internal cyclic pressure, applied with a pressurized water supply, has been investigated by Frost.[41] An approximately saw-tooth waveform was used with a maximum frequency of 0.15 Hz. Leak-detection wire was wrapped around each pipe to monitor pipe leakage. The pipes tested were of internal diameter 3 in with winding angles ±55°. Failure was due to weepage, i.e. through-thickness matrix cracks linking together with delaminations to form a convoluted path through the pipe wall such that there was practically uniform seepage of water along the pipe length. The weepage data were subsequently interpreted to provide fatigue failure envelopes which expressed the number of cycles to weepage in terms of axial and hoop stress within a pipe. These failure envelopes were established from the Tsai–Wu failure criterion and a regression curve fitted to experimental *S–N* data. However, no experimental results had been obtained to corroborate the failure predictions.

Norman *et al.*[42] compared the development of tension–tension fatigue damage ($R = 0.1$ and frequency = 10 Hz) in thin-walled carbon/epoxy (AS4/3501-6) cylinders with the damage within plane coupons of identical quasi-isotropic lay-up, $[0°/\pm45°/90°]_s$. This comparison includes geometric effects and the influence of different boundary conditions since the coupon specimens represent flat plates with free edges whilst the cylinders represent curved plates with no free edges. A series of coupons and cylinders were cycled

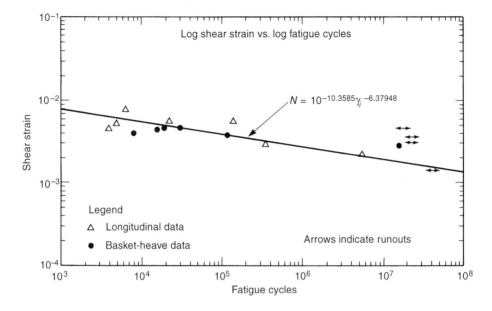

Fig. 22.11   Initial shear strain γ_i vs. fatigue cycles for carbon/fibre/epoxy cylinders.[38]

to catastrophic failure, which occurred within one million cycles except for the tests at lowest fatigue stress levels which were 60% of monotonic failure. In absolute terms, for a given level of maximum applied stress, the cylinders had a fatigue life which was almost an order of magnitude greater than that of the plane coupons. However, when the maximum applied stress was expressed as a percentage of the corresponding monotonic failure stress, the measured fatigue lives of the cylinders and coupons were practically identical. This is significant because of the inherent differences between cylindrical and plane coupons.

22.6.6   Bridges and beams

McCormick[43] performed an accelerated fatigue test on a glass/polyester pedestrian foot-bridge of length 4.9 m. The bridge had been fabricated by bonding three identical open-web GRP trussed girders to pultruded 12 mm thick GRP plates. A more severe load-deflection cycle was used to test the bridge than would have been seen in normal operating conditions. This was done in order to accelerate failure of a connection or an element of the bridge rather than to evaluate its service life. Visible cracks in the epoxy adhesive joints between the flange plates and the horizontal stiffeners were observed at the ends of some of the stiffeners when fatigued for 0.5×10^6 cycles from 7.2 to 17.8 kN at a frequency of 0.15 Hz. This compared with the post-fatigue monotonic failure load of some 74 kN, which indicates that the bridge had been over-designed with a factor of safety in excess of four.

Figure 22.12 gives details the fatigue test configuration for pultruded box-beams and wide flange beams which have been manufactured from unidirectional E-glass/polyester.[44] The wide flange beams exhibited a high resistance to fatigue, with varying strain ranges up to levels as high as 84% of the ultimate monotonic strain of the specimen without failing after 6.86×10^6 cycles. Tests on the box beams, however, with a steel roller as the load-transfer mechanism (i.e. a line load), exhibited three distinct responses: a fibre-breakage failure mechanism, an endurance limit and a transition zone. The fatigue limit response was

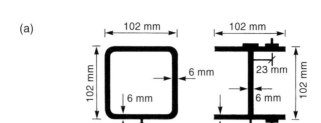

(a)

Box section   WF-section

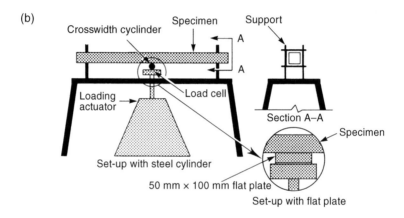

(b)

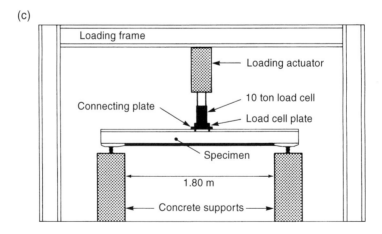

(c)

Fig. 22.12   Three-point flexure testing of box section and wide-flange section beams.[44] (a) Cross-section of test specimens and location of diameter gauges and strain gauges across width and span. (b) Experimental set-up 1. (c) Experimental set-up 2.

(a)

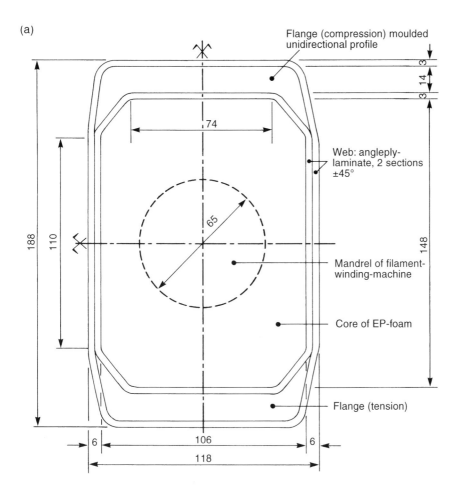

Flange (compression) moulded
unidirectional profile

74

Web: angleply-
laminate, 2 sections
±45°

65

Mandrel of filament-
winding-machine

Core of EP-foam

Flange (tension)

3

14

3

148

188

110

6

106

6

118

(b)

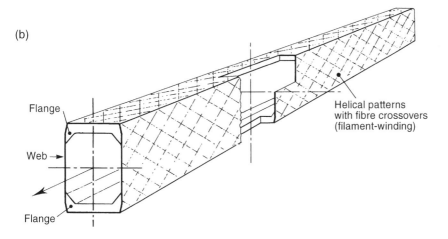

Flange

Web

Flange

Helical patterns
with fibre crossovers
(filament-winding)

Fig. 22.13   (a) and (b) Cross-section of box beams which have been tested under four-point
flexure.[47] Dimensions are in mm and the beam length is 2.8 m. A four-point flexure testing
arrangement is used with loads applied at the quarter points.

seen during a test with a strain range of 0.14% (i.e. 18% of the ultimate strain) which did not cause any damage after 6.9×10^6 cycles. The fibre breakage failure mechanism was seen in tests at higher strain ranges of 0.18%–0.19% with failure after 4500 cycles. The transitional response (failure after 0.85×10^6 cycles at an intermediate strain range of 0.165%) exhibited failure due to a longitudinal matrix crack along the flange-web intersection.

Meier and co-workers[45–47] tested two box-beams in four-point flexure under sinusoidal load-control at a frequency of 2 Hz for 10^8 cycles. The beam flanges were fabricated from unidirectional profiles surrounded by ±45° plies, whilst the webs were filament wound with ±45° plies of E-glass/epoxy. The interior of the section was filled with an epoxy-resin foam. Figure 22.13 details the fabrication of these beams. The maximum loads were 19.1% and 28.6% of the monotonic failure load, i.e. 40 kN and 60 kN, respectively. The corresponding surface tensile strains at the outside of the beam were 0.28% and 0.42%. Tests with greater maximum load levels were not performed. The beam which was subjected to the lowest maximum load did not develop any detectable damage prior to termination of the test, after 10^8 cycles. The bending stiffness of this beam after testing was identical to that before testing. However, in the more highly loaded beam, matrix cracks initiated on the matrix-rich surface of the tensile face after 4×10^6 cycles. A zone of delamination (approximately 20 mm × 20 mm in area) developed at 38×10^6 cycles between the outer ±45° layer and the unidirectional compression flange at the top corner of the beam under the loading point. This delaminated area had extended to 20 mm × 28 mm after 50×10^6 cycles. Further cycling to 10^8 cycles only caused a 2% decrease in the beam bending stiffness.

The present author and co-workers[48–50] have examined the monotonic and cyclic fatigue failure of composite I beams. Both carbon-fibre/epoxy-matrix and glass-fibre/epoxy-matrix composites were used to manufacture the I beams, which had a multi-directional stacking sequence consisting of a balanced lay-up of 0, +45 and –45° plies. Both un-notched and notched I beams have been studied. A four-point flexural configuration was used to test the I beams and in no cases were the beams fatigued above the loads at which buckling of the compression flanges occurred during monotonic testing. The carbon/epoxy and glass/epoxy I beams which were un-notched did not exhibit any detectable damage within 1.2×10^6 and 8×10^6 fatigue cycles, respectively. At these numbers of cycles the fatigue tests were halted. The excellent fatigue behaviour of these un-notched composite I beams was most noteworthy, especially since the maximum fatigue loads which were applied represented typically about 75 to 100% of the loads needed to cause buckling of the compression flange during monotonic testing. Subsequently, the I beams were notched in order to induce failure under the fatigue loads. The most damaging type of notch that was introduced was a 60 mm diameter hole in the web section of the I beam (see Fig. 22.14). The notched I beams then failed under the fatigue loads. For example, in the case of the carbon-fibre/epoxy I beams which were fatigue loaded at 5 Hz from 5 kN to 50 kN (which represented about 9 to 90% of the load at which buckling of the compression flanges occurred during monotonic testing) they failed after 4.78×10^6 cycles. Fatigue failure was due to various types of damage, including delamination, matrix microcracking and fibre fracture, occurring around the 60 mm diameter web notch. The damage mechanisms in the notched CFRP I beams were studied in detail. The most severe of such damage was caused by the tensile stresses which were present around the web notch. The principal mode of damage was matrix cracking, in plies oriented at 90° to the local direct tensile stress. A significant proportion of this damage occurred within the first 0.5×10^6 cycles. The matrix cracking led eventually to delamination and fibre fracture, the latter being the final cause of structural failure of the I beams.

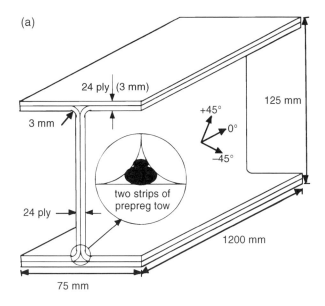

Fig. 22.14(a)   *I* beams manufactured using two channel sections, two flange caps and strips of wound prepreg tow.[48-50] The 24-ply lay-up has a $(-45/0/45°)_{2s}(45/0/-45°)_{2s}$ global stacking sequence, where the global 0° is along the axis of the *I* beam as shown. The corresponding local co-ordinate system (not shown here) used for microscopy around web notches is $(0/-45/90°)_{2s}$ $(90/-45/0°)_{2s}$ (cf. Fig. 22.14(b)).

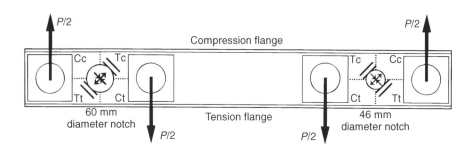

Fig. 22.14(b)   Schematic diagram of the four-point flexure loading arrangement used for flexural fatigue of I beams.[48-50] The shear stress around the web notches can be resolved into direct tensile and compressive stresses which act in four different quadrants, *Tt, Tc, Cc* and *Ct*, as shown. Quadrants *Tt* and *Tc* are subject to a resolved tensile stress state and *Cc* and *Ct* to a resolved compressive stress state. Quadrants *Tt* and *Ct* are adjacent to the tension flange whilst *Tc* and *Cc* are adjacent to the compression flange. Sections for optical microscopy were taken after testing from around the web notches, typically in quadrants *Tt* and *Tc*. Such sections were parallel to the global ±45° orientation (cf. Fig. 22.14(a)).

22.6.7 Panels

Stiffened carbon/epoxy panels have been shown to be less sensitive than comparable metal panels to similar levels of repeated buckling loads.[51] Angle-stiffened shear panels and *I* and *J* stiffened compression panels, shown in Figs. 22.15(a) and (b), were able to sustain a

(a)

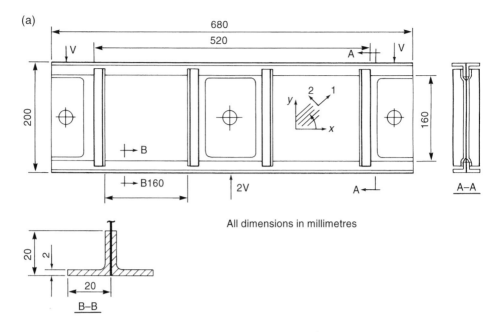

Fig. 22.15(a)   Angle stiffened panels subjected to shear.[51]

specified fatigue life of 0.25×10^6 cycles. The skin of the compression panels buckled first, with the stiffeners failing at approximately five times the initial buckling load. The initial buckling was somewhat reduced by repeated buckling, although the ultimate load-carrying capacity of the stiffened panels was not affected. Panel failure initiated at the stiffener caps of one of the outer stiffeners, followed by failure of the two central stiffeners, these failures being associated with 45° cracks in the skin (parallel to the 45° fibres in the outer plies). No stiffener separation from the skin occurred, this being prevented by overlapping the last two plies in the skin on the flange and by curing the panel in one operation. The development of interlaminar shear stress was thereby avoided and the effect of peeling stresses at the flange–skin intersection reduced. In most of the shear panels significant damage developed with increasing number of repeated buckling cycles, the extent of the damage depending on the working load level. In no case, however, did the damage affect the fatigue life of the panels; even extensive delamination did not result in catastrophic failure. Nevertheless, the residual strength of the panels was reduced by up to 20%. The correct placement of the outer fibres in the stacking sequence of the web was found to be of great importance. Placing these fibres in the tension field direction increased the ultimate shear strength.

22.6.8   Joints

Since joints constitute an integral part of most structures, it seems appropriate to include a brief mention of the fatigue behaviour of both mechanically fastened and bonded joints prior to a fuller treatment of bolted joints by Schön and Starikov in Chapter 23.

   As with structural behaviour, there is not much published information on the fatigue, as opposed to the monotonic, performance of fastened joints. Most relevant papers are given in Herrington and Sabbaghian[52] who also report on their own study. In the latter, the

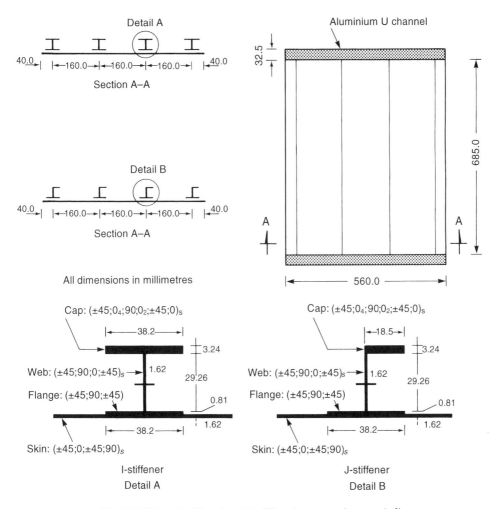

Fig. 22.15(b)   *I*-stiffened and *J*-stiffened compression panels.[51]

influence of laminate orientation, applied stress level and bolt torque were investigated. For quasi-isotropic CFRP Herrington and Sabbaghian[52] determined that the laminate's orientation (relative to the applied load) had an insignificant effect on performance. The applied stress and bolt torque data were found to follow a log-normal distribution. Pin joints (i.e. unclamped) showed significantly shorter lives (two decades) than properly clamped bolts. For maximum stress levels of about 75% of monotonic ultimate run-out at 10^6 cycles was obtained.

Smith and Pascoe[53] working with cross-ply CFRP showed similar general results, although their strengths were only 55% of monotonic ultimate at 10^6 cycles. Significant stiffness loss (i.e. increase in deformation at the bolt hole) was seen one or two decades before failure.

Bonded joints are particularly sensitive to overlap length which, in turn, influences the maximum shear and peel (through-thickness tension) stresses in the joint. Also, the characteristics of the adhesive will be important in determining the joint's performance. Unfortunately, there appears to be no single source in which all of the information is collected.

The work of Kinloch and Osiyemi[54] indicates that unidirectional single-lap joints with structurally realistic overlap-to-thickness ratios (> 30) can sustain a maximum applied load (zero-tension) of about 75% of monotonic ultimate, for a life of over 1.5×10^6 cycles. In contrast, the work of Robson *et al* .[55] indicates that for quasi-isotropic scarf joints, as used for repairs, the maximum load in fatigue may be only 30% of monotonic ultimate at 10^7 cycles.

22.7   Conclusions

This chapter has shown that of the various methodologies used to assess fatigue performance of structures none is totally satisfactory, although the wear-out model offers some promise. However, much still needs to be done to characterize adequately the damage growth rates needed for this approach. Because of the very rapid growth of delaminations in the final stages of fatigue it seems advisable to design for zero growth. Applications were reviewed and it is clear that successful fatigue performance has been obtained in a wide range of circumstances. Equally, it seems, these successes are probably due to low design strain levels. There are indications that coupon data can give a misleading prediction of structural performance.

22.8   References

1. FARROW I R and YOUNG I B (1988), Non-destructive test analysis and life and residual strength prediction of composite structures, *Composite Structures*, **10**, 1–15.
2. CURTIS P T (1986), An investigation of the mechanical properties of improved carbon fibre composite materials. RAE Tech Report 86021, DRA, Farnborough, UK.
3. KEDWARD K T and BEAUMONT P W R (1992), The treatment of fatigue and damage accumulation in composite design, *International Journal of Fatigue*, **14**, 283–294.
4. POURTSARTIP A and BEAUMONT P W R (1986), The fatigue damage mechanics of a carbon fibre composite laminate: II – life prediction, *Composites Science and Technology*, **25**, 283–299.
5. REIFSNIDER K L, HENNEKE E G, STINCHCOMB W W and DUKE I C (1982), Damage mechanics and NDE of composite laminates. *Proceedings of the IUTAM Symposium on Mechanics of Composite Materials*, Virginia, USA, August 16–19, 399–420.
6. HIGHSMITH A L and REIFSNIDER K L (1982), Stiffness-reduction mechanisms in composite laminates. ASTM STP 775, *American Society for Testing and Materials*, Philadelphia, USA, 103–117.
7. O'BRIEN T K (1990), Towards a damage tolerance philosophy for composite materials and structures. ASTM STP 1059, *American Society for Testing and Materials*, Philadelphia, USA, 7–33.
8. LIAO K and REIFSNIDER K L (1993), A life prediction model for fatigue loaded composite femoral prosthesis. ASTM STP 1178, *American Society for Testing and Materials*, Philadelphia, USA, 72–85.
9. CHAMIS C C and GINTY C A (1989), Fibre composite structural durability and damage tolerance. ASTM STP 1012, Vol. 2, *American Society for Testing and Materials*, Philadelphia, USA, 338–355.
10. SHIAO M C and MURTHY P L N (1992), Design for cyclic loading endurance of composites. *Proc 24th Int SAMPE Tech Conf*, Toronto, Canada, October 20–22.
11. TOMASHOFSKI C A, NAGY E J and KEARY P E (1992), Application of generalized force determination to a full scale low cycle fatigue test of the SH-2G helicopter. Presented at the American Helicopter Society 48th Annual Forum, Washington, DC, USA, June 3–5.
12. TOMASHOFSKI C A, NAGY E J and KEARY P E (1992), An improved method of structural dynamic test design for ground flying and its application to the SH-2F and SH-2G helicopters. Presented at the 80th AGARD Symp on Flight Mechanics, Chania, Crete, Greece, May.
13. SCHNEIDER G and GUNSALLUS C (1991), Continuation of the AHS Round Robin on fatigue reliability and damage tolerance. Presented at the American Helicopter Society 47th Annual Forum, Phoenix, Arizona, USA, May 6–8.

14. ZION H L (1991), Safe life reliability: evaluation of new statistical methods. Presented at the American Helicopter Society 47th Annual Forum, Phoenix, Arizona, USA, May 6–8.

15. VISWANATHAN S P, TATA V, BOORLA R, MCLEOD G and SLACK J (1987), A statistical analysis to assess the reliability of a rotorcraft component in fatigue. Presented at the American Helicopter Society 43rd Annual Forum, St. Louis, Mo., USA, May.

16. KRASNOWSKI B R and VISWANATHAN S P (1991), Reliability of helicopter composite dynamic components. Presented at the American Helicopter Society 47th Annual Forum, Phoenix, Arizona, USA, May 6–8.

17. TALREJA R (1985), On design criteria for composite structures under static and fatigue loads. *Proceedings of ICOSSAR '85*, Kobe, Japan, May 27–29.

18. MYERS M R and CHI F (1991), Factors affecting the fatigue performance of metal matrix composites for diesel pistons. SAE Paper No.910833, Society for Automotive Engineers, Warrendale, Pennsylvania, USA.

19. YIN W S and HSU T T C (1990), Uni- and bi-axial compressive fatigue of fibre concrete. *Proceedings of the Conference on Serviceability and Durability of Construction Materials*, ASCE, Denver, CO, USA, August 13–15, American Society of Civil Engineers.

20. FINI G P, MARRONE G, SARTONE L and SENA E A (1993), Qualification tests performed on composite insulators for 132–150kV overhead lines. *Proceedings of the 12th International Conference on Electricity Distribution*, IEEE, Birmingham, UK, May 17–21.

21. CIGRE (1983), Paper presented by Study Committee 22, Working Group 10 (Composite Insulators), Technical basis for nominal requirements for composite insulators, *Electra*, **88**, 89–114.

22. BUDELMANN H, KEPP B and ROSTASY F S (1990), Fatigue behaviour of bond-anchored unidirectional glass-FRPs. *Proceedings of the Conference on Serviceability and Durability of Construction Materials*, ASCE, Denver, CO, USA, August 13–15, American Society of Civil Engineers.

23. RICH M J and MAASS D P (1981) Developing design allowables for composite helicopter structures. *Test Methods and Design Allowables for Fibrous Composites*, ASTM STP 734, C. C. Chamis, Ed., American Society for Testing and Materials, Philadelphia, USA, 181–194.

24. ARDEN R W (1980), Hypothetical fatigue life problem. Presented at the Specialists Meeting on Helicopter Fatigue Methodology sponsored by the Midwest Region of the American Helicopter Society. St. Louis, Missouri, USA, March 25–27. Preprint no. 18.

25. STIEVENARD G (1980), Hypothetical fatigue life problem application of Aérospatiale method. Presented at the Specialists Meeting on Helicopter Fatigue Methodology sponsored by the Midwest Region of the American Helicopter Society. St. Louis, Missouri, USA, March 25–27. Preprint no.19.

26. ALDINIO G and ALLI P (1980), The Agusta solution of AHS hypothetical fatigue life problem. Presented at the Specialists Meeting on Helicopter Fatigue Methodology sponsored by the Midwest Region of the American Helicopter Society. St. Louis, Missouri, USA, March 25–27. Preprint no.20.

27. MCCLOUD G W (1980), A method of determining safe life for helicopter components. Presented at the Specialists Meeting on Helicopter Fatigue Methodology sponsored by the Midwest Region of the American Helicopter Society. St. Louis, Missouri, USA, March 25–27. Preprint no.21.

28. THOMPSON G H (1980), Boeing Vertol fatigue life methodology. Presented at the Specialists Meeting on Helicopter Fatigue Methodology sponsored by the Midwest Region of the American Helicopter Society. St. Louis, Missouri, USA, March 25–27. Preprint no.22.

29. MCDERMOTT I (1980), Hughes Helicopters – fatigue life methodology. Presented at the Specialists Meeting on Helicopter Fatigue Methodology sponsored by the Midwest Region of the American Helicopter Society. St. Louis, Missouri, USA, March 25–27. Preprint no.23.

30. HARDERSEN C P (1980), Fatigue life prediction of helicopter pitch link using Kaman life calculation methods. Presented at the Specialists Meeting on Helicopter Fatigue Methodology sponsored by the Midwest Region of the American Helicopter Society. St. Louis, Missouri, USA, March 25–27. Preprint no.24.

31. MALONEY P F (1980), Structural testing of composites with known defects. Presented at the Specialists Meeting on Helicopter Fatigue Methodology sponsored by the Midwest Region of the American Helicopter Society. St. Louis, Missouri, USA, March 25–27. Preprint no.15.

32. SMITH S and WILSON H (1993), Flight service evaluation of composite components on the Bell model 206L helicopter. Presented at the American Helicopter Society 49th Annual Forum, St. Louis, MO, USA, May 19–21.

33. HAMILTON B K, BELL N W, MURRILL R I, FLORES S E and LUCCHETTO L A (1993), Advanced

composite main rotor flexbeam from optimization to full scale multi-component and whirl tower testing. Presented at the American Helicopter Society 49th Annual Forum, St. Louis, MO, USA, May 19–21.

34. MARDOIAN G H and EZZO M B (1991), Flight service evaluation of composite helicopter components. Presented at the American Helicopter Society 47th Annual Forum, Phoenix, Arizona, USA, May 6–8.

35. LUCAS I I and SAINSBURY-CARTER I B (1972), Effect of specimen geometry on fatigue strength of Boron and Glass Epoxy composites. I Materials, *JMLSA*, **7**, 586–589.

36. SALKIND M J (1976), Early detection of fatigue damage in composite materials. I. *Aircraft*, **13**, 764–769.

37. FRANCIS P H, WALRATH D E, SIMS D F and WEED D N (1977), Biaxial fatigue loading of notched composites. *Journal of Composite Materials*, **II**, 488–501.

38. FUJCZAK R R (1978), Torsional fatigue behaviour of graphite-epoxy cylinders. *Proceedings of ICCM-2*, April 16–20, Toronto, Canada, 635–648.

39. OWEN M J and GRIFFITHS J R (1978), Evaluation of biaxial stress failure surfaces for a glass-fabric-reinforced polyester resin under static and fatigue loading. *Journal of Materials Science*, **13**, 1521–1537.

40. OWEN M J and FOUND M S (1975), The fatigue behaviour of a glass-fabric-reinforced polyester resin under off-axis loading. *Journal of Physical D: Applied Physics*, **8**, 480–497.

41. FROST S (1993), The fatigue performance of glass fibre/epoxy matrix filament wound pipes. Proc ICCM-9, Vol. 5, 684–691, Madrid, Spain, 12–16 July, Woodhead Publishing Limited, Cambridge.

42. NORMAN T L, CIVELEK T S and PRUCZ J (1992), Fatigue of quasi-isotropic composite cylinders under tension-tension loading. *Journal of Reinforced Plastics and Composites*, **II**, 1286–1301.

43. MCCORMICK F C (1990), Laboratory fatigue investigation of a GRP bridge. *Proceedings of the Conference on Serviceability and Durability of Construction Materials*, ASCE, Denver, CO, USA, August 13–15, American Society of Civil Engineers.

44. GANGARAO H V S, SOTIROPOULOS S N and NAGARAJ V (1993), Characterization of fatigue behaviour of fibre reinforced plastic beams and joints. *Proceedings of the Third International Offshore and Polar Engineering Conference*, Singapore, June 6–11.

45. MEIER U VON, MULLER R and PUCK A (1982), GFK-Biegetriiger unter quasistatischer und schwingender Beanspruchung. aus dem Tagungsbericht der 18. Oeffentlichen Jahrestagung der Arbeitsgemeinschaft Verstarkte Kunststoffe e. V. Freudenstadt.

46. MEIER U VON, MULLER R and PUCK A (1983) FRP-box beams under static and fatigue loading. *Proceedings of the International Conference Testing, Evaluation and Quality Control of Composites*, Surrey University, Guildford, UK, September 13–14.

47. MANDELL J F and MEIER U (1983), Effects of stress ratio, frequency, and loading time on the tensile fatigue of glass-reinforced epoxy. Long-term behaviour of composites, ASTM STP 813, T. K. O'Brien, Ed., *American Society for Testing and Materials*, Philadelphia, USA, 55–77.

48. GILCHRIST M D, KINLOCH A J and MATTHEWS F L (1999), Mechanical performance of carbon-fibre and glass-fibre-reinforced epoxy I beams: III – Fatigue observations. *Composites Science and Technology*, **59**(2), 179–200.

49. GILCHRIST M D, KINLOCH A J and MATTHEWS F L (1996), Mechanical performance of carbon-fibre and glass-fibre reinforced epoxy I beams: II – Fractographic failure observations. *Composites Science and Technology*, **56**(9), 1031–1045.

50. GILCHRIST M D, KINLOCH A J, MATTHEWS F L and OSIYEMI S O (1996), Mechanical performance of carbon fibre and glass fibre-reinforced epoxy I beams: I – Mechanical behaviour. *Composites Science and Technology*, **56**(1), 37–53.

51. WELLER T and SINGER J (1990), Durability of stiffened composite panels under repeated buckling. *International Journal Solids Structures*, **26**, 1037–1069.

52. HERRINGTON P D and SABBAGHIAN M (1993), Fatigue failure of composite bolted joints. *Journal Composite Materials*, **27**, 491–512.

53. SMITH P A and PASCOE K J (1987), Fatigue of bolted joints in (0/90) CFRP laminates. *Composites Science and Techology*, **29**, 45–69.

54. KINLOCH A J and OSIYEMI S O (1993), Predicting the fatigue life of adhesively-bonded joints. *J Adhesion*, **43**, 79–90.

55. ROBSON J E, MATTHEWS F L and KINLOCH A J (1993), The fatigue behaviour of bonded repairs to CFRP. *Proc Conf Deformation & Fracture of Composites*, Manchester, UK, March 29–31, Inst of Materials, London, UK.

22.9 Appendix

Equations for stiffness loss from [O'Brien[7], 1990]

(a) Stiffness loss due to matrix cracking in 90° plies of cross-ply laminate:

$$E = \frac{E_{LAM}}{1 + \left(\dfrac{1}{\lambda s}\right)\left(\dfrac{c}{d}\right)\left(\dfrac{E_{22}}{E_{11}}\right)\tanh(\lambda s)} \qquad [22.5]$$

where

$$\lambda = \left(\frac{3G_{12}(c+d)E_{LAM}}{c^2 dE_{11}E_{22}}\right)^{\frac{1}{2}} \qquad [22.6]$$

(nomenclature is given below)

(b) Stiffness loss due to edge delamination:

$$E = \frac{(E^* - E_{LAM})a}{b} + E_{LAM} \qquad [22.7]$$

where E^* is determined from a rule of mixtures expression

$$E^* = \sum_{i=1}^{M} \frac{E_i t_i}{t} \qquad [22.8]$$

(c) Stiffness loss due to delaminations emanating from matrix cracks:

$$E = \left[\left(\frac{a}{1}\right)t_{LAM}\left(\frac{1}{t_{LD}E_{LD}} - \frac{1}{t_{LAM}E_{LAM}}\right)\right]^{-1} \qquad [22.9]$$

where E_{LD} is calculated in a similar manner to E^* in equation [22.8].

(d) Strain concentration factor:

$$K_\varepsilon = \frac{E_{LAM}\, t_{LAM}}{E_{LD}\, t_{LD}} \qquad [22.10]$$

22.10   Nomenclature

a	delamination size
b	laminate half width
c	uncracked ply thickness
d	cracked ply thickness
E	axial modulus of a laminate
E_{LAM}	axial modulus before delamination
E^*	modulus of an edge delaminated laminate
E_{LD}	modulus of a locally delaminated cross-section
E^*_{LD}	modulus of local cross-section with edge and local delaminations
E_0	initial modulus measured
E_{11}	lamina modulus in the fibre direction
E_{22}	lamina modulus transverse to the fibre direction
G_{12}	in-plane shear modulus
K_ε	strain concentration factor
l	laminate length
M	number of sub-laminates formed by edge delamination
$2s$	matrix crack spacing
t	thickness
t_{LAM}	laminate thickness
t_{LD}	thickness of a locally delaminated cross-section
ε	uniaxial strain

23

Fatigue of joints in composite structures

J. Schön and R. Starikov, Swedish Defence Research Agency, Sweden

23.1 Introduction

Two joining techniques of composite materials, mechanically fastened and adhesively bonded joints, have been widely used in civil construction and the aerospace, marine, and transportation industries. Most of the published and available results on composite joints are for quasi-static loading. This chapter includes a short introduction to the general topic of composite joints and two main sections describing fatigue in composite bonded and bolted joints. Further research attempts needed to improve the fatigue design of composite joints are outlined as a logical outcome of this work.

23.2 Composite joints

Although advanced composite materials manufacturing techniques make it possible for the civil, shipbuilding, automobile, and aerospace industries to manufacture large structural components with complex shapes and geometry, they have to be joined together to create the desired structures. There are two main techniques of joining composite components: mechanical fastening and adhesive bonding. Since each method has its own special advantages and drawbacks, particular design criteria and preference are difficult to present unless the type of structure, material, service and loading conditions are specified. In order to make a short comparison Table 23.1 lists the general strong (+) and weak (–) points of each joining method.

In general, when relatively thick structures are used and designed to withstand high levels of loads in service life, or component disassembly is required for inspection and repair purposes, bolted joints are usually preferred. The major drawback of bolted joints is the concentration of high stresses at the bolt holes induced by the notch effect. The hole generation requires specific drilling techniques introducing the possibility of mechanically and thermally induced defects. Finally, the installation of thousands of fasteners results in a large weight penalty.

The functioning principle of bolted joints is based on friction between the joined parts, shear or tensile stresses in fasteners, and contact forces between the fasteners and composite.

Table 23.1 Comparison of joining techniques

Property	Mechanical fastening	Adhesive bonding
Overweight penalty	–	+
Corrosion resistance	–	+
Design of smooth surfaces	–	+
Severity of stress concentrations	–	+
Strength degradation of basic composite	–	+
Manufacturing and life-cycle cost	–	+
Joining of complex shapes	–	+
Required surface preparation	+	–
Sensitivity to peel stress and creep	+	–
Disassembly and removeability	+	–
Possibility of joining thick components	+	–
Sensitivity to environmental attack	+	–

Bolted joints are used extensively by industry to join metal components with composite structures. However, special care should be taken when materials with different electrode potential would be used in the joint. For instance, aluminium and stainless steel fasteners, being installed in carbon fibre/epoxy matrix composites, may result in galvanic corrosion.

There are four basic failure modes, see Fig. 23.1, which may occur in composite bolted joints.

Net-section failure is caused by tangential tensile or compressive stresses at the hole edge in the net-section plane. This mode primarily occurs when the ratio of hole diameter d to plate width w is high, or when the ratio of bypass load (i.e. the load applied to the plate) to bearing load (i.e. the load which passes through the bolt) is high. Net-section failure is common for joints with several bolt rows. Bearing failure mode is governed by compressive stresses acting on the hole surface. This failure occurs when the ratio d/w is low or when the ratio of bearing load to bypass load is high. Bearing failure is common for joints with one bolt row. Shear-out failure mode is caused by shear stresses acting in shear-out planes on the hole boundary in the principal load direction. This mode primarily occurs when the end distance e is short. Shear-out mode is quite common for highly orthotropic laminates. In this case the shear-out failure mode is independent of the end distance. Bolt failure mode is a result of high shear stresses acting in the bolt shank. This failure is governed by the properties of the bolt to support shear and tensile loading and depends on the plate and bolt geometry.

Since the bearing failure usually develops slowly, giving plenty of warning before the ultimate failure occurs, it is recognized as a desirable failure mode in bolted laminates. The other failure modes, i.e., net section and shear out, usually occur suddenly and are therefore catastrophic. Despite the above description of the failure modes being usually associated with static failure of composite bolted joints, the same failure modes can take place during fatigue loading as well.

Although there are many different joint configurations, they may be divided depending on their general geometry and load-transfer capability. Mechanically fastened joints may be implemented with either a single overlap or double lap configuration. The first configuration is recognized as prone to out-of-plane deflection, i.e. secondary bending, during loading. Secondary bending causes bending deflection of the bolt and joint plates which may result in non-uniform stress distributions through the thickness of the composite laminates and high contact forces localized at the top and bottom hole edges.

Depending on the amount of load being transferred, composite joints may be divided into

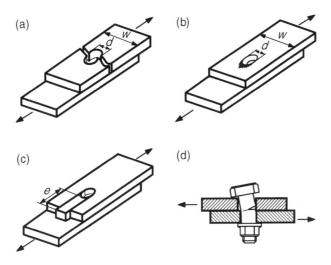

Fig. 23.1   Failure modes of composite bolted joints: (a) net-section failure; (b) bearing failure; (c) shear-out failure; (d) bolt failure.

lightly and heavily loaded. The first group is usually realized in the form of single-row joints, whereas the latter type is implemented as multi-row joints. Although non-catastrophic bearing failures are quite common for single-row joints, net-section failure is common for multi-row joints. Another significant difference between single and multi-row bolted joints is distribution of applied load between the fasteners. In single-row joints all the fasteners transfer the same amount of load, whereas the outer bolt rows in multi-row joints usually transfer more load than the inner bolt rows.

In the cases when thin composite parts or large area components are to be joined and service load levels are expected to be relatively low, adhesive bonding techniques are usually employed. Bonded joints possess the potential of weight saving in comparison to mechanical fastening methods, and make it possible to design smooth surfaces. On the other hand, surface pre-treatment and accurate matching the joint parts as well as the use of adhesives, requiring the time for heating and curing, drastically increase the cost of manufacturing. Despite this, the eventual cost of adhesive joining of large composite structures would still be lower than with mechanical joining.[1] Adhesive joining of dissimilar materials with different coefficients of thermal expansion can cause problems. If the structure is subjected to large temperature variations, large thermal stresses can be introduced.

Composite structures may be bonded by three different techniques: cocuring, cobonding, and secondary bonding. The present work addresses the last method of bonding. A connection by secondary bonding usually consists of an adhesive layer and parts to be joined, adherends. Since in adhesive joints the load transfer depends on chemical bonds between the adhesive and adherends, the adhesive/adherend interface plays an important role in the mechanical performance of the bonded structures under loading. The presence of voids, flaws and inhomogeneities as well as the quality of the interface affect the fatigue performance of the bonded joint, and make it a feature partially depending on the quality of the manufacturing process.[1-4]

Adhesive bonded joints may be classified into three main groups: laps, scarfs, and butts (see Fig. 23.2).

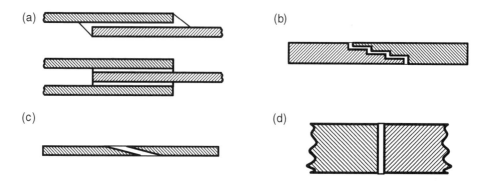

Fig. 23.2   Examples of adhesive joint configurations: (a) single and double overlap joints; (b) stepped lap; (c) single scarf; (d) butt joint.

Lap joints are the most frequently used configuration of adhesive composite joints in engineering applications. There are several basic types of this joint configuration, i.e. single or double overlap, and tubular lap. From a stability point of view, joints with the double overlap configuration would result in a better mechanical performance under loading than the single overlap joint. A modified configuration of the lap joints is a stepped lap configuration shown in Fig. 23.2(b). Bonded joints of this design are able to create bearing resistance to applied compressive loads. In addition, this configuration facilitates the assembly of the bonded joints as it allows the length of the joint overlap to be controlled, which eliminates the use of supporting fixtures. Tubular joints are widely used in the oil industry for joining composite pipes, which offer excellent corrosion resistance in the presence of severe service conditions.

Scarf joints have a very distinguished advantage over other joint configurations being flush and collinear. This results in a better stability of the joint when axial loads are introduced. In scarf joints the normal and shear stresses are dependent on the adherend thickness and the angle of scarf. It is therefore obvious that the preferred joint configuration is when the joint strength would be higher than the strength of adherends and joint fracture would occur in the adherends. Scarf joints are frequently used in the repair of aircraft composite primary parts since aerodynamic smoothness remains intact as well as the higher load carrying capability that joints of this type give compared to other methods of repair.[5]

In comparison to other configurations, butt joints are less complicated and time-consuming to prepare. This configuration of bonded joints is recognized as being relatively free of stress concentrations under axial loads. However, the adhesive layer is usually rather short and therefore the mechanical performance of such joints is limited under axial tensile loads. As a result, this configuration is rarely used by itself in engineering applications. In the case of compressive dominated loads, butt joints may fully utilize the compressive strength of the adherends.

Despite the existence of modern manufacturing techniques and the long term experience in designing composite joints, they are considered as weak points in the structure and may be a source of service breakdown and even catastrophic failure. No matter which industry is considered, modern design philosophy gives the highest priority to safety of people. Almost all structures, such as aircraft bodies, aerospace vehicles, cars, boats and ships, experience a broad range of mechanical loads including fatigue. However, current design procedures are still often based on the well-established static approaches, which are often conservative leading to large safety margins and thus to a high degree of structural weight penalty. Therefore, a review of the state-of-the-art methodologies and achievements by industry and academia in studying the subject of fatigue applied to composite mechanical and adhesive joints would be a challenge.

23.3   Fatigue in adhesive joints

23.3.1   Stress state and fatigue fracture in adhesive joints

A bonded structure may be subjected to a number of different load cases. The bonded structure may be loaded in tension, compression, shear, bending, and/or a combination of these loads. When an engineering structure, consisting of several materials joined adhesively, is loaded, due to differences in elastic properties between the adherends and adhesive as well as possible geometrical asymmetry in the bonded structure, a uniform stress field is not likely to occur. From a number of stress analyses it has been shown that the stress distribution is rather complicated and the stress state tends to be multiaxial. Figure 23.3 shows shear and tensile stress distributions for a bonded lap joint.

   High peel and shear stresses occur at both ends of the joint overlap, which are considered as stress concentration factors. Stress multiaxility in the adhesive layer of butt, scarf, and thick-adherent lap-shear joints varies depending on the configuration of the joints.[6] For example, in lap joints the adhesive shear and peel stress concentrations can be reduced drastically by introducing fillets at the end of the joint overlap.[7] The use of a reverse taper at the end of the adherends can reduce stress concentrations even further.[8]

   When cyclic loading is applied, fatigue cracks normally initiate close to the corner point near the overlap edge where the stress concentration is high. For double-lap joints, both outer and inner adhesive fillet are areas where the corresponding stress and strain concentrations occur. There are three general modes of fatigue failure, see Fig. 23.4, which may occur in composite bonded joints in a single mode or as a combination of different failure modes: adhesive and cohesive debonding, and failure in adherends.[2,9]

   A debond in the form of a fatigue crack may initiate and propagate either in the bulk adhesive (cohesive debonding) or near, or in, the interface between the adherend and adhesive (adhesive debonding). In double-lap joints the initiation of a fatigue crack and its propagation can take place in both bondlines. Moreover, stress redistribution, due to a crack initiated in one of the bondlines, will affect the initiation of cracking in the other bondline.[10]

   In some cases, a crack, initiated in the adhesive layer and after having grown to a certain length, can change fracture mechanisms by deflecting into the adherend and inducing interlaminar delamination in the composite. The interlaminar cracks usually propagate very rapidly in the adherend in comparison with cracks in the adhesive.[8] Since the interlaminar strength of most laminated composites is lower than for common adhesives, instead of the crack initiating in the bondline the joint failure may start from interlaminar fracture in the form of delamination in the composite part. This would be a sign of improper design of the bonded joints.[10]

23.3.2   Fatigue approaches for adhesive composite joints

There are several approaches to predict the service life of adhesively bonded joints. Three basic and most commonly used prediction methods will be discussed now. It should however be noted that only one method is seldom used in the design process. So far the use of several methods in parallel has given the most accurate results due to the

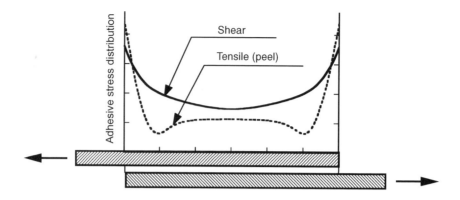

Fig. 23.3   Schematic stress distributions in single lap joint under loading.

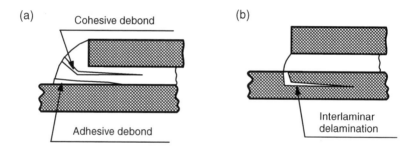

Fig. 23.4   Fatigue fracture modes in adhesive joints: (a) adhesive and cohesive debonding; (b) interlaminar fracture.

problems associated with the complex state of stress distributions, complicated joint geometry, and different fracture mechanisms in composite materials.

23.3.2.1   Stress-life approach

The classical applied stress versus number of cycles $S–N$ curves are a very common method of analysing the fatigue performance of adhesive composite joints (see Fig. 23.5(a)).

In this approach adhesive joints are subjected to fatigue loading at different load levels relative to their quasi-static failure load. In the stress-life approach, fatigue life results have often been presented as maximum load, or load amplitude versus number of cycles, instead of as maximum stress or strain amplitude versus number of cycles.[10–15] This is attributed to the highly non-uniform distribution of stresses along the bondline under loading. It is possible to introduce an average stress as applied load divided by the overlap area.[6,8,16] However, the resulting average stress may be significantly lower than the real values of stresses acting at the ends of the joint overlap.[1,17]

The obtained fatigue lives can be used to determine the endurance limit, i.e. the highest load below which joints of the tested configuration will not fail (see Fig. 23.5(a)). This limit

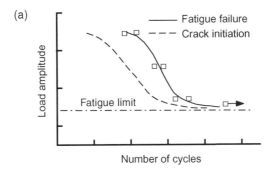

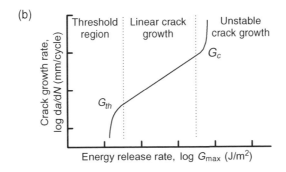

Fig. 23.5   (a) Use of *S-N* curves in fatigue analysis of adhesive joints; (b) three regions in fatigue crack growth *G–da/dN* curve.

is called the fatigue threshold and is usually taken by engineers as corresponding to 10^6 cycles.[10,11,17] In addition, the number of cycles, corresponding to the initiation of a macro-crack, can be tracked as well. For example, the difference between fatigue crack initiation and total fatigue lives can be used to compare the fatigue resistance of adhesive joints with different overlap lengths.[11]

Although the applicability of the stress-life approach is limited by the particular joint geometry being tested, this method can be used together with fracture mechanics or cumulative damage model approaches for the fatigue life prediction of adhesive joints with complex geometries.[10,15] By itself, the stress-life method is usually used to prove the safety of a chosen design of adhesive joints in the prototype stage.[2]

23.3.2.2   Fatigue crack propagation approach

A more informative method, highlighting the fracture and fatigue crack growth in the adhesive, is the Griffith energy approach based on the strain energy release rate *G*. Usually double cantilever beam (DCB) and cracked lap shear (CLS) joints are used to generate *G* versus cyclic crack growth rate *da/dN* data (*a* is the crack length and *N* is the number of fatigue cycles), which are usually presented in logarithmic scale (see Fig. 23.5(b)).

In this approach, the specimens are usually pre-cracked to avoid the crack initiation stage and only the propagation of fatigue crack is monitored. This is attributed to an assumption that fatigue fracture starts to develop from a void or any other flaw, which could have been induced during the assembly process. The fatigue crack growth rate is usually obtained from experimentally determined changes in the crack length over a certain number of fatigue cycles with the use of different experimental measurement techniques and then represented by employing data reduction methods.[17–19]

For the lap configuration the stress state at the crack tip is a combination of the mode I and mode II, and the crack growth is limited to a single bondline; whereas in the case of DCB joints, the crack growth is attributed to the mode I fatigue crack propagation.[20] The mode I loading deformation is the classic opening mode, whereas the mode II involves a shearing or relative sliding of the debonded surfaces. Therefore, since both of these modes are present for the general debonding cases in CLS type joints, the total strain energy release G_T is used as a combination of opening mode strain energy release, G_I, and sliding mode strain energy release G_{II}:

$$G_T = G_I + G_{II} \qquad [23.1]$$

However, in the case of brittle adhesives, the use of only G_I has been proposed.[9,20]

With the help of beam theory, the total energy release rate for bonded joints with simple configurations can be obtained. However, in the case of rather complicated joint geometries, the finite element method is used to not only calculate the total energy release rate, but also to obtain its individual components G_I and G_{II}. The calculated energy release rate is then compared with experimental crack growth rates from DCB or CLS specimens. The comparison is made using G_{max}, i.e. strain energy release rate corresponding to the maximum load in a fatigue cycle, or as range of strain energy release rate ΔG, where $\Delta G = G_{max} - G_{min}$. The first method of presenting strain energy release rate appears to be more commonly used than ΔG.[17,21]

For the intermediate region of the classical fatigue crack growth curve, the crack growth behaviour can be described by the linear relationship between cyclic crack growth rate, log da/dN, and energy release rate, log G (see Fig. 23.5(b)). Due to a direct equivalence between the stress intensity factor and the strain energy release rate, this linear relationship can be presented by a modified equation of the empirical crack growth law by Paris and Erdogan:

$$\frac{da}{dN} = C(G)^m \qquad [23.2]$$

where C and m are constants, and m is the slope on the log–log plot. For double cantilever beam specimens G is equal to G_I; whereas for cracked lap shear joints G is equal to G_T. Note that G can be substituted by other parameters of strain energy release rate, such as G_{max} or ΔG. The values of m range from 4 to 4.5, which are higher than the worst cases for steel, i.e. 2.25–3.25.[2,10,22] This means that the rate of debond propagation in adhesively bonded joints is more sensitive to the applied loads than metal structures.[2,17]

At high growth rates, the G–da/dN curve may become steep, which is due to rapid unstable debond growth followed by final failure of the tested joint. At this stage, strain energy release rate approaches its critical value which is called fracture toughness G_c, and can be obtained during quasi-static testing.

At low levels of the crack growth rate, the curve drops sharply and approaches a vertical asymptote, the fatigue crack growth threshold, with the corresponding strain energy release rate G_{th}. The fatigue crack growth for adhesively bonded joints usually exhibits significant scatter and appears to be very sensitive to minor changes in the applied load and the threshold value G_{th} appears to depend on the adhesive properties and not on the joint's geometry.[2,14,20] Therefore, it has been recommended that the fatigue threshold approach be used, i.e. an infinite life, for designing structural adhesive composite joints in the aerospace industry. The same approach is used for verification of repair procedures for composite aircraft structures with the use of adhesive bonding. However, care should be taken since repair patches may change the local load paths.[23] By fatigue testing a set of adhesive coupons in the same environment, as the adhesive structure will be used in real service condition, a typical G–da/dN curve is obtained and G_{th} is estimated. The energy release rate of the bonded structure is calculated with the finite element method and the design is adjusted such that the energy release rate is less than G_{th}.

Despite the fatigue threshold approach, a finite or total life of adhesive joints may still be predicted. In the first case the approach is based on the linear Paris law, given in equation [23.2]. By integrating Paris law an expression for the fatigue life can be obtained as:

$$N_f = \int_{a_i}^{a_f} \frac{da}{C(G_{max})^m}$$
[23.3]

where N_f is the number of cycles required for the crack to propagate from the initial length a_i to the final length a_f. Because of the large value of m, fatigue life prediction of real structures based on this method is inherently difficult.

Another approach to predicting the total number of fatigue cycles to failure of an adhesive joint uses the full sigmoidal shape of the log da/dN vs. log G curve to obtain:

$$N_f = \int_{a_i}^{a_f} \left(\frac{1 - (G_{max}/G_c)^{m_2}}{Cg_{max}^m [1 - (G_{th}/G_{max})^{m_1}]} \right) da$$
[23.4]

where m_1 and m_2 are additional material constants.[17,24,25]

It should, however, be taken into account that the above methods are only applicable when the joint fracture is due to a fatigue crack propagating in the vicinity of the adhesive layer. In reality, such a crack may enter one of the adherends and propagate further in the form of a delamination. Therefore, in order to achieve more accurate predictions of the joint fatigue life, more complex methods based on damage and fracture mechanics are used, often together with the finite element method.[26]

23.3.2.3   Fatigue approach based on FEM calculations

The finite element analysis can be used in studying fatigue crack growth in adhesively bonded composite joints. It can be used to compare analytical results obtained with beam theory and analyse the stress state ahead of a crack tip. However, in the case of bonded joints with a complex geometry, the required level of accuracy in analytical solutions using conventional continuum-mechanic methods is difficult to achieve since greatly simplifying assumptions have to be made. The finite element method has the advantage of being applicable to any degree of complexity in the joint configuration, taking into account both geometric non-linearity, from large-scale deflections and rotations of the joint, and material non-linearity of the adhesive.

Several methods have been developed in the literature in order to calculate the stress intensity factor and strain energy release rate from the results of finite element analysis. For the stress intensity factor approach, the displacement and stress extrapolation techniques are widely used.[10] The J-integral and virtual crack closure techniques are often adapted to evaluate strain energy release rate.[25,27] The first method can be applied in any stress–strain relationship and therefore takes into consideration the size of the plastic zone at the crack tip.[27] In the second technique, which is due to Irwin's crack closure integral, the sliding and opening displacements of the crack and the nodal forces in the vicinity of the crack tip are used.[3,9,10,15,28] This approach is based on the assumption that the strain energy required to extend a crack by a small amount is equal to the energy required to close the crack to its original dimensions.[19] A significant outcome of this method is that the individual values of G_I and G_{II} for a complex geometry can be obtained.[10,25,28] A major assumption made in this technique is that the studied joint is in plain strain, which allows the creation of two-dimensional finite element models.[6,11,12,20,28,29]

Simplifying assumptions are often made about the composite. Composite adherends are often modelled as linearly elastic, orthotropic solids. This is a reasonable assumption when the main purpose of the composite is to transfer load to the adhesive. However, this approach is less suitable if fatigue failure develops in the composite adherends.[20]

When there are many joint configurations to be studied during the initial design phase, simple two-dimensional models are preferred as they allow modelling and computational time to be saved. However, it has to be taken into consideration that in such models the geometry, boundary conditions, and other properties are constant across the joint width. In reality, it may be far from true when a complex pattern of fatigue damage develops in different directions which may vary across the entire width of the specimen.[15] The nature of fatigue damage developing in bonded structures is another aspect to take into account when crack growth in adhesive joints is studied with the use of finite element technique. In finite element calculations cohesive crack growth is usually adopted. In reality, however, a fatigue crack, initiated in the bulk adhesive in cohesive or adhesive mode, may grow into the adherend.[2,15] Based on these reasons, it has been proposed that simple two-dimensional models be used to analyse qualitatively the stress state in the adhesive joints as well as energy release rates of cracks with the size of fatigue damage; whereas more complex three-dimensional models are preferred when more accurate predictions of the fatigue service life of composite bonded joints are required.[30]

23.3.3   Effect of loading parameters

Although many investigations on the fatigue behaviour of adhesively bonded joints subjected to different loading conditions have been published, there are not so many dealing with the effect of stress ratio $R = \sigma_{min}/\sigma_{max}$ on fatigue performance. A stress ratio of 0.1 has been most frequently used in fatigue testing of adhesively bonded composite joints. However, stress ratio can have a significant effect on cyclic debonding rate. This was shown on DCB and CLS specimens tested with $R = 0.1, 0.3, 0.5$, and 0.75. Two methods to express the debond growth rates were used. In the first one, the fatigue crack growth rate da/dN was correlated with the corresponding maximum strain energy release rate G_{max} (i.e. corresponding to the maximum load). The obtained results of the relationship between G_{max} and da/dN were not the same for the different load ratios, showing that the higher the stress ratio used, the higher the crack propagation rate observed. However, when the strain energy release rate was introduced as $\Delta G = G_{max} - G_{min}$, the relationship between this strain energy release rate range and da/dN was observed to be the same for all stress ratios. It was concluded that ΔG would be the driving parameter for cyclic loads for bonded joints tested with different stress ratios.[21]

The effect of loading frequency was studied on CLS specimens fatigue tested in the frequency range 0.1–10 Hz. No effect of cyclic frequency on the relationship between the total strain energy release rate and fatigue crack growth rate was observed.[21] However, this does not mean that the mechanical behaviour of different types of adhesives is independent of frequency. Different loading frequencies correspond to different strain rates in the adhesive layer. This could affect the fatigue strength and fatigue failure mechanism involving microcracking ahead of the crack tip and void nucleation around particles as well as particle cracking in adhesives with different microstructures.[31]

23.3.4   Effect of joint geometry

It is obvious that the fatigue behaviour of adhesively bonded joints is dependent on different geometrical parameters of the joint configuration. Several parameters are chosen here to characterize the basic relationship between the geometry of bonded joints and their fatigue performance.

In general, an increase in the length of joint overlap improves the fatigue resistance.[32] This can be explained by the effect of creep, which is more prone in short overlap joints than in joints with long overlaps. In long overlap joints, creep occurs at the ends of the joint overlap. In the centre of the joint overlap, the shear stress remain low and elastic, thereby providing resistance to creep of the plastically deformed adhesive at the end of the joint overlap.[3,10,33,34] The effect of creep may become even more significant when joints with short overlaps are fatigue tested at elevated temperatures.[10] Therefore, one of the basic principles for fatigue design of adhesive joints is a sufficient overlap length to decrease the adhesive shear stress and improve the joint resistance to creep and load rate effects.[3] The effect of overlap lengths on the fatigue durability was studied on metal/composite adhesively bonded joints. It was observed that for different overlap lengths the fatigue crack initiation life was the same. Whereas, the remaining fatigue life of the tested joints depended on the crack propagation period until failure, i.e. it was the longest for the longest overlap.[11] However, despite the above, there are experimental results showing the opposite trend, with composite joints with short overlaps yielding a better resistance to fatigue than joints with long overlaps.[13,16,35]

The general dependence of fatigue endurance of adhesive joints on thickness of composite adherends has been reported as decreasing slightly with thickening of adherends.[32] However, it was experimentally observed on DCB composite joints with different adherend thickness that thicker adherends produced slower debond growth rates. Moreover, the thickness effect was the greatest at low values of strain energy release rate and was much greater for specimens tested in load control than for joints tested in displacement control. The influence of thick adherends in lowering crack growth rates was related to the size of the plastic zone and stress distribution ahead of the debond tip. The plastic zone is longer for thicker adherends. The thick adherend joints therefore use a larger percentage of the available energy to create the associated larger plastic zone, thereby leaving less energy to propagate the damage.[28] The adherend thickness effect on fatigue resistance of bonded joints seems to be not obvious and depends on the particular configuration of adhesive joints being fatigue tested.

Single overlap joints were found to be less resistant to fatigue loading than joints with a double overlap configuration.[32] This is attributed to higher stress concentrations in adhesive joints with a single overlap due to this configuration making joints more prone to secondary bending under loading. Therefore, symmetrical adhesive joints are preferred from a fatigue point of view. However, in adhesive double lap joints fatigue cracks may initiate in both bondlines. In this case their propagation is dependent on the stress state and interaction of crack growth in both adhesive layers.[10]

The influence of adhesive thickness on the fatigue behaviour of composite bonded joints seems to be dependent on the particular configuration of joints. According to a fatigue investigation done on single overlap joints, there was no distinct effect of adhesive thickness on the joint fatigue life.[13] On the other hand, the same subject was studied on DCB composite joints with three different bond thicknesses: 0.1, 0.25, and 0.5 mm. At high debond growth rates, joints with the first two bond thicknesses showed similar resistance to fatigue loading, whereas the fatigue resistance of joints with the thickest bond was considerably improved. However, this was not the case at lower debond growth rates (or near the threshold region) where the fatigue resistance of joints with all three adhesive thickness was the same.[36]

The ply orientation can affect not only the fatigue endurance of adhesive joints, but is a factor in the type of joint fatigue failure. For instance, all single overlap joints with 0° unidirectional lay-up adherend failed in the adhesive, whereas the 45°/0°/–45°/0° specimens failed at the 45° ply adjacent to the bondline. Failure in the 45° ply adjacent to the adhesive was attributed to excessive interlaminar and normal stresses in the resin of the ply.[13,35] Similar results were found in another experimental investigation, where two lay-ups were used, 0° unidirectional lay up and +45°/–45°/+45°/0°/+45°/–45°/+45° angle ply lay-up. The joint resistance to fatigue loading was improved using the stiffer adherends, i.e. with 0° oriented layers.[16]

The effect of stacking sequence should be taken into consideration as this affects both failure mode and fatigue durability of bonded joints. Despite the same lay-up used, orientation of the adjacent ply to the adhesive line is very important. Fatigue resistance of CLS joints was lowest when 90° plies were introduced in the adhesive/adherend interface. Moreover, fatigue fracture in such joints was due to transverse cracking in the 90° ply, which then quickly propagated as combined delamination and intraply failure between plies in the adherend. Whereas, in all specimens with 0° and 45° interface plies, fatigue damage initiated with cyclic debonding within the adhesive, which then propagated in cohesive and adhesive modes.[37] Therefore, the use of 90° plies at the adhesive/adherend interface should be avoided.[2,37,38]

23.3.5   Effect of environmental conditions

Critical service conditions may be one of the reasons for in-service failures of bonded structures. Therefore, reliable data of the fatigue behaviour of adhesive joints should not only be determined under realistic load spectra, but also during realistic environmental conditions as well. When dealing with fatigue loading of bonded joints at high temperatures, creep deformations can have a significant influence on the fatigue performance of the joints.[3,10,16,39]

In general, fatigue resistance of composite bonded joints in different environmental conditions is limited by the ability of adhesive and the adhesive/adherend interface to withstand a critical combination of cyclic loading and service environment. For instance, by increasing the temperature in the service range from –50 °C to 90 °C, the fatigue threshold of DCB and CLS joints was increased. It was also observed that the failure mode transferred from the composite adherend to the adhesive layer.[17,20] However, when joints of the same configurations were fatigue tested in the combination of elevated temperature and high level of moisture, it was found that the fatigue threshold of the joints reduced drastically. This was attributed to the effect of moisture, which reduced the glass transition temperature and consequently the mechanical properties of the adhesive to resist fatigue loading at elevated temperatures.[10,20] Care should therefore be taken about the maximum service temperature and humidity condition to which an individual adhesive will be exposed.

In addition, consideration should be taken about the quality of the adhesive/adherend interface, which can be subjected to environmental attack. The presence of voids and flaws can cause a relatively rapid ingress of water and enable pockets of water to develop along the interface. Under loading, such voids create high stress concentrations, which weaken the interface.[1,3] This causes poor interfaces to fail at a low value of G_{th} in wet environmental condition during fatigue loading.[2,4]

23.4   Fatigue in bolted joints

When composite structures are joined to metal structures bolted joints are often used. The slope of the fatigue curve for the metal part of the joint is usually steeper than for the composite part. As a consequence, the metal part often breaks before the composite part during fatigue loading, especially at low load levels. In fatigue tests of single bolt metal-composite joints the metal was found to break.[40–41] There is no fundamental difference in the behaviour of the composite part in a composite–metal joint compared to a composite–composite joint. The coefficient of friction between the parts might be slightly different and the wear properties of the metal part are different. But, those differences do not cause any substantial changes in the behaviour of the composite part in the composite–metal joint compared to the composite–composite joint. Therefore, only composite–composite joints will be treated in this chapter.

If the pre-tension in the fasteners is high a large part of the applied load can be transferred by friction between the joint plates. This will reduce the amount of load transferred by the fasteners and as a result the stresses in the fasteners and on the fastener hole surfaces will be reduced. This will lead to an increased fatigue life. During fatigue loading wear will occur in the joint plates close to the bolt holes. This will reduce the pre-tension in the bolts. Sometimes the nuts on the fasteners will come lose during fatigue loading, causing the pretension to disappear.[42] Therefore, conservative fatigue data of bolted joints should be obtained with fingertight fasteners. Measurements of the coefficient of friction between carbon fibre/epoxy matrix composite, HTA7/6376, in contact with composite or aluminium found that the coefficient of friction increases initially and then decreases slowly. The peak value of the coefficient of friction was about 0.7. It was slightly larger for the composite–composite contact than for the composite–aluminium contact.[42,43]

23.4.1   Hole elongation

A common failure mode during quasi-static testing is bearing failure, which is crushing of the bolt-hole surface. The corresponding failure mode during fatigue loading is hole elongation. The bolt hole is elongated by wear during fatigue loading until failure occur and the joint cannot support the applied load any more. Wear particles are removed from the hole surface and are then often attached to the surface again. Some particles will be transported out of the hole and thereby increasing the available space for the bolt to move.

In load–grip displacement curves measured during fatigue it is often possible to identify the sliding distance of the bolt in the bolt hole. By subtracting the initial sliding distance from the sliding distance during fatigue loading the hole elongation can be measured. This technique has been verified by disassembling specimens in order to physically measure the hole elongation.[44] But, in many cases wear debris are attached to the hole surface, reducing the available space within which the bolt can slide. If the wear debris are removed during disassembly the hole elongation will be larger than that measured from the load-grip displacement curves.[44,45]

A comparison has been made between specimens fatigue loaded in air and submerged in water. Specimens submerged in water had a 25–40% lower hole elongation threshold than specimens tested in air.[46] It was suggested that water could have flushed debris away from the hole surface and thereby continuously exposed undamaged material to loading by the bolt shank. It has been found that if specimens are disassembled and the hole surface cleaned before being put together the hole elongation will grow faster afterwards than it would have done otherwise.[44] In applications joints will be subjected to fatigue loading during several years and wear debris might be removed from the bolt hole by fluid or some other mechanism. This would cause a shorter fatigue life than that measured in laboratory experiments.[44]

During fatigue testing the hole elongation initially increases slowly and close to failure the hole elongation begins to increase rapidly.[40,44,47] A low clamping pressure from the fasteners will result in a higher growth rate of the hole elongation at the beginning of testing than when the clamping pressure is high. Close to failure the increase in growth rate will be softer for joints with a low clamping pressure than for joints with a high clamping pressure which have a very rapid transition to a high growth rate.[40,46] An increased clamping pressure will reduce the hole elongation and increase the fatigue life.[44,45,48] A higher clamping pressure will increase the amount of load transferred between the joint plates by friction and thereby reducing the pressure on the hole surface from the bolt shank.[49] An increased clamping pressure also increases the quasi-static ultimate bearing strength. But, it has been found that, if the fatigue load is applied as a percentage of the ultimate bearing strength, the difference in fatigue life is small.[50]

Most of the load in joints is transferred by the cylindrical part of the fasteners. When protruding head fasteners are replaced with countersunk fasteners the cylindrical part of the fastener is reduced and as a consequence the stresses increases in the composite.[51] In experiments it has been found that the fatigue threshold load was reduced when protruding head fasteners were replaced with countersunk fasteners.[40] Fatigue tests have been done with titanium and thermoplastic fasteners, IM7/PEEK. At equal clamp-up load joints with the titanium fasteners had slightly better fatigue performance than the joints with the thermoplastic fasteners. But, if the titanium fasteners were fully torqued those joints had significantly better fatigue performance than the joints with thermoplastic fasteners.[48]

In a comparison between joints fatigue loaded with $R = -1$, tension–compression, $R = +0.1$, tension–tension, and $R = -\infty$, compression–compression, $R = -1$ resulted in the shortest fatigue life followed by $R = +0.1$. Fatigue loading at $R = -\infty$ resulted in a very flat fatigue curve.[44]

The residual strength of joints stays the same or increases slightly during most of the fatigue loading. Measurements of residual strength of joints with a hole elongation up to 0.25 mm showed only little strength degradation.[44] Measurements of residual strength of specimens, which had reached run out, showed no decrease or a slight increase in residual strength.[48,52]

There does not appear to be any strong influence on fatigue life from the lay-up. Two different lay-ups, 50/40/10 and 30/60/10 (per cent 0°, ±45°, 90°), where fatigue loaded and their 10^6 cycle threshold bearing stress was approximately equal.[40]

Double lap joints with three bolts have been fatigue tested at $R = -1$. Some of the joints had an increased clearance of 240 µm at one bolt hole. This increase in clearance resulted in a slightly shorter fatigue life than without clearance. Clearance caused damage to develop earlier in fatigue testing.[53]

Fatigue testing at an elevated wet environment has been found to reduce the threshold bearing stress compared to room temperature dry testing.[40] In a comparison between room temperature dry, elevated temperature wet, and cold temperature dry testing it was found that elevated temperature wet testing was the critical environment with shortest fatigue life.[44] It has also been found that hydrothermal cycling will reduce the fatigue life.[49]

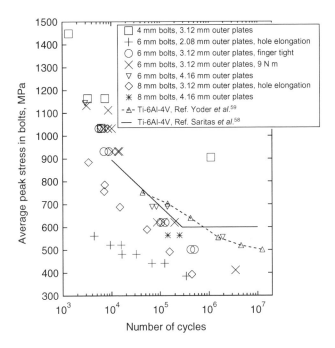

Fig. 23.6 Average peak opening stress in bolts vs. fatigue life for joints.

23.4.2 Bolt failure

Another failure mode often observed in experiments is bolt failure. One or several fasteners break in fatigue. One question is if the composite at the bolt hole becomes damaged during fatigue loading and the fastener then breaks quickly when the composite has reached a certain damage state. Or, if the composite remains fairly undamaged and the fastener breaks due to fatigue of the fastener. One difference between fatigue of metals and composites is how fatigue life is affected by occasional overloads. Composites are known to be sensitive to overloads and the fatigue life is reduced.[54–56] Metals often respond the opposite way to occasional overloads and the fatigue life is increased. Bolted joints were tested at constant amplitude loading and $R = -0.2$, tension dominated loading. Some joints were subjected to occasional tension overloads and those joints had a longer fatigue life than those without overloads. This suggests that the fatigue lives of the fasteners determine the fatigue lives of the joints.

Bolted double lap joints with six fasteners, two columns and three rows, have been fatigue tested. The joints had 4, 6, and 8 mm fasteners and the thickness of the composite plates was varied. They were constant amplitude loaded at $R = -1$. The maximum opening stress, tensile stress, in the fasteners was calculated using the FEM. Each joint had six fasteners and the average maximum opening stress was plotted against the fatigue life of the joints and the results can be seen in Fig. 23.6.[57] Since the fasteners were made of titanium, rotating fatigue life curves for titanium[58,59] were included in the figure, as solid lines. The joints with 6 mm bolts and 2.08 mm thick outer plates and the joints with 8 mm bolts and 3.12 mm thick outer plates failed due to hole elongation. The remaining joints failed due to bolt fracture. The joints, which failed due to bolt fracture, fall into a scatter band and on top of the titanium rotating fatigue life curves. This means that it is possible to predict the fatigue

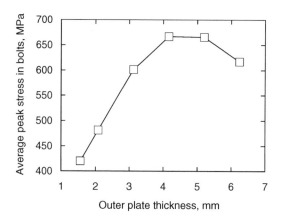

Fig. 23.7   Average peak opening stress in double lap joints with six 6 mm fasteners vs. outer plate thickness.

life of bolted joints which fail due to bolt fracture from the titanium fatigue curve. The joints which fail due to hole elongation are to the left of the titanium fatigue curve. The joints fail due to the failure mode, which results in the shortest fatigue life.

The thickness of the composite plates in the double lap joint were changed in the FE-model and the average peak opening stress in the bolts was calculated, see Fig. 23.7. The applied load to the joints was 10 kN/bolt. When the thickness of the joint increases the opening stress in the bolts increases and reaches a maximum for a constant applied load to the joint. This means that the fatigue life for thin joints, for a given applied load, will decrease when the joint thickness is increased. If the strain or stress in the joint is considered the reduction in fatigue life will be much larger. Usually, the quasi-static failure mode is not bolt fracture. The most common quasi-static failure modes are bearing failure and net-section failure. When the thickness of a joint is increased the total load at quasi-static failure is increased whereas the fatigue life is reduced. As a result thick joints, in comparison with the bolt diameter, can have surprisingly poor fatigue properties in comparison with the quasi-static strength. A double lap joint with 4 mm fasteners and 3.12 mm thick outer plates had a fatigue life of about 6200 cycles when the applied load was 1/3 of the quasi-static strength.[42] The loading was $R = -1$. In experiments it has been found that bolt failure is associated with a large ratio of the laminate thickness to the bolt diameter.[49]

The fatigue life of bolted joints with bolt failure is determined by the opening stress in the bolts. The opening stress in the bolts is related to the amount of load transferred by a bolt. In a joint with three bolt rows the opening stress in the middle bolt was lower than in the outer bolts.[57] But, during fatigue loading damage in the composite at the bolt holes might redistribute the loads such that the opening stress in the fasteners becomes more even. As a result a simple method to estimate the fatigue life of a joint with several fasteners is to calculate the average load on each bolt by dividing the total applied load with the number of bolts. The fatigue life is then estimated from joints with few fasteners. In experiments on double lap specimens with one, two, and three bolt rows it was found that the fatigue results collapsed into one single master curve if the applied load was divided by the total number of bolts.[60] The stiffness of the laminates in one type of joint was increased by increasing the number of 0° plies in the laminates. The fatigue results of those joints also collapsed onto the master curve when the load per bolt was calculated. Using the master curve it is possible to estimate the fatigue life of composite–structure joints. First the load transferred at a section of the joint should be calculated. The load transferred by each bolt is then estimated by dividing the total load by the number of bolts. The fatigue life is then estimated from the master curve. The method should work for all lay-ups as long as the failure mode is bolt failure. The master curve should be for the same type of joint, single lap or double lap and the same laminate thickness. Large double lap joints with 20 fasteners have been fatigue loaded at $R = -0.2$, mainly tension loading. The diameter of the protruding-head fasteners was 6 mm. Two joints had all 20 fasteners present and in two joints two fasteners had been removed in order to complicate the load transfer; the bolt holes were still present.[61] The load per bolt has been calculated and compared with fatigue results of joints with two fasteners. The fatigue results of the large joint were within the scatter band of the results from joints with two fasteners. The large joints fatigue life was slightly shorter than the average for the small joints. Because the fasteners transfer different amounts of load in the large joints some fasteners may as a result transfer more load than the average calculated load.

Since the fatigue lives of joints with bolt failure is determined by the fatigue lives of the fasteners it is reasonable to assume that changing the type of fasteners will affect the fatigue life of the joint. Increasing the diameter of the fasteners will increase the fatigue life of the joint as long as the failure mode is bolt failure. In experiments steel bolts have been replaced with titanium bolts. But, the steel and titanium bolts had almost the same fatigue resistance.[49] In another study protruding head fasteners were replaced with countersunk fasteners. This caused the failure mode to change from hole elongation to bolt failure.[40] Fatigue testing of double lap joints with protruding head and countersunk fasteners found that joints with countersunk fasteners have a shorter fatigue life. The protruding head fasteners broke at the centre of the shank where the bending is largest. The crack in the countersunk fasteners usually passed through the area where the countersink begins on the fastener shank. In many cases it also passed through the cutout in the fastener where a mechanical tool is inserted during mounting. The geometrical feature probably reduces the fatigue life of countersunk fasteners by introducing stress concentrations. Countersunk Huck-comp fasteners do not have a cutout for a mechanical tool and they are installed with a higher pre-stress which increases the amount of load transferred by friction in the joint. As a result the opening stress in the fasteners is reduced and the fatigue life increased. Countersunk fasteners made of composite have also been tested. The fasteners were made of PEEK/long carbon fibre reinforced composite. The fasteners were sheared off at the shear planes of the joints. The fatigue curve was flatter for the composite fasteners than for the titanium fasteners. But, fatigue failure occurred at a lower stress level than for titanium fasteners.[62]

The average opening stress in bolts in a double lap joint with six fasteners was calculated for tensile and compressive loading. For compressive loading the opening stress was 7% lower than for tensile loading when the magnitude of the applied load was the same. This would suggest that compression dominated loading would result in a slightly longer fatigue life than tension dominated loading. Fatigue testing at $R = -0.2$ and $R = -5$ of the joints which were modelled found that the fatigue life was longer for $R = -5$ than for $R = -0.2$.[63] The increase in fatigue life was larger than one would expect from the numerical results. Fatigue testing of joints with two fasteners found a smaller increase in fatigue life for $R = -5$ when compared with $R = -0.2$. When joints tested at $R = -0.2$ and $R = -5$ are compared with joints tested at $R = -1$ the joints tested at $R = -1$ have the shortest fatigue life.

Double lap bolted joints have been spectrum fatigue loaded. The load spectrum was a symmetrical spectrum from a vertical tail of a fighter aircraft. Most of the large load cycles in the load spectrum had a R-value close to -1. The slope of the fatigue curve for the load spectrum was close to the slope of constant amplitude fatigue loaded joints at $R = -1$. Fatigue life predictions using Palmgren–Miner's rule resulted in a slightly longer fatigue life than observed. The original load spectrum contains a large number of load cycles of which many are low amplitude cycles. Load cycles with a peak to peak amplitude less than 50% of the overall peak to peak amplitude of the load spectrum were removed and the results suggest that the fatigue lives were not greatly affected. This operation reduced the number of load cycles by 90%.[63] Specially designed load spectra have been used to test joints. The results suggest that 100 load cycles with a 50% amplitude compared with the amplitude of one large load cycle will reduce the fatigue life. But the number of such load cycles in a realistic load spectrum is small and elimination of those load cycles will not have a large influence on the fatigue life.[42]

The grip displacement often decreases slightly during the first load cycles. This could be explained by the wear particles that are formed in the bolt holes and which reduce the available space for bolt sliding, thereby reducing the joint elongation. The coefficient of friction between the composite plates increases during the first load cycles and this could also reduce the joint elongation.[42] The grip displacement then increases slowly until one bolt breaks after which it increases faster.[60]

Single lap joints with three bolts have been fatigue tested at $R = -1$. Some of the joints had an increased clearance of 240 μm at one bolt hole. This increase in clearance resulted in a slightly shorter fatigue life than without clearance.[53]

23.4.3   Net-section

In quasi-static loading net-section failure is common for joints with several bolt rows. In fatigue experiments net-section failure has only been observed at high load levels, suggesting that the fatigue curve is flat.

As the fatigue load approaches the quasi-static strength of the joint the failure mode during fatigue loading will be the same as during quasi-static loading. This has been observed for two different types of joints with three bolt rows. For one type the failure mode at high load levels was net-section and at lower load levels the specimens failed due to hole elongation. The other type of joint failed due to bolt failure at lower loads.[42] When joints with three bolt rows were loaded at high load levels bolts failed first. Then the joints failed catastrophically from net-section failure. The failure of bolts caused more load to be carried by the net section. At lower load levels the joints failed due to bolt failure.[60,62–64] In aluminium/aluminium joints fretting induced fatigue cracking is common.[65–67] One crack grows and causes failure of the joint. A similar behaviour has been observed for a steel/composite joint. A crack was initiated by fretting on the faying surface in the composite. During further fatigue loading the crack grew and caused failure of the composite.[41] In most cases fretting only causes the polymer layer on the surface of the composite or the first outer ply to be worn away, not causing failure of the joint. During testing the grip displacement decreases slightly during the first load cycles. It then remains fairly constant until catastrophic failure.[60]

Joints have been fatigue loaded with a wing spectrum from the tensile side of the wing. The overall load ratio of the spectrum was –0.2. Some specimens were tested with an eliminated spectrum where cycles with amplitude less than 50% of the overall amplitude of the spectrum were removed. The elimination of load cycles did not appear to increase the fatigue life.[42]

23.4.4   Shear-out

If the quasi-static failure mode is shear-out the failure mode during fatigue loading will be shear out when the applied load approaches the quasi-static strength. Joints with an orthotropic lay-up failed quasi-statically due to shear-out. When they were fatigue tested at $R = -1$ they failed in shear out at a load level of 75% of quasi-static tensile strength. Bolt failure occurred at a load level of 60% of quasi-static tensile strength.[60,64]

When the load ratio R changes, the failure mode might change. Fatigue testing has been done on joints with the lay-up 50/40/10 and $R = 0$, tension–tension. The failure mode was shear-out and load levels below 90% of the quasi-static bearing strength resulted in run out. When the joints were tested at $R = -\infty$, compression–compression, they failed due to local bearing and shear-out. At this R-value run out occurred at 85% of the quasi-static bearing strength. At a load ratio of $R = -1$, tension–compression, the failure mode changed to hole elongation.[40] During testing the grip displacement decreases slightly during the first load cycles. It then remains fairly constant until catastrophic failure.[60]

23.4.5 Prediction of failure modes

As the applied fatigue load approaches the quasi-static strength, the failure mode will become the same in fatigue as in quasi-static loading. As the applied fatigue load decreases, the failure mode often changes to bolt failure. There are several competing failure modes in bolted joints, hole elongation, net-section, shear-out, and bolt failure. The joint will fail due to the failure mode, which results in the shortest fatigue life. At low loads bolt failure is common. Bolt failure is due to metal fatigue whereas the other common failure modes can be characterized as composite material failure modes. The slope of metal fatigue curves is often steeper than for composite materials. As a result bolt failure often results in the shortest fatigue life at lower loads. A schematic of this can be seen in Fig. 23.8.

Since several different failure mechanisms are competing with each other they might interact with each other. The most obvious interactions occur between hole elongation and bolt failure. Hole elongation will change the loading condition of the bolts, giving more space for bolt bending.[64] This will affect the opening stress in the bolts. When a bolt breaks in a joint the remaining bolts will have to transfer its load. This will result in larger stresses in the remaining bolts and also an increased growth rate in hole elongation. At high applied loads bolt failure often results in the specimen breaking due to another failure mode, such as net-section, shear-out or hole elongation.[60]

23.5 Outlook

A significant number of researchers have been studying the fatigue performance of adhesively bonded composite joints. The main focus has been on joints with rather simple configurations and as a result there is a lack of fatigue data for full scale bonded connections of composite structures. Moreover, existing analysis methods, based on the assumption of adhesive/cohesive mode of fatigue crack propagation, are not capable of predicting service life of composite bonded structures experiencing more complex failure mechanisms. Therefore, a universal analysis methodology, which would be able to predict fatigue damage growth as well as the service life of adhesively bonded composite components and deal with multiaxial stress state and complex joint geometries, is required.

Although fatigue of bolted joints has been studied for some time there is still a great deal of information missing. More experimental parameter studies need to be performed; especially, for net-section and shear-out failure modes where the available information is very limited. So far experimental fatigue results are rarely related to calculated stresses and

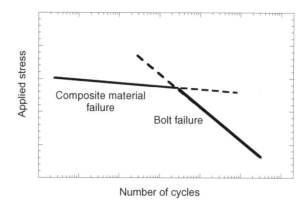

Fig. 23.8   Schematic of fatigue curves for composite material and bolt failure modes.

strains in the joints. Experimental relationships between parameters need to be explained from theoretical considerations. From an applications point of view it is important to be able to predict when the fatigue life will be surprisingly short. In the long term methods to predict failure modes and fatigue life should be developed and it should be possible to handle spectrum loading.

23.6   Summary

During fatigue loading of adhesive joints one major crack usually propagates until failure occurs. The crack can propagate in the adhesive, at the interface between the adhesive and the adherend, or in the adherend as a delamination. The crack is usually modelled with fracture mechanics and a modified Paris law is used to describe the crack growth rate. The crack growth rate is often assumed to depend on the maximum energy release rate or the change in energy release rate. The fatigue life can be estimated by integrating the crack growth rate. Since the exponent in Paris law is large, the fatigue life is sensitive to the applied load. Therefore, the threshold approach is often used in applications. The joint is designed such that no crack growth will occur.

There are four major failure modes in fatigue of bolted joints, hole elongation, bolt failure, net-section, and shear out. In general an increased clamping pressure will increase the fatigue life by increasing the amount of load transferred by friction between the plates; thereby reducing the stresses in the bolts and in the composite close to the bolt hole. During hole elongation the bolt hole is elongated by wear between the bolt shank and the composite hole surface. At the beginning of fatigue loading the hole is elongated slowly and close to failure the hole elongation increases rapidly. Countersunk fasteners will reduce the fatigue threshold compared to protruding head fasteners. Bolt failure can be characterized as metal fatigue failure. The fatigue life of joints with bolt failure can be estimated by calculating the opening stress in the bolts and comparing it with a metal fatigue curve. An increased joint thickness of thin joints promotes bolt failure. Countersunk fasteners have a shorter fatigue life than protruding head fasteners. Net-section and shear out failure have been observed at high load levels for joints, which fail due to those failure modes quasi-statically.

23.7   References

1. HART-SMITH L J (2002), Adhesive bonding of composite structures – progress to date and some remaining challenges, *Journal of Composites Technology and Research*, JC-TRER, **24**(3), 133–153.
2. DE GOEIJ W C, VAN TOOREN M J L and BEUKERS A (1999), Composite adhesive joints under cyclic loading, *Materials and Design*, **20**, 213–221.
3. DAVIS M and BOND D (1999), Principles and practices of adhesive bonded structural joints and repairs, *Adhesion and Adhesives*, **19**, 91–105.
4. KINLOCH A J, LITTLE M S G and WATTS J F (2000), The role of the interphase in the environmental failure of adhesive joints, *Acta Materialia*, **48**, 4543–4553.
5. TRABOCCO R E, DONNELLAN T M and WILLIAMS J G (1988), Repair of composite aircraft, in *Bonded Repair of Aircraft Structures*, ed. Baker A A and Jones R, Martinus Nijhoff Publishers.
6. ISHII K, IMANAKA M, NAKAYAMA H and KODAMA H (1998), Fatigue failure criterion of adhesively bonded CFRP/metal joints under multiaxial stress conditions, *Composites: Part A*, **29A**, 415–422.
7. TSAI M Y and MORTON J (1995), The effect of a spew fillet on adhesive stress distributions in laminated composite single-lap joints, *Composite Structures*, **32**, 123–131.
8. POTTER K D, GUILD F J, HARVEY H J, WISNOM M R and ADAMS R D (2001), Understanding and control of adhesive crack propagation in bonded joints between carbon fibre composite adherends I. Experimental, *International Journal of Adhesion and Adhesives*, **21**, 435–443.
9. MALL S and YUN K T (1987), Effect of adhesive ductility on cyclic debond mechanism in composite-to-composite bonded joints, *Journal of Adhesion*, **23**, 215–231.
10. ABDEL WAHAB M M, ASHCROFT I A, CROCOMBE A D and SHAW S J (2001), Prediction of fatigue thresholds in adhesively bonded joints using damage mechanics and fracture mechanics, *Journal of Adhesion Science Technology*, **15**(7), 763–781.
11. ISHII K, IMANAKA M, NAKAYAMA H and KODAMA H (1999), Evaluation of the fatigue strength of adhesively bonded CFRP/metal single and single-step double-lap joints, *Composites Science and Technology*, **59**, 1675–1683.
12. IMANAKA M, ISHII K and NAKAYAMA H (1999), Evaluation of fatigue strength of adhesively bonded single and single step double lap joints based on stress singularity parameters, *Engineering Fracture Mechanics*, **62**, 409–424.
13. RENTON W J and VINSON J R (1975), Fatigue behavior of bonded joints in composite material structure, *J Aircraft*, **12**(5) 442–447.
14 BRISKHAM P and SMITH G (2000) Cyclic stress durability testing of lap shear joints exposed to hot-wet conditions, *International Journal of Adhesion and Adhesives*, **20**, 33–38.
15. KRUEGER R, PARIS I L, O'BRIEN T K and MINGUET P J (2002), Fatigue life methodology for bonded composite skin/stringer configurations, *Journal of Composites Technology and Research*, **24**(2), 308–331.
16. FERREIRA J A M, REIS P N, COSTA J D M and RICHARDSON M O W (2002), Fatigue behaviour of composite adhesive lap joints, *Composites Science and Technology*, **62**, 1373–1379.
17. ASHCROFT I A and SHAW S J (2002), Mode I fracture of epoxy bonded composite joints 2. Fatigue loading, *International Journal of Adhesion and Adhesives*, **22**, 151–167.
18. Annual book of ASTM standards (1997). Technical standard E647–95a.
19. JABLONSKI D A (1980), Fatigue crack growth in structural adhesives, *Journal of Adhesion*, **11**, 125–143.
20. ASHCROFT I A, ABDEL WAHAB M M, CROCOMBE A D, HUGHES D J and SHAW S J (2001), The effect of environment on the fatigue of bonded composite joints. Part 1: testing and fractography, *Composites: Part A*, **32**, 45–58.
21. MALL S, RAMAMURTHY G and REZAIZDEH A (1987), Stress ratio effect on cyclic debonding in adhesively bonded composite joints, *Composite Structures*, **8**, 31–45.
22. DOWLING N E (1999), *Mechanical Behavior of Materials: Engineering Methods for Deformation, Fracture, and Fatigue*, Upper Saddle River, New Jersey, Prentice Hall.
23. JONES R, CHIU W K and SMITH R (1995), Airworthiness of composite repairs: failure mechanisms, *Engineering Failure Analysis*, **2**(2), 117–128.
24. ABDEL WAHAB M M, ASHCROFT I A, CROCOMBE A D and SMITH P A (2002), Numerical prediction of fatigue crack propagation lifetime in adhesively bonded structures, *International Journal of Fatigue*, **24**, 705–709.
25. CURLEY A J, HADAVINIA H, KINLOCH A J and TAYLOR A C (2000), Predicting the service-life of adhesively bonded joints, *International Journal of Fracture*, **103**, 41–69.

26. HOYT D M, WARD S H and MINGUET P J (2002), Strength and fatigue life modeling of bonded joints in composite structures, *Journal of Composite Technology and Research*, **24**(3), 190–210.

27. ABDEL WAHAB M M, ASHCROFT I A, CROCOMBE A D, HUGHES D J and SHAW S J (2001), The effect of environment on the fatigue of bonded composite joints. Part 2: Fatigue threshold prediction, *Composites: Part A*, **32**, 59–69.

28. MANGALGIRI P D, JOHNSON W S and EVERETT JR R A (1987), Effect of adherend thickness and mixed mode loading on debond growth in adhesively bonded composite joints, *Journal of Adhesion*, **23**, 263–288.

29. KAYUPOV M and DZENIS Y A (2001), Stress concentrations caused by bond cracks in single-lap adhesive composite joints, *Composite Structures*, **54**, 215–220.

30. KRUEGER R, PARIS I L, O'BRIEN T K and MINGUET P J (2002), Comparison of 2D finite element modeling assumptions with results from 3D analysis for composite skin-stiffener debonding, *Composite Structures*, **57**, 161–168.

31. XU X X, CROCROMBE A D and SMITH P A (1994), Fatigue behaviour of joints bonded with either filled, or filled and toughened, adhesive, *Fatigue*, **16**, 469–477.

32. DASTIN S J (1982), *Handbook of Composites*, Lubin G, Ed., New York, Van Nostrand Reinhold Company.

33. HART-SMITH L J (1994), The key to designing durable adhesively bonded joints, *Composites*, **25**(9), 895–898.

34. HART-SMITH L J (1986), Adhesively bonded joints for fibrous composite structures, *International Symposium on Joining and Repair of Fibre-Reinforced Plastics*, Imperial College, London.

35. RENTON J W and VINSON J R (1975), On the behavior of bonded joints in composite material structures, *Engineering Fracture Mechanics*, **7**, 41–60.

36. MALL S and RAMAMURTHY G (1989), Effect of bond thickness on fracture and fatigue strength of adhesively bonded composite joints, *International Journal of Adhesion and Adhesives*, **9**(1), 33–37.

37. JOHNSON W S and MALL S (1986), Influence of interface ply orientation on fatigue damage of adhesively bended composite joints, *Journal of Composites Technology and Research*, **8**(1), 3–7.

38. CVITKOVICH M K, O'BRIEN T K and MINGUET P J (1998), Fatigue debonding characterization in composite skin/stringer configurations, *Composite Materials: Fatigue and Fracture*, Seventh volume, ASTM STP 1330, Bucinell R B, Ed., American Society for Testing and Materials, 97–121.

39. BAKER A A, CHESTER R J, HUGO G R and RADTKE T C (1999), Scarf repairs to highly strained graphite/epoxy structure, *Adhesion and Adhesives*, **19**, 161–171.

40. RAMKUMAR R L and TOSSAVAINEN E W (1986), Strength and lifetime of bolted laminates, *Fatigue in Mechanically Fastened Composite and Metallic Joints*, ASTM STP 927, John M. Potter, Ed., American Society for Testing and Materials, Philadelphia, pp. 251–273.

41. MALLICK P K, LITTLE R E and CUNHAM J W (1986), Fatigue of bolted continuous fiber sheet moulding compound composite–metal joints, *Fatigue in Mechanically Fastened Composite and Metallic Joints*, ASTM STP 927, John M. Potter, Ed., American Society for Testing and Materials, Philadelphia, pp. 274–288.

42. SCHÖN J, Coefficient of friction, quasi-static strength, and fatigue life of composite bolted joints, Deliverable D5-7 in BOJCAS, FOI-memo 82-0012, Swedish Defence Research Agency FOI, 172 90 Stockholm, Sweden.

43. SCHÖN J (2000), Coefficient of friction of composite delamination surfaces, *Wear*, **237**, 77–89.

44. GRANT P, NGUYEN N and SAWICKI A (1993), Bearing fatigue and hole elongation in composite bolted joints, AHS, Annual Forum, Proc. Vol. 1, Saint Louis, Mo, May, American Helicopter Society, pp. 163–170.

45. SMITH P A and PASCOE K J (1987), Fatigue of bolted joints in (0/90) CFRP laminates, *Composites Science and Technology*, **29**, 45–69.

46. CREWS J H JR (1981), Bolt-bearing fatigue of a graphite/epoxy laminate, *Joining of Composite Materials*, ASTM STP 749, pp. 131–144.

47. LIU D, GAU W G, ZHANG K D and YING B Z (1993), Empirical damage evaluation of graphite/epoxy laminate bolt joint in fatigue, *Theoretical and Applied Fracture Mechanics*, **19**, 145–150.

48. WHITWORTH H A (1999), Fatigue evaluation of composite bolted and bonded joints, *Journal of. Advanced Mat*erials, **45**, 25–31.

49. CHEN H S (2001), The static and fatigue strength of bolted joints in composites with hygrothermal cycling, *Composite Structures*, **52**, 295–306.

50. HERRINGTON P D and SABBAGHIAN M (1993), Fatigue failure of composite bolted joints, *Journal of Composite Materials*, **27**, 491–512.
51. IREMAN T (1998), Three-dimensional stress analysis of bolted single-lap joints, *Composite Structures*, **43**, 195–216.
52. RAMKUMAR R L (1981), Bolted joint design, *Test Methods and Design Allowables for Fibrous Composites*, ASTM STP 734, pp. 376–395.
53. MCCARTHY M, LAWLOR V and STANLEY W, Bolt-hole clearance test results Part 2: Fatigue tests, Deliverable D5-10 in BOJCAS, Dept. of Mechanical and Aeronautical Eng., University of Limerick, Limerick, Ireland.
54. NYMAN T, ANSELL H and BLOM A (2000), Effects of truncation and elimination on composite fatigue life, *Composite Structures*, **48**, 275–286.
55. SCHÖN J and BLOM A (2002), Fatigue life prediction and load cycle elimination during spectrum loading of composites, *International Journal of Fatigue*, **24**, 361–367.
56. SCHÖN J (2001), Block loading and elimination fatigue studies of notched composite specimens *Proceedings of ICCM13*, ID 1117.
57. SCHÖN J (2002), Fatigue life prediction of composite bolted joints with bolt failure, FATIGUE 2002, Stockholm, June, **2/5**, 1119–1126.
58. SARITAS S, PROCTER R P M and GRANT W A (1989), Effect of ion implantation on fatigue, fretting and fretting-corrosion of Ti-6Al-4V, *Materials Science Engineering*, **A115**, 307–314.
59. YODER G R, COOLEY L A and CROOKER T W (1985), Observation on a fracture mechanics approach to fatigue crack initiation in Ti-6AL-4V ASTM STP 868. pp. 392–405.
60. STARIKOV R and SCHÖN J (2001), Experimental study on fatigue resistance of composite joints with protruding-head bolts, *Composite Structures*, **55**, 1–11.
61. VAN RIJN J C F N and UBELS L C, 'Test report of Saab Benchmarks', Deliverables D3.9 and D3.12 in BOJCAS, NLR Contract Report 2002-485, National Aerospace Laboratory NLR, The Netherlands.
62. STARIKOV R and SCHÖN J (2002), Fatigue resistance of composite joints with countersunk composite and metal fasteners, *International Journal of Fatigue*, **24**, 39–47.
63. SCHÖN J and NYMAN T (2002), Spectrum fatigue of composite bolted joints, *International Journal of Fatigue*, **24**, 273–279.
64. STARIKOV R and SCHÖN J (2002), Local fatigue behaviour of CFRP bolted joints, *Composites Science and Technology*, **62**, 243–253.
65. SEGERFRÖJD G, WANG G-S and BLOM A F (1997), Fretting fatigue in mechanical joints, Conference Proceeding Computational Methods in Contact Mechanics III, Madrid, Spain, July, pp. 193–206.
66. IYER K, BASTIAS P C, RUBIN C A and HAHN G T (1997), Analysis of fatigue and fretting of three-dimensional, single and double rivet-row lap joints, CAF 97 – Fatigue in new and ageing aircraft; *Proceedings of the 19th ICAF Symposium*, Edinburgh, United Kingdom, June 18–20, **2**, 855–869.
67. ELLIOTT C B III and HOEPPNER D W (1997), The role of fretting fatigue in aircraft rivet hole cracking', CAF 97 – Fatigue in new and ageing aircraft; *Proceedings of the 19th ICAF Symposium*, Edinburgh, United Kingdom, June 18–20, **2**, 883–894.

24

Fatigue in filament-wound structures

D. Perreux and F. Thiébaud, Laboratoire de Mécanique Appliquée RC, France

24.1 Introduction

The process of filament winding makes it possible to produce rotating parts made of composite material containing polymers reinforced with long fibres. Most of the time, this process consists of winding a fibre tow coated with a thermosetting polymeric matrix around a mandrel, thus covering the entire mandrel after successive passages (Fig. 24.1). The mandrel can have a shape of varying complexity. The combination of rotation and transla-tion movements of mandrel or of fibre payout system may require the use of robots with several control axes. The mandrel can be made of metal, polymer, water-soluble sand, etc. (Shen, 1995). Following a polymerization phase, the mandrel can be removed in order to get only the composite structure. In certain cases, the mandrel can be left in place and is then used as a liner.

Filament winding is used for manufacturing gas/fluid vessels (Provenzano et al., 1998; Kim et al., 1998). These vessels generally have a polymer or metal liner. Reinforcing fibres are often made of carbon to obtain a good stiffness. In the field of fluid transportation for nuclear or oil stations, or for marine applications, etc. (Salama, 1994; Davies and Rannou, 1995; Southam, 2000), pipes made of composite materials offer good resistance to adverse environmental conditions. In fact, glass fibres are generally used for these applications. Another significant application is for the repair or rehabilitation of concrete columns on bridges, based on a technique similar to filament winding (Karbhari and Zhao, 2000; Toutanji and Saafi, 2001; Liu et al., 2000). Fabric fibres or bands coated with matrices are rolled up around the columns to reinforce them. This technique offers many advantages with regard to the mechanical performance of columns. This is why it has many other applications for structures in various fields, such as aeronautics, space, automotive or railway industries.

The specific nature of fatigue problems in structures produced through filament winding is very closely related to the type of application in which it is used. The loading of the structures is often a complex phenomenon and involves the study of fatigue behaviour under multiaxial loading. Thus, internal tensile loading-pressure type loading is well suited to vessels or pipes for fluid transportation. Other applications, such as line shafting, require a study of fatigue behaviour under tensile–torsion loading. It is seldom possible to limit the

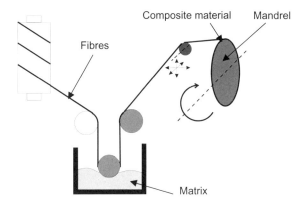

Fig. 24.1   Schematic diagram of the filament winding process.

study of filament winding structures' fatigue behaviour to simple loading cases if one wants to use predictive methods, yet literature in the field of fatigue is scarce. The purpose of this chapter is to provide direction for studying the fatigue of pipe structures.

24.2   Brief overview of literature on pipe behaviour

Various types of pipe structures are used in industry. The literature seldom discusses unidirectional winding or even multidirectional complex structures. Authors usually study bi-directional structures [± θ]. Obviously, winding angles have an impact on the perform-ances of pipes (Rosenow, 1984). Apart from winding angles, the winding pattern results in two major types of fibres arrangement. Helical winding makes it possible to cover the mandrel entirely or partially, depending on the width of band wound around it. Partial covering generally results in crossed structures [± θ] with a pattern close to that of fabrics. Total covering, on the other hand, results in laminated-type structures [+θ/–θ] (Fig. 24.2). Rousseau *et al.* (1999) have highlighted the effect of this pattern on material damage. One can demonstrate that damage of laminated structures takes more time to appear than that of crossed structures.

Most studies of pipes produced through filament winding have examined static behaviour and failure of pipes (criterion, mechanism, etc.), especially those studied by Soden, Hinton and their co-workers on strain and failure mechanisms (Al-Khalil *et al.*, 1996; Curtis *et al.*, 2000). Bai and his co-workers examined the damage mechanisms of pipes containing epoxy matrix and glass fibres [± 55] (Bai *et al.*, 1997a,b). They described in particular the various mechanisms (delamination, micro-cracking, etc.) that can be observed depending on the various combinations of tensile and pressure loading withstood by the pipe. For our part, we have suggested a model of elasto-viscoplastic damaged behaviour of bi-directional pipes (Perreux and Thiébaud, 1994; Thiébaud and Perreux, 1996).

The literature published on fatigue behaviour is more scarce. Most studies relate to glass fibre/epoxy bi-directional helical winding, [± 55]$_n$ or laminate [+ 55, –55]$_n$ (Frost, 1993, 1995; Joseph and Perreux, 1994; Kaynak *et al.*, 2001), because this material is used in fluid transportation circuits. In view of the importance of this structure for industry, we will describe in more detail the fatigue characteristics of such pipes in the next paragraphs. The fatigue of other types of bi-directional arrangements has also been studied. (Macquaire *et*

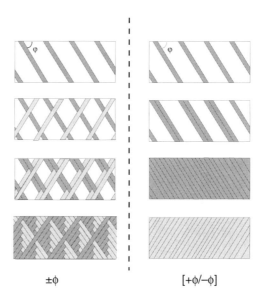

$\pm\phi$ $[+\phi/{-}\phi]$

Fig. 24.2 Main types of winding pattern for pipes.

al., 1994) have studied windings [+45,–45] under torsion and offer an experimental analysis and damage modelling (micro-cracking) of these materials, which can be applied to other types of winding.

There has been little research on multidirectional windings, except for the work of Ellyin and his co-workers. These researchers studied the fatigue behaviour of pipes under pressure loading, which winding sequence was: (outside [+/– 70, ±45$_2$, –70, 0, +45, ±45$_4$]$_T$ inside) (Kujawski *et al.*, 1998). These pipes contained a glass fibre-reinforced epoxy matrix. They analysed the effect of average fatigue constraints and suggested a prediction model of its effect on lifetime. They also showed that significant delaminations appear in 0° angle-directed layers and that matrix cracking is very much present in the ±45° angle directed layers. The study of winding sequence (inside, [±66, 0, ±66$_3$, 0, ±66$_3$, 0, ±66$_5$ 0], outside) (Ellyin and Martens, 2001) was made for various loading ratios of internal tensile loading pressure. The authors concluded that the Poisson's ratio of these materials is a good indicator of damages observed in fatigue.

The literature review shows clearly that the analysis of the fatigue behaviour of pipes produced by filament winding remains an open and vast subject, due to the numerous opportunities offered by the process. It should also be noted that studies of fatigue behaviour have mainly focused on tensile, torsion, internal pressure or multiaxial combinations of these, with no analysis of bending fatigue loading reported, to the best of our knowledge.

24.3   Breadboard fixtures

This section discusses issues related to experimental procedures and suggests some types of fixtures with proven reliability. One of the most significant difficulties of tubular structure fatigue tests is related to test tubes and especially to their fixing onto the testing machine.

24.3.1   Test tubes

As opposed to metal materials, which can be machined to produce desired shapes (cones, threading, shoulders, etc.), composite materials are too delicate for such operations and their machining is not recommended.

Certain authors (Soden *et al.*, 1989; Someardi, 1990) have modified the geometry of their test tubes by adding metal cones or inserts at their ends, held by sticking or filament winding. The use of removable elastic cones seems easier (Perreux *et al.*, 1993; Maire, 1992). Test-pipes are directly cut out in a pipe, and a set of polymer cones slit on its side is fitted to both ends of the pipe. The slit further increases the cone's flexibility and facilitates its insertion inside or outside the test tube. The friction of gripping systems described thereafter ensures the connection between cone and test tube.

24.3.2   Gripping systems

The use of gripping systems specific to each stress type can greatly simplify their development. Nevertheless multiaxial tests require the use of more complex solutions.

24.3.2.1   Gripping systems for uniaxial tests: Tensile test or torsion test
This device uses elastic slit cones, removable and fitted to the pipe's external diameter, as described. The tightening of the cones ensures the connection between the machine and the test tube. Cores inside the pipe prevent its crushing and are also used to align the pipe's axis with the strength cell's axis. On the lower part, a ball is used to align the stress axis of the jack with the pipe's axis and thus prevent inflections induced by fixture.

24.3.2.2   Gripping systems for uniaxial tests: pure internal pressure device
This test can be performed in two different ways. The first method consists of compensating for the tensile force produced by fluid under pressure at the bottom of the test tube (closed ended) by compressing the test tube. This solution thus requires a machine of biaxial tensile (compression)-internal pressure and is limited by the compression capacity of the latter. This solution is a biaxial test, in which the gripping system will be described later.

The second solution uses a compensation method based on a rigid frame. It is essential that test tube ends be free to move in the longitudinal direction to produce a state of pure internal pressure. A neoprene vessel housed in two receptacles is used to seal the device. A polyamide ring prevents extrusion and shearing of the vessel during failure or fatigue tests over a large number of cycles.

Figure 24.3 shows these two experimental devices.

24.3.2.3   Gripping systems for multiaxial tests
Tensile–torsion–internal pressure tests require the use of various loading ratios and a multipurpose fixture (Fig. 24.4). As above, a vessel ensures sealing of the test tube. Conical and slit polyamide cores are fitted inside and outside the pipe. The pipe undergoes compressive forces on its interior and external side faces by means of a set of metal parts (tangential ramps), in which the coning angle is additional to that of the core.

A jack is used to actuate (or release) the ramps by making pipe and metal parts interdependent (or free) and thus allows performing pure internal pressure, torsion, and tensile tests or all combinations thereof. This system is perfectly suited for static or dynamic stresses.

For tests with weeping as the failure mode, the vessel of previous devices can be replaced by a system of joints ensuring direct contact of the liquid under pressure with the composite

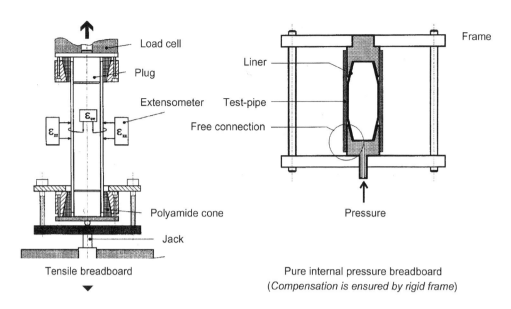

Fig. 24.3   Breadboard devices.

material (Rousseau *et al.*, 1999). Conventional extensometers are used to measure strain, except in torsion type stresses requiring specific systems (Thiébaud *et al.*, 1993).

24.4   Fatigue behaviour of bi-directional [+55/–55] glass-fibre/epoxy-matrix filament-wound pipes

24.4.1   Background

Several studies were made of bi-directional glass fibre/epoxy pipes [+55, –55]$_n$ or [±55]$_n$. The use of these pipes in fluid transportation circuits has generated a greater effort spent on their analysis under tensile–internal pressure loading. A simplified analysis explains the use of a 55° angle for this type of application: this angle is used to ensure the main stress of closed ended pressure loading (circumferential stress = 2 × axial stress: Fig. 24.5) is supported in the direction of the fibres. This elementary calculation leads to an angle such as $\tan^2 \theta = 2$, that is $\theta = 54.74°$. A more complex reliability analysis, taking material parameters (damage, etc.) into account, shows that an angle close to 58.2° for their glass epoxy material is optimal (Richard and Perreux, 2001). In industrial practice, the 55° angle is used.

Frost (1993, 1995) has studied the influence of fatigue loadings by comparing them with the results of static loadings. Kaynak and Mat (2001) have studied unidirectional tensile loading fatigue behaviour and have shown that the damage comprises several stages: craze initiation, craze propagation and densification along fibre direction and finally breakage of the fibre. They have also studied the effect of cycling frequency and have come to the same conclusions as Joseph and Perreux (1994): fatigue life increases with increased frequency.

In order to provide a more precise description of fatigue behaviour for these materials, we later submitted the results obtained on one winding [+55, –55]$_3$. Fibre was made of glass E,

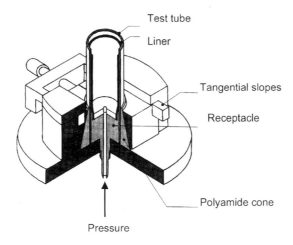

Fig. 24.4   Tensile torsion–internal pressure gripping system.

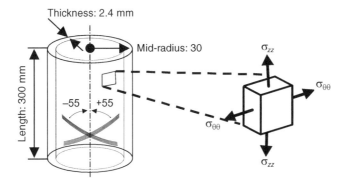

Fig. 24.5   Sample.

the matrix was epoxy, supplied by Ciba Geigy (matrix LY 556, hardener HY 917 and accelerator $\sigma_{\theta\theta}$ DY 70). The glass transition of this matrix is close to 140 °C. The volume fraction of fibres is 55%(±2%). Tested pipes had 60 mm(±0.02 mm) inside diameter, 2.35 mm(±0.1) thickness and approximately 300 mm length.

24.4.2   Static behaviour

Tests under static loading were performed up to failure. Under tensile loading ($\sigma_{\theta\theta} = 0$), final failure occurs with a macro-defect running across the test tube and following the angle of the external layer (in this case +55°). Various loading rates (300 MPa/s, 75 MPa/s, 15 MPa/s) were used to determine the relationship of failure stress with rate of stress. For the rate range under study, no difference was observed. Tests of pure internal pressure ($\sigma_{zz} = 0$) are of the explosion type. The pipe's fracture results from a sudden and local failure of fibre. The same type of failure occurs during closed ended internal pressure loadings of ($\sigma_{\theta\theta} = 2\sigma_{zz}$) with,

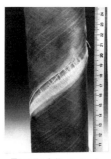 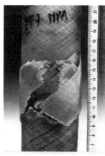 

| Tensile failure mode | Pure internal pression failure mode | Internal pressure with closed end failure mode |

Fig. 24.6   Failure mode.

however, a slower degradation of material (Figure 24.6). The entire set of tests made it possible to identify a failure criterion for axial and circumferential positive stresses. This criterion can be expressed in a Tsai–Wu function. This function is, however, not validated for compression loadings.

$$\left[\frac{\sigma_{zz}}{212}\right]^2 + \left[\frac{\sigma_{\theta\theta}}{234}\right]^2 - \frac{\sigma_{\theta\theta}\,\sigma_{zz}}{171^2} + \frac{\sigma_{zz}}{85} - \frac{\sigma_{\theta\theta}}{122} = 1 \text{ with } \sigma_{\theta\theta} \geq 0 \text{ and } \sigma_{zz} \geq 0 \quad [24.1]$$

24.4.3   Fatigue behaviour: isonumber cycle curves to failure

These materials underwent uniaxial tensile loadings, pure internal pressure or combined loadings of closed ended internal pressure for various stress frequencies. The characteristics of these loadings are given in Table 24.1.

At first, *S–N* curves were analysed according to frequency, but in the case of biaxial tests, using isonumber cycle curves to represent lifetime is more fruitful, since it makes it possible to show how the failure criterion changes with the number of cycles. Figure 24.7 shows the results with a frequency of 0.2 Hz.

Analysis of failure criterion changes in relation to the number of cycles can provide an image close to that resulting from the theory of plasticity. At the time of fatigue, the failure criterion undergoes both negative isotropic hardening causing a reduction of its size and kinematic hardening causing a displacement of its centre, which tends to come close to the origin of the stresses' marks. This distortion of failure criterion shows that the damage

Table 24.1   Fatigue loading

Loading type	R	Frequency Hz	Life end criteria
Tensile loading (σ_{zz})	$R = \dfrac{\sigma_{zz}^{min}}{\sigma_{zz}^{max}} = 0$	0.02	
Internal pressure		0.2	Total loss of stiffness
($\sigma_{\theta\theta} = \beta\,\sigma_{zz}$)		0.5	
with $\beta = 0, 2, \infty$		5	

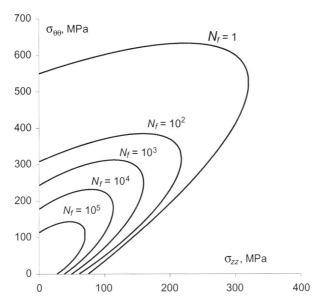

Fig. 24.7   Isonumber cycle curve to failure at 0.2 Hz.

occurring during cycling is not isotropic, but proportionally results in a greater reduction of resistances in the direction where these were initially stronger. It is as if the damage was decreasing the level of the material's anisotropy, regarding failure, despite the fact that fatigue failure modes are identical to those of static tests.

The difference in damage kinetics after loading could be highlighted. The variation of the test tube axial module was monitored during the various tests and shows that the damage level is relatively low for pure internal pressure tests and that it increases in the last cycles. This shows that this loading produces a low density of micro-cracks. On the contrary, for closed ended internal pressure loadings, the speed of damage is important when starting and tends to decrease as the number of cycles increases. However, an axial module variation of about 50% can be observed in these tests. In the case of tensile loading tests, the speed of damage remains constant up to approximately 80% of lifetime and then undergoes a sudden acceleration (Figure 24.8). One should refrain from drawing a hazardous and difficult parallel between the damage measured by stiffness variations (which represent the development of micro-cracks and can be regarded as homogeneous) and the more localized damage leading to the final failure of the test tube, and which is responsible for the distortion of isonumber cycles to failure. Nevertheless, both show that the material's anisotropy changes during fatigue tests.

24.4.4   Role of frequency

Stress frequency has a significant impact on lifetime. Figure 24.9 shows how the number of cycles to failure changes according to frequency during tensile loading tests.

Lifetime increases with frequency for the frequency range under study, and can be five times higher at 1 Hz than at 0.02 Hz. This increase is, however, limited and even null between 1 Hz and 5 Hz. The increase of lifetime can be observed qualitatively for internal pressure loadings with or without closed ends.

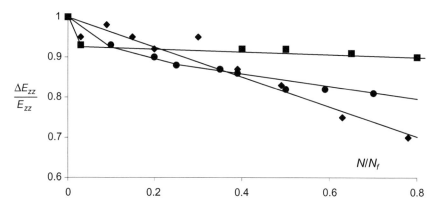

Fig. 24.8   Variation of test tube axial module according to type of loading. (●: $\sigma_{\theta\theta,\mathrm{max}}$ = $2\sigma_{zz,\mathrm{max}}$ = 100 MPa, ■: $\sigma_{\theta\theta,\mathrm{max}}$ = 100 MPa, $\sigma_{zz,\mathrm{max}}$ = 0 MPa, ◆: $\sigma_{\theta\theta,\mathrm{max}}$ = 0 MPa, $\sigma_{zz,\mathrm{max}}$ = 55 MPa)

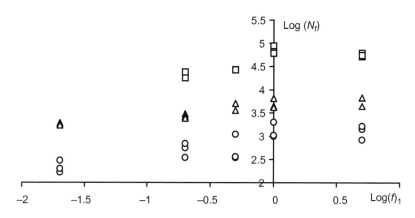

Fig. 24.9   Effect of frequency on the number of cycles to failure N_f. (○: $\sigma_{zz,\mathrm{max}}$ = 55 MPa, Δ: $\sigma_{zz,\mathrm{max}}$ = 45 MPa, □: $\sigma_{zz,\mathrm{max}}$ = 35 MPa)

The effect of frequency is related to two phenomena with opposing action on the lifetime, namely temperature and fatigue–creep coupling.

24.4.4.1   Effect of temperature
Viscoplastic dissipation of energy increases as a function of frequency and results in an increase of test tube temperature during fatigue tests. This is because heat transfer through convection under great frequencies is not sufficient to maintain temperature constant. An increase of temperature decreases the lifetime of test tubes.

This result can be observed in Figure 24.10. These fatigue tests under tensile loading stress were carried out at a low frequency level (0.2 Hz) in order to limit the temperature variation due to viscoplastic heat dissipation. On the other hand, the tests were carried out in an enclosure with the temperature controlled and set from outside.

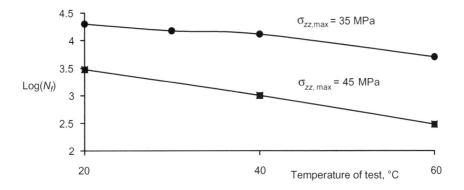

Fig. 24.10   Variation of lifetime according to test tube temperature controlled from outside.

In a fatigue test, the variation of the test tube's temperature not only depends on viscoplastic properties (hence on the material's properties) but also on the way the test tube exchanges heat with heat ambient conditions. This exchange depends on the shape of the test tube. At higher frequencies, the lifetime of a test tube is not intrinsically dependent on the material, but is a function of the coupling of the tube structure with the material. However, in the frequency range under study, the variation of temperature of the test tube remains weak. Therefore, the variation of temperature of the test tube in the course of tests is not a major factor of the test tube's lifetime.

24.4.4.2   Fatigue–creep coupling

The time spent in a cycle with strong stresses increases as the frequency decreases. Under strong stresses, the material creeps more strongly, which involves a more significant strain. Greater strains increase damage, thus leading to a shortened lifetime.

This result can be seen in Fig. 24.11, where minimum and maximum strains are compared during a pure internal pressure test. These two tests were performed under 100 MPa. At 0.2 Hz frequency, the number of cycles to failure is 12 000 cycles, whereas it is 45 000 cycles at a 1 Hz frequency. The figure shows that the strain to failure is lower for the test at higher frequency, despite a greater number of cycles.

For the frequency range under study, fatigue–creep coupling is the major phenomenon, which explains why lifetime increases according to frequency in these tests. It is most likely that, if the frequency range under study had been larger, the lifetime would have increased then decreased according to the change of the prevalent factor. Therefore, there is a frequency of transition for which the lifetime is the largest (Fig. 24.12). Indeed, this result starts showing up for 1 Hz and 5 Hz frequencies, when lifetime appears approximately equal. This frequency of transition would then be equal to a few Hz for the type of geometry of test tubes. Additional tests would be needed to confirm these conclusions.

24.4.5 Moisture effect on lifetime

Pipes used for fluid transportation are often in contact with water. The effect of moisture on the behaviour of composite materials is a complex phenomenon, but generally results in their degradation (Weitsman and Guo, 2002). In order to study the effect of moisture on

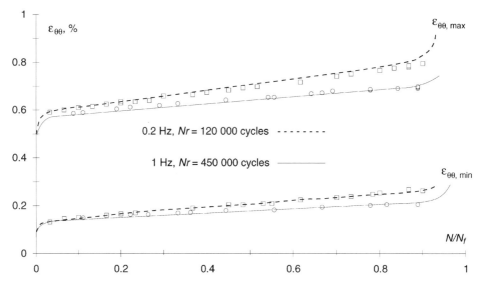

Fig. 24.11   Maximum and minimum strain according to frequency in a pure internal pressure test; □ 0.2 Hz; ○ 1 Hz

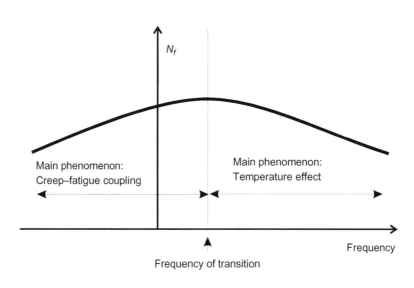

Fig. 24.12   Variation of lifetime according to frequency: a tentative explanation.

lifetime during fatigue tests, test tubes were immersed in water at 60 °C and were then fatigue tested. The water mass absorbed by test tubes depends on time of immersion, but reaches saturation after 24 to 30 months of immersion. Physicochemical degradation occurs after 36 months. In the present study, test tubes were aged up to 18 months. After test tubes had been aged according to various ageing time periods, they were fatigue tested under tensile loading ($\sigma_{zz,max}$ = 55 MPa, f=0.2 Hz). Results are reported in Figure 24.13.

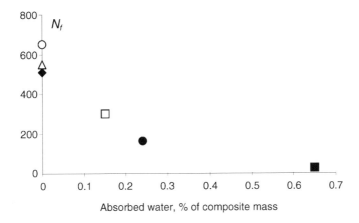

Fig. 24.13   Effect of moisture absorption on sample lifetime under tensile fatigue: ○ oven dried; △ unaged; □ aged for 15 days; ● aged for 2 months; ■ aged for 18 months; ◆ aged for 18 months and oven-dried again.

Moisture has a very important effect on the lifetime of test tubes, and can divide their lifetime by 20 after 18 months of immersion. However, when the test tube is dried after this time of immersion, the former lifetime of the tube, similar to that of an unaged tube can be restored.

As for the effect of temperature, the capacity of a test tube to absorb moisture depends on its shape. The lifetime of a test tube having undergone ageing is thus not an intrinsic property of material, but depends on the coupling of material with the tube structure.

24.5   Conclusions

Filament winding is a production technique well suited to the manufacturing of pipes. Fatigue stresses of tubular structures are often of biaxial type. As regards glass/epoxy pipes $[+55, -5]_n$, this chapter has discussed the effect on lifetime of various stress types (tensile, internal pressure), of frequency and moisture and in certain cases of the rate of damage. Special mention should be made of the very significant influence of frequency on lifetime. We have also studied the opposing action of fatigue–creep coupling and temperature. The role of moisture is also considerable. The study shows also that the role of the material in the results is often hard to demonstrate. Generally, quantitative results (such as the number of cycles to failure, the level of damage after N cycles, etc.) also depend on the shape and dimensions of test tubes. Therefore, the prediction of lifetime or of damage phenomena requires a global approach including factors related to both material and structure. The purpose of this chapter is to suggest an explanation of phenomena at a qualitative level.

24.6   References

AL-KHALIL M F S, SODEN P D, KITCHING R and HINTON M J (1996), The effects of radial stresses on the strength of thin-walled filament wound GRP composite pressure cylinders, *International Journal of Mechanical Sciences*, **1**, 97–120.

BAI J, SEELEUTHNER P and BOMPARD P (1997a), Mechanical behaviour of ±55° filament-wound glass-fibre/epoxy-resin pipes: I. Microstructural analyses, mechanical behaviour and damage mechanisms of composite pipes under pure tensile loading, pure internal pressure, and combined loading, *Composites Science and Technology*, **2**, 141–153.

BAI J, HU G and BOMPARD P (1997b), Mechanical behaviour of ±55° filament-wound glass-fibre/epoxy-resin pipes: II. Micromechanical model of damage initiation and the competition between different mechanisms, *Composites Science and Technology*, **2**, 155–164.

CURTIS J, HINTON M J, LI S, REID S R and SODEN P D (2000), Damage, strain and residual burst strength of filament-wound composite pipes subjected to impact or quasi-static indentation, *Composites Part B: Engineering*, **31**, 419–433.

DAVIES P and RANNOU F (1995), The effect of defect in pipes: Part I. Mode I delamination resistance, *Applied Composites Materials*, **1**, 333–349.

ELLYIN F and MARTENS M (2001), Biaxial fatigue behaviour of multidirectional filament-wound fibreglass /epoxy pipe, *Composites Science and Technology*, **61**, 491–502.

FROST S R (1993), The fatigue performance of glass fibre/epoxy matrix filament wound pipes, in *Proceedings of ICCM 9*, Madrid, Woodhead Publishing Limited, **5**, 684–691.

FROST S R (1995), Predicting the long-term fatigue behaviour of filament wound glass fibre-epoxy matrix pipes, in *Proceedings of ICCM 10*, Whistler, Woodhead Publishing Limited, 649–656.

JOSEPH E and PERREUX D (1994), Fatigue behaviour of glass-fibre/epoxy-matrix filament-wound pipes. *Composites Science and Technology*, **52**, 469–480.

KARBHARI V M and ZHAO L (2000), Use of composites for 21st century civil infrastructure, *Computer Methods in Applied Mechanics and Engineering*, **185**, 433–454.

KAYNAK C and MAT O (2001), Uniaxial fatigue behaviour of filament-wound glass-fibre/epoxy composite pipes, *Composites Science and Technology*, **61**, 1833–1840.

KIM B S, KIM B H, KIM J B and JOE C R (1998), Study on the development of composite CNG pressure vessels, *Cryogenics*, **38**, 131–134.

KUJAWSKI D, ELLYIN F and CULEN M S (1998), The fatigue behaviour of filament-wound fibreglass/epoxy pipes under cyclic pressure, *Journal of Reinforced Plastics and Composites*, **3**, 268–281.

LIU H-K, TAI N-H and CHEN C-C (2000), Compression strength of concrete columns reinforced by non-adhesive filament wound hybrid composites, *Composites: Part A*, **31**, 221–233.

MACQUAIRE B, THIONNET A and RENARD J (1994), Fatigue damage in composite pipe in torsion-torsion, in *Proceedings of International Conference on Composite Materials in Petroleum Industry*, Paris, IFP, 55–65.

MAIRE J F (1992), Etude théorique et expérimentale du comportement de matériaux composites en contraintes planes, PhD Thesis University of Franche-Comté, Besançon.

PERREUX D and THIÉBAUD F (1994), 'Damaged-elasto-plastic behaviour of fibre-reinforced $[+\varphi,-\varphi]n$ composite laminates in biaxial loading'. *Composites Science and Technology*, **54**, 275–285

PERREUX D, VARCHON D, BURTHERET A and OYTANA C (1994), Etude de quelques systèmes d'essais mécaniques en sollicitations complexes adaptés aux matériaux composites, *Matériaux et techniques*, Hors série, 1–6.

PROVENZANO J, SCOTT P B and ZWEIG R (1998), Demonstration of fleet trucks fuelled with PV hydrogen, *International Journal of Hydrogen Energy*, **23**, 289–293.

RICHARD F and PERREUX D (2001), A reliability method for optimisation of $[+\varphi,-\varphi]$ fibre reinforced composite pipes, *Reliability Engineering and System Safety*, **68**, 53–60.

ROSENOW M W (1984), Wind angle effects in glass fibre-reinforce polyester filament wound pipes, *Composites*, **2**, 144–152.

ROUSSEAU J, PERREUX D and VERDIÈRE N (1999), The influence of winding patterns on damage behaviour of filament-wound pipes. *Composites Sciences and Technology*, **9**, 1439–1449.

SALAMA M M (1994), Advanced composites for offshore industry: application and challenges, in *Proceedings of International Conference on Composite Materials in Petroleum Industry*, Paris, IFP, 1–10.

SHEN F C (1995), A filament-wound structure technology overview, *Materials Chemistry and Physics*, **42**, 96–100

SODEN P S, KITCHING E and TSE P C (1989), Experimental failure stresses ± 55° filament wound carbon fibre reinforced epoxy resin pipes, *Third Conference on Computer Aided Design, Composites*, **20**, 125–134.

SOMEARDI T P (1990), Etude du comportement mécanique et de l'endommagement de tubes en composites glass-époxy soumis à des sollicitations axiales et biaxées en statique et en fatigue, PhD Thesis of Ecole Centrale de Paris, Paris.

SOUTHAM D (2000), Filament wound pipe an economic solution, *Reinforced Plastics*, **44**, 40–41.

THIÉBAUD F and PERREUX D (1996), Overall Mechanical behaviour modelling of composite laminate, *European Journal of Mechanics – Solids*, **3**, 423–445.

THIEBAUD F, VARCHON D and PERREUX D (1993), Capteurs de déformations pour un essai de tension-torsion, *Annales des Composites*, **3**, 27–38.

TOUTANJI H and SAAFI M (2001), Durability studies on concrete columns encased in PVC-FRP composite pipes, *Composite Structures*, **54**, 27–35.

WEITSMAN Y and GUO A (2002), Correlation between fluid-induced damage and anomalous fluid sorption in polymeric composites, *Composites Science and Technology*, **62**, 889–908.

25

Fatigue of FRP composites in civil engineering applications

J. M. C. Cadei, FaberMaunsell Ltd, UK

25.1   Introduction

This chapter reviews uses of composite materials in civil engineering and building applications, and the impact of design for fatigue on these applications.

25.2   Composite material applications in civil engineering

Fibre reinforced polymer (FRP) composites have found increasing application in the building and civil engineering industries. Amongst the earliest applications were architectural mouldings for building facades and pultruded profiles for the corrosion market. The early applications tended to follow a material substitution approach in which an FRP composite profile would assume the same shape as a standard rolled steel profile. The intention was that the composite profiles would be connected primarily by bolting following the arrangements established for steel construction. In more recent applications structural forms and connection methods are tailored specifically to suit FRP composites.

Today, composites are mainly found in the following forms:

- pultruded profiles
- filament wound pipes
- spun pipes and tanks
- moulded panels
- sandwich panels
- modular systems
- moulded tanks and vessels
- plates and systems for strengthening.

25.2.1   Structural components and systems

Pultrusions are linear components of constant section that are formed by drawing fibre and resin through a heated die (Fig. 25.1). Pultrusions start at light sections used primarily for applications such as walkways, gratings, ladders, handrails, etc. (Fig. 25.2). These components are primarily aimed at the offshore oil and gas extraction industry, the water and process plant industries, and aluminium and hardwood replacement areas. Most pultrusion manufacturers produce such profiles.

Manufacturers include Strongwell of the USA, Fibreforce of the UK, Fiberline of Denmark, and Creative Pultrusions of the USA. In the middle range are sections targeted at structural framing members. Examples include the Extren range of profiles manufactured by Strongwell, and comparable sections manufactured by Creative Pultrusions.

At the top end are heavy sections such as the 36 inch deep, double web bridge beam manufactured by Strongwell.

Mouldings come in many forms, from low technology hand laminated contact mouldings to closed mouldings using capital intensive equipment such as resin transfer moulding (RTM). Contact mouldings are widely used to manufacture decorative façade panels.

Filament winding is a cost-effective process used to manufacture axisymmetric components such as pipes, cylindrical tanks, and cylindrical chimney stacks. Filament wound pipes have found wide application in the offshore oil and gas industry and in process plants onshore. Examples may be found in the range of large diameter pipes manufactured by the US manufacturer Ameron. In the UK the manufacturer Fibaflo manufactures a range of pipes, pressure vessel components, and storage tanks.

Centrifugal moulding and spray up are typically used to manufacture components from short fibres and resin. These techniques are widely used to manufacture FRP sewer liners, septic and clean water tanks, drainage and sewerage components.

Modular structural systems typically comprise a small number of unique component types which can be combined to build a wide variety of structural forms. The essential difference between these systems and simple pultruded or moulded components is that the systems have the component connectivity built into the system, whereas the method of connection of the non-system components is left to the user or application designer to determine. An example of a modular system is the advanced composite construction system (ACCS) developed by Maunsell (Fig. 25.3). The system comprises a cellular panel component, a connector component, and a toggle component. These components may by combined by mechanical interlock to form platforms, bridge enclosures, monocoque building structures, and cellular bridge beams.

25.2.2   Structural connections

The main types of structural connection open to the composites designer are pinned connections, bonded connections, and mechanical interlock connections. Pinned connections include dowelled, riveted, and bolted connections. Bonded connections feature the bonding together of mating surfaces with a structural adhesive. Mechanical interlock connections include tongue and groove connections, toggle connections, and snap-fit connections. In many real applications elements are connected by a combination of the previously identified elementary types of connection.

All connections produce stress concentrations. Unlike, for example, the case of steel connections, design of FRP connections must take the stress concentrations explicitly into account. Due to the stress concentrations, the fatigue life of a composite structure may be governed by the fatigue life of a connection.

Bonded connections produce stress concentrations in the adhesive and the adherends primarily at the ends of the joint and at any discontinuities (Fig. 25.4). Discontinuities

Fig. 25.1   The pultrusion process.

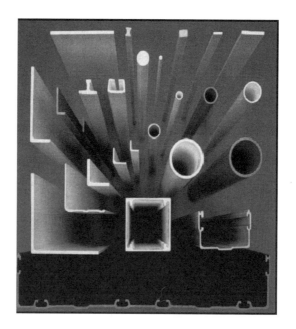

Fig. 25.2   Typical light pultrusions.

Fig. 25.3   Advanced composite component sections.

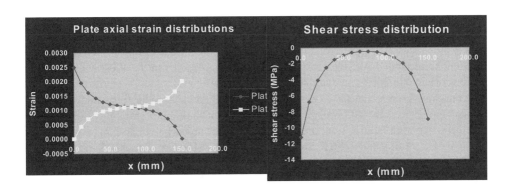

Fig. 25.4   Stress distribution in a bonded joint.

include cracks in the adherends and interlaminar cracks in the adhesive. Generally, in design, only the stress concentrations at bondline ends and at known discontinuities are explicitly taken into account. Stress concentrations due to cracks of a random nature will be implicitly taken into account in the values assumed for the strength parameters.

Pinned connections produce stress concentrations due to several causes. First, when the bolted joint comprises several rows of bolts at right angles to the direction of loading, an elastic distribution of loading between bolts must be assumed up to failure, due to the linear elastic behaviour of the composite material. This contrasts with steel bolted joints where due to the ductility of the bolts and steel substrate it is permissible to assume a plastic distribution of load between the bolts at the ultimate limit state. The elastic distribution of load between the bolts shows that most of the load is taken by the outermost rows of bolts. This is the discrete analogue of the end stress concentration which develops in a loaded bonded joint. Next, the bolt holes produce stress concentrations in the composite material which may extend to the next row of bolts. The stress concentration factors in an anisotropic laminate are higher than in an isotropic material. Finally, a bolt bearing against a bolt hole of a marginally larger diameter in a different material produces concentrated bearing stresses.

Mechanically interlocking joints are subject to stress concentrations due to a number of causes. These include:

*   lack of fit of the components being joined, resulting in locked-in stresses as the components are strained to force them to fit
*   bearing stress concentrations due to uneven contact
*   stress concentrations due to re-entrant corners, notches, holes, and other geometric features of the interlocking joint.

25.2.3   Load bearing structural applications

Bridge engineering is possibly the civil engineering area that has seen the most intense development of composites. Bridge applications range from long-span slender footbridges such as the Aberfeldy Footbridge, Scotland (Fig. 25.5) and Wilcott Footbridge, Shropshire (Fig. 25.6) to all-composite road bridges such as Bond's Mill Lift Bridge, Gloucestershire (Fig. 25.7). Road bridges are particularly demanding from a fatigue point of view due to the high live to dead load ratio for various structural elements, the roadway deck being the principal among them.

There are a number of roadway deck systems currently being developed or used. These include the Maunsell designed roadway panel undergoing fatigue testing at TRL (Fig. 25.8), the Mouchel designed ASSET project panel that was installed in the West Mill bridge in Oxfordshire in late 2002 and a number of US systems.

In buildings composites have been in the main applied in secondary structural elements. Typical applications include wall cladding panels, roof shell units, and lightweight framed structures. Mondial House, London, UK (Fig. 25.9) is an early example in which curtain wall panels were finished in FRP. Sharjah airport, UAE (Fig. 25.10) has a domed roof clad in FRP panels. The Stone Mountain building, USA (Fig. 25.11) has a roof structure constructed as a framework of structural sections in FRP, the choice of FRP having been dictated by the need for radio transparency. Fatigue is seldom a critical design issue in the design of primary structures for buildings, but may be more critical for fastenings and connections.

Poles, pylons and masts belong to a class of structure where lightness, corrosion resistance, and durability are desirable, due to the high cost of maintenance and replacement. Composite solutions are being developed for lighting columns, tall electricity poles (Fig. 25.12), lighting masts, triangulated pylons, and guyed masts. The design of these slender structures is frequently dictated by dynamic response to wind excitation effects. Since the modulus to density ratio of composite materials is not too unfavourable compared to that of steel, composite solutions that meet the dynamic performance criteria can be found. Because of the dynamic sensitivity of these structures, there are likely to be many cycles of wind induced stress over the life of the structure, creating a potential fatigue problem.

In the offshore field, composites are establishing themselves because of the highly corrosive nature of the marine environment, and the high cost of maintenance and replacement of structures due to difficult access. To date, composites have been applied mainly in secondary structures such as gratings, ladders, handrails, caisson linings, risers, and pipework. A recent study (Maunsell, 1999), however, has shown that it is feasible to construct primary structures such as complete topsides entirely in composite materials. Offshore deck structures typically have to be designed for high imposed loads and impact

Fig. 25.5   Aberfeldy Bridge, Scotland, UK.

Fig. 25.6   Wilcott Bridge, Shropshire, UK.

Fig. 25.7   Bond's Mill Lift Bridge, Gloucestershire, UK.

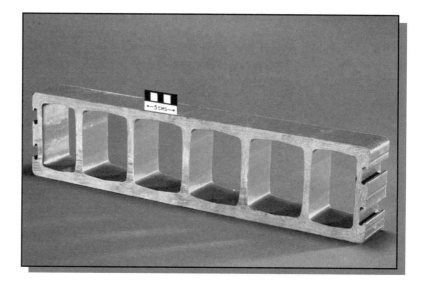

Fig. 25.8   Bridge deck component.

loads. Due to the hazardous environment, structures must meet special fire and blast scenarios. Fatigue is therefore often an issue of secondary importance.

In the field of maritime structures, corrosion and wave loadings are primary design issues. The large wave uplift forces tend to militate against a lightweight structural solution for the deck of a jetty structure, unless porous and adequately anchored. However, composites are beginning to be used in sheet and tubular piles. Concrete-filled composite tubular piles are already available commercially and show promising potential for growth. The reinforcement of concrete structures with composite reinforcing bars and/or profiles also looks promising, particularly when deflection is not a critical design issue. Due to the cyclical nature of wave loading, any composite marine structure could be a candidate for fatigue design.

On account of their corrosion resistance, composites have found wide application in the

Fig. 25.9   Mondial House, London, UK.

Fig. 25.10   Sharjah Airport, UAE.

Fig. 25.11   Stone Mountain building, USA.

Fig. 25.12   Composite electricity poles, USA.

field of pipes and vessels for containing chemically aggressive liquids. Typically, pressure vessels have to be designed for relatively high mean and peak pressures. Creep, hygrothermal, and stress corrosion effects must be taken into account in the design. Although cyclical load counts may be relatively low, the associated high peak pressures may make fatigue strength a potentially critical design issue, particularly for connections and other points of high stress concentration such as apertures.

Environmental enclosures to protect the contents from the environment or vice versa are another area where composites have found a significant role. These include bridge enclosures to protect steel bridges from corrosion, tank covers to contain odours, pump housings to protect the environment from noise, and enclosures for refrigerated containers to maintain high temperature differentials. These structures have much in common with building structures, where fatigue strength is not usually an issue except perhaps in connections.

25.2.4   Externally bonded strengthening of structures

Composite plates and prepregs are being increasingly used for the strengthening of concrete and metallic structures. The purpose of the strengthening may be change of use, to permit structural modification, to compensate for corrosion loss, to rectify design or construction deficiencies, or to extend the fatigue life of the structure.

Composites for strengthening are available in several different forms, each having advantages and disadvantages depending on the particular project circumstances. Preformed pultruded plates or strips are a common form of strengthening material and are used when the substrate is plane and relatively even. Other less common forms of strengthening include hand laminated mats of reinforcement, prepregs cured by the application of pressure and heat, and fibre mats impregnated in situ by vacuum infusion techniques. The forms of strengthening involving *in situ* lamination are more suitable for cases where the surface to which they are to be applied is curved.

Stress concentrations arise in externally bonded FRP laminates, as in any bonded joint, particularly at discontinuities such as at laminate ends, changes in thickness, and cracks in the substrate. Each of these points is the site of a potential delamination crack, which would grow under the action of repeated cyclic loading. Therefore, the fatigue endurance of these applications should be carefully assessed in the design process.

25.3   Typical fatigue loadings in civil engineering structures

There is a large range of fatigue loadings in civil engineering applications. These range from heavy cyclic vehicle axle loads in highway and railway bridges to lighter cyclic loading of slender structures due to their dynamic response to actions such as wind, pedestrian footfall, and waves. Slender footbridges, tall masts, high rise buildings, and offshore and marine structures are all susceptible to a greater or lesser degree to dynamic vibrations causing fatigue cycles.

25.3.1   Fatigue behaviour of composites

The fatigue behaviour of composites is primarily associated with damage to the resin matrix or matrix interface. Composites loaded prevalently in the principal fibre direction exhibit excellent fatigue behaviour because the fibre limits the strain in the matrix. Moreover, since matrix damage is a function of matrix stress level, composites with higher modulus fibres such as carbon fibre tend to exhibit better fatigue performance than composites with lower modulus fibres such as E-glass. Like other matrix dominated behaviour modes, composite fatigue behaviour is sensitive to hygrothermal conditions. Fatigue damage growth is characterized by an increasing crack density in the matrix. If fatigue cracks propagate to the surface of the composite, they create paths for the environment to penetrate the material more rapidly, thereby accelerating the rate of fatigue damage.

Many composites tend to exhibit a 'sudden death' type of fatigue behaviour, in which stiffness is not greatly reduced until shortly before the ultimate fatigue life is reached.

Generally, if strain levels under expected (unfactored) loads are kept below first damage level, fatigue is unlikely to be a critical design issue. Fatigue is more likely to be a critical design issue in matrix dominated failure modes, including interlaminar shear, through thickness peel, adhesion of externally bonded plates, and locally isotropic stresses in highly anisotropic material.

Consider a structure subjected to sinusoidally varying stress cycles (Fig. 25.13), where the minimum and maximum values of the stress in a cycle are σ_{min} and σ_{max}. The stress range σ_r in a cycle is:

$$\sigma_r = \sigma_{max} - \sigma_{min} \tag{25.1}$$

In welded steel structures fatigue is driven by the stress range in a cycle due to the presence of high tensile residual stresses and the ductile stress–strain behaviour of the material. FRP composite structures, by contrast, have a linear elastic stress–strain behaviour up to failure, and have lower residual stresses. Therefore, in FRP composite structures fatigue is driven primarily by the peak stress in a cycle, since this determines the maximum concentrated stress at a flaw or other stress raising detail. This in turn determines the incremental damage in a cycle. Damage usually takes the form of resin cracking. Several distinct types of damage can develop, including resin cracking within laminate plies, interlaminar cracking between plies, fibre debonding, and adhesive debonding.

It has been found that, for a simple loading configuration, the fatigue endurance for a composite component fits the normalized S–N curve equation (Fig. 25.14):

$$\frac{\sigma_{max}}{\sigma_u} = 1 - k \log_{10} N_f \tag{25.2}$$

where σ_u is the quasi-static (or single cycle) strength under the same loading configuration and the same loading rate as the fatigue loading, and k is a slope coefficient. There are two alternative approaches to the determination of σ_u and k. In the first, σ_u is the mean value of the quasistatic strength determined from quasi static tests to failure, and k is the best fit slope to the (σ_{max}/σ_u, log N_f) points. In the second, the two coefficients are determined as best-fit coefficients to the experimental endurance points. The value of σ_u determined by the two approaches is understood to agree reasonably well.

The slope coefficient k is a function of the R ratio, defined by:

$$R = \frac{\sigma_{min}}{\sigma_{max}} \tag{25.3}$$

NPL (Broughton and Lodeiro, 2000) found that, for E-glass/epoxy UD laminates, the relationship between k and R is:

$$k = 0.11 - 0.07R \tag{25.4}$$

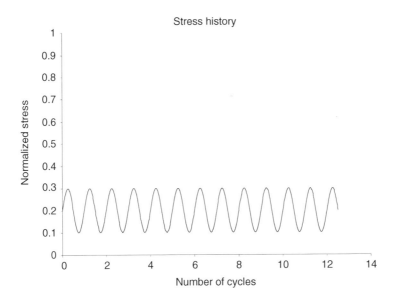

Fig. 25.13   Idealized fatigue loading.

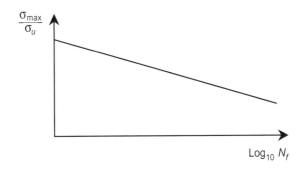

Fig. 25.14   Fatigue endurance curve for a composite component.

It has been found that the above form of fatigue endurance equation is not particularly sensitive to fibre volume fraction, laminate stacking sequence, and environmental conditions, since these are all taken into account in the normalizing stress σ_u.

It should be noted that the ratio σ_{max}/σ_u is always positive. This implies that when the stress in a single load cycle passes from a positive to a negative peak, there are two positive fatigue damage cycles (see Fig. 25.22). This could explain the fact that tension–compression fatigue cycles are found to be considerably more damaging than tension–tension and compression–compression cycles. Since σ_u is typically considerably lower for compression than for tension, compression cycles are more damaging than tension cycles for the same magnitude of peak stress.

S–N curves are usually determined for a value of R of 0.1. Harris and coworkers (Harris *et al.*, 1997; Beheshty *et al.*, 1999) have determined an empirical law for constant life curves valid for variable R values:

$$\frac{\sigma_a}{\sigma_t} = f\left(\frac{\sigma_c}{\sigma_t}, N_f\right)\left(1 - \frac{\sigma_m}{\sigma_t}\right)^{u(N_f)}\left(\frac{\sigma_c}{\sigma_t} + \frac{\sigma_m}{\sigma_t}\right)^{v(N_f)}$$

[25.5]

where σ_a is the stress amplitude in the stress cycle, σ_m the mean stress in the stress cycle, σ_t is the tensile strength, and σ_c is the compressive strength. The coefficients f, u and v are three empirical coefficients to fit the fatigue test points to a Goodman-type constant life curve. They are functions of life N_f.

For a complex multi-stress fatigue loading configuration, the S–N fatigue law may be generalized through the introduction of a scalar, positive-valued, quasi-static failure function f:

$$f(\boldsymbol{\sigma}, \mathbf{R}) > 1$$

[25.6]

where $\boldsymbol{\sigma}$ is a vector of load dependent stresses or stress-resultants, and $\mathbf{R}$ is a vector of independent strength parameters. Examples of the failure criterion f include the Tsai Hill criterion, and the tensor polynomial criterion.

Let the stress history during a fatigue cycle be $\sigma(t)$, and the corresponding history of the failure function be $f(t)$ (see Fig. 25.23). Let the maximum and minimum values of f over the fatigue cycle be f_{max} and f_{min}. The fatigue endurance equation may be recast as:

$$\frac{f_{max}}{f_u} = 1 - k \log_{10} N_f$$

[25.7]

where f_u and k are two experimentally determined best-fit coefficients. The slope coefficient k is a function of the R_f ratio, defined by:

$$R_f = \frac{f_{min}}{f_{max}}$$

[25.8]

Alternatively k may be defined in terms of a modified R_f' ratio,

$$R_f' = \frac{f_{max} - f_{min}}{f_{max} + f_{min}}$$

[25.9]

This represents the normalized stress range expressed as a ratio of the mean normalized stress.

In composite deck and bridge structures the dead load stress in the composite is typically low compared to the allowable stress, due to the high specific strength of the material. Hence the R ratio tends to be close to zero for simply supported elements, and -1 for continuous elements where stress reversals occur in each load cycle. The live to dead load ratio is furthermore affected by the point in the bridge being considered. It is higher for points dominated by local effects, such as the roadway deck, and lower for points dominated by global effects, for example, the bottom flange of a beam.

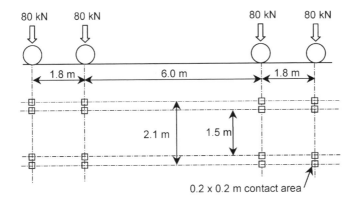

Fig. 25.15   BS 5400 Part 10 standard fatigue vehicle.

25.3.2   Traffic loading fatigue effects
Traffic loading for fatigue effects are specified in BS 5400: Part 10 and in the Highways Agency implementation document BA9/81.

The standard specifies a spectrum of vehicles, defining for each vehicle type weight, axle loads, and frequency on the road. The standard also defines an average fatigue vehicle, that is a single vehicle type which produces the same effects as the underlying vehicle spectrum. The standard fatigue vehicle has a weight of 360 kN and an axle load pattern as shown in Fig. 25.15. The code specifies a bridge design life of 120 years and 2.0×10^6 standard fatigue vehicles per year on the slow lane of a three-lane motorway.

25.3.3   Wind loading fatigue effects
Wind loading effects are a function both of wind turbulence and of the dynamic interaction between wind and structure. Many tall mast structures are characterized by vortex excitation effects which result in cyclic loading. BS 8100: 1995 'Lattice towers and masts: Code of Practice for loading of guyed masts' provides guidance on dynamic loading of masts.

25.3.4   Temperature and other environmental loading fatigue effects
Temperature loadings have a daily and a seasonal cycle. The total number of cycles over the design life of a typical structure is an order of magnitude lower than the total number of cycles of live load, and is therefore frequently negligible in the assessment of fatigue life on the loading side. Temperature and humidity however affect the structural properties of FRP materials and are therefore important in determining the fatigue life of a structure subjected to stress cycles. One approach to assessing their effect is to use an ultimate strength value modified to take into account hygrothermal effects and put this into the fatigue life equation.

25.4   Fatigue behaviour of composite structures and components

25.4.1   Stress concentrations in composites
The most fatigue-critical points in composite components and structures are locations of high stress concentration due to the presence of stress raising details. These include stress

concentrations due to the geometry and boundary conditions of the structure. Examples include holes, notches, changes in thickness, re-entrant corners, and other geometric discontinuities. At the ply level stress concentrations exist at laminate edges, ply drop-offs, and adjacent to intralaminar cracks.

25.4.2   Failure modes

In the case of a single ply, failure modes include tensile rupture or buckling. In the case of a unidirectional ply, tensile rupture may involve cracking of the matrix between the fibres or cracking of both matrix and fibre. In the case of well-configured multiaxial plies and multi-ply laminates, ultimate tensile failure almost always involves cracking of both matrix and fibre, usually at the end of a sequence of ply failures involving progressive matrix cracking. Under fatigue loading damage initiates as matrix cracking. The crack density increases with number of cycles, eventually leading to fibre rupture.

Laminate failure modes include ply tensile rupture or buckling and interlaminar shear or peel failure. Fatigue damage normally initiates as intralaminar cracking in cross plies. The cross ply cracks produce high interlaminar stress concentrations between the cracked ply and the adjacent plies. These result in the formation of interlaminar cracks which eventually lead to loss of integrity of the laminate plies. Interlaminar cracks are driven by compressive cycles as well as tensile cycles. Unless three-dimensional reinforcements are used, the ultimate interlaminar strength is matrix-dominated.

25.4.3   Fatigue behaviour of composite plies

Fibre reinforcements commonly used in structures for civil engineering include unidirectional (UD) rovings and mat, chopped strand mat (CSM), continuous filament mat (CFM), woven rovings (WR) bi-directional mats, and stitch bonded multiaxial mats (MAM). Unidirectional rovings and mats provide the maximum degree of anisotropy that can be achieved with given fibre and matrix materials, while chopped strand mats and continuous filament mats provide a quasi-isotropic behaviour. Multidirectional mats provide a range of behaviour intermediate between isotropic and maximum anisotropic, depending on the directional distribution of fibre. The fibres in woven mats are crimped, i.e. follow an undulating path, whilst fibres in stitch bonded mats and UD rovings are straight. The fibres in chopped strand mats are relatively short, and are arranged in a random orientation. The fibres in the other reinforcement types mentioned are long. The fibres in CFMs, although continuous, continuously vary in direction, so as to give an effectively random distribution of fibre orientation.

At the microstructure level stress concentrations exist in the matrix at fibre ends, fibre changes of direction, and at matrix cracks. Therefore the reinforcement types which have the greatest density of these stress raising features are most sensitive to fatigue. Thus CSMs and WRs are more fatigue sensitive than UDs, MAMs. CFMs are intermediate between the two ends of the scale.

25.4.4   Fatigue behaviour of plane laminates

Stress concentrations exist in interlaminar stresses at ply ends and at ply cracks. In a cross-ply laminate, intralaminar cracking may occur in the cross-ply when the laminate is loaded parallel to the longitudinal ply. When a crack forms in a cross-ply, an interlaminar stress concentration develops between the cross-ply and longitudinal ply. Under a load cycle, the

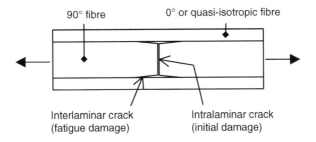

90° fibre   0° or quasi-isotropic fibre

Interlaminar crack   Intralaminar crack
(fatigue damage)   (initial damage)

Fig. 25.16   Cracking pattern in cross-ply laminate under 0° loading.

interlaminar stress concentration may result in an interlaminar crack, which may grow under further load cycles (see Fig. 25.16). Particularly sensitive points from a fatigue standpoint are points of change in thickness, ply drop-off points, and cut edges at bolt holes and notches.

Laminates generally have to carry a combination of in-plane (membrane) loads, and out-of-plane (flexural) loads. In a laminate having a well configured distribution of fibres, in-plane loads are carried primarily by the fibres, except at the laminate edges where interlaminar stress concentrations may arise, depending on the laminate boundary conditions and how the external loads are transferred into the laminate. Laminates under in-plane loading generally exhibit good fatigue performance. The most likely initial damage mode is cracking of plies whose fibres are at right angles to the stress direction. As previously noted, this tends to be followed by interlaminar cracking.

Laminates are usually considerably weaker in compression than in tension. This is due to the second order buckling effects of fibres in compression, which create through thickness bursting stresses. Therefore laminates under cyclic compression loading may be expected to exhibit a shorter fatigue life than laminates under cyclic tension loading.

Under out-of-plane loading, the laminate is subject to interlaminar shear stresses as well as stresses in the plane of the plies. In manufacturing processes such as hand lamination, matrix defects are more likely to exist between plies than within the plies themselves. Moreover, half the laminate section is subject to compression, which is inherently more damaging than tension. Therefore laminates may be expected to exhibit worse fatigue performance under out-of-plane loads than under in-plane loads.

Laminates that do not have sufficient fibre in directions off the primary fibre direction may be subject to significant stresses transverse to ply fibre directions which could contribute to intralaminar cracking damage.

25.4.5 Junctions and intersections in structural sections

Junctions between laminates in structural sections are a point of weakness because of practical difficulties in achieving fibre continuity in the requisite directions local to the junction. Consider, for example, the junction between the web and flange laminates of a pultruded I-section (Fig. 25.17). Tests to failure of *I*-beam sections show that such sections often fail by explosive rupture of the compression flange away from the web. The compression of the flange generates buckling restraint stresses. When these stresses exceed the low pull-off capacity of the flange from the web, the junction fails, and with it the structural integrity of the section.

The junction areas may be thicker than the adjoining laminates and may therefore be not

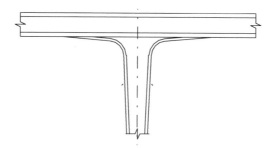

Fig. 25.17   Junction between web and flange of pultruded I-section.

as well cured as the laminates and may incorporate greater curing shrinkage stresses. Both these factors will reduce the strength and fatigue life of the junction.

25.4.6   Sandwich panels
Sandwich panels are formed by bonding or laminating fibre reinforced skin plates onto a lower performance core made of structural foam, balsa wood, or a honeycomb. The skins frequently have a quasi-isotropic fibre configuration.

The most fatigue sensitive points in sandwich panels are the bonded interfaces between skin and core. If the bonding is done manually there is scope for significant incidence of disbonds (bond defects).

Under repeated loading damage may be expected to develop in the skin-core interface or in the weaker core. A repeated concentrated load such as a wheel load may also produce degradation of the core properties due to creep and degradation of the core cell structure.

25.4.7   Stiffened panels
Particularly in naval construction FRP shells stiffened by top hat stiffeners are frequently used. This form of construction is analogous in concept to stiffened steel plate construction used in orthotropic steel bridge decks and steel box girders.

Geometric discontinuities are created by the bonding of the top hat stiffeners (Fig. 25.18). Especially sensitive to fatigue is the reentrant crack between the top hat flange and the shell plate. Under external loadings concentrated peel and shear stresses are induced around this detail. To reduce the stress concentrations and thereby increase the fatigue life of the connection, spew fillets in resin may be incorporated to reduce the notch effect. Considerable research has been carried out to investigate the fatigue performance of this type of joint and the findings are that the blending fillet is effective in improving the static and fatigue strength of the stiffener to shell connection.

25.4.8   3-D components
Three-dimensional components refer to moulded components which have appreciable dimensions in three orthogonal directions. These components may have a significant minimum thickness. They may be reinforced by short fibres, or by pre-forms that are draped to fairly tight surface curvatures. The state of stress is characteristically three dimensional, with no dominant direction over the whole of the component.

Fig. 25.18   Plate stiffened by top-hat stiffeners.

Such components are characterized by stress concentrations associated with geometric features such as chamfers, fillets, fins, holes, deviations of mats, etc. However, components may be designed to keep strain levels at a reasonably low level in relation to the failure strain level, thereby designing out fatigue life as a critical design criterion.

Thick components may have higher residual stresses due to differential curing effects which can adversely affect fatigue life.

25.4.8.1   Holes and notches
Stress concentration factors for holes and notches are given in (Tan and Sen, 1994).

25.4.8.2   Bolted connections
The fatigue life of bolted connections is covered in detail elsewhere. Suffice it to say that the stress concentrations are not only affected by the number of rows of bolts and the ratio of hole diameter to hole spacing, but also by fit-up tolerances. A bolted connection in which one or more bolts do not carry their intended share of the load due to fit-up tolerances will have a shorter fatigue life. Therefore it is important to use close tolerance holes and consider filling any gap between bolt and hole with resin to ensure uniform bearing of all bolts. Some bolt preload to create a compressive through thickness stress can enhance the apparent interlaminar strength of the laminate and extend the fatigue life of the joint.

25.4.8.3   Bonded connections
Under cyclic loading delamination cracks in the adhesive layer, substrate, or bond interface may grow. To reduce the stress concentration at the ends of bonded connections stepped or tapered plates and spew fillets may be used. This will increase the fatigue life. Through thickness composite pins may be employed to increase the peel strength of the joint and act as a crack stopper.

25.4.8.4   Typical S–N curves for composites
Considerable experimental work has been carried out by the NPL to determine the S–N curve of laminates (Broughton and Lodeiro, 2000). These curves have normally shown a reasonably consistent fit with equation [25.2]. The S–N curve slope coefficient k has been found to be reasonably consistently around 0.1. Figure 25.19 shows an S–N curve for an E-glass/913 laminate.

The NPL have also determined experimental S–N curves for bonded joints (Broughton *et al.*, 1999). Again these curves fit well with equation [25.2], with a slope coefficient of 0.1 or less. Figure 25.20 shows a S–N curve for a bonded joint.

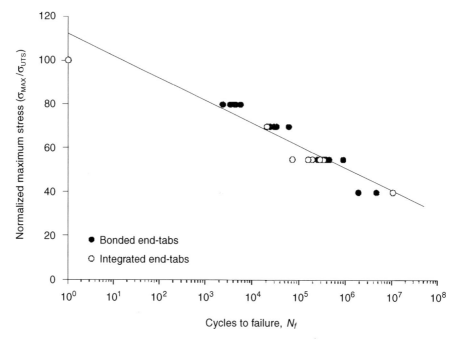

Fig. 25.19   *S–N* curve for E-glass/913 (R = 0.1) (Broughton *et al.*, NPL, 2000).

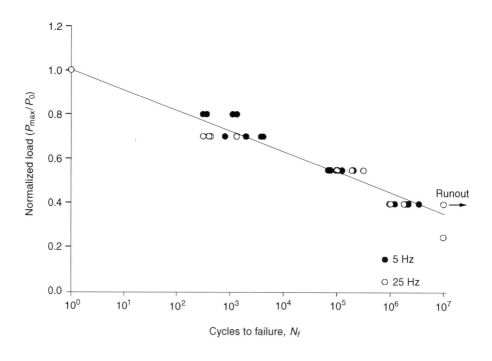

Fig. 25.20   *S–N* curve for bonded joint (Broughton *et al.*, 1999).

25.5   Design and analysis of structures for fatigue

25.5.1   Codes and standards

At the time of writing there are no national codes and standards covering the structural design of composites. The only reference documents are BS 4994 for pressure vessels, Eurocomp (Clarke, 1996), which proposes a Limit State format for a structural code, and a number of standards developed for specific types of structure or sectors, e.g. offshore pipelines. A recent standard for composites in offshore applications is DNV Offshore Standard OS-C501.

A number of design guides have been published for FRP strengthening of concrete structures (e.g. Concrete Society Technical Report No 55, 2000), and a best practice guide on the strengthening of metallic structures is due to be published in 2003 (CIRIA, 2003).

25.5.2   Limit state design methodology and factors of safety

Most current codes and standards for the design of structures for building and civil engineering are based on a semi-probabilistic design methodology. An account of how this may be applied is given in (Cadei, 1998) and in Chapter 3 of Hollaway and Head (2001).

Fatigue endurance is sometimes considered a serviceability limit state because it depends on the cumulative effect of expected (unfactored) load events rather than the effect of a single extreme (ultimate) load event. It is more appropriate, however, to consider it a durability limit state.

An experimental S–N curve exhibits considerable scatter in the experimental points to which the curve is a best fit. For design purposes, the mean curve should not be used, but rather a lower confidence limit curve corresponding to the mean less 2.0 standard deviations (Fig. 25.21).

In most real structures stress histories due to live loads are characterized by variable amplitude stress cycles. In such situations the Palmgren–Miner rule for damage accumulation may be used to assess fatigue life. Because the fatigue of composites is driven by peak stress rather than stress range, the reservoir cycle counting method given in BS 5400 Part 10 to reduce an irregular stress fluctuation history to a series of simple stress cycles is not in principle applicable to composites. It is proposed that, in composites, the cycles be based on peaks of the non-dimensional peak stress or the failure function, but experimental research is required to identify the most suitable approach.

25.5.3   Significance of fatigue limit states in relation to other design limit states

Composite structures are designed to satisfy ultimate limit states (ULSs) such as laminate rupture or buckling and serviceability limit states (SLSs) such as limiting deflections and vibrations. A common approach has been to apply a stress or strain limit under unfactored design loads. The stress or strain limit corresponds to the onset of damage, which, for example, can take the form of matrix cracking in a cross ply. BS 4994 prescribes a limiting strain under unfactored loads of 0.1 of the ultimate failure strain. For glass reinforced polymers a limit of 0.25%–0.30% is applied under 'frequently occurring load events', and a limit of 0.4% under 'rare load events'.

Due to the low modulus, high strength, and high strain to failure of many composites, the serviceability limit states are frequently more critical than ultimate limit states. To demonstrate this, consider the following. At the ultimate limit state the partial material safety factor γ_m is commonly in the range of 2.25 to 3.0. The partial load factor γ_{FL} is in the region of 1.6.

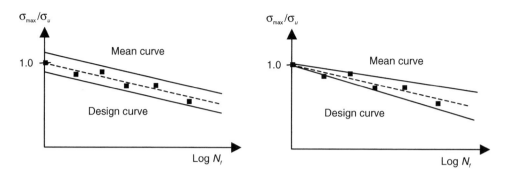

Fig. 25.21 Design vs. mean *S–N* curve.

Therefore the combined factor is in the range of 3.6–4.8. However, at the serviceability limit state γ_{FL} is 1.0 while γ_m is 8–10. Hence the combined factor is 8–10. This is considerably more critical than the ULS combined safety factor.

For a combined SLS factor of safety of 10, $\sigma_{max}/\sigma_u = 0.1$. Putting this in equation [25.1] yields $N_f = 1.0 \times 10^9$ cycles. This is greater than the requirement in many actual applications.

25.5.4   Influence of creep, temperature, and moisture on fatigue properties

As previously pointed out, elevated temperature and moisture content reduce the mechanical properties of the resin and therefore increase the fatigue damage under a given stress cycle. Hence a component loaded cyclically in a hot, humid environment will display a steeper *S–N* curve and a shorter life than a component in a standard environment under the same cyclical loading. A pragmatic approach to taking this effect into account is to assume that the normalized *S–N* curve in the form of equation [25.2] is independent of hygrothermal conditions, and that the normalizing stress σ_u is modified to take into account the hygrothermal conditions. A reduced σ_u value due to adverse hygrothermal conditions increases the value of the normalized stress σ_{max}/σ_u, and hence the life is shortened.

An overview of the influence of environmental exposure on fatigue properties is given in Curtis (1998).

25.5.5   Stress analysis for fatigue assessment

As a general guideline, stress concentrations due to deterministic geometric features such as holes, notches, ply drop-offs, changes in thickness, etc. should be taken into account in the determination of the fatigue stress σ_{max}. The corresponding failure stress σ_u should take into account material variability caused by internal material and workmanship defects.

As previously observed, geometric discontinuities cause stress concentrations in the vicinity of the stress raising detail. For example, the adhesion and peel stresses acting between a bonded FRP plate and a substrate in a dissimilar material will be highly localized to the end of the plate or a crack in the substrate. It may be found that the theoretical value of the peak stress is dependent on certain geometric or material parameters which are in themselves variable and therefore better characterized on a probabilistic basis rather than a deterministic basis. For example, the aforementioned adhesion stresses between the FRP plate and the substrate are sensitive to the values assumed for the thickness and shear modulus of the adhesive layer. Given the potential unevenness of the substrate surface and the variability of the workmanship, it is difficult to put narrow bounds on the bondline thickness. To circumvent this problem there are two alternative approaches.

- Retain the stress-based approach, but use a consistent nominal adhesive thickness in the calculations and in the analysis of test results. Do a sufficient number of tests to be able to determine the mean and standard deviation of the peak stress based on a nominal bondline thickness. Use a factored characteristic value in design.
- Use an ultimate fracture mechanics-based approach, which abstracts from the thickness and stiffness characteristics of the adhesive layer.

In the stress-based approach, peak stresses taking stress concentration effects into account may be determined from closed form solutions, where available, or from a numerical analysis of the detail. Finite element analysis is frequently used for this purpose, although the boundary element method (BEM) may be better suited to this type of problem. The disadvantage of the finite element analysis approach is that the accuracy of the predicted peak stress is highly dependent upon the choice of the mesh density in the region of the discontinuity. Modifying the mesh density to verify that a converged solution has been obtained is a time-consuming process. The boundary element method utilizes Green's function type stress functions which satisfy equilibrium and assume concentrated stresses in the first place. There is still a mesh density issue in the BEM in the choice of the mesh density along boundaries, but the issue is of a lower order of importance.

The fracture mechanics approach is based upon considering the energy release rate per unit extension of crack. The simplest formulation considers the elastic strain energy released as a function of a unit extension of the crack. Consider for example the case of a ply drop-off. An expression for the energy release rate is

$$G = \frac{N^2}{2B}\left(\frac{1}{EA_1} - \frac{1}{EA_2}\right)$$

[25.10]

where G is the energy release rate, N is the load applied to the laminate, B is the breadth of the laminate, and EA_1, EA_2 are the laminate stiffness values on either side of a crack tip.

When considering fatigue, the maximum G value per cycle would be used to assess the fatigue life. The fatigue life curve could be couched in the following terms:

$$\frac{G_{max}}{G_u} = 1 - k\log_{10}N_f$$

[25.11]

where G_{max} is the energy release rate corresponding to N_{max} and G_u is the failure energy release rate as determined from tests.

25.6   Case study: FRP road deck fatigue performance (TRL test programme on ACCS Roadway Panel)

The Transport Research Laboratory (TRL) were commissioned by the UK Highways Agency (HA) to undertake a research project to investigate the fatigue performance of a cellular roadway panel in E-glass and vinylester resin and develop generic design guidelines for roadway panels (Daly and Duckett, 2002). The roadway panels are designed to replace a

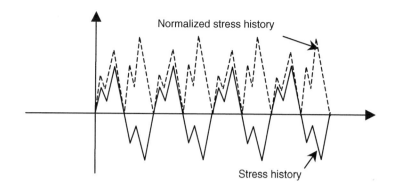

Fig. 25.22   Stress history vs. normalized stress history.

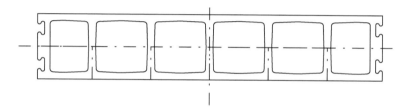

Fig. 25.23   Test roadway panel (courtesy of FaberMaunsell).

reinforced concrete deck slab in slab and beam bridge decks. The project commenced in February 2000 and is expected to be completed in 2003.

The project brief was to develop experimental data upon which to base generic fatigue requirements for the technical approval of FRP deck systems, i.e. to define the evidence needed and to develop a method of providing assurance of fatigue durability. To this end, laboratory tests were undertaken to investigate the performance of the road panel under highway traffic loading.

The panel, designed by Maunsell, is shown in Fig. 25.23. The FRP deck was designed to withstand the highway loading specified in HA document BD 37 with 45 units of HB, and the fatigue loading specified in BS 5400: Part 10. The load partial safety factors for the serviceability and the ultimate limit states were in accordance with BD 37/88. The most significant design loadings are:

- HA Loading: Wheel load of 100 kN over a circular or square contact area giving a contact pressure of 1.1 MPa.
- HB Loading: Wheel load of 112.5 kN over a circular or square contact area giving a contact pressure of 1.1 MPa.
- HB Longitudinal Load: A longitudinal braking load of 56.25 kN combined with the nominal vertical HB load above.
- Fatigue loading: 'Standard fatigue vehicle' (Fig. 25.16) of 320 kN, wheel loads of 20 kN, and 2.0 million cycles per annum in slow lane of motorway, or the spectrum of commercial vehicles defined in Table 11 of BS 5400: Part 10, whichever produces the worse damage.

The loading partial safety factors are:

	SLS		ULS	
	γ_{fl}	γ_{f3}	γ_{fl}	γ_{f3}
HA	1.20	1.0	1.50	1.1
HB	1.10	1.0	1.30	1.1
HB + Braking	1.00	1.0	1.10	1.1

The cellular panel is 500 mm wide and 115 mm deep. In order to withstand the high local stresses imposed by HB vehicle wheel loads, the skin thickness of the panel is 12–15 mm and the web thickness is 12 mm. By limiting the width of the unit to 500 mm, the weight of the component is limited to about 37 kg/m, thereby facilitating its manufacture by the pultrusion process. To construct a roadway deck, panels are laid side by side and joined along their mating edges by adhesive bonding and the insertion of a pair of toggles.

The panel design concept is such that the panel spans predominantly in the longitudinal direction of the webs, as it is relatively flexible in its transverse direction due to Vierendeel action. Thus stress resultants that have to be transmitted across the bonded joints between panels are minimized.

The panel was designed for strength, serviceability, and fatigue endurance, assuming a normalized S–N curve having a k value of 0.1. Of course, in the absence of any experimental data, the S–N curve assumed in the design phase is in the nature of a presumption, and the testing to be carried out under the project is to determine the true S–N curve, which will enable the panel design to be adjusted accordingly.

The designers recognized that when the panel is laid transverse to the direction of traffic flow, the T-junction between the web and the flange laminate is subjected to a large number of stress cycles. Due to the flexure of the skin plate caused by concentrated wheel loads, frame type continuity moments are induced in the web. Thus for each wheel passage the surface mat of the web is subjected to a stress cycle. The surface mat is not straight but goes around the corner at a radius determined by the fillet radius. The curvature of the mat generates radial through thickness tensile stresses, tending to cause delamination. Delamination of the surface mat, therefore, was predicted to constitute a likely fatigue damage mechanism. Moreover, in each load cycle the surface mat is subjected to a stress reversal from tension to compression. When under compression, peel stresses may be induced between the straight section of the surface mat and the core, adding to the fatigue driving effect.

Two series of fatigue tests were carried out. In the first series a complete assembly of roadway panels were supported on a full-scale composite primary structure and were subjected to multiple cycles of a full-scale rolling wheel trundling back and forth at about 1 cycle per second. In the second series of tests roadway panel samples were loaded with high frequency servo-hydraulic actuators (5 Hz) and specially designed loading jigs. The tests were designed to run to fatigue failure at relatively large numbers of cycles and the intention was to carry out a sufficient number of tests at different peak stresses to construct a full S–N curve.

The rolling wheel tests were carried out using the Trafficking Test Facility (TTF) at TRL

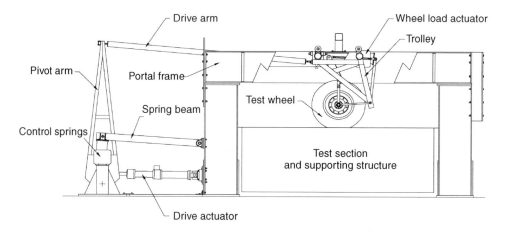

Fig. 25.24   Trafficking test facility at TRL.

(Fig. 25.23), which was originally constructed to test the durability of bridge deck joints. The wheel (Fig. 25.24) was kept under a constant load of 35 kN, a substantially higher value than the 20 kN wheel load specified for the standard fatigue vehicle in BS 5400 Part 10. The effect of the standard fatigue vehicle's other three wheels on a given axle is expected to be small due to the short length of the transverse influence line.

Two rolling wheel tests were carried out for different types of roadway panel. In the first test thin-walled ACCS panels not designed to carry highway wheel loads directly were used. The purpose of this preliminary test was to reach fatigue failure in a relatively small number of cycles and identify the likely fatigue failure modes and locations. In the second test the newly designed Roadway Panels were tested. It was predicted that the Roadway Panel would not fail during the 350 000 cycles of the test. Strain gauges were attached to the panels at the potentially critical locations identified in the preliminary test in order to obtain strain histories during the test. This data was used to determine corresponding normal stress histories at the critical locations and subsequently to plan the second series of tests. The normal stress data can be used as input to a detailed finite element analysis to compute interlaminar shear and through thickness stresses that cannot be readily measured directly by strain gauges. If a relevant interlaminar stress is shown to drive fatigue damage, it could be used as the reference stress in the S–N curve for the critical detail, and employed to predict the fatigue life of the component under actual highway fatigue loading. However, this level of detail is unnecessary if the normalized S–N curve is used for design, since this only requires the ratio of fatigue load to ultimate load.

The preliminary test using the light duty ACCS panels to form the running surface was carried out at a reduced wheel load of 6 to 8 kN. The first signs of failure were recorded at 5000 cycles and the test was stopped at 80 000 cycles. As predicted, the failure occurred at the junction of the webs and the top skin of the panel. Cracking was visible in the top surface of the panel adjacent to the webs and is believed to be due to hogging moments at that location.

The second test using the heavy duty Roadway Panels was stopped after 4.56 million cycles. Assuming an S–N curve k value of 0.1, this corresponds to a life in excess of 37 million fatigue vehicles. After this period of testing there was no visible sign of deterioration in the performance of the Roadway Panels and it was concluded that, if this was a real life structure, there would be no cause for concern about fatigue performance. However, some

Fig. 25.25   Test wheel.

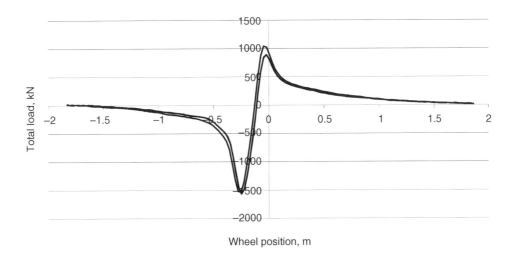

Fig. 25.26   Influence line in terms of microstrain vs. wheel position.

of the strain gauges did appear to indicate a local failure. It was not clear whether this was a failure of the gauge or an indication of delamination of the outer ply. Further investigation and coring of the test sample was undertaken at these locations, but no visual indication of damage was found.

On the basis of the test, TRL independently estimated a fatigue life of at least 30 years under normal UK traffic conditions. Both these estimates should be treated with due caution, given that the slope of the S–N curve beyond 10^7 cycles is not known at this stage.

The influence lines for the various strain gauges were plotted and by inspection the critical stress occurs at the top of the internal webs where a stress reversal also occurs. A plot of this influence line is shown in Fig. 25.26. The R ratio ($\sigma_{min}/\sigma_{max}$). at this location was –0.67.

The number of cycles in the rolling wheel test was limited by the relatively slow rate of testing and the cost associated with the duration of the test. In the second series of tests, a conventional servo-hydraulic testing machine operating at up to 5 Hz was used to obtain lives of up to 10 million cycles. The small-scale specimens consisted of full-scale sections cut from standard roadway panels. Strain gauges were installed at the same locations as in the rolling wheel tests and were used to set up a loading configuration that gives the correct stress distribution.

A special loading jig was designed to simulate the passage of a wheel from one side of a web to the other in an actuator load cycle. Thus the strain history at the critical location in a single cycle closely matches the history measured in the rolling wheel test.

The objective of the second series was not only to determine an experimental S–N curve for the roadway panels but also to devise and validate a suitable fatigue test method that can be carried out relatively quickly on deck specimens. The test could be used to certify the actual fatigue performance of commercial roadway panels.

25.7   Operational aspects

It is important that a materials and workmanship specification be produced to prescribe the tolerances assumed in the design of the components for ultimate, serviceability, and fatigue loads. Similarly a fabrication specification is required to define fabrication processes, fit-up tolerances, bonding processes, bonding tolerances, bolting, and training and supervision of operatives. An important aspect of bonded joints is that the hygrothermal dependency of the strength of the joint is dependent on the glass transition temperature T_g of the adhesive. The curing temperature of the adhesive affects the T_g value. Therefore both the static and fatigue strength of the joint is critically dependent upon achieving the T_g value assumed in the design through correct curing of the adhesive.

Prior to manufacture of components, type approval tests are required to validate the manufacturer's or fabricator's proposed materials and manufacturing processes. These could include adhesives and bonding procedures for bonded joints, assembly and connection of bolted structures, minimum strength and stiffness properties of components and connectors, etc.

During manufacture or fabrication, further quality control tests are required to demonstrate that the requisite quality is consistently being obtained.

Accurate non-destructive defect detection of composite structures and bonded joints is still an area of ongoing research. Practical examination techniques for bonded joints tend to be limited to such basic techniques as tap tests, although thermographic techniques show promise for the future. Therefore rather than rely on the detection of major flaws, critical connections should receive close control of the application process, and independent checking of the design.

During service embedded or surface mounted strain sensors, and acoustic emission sensors, may be used to detect damage events. Regular inspections of structures subject to significant fatigue loads should be carried out to check for evidence of incipient fatigue damage. Nascent fatigue cracks can be stopped relatively easily by appropriate repair techniques. These include overlaminating or bonding of strengthening patches and the introduction of crack stoppers.

25.8   Concluding remarks

FRP composites are finding increasing application in civil engineering due to their corrosion resistance and light weight. With working strain levels frequently dictated by serviceability design criteria, fatigue is often not a critical limit state. It is, however, potentially critical in matrix dominated failure modes such as interlaminar shear and in connections characterized by stress concentrations. Amongst the most demanding applications from the point of view of fatigue performance are FRP bridge decks. These are required to withstand tens of millions of heavy goods vehicle wheel loading cycles. Roadway panels recently tested at TRL have demonstrated that FRP solutions can achieve satisfactory fatigue lives under demanding loading conditions.

25.9   References

BEHESHTY M H, HARRIS B and ADAM T (1999), 'An empirical fatigue-life model for high performance fibre composites with and without impact damage', *Composites: Part A*, **30**, 971–87.
BS 4994: 'Design and construction of vessels and tanks in reinforced plastics'.
BS 5400: Part 10: 1980 'Steel, concrete and composite bridges. Code of Practice for fatigue'.
BS 8100: 1995 'Lattice towers and masts: Code of Practice for loading of guyed masts'.
BROUGHTON W R and LODEIRO M J (2000), 'Fatigue testing of composite laminates', *NPL Report CMMT(A)* 252, November.
BROUGHTON W R and MCCARTNEY L M (1998), 'Predictive models for assessing long-term performance of polymer matrix composites', *NPL Report CMMT(A)* 95.
BROUGHTON W R, MERA R D and HINOPOULOS G (1999), 'Cyclic Fatigue Testing of Adhesive Joints Test Method Assessment', *NPL Report CMMT(A)* 191, September.
CADEI J M C (1998), 'Factors of safety in the Limit State design of FRP composite structures', Designing Cost-effective composites, *I.Mech.E.*, September.
CIRIA (2003), Report 645, 'Strengthening of metallic structures using externally bonded fibre-reinforced polymers', (expected).
CLARKE J L (ED) (1996), *Eurocomp Design Code and Handbook*, Spon.
CONCRETE SOCIETY TECHNICAL REPORT 55 (2000), 'Design guidance for strengthening concrete structures using fibre composite materials'.
CURTIS P T (1998), 'Designing for fatigue and environmental effects in polymer composites', Designing cost-effective composites, *I.Mech. E.*, September.
DALY F R and DUCKETT W G (2002), 'The design and testing of an FRP composite highway deck', *ACIC 2002*, Spon.
DNV OFFSHORE STANDARD OS-C501, 'Composite Materials'.
HARRIS B, GATHERCOLE N, LEE J A, REITER H and ADAM T (1997), 'Life prediction for constant-stress fatigue in carbon-fibre composites', *Phil. Trans. R. Soc. Lond. A355*, 1259–94.
HOLLAWAY L C and HEAD P R (2001), *Advanced Composites and Polymers in the Civil Infrastructure*, Elsevier.
MAUNSELL, S L P (1999), ARP, 'Project CP 4353 – Detailed conceptual design and cost assessments of composites topsides'.
TAN SEN C (1994), 'Stress concentrations in laminated composites', Technomic, USA.

26

Fatigue in aerospace applications

A. J. Davies, QinetiQ, UK and P. T. Curtis, Dstl, UK

26.1   Introduction

Since the far-reaching introduction of light alloys into airframes and the failures of aircraft such as the Comet, fatigue has been a subject of considerable interest to the aircraft industry. Problems associated with metallic fatigue have been widespread in this industry and, as a result, fatigue features strongly in the design of metallic aircraft and dominates maintenance issues.

The introduction of polymer composite materials into primary airframe structures has brought many benefits, including a significantly higher tolerance to fatigue loading than metallic materials. Although less sensitive to fatigue, the increased use of composite materials has emphasized the fact that their fatigue behaviour is more complex than that of metals. In a metal, fatigue damage develops as clearly defined sharp cracks, the initiation and propagation of which can be reasonably well predicted by fracture mechanics analysis.[1]

In a composite material, fatigue damage can take the form of any, or all, of the following: delamination, matrix cracking, fibre failure, matrix crazing, fibre/matrix debonding and void growth, forming a discrete but complex damage zone (Fig. 26.1). This is dependent upon variables associated with the testing conditions and the construction and composition of the material.

Until recently, aircraft designs using composite materials have been limited by static properties, including damage tolerance and compressive behaviour. Fatigue behaviour has usually not been an issue, as at the strain levels dictated by the static properties, damage would not grow in fatigue (there are notable exceptions to this philosophy, such as rotor blades, propellers, suspension parts etc.). Improvement in these properties and a greater understanding of the static properties of the materials has raised design strains to the point that zero growth in fatigue cannot be guaranteed. At present there are major deficiencies in life prediction methodologies for composite materials, which often force large factors of safety to be adopted. That is, composite structures used in high-cycle fatigue applications are often over-designed and are therefore somewhat heavier and more costly than necessary. Increasing design strains will further exacerbate this problem.[2]

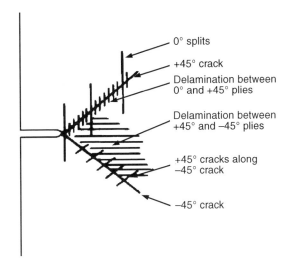

Fig. 26.1   Typical damage zone at a sharp crack after fatigue testing.

26.1.1   History of aerospace composite usage

Lifting a payload against gravity, whether it is in the form of freight, or perhaps a weapons payload, or, indeed, people, is an expensive process. To minimize the weight of the aircraft and maximize the weight of the payload, designers are always looking to design structures so that they are both efficient and lightweight.

The first usage of composite materials (as we would know them today) for primary structures was seen in 1940 when a main spar on a Blenheim aircraft was built from unbleached flax thread skin formed with phenolic resin in a heated press to form what was possibly the first aerospace composite structure. This process was developed by Dr Norman de Bruyne at Aero Research Ltd at Duxford, the forerunner of Ciba Composites (now Hexcel Composites). De Bruyne had also investigated another common aerospace material, the honeycomb sandwich, back in 1937, which was first used in balsa form on the De Havilland Albatross and the Mosquito.

Fibrous composites were first used in 1947 in the form of Durestos, a chrysotile asbestos fibre reinforcing a phenolic resin. By 1966 Watt, Johnston and Philips at the Royal Aircraft Establishment, Farnborough, (now QinetiQ/DSTL) had perfected a technique to produce high-performance carbon fibres with a diameter of 8 mm, considerably less than that of boron, which was posing some fabrication difficulties, since at 100 μm it was too thick to be formed easily into complex shaped components. The Grumman Corporation was one of the first companies to use boron/epoxy composite materials in primary aircraft structures, for the horizontal stabilizer for the F-14A Tomcat naval fighter.

The number of fibres in use today has escalated, with many ceramic and polymer fibres such as aramids, silicon carbide, quartz, polyethylene, alumina, etc. also being available today. Carbon fibre continues, however, to dominate the aerospace composites market, followed by glass fibres, often used for its radar transparency for radome applications.

Since those early days, the percentage of composite structures used in primary, secondary or tertiary applications has increased considerably in both civil and military aircraft. Although, as often happens, military aircraft lead the way in the use of new technologies, today the drive for increased performance at reduced cost has led to extensive usage of these materials in the civil aerospace industry.

The use of composites in aerospace became more widespread in the 1950s and 1960s and indeed the world's first all-composite aircraft, the Learfan, was conceived by Bill Lear in 1954. However, the Learfan's maiden flight was not until New Year's Day 1981. Composite parts for this aircraft were many and varied including driveshafts, propellers and fuselage. However, the project was cancelled as a result of unforeseen problems, delays and a lack of funding. Undeterred, there have been numerous designers who have harnessed the unique properties of composite materials to develop aircraft; amongst the most publicised is Burt Rutan who flew non-stop around the world in 1986 in his aircraft Voyager.

At the top end of the civil-aviation market, airliners have been taking advantage of composite materials to reduce weight and to decrease manufacturing costs. The Airbus range of aircraft has the highest utilization of composite materials yet seen. In 1972 the A300 had the vertical fin, leading edge and various fairing panels made of glass fibre. The composite usage was further increased with the addition of a carbon-fibre tail-fin box in the years between 1985 and 1987. Figure 26.2 shows a breakdown of the composite parts on the Airbus A320. The A330 and the new A340 follow a similar design philosophy.[3] Figure 26.3 compares the composite usage in various Airbus aircraft.

In military aircraft, weight saving is of great importance, particularly in the case of V/STOL aircraft. The development of the Harrier by BAe Systems and McDonnell Douglas into the AV-8B/GR5-7 afforded an opportunity to exploit composites to their economic limit. In total, 25% of the airframe weight is of composite materials. Based upon this and the experience gained with BAe Systems EAP, the European Fighter Aircraft (EFA) has made even greater usage of composite materials. US military aircraft such as the F16, F18, F22 and the unconventional Osprey make very extensive usage of composite materials. As issues such as the drive for reduced cost, increased temperature capability, fabrication flexibility and reduced signatures are addressed we can expect to see the majority of future military airframes made from these materials.

Alongside the growth in usage in fixed-wing aircraft, one must not forget the dominating position that composite materials have established in the rotary-wing industry. Whilst in the 1960s most helicopters had rotor blades made from metallic materials, most today use all-composite rotor blades. The drive for this has indeed been one of increased component life and reduced cost. Typically, metallic rotor blades might last for around 1000 hours of use, whereas today's composite blades are expected to last for at least 20 000 hours and in some cases as long as the life of the vehicle. The principal reason for this is the much better fatigue performance of composite materials, here used in an application where designers must allow for tens of millions of fatigue load cycles.

26.2   Overview of fatigue performance of aerospace materials

Typical plots of peak tensile strain vs. cycles to failure (S–N plots) for unidirectional composite materials are shown in Fig. 26.4[4] for a range of carbon-fibre-reinforced materials. Since, for unidirectional materials under tensile loading, the fibres carry virtually all the load, the tensile fatigue behaviour might be expected to depend solely on the fibres, and since carbon fibres are not sensitive to fatigue loading, good fatigue behaviour should result. However, experimental evidence has shown that the slopes of the S–N curves are determined principally by the strain in the matrix.[5,6] Consequently plots of mean strain versus cycles to failure are often more instructive.[5]

A320 Composite applications

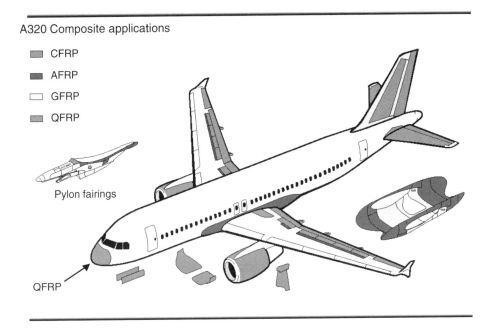

Fig. 26.2   Composite usage in A320 (Reproduced with kind permission of ⊘ AIRBUS).

Composite structure distribution – percentage

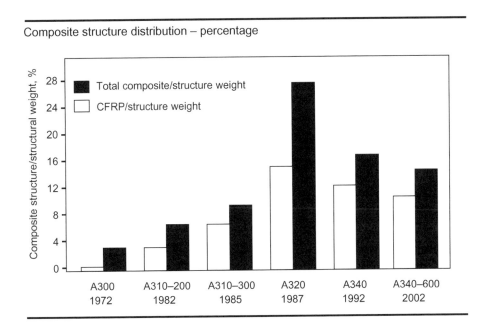

Fig. 26.3   Percentage composite structure distribution (Reproduced with kind permission of
⊘ AIRBUS).

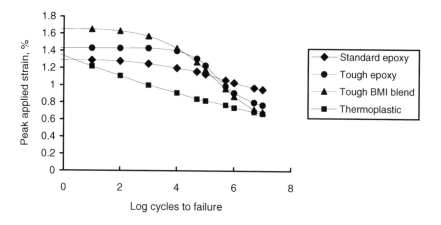

Fig. 26.4 Typical *S–N* fatigue data for unidirectional carbon fibre composites.

It is clear from Fig. 26.4 that, even after 10 million fatigue loading cycles, sustainable strains are still well above the 4000 $\mu\varepsilon$ (0.4%) limit reinforcing the designers' confidence in assuming that fatigue is generally not a problem. The data in Fig. 26.4 are for unidirectional materials, but composite materials are usually used in laminated form, layers being arranged so that the fibres are oriented in several directions to carry the principal stresses. On increasing the percentage of off-axis fibres in a laminate, the static properties are reduced as there are fewer fibres available to support the applied stresses. The slope of the *S–N* fatigue curve increases in relation to the reduction in monotonic strength (Fig. 26.5), as the layers with off-axis fibres, whose mechanical properties are resin dependent, are more easily damaged in fatigue. Transverse plies, with fibres at 90° to the test direction, develop transverse cracks upon the first tensile load cycle or with increasing numbers of cycles.[7] Angled plies, with fibres typically at ±45°, will also develop intraply damage. Since these layers support little axial load, the damage has a minimal effect on the axial tensile strength or stiffness. However, this damage can have a noticeable effect in fatigue loading. The stress concentrations at the ends of intraply cracks can lead to the initiation of delamination between the layers, which may lead to a loss of integrity with potential for environmental attack and certainly reductions in compressive strength.[7,8] Alternatively the cracks may propagate into adjacent primary load-bearing layers and seriously weaken the material.[4]

At present, the compressive properties of carbon-fibre composites are a factor limiting their wider usage in aerospace applications. In fatigue loading, carbon composites are much more sensitive to compression loading than to tension. Ultimately, the worst fatigue case for carbon composites is fully reversed fatigue or tension–compression loading. The poorer behaviour (Fig. 26.6) is because many of the laminate plies, without fibres in the test direction, develop intraply damage, which causes local layer delamination at relatively short lifetimes. In tensile fatigue this is less serious, since the layers containing fibres in the test direction continue to support the majority of the applied load. In compression, however, tensile induced damage of this type can lead to local layer instability and layer buckling leading to macro-instability failure at relatively short lifetimes.

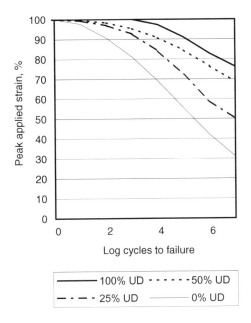

Fig. 26.5   Effect of UD plies on fatigue sensitivity.

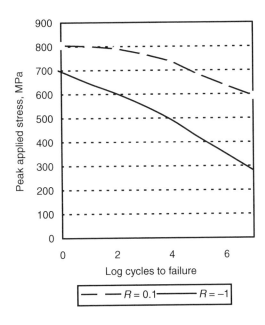

Fig. 26.6   Composition of typical fatigue behaviour for tension and tension–compression loading.

26.3   Fatigue life prediction

There have been numerous studies[9,10] on predicting fatigue life in polymer composites; which have led to the development of empirical relationships or theoretical equations. The three main types are based upon one of the following:

- changes in modulus
- degradation of residual strength
- actual damage mechanisms

There are also many empirical relationships for predicting fatigue life such as Basquin's Law (power law), straight-line fits to S–N curves, Miner's rule, and the Coffin and Manson Law. Some models show good agreement of what are essentially power laws with experimental data. At present, however, no single model can reliably predict fatigue life and residual strength in composite structures. This section briefly reviews some of the key work done to date on fatigue life prediction and suggest ways of progressing the current understanding.

26.3.1   Residual strength degradation

Many life-prediction methods have been based on residual strength degradation.
    These have been developed on the basis of one or more of the following three assumptions:

- the statistical variability of the static strength of the material can be described by a two-parameter Weibull distribution,
- the residual strength after N cycles of fatigue loading can be related to the static strength by a deterministic equation,
- when the residual strength decreases to the maximum applied stress, fatigue failure occurs.

These approaches can be broadly characterized as being either mechanistic or phenomenological. Mechanistic models quantitatively account for damage progression in composites with a minimal amount of experimentally obtained input. Phenomenological models characterize residual strength and life in terms of macroscopically observable properties, such as strength and stiffness. The primary drawback of phenomenological approaches is their dependency on large amounts of experimental input for each material, lay-up and loading of interest and the difficulty in extrapolation to different conditions.

    A good example of such a model is that developed by Schaff and Davidson[11,12] which is a phenomenological strength-based wear-out model, which could be used to predict the residual strength and fatigue life of composite laminates subjected to constant amplitude and two stress level loadings. The model was derived on the basis of the fundamental assumption that the laminate or structure of interest was subjected to proportional loading; that strength was a monotonically decreasing function of the number of cycles; and that both the distribution of fatigue life due to constant amplitude loading and the residual strength distribution after an arbitrary load history could be represented by two-parameter Weibull functions. To verify the accuracy of the model and the procedures involved in characterization, predicted fatigue–life distributions were compared to a variety of uniaxial spectrum fatigue loadings. For the cases considered, good correlation was obtained.

    Another example is that of Yang and Shanyi[13] who conducted an exploratory study into the fatigue behaviour of composite materials under spectrum loading. They modified a fatigue and residual-strength model for constant-amplitude cyclic loading and applied it to the fatigue of composites. The study used baseline constant amplitude data to describe the fatigue behaviour subjected to spectrum loading.

26.3.2   Stiffness reduction
Theories for fatigue based on the reduction in stiffness have one significant advantage over the residual strength theories, namely that the remaining life can be assessed by non-destructive means. A typical stiffness-reduction model relates the degradation of modulus to the fraction of life expended at a given stress amplitude, assuming that the residual stiffness decreases monotonically as the number of load cycles increases.

For this approach to succeed a comprehensive database is required, based on the stiffness reduction, unless mathematical relationships can be developed to relate the residual stiffness degradation to other readily measurable materials properties such as residual strength and fatigue life. If such a relationship could be established, extrapolation of data at various stress levels would be possible, thus greatly reducing the amount of test data needed to characterize the material's behaviour.

Various researchers have reported stiffness reduction caused by fatigue loading. Whitworth,[14] for example, proposed a model to relate the stiffness degradation to the fractional life expended at a given stress level and also to the residual strength degradation. The model formulated was phenomenological in nature and was limited to specimens subjected to constant-amplitude fatigue loading. For a given specimen, a rate equation was proposed, which assumed that the rate of residual modulus reduction was inversely proportional to a certain power of the residual modulus itself. The model is capable of predicting the statistical distribution of the residual strength for any ratio of residual-to-initial stiffness from a limited amount of base-line experimental data and is applicable to constant amplitude fatigue loading.

Reifsnider et al.[15] also investigated the use of stiffness change as a non-destructive fatigue damage parameter. Generally they found that the stiffness change could be quantitatively related to the fatigue life and the residual strength of composite laminates through various models based on the observed micro-damage. A cumulative-damage scheme based on the critical element model was used to predict the fatigue behaviour of laminates. The critical element model (Fig. 26.7) assumed that the laminate was composed of sub-critical and critical elements. The fibres were assumed to be the load-carrying members and are denoted as the critical elements; the matrix was designated as the secondary, sub-critical elements. Non-catastrophic damage such as matrix cracking was called subcritical. They proposed a cumulative-damage scheme for 0°/90° laminates based on the critical element model.

26.3.3   Strength-life equal-rank assumption
The possibility of a correlation between the static strength and fatigue life distributions for composite materials was first suggested by Hahn and Kim[16] though this was first encapsulated in the strength-life equal-rank assumption by Chou and Croman.[17]

Hahn and Kim demonstrated the existence of a unique relationship between the monotonic strength and the number of cycles to failure for a composite material. Firstly, it was hypothesized that a sufficient number of specimens should be tensile tested and the monotonic strength distribution obtained. The same number of specimens with the same population should then be subjected to cyclic fatigue loading. Then a specimen of a certain rank in the fatigue life distribution would be equivalent in strength to the specimen of the same rank in the static strength distribution, i.e. there was a unique relationship between the static

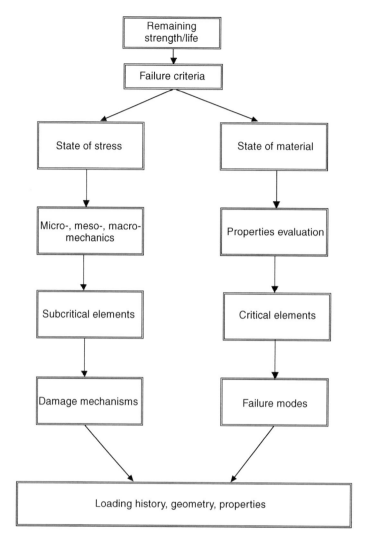

Fig. 26.7   Schematic of the critical element model.

strength and fatigue life, such that a monotonically strong specimen is strong in fatigue. Implicit in this is the assumption that fatigue failure is by the same mechanism as static failure.

Hahn and Kim also introduced the concept of rate of change of residual strength, without referring to any damage mechanisms or cracks. They assumed that the time rate of decrease of residual strength was inversely proportional to the residual strength to a certain power. From this deterministic residual strength equation, and the static strength distribution, they derived the fatigue life distribution.

The strength–life equal-rank assumption (SLERA), although potentially very useful in predicting the fatigue life of composite materials, has not found wide support in the literature for two main reasons; firstly, it cannot be proved, secondly it cannot be applied to notched or impacted composites, because failure mechanisms are different in monotonic and fatigue loading.

Barnard et al.[18] presented evidence to validate and extend the SLERA theory. They stated that the argument that notched specimens invalidate the SLERA are false, as it makes no assumption about residual properties, only stating that there is a correlation between the monotonic strength and fatigue-life expectancy of a nominally identical sample. The strength of each of these components changes as the fatigue life progresses, but there will still be a correlation between the residual strength and residual life expectancy. Thus the correlation need not be the same as the initial one. They reported that the scatter in fatigue data has two components, a fatigue part and a static part. The SLERA will only apply if the fatigue component of the fatigue scatter is very small or in some way a function of the static component.

The SLERA does have its limitations. It cannot predict changes in failure modes as a function of stress levels, it also tends to give conservative estimates for fatigue life.

26.4   Damage mechanisms

Theories of fatigue behaviour based on damage mechanisms must model the development of complex damage zones and are thus generally mechanistic in nature. This approach has usually proved too challenging and researchers have tended to try and restrict models to circumstances where one type of damage predominates, as would be the case in metallic materials. A typical approach would be to model the intrinsic defects in the matrix as small cracks parallel to the fibre, and the propagation of these cracks might be predicted by a linear fracture-mechanics analysis. Alternatively delamination might be modelled as a single crack.

The work by Robinson and Davies[19] Martin[20] and O'Brien et al.[21] is typical. O'Brien et al. developed a life-prediction methodology for composites subjected to tensile fatigue loading that incorporated both the generic fracture mechanics characterization of delamination and the assessment of the influence of damage on laminate fatigue life. They reported that several damage mechanisms may reduce the stiffness of a composite laminate, the most common ones being matrix cracking and delamination.

Figure 26.8 shows the influence of damage on laminate stiffness. As damage forms and grows in the laminate, the global strain in the laminate increases. The amount of stiffness loss associated with matrix cracking depends upon the ply orientation of the cracked ply, the lay-up of the laminate, the relative moduli of the fibre and the matrix and the crack spacing or crack density in the ply. As the crack density increases, the stiffness will decrease. As edge delaminations form and grow at a particular interface, the laminate stiffness further decreases as the delamination size increases.

To predict stiffness loss as a function of the number of fatigue cycles, the onset and growth of matrix cracks and delaminations must be characterized in terms of a generic parameter that is representative of the composite material being tested, but independent of the laminate structural variables such as stacking sequence, lay-up and ply thickness. A large number of researchers have attempted to use the strain energy release rate G associated with matrix cracking and delamination.

Figure 26.9 shows the steps that O'Brien et al. used to predict stiffness loss as a function of fatigue cycles using a strain-energy release rate G characterization of damage onset and growth.

Firstly, plots of G vs. log N were generated to characterize delamination onset, then power-law relationships between G and the rate of growth of delamination with fatigue cycles are needed to characterize damage growth (Fig. 26.9(a)). By the use of these material

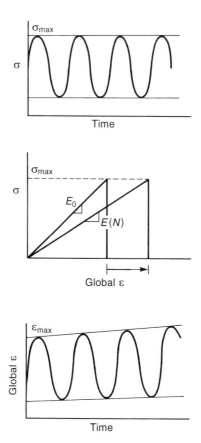

Fig. 26.8   Influence of damage on laminate stiffness.

characteristics, the decrease in matrix crack spacing $2s$, and the increase in delamination size a, with fatigue cycles can be predicted (Fig. 26.9(b)). The material characteristics, such as elastic modulus decrease with cycles, may then be predicted for particular laminates of interest, which for a constant stress amplitude is analogous to predicting the increase in global strain with cycles (Fig. 26.9(c)).

Application of this technique is difficult because of the interaction of various damage modes, which complicates the characterization of each singular damage mechanism in terms of G. This technique is more applicable where there is one dominant damage mechanism.

Bergmann and Prinz[22] tried to separate the damage development during fatigue into distinct zones to permit them to simplify the interaction problem. They state that the damage growth in multidirectional laminates during cyclic loading can be classified into four load-related phases and they found some success in residual strength and life prediction.

Song and Otani[23] predicted the fatigue life of cross-ply laminates. Various critical strengths consisting of the strength of the composite and damage occurring at fibre, matrix and fibre/matrix interface were investigated from a microscopic viewpoint. The composition of fatigue strength, the influence of microdamage on the various critical strengths, the contribution of these critical strengths to the fatigue life are examined and the fatigue life predicted. The predicted life was conservative at low numbers of cycles but mostly showed good agreement with experiment.

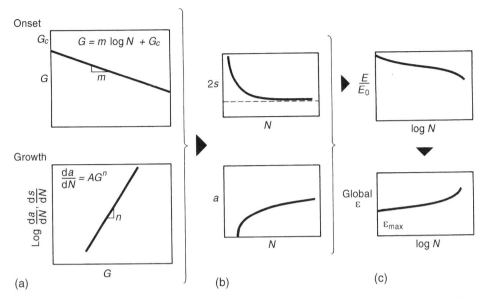

Fig. 26.9   Prediction of stiffness loss in composite laminates: (a) characterization of stiffness loss in laminate; (b) prediction of matrix cracking and delamination within the fatigue cycle, and (c) prediction of stiffness loss with fatigue cycles.

26.4.1   Curve fitting

Harris *et al.* have undertaken a large body of work[24–28] on the study of the fatigue behaviour of hybrid composites especially carbon-glass[24] and carbon–Kevlar[25–28]. The results were analysed in terms of a fatigue function, which permitted the representation of all data in a single two-parameter fatigue curve (Fig. 26.10).

The following equation was developed to describe the shape of the Goodman curve:

$$a = f(1 - m)^u (c + m)^v$$

where f, u and v are dependent on the logarithm of life.

From previous work it was found that f mainly controlled the height of the curve, u the slope of the contour in the 'tensile' mean stress zone and v the slope in the 'compressive' mean stress zone. These parameters were not thought to have a significant relationship to the structures and properties of the materials. From reference 28 it appeared, however, that there may have been a relationship between the tensile strength of the laminate and f. The model can predict the fatigue response of the composite needing only the tensile and compressive properties of the composite in question.

Wright[29] also uses Goodman-type diagrams in his empirical approach. He assumes that the right- and left-hand sides of the diagram are mirror images, which are displaced about the abscissa. This assumption would simplify greatly the predictions, and the analysis could be done with Miner type summations as used with metallic materials. It is reported that difficulties could occur if the two sets of curves would overlap, i.e. in regions of high tensile and compressive loading. Wright ignores any synergistic effects that may occur in this region and simply sums the two loads. A simple Miner-type summation is then performed

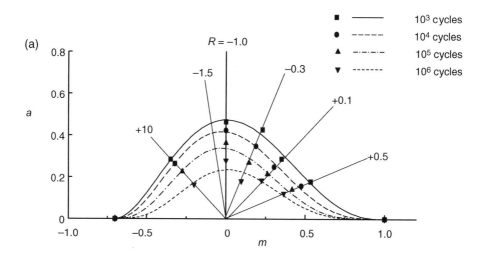

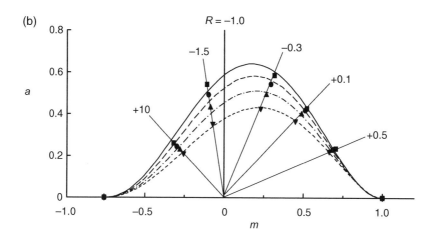

Fig. 26.10   Constant-life plots for (a) E-glass/913 and (b) HTA/982 laminates of $[(\pm45,0_2)_2]_s$ lay-up in the virgin condition.

to allow for damage generated by each loading block, permitting predictions of fatigue life or remaining life to be calculated.

   The same approach is used whether the loading is fully tensile, fully compressive or part tensile–compressive. The predictions made were reasonable for design-critical conditions of matrix-dominated behaviour where deterioration in performance due to fatigue is most pronounced. His predictions are reported to agree well with experiments.

26.5   Airframe structural elements

Although a large percentage of the research undertaken on fatigue–life prediction has been coupon-based, some work has been reported on both predictive modelling and the effect of fatigue on structural elements that would typically make up a composite airframe. Typically stringer configurations (I, J and T shape), parts of stringers (foot) and stringer stiffened panels have been studied (Fig. 26.11).

26.5.1 Stringer stiffened panels

The effect of fatigue on impact-damaged skin/stringer panels has been studied by NASA[30–32] and specifically the influence of impact energy on the onset of delamination growth under cyclic compression loading.[33] It was concluded from this research that the onset of delamination growth was mainly dependent on the impact energy. This phenomenon was further investigated, and the damage tolerance of stiffened panels compared to that of unstiffened panels in references 33, 34. It was found that unstiffened panels were sensitive to low-energy impact damage (2.5–10 J) under tension–compression fatigue. This was thought to be due to a lack of anti-buckling support of the delaminated parts, since the stiffened panels were much more damage tolerant under the same loading conditions.

The influence of stacking sequence on the fatigue failure of a skin stringer bond has been investigated using a four-point bend test.[35] The skin/stringer panel was simulated by using a tapered composite flange bonded onto a composite skin as shown in Fig. 26.12. It was reported that, once matrix cracks were present in the panel, the number of cycles to delamination onset did not strongly depend on skin lay-up.

The durability under repeated buckling of carbon/epoxy I and J stiffened panels under axial compression has been investigated.[36,37] The initial buckling load of the skin was affected by the fatigue cycling and decreased as the number of cycles increased. In the post buckling region a large increase in the share of the load carried by the stiffeners was observed. It was also found that repeated buckling (200–300 cycles) was not detrimental to the ultimate load-carrying capacity of the panel. Manufacturing defects (mainly porosity) and geometrical imperfections were found not to affect initial buckling loads but were found to affect final failure loads.

The performance during fatigue loading of impact-damaged stiffened panels has been compared with that of coupons for both thermoplastic and thermoset matrix composites.[38] When the stiffened panel test data were compared to the coupon test results the coupons were shown to be adequate for ranking the relative damage tolerance of various materials. However, component tests were required to predict structural performance accurately.

What does the literature tell us about how these fatigue tests on impact-damaged skin stringer panels have actually been carried out and when damage can be expected to grow? Impacts are commonly sited in the middle of the bay, over the stringer foot and over the stringer centreline. In the middle of the bay the impacts have been shown to lead to extensive matrix cracking, delamination, and in some cases fibre fracture.[39] As the impact moves over the stringer, more energy is absorbed through elastic structural response. Most of the energy is absorbed in this way when the impact is over the stringer centreline, although damage can be induced in the stringer.

Impact energies used in the papers discussed here were found to vary from 1.95 J to over 40 J although 50 J is the maximum typically expected for this type of structure. The 1.95 J impact was only intended to produce barely visible impact damage. In a study by NLR and QinetiQ on compression testing of impact-damaged skin/stringer panels it was estimated that an impact of between less than 15 J and more than 40 J is needed to cause delamination initiation depending on the panel configuration.[40] The NLR chose 35 J as a single impact energy to compare performance of different configuration panels impacted at different sites.

The number of cycles before damage growth occurs depends upon impact energy, load level, load cycling and geometry of sample. Many different results have been seen in the

Fig. 26.11   Stringer stiffened panel.

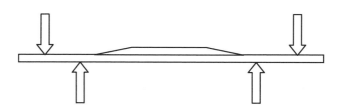

Fig. 26.12   Four-point bend configuration of simulated skin stringer panel.

papers included here, for example delaminations have been shown not to grow outside the area of impact damage during the first 1.3×10^6 cycles in one study. In another, after a 15 J impact no significant growth in delaminations could be seen after 80 000 cycles with maximum loads of ± 30 kN. In the same study after a 20 J impact no growth in delaminations could be seen after 200 000 cycles. The damaged area was shown to have increased by less than 10% after a 1.95 J impact and 2×10^5 cycles at 100 kN in a further study. However, after a 4.2 J impact significant delamination growth was seen to occur at 70 000 cycles and with a 5.75 J impact damage growth was observed in the first 5000 cycles.

In summary the parameters of a fatigue test on an impact-damaged skin/stringer panel are:

- impact location – in the bay, over the stringer foot or over the stringer
- impact energy – between approximately 15J and 50J (to produce visible impact damage)
- fatigue cycling – typically tension–compression, zero-compression and compression–compression.
- loading levels – should be a significant proportion of the ultimate failure strain
- number of cycles before damage growth occurs – will depend upon impact energy, load level, load cycling and geometry of sample.

O'Brien *et al.*[41] have written a recent article on a fatigue-life methodology for bonded composite skin/stringer configurations. The methodology is based on delamination fatigue characterization data and geometric non-linear finite element analysis. The onset of both matrix cracks and delamination was predicted and was seen to be in good agreement with test data.

The first objective of this work was to investigate the damage mechanisms in bonded composite skin/stringer specimens under tension fatigue loading conditions. Microscopic investigations of the specimen edges were used to document the onset of matrix cracking and delamination as a function of fatigue cycles and to identify typical damage patterns.

The second was to develop an analytical methodology accurately to predict the onset of matrix cracking and delamination. The tension loading was simulated in a geometrically non-linear analysis using a two-dimensional plane stress finite element model. A stress analysis was used to predict the location and orientation of the first transverse crack based on the principal transverse tension stress distribution in the flange tip area. A fracture-mechanics approach was used to determine delamination onset from this transverse crack.

26.5.2 I-beams

A series of papers have been written, reporting on the work undertaken on I beams[42–45] at Imperial College. They detail the mechanical behaviour, finite-element predictions and fractographic observations of the failure of composite I-beams. Both notched and un-notched beams were loaded monotonically and in fatigue in a four-point bend configuration. CFRP and GRP beams were investigated. It was found that, when fatigued at loads less than the monotonic buckling load, the un-notched beams showed no detectable damage up to 8 million cycles. The notched beams, however, failed as a result of delamination, and of matrix, and fibre failure around the notches.

A finite-element-based procedure has been developed at Imperial College[46] for predicting fatigue lifetimes for composite plates containing a central hole. The method uses the stress distribution from two-dimensional FE analysis to calculate strain-energy release rates, which, in combination with fracture mechanics concepts, predicts fatigue lifetime via a Paris–Law approach. Damage is taken to be due only to matrix cracking, and any stiffness reduction of the composite laminate is based solely on this form of damage.

Recent work has progressed from an I-beam containing holes in the web to skin/stringer panels which have sustained impact damage. The current approach involves three-dimensional finite-element analysis (utilizing a global/local approach) but is restricted in terms of the number of off-axis plies that can be interrogated for possible damage; the computer coding will be generalized to account for any number of ply orientations (any lay-up). The proposed computer model will track the development of damage in the structure (inter-fibre cracking when a threshold strain is exceeded), calculate the strain-energy release rate and link the latter to number of cycles.

The major aim of the proposed investigation was to extend the methodology described above to skin/stringer panels that have sustained impact damage. The principal objective was to predict the number of fatigue cycles the structure can withstand before damage starts to grow. To cope with the additional complexity, it was necessary to formulate a three-dimensional FE model in the vicinity of the damage. The damaged area was represented as a circular region of reduced stiffness, which was located in different parts of the panel (i.e., partly under a stringer foot, and in the middle of a bay (skin between two stringers).

It was also necessary to add delamination initiation and growth to the current model, as this mode of damage is always caused by impact. This addition simulated damage more fully, such that calculated strain-energy release rates were then dependent on both matrix cracking and delamination. The delamination was then modelled by the virtual crack closure method, which could readily be implemented in ABAQUS. The criterion for growth of the damage was a 5% increase in the original damage area. Work is continuing on this model and it should show good agreement with actual tests.

26.5.3 No-growth design philosophy

To date, where composite materials have been used, most aerospace design philosophy has effectively been based on a critical maximum strain criterion. The maximum strain level has been set on the basis of coupon tests for what are seen as design critical properties: notched compression, compression after impact, tension after impact, etc. This is how the often-quoted 4000 µε ultimate strain level now being used in many applications has been derived. It is certainly true that, at this level, or certainly at the working design limit strain of around 2700 µε, fatigue is unlikely to be a problem. Composite materials comfortably withstand large numbers of fatigue cycles, equivalent to many aircraft lifetimes at this strain level, without failing, and additionally it has been found that damage does not usually grow at these low applied strains. Indeed, the no-growth philosophy has become the key basis on which many aircraft composite structures have been validated, designs thus being based solely on monotonic properties. Another key factor is that any reduction in strength due to fatigue loading has been small compared with the reductions in monotonic strength observed as a result of notches and impact, hence the use of these properties in setting the maximum strain criterion.

Experiment has shown that impact damage will not usually grow during fatigue loading. Typical data are shown in Fig. 26.13 for a range of materials.[47] These data were generated for thin quasi-isotropic panels impacted at a level of 7 J then fatigue loaded in either tensile or compressive fatigue. The strains quoted represent a no-growth limit strain for one million fatigue cycles. Materials range from a fairly standard carbon-fibre/epoxy system, XAS/914, to much tougher newer materials and the thermoplastic-based material IM8/PEEK. The threshold strains for damage growth in tension for the new tough materials were generally much improved over the standard material (XAS/914), with three of the materials exhibiting values in excess of 0.8%. The IMS/927 material from Hexcel Composites required a strain in excess of 1% for damage to grow in tension. In compression, the improvements for the new tough materials were more modest, with two of the materials exhibiting damage growth threshold strains just under 0.4% and the best material, the IM7/977, a strain of 0.5% compared with a figure of 0.34% for the standard material. This does imply, however, that, if working strains reach 0.4% strain in compression, which is likely as these tougher materials are employed at higher design strains, damage growth in fatigue will have to be a

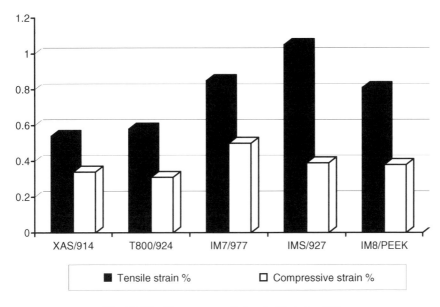

Fig. 26.13   Damage growth threshold strains (%).

serious design consideration. It is very important, therefore, to develop a damage-growth-predictive methodology and fatigue–life prediction capability for composite materials if the advantages of these tough materials are to be exploited through designs at higher strains and stresses.

26.5.4   Designing for strength reduction and damage growth
A number of empirical equations have been proposed to predict the residual static strength of a fatigued laminate. The simplest is based on a basic Miner summation and considers a linear strength reduction given as:

$$\sigma_{residual} = \sigma_u - (\sigma_u - \sigma_{max})\frac{N}{N_f}$$

where $\sigma_{residual}$ is the residual strength after N cycles at $S = \sigma_{max}$ and N/N_f the fractional fatigue life spent at the cyclic peak stress σ_{max}. σ_u is the static strength. The key to this type of expression is understanding and then modelling the degradation during fatigue. This assumes a linear reduction in strength, which is unrealistic for most polymer composites, where strength reduction more usually follows the form shown in Fig. 26.14.

It is important for design purposes to know not only fatigue life, but also how performance is degraded during life by damage and how failure occurs. There have also been many efforts to predict the onset of damage growth in polymer composites and most of these centre around the use of fracture mechanics approaches. Work at Imperial College by Robinson and Davies,[19] Martin and Jackson[20] and Hiley and Curtis[48] is typical. The key to the approach is to generate data of the form shown in Fig. 26.15, which presents $G_{1\text{-max}}$ against cycles to the onset of damage growth. This shows that damage may develop more readily after fatigue cycling. From such data it is relatively simple to predict a stress–life curve for the material.

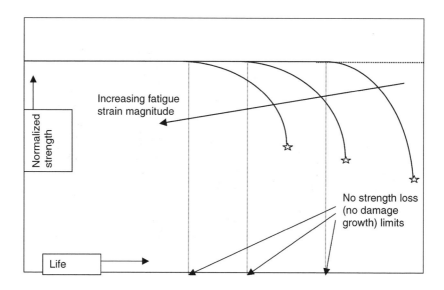

Fig. 26.14   Schematic diagram of strength loss vs. life of polymer composites in fatigue life.

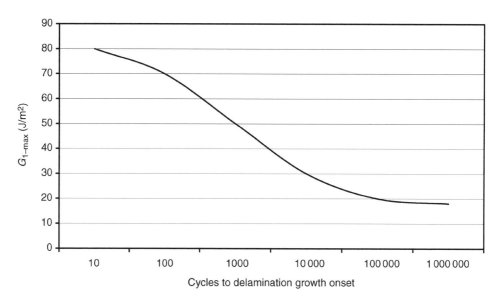

Fig. 26.15   Schematic diagram of fatigue fracture toughness.

However, the key here is to be able to extrapolate the data in Fig. 26.15 to other circumstances without having to regenerate the data every time. If this can be solved, then we have the beginnings of a valuable predictive methodology. Indeed Robinson and Davies at Imperial College have demonstrated an ability to be able to predict strain-energy release rates numerically which may provide a way forward.

Predicting damage growth is also difficult, but fracture mechanics approaches are an option when growth is by the progression of a single crack, such as a delamination.

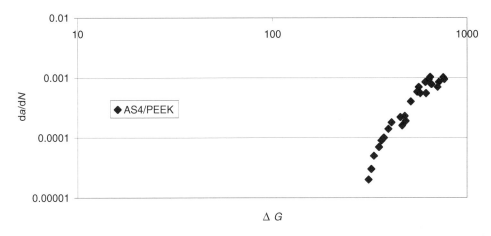

Fig. 26.16   Paris plot for mode II crack growth in fatigue.

Figure 26.16 shows typical data for crack growth, in this case in mode II, versus ΔG showing that fracture-mechanics fits can be used to model delamination growth. Indeed the figure also nicely shows the lower limit to damage growth, effectively the no-growth threshold, which forms the basis of many current design approaches. This is just one example and there are several approaches in the literature dealing with this simple case. However, in real life damage is a complex mixture of fibre fractures, splits, transverse cracks and delamination and modelling the totality of this problem is proving challenging to most current researchers.

26.5.5   Airworthiness clearance issues

The static test of a metal airframe structure tells us nothing of any real value about the performance of that structure under fatigue loading. This is because those types of structural feature which are susceptible to fatigue damage must be designed to allowable values of stress which are lower than the 'B' values used for static design. For combat aeroplanes, it is not unusual to find that the stresses at fastened joints must be below the 'B' value by 40% or more. In consequence, a feature that was correctly sized to fatigue considerations would have a static strength, which was a corresponding amount above the design ultimate load. The fatigue test of a metal structure can therefore be thought of as a process of conditioning the structure in readiness for a degraded static test – in a sense it is an exact parallel to the moisture conditioning process that is necessary for a composite structure.

   The static test of a composite structure, on the other hand, provides vital evidence in relation to fatigue. This is because composite materials remain essentially elastic up to failure and in consequence the ratio of fatigue to static strength is much higher than for metals. Put another way, composites do not have the ductility of metals under extreme static loads and so are not plagued by an entirely new family of failure modes under repeated loading.

   If the designer has been successful in exploiting the properties of the fibre in the composite, the critical failure under static loading will be brittle in nature (thus fibre dependent, not matrix dependent). For carbon-fibre composites, it is well established that in these circumstances S–N curves are very flat indeed and there would be no possibility of this mode of failure giving a fatigue problem in service. However, just as in the interpretation of a major fatigue test on a metal structure, other types of feature which are known to be of marginal strength and which therefore might have been on the point of failure will need to be determined. The 'steepest' of these curves must then form the basis of the fatigue substantiation of the structure.

Since even the steepest of these $S-N$ curves is likely to be relatively flat, it is expected that there will usually be room for sufficient conservatism to enable a simplistic substantiation to suffice. Specifically, if the curve shape can be shown to be conservative and if this is reduced on stress/strain by a 'scatter' factor of 1.5 (after having been located by the stress/strain achieved in the static test), then this curve can probably be used with a conservative cumulative damage method to show the safe life of the structure is at least equal to the specified life. Put another way, the calculation would need to show that the stress/strain sustained by the feature at the design ultimate load was not higher than the allowable value for fatigue. If the fatigue allowable value were calculated to be higher than the 'B' value then, by using this conservative approach, it would follow that a successful static certification would provide the necessary confidence in fatigue performance.

The procedure outlined above makes no mention of hygrothermal degradation because this is an essential part of the static certification procedure upon which the fatigue substantiation is based. The $S-N$ curves used must relate to the appropriate degraded condition, but experience so far indicates that there is usually sufficient conservatism in the analysis for any fatigue testing that might be necessary to be done under normal laboratory conditions. For tests on helicopter rotor components, it is usual to increase the loads by a factor of about 1.1 to compensate for this, but higher factors would be needed to allow for the greater degradation that occurs in combat aircraft applications. In principle, suitable factors might be applied to an $S-N$ curve obtained under unfactored loads.

Further information on airworthiness clearance of composite structures may be found in Defence Standard 00-970, which is available on the internet.[49]

26.6   Conclusions

Fatigue–life prediction of composite materials has generally not been a major issue in the design of composite structures, which has been dominated by impact and monotonic notch performance. At present, the ultimate design strain levels are kept low, in the region of 4000 $\mu\epsilon$, where composite materials can withstand large numbers of fatigue cycles without failing, thus at this strain level damage growth is not seen as a major problem.

To use composite structures to their full potential, design strain levels will have to rise and a partial growth criteria needs to be adopted; if this is to happen, an accurate fatigue lifing methodology needs to be established.

Of the many papers written on fatigue–life prediction, including damage accumulation models, data manipulation models, and statistical accounts of monotonic and fatigue failure distributions by the use of Weibull functions, only a few are physically based.

It is essential that improved life–prediction methodologies are developed if polymer composites are to be used more widely at higher stresses and strains and the enormous benefits of these materials in performance and cost can be realized in structural applications. Key to this is the understanding of the effects of various damage mechanisms on fatigue life.

In conclusion, although fitting curves to data to predict fatigue life offers reasonable accuracy, it is a method that cannot be entirely relied upon and will by its nature always predict a conservative life value. To be able to use composite materials to their full potential, our understanding of composite materials undergoing fatigue failure needs to be broadened. To do this, we need to establish links between observable damage/failure mechanisms and fatigue life. At present, however, no one model can reliably predict fatigue–life and residual strength in composite structures.

26.8   Acknowledgements

Much of the experimental work in this review was supported by the UK Ministry of Defence. The authors thank other researchers for access to data and results.

26.9   References

1. HUSTON R J (1994), *Int. J. of Press. Ves & Piping*, **59**, Elsevier Science Limited.
2. CURTIS P T (2000), *J. Defence Science*, January.
3. MIDDLETON D H (1992), *Aircraft Engineering*.
4. CURTIS P T (1987), RAE Technical Report TR87031.
5. CURTIS P T (1986), RAE Technical Report TR86021.
6. TALREJA R (1981), *Proc. Roy. Soc., Lond.*, **A378**, 461.
7. BADER M G and BONIFACE L (1985), *Proc. ICCM V*, San Diego.
8. JAMISON R D and SHULTE K (1983), Characterisation and analysis of damage mechanisms in tension–tension fatigue of graphite/epoxy laminates, in ASTM STP 836 – 'Effects of Defects in Composite Materials'.
9. HWANG W and HAN K S (1986), *J. Comp. Mater.*, **20**.
10. CURTIS P T and DAVIES A J (2000), Fatigue life prediction of polymer composite materials, *Proceedings of ECCM 9*, Brighton.
11. SCHAFF J R and DAVIDSON B D (1997), *J. Comp. Mater.*, **31**, 128–157.
12. SCHAFF J R and DAVIDSON B D (1997), *J. Comp. Mater.*, **31**, 158–181.
13. YANG J N and SHANYI D (1983), *J. Comp. Mater.*, **17**.
14. WHITWORTH H A (1987), *J. Comp. Mater.*, **21**.
15. REIFSNIDER K L, SUBRAMANIAN S and STINCHCOMB W W (1997), *Int. J. Fatigue*, **17**.
16. HAHN H T and KIM R Y (1975), *J. Comp. Mater.*, **9**.
17. CHOU P C and CROMAN R J (1978), *J. Comp. Mater.*, **12**.
18. BARNARD P M, BUTLER R J and CURTIS P T (1988), *Int. J. Fatigue*, **10**.
19. DAVIES G A O and ROBINSON P, AGARD Conference Proceedings 530, NATO, Greece 199211.
20. MARTIN R and JACKSON W C (1993), *ASTM STP* 1156, 105–126.
21. O'BRIEN T K, RIGAMONTI M and ZANOTTI C (1989), *Int. J. Fatigue*, **11**.
22. BERGMANN H W and PRINZ R (1989), *Int. J. Numerical Methods*, **27**.
23. SONG D-Y and OTANI N (1997), *Mater. Sci. Eng.*, **A238**.
24. DICKSON R F, FERNANDO G, ADAM T, REITER H and HARRIS B (1989), *J. Mater. Sci.*, **24**.
25. ADAM T, FERNANDO G, DICKSON R F, REITER H and HARRIS B (1989), *Int. J. Fatigue*, **11**.
26. FERNANDO G, DICKSON R F, ADAM T, REITER H and HARRIS B (1988), *J. Mater. Sci.*, **23**.
27. HARRIS B, REITER H, ADAM T, DICKSON R and FERNANDO G (1990), *Composites*, **21**.
28. BEHESHTY M H, HARRIS B and ADAM T (1999), *Composites, Part A*, **30**.
29. WRIGHT B D (1991), 16th Symp. ICAF, May, Tokyo, Japan.
30. O'BRIEN T K, KRUEGER R, CVITKOVICH M K and MINGUET P J (1999), Testing and analysis of composite skin/stringer debonding under multi-axial loading. *NASA/TM-1999-209097 ARL-MR-439*, February.
31. MINGUET P J and O'BRIEN T K (1996), Analysis of test methods for characterizing skin/stringer debonding failures in reinforced composite panels, composite materials: testing and design. Twelfth Volume, *ASTM STP 1274*, August, 105–124.
32 MINGUET P J and O'BRIEN T K (1995), Analysis of composite skin/stringer bond failures using a strain energy release rate approach, *Proceedings of the Tenth International Conference on Composite Materials*, **1**, Woodhead Publishing Limited.
33. GEIR B, GOETTING H C, HILLIGER W, KLEIN H, PABSCH A and ZIMMERMAN R (1996), Fracture mechanics of composites, *ESA/ESTEC* Contract No 10228/92/NL/PP, September.
34. KLEIN H, GREIER B, GOETTING H C, HILGER W, PABSCH A and ZIMMERMAN R (1996), Buckling tests

with curved, stiffened CFRP panels damaged by impact, *Proc. Conf on Spacecraft Structures, Materials and Mechanical Testing*, Grand Hotel Huis ter Duin, Noordwijk, Netherlands, 27–29 March.

35. CVITKOVICH M K, O'BRIEN T K and MINGUET P J (1997), Fatigue debonding characterisation in composite skin/stringer configurations, *NASA/TM-1997-110331*.

36. WELLER T and SINGER J (1990), Durability of stiffened composite panels under repeated buckling, *Int. J. Solids Struct.*, **26**(9/10), 1037–1069.

37. FROSTIG Y, SEGAL A and SHEINMAN T W (1989), Post buckling of flat stiffened graphite/epoxy panels under cyclic loading, ECCM3 France, 333-340.

38. GRIFFIN C F and BECHT G J (1991), Fatigue of impact damaged BMI and thermoplastic graphite composites, *36th International SAMPE Symposium*, April 15–18.

39. GREENHALGH E, HUGHES D, SINGH S and ROBERTS D (1996), Impact damage and failure of carbon-fibre reinforced plastic skin stringer panels, DRA/SMC/CR961118/1.0.

40. VERCAMMEN R W A, WIGGENRAAD J F M and UBELS L C (2000), Fabrication concept and impact test programme for wing panels with increased damage resistance, NLR-CR-2000-002.

41. O'BRIEN T K, KRUEGER R and PARIS I (2000), Fatigue life methodology for bonded composite skin/stringer configurations, *Proc. Am. Soc. Composites*, 15th Tech. Conf. 2000, pp. 729–736.

42. GILCHRIST M D, KINLOCH A J, MATTHEWS F L and OSIYEMI S O (1996), Mechanical performance of carbon fibre and GFRP epoxy I-beams: I. mechanical behaviour, *Comp. Sci. Tech.*, **56**, 37–53.

43. GILCHRIST M D, KINLOCH A. J, MATTHEWS F L and OSIYEMI S O (1996), Mechanical performance of carbon fibre and GFRP epoxy I-beams: II. Fractographic failure observations. *Comp. Sci. Techn.*, **56**, 1031–1045.

44. GILCHRIST M D, KINLOCH A J, MATTHEWS F L and OSIYEMI S O (1999), Mechanical performance of carbon fibre and GFRP epoxy I-beams: III. Fatigue performance, *Comp. Sci. Tech.*, **59**, 179–200.

45. GILCHRIST M D, KINLOCH A J, MATTHEWS F L and OSIYEMI S O (1993), Fatigue performance of composite structural I-beams. *ECCM 6*, Bordeaux, France.

46. ATTIA O, KINLOCH A J and MATTHEWS F L, Modelling the fatigue life of PMC components, *Comp. Sci. Tech.*

47. CURTIS P T, GATES J and MOLYNEUX C G (1993), DRA TR93009, DERA.

48. HILEY M J and CURTIS P T (1992), Mode II damage development in carbon fibre reinforced plastics, *AGARD Conference Proceedings* 530, NATO, Greece.

49. www.dstan.gov.uk.

27

Fatigue and durability of marine composites

P. Davies and D. Choqueuse, IFREMER, Centre de Brest, France and A. Roy, CRITT Matériaux, Rochefort, France

27.1 Introduction

Polymer matrix composites are widely used in marine structures. A good overview of these applications may be found in several references,[1-4] and some examples will be given below. It should be emphasized, however, that the materials used in traditional marine structures are significantly different from those employed by the aerospace industry. There has been a very widespread use of hand lay-up or contact moulding of woven and mat glass reinforcements impregnated with polyester resins and these are the typical marine composites. Nevertheless this situation is evolving rapidly, and infusion impregnation methods have become increasingly common over the last five years. Thermoplastic matrix resins and carbon fibre reinforcements are also being explored.[5,6]

In this first section some typical marine applications and their loadings will be briefly presented. These include:

- pleasure and racing craft
- fast ferries
- military minesweepers, superstructures
- underwater structures
- offshore structures

Particular emphasis will be placed on design requirements and durability of these structures.

Composites have been used for over 50 years by the small boat industry. The materials are chosen primarily on a cost basis, and glass fibres in the form of mat or woven rovings are widely used, impregnated with polyester resins. In the past this industry has mainly employed spray and hand lay-up but recent and imminent European legislation aimed at reducing styrene emissions has had a significant impact, and many boatyards have experimented with infusion methods. The dimensioning of small boats is a combination of experience and classification society rules. Durability aspects such as fatigue loading are not explicitly considered, but the overall safety factors employed are assumed to account for long-term integrity and there is considerable service experience supporting this approach.

At the other end of the budget scale the America's Cup teams are using very high

Fig. 27.1   America's Cup racing yacht.

technology fabrication methods based on carbon fibre prepreg and sandwich materials. This competition allows designers and architects to innovate and optimize the composite hulls and mast structures within a strict set of rules governing minimum gauge and weight. Figure 27.1 shows one of the contenders for the 2003 edition of the cup, the hull is carbon-fibre-reinforced epoxy resin on honeycomb sandwich.

In the design of these racing yachts durability considerations are secondary, but this and other ocean races provide a platform for trying out innovative materials and structures with very low safety factors.

Another application in which weight is critical is for high-speed ferries. Extensive developments in Scandinavia for coastal ferries have resulted in a comprehensive set of rules from the DNV.[7] These include safety factors for different areas of the vessel and material requirements and will be discussed further below, in Sections 2 and 7.

There have been several large composite structures manufactured for military vessels since the original UK minesweeper in the 1960s. There is much current interest in composite superstructures and the 'Lafayette' frigates involved large composite/balsa sandwich panels.[8] The design requirements for such a structure include survivability with respect to missile attack and blast, but also low weight, stealth, electromagnetic protection of equipment and fire resistance. A key issue is the assembly of the composite to the metal hull and innovative solutions have been developed which enable existing welding assembly to be used.

Composites are particularly attractive for underwater applications where weight is at a premium. Around 50% of the external surfaces of modern submarines are composites but the structural hulls remain metallic.[9] Several recent projects in the USA, Russia and Europe have evaluated composites for submarine hulls. Durability aspects of this application will be considered in more detail in Section 8.

A final area receiving particular attention at present is the offshore oil and gas industry.

Gibson gave an overview of potential applications topside[10] and several recent research projects have examined the use of composites offshore.[11] A particularly demanding application is for composite risers.[12] These are essentially long tubes connecting the wellhead to the platform. They are subjected to internal and external pressure as well as tensile fatigue due to wave and current loading. Extensive testing has been performed on these carbon/epoxy structures, including fatigue and stress rupture.[13,14] The first sea trials began in 2001.

It is not possible to treat all of these structures in detail so the chapter is organized as follows. First, the marine environment, and the particular design loads and constraints which it imposes, will be presented. Then marine composites and their damage mechanisms will be briefly described. Two sections on the durability of marine composite laminates and sandwich materials follow. Three case studies are then discussed in more detail, assemblies of marine composites, wave impact loading of surface craft and pressure loading of underwater composite structures. Finally, some areas of future work are indicated, and references allow the reader to obtain more details of these applications.

27.2   Specific nature of the marine environment

A major component in the design of ocean structures is the period of time over which the structure is expected to perform its function, the design life. Generally, the design life is at least 20 years, over which time all the environmental and mechanical effects on the material and structural behaviour must be accounted for. Contact with water and humidity is the main parameter which governs the environmental behaviour of the material and this can affect the fatigue and long term performance. However, ageing resistance tends to be considered in material selection rather than during mechanical design. The temperature range is generally small and not a critical parameter, the sea temperature varying from 15 to 30 °C at sea level and becoming almost constant below 300 metres depth at around 4 °C. The main parameter governing the design life of marine structures is the mechanical loading. There are two types of loading. The first is related to the hydrodynamic forces induced mainly by the waves and this has to be taken into account in the design of ships, boats, offshore and coastal structures.[15] The second is the variation of the pressure forces induced by the hydrostatic pressure and this is the main design parameter for underwater structures.

27.2.1   Fixed structures and ships

Waves are created by the action of the wind on the water surface. Their amplitude, frequency and direction are entirely dependent on the location and the period of the year. Some data are available, and large measurement campaigns have been carried out. Oceanographic satellites are also now used to provide information about sea states and waves at different locations around the world. Figure 27.2 illustrates the variability of the nature of the waves with time. In Fig. 27.2(a) the significant wave heights measured at a site in the North Sea are reported for a period of 2 years. The significant wave height is generally used as the parameter to characterize the amplitude of waves. It corresponds to the mean of the upper third of measured wave heights during a certain period of time (here the period of time used is 3 hours). This shows clearly the seasonal influence, with a significant wave height about ten times higher during winter than during the summer.

In Fig. 27.2(b) the variability and the complexity of the wave height is reported over a shorter time scale, for a period of 100 s. The characteristics of this sea state are a significant

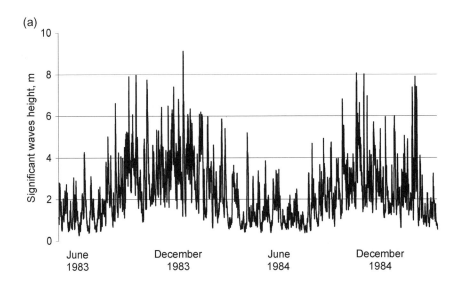

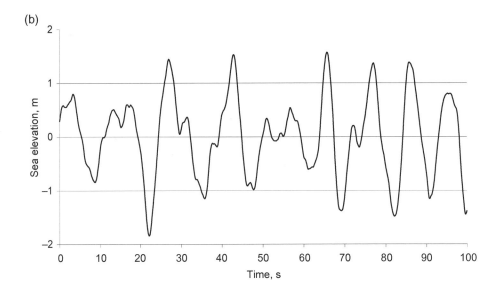

Fig. 27.2   Wave data. (a) Significant wave heights over a 2-year period (ifremer data). (b) Temporal representation of the sea level for a 100 s interval.

wave height of 3 metres and a period of 10 s. The period of the wave can vary but 10 to 12 s is generally assumed for the open sea. Taking into account this period and a design life of 20 years, a fixed structure will have to support more than 10^7 cycles. During its lifetime, the hull structure of a high speed light craft may be subjected to more than 10^8 slamming cycles.[16] This underlines the need for high cycle fatigue data in fast ship design.

A histogram of loading for a 60 metre long composite mine-hunter was proposed by Smith,[1] and the number of cycles by range of loading coefficient is shown in Table 27.1. The loading coefficient is proportional to the bending moment applied, the highest range of this parameter corresponds to 0.6 of the design bending moment of the structure.

Table 27.1 20-year lifetime bending moment histogram for composite material mine hunter vessel (after Smith[1]).

Range of loading coefficient	Number of cycles
0–0.00025	3.0×10^7
0.00025–0.00050	1.0×10^7
0.00050–0.00075	1.2×10^6
0.00075–0.00100	1.1×10^5
0.00100–0.00125	1.0×10^4
0.00125–0.00150	9.5×10^2
0.00150–0.00175	3.0×10^1

Experimental studies have been performed on composite vessels at sea in order to estimate the nature of the loading signal during navigation. To illustrate the loads which can be experienced Fig. 27.3 shows strain and acceleration signals measured by the authors during navigation of a high speed boat. This 21.5 metre long composite craft, manufactured by resin infusion under vacuum (glass and carbon fibre construction), can navigate at speeds up to 45 knots. The acceleration was recorded at the centre of mass of the boat and the strains were measured on a stiffener placed in the engine room. The upper graphs show a 1000 s long sequence while speed was increasing (10 knots to 35 knots). The lower graphs show a 100 s long sequence during speed stabilization at 35 knots. The data show the strong correlation between speed and dynamic signal amplitude (acceleration and strain) and the large spectral content of the dynamic signal. By comparison with Fig. 27.2(b) (time base representation of the wave level during 100 seconds), the graph representing the 100 s long sequence shows a higher frequency content of the signal, which is due to the internal vibration of the structure and the increased frequency of contact with the swell due to the speed of the boat. Fourier analysis shows that the maximum energy of the signal is in a bandwidth of 0.1 to 1.5 Hz.

Currently, the design methods for composite ships only take into account the quasi static loading and safety factors are used in order that the level of stress induced by the dynamic loading is sufficiently low that the fatigue phenomena are theoretically not induced. For example, DNV recommends safety factors from 3 to 6 for the hull structural design for fibre composite and sandwich constructions of high speed and light craft, depending on the nature of the structure, the type of construction and the type of loading considered.[7] Table 27.2 presents the maximum allowed bending stress ratio for the design of stiffeners.

Table 27.2 Ratio between calculated bending stress and nominal ultimate stress of the material[7]

Structural area	Coefficient
Bottom plates exposed to slamming	0.25
Remaining bottom and inner bottom	0.25
Side structures	0.25
Deck structures	0.25
Bulkhead structures	0.25
Superstructures	0.25
Deckhouses	0.25
All structures exposed to long time static loads	0.15

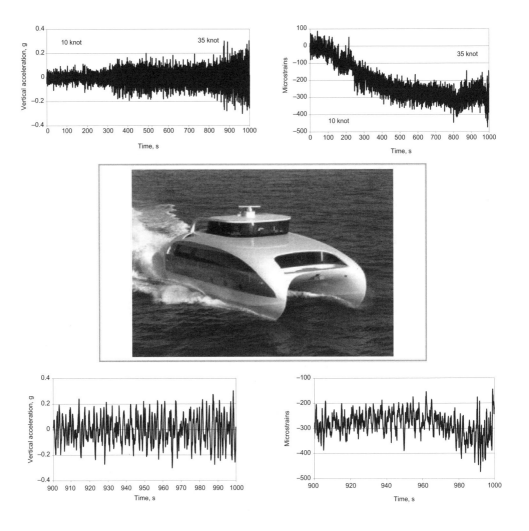

Fig. 27.3   Acceleration and strain temporal response of a pleasure vessel measured at sea (courtesy Kingcat).

Slamming loading will be discussed in more detail in Section 7. It should be noted that design of composite structures does not currently involve the formal approach which is now used in the design of metallic structures, where a distribution of loading sequences allows lifetime to be determined from fatigue crack initiation and propagation predictions.[17]

27.2.2   Underwater structures

For submarine applications the loading stresses are generated by the hydrostatic pressure, which increases with the depth of immersion according to the expression:[18]

$$P = 0.001\,H + 0.05 \times 10^{-6}\,H^2$$

where:

P = pressure (MPa)

H = immersion depth (m)

Submarine applications are generally static and the long-term behaviour is mainly governed by the creep behaviour of the structure. However, for some specific applications (oceanographic submersibles) cyclic loads can be designed for by taking into account the number of dives, which is generally very low. For example, the exploration submarine *Nautile* has been designed for 20 years with around 100 dives per year or a maximum number of cycles of 2000. These applications will be described in more detail in Section 8.

27.3   Marine composites

The composite materials employed in marine applications may be classified in three groups, laminates, sandwich and buoyancy materials. These will now be presented and their properties and damage mechanisms will be briefly described. Table 27.3 gives an overview of the three material types.

Table 27.3   Marine composites

Type	Reinforcement	Matrix	Density kg/m³
Laminates	Woven Rovings Chopped strand mat *Rovimat*	Polyester Vinyl ester Epoxy	1800
Sandwich	Facings: Laminates or prepreg	Cores: PVC, Balsa, Nomex honeycomb	Cores: 40–200
Buoyancy Syntactic foam	Hollow glass spheres	Epoxy	500

27.3.1   Laminated materials

The most widely used marine composites are composed of E-glass woven rovings and/or mat reinforced polyester. In many cases layers of these two reinforcements are combined as 'rovimat' or 'combimat'. The fibre content is usually around 0.3 by volume, much lower than in aerospace composites. Other reinforcements include stitched biaxial (0/90°) or quadriaxial (0/90/+45/–45°) cloths. Various polyester matrix resins are used, the cheapest orthophthalic polyesters are being replaced by isophthalic versions or vinyl esters, often rubber toughened, with superior ageing resistance. Low viscosity vinyl esters are suitable for infusion moulding and fibre volume fractions around 0.5 are then more common. In some applications phenolics, for fire resistance, or epoxies for improved performance are also used. Epoxies are also widely used in filament wound structures for underwater structures. Much higher fibre volume fractions, in excess of 0.6, are then achieved. The surfaces of marine laminates are generally protected by gel-coats, a layer of resin intended to provide aesthetic qualities (colour and smooth surface finish) and some measure of protection from the environment.

27.3.2   Sandwich materials

Sandwich structures, consisting of lightweight cores between laminated facings, are widely used in marine structures.[19] Cores may be closed cell foams, PVC (poly vinyl chloride) is very popular, balsa wood or, mainly for racing craft, Nomex™ honeycomb. Densities are usually in the range from 40 to 200 kg/m³. More details are available elsewhere.[20,21]

27.3.3 Buoyancy materials

While not used as structural materials, the choice of buoyancy material may be critical for the long-term durability of marine structures, particularly for those employed underwater. The syntactic foams, hollow glass spheres dispersed in an epoxy matrix, are an example of a composite system tailored specifically for this application. These materials are currently being studied extensively for thermal insulation of deep-sea flow-lines.[22]

27.3.4 Damage mechanisms

Several mechanisms may contribute to failure. Matrix cracking often appears first, frequently caused by debonding of the reinforcement (whether fibres or micro-spheres). This is conditioned by matrix toughness and interface quality, and the latter may be degraded by long-term immersion in water. When woven glass reinforced polyester composites are tested in tension this first damage may occur around 0.2 to 0.4% strain. In mat reinforced materials damage may occur even earlier. These micro-cracks may coalesce, or may initiate delaminations and large-scale crack propagation. In sandwich materials the facing/core interface may debond or core yielding and damage may lead to failure. Fibre failure may arise in a number of ways from tension or compression overload, micro-buckling, or cracking due to stress corrosion. The latter is treated elsewhere in this book.

In order to put these marine materials into context with respect to aerospace composites, Table 27.4 presents delamination fracture energies for different materials and interfaces. The values given are typical values.

These figures should be used qualitatively rather than quantitatively, there is still considerable discussion over delamination test methods particularly for mode II (in-plane shear) tests.[28] Nevertheless they indicate that the traditional woven glass fibre reinforced polyester marine composites show similar resistance to delamination initiation as that of traditional aerospace composites and may be significantly more damage tolerant. Their long term durability will be discussed in the next section, but before addressing this issue it is important to consider the influence of sample size and scale effects.

27.3.5 Size and scale effects

The majority of the tests performed to characterize marine composites under both short- and long-term loads are performed on small specimens taken from laboratory produced panels. There have been concerns expressed over whether such tests are representative of the materials used in real structures, which are often very thick (tens of millimetres) and produced industrially. There are two aspects to consider: first whether there is an intrinsic bias in test methods when small specimens are tested, and second whether the fabrication procedure for specimens corresponds to that used industrially. With respect to the first point, the weave repeat unit cell is often quite large, 10 mm or more, so it is important to dimension the specimen to include several of these. A series of tests on the rovimat/polyester material described above, which has a weave repeat unit of 10 mm, showed scale effects only for tensile tests on ±45° samples, which appeared to correspond to the capacity of the cross section to sustain damage.[29] The second point can be partly addressed by testing specimens produced by the same fabrication methods as the full-scale structure, but only correlation with results from tests on structural elements will allow doubts over the representative nature of the specimen tests to be removed.

Table 27.4   Values of delamination fracture toughness at initiation

Material	G_{Ic} J/m²	G_{IIc} J/m²	Reference
Carbon/epoxy UD	180	600	23
Glass/polyester UD	100	700	24
Roving/roving	130	500	
Glass/epoxy UD	250	1700	25
Filament wound			
Balsa sandwich	900	1100	26,27
Interface debonding			

27.4   Durability of marine laminates

The ability of marine composites to retain their properties over long periods has been convincingly demonstrated by the anti-mine vessels, from which over 20 years experience at sea is now available. Early work on creep and fatigue of glass/polyester composites for these applications has been described by Smith.[1]

A good overview of the durability of reinforced plastics can be found in a recent volume.[30]

27.4.1   Creep loading

Creep and creep rupture of glass/polyester composites have been studied in detail by Phillips and colleagues,[31] while the stress corrosion phenomenon (failure of certain laminates when subjected to load and liquid environments) has been described by Hogg and Hull[32] and more recently by Pauchard.[33]

Some results from tensile creep tests on glass rovimat reinforced polyester laminates are shown in Fig. 27.4.

Creep of tensile specimens immersed in seawater occurs a little faster than in air at all loads.

27.4.2   Fatigue loading

Within a recent project tensile fatigue tests were performed on the same glass/polyester composite as that tested in creep.[34] Figure 27.5 shows examples of applied stress versus number of cycles to failure (S–N) for specimens loaded in the 0° and 45° directions. Also shown are results from tests in which specimens were loaded to 0.2% and 0.6% tensile strains before the fatigue loading. These were intended to indicate whether matrix cracking damage influences subsequent fatigue behaviour.

To a first approximation the results can be plotted as a straight line on a semi-logarithmic basis, as proposed by Mandell.[35] There is no significant influence of the pre-strain on subsequent fatigue lifetime.

Other fatigue test results for glass composite laminates have been generated within wind energy projects and Echtermeyer has summarized many of these.[36]

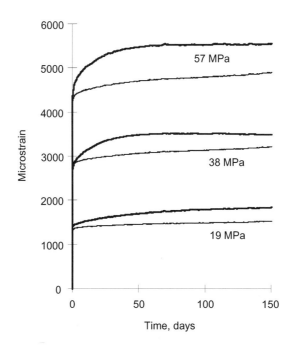

Fig. 27.4   Tensile creep of rovimat/polyester laminates in air and water. NB Failure stress
230 MPa. Upper curves correspond to immersed specimens for each stress level.

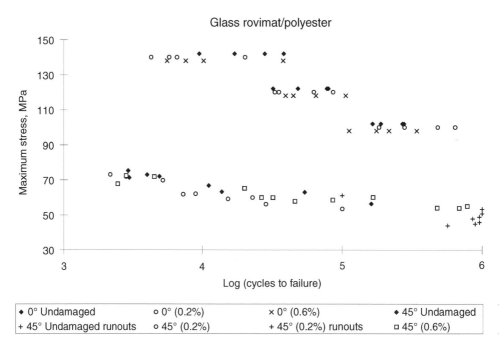

Fig. 27.5   Tensile fatigue of rovimat/polyester laminates.

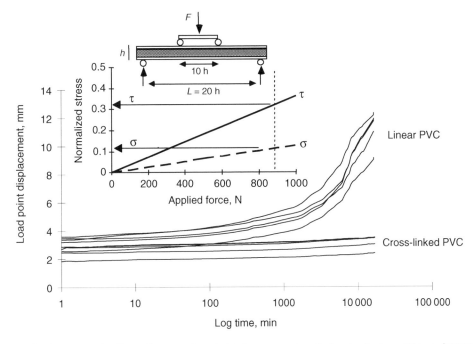

Fig. 27.6   Four-point flexural creep of sandwich beams, rovimat/polyester facings, 80 kg/m³ PVC core.

27.5   Durability of sandwich materials

The long-term durability of marine sandwich materials is generally governed by the shear response of the core. This is particularly true for light PVC cores, and a number of studies have concentrated on the measurement of core shear strength of this material.

27.5.1   Creep behaviour

Several authors have studied foam creep in shear.[37,38] Using time-temperature equivalence it is possible to obtain long-term creep data. These data can then be used to predict the long-term response of sandwich structures and some simple examples are available.[38] Figure 27.6 shows one case, for a sandwich beam based on the same rovimat reinforced polyester facings as described above, where two 80 kg/m³ density PVC foam cores, one cross-linked and the other linear are compared.

27.5.2   Cyclic loading

Surprisingly few studies have been published on fatigue of sandwich materials. Some data for mode I fatigue crack propagation in foam cores were presented by Zenkert and co-workers.[39] S–N curves for the shear fatigue of foams have also been measured using four point flexure tests on sandwich beams.[40–42]

Burman tested sandwich beams with three foams. Fatigue thresholds were found to depend on R ratio but below 20% of the static shear strength no damage was noted after 5 ×

10^6 cycles. Initiation lasted at least 90% of the fatigue life. Clark examined fatigue models and found that for a 130 kg/m^3 cross-linked PVC foam core an exponential stiffness degradation model could be fitted to experimental data.[43] Unfortunately these are rather isolated examples and more fatigue data are needed to extend these models.

27.6   Assemblies

The most frequent locus for failure in composite structures is not the composite material itself but the assembly regions. These may be hull/stiffener joints, hull/bulkhead assemblies or interfaces between composites and metallic components. Fatigue in joints is discussed elsewhere in this book (Chapter 23) so here only the results of some recent tests performed on marine composite assemblies will be presented.

Adhesive bonding holds great potential for marine applications and several studies have been performed in collaboration between IFREMER, L'Ecole Nationale Supérieure de Mécanique et d'Aérotechnique Poitiers and the CRITT (Centre Régional d'Innovation et de Transfert de Technologie) Matériaux in Rochefort, to characterize the durability of bonded assemblies. To date these have involved glass rovimat reinforced orthophthalic polyester substrates (six layers of 500 g/m² woven roving with 300 g/m² mat) bonded either to itself or to mild steel substrates using a structural epoxy adhesive (Redux 420). Simple lap shear specimens were used, each substrate measured 100 mm by 25 mm and a 12.5 mm overlap was employed. The adhesive was applied to the woven roving rather than the mat side of the substrate, as this was the configuration shown in preliminary tests to give the higher static strength.

A numerical and experimental study of joint behaviour was performed first, to identify the damage mechanisms for these assemblies under monotonic tensile loading.[44,45] Damage initiation was observed to occur as one or two cracks in the first layer of the composite, in the stress concentration region at the end of the joint overlap. The load at which first damage appears is roughly one-third of the load at failure, Failure occurs at 6000 N for the composite/composite assembly and 6500 N for the steel/composite. In the former mixed mode (I/II) loading is present while the steel/composite joint is subjected to mainly mode I. Propagation appears to follow the fibre/matrix interface. Significant scatter was noted in static failure loads. A small influence of loading rate was noted.[44,46]

The fatigue behaviour of these joints was then studied as a function of loading parameters. A sinusoidal load waveform was applied at 5 Hz (no effect of frequency was noted between 0.05 and 50 Hz). Either cycling around a constant mean load or complete unloading with a constant R-ratio were applied. Results are shown in Fig. 27.7.

In all cases when the joint is loaded above the damage initiation threshold determined in the monotonic tensile tests, the fatigue damage observed involves the creation of a small crack in the first few cycles and then the majority of the lifetime involves propagation. The first point to note on the plots is that scatter in fatigue data is very low. This may be the result of stress relaxation at the ends of the joint overlap.

For the composite/composite joints, Fig. 27.7(a), the results from both types of loading (constant mean load and constant R ratio) fall on the same curve. In this case it is the maximum load which governs the fatigue mechanisms, amplitude has no effect. This was confirmed by additional tests with constant maximum load, which showed that provided the minimum load was sufficient to keep the crack open the crack could advance. If this is not the case then friction due to the mode II (shear) component of loading will slow the crack propagation.

For the steel/composite assemblies, however, Fig. 27.7(b), there is a significant difference

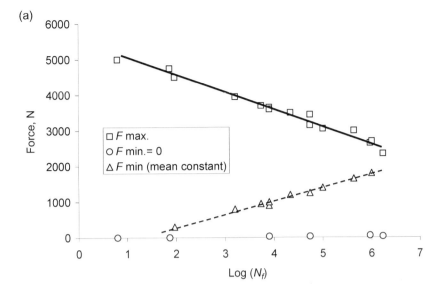

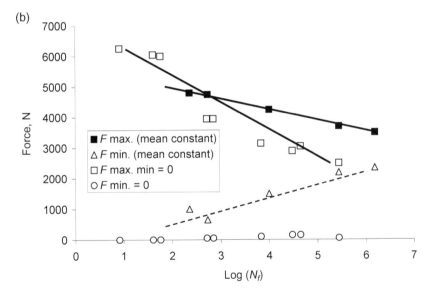

Fig. 27.7 Tensile fatigue of bonded assemblies, rovimat/polyester. (a) composite/composite. (b) composite/steel.

between constant mean load and constant R ratio and both maximum load and load amplitude affect the fatigue lifetime. Here the loading is mainly mode I so friction does not contribute but plastic deformation of the steel substrate during the test will also affect the stress state.

It is interesting to note for both types of assembly that the fatigue endurance limit appears to correspond to the first damage load in the monotonic tensile test. This is consistent with another study, performed on steel/composite assemblies under creep loading.[47,48] In that

Table 27.5   Indication of fatigue effect for marine composites and assemblies

	Composite 0°	Composite 45°	Composite/ composite	Composite/ steel	E-glass[35]
Loss per decade/static strength	13%	7%	9%	10%	10%

study it was shown that, even after 3 years under creep load provided the load level is below the damage initiation threshold no crack will appear. However, a strong coupling was found between the mechanical loads and the environment. In particular when tests are performed on specimens immersed in water cracks may be induced at loads below the damage initiation threshold. Water also accelerated the propagation phase (by up to ten times). This coupling effect shows the complexity of lifetime predictions for assemblies in a marine environment but also clearly indicates that it is the composite, not the adhesive, which is the weak link in the assembly. Fatigue lifetimes can be improved by improving the resistance of the composite to crack initiation and propagation. Tougher composites are, of course, available but not at the same cost as the basic polyester composites.

It is interesting to examine the slopes of the S–N plots of both composites (Section 27.4.2) and adhesively bonded composites. Fitting both to semi-log plots allows a strength loss per decade to be established. This value is given in Table 27.5 and indicates that, to a first approximation, both composites and assemblies lose roughly 10% of their initial static strength per decade. Published values for E-glass strands are also shown.

Of course, this very simplified approach gives no indication of the physical mechanisms involved, and as Harris has pointed out it is very unlikely that only one mechanistic model can be applied when both fibres and matrix are involved.[49] Nevertheless it gives an indication of the order of magnitude of fatigue effects.

Work at Southampton University has focused on the behaviour of stiffener and tee joint assemblies under static and cyclic loading.[50,51] Read has examined the different fatigue mechanisms in overlaminated tee joints and noted that the first damage under 45° pull-off loading depended on the overlaminate lay-up. Delamination or matrix cracking in the overlamination region due to high through thickness stresses and cracking at the overlaminate/ base laminate interface can occur. Different fatigue lifetime models have been examined and predictions were compared to experimental data.

27.7   Slamming impact response

Ship structures must be designed to resist repeated wave impact loading. This is a particularly important point for fast craft, which are subjected to repeated wave impact both to the bottom and bow areas. As a result this subject has received considerable attention in recent years. The design of small fast vessels with respect to slamming loads involves three steps. First, according to the sea state and service conditions of the vessel a vertical acceleration is estimated. This allows a vertical force to be obtained. From this an effective slamming pressure is determined based on assumptions for the pressure distribution. This equivalent static pressure can then be used as input in a stress analysis of the hull. This procedure contains many inherent uncertainties, which have been discussed in a recent paper.[52] In order to improve the approach for composite hulls, and in particular to measure the response of hull sections to slamming loads, several large-scale tests have been performed. These have ranged from dropping test sections into wave basins to tests at sea on instrumented vessels.

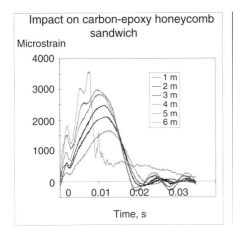
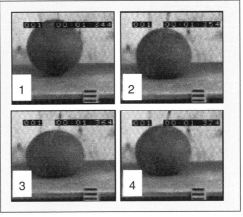

Fig. 27.8   Simple test to simulate slamming damage. Example of strain gauge response at increasing drop heights. Delamination at 6 metre drop.

Considerable work was performed in the late 1980s and early 1990s at DNV (Det Norske Veritas) to examine the slamming response of composite sandwich panels. A number of interesting results emerged, which have been summarized by Hayman.[53] In order to examine pressure distributions instrumented hull sections were dropped into a fjord from different heights.[54] The results showed that the peak pressure is proportional to the velocity squared but also depends on the slamming angle. Pressures of several bars were measured and the pressure peak moved across the hull as it entered the water. Core shear failure was shown to be the critical failure mechanism, though it is preferable that the core fails before the sandwich facings, as core failure is not catastrophic, Hayman and colleagues showed that, if panels are designed by use of the conventional approach for metallic hulls, the safety coefficients for core shear failure will be underestimated, and premature core failure may occur. Another important result from this work was that no significant difference in lifetime was observed from sinusoidal tests at normal rates (1–4 Hz) and slamming rate tests, suggesting that material evaluation can be performed using conventional test procedures.

A simpler test was developed by the authors to compare the resistance of different laminate and sandwich panels to slamming impact, using a soft impact set-up.[55] An example is shown in Fig. 27.8, a 20 kg bladder filled with sand is dropped from different heights onto simply supported instrumented sandwich panels. The damage induced is similar to that observed in service and the test allows damage thresholds to be compared. An example of the response of a strain gauge on the lower facing of a sandwich panel at progressively higher drop heights is also shown.

A difficulty with testing structural elements is transferring the results to full size vessels. An alternative is to instrument complete vessels and to test them at sea, but careful characterization of the sea conditions is necessary if we are to be able to interpret the results. In a current project aimed at measuring the response of assemblies in composite motor vessels, both instrumented boat-drop tests and tests at sea have been performed.[56] Figure 27.9 shows an example.

Results have enabled material development tests to be designed to correspond more closely to service conditions. Little work has been presented on the optimization of material selection to resist slamming loads. One such study on the effect of slamming pressure on the

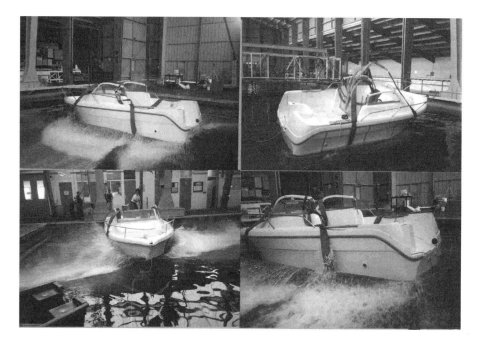

Fig. 27.9   Instrumented boat drop tests, IFREMER wave basin.

interlaminar behaviour of laminated composite ship panels has been presented by Parga-Landa and colleagues.[57] These authors use a model based on stress wave propagation to examine through thickness stresses. Different lay-ups have been examined and recommendations are given to reduce the interlaminar stress concentration factors.

Finally, results have been reported very recently from slamming tests on panels with more sophisticated instrumentation based on optical fibres.[58] This technique may in the future provide exciting possibilities for implanting such fibres during boat construction and obtaining a much wider database on the structural response of fast vessels during their service life.

27.8   Cylinders for underwater applications

Deep ocean exploration, whether by manned submersibles or autonomous underwater vehicles (AUVs), requires pressure resistant hull structures. The hydrostatic pressure increases directly with depth according to the expression given in Section 27.2. Thus at 6000 metres depth a pressure hull is subjected to around 625 bars or 63 MPa external pressure. In order to achieve a buoyant vessel, it is essential to reduce hull weight as much as possible. Fibre-reinforced composites are very attractive for such applications as they offer high specific stiffness and strength compared to metals.[59] Considerable testing experience now exists, and an example of a large filament-wound carbon/epoxy cylinder entering into a pressure vessel before an implosion test is shown in Fig. 27.10.

Fig. 27.10   Carbon/epoxy cylinder 1.25 metres long, 450 mm internal diameter being lowered into 1000 bar pressure vessel.

27.8.1   Quasi-static failure mechanisms

Composite cylinders tested monotonically to failure under hydrostatic pressure fail by one of two mechanisms, buckling or compressive material failure. The former has received considerable study as thin walled cylinders are used in many applications apart from deep sea vessels, so designers are generally happier with designing for buckling than for material failure. However, as thickness-to-diameter ratio increases above 0.1 material failure under biaxial compression becomes more likely. This failure mechanism is complex and relatively few test results are available even for quasi-static loading. Hinton and colleagues performed a series of tests on glass/epoxy tubes under biaxial stresses including compression and showed the limitations of conventional failure criteria.[60] The failure under hydrostatic pressure (hoop stress twice axial stress) of tubes wound at ±55° to their longitudinal axis were reasonably well predicted by a progressive failure criterion, but the predictions were very sensitive to the input ply compression strength. The latter is notoriously difficult to measure accurately and so tests on tube specimens are probably more promising for analysing long term performance.

27.8.2   Creep under hydrostatic pressure

When composite cylinders are used as instrumentation housings for oceanographic studies they may remain at great depths for several years. Creep deformation may then become

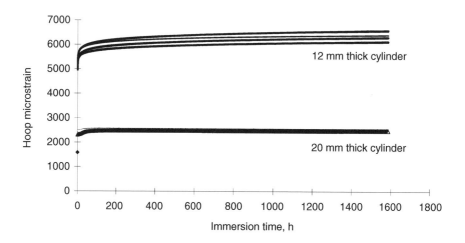

Fig. 27.11 Creep vs. time for two cylinders, 12 and 20 mm wall thickness 152 mm internal diameter, glass/epoxy wound at ±55° to the cylinder axis. Strains recorded during immersion at 2400 metres depth.

critical, and creep induced buckling may occur. It is not economic to study this behaviour in expensive pressure vessels, so in order to measure creep in glass/epoxy cylinders tests have been performed at sea. Two glass/epoxy cylinders were instrumented with strain gauges. They were connected to autonomous programmable data loggers and were immersed at 2400 metres depth in the Mediterranean Sea. Some results from this project have been presented recently,[61] Figure 27.11 shows an example of the creep responses of the two cylinders.

In another recent European project carbon/epoxy cylinders were immersed for 1 year at 2000 metres depths.[62] Such demonstrator projects have shown the capability for design and fabrication of composite pressure vessels for deep sea applications under static loading conditions. Less attention has been paid to cyclic loading.

27.8.3   Cyclic pressure loading

Very little published data is available on the fatigue behaviour of composite cylinders under external pressure. Tests are known to have been performed within military projects, but the results are not in the public domain. For oceanographic applications the numbers of cycles involved are relatively low, typically a few hundred cycles per year at most, so the tests of interest are low-cycle high-load fatigue.

Some recent tests were performed on small glass/epoxy cylinders, 55 mm internal diameter, cycled for 500 cycles from 1 to 625 bars, 50% of the nominal quasi-static implosion pressure. After cycling the cylinders were pressurized to implosion. The results showed that at least 85% of the initial quasi-static implosion pressure was retained after cycling. While this suggests that for oceanographic applications fatigue may not be a problem more results are needed if high load cycle applications are envisaged.

27.8.4   Future underwater composite requirements

To date, there have been relatively few applications of composites in deep sea but recent oil and gas finds down to 3000 metres depth have led to renewed interest in composites. An example is the possibility of increased sub-sea operations such as separation of oil from water and other contaminants on the sea floor, instead of pumping and separating topside. Weight requirements indicate that the structure of such deep sea separators could not be steel and one option is a composite pressure vessel. This is a very challenging application, with internal and external pressures, elevated temperatures and corrosive fluids. This involves a significant step from the small pressure vessels being used for deep sea instrumentation, and ensuring long term durability (20 years or more in service) will be paramount to the success of such a structure.

27.9   Future directions

This chapter has presented an overview of the durability and fatigue performance of marine composites. The performance of monolithic glass/polyester laminates, then the same materials as sandwich facings and in bonded assemblies, have been described. Filament wound composite pressure vessels have also been discussed.

It is clear that these composites are liable to damage at quite low strains but their overall damage tolerance is very good. While durability is a factor in the design of all the structures considered here, fatigue loading tends to be accounted for in a general safety factor for long term behaviour. Nevertheless there are structures for which the response to repeated loading is the dimensioning characteristic. Two examples are given, fast vessels subjected to repeated impact (slamming), a high cycle fatigue loading, and pressure vessels for underwater use, a low cycle high load case. More experimental data are required for both if structures are to be optimized.

Finally, it is interesting to note that there is a strong tendency in marine design towards a reliability approach to lifetime prediction. This is very noticeable in the offshore industry where it is being very actively encouraged.[63]

27.10   References

1. SMITH C S (1990), *Design of Marine Structures in Composite Materials*, London, Elsevier Applied Science.
2. SHENOI R A and WELLICOME (eds.) (1993), *Composite Materials in Maritime Structures*, Cambridge Open Technology Series.
3. DAVIES P and LEMOINE L (eds.) (1992), *Nautical Construction with Composite Materials*, Proceedings of Conference in Paris, December 1992, IFREMER Actes de Colloque no. 15, Brest.
4. GREENE E (1998), *Marine Composites*, Second Edition, available from the author, Eric Greene Associates, Inc. 86 River Drive, Annapolis, MD 21403 USA.
5. SHARP R, HOLMES S and WOODALL C (1995), Material selection/fabrication issues for thermoplastic fiber placement, *Journal of Thermoplastic Composite Materials*, **8**, January, 2–14.
6. LONNO A and HELLBRATT S-E (1995), Use of carbon fibre in a 63 m high-speed vessel for the Swedish Navy, *Proceedings of Sandwich Construction 3*,, EMAS, 3–14.
7. DET NORSKE VERITAS (DNV) (1991), Hull structural design, fibre composite and sandwich constructions, Part 3, Chapter 4 in *Rules for Classification of High Speed and Light Craft*, January.
8. LELAN J Y, PARNEIX P and GUEGUEN P L (1992), Composite Materials Superstructures in *Nautical Construction with Composite Materials*, Proceedings of Conference in Paris, December, 399–411.
9. LEMIÈRE Y (1992), The evolution of composite materials in submarine construction, in *Nautical Construction with Composite Materials*, Proceedings of Conference in Paris, December, 441–449.
10. GIBSON A G (1993), Composites in offshore structures, Chapter 11 in *Composite Materials in Maritime Structures*, Cambridge Open Technology Series.
11. REVUE DE L'INSTITUTE FRANÇAIS DE PÉTROLE (1995), *Composite Materials in the Petroleum Industry*, January, no. 1.

12. SALAMA M M, MURALI J, BALDWIN D D, JAHNSEN O and MELAND T (1999), Design considerations for composite drilling riser, *Proceedings of Offshore Technology Conference*, Houston Texas, OTC 11006.

13. SPARKS C P, ODRU P, BONO H and METIVAUD G (1988), Mechanical testing of high performance composite tubes for TLP production risers, *Proceedings of Offshore Technology Conference*, Houston, OTC 5797.

14. JOHNSON D B, BALDWIN D D and LONG J R (1999), Mechanical performance of composite production risers, *Proceedings of Offshore Technology Conference*, Houston, OTC 11008.

15. HASSON D F and CROWE C R (eds.) (1988), *Materials for Marine Systems and Structures*, Academic Press.

16. HELLBRATT S E and GULLBERG O (1989), The development of the GRP-sandwich technique for large marine structures, *Proceedings 1st Sandwich Construction Conference*, EMAS, 425–442.

17. TOMITA Y, HASHIMOTO K, OSAWA N and TERAI K (2000), Fatigue strength evaluation of ship structural members based on crack growth analysis, in *Proceedings of NAV 2000*, 10.4.1–11

18. AFNOR STANDARD XP X 10-812 (1995), Marine environment, oceanographic equipment, environmental test and recommendations for test equipment.

19. WEISSMAN-BERMAN D (1992), Marine sandwich structures, Parts 1 and 2, *SAMPE Journal*, **28**(4), 21–28 and (5), 9–17.

20. ALLEN H G (1969), *Analysis and Design of Structural Sandwich Panels*, Pergamon Press.

21. ZENKERT D (1997), *An Introduction to Sandwich Construction*, EMAS Publishers.

22. CHOQUEUSE D, CHOMARD A and BUCHERIE C (2000), Thermal insulation for ultra deep pipelines, Proceedings of DOT (Deep Offshore Technology).

23. PREL Y J, DAVIES P, BENZEGGAGH M L and DE CHARENTENAY F X (1989), Mode I and Mode II delamination of thermosetting and thermoplastic matrix composites, *ASTM STP 1012*, 251–269.

24. DAVIES P (1996), Fracture of marine composites in *Fracture of Composites*, ed. Armanios E A, Transtec Publications, Switzerland, 583–596.

25. OZDIL F, CARLSSON L A and DAVIES P (1999), Characterization of delamination toughness of angle ply glass/epoxy cylinders, *Proceedings of ICCM 12*, Paris.

26. CANTWELL W J, SCUDAMORE R, RATCLIFFE J and DAVIES P (1999), Interfacial fracture in sandwich laminates, *Composites Science and Technology*, **59**, 2079–2085.

27. CARLSSON L A, SENDLEIN L S and MERRY S L (1991), Characterization of face/core shear fracture of composite materials, *Journal of Composite Materials*, **25**, 101.

28. DAVIES P, BLACKMAN B R K and BRUNNER A J (1998), Standard test methods for delamination resistance of composite materials, *Applied Composite Materials*, **5**, 345–364.

29. DAVIES P and PETTON D (1999), An experimental study of scale effects in marine composites, *Composites Part A*, **30**, 267–275

30. PRITCHARD G (ed.) (1999), *Reinforced Plastics Durability*, CRC/Woodhead Publishing, Cambridge.

31. WHITE R J and PHILLIPS M G (1985), Environmental stress–rupture mechanisms in glass fibre/polyester laminates, *Proceedings of ICCM5*, 1089–1099.

32. HOGG P J and HULL D (1983), Corrosion and environmental deterioration of GRP, Chapter 2 in *Developments in GRP Technology*, ed. Harris B, Elsevier Applied Science, 37–90.

33. PAUCHARD V, GROSJEAN F and CAMPION-BOUKHARTS H and CHATEAUMINOIS A (2002), Application of a stress corrosion model to the analysis of the durability of glass/epoxy composites in wet environments, *Composites Science and Technology*, **62**, 493–498.

34. ROY A, ROYER J and DAVIES P (1997), Fatigue behaviour of marine composites in *Proceedings of 1st International Conference on Fatigue of Composites*, Paris, June, 439–446.

35. MANDELL J F (1991), Fatigue behaviour of short fibre composite materials, Chapter 7 in *Fatigue of Composite Materials*, ed. Reifsnider K L, Elsevier.

36. ECHTERMEYER A T, HAYMAN E and RONOLD K O (1995), Comparison of fatigue curves for glass composite laminates, Chapter 14 in *Design of Composite Structures Against Fatigue: Applications to Wind Turbine Blades*, ed RM Mayer, Professional Engineering publishing, London.

37. CAPRINO G, TETI R and MESSA M (1995), Long term behaviour of PVC foam cores for structural sandwich panels, *Sandwich Constructions 3*, EMAS Publishers, 269–280.

38. DAVIES P and CRAVEUR L (1996), Prediction of long term behaviour of sandwich structures, *Proc ECCM-7*, Woodhead Publishing, **2**, 367–76.

39. SHIPSHA A, BURMAN M and ZENKERT D (1999), A comparative study of mode I fatigue crack propagation in foam cores for sandwich structures by using different test specimens, *Proc. ICCM-12*, Paris.

40. BURMAN M and ZENKERT D (1997), Fatigue of foam core sandwich beams –1, *International Journal of Fatigue*, **19**(7), 551–561.

41. BUENE L, ECHTERMEYER A T, HAYMAN R, SUND O E and ENGH B (1992), Shear properties of GRP sandwich beams subjected to slamming loads, *Proceedings Sandwich Constructions 2*, EMAS publishers, Florida, March 9–12.

42. THOMSON R S, SHAH KHAN M Z and MOURITZ A P (1998), Shear properties of a sandwich composite containing defects, *Composite Structures*, **42**, 107–118.

43. CLARK S D, SHENOI R A and ALLEN H G (1999), Modelling the fatigue behaviour of sandwich beams under monotonic, 2-step and block loading regimes, *Composites Science and Technology*, **59**, 471–486.

44. ROY C (1994) Comportement mécanique en sollicitation monotone et cyclique d'assemblages collés composite/composite et composite/acier – Thèse de Doctorat de l'Université de Poitiers, 17/01/1994.

45. ROY A, MABRU C, GACOUGNOLLEJ L and DAVIES P (1997), Damage mechanisms in composite/composite bonded joints under static tensile loading, *Applied Composite Materials*, **4**, 95–119.

46. ROY A, BLACKMAN B, GACOUGNOLLE J L, KINLOCH A and DAVIES P (1996) Influence of the strain rate on damage and failure mechanisms of composite bonded joints and substrates, *Proceedings of the Eleventh European Conference on Fracture*, Sept, 1747–1752.

47. GONTCHAROVA-BERNARD E (1997), Vieillissement d'assemblages collés acier/composite dans l'eau et sous charge, Thèse de Doctorat de l'Université de Poitiers, 16/10/1997.

48. ROY A, GONTCHAROVA E, GACOUGNOLLE J-L and DAVIES P (2000), Hygrothermal effects on failure mechanisms in composite/steel bonded joints, *ASTM STP 1357*, 353–371.

49. HARRIS B (1996), Fatigue behaviour of polymer based composites, in *Durability Analysis of Composite Structural Systems*, ed. Cardon AH, Balkema Press, 49–84.

50. SHENOI R A, READ P J C L and HAWKINS G L (1995), Fatigue failure mechanisms in fibre reinforced plastic laminated tee joints, *International Journal of Fatigue*, **17**(6), 415–426.

51. READ P J C L and SHENOI R A (1999), Fatigue behaviour of single skin FRP tee joints, *International Journal of Fatigue*, **21**, 281–296.

52. KOELBEL J G JR (2000), Structural design for high speed craft, *Professional Boatbuilder*, Oct/Nov, 31–46

53. HAYMAN B (1993), Response of Sandwich structures to slamming and impact loads, Chapter 9 in *Composite Materials in Maritime Structures*, Cambridge Open Technology Series, 161–177.

54. HAYMAN B, HAUG T and VALSGARD S (1992), Slamming drop tests on a GRP sandwich model, *Proceedings of Sandwich Constructions 2*, EMAS Publishers, Florida, March 9–12.

55. CHOQUEUSE D, BAIZEAU R and DAVIES P (1999), Experimental studies of impact on marine composites, *Proceedings of ICCM-12*, Paris.

56. BAUR P, ROY A, CASARI P, GACOUGNOLLE J L, CHOQUEUSE D and DAVIES P (2002), Recherche de la nature des efforts transmis par les liaisons structurales d'un bateau, *Proceedings Matériaux 2002*, Tours.

57. PARGA LANDA B, VLEGELS S, HERNANDEZ-OLIVARES F and CLARK S D (1999), An analytical study of slamming pressures on the interlaminar behaviour of composite panels, *Composite Structures*, **46**, 357–365.

58. JENSEN A E, PRAN K, HAVSGARD G B, WANG G, VOHRA S T, DAVIS M A and DANDRIDGE A (2000), Wet deck slamming experiments with a FRP sandwich panel using a network of 16 fibre optic Bragg grating strain sensors, *Composites Part B*, **31**, 187–198.

59. GARVEY R E (1990), Composite hull for full ocean depth, *MTS Journal*, **24**(2), 49–58.

60. HINTON M J, SODEN P D and KADDOUR A S (1996), Strength of composite laminates under biaxial loads, *Applied Composite Materials*, **3**, 151–162.

61. DAVIES P and LEFLOUR D (2001), Long term behaviour of fibre reinforced structures for deep sea applications, in *Proceedings of Oilfield Engineering with Polymers*, 3rd MERL Conference, November 2001, RAPRA, 255–268.

62. LIVINGSTONE F (2002), Lightweight composite pressure housings for mid-water and benthic applications, Final report MAST3 project CT97-0091, March.

63. HEALTH & SAFETY EXECUTIVE (HSE) Rationalisation of FPSO design issues, Offshore Technology report 2000/097.

Index

A sizing 152–3
A-scan ultrasonics 243, 244–5
Aberfeldy Footbridge 662, 663
acoustic emission 254–6
acousto-ultrasonics 249–51
acoustography 252–4
adhesive joints 623–4, 625–33
    crack propagation 627–9
    debonding 625
    environmental conditions 632–3
    finite element modelling (FEM) 629–30
    geometry of joints 631–2
    life prediction methods 625–30
    loading parameters 630–1
    in marine composites 720
    stress state/distribution 625
    stress-life analysis 626–7
advanced load-carrying materials 334–5
advanced resin systems 121–2
aerospace applications 526, 686–707
    airframe structural elements 698–706
    airworthiness clearance 705–6
    carbon fibres 687
    civil aviation market 688
    damage growth predictions 704–5
    damage mechanism based theories 695–8
    fatigue performance 688–91
    Goodman diagrams 697–8
    history of composite usage 687–8
    I-beams 701–2
    life prediction 692–5
    military aircraft 687, 688
    no-growth design philosophies 702–3
    residual strength degradation 692–3
    stiffness reduction 693
    strength reduction 703–5
    strength-life equal-rank assumption
        (SLERA) 693–5

    stringer stiffened panels 699–701
airframe structural elements 698–706
airworthiness clearance 705–6
all-tension (TTTT) experiments 27
Almond, D.P. 569–88
amplitude
    constant stress amplitude fatigue 580–1
    variable amplitude tests 514–16
anchoring systems 601–2
angle-ply
    delamination 498
    fatigue life tests 98–100
    matrix cracking 471, 484
    stiffness properties 480–4
anisotropy 4, 118
Ansell, M.P. 339–59
aqueous environments
    Fickian laws of moisture diffusion 117–20
    humidity 118
    interface degradation 159–63
    lifetimes of composites under load 132–5
    moisture sensitivity of resins 120–3
    thermal fatigue 127–9
    thermal spiking 123, 126
    thermal stresses 126–7
    thermomechanical response of resins 123–6
    see also marine composites
aramid fibres 14–15, 21, 25, 142, 391
Arrhenius' law 369
artefacts in testing 42–52
artificial neural networks (ANNs) see neural
    networks
AS-4/3501-6 cross-ply laminates 453–61, 470–
    1
ASTM standards 52, 54–5, 60, 91
autocatalytic reactions 204
autogenous heating 45–6, 53
autonomous underwater vehicles (AUVs) 724

beams 609–13
bearing failure 622
bearing fatigue 55
Beaumont, P.W.R. 365–410
Bergland, L.A. 314–35
bi-directional glass-fibre/epoxy pipes 648–55
biological neural networks 570
blister-resistant composites 122–3
block-loading data analysis 25–7, 582–3
block-type loading spectrum 528–32
boat pox 122
bolted joints 621–2, 633–9, 661–2, 675
    bolt failure 635–8
Bond's Mill Lift Bridge 662, 664
bonded joints 615, 623–6, 659, 675
bonded-in rods 357–8
boron fibres 20
box-beams 609–12
breadboard fixtures 646–8
bridges 609–13, 662, 670
brittle failure 155
buckling under compression 25, 46–7
building block design 366
buildings 662
bundle aspect ratio 274, 292
buoyancy materials 716
butt joints 624

C-glass 142
    see also glass fibre
C-scan ultrasonics 243, 244, 247–8
Cachan, L.M.T. 432–41
Cadei, J.M.C. 658–85
Caprino, G. 269–92
carbon fibres
    in aerospace applications 687
    fibre sizing/coating 152–3
    fibre surface treatment 148–9
    glass/carbon hybrids 191, 194
    high temperature off-axis fatigue 163
    Kevlar/carbon hybrids 194–5
    and modulus decrease 280–1
    and stress-corrosion resistance 142
carbon-fibre composite laminates 461–3
carbon-fibre-reinforced plastics 1–30
    complex stresses 28
    constant-life diagrams 16–17
    damage accumulation 4–6, 17–20, 27
    fatigue lives 7–8
    fibre type 20
    hybrid composites 21
    interleaving 24
    loading conditions 24–5
    matrix plastic 20–1, 23–4
    prior impact damage 29
    residual stiffness and strength 17–20
    resin content 20–1
    short-fibre composites 22–4

strain/life curves 9–16
    stress/life/probability (S/N/P) diagram 8
    stress/life curves 9–16, 21
Case, S. 413–30
CEN (Comitte European de Normalisation) 52
centrifugal moulding 659
ceramic fibres 414–15, 599
chemically resistant resins 137
chipboard 341, 347, 357
chopped strand mat (CSM) 269, 270, 286, 672
Choqueuse, D. 709–27
civil aviation market 688
civil engineering applications 658–85
    bridges 609–13, 662, 670
    buildings 662
    composite plies 672
    fatigue loadings 667–71
    maritime structures 662, 664
    offshore oil and gas industry 662, 664, 711
    standards and codes 677
    temperature loading fatigue effects 671
    traffic loading fatigue effects 662, 671, 679–84
    wind loading fatigue effects 671
    see also structural components
coating and sizing 152–4
cobonding 623
cocuring bonding 623
Comitte European de Normalisation (CEN) 52
complex stresses 28
component fatigue testing 55–6
composite joints 621–5
composite plies 672
compression
    buckling under compression 25, 46–7
    fibre compression failure criteria 66
    fibre compression property degradation 69
    and hybrid composites 197–8
    longitudinal compressive tests 83–5
    matrix compression
        failure criteria 67
        property degradation 70
    normal compression
        failure criteria 67–8
        property degradation 70
    strength of wood panel products 347, 349
    tension/compression fatigue of hybrids 221–3
    and thermoplastic composites 325–6
    transverse compressive tests 85–9
compression panels 613–14
constant stress amplitude fatigue 580–1
constant-life models 16–17
    fibre-reinforced plastics 546–67
    GRP (glass-reinforced plastic) 557–8
    and variable plane stress 511–14
    see also life-prediction models
constitutive models 368, 369, 373

continuous fibre composites 194–5, 242, 321–31
continuum modelling 368
cotton 358
coupling agents 154
coupon fatigue testing 53–5
crack growth 4, 5, 17, 54–5
    adhesive joints 627–9
    and fracture mechanics 547–8
    in glass fibres 137
    Irwin equation 131
    of matrix cracks 384–5
crack-tip damage 547
creep behaviour
    creep-fatigue interaction 332–3
    fatigue-creep coupling 653
    marine composites 717–19
    and structure design 678
    under hydrostatic pressure 725–6
    wood panel products 347
critical element modelling 443, 445, 446, 597
cross-ply laminates
    AS-4/3501-6 453–61, 470–1
    delamination 450–3, 468, 497–8
    fatigue life tests 97–8
    fatigue performance 461–3
    matrix cracking 471
    physical modelling 374–5
    shear-lag model 450–3, 468
    stiffness properties 480
crystallinity 319–20, 326–7
CSM (chopped strand mat) 269, 270, 286, 672
curing 122, 155–8, 200, 202–6, 236
Curtis, P.T. 686–707
curvature of fibres 207–8
cyclic loading 4, 5
    marine composites 717–20
    pressure loading 726
cylinders 55, 606–9, 724–7

damage development
    cycle counting strategy 508–9
    fibre-reinforced composites 4–6, 17–20, 27, 443, 445, 546–7
    framework 365–7
    growth rates 398–400
    GRP (glass-reinforced plastic) 4–5
    hybrid composites 223–32
    marine composites 716
    micro-mechanical modelling 414–15
    predictions in aerospace applications 704–5
    and stiffness reduction 595–6
    in structural components 595–7
    wood panel products 356–7
    see also physical modelling of damage development
damage mechanics 375
damage tolerance methodology 594

data
    precision of 56, 372
    presentation 58–9
    processing 41, 58
    requirements 36–8
Davies, A.J. 686–707
Davies, P. 709–27
De Bruyne, Norman 687
debonding 5, 148, 165
    of adhesive joints 625
    and interface parameters 148, 165
    short-fibre thermosets 272, 278
    woven-fibre thermosets 299
definitions of failure 6–7, 8–9
degradation
    generalized material property degradation 77–8, 93–6, 108
    gradual material property degradation 68, 70–3
    interfacial degradation 141–2
    material degradation properties 68–78
    normalized strength degradation model 70–1
    short-fibre thermoset composites 281–2
    sudden material property degradation 4, 68–70, 668
delamination 173–87, 255
    angle-ply 498
    areas of concern 175
    cross-ply composites 450–3, 468, 497–8
    edge delamination 470
    growth per fatigue cycle 178
    growth prediction 486–96
    hybrid composites 192–3, 209
    interlaminar fracture modelling 174, 175–6, 183–7
    matrix crack induced 386–91, 470–1, 488
    peel stresses (mode I) 177, 179–80, 182, 184, 492–6
    physical modelling 377–82, 408
    shear deformation theory 487
    shear stresses (mode II and III) 177, 180–3, 184, 492–6
    shear-lag model 450–3, 468
    stiffness degradation 477–80, 497
    stiffness properties 471–86
        angle-ply laminates 480–4
        constraining ply orientation 484–6
        cross-ply laminates 480
    strain-energy release rates 183–4, 210, 486, 488
        equivalent laminate concept 489–92
    stress analysis 473, 474–7
    structural integrity predictions 187
    testing 173, 177–81
design
    building block approach 366
    conventional mechanical design 367–9
    design life of marine composites 711
    limit state design 677

limit states 677–8
no-growth design philosophies 702–3
Diao, X. 442–68
dicyandiamide (DICY) 122
differential scanning calorimetry (DSC) 196
displacement measurements 40
double-cantilever-beam test 179–80
DSC (differential scanning calorimetry) 196
ductility effects 327–30
DuPont Lanxide 427
durability
    of laminated materials 717–18
    of sandwich materials 719–22
Durestos 684
dynamic models 370

E-glass 601
    see also glass fibres
eddy currents 259
edge delamination 470
electrolytic anodization 148
EN ISO standards 37, 48, 52–6
enclosures 667
end-loaded split specimen (ELS) tests 180–1
end-notched flexure (ENF) tests 180–1
energy release rates 435, 439
environmental effects on the interface 158–63
environmental enclosures 667
environmental stress-corrosion cracking
    (ESCC) 135, 137–43
EPET573 spectrum 514–16, 517, 519
epoxy compatible sizing (EP) 154
epoxy resins 120
equipment for testing 39–42
    fatigue machines 197
equivalent laminate concept 489–92
extreme-value models 8

failure criteria 36–7, 53, 63–8
failure strain 209
failure tensor polynomial (FTPF) 506–7
fatigue machines 197
fatigue-creep coupling 653
feed-forward networks 570–1
FEM (finite element modelling) 166, 400, 487,
    629–30
Fernando, G.F. 189–238
fibre skin hybrids 190
fibre-matrix shearing
    failure criteria 66
    property degradation 69
fibre-reinforced composite laminates 442–68
    carbon-fibre 461–3
    critical elements 443, 445, 446
    cross-ply 450–3, 461–3
        AS-4/3501-6 453–61
    damage development 443, 445
    life-prediction model 448–9

matrix crack density 445, 452
physical model 445
probability of failure 448
residual strength reduction 443, 445, 447,
    448–9
shear-lag model 450–3, 468
statistical model 447–9
    development 445–6
stiffness reduction 446, 452
strength degradation model 447–8
stress redistribution function 446, 449–53
subcritical elements 443, 446
unidirectional laminates 454, 455, 461
wear out model 442
fibre-reinforced concrete 601
fibre-reinforced plastics 546–67
    see also carbon-fibre-reinforced plastics
fibre-reinforced polymer (FRP) 658–85
    load bearing applications 662–7
    mouldings 659
    pultrusions 658–9
    road deck fatigue performance 679–84
    strengthening composites 667
    structural connections 659–62
Fibredux 199
Fibrefax 599
fibres
    bundles under static fatigue 131–5
    compression failure criteria 66
    compression property degradation 69
    curvature 207–8
    sizing/coating 152–4
    surface treatment 148–52
    tension failure criteria 63–4, 65–6
    tension property degradation 69
    unkinking model 391–2
    waviness 207–8
Fickian laws 117–20
filament-wound structures 644–55, 659
    breadboard fixtures 646–8
    gripping systems 647–8
    helical winding 645
    mandrel 644
    multidirectional winding 646
    pipes 644–6, 648–55
    test tubes 647
filler content 274, 276
finite element modelling (FEM) 166, 400, 487,
    629–30
flax fibres 150–1
flexural fatigue 343
flexure tests 48
four-point end-notched flexure (4ENF) tests
    180–1
fractography 233–6
fracture analysis 174, 175–6, 183–7
fracture stress model 398–402
frequency effects 165, 182, 283, 330–1, 651–3
    variable amplitude tests 514–16

fretting 48
Fu, K.E. 526–45

Galiotis, C. 147–70
Gamstedt, E.K. 314–35
gas cylinders 55
gas industry 662, 664, 711
generalized force determination (GFD) 598
generalized material property degradation 77–8, 93–6, 108
geometry of joints 631–2
Gilchrist, M.D. 593–616
glass ester laminates 162–3
glass fibres 20
    bi-directional glass-fibre/epoxy pipes 648–55
    crack growth 137
    environmental stress-corrosion cracking (ESCC) 137–8, 142
    fibre sizing/coating 153–4
    fibre surface treatment 149–50
    glass/carbon hybrids 191, 194
    glass/epoxy composites 236–7
    long-term environmental fatigue 161
    monotonic strength 284–5
    static fatigue 129–35
    time-dependent fracture 130
glass-mat thermoplastics (GMT) 332
glass/carbon hybrids 191, 194
glass/epoxy composites 236–7
Goodman diagrams 16, 697–8
gradient descent learning 575–6
gradual material property degradation 68, 70–3
Griffith flaws 129
gripping systems 48, 197, 647–8
GRP (glass-reinforced plastic)
    adding CFRP to 21
    constant-life model 557–8
    crack-tip damage 547
    damage development 4–5
    environmental stress-corrosion cracking 137–43
    interleaving 285
    monotonic strength 284–5
    offshore pipes 55
    physical modelling 394–5
    stress/strain life curves 12–14

hardboard 341
Harris, B. 3–31, 546–67
helical winding 645
helicopter industry 599, 602–6
    rotor blades 520–1, 599, 688
hemp fibres 358
hierarchy of structural scales 366
high-speed ferries 710
Highways Agency 679
hip implants 596

holes and notches 396–7, 416
    hole elongation 633–4
    hole size effect 400
Hooke's law 367
humidity 118
hybrid composites 21, 189–238
    classification of 189–90
    compressive loading 197–8
    continuous fibre 194–5
    curing 200, 202–6, 236
    cycles to failure 216–21
    damage development 223–32
    delamination 192–3, 209
    failure strain 209
    fibre skin hybrids 190
    flexural strength 209
    fractography 233–6
    glass/epoxy composites 236–7
    interface 195–6
    interleaving 192–3, 199
    interply fibre hybrids 189–90
    intraply fibre hybrids 189–90
    macroscopic failure modes 235–6
    manufacturing methods 196–7, 199–201
    material selection 198–9
    mechanical properties 206–14, 236
    organic-matrix hybrid composites 189–92
    quality control 195–6, 196–7, 200–1
    resins 195–6, 199, 215–16, 221–3, 225, 228, 233, 235–6
        quality 195–6
    short-fibre composites 193–4
    strength 209
    surface treatments 196
    tensile strength 209
    tension/compression fatigue 221–3
    tension/tension fatigue 214–20
    testing 197, 201
    thermal analysis 201
    void content 196
hybrid effect 191
hygrothermal ageing 160–1

_I_ beams 612–13, 701–2
impact damage 9, 29
    slamming impact response 722–4
imperfect interface 147–8
in-plane shear tests 89–91
infra-red thermography 357
interface 135, 147–70
    in aqueous environments 159–63
    curing process 155–8
    degradation 141–2, 159–63
    environmental effects 158–63
    fatigue loading effects 163–8
    fibre sizing/coating 152–4
    fibre surface treatment 148–52
    hybrid composites 195–6

imperfect interface 147–8
meso-damage model 440
modifiers 154–5
sheer stresses (ISS) 170
short-fibre thermoset properties 276
interlaminar fracture modelling 174, 175–6, 183–7
interlaminar stresses 175
interleaving
  carbon-fibre-reinforced plastics 24
  GRP laminates 285
  hybrid composites 192–3, 199
interphase 117
interply fibre hybrids 189–90
intersections 673–4
intraply fibre hybrids 189–90
Irwin equation 131
ISO (international Standardization Organization) 37, 48, 52–6, 60
isonumber cycle curves 650–1
isophthalic polyester composites 161–2

joints 614–16, 621–40
  adhesive joints 623–4, 625–33
  bearing failure 622
  bolted joints 621–2, 633–9, 661–2, 675
  bonded joints 615, 623–33, 659, 675
  butt joints 624
  composite joints 621–5
  failure modes 622
  hole elongation 633–4
  lap joints 624
  in marine composites 720–2
  net-section failure 622, 638
  scarf joints 624
  shear-out failure 622, 638–9
  single-lap joints 616
  timber joints 357–8
Jones, F.R. 117–45
junctions and intersections 673–4
jute fibres 150–1, 358

kapok 358
Kashtalyan, M. 470–98
Kevlar (aramid) fibres 14–15, 21, 25, 142, 391
Kevlar/carbon hybrids 194–5
kinetic model of fibre stiffening 391–6
kinetic theory 422–3
Koimtzoglou, C. 147–70

Ladevèze, P. 432–41
Lamb waves 251–2
lap joints 624
Lear, Bill 688
Lee, J.A. 569–88
Lee, L.J. 526–45
lengthscale 366, 367
Lessard, L.B. 63–109

life-prediction models 7–8, 27, 30
  adhesive joints 625–30
  aerospace applications 672–95
  angle-ply 98–100
  aqueous environments 132–5
  carbon-fibre-reinforced plastics 7–8, 16–17
  constant-life models 16–17, 511–14, 546–67, 557–8
  cross-ply composites 97–8
  fibre bundles under static fatigue 131–5
  fibre-reinforced composites 448–9, 546–67
  mesodamage model 432–40
  neural network approach 569–88
  normalized fatigue life model 73–6
  physical modelling 378–82
  under service loading 526–44
  shear fatigue conditions 76–7
  simulation of fatigue life 96–100, 106–7
  strain/stress life curves 8, 9–16, 21
  strength data 554
  structural components 595–7
  thermoplastic composites 315
  and variable plane stress 504–23
  wood panel products 343–9
  woven-fibre thermoset composites 308
limit state design 677
loading
  block loading 25–7, 528–32, 582–3
  compression loads 46–8
    hybrid composites 197–8
  concentration points 48
  load conditions 24–5
  load cycles 4, 5, 36, 38–9
  monotonic loading 4
  service loading 526–44
    stiffness degradation model 526–30
    stress cycles 528
  variable amplitude loading 381–2
  see also stress
longitudinal compressive tests 83–5
longitudinal cracking 17
longitudinal tensile tests 80–3

macroscopic failure modes 235–6
MAH-PP treatment 151
Mai, Y-W. 442–68
mandrel 644
Marco-Starkey model 26
marine composites 709–27
  adhesive joints 720
  buoyancy materials 716
  creep behaviour 717, 719
    under hydrostatic pressure 725–6
  cyclic loading 719–20
  cyclic pressure loading 726
  cylinders for underwater applications 724–7
  damage mechanisms 716
  design life 711

durability
  of laminated materials 717–18
  of sandwich materials 719–20
  fatigue loading 717
  high-speed ferries 710
  joint behaviour 720–2
  laminated materials 715, 717–18
  military ships 710
  offshore oil and gas industry 711, 724–7
  racing yachts 710
  sandwich materials 715, 719–20
  ships 711–14
  size and scale effects 716
  slamming impact response 722–4
  submarines 710, 714–15, 724
  wave impact 711–12, 722–3
  see also aqueous environments
maritime structures 662, 664
Martin, R. 173–87
material degradation properties 68–78
Materials Response Group 426
matrix composites 60
  compression failure criteria 67
  compression property degradation 70
  ductility effects 327–30
  and environmental stress-corrosion cracking
    (ESCC) 135
  fibre-matrix shearing failure criteria 66
  fibre-matrix shearing property degradation
    69
  organic-matrix hybrid composites 189–92
  plasticization of the matrix 118
  polymer-matrix composites 296
  short-fibre thermoset composites 290–1
  solubility parameters 143
  tension failure criteria 66–7
  tension property degradation 69
  thermoplastic composites 320
matrix cracking
  angle-ply 471, 484
  crack growth rate 384–5
  crack induced delamination 470–1, 488
  cross-ply composites 471
  fibre-reinforced composites 445, 452
  physical modelling 382–6
    linked to delamination 386–91
  transverse ply matrix cracking model 382–6
  woven-fibre thermoset composites 298–9
mechanical properties of wood 341–2
medium density fibre board (MDF) 341
mesodamage model 432–40
  3D damage model 433–4
  basic interface problem 440
  damage scenarios 432–3
  micro-mesomodel 434–7
metal-matrix composites 599–601
metallic fatigue 3
metarules 369
micro-cellular damage 349

micro-mechanical modelling 368–9, 375, 413–
  30
  applications 426–9
  critical element method 419–21
  damage accumulation 414–15
  fatigue development law 438–40
  stiffness changes 416–17
  strength of materials
    changes in 417–18
    critical element method 419–21
    evolution 421–6
    non-uniform stress states 421
  see also physical modelling of damage
    development
micro-mesomodel 434–7
microcracking 143–5, 432, 434–6
microscopic failure modes 272–4, 278–80
microstructural damage 356, 357
microstructure of thermoplastic composites
  333–4
military aircraft 687, 688
military ships 710
Miner's rule 5, 27, 106–7
modifiers 154–5
modular structural systems 659
modulus decay 280
Moiré interferometry 259–61
moisture
  absorption responses 120–6
  and civil engineering applications 678
  content of wood panel products 345
  effect on pipe lifetimes 653–5
  sensitivity of resins 120–3
  see also aqueous environments; marine
    composites
Mondial House 662, 665
monotonic loading 4
monotonic strength 284–5
mouldings 659
  temperature 157–8
Mouritz, A.P. 242–62
MRLife code 426
multi-layer perception 574–6
multi-variate non-linear mappings 570–3
multiaxial stress systems 63–109
  failure criteria 63–8
  material degradation properties 68–78
  progressive fatigue damage modelling 78–
    80, 108–9
    evaluation 96–107
  testing material characterization 80–93
multidirectional winding 646
MWISPERX 514, 516, 517–19

Naik, N.K. 296–311
natural fibre composites
  fatigue in 358
  fibre surface treatment 150–1

NDE *see* non-destructive evaluation
net-section failure 622, 638
neural networks 569–88
    biological neural networks 570
    block-loading data analysis 582–3
    compared to other methods 585–8
    constant stress amplitude fatigue 580–1
    fatigue life data analysis 579
    feed-forward networks 570–1
    gradient descent learning 575–6
    life-predictions 583–5
    model construction 577–8
    multi-layer perceptron 574–6
    multi-variate non-linear mappings 570–3
    neuron model 573–4
    new material application 581–2
    optimum architecture 580
    radial basis function networks 576–7
    sigmoidal function 576
    single-layer perceptron 574
    tanh function 576
    training data 578, 580
neuron model 573–4
non-destructive evaluation (NDE) 242–62
    acoustic emission 254–6
    acousto-ultrasonics 249–51
    acoustography 252–4
    eddy currents 259
    Lamb waves 251–2
    Moiré interferometry 259–61
    objectives 242–3
    radiography 256–8
    thermo-acoustic emission 256
    thermography 259, 357
    ultrasonics 243–9
    vibrothermography 259
normal compression failure criteria 67–8
normal compression property degradation 70
normal tension failure criteria 67
normal tension property degradation 70
normalized fatigue life model 73–6
normalized stiffness degradation model 71–3
notches and holes 396–7, 416
    hole size effect 400

O sizing 152–3
observation techniques 371–2
offshore oil and gas industry 662, 664, 711
organic-matrix hybrid composites 189–92
oriented strand board (OSB) 341
osmosis 122
out-of-plane shear tests 91–3

Palmgren-Miner's rule *see* Miner's rule
panels 610–11, 674
    stringer stiffened 699–701
Paris law 333, 548
PEEK (polyetheretherketone) 17, 121, 317,

321, 323, 327–8, 461–3
peel stresses (mode I) 177, 179–80, 182, 184,
    492–6
penetrant-enhanced X-ray radiography 257
Perreux, D. 644–55
phase-insensitive tone-burst spectroscopy 249
Philippidis, T.P. 504–23
physical ageing 319–20
physical modelling of damage development
    365–410
    accumulation rates 376–7
    choosing a model 370
    computer implementation 408
    constitutive models 368, 369, 373
    constructing a model 373–5
    continuum modelling 368
    cross-ply composites 374–5
    definition 369
    delamination model 377–82, 408
        linked to matrix cracking 386–91
    dynamic models 370
    empirical models 370, 372
    fibre unkinking model 391–2
    fibre-reinforced composites 445
    finite element model 400
    fracture stress model 398–402
    holes and notches 396–7, 416
        hole size effect 400
    inputs and outputs 371, 373
    kinetic model of fibre stiffening 391–6
    life-prediction model 378–82
    matrix cracking model 382–6
        linked to delamination 386–91
    metarules 369
    notches and holes 396–7, 416
        hole size effect 400
    observation techniques 371–2
    precision 372
    problem identification 370–1
    static models 370
    at stress concentrators 396–408
    tensile strength model 402–8
    thermally activated chemical kinetics 369
    transverse ply matrix cracking 382–6
    see also micro-mechanical modelling
pipes 55, 606–9, 644–6
    bi-directional glass-fibre/epoxy pipes 648–
    55
plain weave fabrics 301
plane laminates 672–3
plasticization 118, 122, 123, 126
plies 672
polyester resin 192–3
polyetheretherketone (PEEK) 17, 121, 317,
    321, 323, 327–8, 461–3
polyethylene (PE) fibres 199
    sizing 154
    surface treatment 151–2

polymer-matrix composites 296
precision 56, 372
prepreg systems 195, 198–9, 199
presentation of data 58–9
pressure loading 726
prior impact damage 29
processing of data 41, 58
progressive failure 155
progressive fatigue damage modelling 78–80,
    108–9
    evaluation 96–107
    testing methods 80–93
pulse-echo (A-scan) ultrasonics 243, 244–5
pultrusions 658–9

quality control 196–7, 200–1
    resin quality 195–6

R-glass 142
    see also glass fibres
racing yachts 710
radial basis function networks 576–7
radiography 256–8
Raman spectroscopy 168
recrystallization 319–20
recyclability 335
Reifsnider, K. 413–30
reinforcement architecture 296–7
    short-fibre thermoset composites 269, 270,
    276–7
reliability analysis 594, 599
replicate testing 6–7
representative units testing 61
residual stiffness and strength 17–20
    degradation 692–3
    fibre-reinforced composites 443, 445, 447,
    448–9
    simulation 100–6
resins
    advanced resin systems 121–2
    blisters 122–3
    chemically resistant resins 137
    content in carbon-fibre-reinforced plastics
    20–1
    crack-growth 5, 137
    curing agents 122
    epoxy resins 120
    fracture toughness 135, 137
    in hybrid composites 195–6, 199, 215–16,
    221–3, 225, 228, 233, 235–6
    moisture absorption responses 120–6
    moisture sensitivity 120–3
    and osmosis 122
    plasticization 122, 123, 126
    polyester resin 192–3
    and stress-corrosion resistance 142–3
    styrenated resins 122
    thermomechanical responses 123–6
    urethane resin 193

road deck fatigue performance 662, 679–84
rotating structures 314–15
rotor blades 520–1, 599, 688

S-glass 142
    see also glass fibres
safe-life/reliability methodology 594
safety factors 677
Saffil 599
sandwich materials 715, 719–20
    panels 674
scarf joints 624
Schön, J. 621–41
secondary bonding 623
service loading 526–44
    stiffness degradation model 526–30
    stress cycles 528
    see also loading
serviceability limit states (SLSs) 677
servo-test machines 39–41
shadow Moiré interferometry 259–60
Sharjah Airport 662, 665
shear-lag model 450–3, 468
shear-out failure 622, 638–9
shearing
    deformation theory 487
    fatigue conditions 76–7
    fibre-matrix shearing failure criteria 66
    fibre-matrix shearing property degradation
    69
    in-plane shear tests 89–91
    mode II and III conditions 177, 180–3, 184,
    492–6
    out-of-plane shear tests 91–3
    shear weakness 25
sheet moulding compounds (SMCs) 269, 270
ships 708–11
    see also marine composites
Shokrieh, M.M. 63–109
short-fibre thermoset composites 22–4, 193–4,
    269–92, 331–4
    bundle aspect ratio 274, 292
    composition 270, 274–8, 284–9
    crack density/orientation 278–9
    debonding 272, 278
    degradation 281–2
    fatigue behaviour 278–92
    fatigue sensitivity 282, 285, 287–8
    fibre types 277–8
    fibre volume fraction 274–5
    filler content 274, 276
    frequency effect 283
    interface properties 276
    loading conditions 289
    matrix-dominated fatigue 290–1
    microscopic failure modes 272–4, 278–80
    modulus decay 280
    reinforcement 269, 270, 276–7

sheet moulding compounds (SMCs) 269, 270
  static behaviour 270–8
  stiffness 280, 281–2
  strain levels 289–90
  stress/life curves 282–92
  stress/strain curves 270–2, 277
  structure 270
sigmoidal function 576
signal attenuation coefficient 244–6
silane coupling agents 154
silicon carbide fibres 199
Sims, D. 36–62
SIMS (surface ion mass spectrometry) 196
simulation of fatigue life 96–100, 106–7
sine waveforms 41
single-lap joints 616
single-layer perceptron 574
sisal fibres 358
sizing/coating
  carbon fibres 152–3
  glass fibres 153–4
  interface 152–4
slamming impact response 722–4
softening strips 24
Soutis, C. 470–98
SPATE technologies 259
spectrum test loads 514–16
standards
  for structural components 677
  in testing 37–8, 52–6, 60
Starikov, R. 621–41
static models 370
statistical model 447–9
  development 445–6
stiffened panels 674
stiffness 41, 471–86
  and aerospace applications 693
  angle-ply laminates 480–4
  constraining ply orientation 484–6
  cross-ply laminates 480
  degradation 477–80, 497, 526–30
  fibre-reinforced composites 280, 281–2,
    308, 446, 452
  kinetic model of fibre stiffening 391–6
  micro-mechanical modelling 416–17
  normalized stiffness degradation model 71–
    3
  reduction 446, 452, 595–6, 693
  short-fibre thermoset composites 280, 281–2
  woven-fibre thermoset composites 308
  see also residual stiffness and strength
Stone mountain building 662, 665
strain levels 289–90
strain measurements 40, 41
strain-energy release rates 183–4, 210, 486,
    488
  equivalent laminate concept 489–92
strain/life curves 9–16

strain/stress life curves 8, 9–16, 21
strength
  and aerospace applications 703–5
  degradation model 27, 70–1
    fibre-reinforced composites 447–8
  direct characterization measurement 504,
    509
  fatigue strength criterion 506–8
  flexural strength of hybrids 209
  life-prediction from strength data 554
  micro-mechanical modelling 417–26
  normalized strength degradation model 70–1
  physical modelling 402–8
  simulation 100–6
  strength-life equal-rank assumption
    (SLERA) 693–5
  tensile strength of hybrids 209
  tensile strength model 402–8
  and variable plane stress 504–23
  woven-fibre thermoset composites 308
  see also residual stiffness and strength
stress
  in adhesive joints 626–7
  complex stresses 28
  concentration points 48, 50–2, 396–408,
    671–2
  in cracked transverse ply 384
  cycles 528
  and delamination 473, 474–7
  environmental stress-corrosion cracking
    135, 137–43
  fibre-reinforced composites 446, 449–53
  interfacial sheer stresses (ISS) 170
  interlaminar stresses 175
  redistribution function 446, 449–53
  shear weakness 25
  state/distribution 625
  stress/life curves 9–16, 21
    short-fibre thermoset composites 282–92
  stress/life/probability (S/N/P) diagram 8
  stress/strain curves 270–2, 277
  structural components 671–2, 678–81
  swelling stresses 143
  transfer efficiency 168
  variable stresses 25–7, 504–23
  see also multiaxial stress systems
stringer stiffened panels 699–701
structural components 593 616
  anchoring systems 601–2
  beams 609–13
  bridges 609–13
  creep influence 678
  critical element model 597
  cylinders 55, 606–9
  damage growth 595–7
  damage tolerance methodology 594
  design limit states 677–8
  failure modes 672

fibre reinforced polymer (FRP) composites
    659–62
fibre-reinforced concrete 601
generalised force determination (GFD) 598
helicopter industry 599, 602–6
    rotor blades 520–1, 599, 688
hierarchy of structural scales 366
integrity predictions 187
junctions and intersections 673–4
    see also joints
life prediction 595–7
limit state design 677
metal-matrix composites 599–601
modular structural systems 659
and moisture 678
panels 613–14, 674
pipes 55, 606–9
reliability analysis 594, 599
safe-life/reliability methodology 594
safety factors 677
sandwich panels 674
standards 677
stiffened panels 674
stress analysis 678–81
stress concentrations 671–2
and temperature 678
testing 173, 598
3-D components 674–5
wear-out methodology 594–5
    see also civil engineering applications;
        filament-wound structures
structural connections see joints
styrenated resins 122
subcritical elements 443, 446
submarines 710, 714–15, 724
sudden material property degradation 4, 68–70,
    668
surface ion mass spectrometry (SIMS) 196
surface treatment 148–52
    glass fibres 149–50
    hybrid composites 196
    interface 148–52
swelling stresses 143

tanh function 576
temperature 118, 652–3
    high temperature off-axis fatigue 163
    loading fatigue effects 671
    moulding temperature 157–8
    structural components 678
    and testing 45–6, 48
    thermal analysis of hybrid composites 201
    thermal fatigue 127–9, 248–9
    thermal spiking 123, 126
    thermal stresses 126–7
    thermally activated chemical kinetics 369
    thermomechanical response of resins 123–6
tensile properties of hybrids 206–8

tensile strength of hybrids 209
tensile strength model 402–8
tensile testing 48, 54
tension
    fibre tension failure criteria 63–4, 65–6
    fibre tension property degradation 69
    longitudinal tensile tests 80–3
    matrix tension failure criteria 66–7
    matrix tension property degradation 69
    normal tension failure criteria 67
    normal tension property degradation 70
    tension/compression fatigue 221–3
    tension/tension fatigue 214–20
    transverse tensile tests 85
test tubes 644
testing 3, 36–61
    all-tension (TTTT) experiments 27
    analysis of results 58
    artefacts in testing 42–52
    autogenous heating 45–6, 53
    bearing fatigue 55
    buckling under compression 46–7
    component fatigue testing 55–6
    control facilities 41
    coupon fatigue testing 53–5
    crack growth 54–5
    data
        precision of 56
        presentation 58–9
        processing 41, 58
        requirements 36–8
    delamination 173, 177–81
    displacement measurements 40
    equipment 39–42
        fatigue machines 197
    failure criteria 36–7, 53, 63–8
    flexure tests 48
    gripping systems 48, 197, 647–8
    hybrid composites 197, 201
    in-plane shear tests 89–91
    load conditions 24–5
    load cycles 36, 38–9
    longitudinal compressive tests 83–5
    longitudinal tensile tests 80–3
    out-of-plane shear tests 91–3
    precision data 56
    rate dependence effects 43–5, 53
    reasons for 36
    replicate testing 6–7
    representative units testing 61
    sine waveforms 41
    standards 37–8, 52–6, 60
    strain measurements 40, 41
    stress concentrations 48, 50–2
    structural components 173, 598
    and temperature 45–6, 48
    tensile testing 48, 54
    transverse compressive tests 85–9

transverse tensile tests 85
  woven-fibre thermoset composites 303–4
  see also non-destructive evaluation (NDE)
textile composites 296–7
  see also woven-fibre thermoset composites
thermal analysis of hybrid composites 201
thermal fatigue 127–9, 248–9
thermal spiking 123, 126
thermal stresses 126–7
thermally activated chemical kinetics 369
thermo-acoustic emission 256
thermography 259, 357
thermomechanical response of resins 123–6
thermoplastic composites 314–35
  advanced load-carrying materials 334–5
  advantages and drawbacks 316–17
  compressive loading 325–6
  continuous fibre composites 321–31
  creep-fatigue interaction 332–3
  crystallinity 319–20, 326–7
  frequency effects 330–1
  high-temperature use 317
  life diagrams 315
  manufacturing principles 331–2
  materials 315–16, 331–2
  matrix ductility effects 327–30
  as matrix materials 320
  mechanical and physical properties 317–19
  microstructure 333–4
  physical ageing 319–20
  recrystallization 319–20
  recyclability 335
  rotating structures 314–15
  short-fibre composites 331–4
  transcrystallinity 319, 326
Thiébaud, F. 644–5
three-dimensional (3D) components 674–5
three-dimensional (3D) damage model 433–4
three-dimensional (3D) textile composites
  296–7
through-transmission (C-scan) ultrasonics 243,
  244, 247–8
timber 339–40
  joints 357–8
time-dependent fracture 130
tow-hybrids 189–90
traffic loading fatigue effects 662, 671, 679–84
training data in neural networks 578, 580
transcrystallinity 319, 326
transverse compressive tests 85–9
transverse tensile tests 85
transverse-ply cracking 17, 193, 473
  matrix cracking model 382–6
TRL (Transport Research Laboratory) 679–84
two-dimensional (2D) textile composites 297

ultimate limit states (ULSs) 677
ultrasonics 243–9

acousto-ultrasonics 249–51
  limitations 247–8
  phase-insensitive tone-burst spectroscopy
    249
  pulse-echo (A-scan) ultrasonics 243, 244–5
  signal attenuation coefficient 244–6
  and thermal fatigue 248–9
  through-transmission (C-scan) 243, 244,
    247–8
unidirectional composites 296–7, 298, 301,
  321–3, 454, 455, 461, 669
unkinking model 391–2
urethane resin 193

VAMAS 52, 55
variable amplitude loading 381–2
variable amplitude tests 514–16
variable plane stresses 25–7, 504–23
Vassilopoulos, A.P. 504–23
vibrothermography 259
vinyl ester laminates 162–3
viscoplastic dissipation of energy 652
void content of hybrid composites 196

water *see* aqueous environments; marine
  composites; moisture
wave impact 711–12, 722–3
waviness of fibres 207–8
wear-in 4
wear-out model 4, 5, 442, 594–5
Weibull model 7–8, 129, 562
welded steel structures 668
Wellstream Corporation 427–8
wide flange beams 609
Wilcott Footbridge 662, 663
wind loading fatigue effects 671
WISPERX spectrum 349, 514, 520
wood panel products 339–58
  bonded-in rods 357–8
  chipboard 341, 347, 357
  classification of 341
  complex loading 349
  compressive strength 347, 349
  damage development 356–7
  dynamic property changes 349–55
  fatigue in compression 343–6
  fatigue and creep 347
  fatigue in tension 343–6
  fatigue in wood 342–3
  flexural fatigue 343
  infra-red thermography 357
  life-prediction models 343–9
  mechanical properties of wood 341–2
  micro-cellular damage 349
  microstructural damage 356, 357
  moisture content 345
  structure of wood 339–40
  timber joints 357–8

woven rovings 672
woven-fibre thermoset composites 296–311
    debonding 299
    fatigue damage 304–8
    laminated composites 296–7, 298–9
    life diagrams 308
    matrix cracking 298–9
    reinforcement architecture 296–7
    stiffness 308
    strength 308
    testing 303–4
    unidirectional (UD) layers 296–7, 298, 301
    woven-fabric laminated composites 299–
        303, 304–8

X-ray radiography 256–8

yachts 710
Ye, L. 442–68